Forensic Science

FUNDAMENTALS & INVESTIGATIONS

2nd Edition

Anthony J. Bertino
Canandaigua Academy High School
Canandaigua, New York

Patricia Nolan Bertino
Scotia-Glenville High School
Scotia, New York

NATIONAL GEOGRAPHIC LEARNING | SOUTH-WESTERN CENGAGE Learning

Australia · Brazil · Mexico · Singapore · United Kingdom · United States

Wraparound Teacher's Edition
Forensic Science: Fundamentals and Investigations,
Second Edition

Anthony J. Bertino, Patricia Nolan Bertino

SVP Global Product Management, Research,
School & Professional: Frank Menchaca

General Manager, K-12 School Group: CarolAnn
Shindelar

Publishing Director: Eve Lewis

Acquisitions Editor: Jeff Werle

Executive Editor: Dave Lafferty

Marketing Manager: Kelsey Hagan

Sr. Content Project Manager: Martha Conway

Sr. Media Editor: Mike Jackson

Website Project Manager: Ed Stubenrauch

Manufacturing Planner: Kevin Kluck

Consulting Editor: Lisa Furtado Clark

Development, Ancillaries: Marce Epstein

Production Service: Integra

Sr. Art Director: Michelle Kunkler

Cover and Internal Designer: Ke Design

Cover Image: © Larysa Ray/Shutterstock.com

Intellectual Property Project Manager: Lisa Brown

Intellectual Property Analyst: Kyle Cooper

Photo Researcher: Darren Wright

Permissions Researcher: Lumina Datamatics

Design Images: Crime-scene tape: Ferrerivideo/
iStock/Thinkstock; Mobile phone: © Radu
Bercan/Shutterstock.com; Thumbprint data:
Maksim Kabakou/iStock/Thinkstock; Scan of
Hand: © cluckva/Shutterstock.com; DNA helix:
© wavebreakmedia/Shutterstock.com; DNA
fingerprints: © isak55/Shutterstock.com;
Tablet PC: © Thaiview/Shutterstock.com

For product information and technology assistance, contact us at
Cengage Learning Customer & Sales Support, 1-800-354-9706

For permission to use material from this text or product,
submit all requests online at **www.cengage.com/permissions**
Further permissions questions can be emailed to
permissionrequest@cengage.com

Instructor's Edition: 978-1-305-10792-2
Student Edition: 978-1-305-07711-9

Cengage Learning
20 Channel Center Street
Boston, MA 02210
USA

Cengage Learning is a leading provider of customized learning solutions
with employees residing in nearly 40 different countries and sales in more
than 125 countries around the world. Find your local representative at
www.cengage.com

Cengage Learning products are represented in Canada by
Nelson Education, Ltd.

Visit National Geographic Learning online at **ngl.cengage.com**

Visit our corporate website at **www.cengage.com**

Printed in the United States of America
Print Number: 01   Print Year: 2015

DEDICATION

To my parents, Joe and Alice Bertino, who taught me the meaning of "doing what you like brings freedom but liking what you do brings happiness."

–Anthony (Bud) Bertino

To my father, Arthur J. Nolan, for his keen interest, guidance, and encouragement during my teaching career and his invaluable technical support of this book.

–Patricia Nolan Bertino

PREFACE

Welcome To
Forensic Science: Fundamentals and Investigations 2e

This new edition provides the science behind forensics, as well as labs and activities appropriate for high school students! *Forensic Science: Fundamentals and Investigations 2e* is student *and* teacher friendly. Students enjoy a hands-on approach to forensics. Extra support is offered both for at-risk students and gifted learners through differentiated learning activities in the teacher's edition. Teachers can conduct a full-year's study of forensics or select topics that can be incorporated into a half-year course. As another option, teachers can use the textbook to motivate students in all science classes by using forensics to teach basic science concepts. *Forensic Science: Fundamentals and Investigations 2e* integrates science, mathematics, technology, history, and political science along with writing and presentation skills using real-life applications and case studies, providing complete flexibility for any science program. *Forensic Science: Fundamentals and Investigations 2e* is the new standard in high school forensic science . . . case closed!

GETTING STARTED

Forensic Science: Fundamentals and Investigations 2e reveals the science used in forensic science techniques. It provides a chapter-by-chapter description of specific types of evidence and the techniques to collect, analyze, and evaluate the evidence. As students progress through the course, they refine the techniques and apply them to other areas of study. The topics covered in the 18 chapters include crime-scene investigation; the collection, handling, and analysis of trace evidence such as hair, fibers, soil, pollen, and glass; fingerprints; blood and blood-spatter examination; forensic analysis of DNA, insects, drugs, glass, handwriting, and tool-marks and impressions; firearms and ballistics; forensic anthropology; and the determination of the manner, mechanism, and cause of death and the estimation of post-mortem interval. New chapters include entomology; expanded chapters includes updated DNA content, expanded autopsy coverage, increased hands-on crime-scene investigation, and forensic botany.

One of the strengths of the textbook is student motivation. Areas of study are introduced in scenarios taken from headlines and popular media. These features engage students as they describe the historical development of forensic science techniques. Inexpensive, easy-to-perform labs provide students with opportunities for successful laboratory experiences as well as an appreciation of the true nature of forensic science problem-solving techniques. Suggestions for research projects extend and enrich student learning and interest.

CHAPTER FEATURES

Each chapter of *Forensic Science: Fundamentals and Investigations 2e* begins with a true-life story, student objectives, key vocabulary, and a Topical Sciences Key. The Topical Sciences Key identifies biology, Earth science, chemistry, physics, literacy, or mathematics concepts integrated into chapter topics.

Special features include **Did You Know** margin notes that provide additional interesting facts and information, and **Digging Deeper**, additional research topics that refer students to the free online database from Gale Publishing called the Forensic Science eCollection Database.

At the end of each chapter, a **Summary** reviews the main points of the chapter. Nonfiction high interest books are listed next to the summary to encourage student's outside reading. A series of short **Case Studies** offer high-interest topics for critical thinking, writing, and class discussion. **Careers in Forensics** describes an occupation related to forensic science. On the bottom of the career page, inexpensive or free forensic Apps are often referenced. A **Chapter Review** contains both objective and short-answer questions requiring critical thinking skills to assess student understanding. A chapter bibliography lists print and online research sources.

Each chapter has *Activities* that provide hands-on experiences with forensic science techniques. Each activity has clear, step-by-step directions for students of all reading levels. For teachers, they offer easy, quick preparation and minimal expense for materials. Each activity includes objectives, materials, safety precautions, procedures, and other learning support.

FOR THE TEACHER

The *Wraparound Teacher's Edition (WTE)* contains teaching strategies and tips to engage students. The WTE provides clarification of science content and forensic science procedures, ideas to help stimulate students, evaluation opportunities, additional questions, and suggestions for further exploration and research. Additional teaching tips are added to help address the needs of English-language learners, gifted students, and at-risk students.

An *Instructor's Resource CD-ROM (IRCD)* is available to teachers who adopt a classroom set of *Forensic Science: Fundamentals and Investigations 2e.* The IRCD contains additional activities, PowerPoint presentations, student handouts, lesson plans with chapter outlines, and enrichment materials, as well as Student Learning Objectives (SLOs) for each chapter.

Cengage Learning Testing Powered by Cognero is a flexible, online system that allows you to author, edit, and manage test bank content from multiple Cengage Learning solutions; create multiple test versions in an instant; and deliver tests from your learning management system, your classroom or wherever you want!

MindTap for Forensic Science Fundamentals and Investigations 2e is a personalized teaching experience with an eBook reader with relevant assignments that guide students to analyze, apply, and improve thinking, allowing you to measure skills and outcomes with ease.

Cengage maintains a **Website** to support this text. Both students and teachers using *Forensic Science: Fundamentals and Investigations 2e* may access the Website at **ngl.cengage.com/forensicscience2e**. The site provides teacher resources and information about related products. Student resources on the site include forms, additional projects, and links to related sites. In addition, a link is provided to the *Gale Forensic Science eCollection database* which allows free online research in various journals and the Gale Virtual Reference Library.

ABOUT THE AUTHORS

Anthony (Bud) Bertino has taught science for 40 years. He has served as biology teacher and science supervisor at Canandaigua Academy. His awards include Outstanding Biology Teacher (NY, NABT), Woodrow Wilson Fellowship Award, Tandy Scholars' Award, and Outstanding Teaching Award from the University of Rochester. He is co-author of "Where's the CAT," and author of "The Cookie Jar Mystery," and many other published activities. He has served as an AP Biology consultant for the College Board and as a clinical supervisor for the University of Albany (NY), Graduate School of Education.

Patricia Nolan Bertino has taught science for 34 years. Her awards include Outstanding Biology Teacher (NY, NABT), Woodrow Wilson Fellowship Award, and the Tandy Scholars' Award. She has served as a scientific consultant for Video Discovery, Neo Sci, and several publishers. Patricia developed curricula and taught high school forensic science and biology at Scotia-Glenville High School for several years.

The Bertinos live near Schenectady, New York and conduct summer workshops in forensic science education for teachers. They are frequent co-presenters at the National Science Teachers Association (NSTA) and many state science teacher conferences.

REVIEWERS

Dr. David R. Foran, Ph.D.
Michigan State University
East Lansing, MI

Myra Frank
Marjory Stoneman Douglas High
  School
Parkland, FL

Stacey Hervey
CEC Middle College of Denver
Denver, CO

Kristen Kohli
Estrella Foothills High School
Goodyear, AZ

Carol Robertson
Fulton High School
Fulton, MO

Dr. Ruth Smith
Michigan State University, School
  of Criminal Justice
East Lansing, MI

Dr. Roshan Strong
Austin, TX

Karen Lynn Cruse Suder
The Summit Country Day School
Cincinnati, OH

BRIEF CONTENTS

Mauro Fermariello/Science Source

© iStock.com/pkripper503

AP Images/The Albuquerque Journal, Pat Vasquez-Cunningham

CONTENTS

CHAPTER 9 Forensic Toxicology 282

CHAPTER 10 Handwriting Analysis, Forgery, and Counterfeiting 314

CHAPTER 14 Forensic Anthropology 442

CHAPTER 15 Glass Evidence 482

CHAPTER 18 **Firearms and Ballistics** 584

STRAIGHT FROM THE SOURCE, NO ASSUMPTIONS

THE CONTENT YOU REQUESTED HAS BEEN IMPROVED

THE OVERWHELMING SUCCESS OF THE FIRST EDITION BRINGS YOU A NEW EDITION AND UPDATE!

This program's balance of relevant content and hands-on lab activities are a direct result of your input at every stage! No other forensic science program delivers precisely what you need for your students and your course.

A review board, focus groups, and ongoing educator feedback guided each decision to ensure that the program meets the educational needs of your students.

Student and teacher supplements support the workflow with time-saving tools. Innovative digital resources include the innovative **Forensic Science eCollection database** and the new **MindTap**™ **with Virtual Labs.**

Forensic Science combines topics from math, chemistry, biology, physics, literacy, and Earth science into a single course with all materials clearly aligned with the **National Science Education Standards, NGSS,** and **CCSS.** Distinctive icons identify topics in the chapter opener and throughout the text.

TOPICAL SCIENCES KEY

BIOLOGY
CHEMISTRY
EARTH SCIENCES
PHYSICS
LITERACY
MATHEMATICS

LITERACY

Stuart H. James, Paul E. Kish, T. Paulette Sutton, William G. Eckert. *Principles of Bloodstain Pattern Analysis.*

- Blood consists of cellular components and plasma containing dissolved ions, proteins, and other substances.
- Blood types result from the presence of antigens on the surface of red blood cells and vary among individuals. Although considered class evidence, blood type is used today to exclude suspects.
- Blood-spatter analysis can be used to help recreate a crime scene.

New Second Edition

Copyright Update

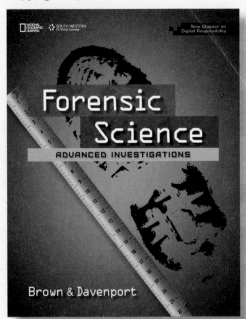

WHAT'S NEW IN THE NEW EDITION (BERTINO AND BERTINO) AND COPYRIGHT UPDATE (BROWN AND DAVENPORT)

- **What's NEW!—** *Forensic Science Fundamentals & Investigations, 2e*, new coverage for various topics such as:

    ○ A new chapter (11) on entomology

    ○ Scientific changes in DNA technologies (7)

    ○ More coverage of autopsy (12)

    ○ More coverage in crime-scene investigation (2)

    ○ Pollen chapter is now Forensic Botany (5)

- **What's NEW!—** *Forensic Science Advanced Investigations, CU*, new coverage for various topics within such as:

    ○ A new chapter (15) on Digital Responsibility and Social Networking

- **Aligned to National Standards—**This text combines topics from math, chemistry, biology, physics, literacy, and earth science into a single course with all materials clearly correlated to the National Science Education Standards, NGSS, and CCSS. The topics are identified by distinctive icons in the chapter opener as well as throughout the text.

- **A Wide Variety of High-Interest Lab Activities—**Many updated end-of-chapter lab activities give students the hands-on experience needed to fully understand and truly integrate their knowledge of science and related subjects.

- **Capstone projects** are updated and give students the opportunity to apply key topics learned throughout the year, as well as extend the learning process with the opportunity to synthesize this knowledge and new content.

- **The Gale Forensic Science eCollection™—**This database allows you and your students to investigate the mysteries of forensic science in-depth with online access to hundreds of recent articles—from highly specialized academic journals to general science-focused magazines.

- **NEW—Forensic Science MindTap™ and Virtual Labs—**Give your students real-world lab experience within an online environment with MindTap! **MindTap** is a fully online, highly personalized learning experience that combines readings, multimedia, activities, and assessments into a singular Learning Path. **Virtual Lab** activities include: background information, 3-D crime scenes, clear instructions, Toolkits, post-lab assessments, and critical-thinking and research activities.

- **NEW APPS** feature that discusses Web Apps for related tools and topics. Available with Forensic Science Fundamentals & Investigations.

- **NEW "Further Reading"** for CCSS literacy details additional reading references. Available with Forensic Science Fundamentals & Investigations.

THE FUNCTIONS OF HAIR

BIOLOGY

All (and only) mammals have hair. Its main purpose is to regulate body temperature—to keep the body warm through insulation. Hair also decreases friction, protects the skin against sunlight, and acts as a sense organ. The very dense hair of some mammals is referred to as fur.

Treated Hair

CHEMISTRY

Hair can be treated in many different ways. Bleaching hair oxidizes the natural pigment, lightening it (Figure 3-8). It also makes hair brittle and can disturb the scales on the cuticle. Artificial bleaching shows a sharp demarcation along the hair, while bleaching from the sun leaves a more gradual mark. Peroxide in bleach can also dam-

APPS

▶ **Time Of Death app considers ambient temperature, body weight, amount and type of clothing, and body location when calculating postmortem interval.**

Figure 4-13 Weave patterns.

Type of Weave	Diagram	Description	Characteristics
Plain		Alternating warp and weft threads	• Firm and wears well • Snag resistant • Low tear strength • Tends to wrinkle
Basket		Alternating pattern of two weft threads crossing two warp threads	• An open or porous weave • Does not wrinkle • Not very durable • Tends to distort as yarns shift • Shrinks when washed
Satin		One weft crosses over three or more warp threads.	• Not durable • Tends to snag and break during wear • Shiny surface • High light reflectance • Little friction with other garments
Twill		Weft is woven over three or more warps and then under one. In the next row, the pattern is shifted over one to the left or right by one warp thread	• Very strong • Dense and compact • Different faces • Diagonal design on surface • Soft and pliable
Leno		This uses two warp threads and a single weft thread. The two adjacent warp threads cross over each other. The weft travels left to right and is woven between the two warp threads.	• Open weave • Easily distorted with wear and washing • Stretches in one direction only

IT'S ALL IN THE DETAILS

RIVETING DESIGN AND FEATURES OFFER A NEW WAY TO EXPERIENCE SCIENCE

TRACING THE CLUES TO STUDENT SUCCESS

From a dynamic design to captivating images, practical applications, intriguing case studies, and glimpses into actual crime and lab scenes, every part of this text appeals to students; the program presents information the way students learn best.

Chapter-opening scenarios highlight intriguing news shaping forensic science. These exciting stories, taken directly from gripping headlines, draw students into the learning path of the text. Scenarios feature well-known cases, such as Cory Monteith, Michael Jackson, Jodi Arias, and more.

Clear Learning Objectives guide how students study, helping them focus on the key topics. Chapter content and assessment materials, tagged to specific learning objectives, provide a strong framework for mastering key concepts.

Scientific Terms and Vocabulary, highlighted in each chapter, introduce key terms, ensuring students are able to understand their meaning.

Case Studies bring closure to the chapter concepts using intriguing case facts drawn from actual forensic investigations. Questions prompt discussion and facilitate students' critical-thinking skills.

Careers in Forensic Science sections focus on the hottest careers related to forensic science today, detailing job requirements, necessary preparation, and challenges.

End of Chapter Review Questions, including true-false, multiple choice, and short answer, highlight cross-curricular connections and ensure students thoroughly comprehend principles before moving ahead.

ENGAGE THEM WITH HANDS-ON ACTIVITIES FOR THE REAL WORLD APPLICATION

The variety of high-interest lab activities (3–5 per chapter) saves you time, while giving students the hands-on experience needed to integrate their knowledge of science and related subjects. These activities outline the objectives, time required, materials, safety precautions, scenarios, background information, detailed procedures and data tables, follow-up questions, and research opportunities. Plus the affordable materials allow labs to be completed with minimal investment.

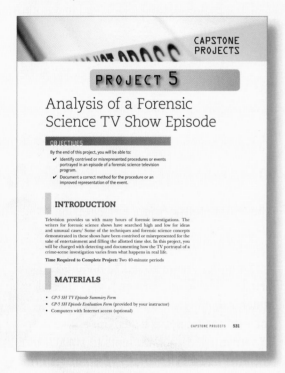

Capstone Crime Scene projects give students the opportunity to apply key topics throughout the course.

P.A.C.T.™ Activities (Preventing Adolescent Crime Together) provide service learning opportunities through projects addressing issues such as anti-bullying and social responsibility. Available with Forensic Science Advanced Investigations.

Crime Scene S.P.O.T (Student Prepared Original Title) offers short stories written by actual students followed by critical-thinking questions and a writing activity. S.P.O.T. provides interdisciplinary instruction integrating reading and writing throughout the text. Available with Forensic Science Advanced Investigations.

DOWN AND DIRTY

ENABLE STUDENTS TO EXPLORE THE TOOLS OF THE TRADE WITH DYNAMIC ONLINE RESOURCES

The Forensic Science companion websites take learning to a new level with a wealth of learning and teaching resources with access to the eCollection database.

ngl.cengage.com/forensicscience2e
ngl.cengage.com/forensicscienceadv

FORENSIC SCIENCE ECOLLECTION™ DATABASE

- Web links to other dynamic science sites
- Interactive flashcards and crossword puzzles to review key terms
- Lab forms to complete in-text lab activities
- Lesson Plans
- PowerPoint® presentation slides

Digging Deeper with Forensic Science eCollection guides students in exploring specific areas of interest related to forensic science for additional reinforcement.

DIGGING DEEPER
with Forensic
Science
eCollection

Are fingerprints really unique? How much of the interpretation of fingerprints is subjective on the part of the fingerprint analyst? Search the Gale Forensic Science eCollection for answers at **ngl.cengage.com/forensicscience2e**.

The Gale Forensic Science eCollection™ allows you and your students to systematically investigate the mysteries of forensic science with online access to hundreds of articles via InfoTrac®. From highly specialized academic journals to general science-focused magazines articles, the eCollection allows you and your students to stay current with the latest scientific developments in this growing field. No other publisher offers such a complete, exclusive resource as a free supplement on the textbook companion website.

COMPREHENSIVE INSTRUCTOR RESOURCES PROVIDE THE BACKUP YOU NEED

WE'VE GOT YOU COVERED WITH THE FINEST INSTRUCTOR RESOURCES AROUND

Wraparound Teacher's Edition (WTE) provides reduced student pages with comprehensive related teaching tips and support that expand upon the topics presented on each page. Teaching notes and overviews include:

- The Big Ideas highlight the key science focus of the chapter content
- Teaching Resources
- Tips for Differentiated Learning
- Teaching Tips to engage, teach, explore, evaluate, and close the lesson
- Answers to end of chapter reviews and activities with additional details related to lab materials, safety precautions, procedures, data tables, and further student research
- Expanded cross-curricular information that connects biology, chemistry, Earth science, physics, math, and literacy

     Fundamentals & Investigations ISBN: 9781305107922
     Advanced Investigations ISBN: 9781305120723

Instructor's Resource CD places key instructor resources at your fingertips, including Lab Activity Forms, additional Activities, Chapter outlines, Instructor Notes, Lesson Plans, Objective Sheets, PowerPoint Presentation Slides, and Rubrics.

Fundamentals & Investigations ISBN: 9781305107946
Advanced Investigations ISBN: 9781305120730

Cengage Learning Testing Powered by Cognero is a flexible, online system that allows you to: author, edit, and manage test bank content from multiple Cengage Learning solutions;
create multiple test versions in an instant; deliver tests from your learning management system, your classroom, or wherever you want!

Fundamentals & Investigations ISBN: 9781305108721
Advanced Investigations ISBN: 9781305120808

Instructor Companion Website provides online access to instructor resources and professional development webinars.

ngl.cengage.com/forensicscience
ngl.cengage.com/forensicscienceadv

OBSERVE THE EVIDENCE

NEW! FORENSIC SCIENCE FOR MINDTAP™ AND VIRTUAL LABS LEADS STUDENTS TO THE RIGHT CONCLUSION

Forensic Science MindTap™ and Virtual Labs—**MindTap** is a fully online, highly personalized learning experience that combines readings, multimedia, activities, and assessments into a singular Learning Path. **Virtual Lab** activities include: background information, 3-D crime scenes, clear instructions, Toolkits, post-lab assessments, critical-thinking questions, and research activities.

FORENSIC SCIENCE MINDTAP™

MindTap contains relevant assignments that guide students to analyze, apply, and improve critical-thinking skills; allowing you, as instructor, to measure skills and outcomes with ease. Included with MindTap are:

MindTap Reader is an interactive reading resource that allows learners to make notes, highlight text, and find definitions. In addition, the Learning Path provides instant access to various resources needed to personalize tour course. Included are these additional resources:

- Chapter sections are linked for navigation
- Chapter objectives are linked to activities and key concepts to show correlation
- Terms and definitions linked to the glossary for clarification
- Flashcards, Web links, Merriam-Webster's Dictionary, and ReadSpeaker are other useful tools for research, reinforcement, and enhanced accessibility
- Photos and illustrations are linked to chapter references for navigation

Link to Digging Deeper eCollection provides immediate access for further online research.

Interactivities for quick virtual interactive learning reinforcement.

MindApps are learning Apps with tools to help you succeed.

SET THE SCENE FOR ONLINE LEARNING SUCCESS!

THE VIRTUAL LABS WITHIN MINDTAP

Now you can give your students real-world lab experience within an online environment! Within MindTap, each chapter will include an interactive lab within the Learning Path. Students will use these labs to solidify their understanding of the concepts presented within the chapter.

Also included within Mindtap is a Virtual Lab which can be used as a final assessment for the course. Each lab activity includes:

- Background information
- Clear instructions
- Toolkit

- Lab assessments
- Critical-thinking questions
- Research activities

As students work through the lab, they will record their findings within an auto-graded assignment. After they have completed the lab and recorded the data, there is a post-lab assessment covering the topics and techniques used within the lab.

Fundamentals & Investigations MindTap with Interactive labs and Death of Rose Cedar Virtual Lab
ISBN IAC: 9781305397804
ISBN PAC: 9781305397835

Advanced Investigations MindTap with Interactive Labs and Bones in the Yard Virtual Lab
ISBN IAC: 9781305270176
ISBN PAC: 9781305270190

Digital Course Support: http://services.cengage.com/dcs/

When you adopt from Cengage Learning, you have a dedicated team of Digital Course Support professionals, who will provide hands-on, start-to-finish support, making digital course delivery a success for you and your students.

Chapter Overview

The skill of observation is critical to the field of forensic science. Many factors affect our observational skills, such as our mood and whether we are alone or in a group. At times, how our brains perceive what goes on around us may not reflect reality. To be good observers, we must be systematic about how we examine our surroundings and not jump to conclusions. Sometimes a person is wrongly convicted of a crime because of faulty eyewitness testimony. People often remember things differently from how the events actually occurred. The purpose of the Innocence Project is to use DNA evidence to reexamine some of these cases.

The Big Ideas

Observation is how you perceive your surroundings. Your brain affects your observations by filtering the information you take in from your environment. Many factors affect eyewitness accounts of a crime. Investigators must understand these factors when determining the accuracy of a witness's testimony. With practice and patience, you can train yourself to be a good observer. Forensic science attempts to uncover evidence in order to discover the facts of a crime. Forensic scientists do not try to prove whether someone is innocent or guilty. They are only interested in collecting and examining evidence.

CHAPTER 1
Observation Skills

Was Someone Stealing the Trees?

An officer with the Department of Natural Resources was called to a farm where a landowner had discovered missing trees. The trees were black walnut, a valuable wood used to make expensive furniture. The officer found six stumps where once there were living trees. The limbs and branches were left behind. Scattered around the woods were 20 empty beer cans.

The officer examined the area and found tracks left by a truck leading across a neighbor's field; the perpetrator of the theft had then cut through the boundary fence. By following the tracks, the officer found where the truck had slid sideways and scraped against a tree, leaving a small smear of paint. These pieces of evidence were photographed and sampled.

The landowner remembered having seen similar tire marks leading into another wooded area two miles up the road. The officer investigated these marks and found several more black walnut stumps and more empty beer cans. The officer documented numerous forms of evidence—a paint sample from the truck, tire tread impressions, and one fingerprint lifted from a beer can. The thefts stopped, and the case was considered unsolved.

Two years later, a man was caught stealing black walnut trees a couple of counties away, and his truck was impounded. The officer compared the original paint sample to matching paint from the truck. A receipt in the truck from a veneer mill (veneer is the thin layer of high-value wood put on the surface of low-quality woods to be used in furniture) suggested that the man had been selling logs for some time.

The paint on his truck was consistent with paint found at the crime scene, and his fingerprints matched the fingerprint found on the beer can at the scene. Based on the evidence, he was convicted, fined, and sent to prison for six years. An observant investigator was able to collect sufficient evidence for a jury to find the man guilty of stealing the trees.

An investigator examines paint evidence.

2

SCENARIO

What evidence was the most valuable in convicting the suspect? Why?
What tools did the investigator use to gather the evidence?

Biology: DNA, genetic code

OBJECTIVES

By the end of this chapter, you will be able to:

1.1 Define observation, and describe what changes occur in the brain while observing.

1.2 Describe examples of factors influencing eyewitness accounts of events.

1.3 Compare the reliability of eyewitness testimony to what actually happened.

1.4 Relate observation skills to their use in forensic science.

1.5 Define forensic science.

1.6 Practice and improve your own observation skills.

TOPICAL SCIENCES KEY

BIOLOGY CHEMISTRY

EARTH SCIENCES PHYSICS

LITERACY MATHEMATICS

VOCABULARY

■ **analytical skills** the ability to identify a concept or problem, to isolate its component parts, to organize information for decision making, to establish criteria for evaluation, and to draw appropriate conclusions

■ **deductive reasoning** deriving a conclusion from the facts using a series of logical steps

■ **eyewitness** a person who has seen someone or something related to a crime and can communicate his or her observations

■ **fact** a statement or information that can be verified

■ **forensic** relating to the application of scientific knowledge to legal questions

■ **logical** reasoned from facts

■ **observations** what a person perceives using his or her senses

■ **opinion** personal belief founded on judgment rather than on direct experience or knowledge

■ **perception** information received from the senses

OBSERVATION SKILLS   3

Teaching Tip
Refer to the Instructor Resource CD (IRCD) for activity student handouts (Act SH) and other student and teacher support materials. (A list appears below.) The IRCD is organized by chapter.

Teaching Tip
See IRCD, Ch01 First Day Activity

Teaching Tip
Student Learning Objectives (SLOs) for Chapter 1 are found on the IRCD. These are single-concept, testable skills. SLOs not only help the student, but also help the teacher know what is included in the chapter. Use the SLOs throughout the chapter to periodically assess student comprehension. We suggest forming small collaborative groups to have students discuss the objectives. Rather than review all of the objectives at once at the completion of the topic, it is more effective to have students periodically review a few objectives throughout the chapter.

TEACHING RESOURCES

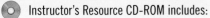

Instructor's Resource CD-ROM includes:
- Activities and Student Handouts
- Alternative Assessments
- Consolidated Bibliography
- Correlations to NGSS and CCSS
- Figure Files
- Lesson Plans with Chapter Outlines
- MST

- Nonfiction Readings
- PowerPoint Presentations
- Student Learning Objectives (SLOs)
- WTE page files

CL Testing powered by Cognero

Website: ngl.cengage.com/forensicscience2e

INTRODUCTION

Figure 1-1 *A crime scene is often laid out in a grid to ensure that all evidence is found.*

AP Images/Charles Bennett

One of the most important tools of the **forensic** investigator is the ability to observe, interpret, and report **observations** clearly. Whether observing at a crime scene or examining collected evidence in the laboratory, the forensic examiner must be able to identify the evidence, record it, and determine its significance. The trained investigator collects all available evidence, without making judgments about its potential importance. That comes later. Knowing which evidence is significant requires the ability to re-create the series of events preceding the crime. The first step is careful and accurate observation (Figure 1-1).

WHAT IS OBSERVATION? *Obj. 1.1, 1.4*

Every single moment, we are gathering information about what is around us, through our senses—sight, taste, hearing, smell, and touch. We do this largely without thinking, and it is very important to our survival. Why are we not aware of all the information our senses are gathering at any time? The simple answer is that we cannot pay attention to everything at once. Instead of a constant flow of data cluttering up our thoughts, our brains select what information they take in; we unconsciously apply a filter (Figure 1-2). We simply pay attention to things that are more likely to be important. What is important is decided by various factors, including whether the environment changes. For example, if you are sitting in a room and everything is still, you are unlikely to be filled with thoughts about the color of the sofa, the shade of the light, or the size and shape of the walls. But if a cat walks in, or you hear a loud bang, you will perceive these changes in your environment. Paying attention to the details of your surroundings requires a conscious effort.

Figure 1-2 *How information is processed in the brain.*

| Information from our senses | What we pay attention to | Perception | Short-term memory | Long-term memory |

It is difficult to believe, but our brains definitely play tricks on us. Our **perception** is limited, and the way we view our surroundings may not accurately reflect what is really there. Perception is faulty; it is not always accurate, and it does not always reflect reality. For example, our brains will fill in information that is not really there. If we are reading a sentence and a word is missing, we will often not notice the omission but instead predict the word that we think should be there and read the sentence as though it is complete.

Our brains will also apply knowledge we already have about our surroundings to new situations. In experiments with food coloring, a creamy pink dessert is perceived to be strawberry flavored even though it is vanilla flavored. Our minds have learned to associate pink with strawberries and apply that knowledge to new situations—even when it is wrong. An interesting aspect of our perception is that we believe what we see and hear, even though our ability to be accurate is flawed. People will stick to what they think they saw, even after they have been shown that it is impossible.

If you are feeling like your brain is defective, do not worry: the brain, while faulty, is still good at providing us with the information we need to survive. Filtering information, filling in gaps, and applying previous knowledge to new situations are all useful traits, even if they do interfere sometimes. Understanding our limitations helps us improve our observation skills, which is extremely important in forensic science. Criminal investigations depend on the observation skills of all parties involved—the police investigators, the forensic scientists, and the witnesses.

DIGGING DEEPER
With Forensic Science eCollection

Can a beer can in the woods lead to a conviction? A smashed dial on a safe betray the suspect? They have, and now it's your turn. Search the Gale Forensic Science eCollection on **ngl.cengage.com/forensicscience2e** to find a case study and demonstrate in writing how good observation skills led to the solution of a crime.

OBSERVATIONS BY WITNESSES

Obj. 1.2, 1.3, 1.4, 1.6

One key component of any crime investigation is the observations made by witnesses. Not surprisingly, the perceptions of witnesses can be faulty, even though a witness may be utterly convinced of what he or she saw. Have you ever noticed that you can walk along the street or ride in a car and be totally unaware of your surroundings? You may be deeply involved in a serious conversation on your cell phone and lose track of events happening around you. Your focus and concentration may make an accurate accounting of events difficult.

Our emotional state influences our ability to see and hear what is happening around us. If people are very upset, happy, or depressed, they are more likely not to notice their surroundings. Anxiety also plays a big part in what we see and what we can remember. Our fear at a stressful time may interfere with an accurate memory. Victims of bank robberies often relate conflicting descriptions of the circumstances surrounding the robbery. Their descriptions of the criminals committing the robbery often do not match.

OBSERVATION SKILLS   5

Explore
Perception may be a difficult term for some students to understand. Have students perform an activity that illustrates perception, such as touching an unseen object and guessing what the object is. Did the students guess correctly? Ask them what information they used to form their perception.

We use our five senses to make observations. Ask students what observations they can make about the classroom. What was the teacher in the previous class period wearing? Was a demonstration of some kind given? What evidence do they have? Have students recall what you were doing as they entered the classroom. Can they remember details? Why or why not? Have students brainstorm situations when their senses are heightened and they are more conscious of their surroundings. What similarities do these situations share?

Paul Ekman, who is featured in the Careers section, can often tell if someone is lying. Discuss with students how they think they can tell if someone is not telling the truth. What clues ("tells") do they look for?

DIFFERENTIATED LEARNING

Teaching At-Risk Students
Ask for a student to volunteer to empty his or her backpack contents on a table and leave them there for a few minutes, while the others observe. Put the items back, and have the students return to their desks. Now ask them to write down all of the items they remember. How much detail can they recall? Was anything missed? Discuss why students remembered certain items and not others.

Evaluate

Ask students to discuss why eye-witness accounts of a crime often differ. They should note that the accounts are based on different individuals' observations, and that each person brings a different set of physical and emotional tools to every situation.

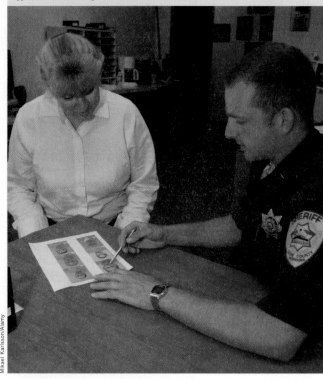

Figure 1-3 *This eyewitness is searching a mug book for previous offenders who might have committed the crime she witnessed.*

Mikael Karlsson/Alamy

Nevertheless, eyewitness accounts of crimes can be valuable evidence (Figure 1-3). Bystanders who are unaware that they are watching a crime unfold are not subject to the anxiety victims are, and may provide valuable evidence. And some victims are less subject to the disruptive effects of anxiety on memory.

Other factors affecting our observational skills include:

- Whether you are alone or with a group of people
- The number of people and/or animals in the area
- What type of activity is going on around you
- How much activity is occurring around you

All of these factors influence the accuracy of a witness's observations.

Eyewitness Accounts

What we perceive about a person depends, in part, on his or her mannerisms and gestures. How a person looks, walks, stands, and uses hand gestures all contribute to our image of his or her appearance. Think about your family members. How would you describe them? What makes them unique? We also form images of familiar places. Our homes, school, and other places we often visit (e.g., a favorite store or restaurant) are burned into our memories and easy to recognize and remember.

Eyewitness accounts of crime-scene events vary considerably from one person to another. What you observe depends on your level of interest, stress, concentration, and the amount and kind of distraction present. Our prejudices, personal beliefs, and motives also affect what we see. Memory fades with time, and our brains tend to fill in details that we feel are appropriate but may not be accurate. These factors can decrease an eyewitness's accuracy in recalling a crime. The testimony of an eyewitness can be very powerful in persuading the jury one way or another; knowing the shortcomings of eyewitness testimony is necessary to ensure that justice is carried out appropriately.

The Innocence Project

The Innocence Project at the Benjamin N. Cardozo School of Law at Yeshiva University in New York was created by Barry C. Scheck and Peter J. Neufeld in 1992. Its purpose is to reexamine post-conviction cases (individuals convicted and in prison) using DNA evidence to provide conclusive proof of guilt or innocence (Figure 1-4). After evaluating hundreds of wrongful convictions in the United States, the Innocence Project found that faulty eyewitness identification contributed up to 87 percent of those wrongful convictions. Eyewitness errors included mistakes in describing the age and facial distinctiveness of the suspect. These mistakes resulted from disguised appearances, too-brief sightings of the perpetrator, cross-gender and cross-racial bias, and changes in the viewing environment (from crime scene to police lineup).

When evaluating eyewitness testimony, the investigator must discriminate between **fact** and **opinion**. What did the witness actually see? Often what we think we saw and what really happened differ. Someone fleeing the site of a shooting might look like a suspect but could merely be an innocent bystander running away in fear of being shot. Witnesses have to be carefully examined to ensure that they describe what they saw (eyewitness evidence), not what they thought happened (opinion).

After witness examination, the examiner tries to piece together the events (facts) of the crime into a **logical** pattern. The next step is to determine if this pattern of events is verified by the evidence and reinforced by the witness testimony.

How to Be a Good Observer

We can apply what we know about how the brain processes information to improve our observation skills. Here are some basic tips:

1. *We know that we are not naturally inclined to pay attention to all of the details of our surroundings.* To be a good observer, we must make a conscious effort to examine our environment systematically. For example, if you are at a crime scene, you could start at one corner of the room and run your eyes slowly over every space, looking at everything you see. Likewise, when examining a piece of evidence on a microscope slide, look systematically at every part of the evidence.

Figure 1-4 *Gary Dotson was the first individual shown to be innocent by the Innocence Project.*

AP Images/Seth Perlman

Science
BIOLOGY

BIOLOGY
Why is DNA used in forensics? What is unique about DNA? Review students' understanding of DNA. Make sure they understand that DNA is the blueprint of a person's inherited characteristics. Everyone's DNA is different, with the exception of identical twins.

Teaching Tip
A quick activity reviewing quantitative data and qualitative data can help students make detailed observations about an object. Some students have trouble distinguishing between a factual statement and an opinion. A brief exercise defining the two may be helpful.

For example, a fact about a maggot might be: 2.1 cm. long. The associated opinion might be: "Maggots are gross!"

Teaching Tip
Search the Gale Forensic Science eCollection on ngl.cengage.com/forensicscience2e, along with other resources, for articles pertaining to the Innocence Project. Many of the exonerated individuals were convicted on the basis of eyewitness testimony.

2. *We know that we are naturally inclined to filter out information we assume is unimportant.* However, at a crime scene, we do not know what may turn out to be important. In this situation, we need to consciously observe everything, no matter how small or how familiar, no matter what our emotions or previous experiences. So we train ourselves to turn off our filters, and instead act more like data-gathering robots.

3. *We know that we are naturally inclined to interpret what we see, to look for patterns, and make connections.* To some degree, this inclination can lead to us jumping to conclusions. While observing, we need to be careful that we concentrate first and foremost on gathering all of the available information and leaving the interpretation until we have as much information as possible. The more information we have, the better our interpretations will be.

4. *We know that our memories are faulty.* While observing, it is important to write down and photograph as much information as possible (Figure 1-5). This will become very important later when we, or our investigating team members, are using our observations to try to piece together a crime. Documentation also is important when acting as an expert witness. A judge will only accept hair evidence that has been documented in writing and with photographs taken at the crime scene. The verbal testimony of a forensic scientist alone may not be entered into evidence without the proper documentation.

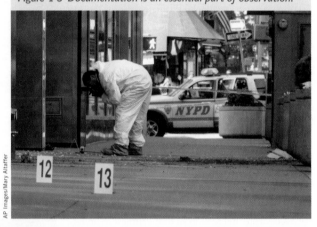

Figure 1-5 *Documentation is an essential part of observation.*

AP Images/Mary Altaffer

DIGGING DEEPER with Forensic Science eCollection

Observation is as much about finding evidence as it is about spotting patterns of criminal behavior. We know that, on average, most thieves who come in through a window will leave by a door. Search the Gale Forensic Science eCollection on **ngl.cengage.com/ forensicscience2e** for articles on patterns of criminal behavior. Discuss with the class how a knowledge of criminal behavioral patterns can help to solve crimes.

OBSERVATIONS IN FORENSICS *Obj. 1.5*

Forensics: the word conjures up images of *CSI: Miami*, lab coats, and dimly lit laboratories. "Forensic" derives from the Latin word *forensis*, which means "of the forum." The ancient Roman forum was an open area where scholars would gather to debate issues. The forum was something like modern-day court. Crimes were solved by forum debates. Sides for the suspect and victim would give speeches, and the public would decide who gave the best argument.

However, debating is not forensic science. Forensic science is concerned with uncovering evidence. It is using science to help resolve legal matters, such as crimes. A forensic investigator is interested only in collecting and examining physical evidence, reporting results to law enforcement, and possibly testifying in court. The lawyers partake in more Roman-style forensics when they try to persuade juries.

What Forensic Scientists Do

So—what do forensic scientists do? Their first task is to find, examine, and evaluate evidence from a crime scene. A good forensic scientist is skilled at making observations and applying scientific knowledge to analyze the crime scene. However, a forensic scientist must also be a good communicator who is able to convince a jury that his/her analysis is both reliable and accurate (Figure 1-6). Generally, specialists deal with certain types of evidence. Ballistics experts work with bullets and firearms; pathologists work with bodies to determine the cause of death through the examination of injuries. Textile experts, blood-spatter experts, vehicle experts, and animal experts all rely on observation skills to do their jobs.

Police officers must also be trained to have good observation skills. Part of their training is learning to take in the entire scene before making a final assessment based on their observations. Police are trained to not only observe but also to carefully analyze what they see. The ability to solve a crime depends on observing all of the evidence left at a crime scene. **Analytical skills** of this type require patience and practice.

The character Sherlock Holmes had excellent observation skills that made him an extraordinary detective. He could look at a situation and find clues in the ordinary details that others missed. Then, he worked backward from the evidence to piece together what happened leading up to the crime. Holmes used **deductive reasoning** to verify the actual facts of the case. The abilities to observe a situation, organize it into its component parts, evaluate it, and draw appropriate conclusions are all valuable analytical skills used by forensic examiners. Forensic scientists are all, in their own way, modern-day Sherlock Holmeses.

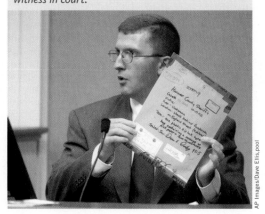

Figure 1-6 *A forensic scientist acting as an expert witness in court.*

AP Images/Dave Ellis,pool

DIFFERENTIATED LEARNING

Teaching Gifted Students

Ask students to develop a scenario that is consistent with the following observations: a strong odor inside a house; two people lying on the floor of a room in the house, one of them grasping a newspaper in his hand; three other people standing or sitting in other rooms in the house; a group of five-year-olds playing outside the house; and a fire truck outside the house.

Engage

Discuss with students how a person's experiences strongly influence what he or she interprets and remembers. Ask students to discuss what they think happens in such a situation.

Teaching Tip

Qualitative data are descriptive data, such as color or shape. We collect qualitative data using our senses. *Quantitative* data are numerical data, such as weight, height, and mass.

Teaching Tip

Scientists have established a rigorous study procedure called the scientific method. The steps are 1) state the problem or question, 2) propose a hypothesis based on prior knowledge or observation, 3) conduct an experiment, 4) collect data, 5) analyze data, and 6) draw a conclusion based on the data.

A *hypothesis* is an investigator's possible explanation of a question or problem based on prior knowledge or observation. It is not a guess.

In student investigations, students are sometimes expected to make observations, and then state a claim based on those observations.

LITERACY

NONFICTION
READINGS
Ekman, Paul,
Emotions Revealed

SUMMARY

- Our ability to observe is affected by our environment and the natural filters of sensory information in our brains.
- The observations of witnesses to crimes can be faulty, but in some cases can be precise.
- The Innocence Project has found that up to 87 percent of their wrongful conviction cases resulted from flawed eyewitness testimony.
- Police officers and crime-scene investigators are trained in good observation practices.
- Forensic scientists find, examine, photograph, document, and evaluate evidence from a crime scene and provide expert testimony to courts.

CASE STUDIES

Carlo Ferrier
(1831)

Fuse/Jupiter Images/Getty Images

In 1831, three men aged 33, 30, and 26 were tried in a court in London, England, for the murder of a 15-year-old Italian immigrant, Carlo Ferrier. John Bishop, James May, and Thomas Williams brought the body in a sack to a local university, King's College, seeking money in exchange for the corpse. It was common practice at the time for universities and hospitals to buy bodies of people who had died from natural causes to use for anatomy lessons and research. However, the university staff member noticed that this body looked particularly fresh, and he turned the three men over to the police because of his suspicion. The conviction of the suspects rested on a variety of evidence that was collected because of excellent observation skills. A surgeon carefully examined the body and noticed that all of the organs were healthy; the cause of death did not appear natural. Blood pooled around the spinal cord at the back of the neck was the only sign of violence, and was in keeping with what would be expected from a blow to the back of the neck. Other evidence included bloodstained clothes belonging to the dead boy, which were found buried in the back garden of the accused. These articles were recovered when a policeman inspecting the residence noticed a patch of soft earth in the garden. Bishop, May, and Williams were sentenced to death.

Three Wrongful Convictions

In August 2003, charges were dropped against two men who were wrongly identified and imprisoned for 27 years based on a faulty eyewitness account. In 1976, Michael Evans and Paul Terry were tried and sent to prison for the rape and murder of nine-year-old Lisa Cabassa. They were convicted on the testimony of one purported witness. DNA tests proved that the men were not guilty of the charges.

In a Florida case, death row inmate Frank Lee Smith died of cancer in January 2000 while in prison. He was convicted in 1986 of the rape and murder of an eight-year-old child, even though no physical evidence was found. He was found guilty largely on the word of an eyewitness. Four years after the crime, the eyewitness recanted her testimony, saying she had been pressured by police to testify against Smith. Despite this information, prosecutors vigorously defended the conviction and refused to allow Smith a postconviction DNA test he requested. After his death, the DNA test exonerated him.

AP Images/Jamie Rector, Pool

Think Critically

Review the Case Studies and the information on observation in the chapter. Then state in your own words how eyewitness evidence impacts a case.

Close

Review the five senses and how each one contributes to observation. Make sure students understand that while we rely strongly on the senses of sight and hearing, the other senses are also important in observation.

Have students identify factors that can influence observation. Create a class list on the board or projecting device. Select factors from the list and ask students to explain how and why each factor affects observation. Elicit from students their ideas of the forensic significance of understanding how our perceptions and memories are formed.

Careers
in Forensics

As a class, discuss other forensics professions in which psychology would be a valuable component (e.g., detective, interrogator, post-trauma counselor, or rehabilitation counselor). For example, a post-trauma counselor provides counseling and evaluation for the survivors of tragedies and disasters and their families and associates.

Invite interested students to read Paul Ekman's *Emotions Revealed* or *Unmasking the Face*. Encourage volunteers to report to the class what they learned.

Teaching Tip
Apps will be mentioned throughout the text. They are not intended to replace an understanding of forensic procedures but to enhance data collection.

Explore
A television program called *Lie to Me* was based on the work of Paul Ekman. Episodes are still available streaming or on DVD. If possible, have students view segments of the program where the main character uses microexpressions to help reveal when a person is not telling the truth. Season 1, Episodes 1 and 2 (the first five minutes) may be sufficient.

Careers *in Forensics*

Paul Ekman

Courtesy, Dr. Paul Ekman

Paul Ekman

Very few people can lie to Paul Ekman and get away with it. He can read faces like an open book, spotting the most subtle changes in expression that reveal if a person is lying. A psychologist who has spent the last 50 years studying faces, Ekman is a leading expert on facial analysis and deception. This skill puts him in high demand by law-enforcement groups around the world, such as the Federal Bureau of Investigation (FBI), Central Intelligence Agency (CIA), Scotland Yard, and Israeli Intelligence.

When looking for deception, Ekman watches for inconsistencies, such as facial expressions that do not match what is being said. He can also detect what are called *microexpressions*—rapid changes in expression that last only a fraction of a second but reveal a person's true feelings. It is a rare talent to be able to spot these microexpressions. Only 1 percent of people are able to do so without training.

Ekman was the first to determine that a human face has 10,000 possible configurations and which muscles are used in each. He then created the Facial Action Coding System. This atlas of the human face is used by a variety of people looking to decode human expression, including investigators, psychologists, and even cartoon animators.

Ekman has turned his expert gaze onto many famous faces. He thinks the mysterious Mona Lisa is flirting, and he can identify the exact facial muscles a witness uses when he lies in court. He has studied tapes of Osama bin Laden to see how his emotions changed leading up to the 9/11 terrorist attacks.

Ekman first became interested in facial expressions at the age of 14, after his mentally ill mother committed suicide. He hoped to help others like her by understanding emotional disorders. From his experience as a photographer, he realized that facial expressions would serve as a perfect tool for reading a person's emotions.

Ekman's early research led to a major discovery that changed how scientists view human expression. Experts used to believe that facial expressions were learned, but Ekman thought otherwise. He traveled around the world and found that facial expressions were universally understood, even in remote jungles where natives had never before seen a Westerner. It could mean only one thing: our expressions are biologically programmed. This opened the door for Ekman to study human expression in a completely new way.

Fifty years of groundbreaking research followed Ekman's discovery. He served first as Chief Psychologist for the U.S. Army, and then as a professor at the University of California. Now in his eighties, Ekman continues to train others to detect deception and improve safety and security. His work was the basis for the TV series *Lie To Me*.

Learn More About It
▸ To learn more about Paul Ekman and the work of forensic psychologists, go to **ngl.cengage.com/forensicscience2e**.

APPS

▸ **Lie Detector**
▸ **FaceORama**
▸ **SoER Free**

Teaching Tip
Refer to Capstone 7, Forensic Science Career Exploration, in which student teams investigate and report on different careers related to forensics.

Teaching Tip
Among poker players, there's a concept called a "tell." When a player is pretending to have a better hand than he or she does, he or she often has a tell-tale mannerism, or "tell," such as a finger tapping. Detectives are trained to look for similar mannerisms when interrogating suspects.

True or False

1. The word *forensic* refers to the application of scientific knowledge to legal questions. *Obj. 1.5*
2. Good observation skills come naturally to investigators; they do not need to be trained. *Obj. 1.1*
3. If we remember seeing something happen, we can trust that it happened just as we think it did. *Obj. 1.2, 1.3*
4. The Innocence Project is an organization that seeks to get convicted killers out of prison. *Obj. 1.2, 1.3*

Multiple Choice

5. A forensic scientist is called to a court of law to provide *Obj. 1.5*
   a) facts
   b) opinion
   c) judgment
   d) reflection
6. The Innocence Project found that most faulty convictions were based on *Obj. 1.2, 1.3*
   a) out-of-date investigating equipment
   b) poor DNA sampling
   c) inaccurate eyewitness accounts
   d) officers not thoroughly observing a crime scene

Short Answer

7. Describe why two people might perceive a crime scene in different ways. *Obj. 1.2, 1.3*
8. Briefly describe what can be detected by observing facial expressions. *Obj. 1.2, 1.3, 1.4*
9. Analyze the Case Study of Carlo Ferrier in the text. List the physical evidence observed at the crime scene, and describe its significance in solving the crime. *Obj. 1.4, 1.5*
10. Refer to the section in the text entitled "How to Be a Good Observer." Summarize methods used by forensic scientists to ensure that no evidence is overlooked. *Obj. 1.2, 1.4, 1.6*
11. Many states have passed legislation that imposes serious fines on anyone who is using a cell phone while driving. *Obj. 1.1, 1.2, 1.3*
    a) What are the laws in your state regarding texting or phoning while driving?
    b) What are some of the reasons people give as to why they text or phone while driving?
    c) Using the information from the text about observational skills, give two reasons that would convince a friend that using a cell phone while driving is a dangerous situation.

Chapter 1 Review

True or False

1. True
2. False
3. False
4. False

Multiple Choice

5. a
6. c

Short Answer

7. Two people may perceive a situation differently due to these factors:
   - Some people are more observant than others.
   - The situation may be more distracting for one person than another and, therefore, they would not notice the same things.
   - People may be focused on different things, such as a person, object, or action, so they notice different things.
   - People's memories differ.
8. Facial expressions often reveal deception. If a person is lying, then small microexpressions may be noted. His or her face may reveal inconsistencies between what is being said and his or her facial expression.
9. Body fresh—recent death
   All organs healthy—did not die from natural causes
   Blood pooled around spinal cord—violence to back of head
   Disturbed earth in garden—recent disturbance
   Buried blood-stained clothes belonging to victim—homicide
10. Look at area systematically, examining all areas. View everything, and do not prejudge what is significant and what is not. Gather all information and evidence. Take photographs, make sketches, and document all evidence.

11. A. Answers will vary.
    B. Responses might include: a need to communicate quickly with family, friends, and businesses; lack of time to pull over, feeling they are capable of doing multiple things at a time well.
    C. Statistics show that a large percentage of traffic accidents and fatalities from traffic accidents are due to drivers distracted by cell phones or other electronic devices. If you are distracted by a phone or other electronic device, then you cannot devote 100 percent of your attention to making observations regarding driving and driving conditions. You fail to observe your surroundings, such as obstacles in the road or changes in the driving patterns of other drivers.
12. Answers will vary but should include observable evidence that is characteristic of each category. Additional information is available on the Instructor's Resource CD-ROM.
13. Answers will vary. Students may refer to the TED talk on eyewitness accounts, provide the link to Project Innocence, cite the book *Picking Cotton* by Jennifer Thompson Cannino, and/or provide examples of TV crime shows: *Forensic Files, NCIS, CSI, Bones*, etc.
14. Answers will vary.

Teaching Tip

Teacher Note: Question 12—See IRCD Chapter 1, for student handout entitled CH01 CR 12 Physical Evidence.

12. Much can be learned about a person through observation. Form groups of four and choose one of the following categories to discuss. List observable clues that indicate each of the following about a person. Select one person to be the recorder. Other team members should share observations that would support their descriptions. *Obj. 1.2, 1.6*
    a) Occupation
    b) Family status
    c) Age
    d) Personality traits and habits

Going Further

13. View a TV crime show, listen to a TED talk, or read a book or article that describes why eyewitness accounts tend to be unreliable. Summarize the information and provide evidence to support the statement that eyewitness accounts are not the most reliable form of evidence.

14. Design and prepare a crime scene including various types of physical evidence. The crime scene can be presented as a written description, photograph, projected image, or poster. Ask students in the class to make observations of the crime scene and list what they observe.

Bibliography

Books and Journals

DiSpezio, Michael, *Classic Critical Thinking Puzzles*. New York: Sterling Publishing Company, 2005.
Ekman, Paul, *Emotions Revealed, 2nd Edition*, New York: Henry Holt & Company, 2007.
Loftus, E. F. *Eyewitness Testimony*. Cambridge, MA: Harvard University Press, 1996.
Munsterbe, Hugo. *On the Witness Stand: Essays on Psychology and Crime*. South Hackensack, NJ: Fred Rothman and Company, 1981.
Thompson, Jennifer, and Ronald Cotton, with Erin Torneo. *Picking Cotton*. New York: St. Martin's Griffin, 2009.
United States. *Federal Rules of Evidence*. New York: Gould Publications, a division of LexisNexis, 1991.

Internet Resources

Gale Forensic Sciences eCollection, ngl.cengage.com/forensicscience2e
The Innocence Project, www.innocenceproject.org
Apps "Lie Detector"; "FaceORama"; "SoER Free"
How Stuff Works podcast and www.howstuffworks.com "How Lie Detectors Work"
TED Talks https://new.ted.com Scott Fraser, "Why Eyewitnesses Get It Wrong"
www.YouTube.com searches "Awareness Test Gorilla Basketball," "Awareness Test Dancing Bear," "Awareness Test Card Trick"

ACTIVITY 1-1

Learning to See *Ch. Obj. 1.2, 1.3, 1.4, 1.6*

Objectives:

By the end of this activity, you will be able to:

1. Describe some of the problems in making good observations.
2. Improve your observational skills.

Time Required to Complete Activity: 25 minutes

Materials:

Act 1-1 SH Learning to See
Act 1-1 SH Photo 1
Act 1-1 SH Photo 2
Act 1-1 SH Photo 3
pencil

SAFETY PRECAUTIONS:

None

Procedure:

1. Your teacher will provide you with Photograph 1 and a question sheet.
2. Study Photograph 1 for 15 seconds.
3. When directed by your teacher, turn over your question paper and answer as many of the questions as you can in 3 minutes.
4. Repeat the process for Photographs 2 and 3.
5. Discuss the answers to the questions below with your classmates.

Questions (for class discussion):

1. Did everyone answer all of the questions correctly?
2. If everyone viewed the same photograph, list some possible reasons their answers differed.

Further Research and Extensions

Look at the photos from this activity and answer the questions about them again several days later. Tell students that this is similar to revisiting a crime scene. Did students notice different things the second time? Did they fill in more details?

Background

During this activity, students will use their observation skills to answer questions about three photographs they study for a few seconds each. They will then compare their answers with the rest of the class and discuss the reasons they think answers differed.

Materials

Student Handouts (IRCD), Teacher Resources, Activities

- Act 1-1 SH Learning to See
- Act 1-1 SH Photo 1
- Act 1-1 SH Photo 2
- Act 1-1 SH Photo 3
- pencil

Safety Precautions

None

Procedures

1. Print and copy Act 1-1 SH Learning to See. These question sheets could be copied and handed out separately to avoid students reading questions in advance of the activity.

2. Print and copy Act 1-1 SH Photo 1, 2, and 3 from the IRCD.

3. Do not give all three photographs to the students at once.

4. Do not let students read the questions before studying the photographs.

5. Make sure all students are able to see the pictures in the given time.

Answers

1. Answers will vary, but students will likely note that everyone did not answer every question correctly.

2. Possible answers: the time allotted to answer the questions, everyone's brain fills in gaps differently, the mood of the observer, distractions in the environment of the observer, past experiences of the observer.

Background

During this activity, students will be given a time limit of three minutes to observe a photograph of a crime scene and then answer questions about the scene. They will get an idea of how good an eyewitness they might be by how well they answer the questions. Students will also have an opportunity to access their observation skills.

Materials

Teacher Resources, Activities,
- Act 1-2 SH Jane's Photo
- Act 1-2 SH Jane's Questions

Safety Precautions

None

Procedures

1. Print and copy Act 1-2 SH Jane's Photo from the IRCD.
2. Print and copy Act 1-2 SH Jane's Questions.
3. Distribute the photos individually.
4. Do not let the students read the questions before studying the picture.
5. Make sure all students are able to see the picture in the given time.

Answers

1. Answers will vary.
2. Not all eyewitness testimony may be helpful in court. Eyewitnesses may not remember everything correctly. One witness's account may differ from another's.
3. Possible answers: my mood, the time I had to observe the crime scene and write down my answers, and my own experiences.
4. Possible answer: learn to look at everything and do not judge whether something is important or not.

ACTIVITY 1-2

You're an Eyewitness! *Ch. Obj. 1.2, 1.3, 1.4, 1.6*

Objectives:

By the end of this activity, you will be able to:
1. Assess the validity of eyewitness accounts of a crime.
2. Test your own powers of observation.

Time Required to Complete Activity: 45 minutes

Materials:

(per student)
Act 1-2 SH photo of Jane's Restaurant
Act 1-2 SH Jane's Questions

SAFETY PRECAUTIONS:
None

Procedure:

1. Obtain the image of Jane's Restaurant, the crime scene, from your teacher.
2. Study the image for three minutes.
3. When given the signal, turn over the image, and answer the questions about Jane's Restaurant, the crime scene.

Discussion Questions:

1. How well did you do in remembering the details in this picture?
2. What do the results of this activity say, if anything, to you about the usefulness of eyewitness accounts in a court?
3. What factors influenced your observations?
4. How could you improve your observation skills?

16   Observation Skills

Further Research and Extensions

Have one student look at a crime scene and then dictate his or her observations to another student to see if that student can sketch what the person is describing. How similar is the sketch to the observations?

DIFFERENTIATED LEARNING

Teaching English Language Learners and At-Risk Students
Find "TED Talks and Eyewitness Accounts" on the Internet; note that TED Talks are available in Spanish.

ACTIVITY 1-3

What Influences Our Observations? *Ch. Obj. 1.2, 1.3, 1.4, 1.6*

Objectives:

By the end of this activity, you will be able to:

1. Test your ability to make observations during events.
2. Design an experiment involving a television commercial or magazine ad that demonstrates how different factors influence one's ability to observe.

Introduction:

Television commercials or magazine ads can test your observational skills.

Time Required to Complete Activity: 45 minutes

Materials:

television commercial (taped or online) or magazine ad
Act 1-3 SH What Influences Our Observations?
Act 1-3 SH Student-Designed Experiment Template
pen or pencil

SAFETY PRECAUTIONS:

None

Procedure Part 1:

1. View the television commercial or magazine ad.
2. Answer the questions on the handout "What Influences Our Observations?"

©bikeriderlondon/Shutterstock.com

Background

Students will test their observation skills when viewing a series of events. Students then design an experiment to test factors affecting people's observation skills.

Materials

Act 1-3 SH What Influences
Act 1-3 SH Student-Designed Ex
pen or pencil

Safety Precautions

None

Procedure Part 2

1. Print and copy Act 1-3 SH What Influences from the IRCD.

2. Ask students if the presence or absence of sound affects their observational skills.
   Experimental design: Play a commercial to Group 1 with sound and then to Group 2 without sound.
   Students may need to test several groups to get sufficient data.
   Factor: Sound
   Group 1: No sound
   Group 2: With sound

3. After playing the commercial to both groups, have students answer the questions on Act 1-3 SH What Influences.

4. After analyzing their results, ask students if there is adequate evidence to determine if the presence or absence of sound affects observational skills.

5. Ask students how they think their conclusions relate to forensics.

Questions

Answers will vary.

Procedure Part 2: Student-Designed Commercial Activity

Provide the following format for students:

- Question
- Hypothesis
- Experimental Design
- Observation and Data
- Analysis
- Conclusion

See IRCD, Template Forms, Chapter 1

Ch01 TF Student-Designed Experiment

1. Print and make copies of Act 1-3 SH Student-Designed Ex for your students.

2. A list of suggested factors that students can consider in designing their experiment is found on student page 19.

3. Remind students that they need to *describe* the experiment and explain *what* is to be measured and *how* it is to be measured.

4. Have students present their experiment and discuss whether their claim is supported by their observations.

Questions:

1. How many people are in the commercial or ad?
2. Describe the main character(s) in the commercial in terms of
   a. Size
   b. Age
   c. Skin color
   d. Height
   e. Weight
   f. Hair: style, color, length
   g. Clothing
   h. Hat
   i. Glasses
   j. Distinguishing features
   k. Jewelry
   l. Beard or no beard
   m. Any physical limitations
3. Describe the other people in the commercial.
4. Describe the area where the video was filmed.
5. What furniture, if any, was in the commercial?
6. Was the time noted?
7. Was it possible to determine the season?
8. What were the people doing in the commercial?
9. Were there any cars in the commercial? If so, describe the:
   a. Model
   b. Year
   c. Color
   d. License plate number
10. How long was the video?

Procedure Part 2: Student-Designed-Commercial Activity

Design an activity involving commercials that would demonstrate how different factors influence our ability to observe. You should include the following:

1. Question
2. Hypothesis
3. Experimental design
   a. Control
   b. Variable
4. Observations
   a. What you will measure and how you will measure it
   b. Data tables with your measurements
5. Conclusion based on your data

Further Research and Extensions

Have students find some real-life experiments similar to theirs. Researchers for political candidates create experiments for campaign ads. Have students write reports on the findings.

Suggested Factors to Be Tested:

1. Will the number of people in the room affect someone's observational skills?
2. Will someone's observational skills be affected if he or she is listening to music while making the observation?
3. Are men less observant of the surrounding environment if the commercial features an attractive woman?
4. Are women less observant of the surrounding environment if the commercial features a handsome man?
5. Are young people less observant of an older person in a commercial as opposed to a younger person?
6. Are older people less observant of younger people in a commercial as opposed to an older person?
7. Will famous people (e.g., actors, actresses, singers, athletes) in a commercial encourage someone to watch the commercial and therefore be more observant of the product information?
8. Does racial background affect someone's ability to recognize someone of a different race?
9. Does the color of someone's clothing make the person more noticeable?
10. Are bald men more difficult to recognize than men who have hair?
11. If the person wears a hat, does that make him or her more difficult to recognize or more likely to be recognized?
12. Does a person's style of clothing make him or her more or less noticeable? (For example, are there differences in responses regarding a man wearing a suit as opposed to a man wearing jeans?)
13. Does the presence of a beard make someone less noticeable or more noticeable?
14. Is an overweight person less likely to be observed than someone of normal weight?

Further Research and Extensions

Have students choose several different commercials and describe specific elements in each that are used to target children, parents, teens, and senior citizens.

Chapter Overview

A crime cannot be committed without the perpetrator leaving some sort of evidence at the scene, no matter how minute. Trace evidence—small amounts of material physically transferred when two people or objects come into contact with each other—can be in the form of hair, clothing fibers, blood, or skin cells. Trace evidence can help investigators piece together details of a crime. Because this evidence can be easily lost or contaminated, the crime scene must be properly secured as soon as possible. All evidence must be properly collected and preserved.

The Big Ideas

Crime-scene investigators recognize, document, collect, and organize evidence left at the scene of a crime. Investigators apply specific procedures and techniques to collect trace evidence, a kind of circumstantial evidence. It is extremely important to preserve both *direct* and *indirect* evidence so that professionals can recreate as complete a picture as possible of what took place before, during, and after a crime. Investigators must secure the crime scene; separate witnesses; take photographs and sketch the scene; and search, secure, and properly package evidence.

CHAPTER 2

Crime-Scene Investigation and Evidence Collection

Lessons from the Jonbenet Ramsey Case

The 1996 homicide investigation of six-year-old JonBenet Ramsey provides valuable lessons in proper crime-scene investigation procedures. From this case, we learn how important it is to secure a crime scene. Key forensic evidence can be lost forever without a secure crime scene.

In the Ramsey case, the police in Boulder, Colorado, allowed extensive contamination of the crime scene. Police first thought JonBenet had been kidnapped because of a ransom note allegedly found by her mother. For this reason, the police did not search the house until seven hours after the family called 911. The first-responding police officer was investigating the alleged kidnapping, so he did not think to open the basement door and did not discover the body of the murdered girl.

Believing the crime was a kidnapping, the police blocked off JonBenet's bedroom with yellow and black crime-scene tape to preserve evidence her kidnapper may have left behind. But they did not seal off the rest of the house, which was also part of the crime scene. The victim's father, John Ramsey, discovered his daughter's body in the basement of the home. He covered her body with a blanket and carried her to the living room. In doing so, he contaminated the crime scene and may have disturbed evidence. That evidence might have identified the killer.

Once the body was found, family, friends, and police officers remained close by. The Ramseys and visitors were allowed to move freely around the house. One friend helped clean the kitchen, wiping down the counters with a spray cleaner—possibly wiping away evidence. Many hours passed before police blocked off the basement room. A pathologist did not examine the body until more than 18 hours after the crime took place.

Officers at this crime scene obviously made serious mistakes that may have resulted in the contamination or destruction of evidence. To this day, the crime remains unsolved. Go to the Gale Forensic Science eCollection for more information on this case.

The Ramsey Home in Boulder, Colorado.

20

SCENARIO

Divide the class into groups of three or four students, and have each group read the scenario. As a class, discuss the following questions:
What mistakes were made by the Boulder Police Department in securing the crime scene?
What specific kinds of evidence may have been compromised?
What could the police have done differently to secure the crime scene and the evidence?

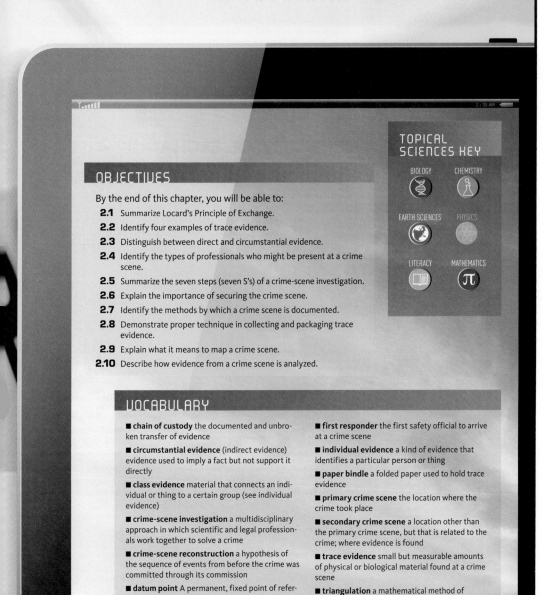

Biology: blood typing

Earth sciences: different ways to study soil

Mathematics: calculating odds

Chemistry: chemical analysis of evidence

OBJECTIVES

By the end of this chapter, you will be able to:

2.1 Summarize Locard's Principle of Exchange.

2.2 Identify four examples of trace evidence.

2.3 Distinguish between direct and circumstantial evidence.

2.4 Identify the types of professionals who might be present at a crime scene.

2.5 Summarize the seven steps (seven S's) of a crime-scene investigation.

2.6 Explain the importance of securing the crime scene.

2.7 Identify the methods by which a crime scene is documented.

2.8 Demonstrate proper technique in collecting and packaging trace evidence.

2.9 Explain what it means to map a crime scene.

2.10 Describe how evidence from a crime scene is analyzed.

TOPICAL SCIENCES KEY

BIOLOGY CHEMISTRY

EARTH SCIENCES PHYSICS

LITERACY MATHEMATICS

VOCABULARY

■ **chain of custody** the documented and unbroken transfer of evidence

■ **circumstantial evidence** (indirect evidence) evidence used to imply a fact but not support it directly

■ **class evidence** material that connects an individual or thing to a certain group (see individual evidence)

■ **crime-scene investigation** a multidisciplinary approach in which scientific and legal professionals work together to solve a crime

■ **crime-scene reconstruction** a hypothesis of the sequence of events from before the crime was committed through its commission

■ **datum point** A permanent, fixed point of reference used in mapping a crime scene

■ **direct evidence** evidence that (if authentic) supports an alleged fact of a case

■ **first responder** the first safety official to arrive at a crime scene

■ **individual evidence** a kind of evidence that identifies a particular person or thing

■ **paper bindle** a folded paper used to hold trace evidence

■ **primary crime scene** the location where the crime took place

■ **secondary crime scene** a location other than the primary crime scene, but that is related to the crime; where evidence is found

■ **trace evidence** small but measurable amounts of physical or biological material found at a crime scene

■ **triangulation** a mathematical method of estimating positions of objects at a location such as a crime scene, given locations of stationary objects

CRIME-SCENE INVESTIGATION AND EVIDENCE COLLECTION **21**

Consider the Capstone Activities that focus on evidence, such as the following:

Capstone 1 Physical Evidence Case Studies

Capstone 2 Personal Evidence Portfolio

Capstone 3 How Reliable Is the Evidence?

Capstone 4 Landmark Cases in Acceptance of Evidence

Capstone 5 Analysis of a Forensic Science TV Show Episode

Capstone 6 Forensic Dumpster Diving

Capstone 8 Mock Crime-Scene Development and Processing

Capstone 10 Grave Site Excavation

TEACHING RESOURCES

 Instructor's Resource CD-ROM includes:

- Activities and Student Handouts
- Alternative Assessments
- Consolidated Bibliography
- Correlations to NGSS and CCSS
- Figure Files
- Lesson Plans with Chapter Outlines
- MST

- Nonfiction Readings
- PowerPoint Presentations
- Student Learning Objectives (SLOs)
- WTE page files

CL Testing powered by Cognero

Website: ngl.cengage.com/forensicscience2e

Engage

Share the following scenario with your students: after seeing a movie, you and a group of friends walk to your car in the movie theater parking lot to find the driver's-side window shattered and the door wide open. Looking inside the car, you find that the car stereo and all of your CDs have been stolen. What specific evidence could have been left in or around your car that could help reveal who committed this crime? What precautions should you and your friends take to preserve any evidence?

INTRODUCTION

How is it possible to identify the person who committed a crime? A single hair or clothing fiber can allow a crime to be reconstructed and lead police to the responsible person. The goal of a **crime-scene investigation** is to recognize, document, photograph, and collect evidence at the scene of a crime. Solving the crime depends on piecing together the evidence to form a picture of what happened at the crime scene.

PRINCIPLE OF EXCHANGE Obj. 2.1, 2.2

Whenever two people come into contact with each other or with an object, a physical transfer occurs. Hair, skin cells, clothing fibers, pollen, glass fragments, debris from a person's clothing, makeup, or any number of different types of material can be transferred from one person or object to another. To a forensic examiner, these transferred materials constitute what is called **trace evidence**. Some common examples of trace evidence include:

- Pet hair on clothes or rugs
- Hair on brushes
- Fingerprints on a glass
- Soil tracked into homes or buildings on shoes
- A drop of blood on a T-shirt
- A used facial tissue
- Paint chips
- Broken glass fragments
- A fiber from clothing

The first person to note this was Dr. Edmond Locard, director of the world's first forensic laboratory in Lyon, France. He established several important ideas that are still a part of forensic studies today. **Locard's Principle of Exchange** states that when a person comes into contact with an object or another person, a cross-transfer of physical evidence can occur. The exchanged materials indicate that the two entities were in contact. Trace evidence can be found on both entities because of this cross-transfer. This evidence that is exchanged bears a silent witness to the criminal act. Locard used transfer (trace) evidence from under a female victim's fingernails to help identify her attacker.

The second part of Locard's Principle states that the *intensity, duration,* and *nature* of the entities in contact determine the extent of the transfer. For example, more transfer would occur if two individuals engaged in a fistfight than if a person simply brushed past another person. However, exchanges are not always useful evidence. Finding a fingerprint on an object or a hair on a surface does not often provide clues as to *when* the exchange occurred.

Teaching English-Language Learners
Make sure students understand the meanings of *direct* and *indirect (circumstantial)* evidence. Ask students to list the following types of evidence: blood stain on a T-shirt—*indirect*; tire tracks in the mud—*indirect*; lip print on a glass—*indirect*; eyelash found on a bathroom sink—*indirect*; videotape from a bank—*direct*. Now have them differentiate between direct and indirect types of evidence collected at a crime scene you provide them by writing "direct" or "indirect" next to each type of evidence.

Teaching Gifted Students
Allow students to design a spreadsheet in which class members can enter all the types of crime evidence they encounter during this course, by category (class, individual).

TYPES OF EVIDENCE *Obj. 2.3*

Evidence can be classified into two types: direct evidence and circumstantial evidence (Figure 2-1). **Direct evidence** includes firsthand observations such as eyewitness accounts or police dashboard video cameras. For example, a witness states that she saw a defendant pointing a gun at a victim during a robbery. In court, direct evidence involves testimony by a witness about what that witness personally saw, heard, or did. Confessions are also considered direct evidence.

Circumstantial evidence is indirect evidence that can be used to imply a fact but that does not prove it. No one, other than the suspect and/or victim, actually knows when circumstantial evidence is produced. Circumstantial evidence found at a crime scene may provide a link between a crime scene and a suspect. For example, finding a suspect's gun at the site of a shooting is circumstantial evidence of the suspect's presence there.

Circumstantial evidence can be either physical or biological in nature. Physical evidence includes impressions such as fingerprints, footprints, shoe prints, tire impressions, and tool marks. Physical evidence also includes glass, soil, fibers, weapons, bullets, and shell casings. Biological evidence includes DNA in tissue, bodily fluids, hair, plants, pollen, and natural fibers. Most physical evidence, with the exception of fingerprints, reduces the number of suspects to a specific, smaller group of individuals. Biological evidence such as blood or DNA may make the group of suspects very small. In the case of DNA, it may reduce the group to a single individual, which is more persuasive in court. Trace evidence is a type of circumstantial evidence, examples of which include hair found on a brush, fingerprints on a glass, blood drops on a shirt, and soil tracked into a house (Figure 2-2).

Evidence can also be divided into class evidence and individual evidence. **Class evidence** narrows an identity to a group of persons or things. Knowing the ABO blood type of a sample of blood from a crime scene tells us that one of many persons with that blood type may have been there. It also allows us to exclude anyone with a different blood type. **Individual evidence** narrows an identity to a single person or thing. Individual evidence typically has such a unique combination of characteristics that it could only belong to one person or thing, such as a fingerprint or DNA.

Figure 2-1 *Classification of types of evidence.*

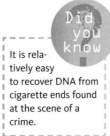

It is relatively easy to recover DNA from cigarette ends found at the scene of a crime.

Figure 2-2 *Common examples of trace evidence.*

Animal or human hair
Fingerprints
Soil or plant material (including pollen)
Body fluids such as mucus, semen, saliva, or blood
Fiber or debris from clothing
Paint chips, broken glass, or chemicals such as drugs or explosives

EARTH SCIENCES   BIOLOGY   CHEMISTRY

Explore

Ask students to write a paragraph explaining the differences between class and individual evidence, making sure to give examples for each. Have them include answers to the following questions in their discussion:

- Would class or individual evidence be considered direct or circumstantial?
- Could biological evidence be circumstantial? Explain.

Science   EARTH SCIENCES

EARTH SCIENCES

Pedologists, or soil scientists, are interested in the way the five soil-forming factors (i.e., parent material, climate, topography, organisms, and time) affect the properties of the soil in its natural, undisturbed state. To help solve a crime, forensic geologists study soil at a crime scene that has been disturbed or moved. They obtain soil samples from in and around crime scenes from which soil may have been transported, perhaps by a tire tread or the bottom of a shoe. Each type of soil has unique characteristics that allow forensic geologists to use soils as evidence in criminal investigations.

Science   CHEMISTRY

CHEMISTRY

Chemical analysis is used to identify the presence of drugs, toxins, paints, solvents, and explosives. Chemical analysis of decomposition gases at a grave site (if present) can provide clues to time of death.

Science   BIOLOGY

BIOLOGY

Everyone has a blood type. The most common blood-type classification system is the ABO (say "A-B-O") system discovered by Karl Landsteiner in the early 1900s. There are four types of blood in the ABO system: A, B, AB, and O. (There are eight blood types if you include Rh factors.) However, today's forensic scientists rely more on DNA profiling and antibody testing than on blood typing.

Explore

Discuss different crime-scene participants.

Police officers: Most police officers are trained in basic forensic techniques. Officers must have a working knowledge of evidence so they do not inadvertently compromise it. They may be asked to collect evidence, especially in small police departments that do not have a CSI unit. Police officers in small towns or communities might bag trace evidence, dust for fingerprints, or use tape to collect hairs or fibers. They would also be links in the chain of custody.

Specialists: A forensic anthropologist studies human bones to determine factors such as sex, age, height, weight, and ethnic background of the victim. A botanist might be able to determine the time of year or region of the world in which a crime took place by studying plant material, including pollen that may have been left at a crime scene. An entomologist might be able to estimate the time since death, or *postmortem interval,* by studying insects colonizing a body. A forensic pathologist autopsies the body and determines the cause of death.

Evaluate

Record an episode of a CSI show. Let the class view all or part of the program. As students watch, ask them to answer the following questions and be ready to discuss them after watching the show:
- What are some examples of direct, indirect, physical, biological, and/or trace evidence?
- How was the crime scene secured?
- What mistakes, if any, were made in securing the crime scene?
- What evidence could have been compromised?

CAPSTONE ACTIVITY

Capstone 5 Analysis of a Forensic Science TV Episode.

CHAPTER

1
2
3
4
5
6
7
8
9
10
11
12
13
14
15
16
17
18

Did you know

Crime-scene investigation teams do not clean up the scene. This dirty job often falls to the victim's family. Professional crime-scene cleaners can be hired to do this job.

CAPSTONE ACTIVITY

#10 "Gravesite Excavation"

THE CRIME-SCENE INVESTIGATION TEAM *Obj. 2.4*

Who is involved in a crime-scene investigation? The team is made up of legal and scientific professionals who work together to solve a crime. Professionals at the scene of a crime may include police officers, detectives, crime-scene investigators, district attorneys, medical examiners, and scientific specialists.

- *Police officers* are usually the first to arrive at a crime scene. They secure the scene and direct activity. A district attorney may be called to the scene to determine whether a search warrant is necessary for the crime-scene investigators.
- *Crime-scene investigators* document the crime scene in detail and collect physical evidence. Crime-scene investigators record the data, sketch the scene, and take photos of the crime scene.
- *Medical examiners* (or coroners) determine the manner of death: *natural, accidental, homicide, suicide,* or *undetermined.*
- *Detectives* interview witnesses and talk to the crime-scene investigators about the evidence.
- *Specialists* such as entomologists (insect biologists), forensic scientists, and forensic psychologists may be consulted if the evidence requires their expertise.

THE SEVEN S'S OF CRIME-SCENE INVESTIGATION

Obj. 2.5, 2.6, 2.7, 2.8

Securing the Scene

Securing the scene is the responsibility of the first-responding law-enforcement officer (**first responder**). The safety of all individuals in the area is the first priority. Preservation of evidence is the second priority. This means the officer protects the area within which the crime has occurred, restricting all unauthorized persons from entering. Transfer, loss, or contamination of evidence can occur if the area is left unsecured (Locard's Principle of Exchange). The first officer on the scene keeps a security log of all those who visit the crime scene. The officer collects pertinent information and requests any additional requirements for the investigation. He or she may ask for more officers to secure the area. Depending on the nature of the crime, the first-responding officer may request various teams of experts to be sent to the crime scene.

Separating the Witnesses

Separating the witnesses is the next priority. Witnesses must not be allowed to talk to each other. Crime-scene investigators will compare the witnesses' accounts of the events. Witnesses are separated so they do not work together to create a story (collusion).

DIFFERENTIATED LEARNING

Teaching English-Language Learners

Have students cut 12 three-by-five-inch cards in half. Write a chapter vocabulary word on one side of a card and the definition for the word on the back. Have students refer to the cards as often as necessary throughout the study of the chapter. If possible, have students use the last two to three minutes of each class period to review their flash cards.

The following questions need to be asked of each witness:

- When did the crime occur?
- Who notified law enforcement?
- Who is the victim?
- Can the perpetrator be identified?
- What did you see happen?
- Where were you when you observed the crime scene?

Scanning the Scene

The forensic crime-scene examiners first need to scan the scene to determine where photos should be taken. A determination may be made of a primary crime scene and secondary crime scene and priorities assigned regarding examination. (The location of the crime is the **primary crime scene**. If movement to a new location occurs, that location is considered a **secondary crime scene**.) A robbery in front of a store might be the primary scene, and the home of a suspect might be the secondary scene. A murder may have taken place at one location (primary scene) and the body found at another (secondary scene).

Seeing the Scene

The crime-scene examiner needs to see the scene. Photos of the overall area and close-up photos with and without a measuring ruler should be taken. *Triangulation* should be included in the photos. **Triangulation** is a mathematical method of calculating the location of an object from the locations of other objects. Close-ups and photos from varying distances of any evidence and remains should be taken.

 ▶ **Theodolite**

Sketching the Scene

A crime-scene investigator eventually makes an accurate sketch of the crime scene, noting the position of the remains (if any) and any other evidence. (You can see a reduced sketch form in Figure 2-3.) All objects should be

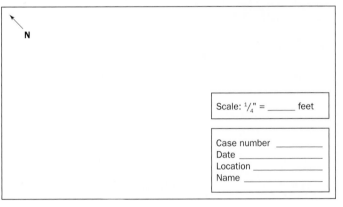

N

Scale: ¹/₄" = _____ feet

Case number _____
Date _____
Location _____
Name _____

Figure 2-3 *A reduced blank crime-scene sketch form showing the information that must be provided with the sketch.*

Teaching Tip

If possible, take students outside or to the school's auditorium or gym to use different search patterns. "Plant" evidence for students to discover. Divide students into four groups and assign each a search pattern that covers one quarter of the area. Make the search more rewarding by recording the search patterns of each group and how much evidence was discovered by each group.

Teaching Tip

One misconception students may have is that all of the evidence at a crime scene will be found and all of it will be in good condition and useful to the investigation. For instance, many fingerprints are smudged, faint, distorted, or partial. This is a good time to remind students why it is so important to properly secure a crime scene. A suspect may be found not guilty because evidence was not properly collected or stored, the chain of custody was broken, or other procedures within and around a crime scene were not correctly followed.

Teaching Tip

Refer to IRCD, Chapter 2, Template Forms to download:
CH02_TF_Paper Bindle
CH02_TF_Evidence Marker
CH02_TF_Mini Notebook
Ch02_TF_Evidence Inv Label

measured from two immovable landmarks. On the sketch, north should be labeled, and a distance scale should be provided. Any other objects in the vicinity of the crime scene, such as doors, windows, and furniture, should be included in the sketch. If the crime scene is outdoors, the positions of trees, vehicles, hedges, and other structures or objects should be included in the sketch. Later, a more accurate, final copy of the crime scene should be made for possible presentation in court, likely with specialized software.

Searching for Evidence

The type of search pattern varies depending on the size of the area to be searched and the number of investigators. Single investigators might use a gridded, linear, or spiral pattern. A group of investigators might use a linear, zone, or quadrant pattern. These patterns are used systematically, ensuring that no area is left unsearched (Figure 2-4).

Figure 2-4 *Four crime-scene search patterns.*

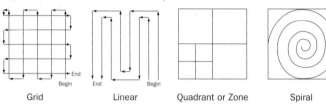

Grid   Linear   Quadrant or Zone   Spiral

All evidence should be photographed, sketched, labeled, and documented. Additional light sources such as flashlights or black lights are used to locate hair, fibers, or body fluids. New technologies, including thermal and satellite imaging and ground-penetrating radar, can be used to help locate remains

Did you know

Research how thermal imaging helped to locate the alleged Boston Marathon bomber.

DIGGING DEEPER

with Forensic Science eCollection

What happened to Natalee Holloway in Aruba in 2005? This is an unsolved case in which questions have been raised about why crime-scene investigators have not been able to find her body. In fact, investigators searched the island with an array of cutting-edge tools, from a remote-controlled submersible equipped with a video camera and sonar used for probing the water under bridges and in lagoons, to telescoping rods tipped with infrared sensors and cameras used for searching beneath manhole covers and into shadowy caverns. Go to the Gale Forensic Science eCollection on **ngl.cengage.com/forensicscience2e** and research the case. Conduct your own investigation by reading the primary sources available on the Website. Write a brief explanation that summarizes the forensic tools used to find Holloway's body and any evidence that was discovered during the search.

and other evidence. Thermal imaging helped law-enforcement teams pinpoint the location of the Boston Marathon bombing suspect in April 2013 (Figure 2-5).

Securing and Collecting Evidence

All evidence needs to be properly packaged, sealed, and labeled. Specific procedures and techniques for evidence collection and storage must be followed. Liquids and arson remains are stored in airtight, unbreakable containers. Moist biological evidence is stored in breathable containers so the evidence can dry out, reducing the chance of mold contamination. After the evidence is allowed to air dry, it is packaged in a **paper bindle**. The bindle (also called a druggist's fold) can then be placed in a plastic or paper container. This outer container is then sealed with tape and labeled with the signature of the collector written across the tape. An evidence log and a **chain of custody** document must be attached to the evidence container.

The evidence log should contain all pertinent information, including:

- Case number
- Item inventory number
- Description of the evidence
- Name of suspect
- Name of victim
- Date and time of recovery
- Signature of person recovering the evidence
- Signature of any witnesses present during collection

PACKAGING EVIDENCE

The paper bindle is ideal packaging for small, dry, trace evidence. The size of the bindle depends on the size of the evidence. If the evidence is small, the bindle can be constructed from a sheet of paper. If the evidence is large, the bindle might be constructed from a large sheet of wrapping paper. The packaging techniques are shown in Figure 2-6 on the next page. The steps are as follows:

1. Choose the appropriate-size sheet of clean paper for the bindle.
2. Crease the paper as shown.
3. Place evidence in the location shown by the X.
4. Fold the left and right sides in.
5. Fold in the top and bottom.

Figure 2-5 *Thermal image of the alleged Boston Marathon bomber, Dzhokhar Tsarnaev, hiding in a boat just before being captured.*

Handout/Getty Images

Explore

Have students research how new technologies such as thermal imaging, ground-penetrating radar, and satellite photos can be used to locate bodies and/or evidence. Present photos illustrating the latest technologies.

Explore

Discuss with students how the hiding spot of the Boston Marathon bomber was discovered by thermal imaging tomography.

Teaching Tip

Package evidence using either a paper bindle (Figure 2-5) or plastic container, depending on whether evidence is wet (into paper) or dry (either container). Each time a bag of evidence is examined, the bag is cut along an *unopened, unsealed* edge and resealed with the date and the name of the examiner. Emphasize that when an evidence bag is opened, the examiner must *never* break a seal. The bag is opened in a new place and resealed with all of the pertinent information. For example, there should be two names written along two different parts of a bag if two people opened and then sealed it. This process allows others to see who opened the bag and when.

CHEMISTRY

Teaching Tip

Demonstrate how blood evidence can be detected using Luminol or Bluestar. Note that several laundry detergents and cleaners can be used as a substitute for blood. These substitutes can be identified using a black light. Have students research the chemistry behind the reaction. Tide, Mr. Clean, club soda, and antifreeze will also glow (fluoresce) under black light and can interfere with evidence recovery. Instead of spatter, for example, the surface will look wiped.

Explore

The prosecution of criminal cases in the United States is terribly backlogged. This has a lot to do with the time it takes to analyze evidence. Not all forensic labs have all of the personnel, budget, or equipment needed to process all of the evidence. For instance, equipment to analyze DNA is too expensive for some crime labs, so they must send their DNA samples to another lab and pay for the analysis. Some crime labs hire private firms to do their testing or to confirm their results. All of this takes time and money.

Ask students to research how DNA evidence is processed in their community. Where is the processing center located? What does a DNA analysis cost? Who pays for the testing?

Teaching Tip

Have students package hair evidence in a paper bindle, seal it, and label it. Have each student pass the evidence to another student. The recipient should open the evidence, examine the evidence, complete the chain of custody portion of the Evidence Inventory Label properly, and reseal it using the proper technique.

DIGGING DEEPER

Orenthal James Simpson, or O.J., is one of the most infamous players in American football history. He was a star running back for the USC Trojans, setting NCAA records and winning the Heisman Trophy. The majority of his professional career was spent with the Buffalo Bills. After he retired from football, Simpson served as a sports commentator and actor for some time.

Figure 2-6 *Demonstration of packaging of dry evidence.*

a. Placement of evidence.

b. Place dried evidence on bindle paper.

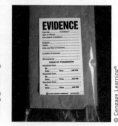

c. Secure bindle in labeled evidence bag using stick-on label.

d. Write the collector's signature across the bag's taped edge.

6. Insert the top flap into the bottom flap; then tape the bindle closed.
7. Place the bindle inside a plastic or paper evidence bag. Fold the bag closed.
8. Place a seal over the folded edge of the evidence bag.
9. Have the collector write his or her name over the folded edge.

If a wet object to be packaged is large, it should be placed in a paper container and sealed to allow it to air dry. Wet evidence should never be packaged in a plastic container while wet. Any DNA present will degrade and evidence may become moldy and useless.

There are standards for collecting different types of evidence that describe how to collect and store the evidence. The Federal Bureau of Investigation and state police agencies publish descriptions of the proper procedures.

Control samples, including hair and fibers, must also be obtained from the victim for the purpose of exclusion. For example, blood samples found on a victim or at a crime scene are compared with the victim's blood.

O.J. Simpson was tried and acquitted for the murder of his ex-wife Nicole Brown Simpson and her friend Ronald Goldman in 1994. The O.J. Simpson murder trial is often cited as a classic example of how crucial evidence was lost, altered, or contaminated. Go to the Gale Forensic Science eCollection on **ngl.cengage.com/forensicscience2e** and research the case. Cite specific examples of how evidence was damaged, lost, or contaminated by crime-scene personnel. Write a brief explanation summarizing your findings, making sure to back up your argument with reliable sources for which you cite dates of the publications.

28   CHAPTER 2

DIFFERENTIATED LEARNING

Teaching Gifted Students
Several people involved in the Simpson murder trial have written books about their experiences. Have students read one of these books and prepare a presentation to give to the class. They should discuss whether crucial evidence was contaminated or made to seem unreliable and what particular factors might have been involved in the not-guilty verdict.

If they match, the samples are excluded from further study. If the blood samples do not match, then they may have come from the perpetrator and will be further examined.

CHAIN OF CUSTODY

In securing the evidence, maintaining the chain of custody is essential. The individual who finds evidence bags the evidence in a plastic or paper container. The final container for the evidence is a collection bag or box, which is labeled with the pertinent information. The container is then sealed, and the collector's signature is written across the sealed edge.

The container is given to the next person. That person takes it to the lab and signs it over to a technician, who opens the package at a location other than the sealed edge. On completion of the examination, the technician repackages the evidence in its original packaging, inserts and reseals the evidence in new packaging, and signs the chain-of-custody log attached to the packaging. This process ensures tracking of the evidence as it passes from the crime scene to a courtroom (Figure 2-7).

Teaching Tip
Some students may need instruction and practice using a compass. This should be done before setting up a collection site for evidence. Give all students instruction and practice time, and be sure all students are competent before beginning the exercise.

Figure 2-7 *Chain-of-custody procedures.*

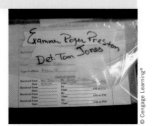

a. Original evidence bag.

b. Opened evidence bag maintaining signature on first seal.

c. Original evidence bag with uncut seal and signature, updated chain-of-custody log in a new sealed and signed evidence bag.

Mapping the Outdoor Crime Scene

In establishing an area around a crime scene for outdoor evidence collection, use either a triangular, square, or rectangular region surrounding the evidence (Figure 2-8). All evidence should be accurately documented as to its precise location.

Figure 2-8 *Establishing a crime scene.*

DATUM POINTS AND SUBDATUM POINTS

If possible, establish a **datum point**, a permanent, fixed point of reference such as a corner of a building or a tree. Measurements and directions can be established from the datum point to a corner stake of your crime scene marking the *subdatum point.* Use a piece of rebar or wooden stake pounded into

Science

MATHEMATICS

MATH
Recall that a right triangle has one 90-degree angle. The side opposite the right angle is called the hypotenuse. If you examine one of the other angles, called the angle of interest, then a side next to the angle of interest is called an adjacent side. The side across from the angle of interest is known as the opposite side.

Teaching Tip

Refer to Activity 5-4 *Processing a Crime Scene for Botanical Evidence* and Capstone 10 *Gravesite Excavation* for additional activities involving searches for evidence at crime scenes.

the ground at the corner of your crime scene as your subdatum point. The rebar can later be located using a metal detector. Any evidence collected will be measured from this subdatum point using two tape measures and a compass.

Pound the rebar or stake into the ground at the north corner of your crime scene at least 1 meter away from any evidence. This marks the first corner (subdatum) of your crime scene. The rebar is used and left in the ground so the crime scene can be revisited.

Using a compass, establish a north-south baseline from this first corner. Run a measuring tape from the rebar located in the first corner (northern end) along this north-south baseline extending the tape measure at least one meter beyond any evidence. Put in a stake at this second corner subdatum (located along the south end of your north-south baseline). Record the distance of this north-south baseline to stake 2.

MARKING EVIDENCE COLLECTING LIMITS

From the first north corner, stake 1, use a compass to form a second line located at 90 degrees east of the first corner. Extend the metered tape at least 1 meter beyond your evidence. Put in a stake into this third corner, 3. Record the length of this second line. Position stake 4 so that a rectangle (or square) is formed around the evidence. Be sure all corners are right angles (see Figure 2-9).

Ensure that you have formed right angles (90 degrees) at each of the corners. Using your north-south perimeter length (*a*) (corner 1 to corner 2) and your north-east perimeter length (*b*), (corner 1 to corner 3), calculate the hypotenuse (*c*) of the right triangle formed by these two sides. Recall the Pythagorean theorem, $a^2 + b^2 = c^2$, where *a* and *b* are the congruent sides of a right triangle, and *c* is the hypotenuse, the side that connects them. For example, if your north-south baseline (*a*) was equal to 3 meters, and your second north-east line (*b*) was equal to 4 meters, then the length of your hypotenuse (*c*) would be 5 meters ($3^2 + 4^2 = c^2$) or ($9 + 16 = c^2$). The square root of 25 is 5, so your hypotenuse is 5.

If you tie a string around corner 3 (northeast corner) equal to the length of your calculated hypotenuse and extend it to corner 2 (southwest corner), it should connect to corner 2. If the string (your hypotenuse) is either too long or too short, then your corners are not 90 degrees. If they are not, go back and check your compass settings are 90 degrees. The length of your calculated hypotenuse should fit the distance between corner 3 and corner 2. Use the same procedure to check the other sides of your rectangle.

MEASURING AND MARKING EVIDENCE POSITIONS

The location of any evidence is measured by the perpendicular distances from the evidence to the two reference lines along the perimeter of your rectangle (Figure 2-10). For example, the distance could be measured from the perpendicular distance from the north–south baseline and the

MATHEMATICS

Figure 2-9 *Evidence collecting limits.*

North

NW Corner #1 ☆　　　　　　　☆ NE Corner #3

SW Corner #2 ☆　　　　　　　☆ SE Corner #4

DIFFERENTIATED LEARNING

Teaching At-Risk Students
Motivate students to master use of a compass by hiding rewards (bonus points, for example) around the classroom. Provide the students with directions that demonstrate compass competence.

Figure 2-10 *Measuring the position of evidence.*

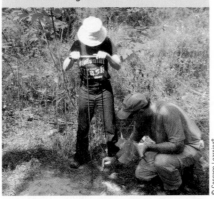

Figure 2-11 *Probing a collection site for evidence belowground.*

Teaching Tip

Before having students map out the crime scene, have them practice identifying compass headings of objects in the classroom or just outside the windows.

perpendicular measurement from your east–west line. You can also cite the compass heading of the evidence taken from the rebar stake or subdatum point in corner 1 to validate the position of the evidence.

To express locations of evidence above or below the ground (Figure 2-11), use the ground as your baseline. Express distances aboveground as positive numbers and distances belowground as negative numbers.

Refer to Figure 2-12. The evidence location (green dot) could be noted as 2 meters from the north line and 2 meters from the west line. The compass heading from subdatum corner 1 is 45 degrees.

Figure 2-12 *Establishing the location of evidence at the collection site.*

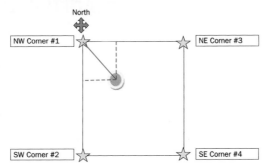

ANALYZE THE EVIDENCE *Obj. 2.9*

Following crime-scene processing, the forensic laboratory work begins (Figure 2-13). A forensic lab processes all of the evidence processed at the crime-scene. Unlike the characters on CSI television programs, forensic lab technicians are specialized and process only one type of evidence.

The laboratory results are sent to the lead detective. The detective looks at the evidence and attempts to determine how it fits into the overall crime scenario. The evidence is examined and compared with the witnesses' statements to help determine the reliability of their accounts. Evidence analysis can link a suspect with a scene or a victim, establish the identity of a victim or suspect, confirm verbal witness testimony, or acquit the innocent. Investigators must consider

Figure 2-13 *A modern forensics laboratory.*

CRIME-SCENE INVESTIGATION AND EVIDENCE COLLECTION   31

Explore

In 1960, crime-scene investigators only had presumptive blood tests and blood identification tests. The former tests only determine if the sample is blood or not. The latter test will tell if the blood is human or from another animal. Blood identification, or typing, tests could also tell which of the four types of blood (i.e., A, B, AB, or O) was present. Have students investigate the following topics: the different types of presumptive blood tests, how it is possible to determine whether blood is human or animal, or blood type information used in forensic blood testing.

CAPSTONE ACTIVITY

#3 "How Reliable Is the Evidence?"

#4 "Landmark Cases in Acceptance of Evidence"

all possible interpretations of the evidence. Direct evidence is more convincing than circumstantial evidence. During legal proceedings, in the process of discovery, all information in the possession of the prosecution must be shared with the defense.

CRIME-SCENE RECONSTRUCTION

Crime-scene reconstruction involves forming a hypothesis of the sequence of events from before the crime was committed through its commission. The evidence is examined and compared with the witnesses' statements to help determine the reliability of their accounts. The investigator looks at the evidence and attempts to determine how it fits into the overall crime scenario. The evidence does not lie, but it could have been staged. It is important that investigators maintain an open mind as they examine all possibilities.

STAGED CRIME SCENES

Crime scenes that are faked, or *staged*, by criminals pose a unique problem. The evidence will not match the testimony of witnesses. Here is a list of some commonly staged types of crime scenes:

- *Arson.* The perpetrator stages a fire to cover some other crime such as murder or burglary.
- *Murder staged to look like suicide.* A victim is murdered, and the perpetrator stages the scene to look like a suicide. The death may be caused by alcohol or drug overdose, or it may be caused by violence. The motive could be insurance money, release from an unhappy marriage, or simply robbery.
- *Burglary.* A burglary may be staged to collect insurance money.

In the determination of whether a crime scene is staged, the following points should be considered:

- Initially treat all death investigations as homicides.
- Are the type(s) of wounds on the victim consistent with the suspected weapon employed?
- Could the wounds be easily self-inflicted?
- Establish a profile of the victim through interviews with friends and family.
- Evaluate the behavior (mood and actions) of the victim before the event.
- Evaluate the behavior (mood and actions) of any suspects before the event.
- Corroborate statements with evidential facts.
- Reconstruct the event.

SUMMARY

- Locard's Principle of Exchange states that contacts between people and objects during a crime can result in a transfer of material.

- Evidence may be direct, as in eyewitness accounts, or circumstantial, which does not directly support a fact.

- Evidence may be physical or biological. Trace evidence is a small amount of physical or biological evidence.

- A crime-scene investigation team consists of police officers, detectives, crime-scene investigators, medical examiners, and specialists.

- A crime-scene investigation consists of recognizing, documenting, photographing, and collecting evidence from the crime scene.

- First-responding officers must identify the extent of a crime scene, including primary and secondary scenes when possible, secure the scene(s), and segregate witnesses.

- After examining the crime scene(s) and identifying evidence, the crime-scene investigators document the scene(s) with photographs and sketches.

- Crime scene(s) are sometimes precisely mapped to ensure that no evidence is overlooked.

- Evidence must be properly handled, collected, and labeled so that the chain of custody is maintained.

- Evidence is analyzed in a forensic laboratory, and the results are provided to detectives, who develop a possible crime-scene scenario.

LITERACY

Erzinclioglu, Zakaria.
*The Illustrated
Guide to Forensics:
True Crime Scene
Investigations*

Close
Organize students into two teams. Tell them that they will have five minutes to list the potential problems with securing a crime scene and techniques to avoid those problems. When they have finished, have teams alternate naming a potential problem and its solution.

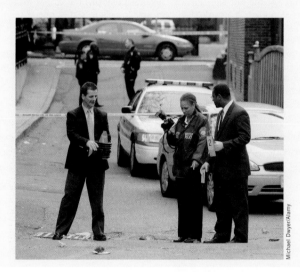

Michael Dwyer/Alamy

Teaching Tip

Make sure students understand that *clemency* means the lessening of the penalty of the crime without forgiving the crime itself. It is a reprieve. Clemency is different from a *pardon* because a pardon is the forgiveness of a crime and the penalty associated with it.

Evaluate

Have students discuss how the Oetting case was handled. What questions do they have about the testing of the blood, the time frame of testing, and the handling of evidence? How do they feel about the number of times a potential suspect should be questioned or asked to submit to a lie-detector test? Why do they think the blood on Weger's jacket was found to be animal blood during testing by the state crime lab, but after being tested by the FBI crime lab was found to be human blood that consistent with the blood of one of the victims?

Science

MATHEMATICS

MATH

Probability is the chance of something occurring. It is calculated by dividing the number of favorable outcomes by the number of possible outcomes. The *theoretical probability* of how a coin will land when it is tossed 100 times is half, or 50 heads and 50 tails. If you actually flip the coin 100 times, you will find the *experimental probability,* which may be 60 heads and 40 tails, or whatever your results turn out to be.

CASE STUDIES

CHAPTER 2

Lillian Oetting (1960)

Three Chicago socialites were murdered in Starved Rock State Park, Illinois. All three women had fractured skulls. Their bodies, bound with twine, were found in a cave. Near the bodies of the women, a bloodied tree limb was found and considered to be the murder weapon. Because all three women had been staying at a nearby lodge, the members of the lodge staff were questioned. Chester Weger, a 21-year-old dishwasher at the lodge, was asked about a blood stain on his coat. He said it was animal blood. He agreed to take a lie detector test and passed it. He was requestioned and took a second lie detector test and passed it as well. The blood was examined by the state crime lab and found to be animal blood as Weger had indicated at questioning. The case reached a dead end.

Investigators decided to revisit the evidence. The rope used to bind the women was examined more carefully. It was found to be 20-stranded twine sold only at Starved Rock State Park. Twine consistent with that used in the crimes was found in an area accessible to Weger. He again became a prime suspect. The blood on his coat was reexamined by the FBI Crime Lab and found to be human and compatible with the blood of one of the victims. Weger submitted to another lie detector test and failed it. Weger was found guilty for the murder of one of the women, Lillian Oetting, and has spent more than 50 years in prison. He recently petitioned the Governor of Illinois for clemency, saying he was beaten and tortured into making the confession. He still maintains his innocence.

The Atlanta Child Murders (1979–1981)

Wayne Williams is thought to be one of the worst serial killers of adolescents in U.S. history. His victims were killed and thrown into the Chattahoochee River in Georgia. Williams was questioned because he was seen close to where a body had washed ashore. Two kinds of fiber were found on the victims. The first kind was an unusual yellow-green nylon fiber used in floor carpeting. Through the efforts of the FBI and DuPont Chemical Company, the carpet manufacturer was identified. The carpet had been sold in only 10 states, one of them being Alabama, where Williams lived. The fibers found on the victims were linked to carpet fibers found in Williams' home.

Another victim's body yielded the second type of fiber. This fiber was determined to be from carpeting found in pre-1973 Chevrolets. It was determined that only 680 vehicles registered in Alabama had a matching carpet. Williams owned a 1970 Chevrolet station wagon with matching carpet. Williams was convicted and sentenced to two life terms.

Think Critically

Review the Case Studies and the information on investigating crime scenes in the chapter. Explain how evidence obtained at a crime scene is crucial to solving a case.

34   CHAPTER 2

DIFFERENTIATED LEARNING

Teaching Gifted Students

Have students discuss the answers to these questions:
- If the victims were found in the river, how were investigators able to find and test fibers?
- Would it be reasonable to assume that fibers on a body prior to being dumped in the river would be washed away over time?
- Is it possible that these fibers were found somewhere else and traveled down the river and collected on the bodies?
- Have students suppose they were the defense attorney for Wayne Williams. How would they have created reasonable doubt and persuaded the jury to find Williams innocent?

Careers *in Forensics*

Crime-Scene Investigator

Crime-scene investigators at work in the field.

The crime-scene investigator has a challenging job. His or her specialty is processing a crime scene. To be well-versed in the field, extensive study, training, and experience in crime-scene investigations are needed. He or she must be knowledgeable in the areas of recognition, documentation, and preservation of evidence at a crime scene to ensure that recovered items will arrive safely at a lab. Investigators generally submit the evidence to forensic specialists for analysis. However, they may have to testify in court about the evidence collected, the methods used to recover it, and the number of people who came into contact with the evidence.

Is the job of a crime-scene investigator accurately portrayed on television? Let's ask a real-life CSI. Carl Williams of Jupiter, Pennsylvania, a retired Pennsylvania State Police detective, had more than 25 years of crime-scene investigation experience. Carl says, "The television shows are for entertainment, not reality. The crime scene doesn't wrap up in an hour, never mind an entire investigation. That can take months. Also, television doesn't show the real horror of what one human being can do to another. Not a lot of people can stomach it. But if you can take it, the job can be fascinating work. Every day was different. It was interesting. I helped stop the people who committed horrendous acts before they could do it again. I'm proud of the work I've done."

What is a typical day like? Here is one scenario: At the beginning of a shift, you might be given a list of calls that have come in from police officers overnight. You will need to prioritize them and plan to investigate them in a logical order. Once you arrive at the crime scene, you will work with the first-responding officer and decide what the best methods are for you to obtain evidence. You will then record the scene using photography and video and gather evidence such as shoe prints, clothing fibers, blood, and hair. You may discover fingerprint evidence by brushing surfaces with special powders and take impressions of fingerprints from anyone who has accessed the crime scene. Finally, you will secure all of your samples in protective packaging and send them to forensic laboratories for analysis.

What does it take to become a crime-scene investigator? It is usually necessary to obtain a degree in crime-scene investigation through college degree programs or certification programs. The crime-scene investigator should have an associate's or bachelor's degree either in science with emphasis in law enforcement and crime-scene processing or a criminal justice degree with an emphasis in science.

Learn More About It
▷ To learn more about crime-scene investigation, go to **ngl.cengage.com/forensicscience2e**.

APPS

▷ **Apps that might be used at a crime scene:**
▷ **Theodolite (surveyor app)**
▷ **Real Tools (measuring, temperature, angles)**
▷ **Photosynth (panoramic photos of crime scene)**

Careers

Forensic science is a multidisciplinary science that provides impartial scientific evidence for use in the court of law. This multidisciplinary science draws primarily from chemistry, biology, physics, geology, and mathematics. In a forensic science degree program, students learn how to identify a crime scene and search the scene for specific types of evidence. They also take laboratory courses that teach them forensic tasks such as lifting fingerprints and performing basic chemical tests on evidence.

CAPSTONE ACTIVITY

In Capstone Activity 7, *Forensic Science Career Exploration*, students research different careers in forensics and share their results with the class.

Chapter 2 Review

Multiple Choice

1. b
2. c
3. d
4. d

Short Answer

5. Class evidence narrows an identity to a group of persons or things. Knowing the ABO blood type of a sample of blood from a crime scene tells investigators that one of many persons with that blood type may have been there. It also allows them to exclude everyone with a different blood type.

6. a. The recorder would need to get the following information from the first responder:

   Date, time, location, and name of collector for all evidence that was found by completing an Evidence Inventory Label for each piece of evidence recovered.

   b. Photos of the crime scene, noting the four points of the compass, the entrance and exit points in the area, any disturbances (damage) at the scene, etc.

   Photographs taken of any evidence encountered both with and without a ruler.

   c. From the sketch artist, the recorder would need to get the rough sketch that was made at the crime scene and the computer-generated sketch that is made later.

   d. From the evidence collection team, the recorder would need to get the search pattern in the crime scene and all properly handled, bindled, and packaged items that are considered evidence.

7. a. Transporting the body in a closed body bag keeps

CHAPTER 2 REVIEW

Multiple Choice

1. Locard's Principle of Exchange implies all of the following except *Obj. 2.1*
   a) Fibers can be transferred from one person to another.
   b) Blood spatter can be used to identify blood type.
   c) Cat hair can be transferred to your pants.
   d) Soil samples can be carried from the yard into your home.

2. The reason it is important to separate the witnesses at the crime scene is to *Obj. 2.5, 2.6*
   a) prevent contamination of the evidence
   b) prevent fighting among the witnesses
   c) prevent the witnesses from talking to each other
   d) protect them from the perpetrator

3. Correct collection of evidence requires which of the following? *Obj. 2.8*
   a) documenting the location where the evidence was found
   b) correct packaging of evidence
   c) maintaining proper chain of custody
   d) all of the above

4. A crime-scene sketch should include all of the following except *Obj. 2.5, 2.7*
   a) a distance scale
   b) date and location of the crime scene
   c) a north heading
   d) the type of search pattern used to collect the evidence

Short Answer

5. Blood type is considered to be class evidence. Although it may not specifically identify the suspect, explain how it still could be useful in helping to investigate a crime. *Obj. 2.3*

6. The recorder at the crime scene needs to work with all of the police personnel at the crime scene. What type of information would the recorder need to obtain from each of the following persons? *Obj. 2.4, 2.7*
   a) first-responding officer
   b) photographer
   c) sketch artist
   d) evidence collection team

7. When the crime-scene investigators arrive at a potential homicide scene, one of their duties is to collect evidence from the victim's body. However, some evidence needs to be collected from the body at a later time in the morgue. For each type of situation listed, describe the type(s) of evidence that could be obtained by: *Obj. 2.6, 2.7, 2.8, 2.9*
   a) transporting the body in a closed body bag
   b) taking nail clippings from the deceased
   c) placing a plastic bag over the hands of the deceased before transporting the person's body to the morgue
   d) brushing the clothing of the victim with a clothes brush

it free from outside contaminants. An autopsy can be done to determine the cause of death. A toxicology report can be made to determine any toxins or drugs found in the victim's blood. Insect evidence that might not be found initially will also be preserved for examination.

b. Material found underneath the nails can be tested specifically for skin or blood (DNA analysis) or soil analysis (location of crime).

c. Any material (hair, soil, fibers, blood, gunshot residue, etc.) that may be found on the hand or under the fingernails will be preserved if the hand is bagged.

d. Brushing the victim's clothes at the scene allows investigators to collect trace evidence found on the body at the crime scene. While in transport, material may fall onto the victim no matter how careful investigators are. If they take evidence samples immediately, they are more likely to get only the material found on the victim at the time of death.

8. Identify the errors in each of the following cases: *Obj. 2.5, 2.7, 2.8, 2.9*

Case 1

A dead body and a gun were found in a small room. The room was empty except for a small desk and a chair. The room had two windows, a closet, and a door leading into a hallway. The crime-scene sketch artist measured the perimeter of the room and drew the walls to scale. He sketched the approximate position of the dead body and the gun. He sketched the approximate location of the chair and the desk. What did he forget to do?

Case 2

At the scene of the crime, the evidence collector found a damp, bloody shirt. The evidence collector quickly wrapped the shirt in a paper bindle. He inserted the paper bindle with the shirt into an evidence bag. The bag was sealed with tape, and the collector wrote his name across the tape. The CSI also picked up three cigarette butts and put them into a plastic evidence bag, which he sealed and labeled. An evidence collection log was completed and taped to each of the evidence bags. What did he do incorrectly?

Case 3

Several different labs often need to share a small amount of evidence. It is important that the chain of custody be maintained. If the chain of custody is broken, then the evidence may not be allowed in a court proceeding. Identify the break in the following chain of custody.

After obtaining evidence, a lab technician removed the tape that contained the signature of the crime-scene evidence collector. Upon completion of her examination of the evidence, the lab technician put the evidence back into a paper bindle, and inserted the bindle into an evidence bag. The technician resealed the bag in the same place as the original crime-scene investigator. After carefully sealing the bag, the lab technician signed her name across the tape. She completed the chain-of-custody form on the outside of the evidence bag and brought the evidence to the next lab technician at the crime lab.

9. Analyze the JonBenet Ramsey case described in the beginning of the chapter.
   a) The crime-scene investigators who first arrived at the scene had a preconceived idea that JonBenet was kidnapped. Describe how important evidence may have been lost or destroyed because they assumed they were investigating a kidnapping as opposed to a murder. *Obj. 2.5, 2.6*
   b) Describe how the father's actions upon finding the body resulted in a loss of evidence and/or contamination of the evidence. *Obj. 2.6*

10. Refer to the case study of the Atlanta Child Murders as you answer the following questions.
    a) Describe the direct evidence linking Wayne Williams to the crimes. *Obj. 2.2, 2.3*
    b) What type of circumstantial evidence linked Wayne Williams to the crimes? *Obj. 2.2, 2.3*
    c) Using specific examples from the Wayne Williams case, explain how crime-scene investigations can use information obtained from manufacturers when evaluating evidence. *Obj. 2.9*

8. **Case 1:** He forgot to include the closet and hallway doors. All objects should be measured from two immovable landmarks. On the sketch, north should be labeled, and a scale of distance should be provided.
   Case 2: The blood on the shirt was not allowed to dry prior to being collected.
   Case 3: The evidence bag should be opened along a different edge from the edge that was sealed and signed earlier. It should then be resealed along the edge that was newly opened and signed. There should now be two signatures and two sealed edges.

9. Possible answers:
   a. Investigators did not look in the basement, assuming the crime scene was the bedroom; only the bedroom was blocked off; friends and family moved freely around the house—as a result evidence could have been altered, disturbed, or destroyed, and the additional people added many more fingerprints, footprints, hair, and fibers to the crime scene; because of the delay in finding the body, the pathologist did not examine the body for more than 18 hours.
   b. The body was covered in a blanket and carried from the basement to the living room. Evidence left by the murderer was contaminated or lost. The blanket added additional contaminating fibers. By moving the body the crime-scene investigator's information about how and when the murder occurred could be affected.

10. a. Wayne Williams was seen near the area where the body had washed ashore.
    b. Two different types of fibers were found on the victims. One was an unusual yellow-green fiber used in carpeting. The same type of fiber was found in Wayne Williams's home. The second fiber found on the victim's body was used only in pre-1973 Chevrolets. Williams owned a 1970 Chevrolet with matching carpet. Both fibers linked Wayne Williams to the crime because both fibers were found in Wayne Williams's home and car. Also, he was seen in the area where a body had washed ashore.

c. First, they identified the manufacturer of the residential carpet fibers. Once it was identified as DuPont, the company could review its sales to determine where it sold the carpets. The fibers were sold in only 10 states, one of which was Alabama, where Wayne Williams lived. The other fibers were identified as carpet used in Chevrolets made in 1972 or before. Using records from the carpet manufacturer and the motor vehicle bureau, it was determined that only 680 cars registered in Alabama had a matching carpet.

11. The hair evidence recovered from the crime scene may be consistent with the suspect's hair. However, hair evidence (without nuclear DNA) is considered to be class evidence that does not prove a particular suspect was ever at the home. Although the fingerprint evidence is individual evidence and shows that the suspect was at the home, it does not provide any clues as to *when* the suspect left the fingerprint. Both the hair and the fingerprint are circumstantial evidence and imply the suspect was at the home where the murder occurred but not direct evidence that the suspect was the murderer.

11. A suspect is linked to a murder by the presence of hair found on a chair at the victims' house and a fingerprint found on the coffee table. Crime-scene investigators found a fingerprint consistent with a suspect's fingerprint, and they found the hair to be similar to the hair from the head of the same suspect. Provide arguments that this evidence is not sufficient to prove the suspect was the murderer. Include the following terms in your answer: *Obj. 2.1, 2.2, 2.3*
- Circumstantial evidence
- Class evidence
- Individual evidence
- Direct evidence

Going Further

12. Research cases where evidence was thrown out or declared inadmissible due to errors made by CSI personnel. Your sources can be TV programs, actual cases, or creative writing.

13. Research the role of a grand jury in criminal investigations.

Bibliography

Books and Journals

Bennett, Wayne W. and Karen M. Hess. *Criminal Investigations, 8th Edition,* Belmont, CA: Wadsworth Publishing, 2006.

"Crime Scene Response Guidelines," in the California Commission on Peace Officer Standards and Training's Workbook for the Forensic Technology for Law Enforcement Telecourse, 1993.

Dupras, Tosha L., John J. Schultz, Sandra M. Wheeler, Lana Williams. *Forensic Recovery of Human Remains: Archaeological Approaches, 2nd Edition,* Florida: CRC Press, 2011.

Erzinclioglu, Zakaria. *The Illustrated Guide to Forensics: True Crime Scene Investigations.* New York: Barnes & Noble, 2004.

Gardner, Ross M., and Tom Beuel. *Practical Crime Scene Analysis and Reconstruction.* Florida: CRC Press, 2009.

Kirk, P. L. *Crime Investigation.* New York: Interscience, John Wiley & Sons, 1953.

L.A. Department of Public Safety and Corrections, Office of State Police, Crime Laboratory, "Evidence Handling Guide." Los Angeles, CA.

Lee, Henry. *Physical Evidence in Forensic Science.* Tucson: Lawyers & Judges Publishing, 2000. Company.

Locard, E. *L'Enquete Criminelle et les Methodes Scientifique.* Paris: Ernest Flammarion, 1920.

Internet Resources

Byrd, Mike. "Proper Tagging and Labeling of Evidence for Later Identification," www.crime-scene-investigator.net

Hencken, Jeannette. "Evidence Collection: Just the Basics," www.theforensicteacher.com

Ruslander, H. W., S.C.S.A. "Searching and Examining a Major Case Crime Scene," www.crime-scene-investigator.net

Schiro, George. "Collection and Preservation of Evidence," www.crime-scene-investigator.net
www.howstuffworks.com forensics links or How Stuff Works podcasts, including.
How Crime Scene Clean-up Works
How Crime Scene Investigation Works
How Locard's Exchange Principle Works
Also check state police Websites for evidence-handling guides.

Locard's Principle of Exchange *Ch. Obj. 2.1, 2.2, 2.6, 2.7, 2.8*

Introduction:

Locard's Principle of Exchange states that trace evidence can be exchanged among a crime scene, victim, and suspect, leaving trace evidence on all three.

Objectives:

By the end of this activity, you will be able to:

1. Demonstrate how transfer of evidence occurs.
2. Identify a possible crime-scene location based on trace evidence examination.

Materials:

(per group of four students)

Activity 2-1 Student Handouts (IRCD, Teacher Resources)
Act 2-1 SH Evidence Inventory Label
Act 2-1 SH Locard's Questions
Act 2-1 SH Paper Bindle
3 fabric squares each about inches in three separate evidence resealable plastic bags
1 white sock in an evidence plastic bag
4 pairs of tweezers (forceps)
1 permanent marker
2 hand lenses or microscopes
1 roll of clear ¾-inch-wide adhesive or masking tape
2 pencils
4 sheets white paper (8½" × 11") for bindle making
4 pairs of plastic or latex gloves
4 resealable plastic bags
1 pair of scissors
4 copies of the evidence inventory label

SAFETY PRECAUTIONS:

Wash your hands before starting work.
Refrain from touching hair, skin, or clothing when collecting evidence.
Wear gloves while collecting evidence.

Scenario:

A dead body has been found. The crime-scene investigators determined that the body was moved after the killing. Trace evidence was found on the victim's sock. It was determined that the crime could have occurred at three different sites. Can you match the trace evidence on the victim's sock with trace evidence collected from the three sites and determine which was the crime scene?

Crime-Scene Investigation and Evidence Collection 39

Background

During this activity, students will demonstrate how transfer of evidence, as described by Locard's Principle of Exchange occurs. Students will work in groups of four to collect and examine trace evidence from three different sources (e.g., library, computer lab, used classroom). The purpose of this activity is to show how transfer of evidence occurs and to give students a chance to determine, by an examination of the evidence, where a crime occurred.

Safety Precautions

Danger to students is minimal, but remind students about ways in which crime scenes are contaminated. To decrease the chance of contamination, students will need to wash their hands before beginning this activity and wear gloves while collecting and examining evidence. If possible, they should change into a new pair of gloves before examining each bag of evidence so they do not transfer evidence from one crime scene to the next. Students should also take care to not touch their hair, skin, or clothing while collecting evidence. After choosing the crime scenes, check for and eliminate any hazards that students might encounter there. Make sure students use caution when cutting the plastic bags open.

Teaching Tip

Student handouts are on the IRCD, Chapter 2.

    Act 2-1 SH Evidence Inv Label
    Act 2-1 SH Locard's Questions
    Act 2-1 SH Paper Bindle
    Ch02 TF Evidence Marker
    Ch02 TF Mini Notebook
    Ch02 TF Evidence Inv Label
    Ch02 TF Paper Bindle

Teaching Tip

Use the template for evidence inventory labels to construct numbered evidence labels that can be reused for other crime scenes. Trace the template onto a manila folder. Multiple copies of evidence inventory labels and paper bindles should be prepared for each team.

Procedures

1. Print, copy, and distribute the Act 2-1 SH and TF from the IRCD.

2. Use white fabric squares so it will be easier to see the evidence.

3. Make sure to let the students know what they should write in for suspect, victim, and types of offense on the Evidence Inventory Label.

4. You may want to collect evidence on socks and prepare it in bindles yourself. When students are finished examining the evidence they collected from each of the three crime scenes, they can receive the "unknown" sample from you. This will allow all students to stay on task during the entire activity.

5. This activity has two parts. Make sure students read all procedures before beginning any collection.

6. Before they enter the first crime scene, tell students to take all of their materials with them: 3 resealable plastic bags, 3 fabric squares, a permanent marker, 3 sheets of paper for bindling, 3 copies of the Evidence Inventory Label, and a roll of tape. Obtain a digital camera for each group, or have them use a good phone or tablet camera.

7. Remind students that contamination is a concern. Therefore, only the student collecting evidence should be walking near the crime scene. Before collecting any evidence, groups should discuss what evidence they see, if any.

8. Whichever group member collects the evidence needs to hold onto the evidence until returning to the classroom to analyze it.

9. During the examination of the evidence, students should open only one plastic bag at a time, examine the evidence

Procedure:

PART A: EVIDENCE COLLECTION

1. After washing your hands and putting on your gloves, visit the school library. Touch as little as possible after putting on your gloves.

2. Using a clean fabric square, lightly rub a 3 foot by 3 foot area of the floor three times. Place the fabric square in a paper bindle, then into a plastic bag, and seal the plastic bag.

3. Complete an evidence inventory label and tape it to the outside of the plastic bag. Seal the bag.

4. Place a piece of tape over the sealed edge of the plastic bag and write your name with a permanent marker across the tape so that your signature begins off one side of the tape and ends off the other side.

5. Repeat steps 1 through 4 at collection site 2 (determined by your instructor).

6. Repeat steps 1 through 4 at collection site 3 (determined by your instructor).

7. Return to your classroom with the three labeled samples.

PART B: EVIDENCE EXAMINATION AND DATA COLLECTION
Examination of evidence samples

1. Students should wear gloves while examining all evidence.

2. Open the plastic bag and bindle from collection site 1. Cut the plastic bag in an area that will not disrupt the taped signature. See Figure 2-7.

3. Using forceps and a hand lens or microscope, examine, describe, and identify items found on the fabric square.

4. Record your findings in the evidence inventory label provided. Be sure to include:
   a. Who collected the sample
   b. When it was collected
   c. Why it was collected
   d. Date
   e. Exact site of collection

5. Press a piece of tape onto the surface of the fabric to remove any additional evidence that the tweezers cannot pick up. Place the tape on white paper and examine it. Add new items found to your list of evidence.

6. Return the fabric square for collection site 1 and all evidence examined to the correct bindle and plastic bag. Seal the plastic bag, complete the chain of custody section on the evidence inventory label, and sign off on the plastic bag as described previously in Figure 2-7.

7. Repeat steps 1 through 6 for the collection site 2 evidence plastic bag.

8. Repeat steps 1 through 6 for the collection site 3 evidence plastic bag.

thoroughly, and reseal the plastic bag properly before examining another bag.

10. Students should examine the side of the fabric that was rubbed on the floor using a hand lens and forceps first, and then use the forceps to place the fabric square under the microscope. They should record as much detail as possible about what each group member sees. Only after examining the fabric under the microscope should they use tape to collect additional evidence from the fabric square.

11. Students should decide who will return to one of the evidence rooms only after all three evidence bags have been examined. This person should make sure to take all of the materials he or she needs: resealable plastic bags, fabric square, a permanent marker, sheet of paper for bindling, Evidence Inventory Label, and a roll of tape.

12. Remind the students returning to a crime scene to put the sock on over their own sock and walk around. They should not simply rub the sock on the floor.

PART C: RETURN TO COLLECT MORE EVIDENCE

1. Select one member from your group to return to one of the three previous areas examined (i.e., collection site 1, 2, or 3).

2. The chosen group member should then decide which of the three previous sites should be considered the crime scene. He or she should then return to that site and put on gloves. This group member will not divulge the crime scene to his or her fellow examiners.

3. The group member puts on the clean sock from the plastic bag over his or her own sock. The group member walks around in the selected location. This sock will serve as the victim's sock, which is now covered with trace evidence from the crime scene.

4. While at the crime scene, the chosen team member carefully removes the sock and places it in a bindle and then a plastic bag. It should then be sealed and labeled with "crime scene," date, time, and collector's name, etc., as before.

5. The group member returns to the meeting room to have his or her partners examine the sock evidence.

6. Crime-scene trace evidence should now be treated as described in steps 1 through 6 of Part B, "Examination of evidence samples."

7. Complete the evidence inventory label for the crime scene, listing all evidence collected from the sock with your partner investigators.

8. Your team must try to determine which of the three original sites matches the crime-scene site by comparing evidence collected from the "crime scene" with evidence from the three previous sites.

Questions:

1. Based on your examinations of the trace evidence, which of the three sites was probably the crime scene? Justify your answer.

2. Did your team correctly identify the crime scene? Explain.

3. Describe ways of improving your evidence collection that would provide more accurate results.

4. What other instruments could be used to improve on your ability to identify evidence?

5. A suspect's shoes and clothing are confiscated and examined for trace evidence. List at least five examples of trace evidence from the shoes or clothing that could link a suspect to a crime scene.

6. A home burglary has occurred. It appears the perpetrator entered after breaking a window. A metal safe had been opened by drilling through its tumblers. A suspect was seen running through the garden. Three suspects were interrogated and their clothing examined. List at least three examples of trace evidence that might be found on the suspect, based upon the evidence found at the crime scene.

7. Some examples of trace evidence are listed in the following table. For each item, suggest a possible location where the trace might have originated. For example, glass fragments—car accident involving a broken headlight. Record your answers in the data table.

Questions

1. Answers will vary.

2. Yes, if a good sample was obtained.

3. Sample answers: Standardize the sampled area; for any given area, use more than one piece of fabric to obtain a better sample; collect from a larger area; use a vacuum with millipore filter; use a fabric with a tighter weave.

4. Sample answers: A microscope, black light, and flashlight can also be used. A metal detector would identify metallic evidence. Using a large magnifying glass would help.

5. Possible answers: mud or dirt, blood from the victim, carpet fibers, hair, glass fragments, or plant parts

6. Possible answers: mud, dirt, plant parts or pollen from the garden on their shoes; metal fragments on their clothing or shoes from drilling into the safe; glass fragments from the broken window, consistent fingerprints on the safe or window.

7. Possible answers:

Trace evidence (left column head)
- Kidnapping from a beach location
- Theft from a paper mill
- Found in the bed of an abandoned pickup truck
- Makeup found on a murder victim
- On the end of a pipe thought to be used as a murder weapon
- A rug used to wrap up a murder victim

Source or location (right column head)
- Drugs at the scene of a crime consistent with drugs found in the car of the suspect
- Found below a safe that was broken into
- Car oil stain found on the ground outside a bank that was robbed
- Found in a tire tread
- Maggots found on a decaying body

Trace Evidence	Source or Location
Example: glass fragments	car accident involving broken headlight
sand	
sawdust	
pollen	
makeup	
hair	
fibers	
powders or residues	
metal filings	
oil or grease	
gravel	
insects	

Evidence Inventory Label

Case # _____   Inventory # _____

Item # _____   Item description _____
_____
_____

Date of recovery _____   Time of recovery _____

Location of recovery _____

Recovered by _____

Suspect _____

Victim _____

Type of offense _____

Chain of Custody

Received from _____   By _____
Date _____   Time _____ AM or PM
Received from _____   By _____
Date _____   Time _____ AM or PM
Received from _____   By _____
Date _____   Time _____ AM or PM
Received from _____   By _____
Date _____   Time _____ AM or PM

Further Research and Extensions

If any group finishes early, have students develop and prepare a new crime scene using evidence that would help identify a specific room. The other teams could then examine this additional crime scene. As another option, have students do the discovery portion of this activity again, either by sending a different student into another room with a sock, or by providing them with a sock and evidence already prepared by the teacher.

Crime-Scene Investigation *Ch. Obj. 2.5, 2.6, 2.7, 2.8*

Objectives:

By the end of this activity, you will be able to:
1. Explain the correct procedure for securing and examining a crime scene.
2. Demonstrate the correct techniques for collecting and handling evidence.

Introduction:

The crime-scene investigation is a way to review many of the skills described in this chapter. A crime has occurred, and you and your investigative team must secure the area and properly collect the evidence.

Time Required to Complete Activity:

60 to 90 minutes (six students per team)

Scenarios:

Two crime scenes prepared in advance by your instructor with approximately five pieces of evidence

Materials:

(Per group, with six students in each group)
Student handouts from IRCD, Teacher Resources
Checklists 1-5:
    Act 2-2 SH First Responder
    Act 2-2 SH Recorder
    Act 2-2 SH Artist
    Act 2-2 SH Photographer
    Act 2-2 SH Evidence Collector
Act 2-2 SH Evidence Inv Label
Ch02 TF Paper Bindle
Ch02 TF Evidence Inv Label
Ch02 TF Mini Notebook
Ch02 TF Evidence Marker
10 evidence markers from IRCD
10 evidence inventory labels from IRCD
10 resealable plastic bags, 6-gallon size
10 resealable plastic bags, 6-quart size
4 paper collection bags
6 permanent marking pens
6 pairs plastic gloves
1 roll crime-scene tape

DIFFERENTIATED LEARNING

Teaching At-Risk Students

During this activity, allow students to pick their role in the group. Allowing them to choose photographer, sketch artist, or recorder will give them the chance to choose something that interests them and plays to their strengths. A student with a role that fits his or her interests is more motivated to perform.

Background

Two crime scenes are prepared in advance for students to enter. Students will use the knowledge gained throughout this chapter to secure and examine the crime scene and properly collect evidence. Students should work in teams of six, with each student assigned to a specific job: first responder, recorder, sketch artist, photographer, and two evidence collectors. Each crime-scene team will complete and turn in an investigation log, checklists 1 through 5, two sketches, photographs, and bagged evidence.

Safety Precautions

Danger to students is minimal, but remind students about ways in which crime scenes are contaminated. To decrease the chance of contamination, students must wash their hands before beginning this activity and wear gloves while collecting and examining evidence. If possible, they should change into a new pair of gloves before examining each bag of evidence so they do not transfer evidence. Students should also be careful to not touch their hair, skin, or clothing while collecting evidence. (You may remind students that real CSIs would also have their feet and hair covered, but school budget constraints do not allow for those coverings in this activity.) Stress that they should use caution when cutting the plastic bags open.

Teaching Tip

Copy and distribute all IRCD Act 2-2 student handouts (SH) listed in the Materials list. Student should have at least one Evidence Inventory label for each evidence item.

Teaching Tip

Keep it simple! Keep evidence to a minimum. The point of the activity is for students to practice the crime-scene roles.

Procedures

1. You may need to set up more than two crime scenes depending on the size of your class. Another alternative is to have two crime scenes and have two groups (total of 12 students) go in and perform all parts of the activity. The rest of the class will stay in the classroom and complete an alternate assignment, possibly viewing a video of the processing of a crime scene. The next class period, the students who watched the video will go to the crime scenes and perform the activity. This will allow you time to go into the crime scenes and set them back up after the first group gets finished. During the second day, the students who have already secured the crime scene and collected evidence are ready to stay in the classroom and analyze the evidence. Later, they can watch the video the other group watched.

2. Students should read all directions before beginning this activity.

3. Instruct students to do all cursory investigation immediately after securing the scene because this will be the only time the scene will be pristine, without outside contamination.

4. Photographs should be taken before evidence collection.

5. Have students go through each checklist to make sure all steps are followed.

6 compasses
1 videocamera (optional)
"bunny suit" (optional)
6 forceps (one pair per person)
1 flashlight or penlight per person
2 floodlights
1 digital camera or cell phone/computer tablet with good camera
10 bindle paper sheets, both large and small
6 hand lenses
sketch paper
2 photographic rulers
1 25-foot tape measure
1 roll ¾-inch masking tape

Procedure:

Your crime-scene team is composed of six students. Each team of students has a first-responding officer, a recorder, a photographer, a sketch artist, and two designated evidence collectors.

By the completion of this part of the activity, each team of students must submit the following:

- A log maintained by the first responder
- Checklists 1 through 5 completed, dated, and signed
- Two sketches—a rough sketch and a quality sketch, both with accurate measurements
- A series of digital images that adequately encompass the crime-scene location; close-up shots of any evidence, evidence numbered and photographed next to a ruler
- Evidence bags properly packaged, labeled, and sealed

PART A: SECURING AND PRESERVING THE CRIME SCENE

1. The crime scene is secured by the first officer to arrive. His or her job is to limit access to the crime scene and preserve the scene with minimal contamination. He or she has primary responsibility for:

   - Securing the safety of individuals at the scene; approach the scene cautiously (look, listen, smell) and determine if the site poses any danger
   - Obtaining medical attention for anyone injured at the scene; call for medical personnel for the injured
   - Calling in backup help, including medical personnel to help the injured, and/or lab personnel
   - Separating the witnesses so they may be interrogated separately to see if their stories match.
   - Performing an initial walk-through of the area (scan the scene) to provide an overview of the crime scene
   - Searching the scene briefly (scan the scene) to notify lab personnel what equipment is needed

- Collecting information, including the crime-scene address/location, time, date, type of call, and the names and addresses of all parties involved and present
- Securing the integrity of the scene by establishing the boundaries of the crime scene by setting up a physical barrier (tape) to keep unauthorized personnel (and animals) out of the area
- Documenting the entry and exit of all authorized personnel
- Providing a brief update to the next-of-command officer to arrive on the scene

The first-responding officer can use checklist 1 to complete all necessary procedures.

Note: Later-arriving police or CSI will set up barricades to prevent unauthorized persons from entering the crime-scene area.

PART B: SEARCH AND EVIDENCE COLLECTION

Once your designated crime-scene specialists arrive, evidence collectors will collect the evidence for processing back in the lab.

1. The photographer has the responsibility of:
   - Working with the sketch artist and recorder to document the crime scene.
   - Photographing any victims and suspects.
   - Taking photos of the crime scene, noting the four points of the compass, the entrance and exit points in the area, any disturbances (damage) at the scene, etc.
   - Noting and photographing any evidence encountered both with and without a ruler.
   - Completing the photographer's checklist.

2. The recorder has the responsibility of working with the primary officer to maintain updated records. The recorder will complete checklist 2. The recorder will:
   - Document by date, time, location, and name of collector all evidence that is found.
   - Work with the sketch artist to measure and document the crime scene.
   - Help search for evidence, if necessary.

3. The sketch artist has the responsibility of drawing accurate and detailed sketches of the crime scene. At the crime scene, a rough sketch is made with accurate measurements. At a later time, a neater (or computer-generated) sketch is completed. The sketch artist working with the recorder will complete Checklist 3.

4. The evidence collectors have the responsibility of:
   - Marking off the area around the victim and keep all unnecessary spectators out.
   - Working within the crime scene, wearing gloves and a "bunny suit," if necessary, to collect evidence.
   - Walking an appropriate search pattern in the crime-scene area. The pattern will be chosen by your instructor. It may be a spiral, grid, or linear pattern, or the area may be divided into zones for examination.

Questions

Each crime-scene team will complete and turn in an investigation log, checklists 1 through 5, two sketches, photographs, and bagged evidence. Students can be graded on accuracy and completeness of each item. Group participation can be assessed by having each student draw a circle and divide that circle up into pieces—like pieces of a pie graph—based on how they feel each group member performed (i.e., if all group members performed their jobs equally and accurately, then the graph would have six equal pieces). You can then assess each member's group participation based on other group members' assessments and your own observations.

- Properly handling and packaging any materials considered to be evidence. Remember that the size of a bindle can vary from very small to large enough to package evidence as large as an overcoat.
- Complete the evidence collector's checklist.

5. The proper handling of evidence includes being aware that:
- Proper evidence collection guidelines should be followed.
- Wet or damp evidence should be placed in a paper bag and sealed.
- DNA evidence should never be placed in a plastic container.
- Dry evidence should be placed in a paper bindle and then packaged in plastic bags or envelopes and sealed.
- Liquid evidence should be stored in sealed, unbreakable containers.
- Care must be taken to prevent any contamination or damage to the evidence collected.
- Flashlights and penlights can be used to search for hair, fibers, and other small or fine trace evidence.
- All evidence containers should be identified with an evidence inventory inventory label taped to the container or placed inside the container. Labels will be provided by your instructor. The name or initials of the collector should be written over the tape sealing the container. The last page in this activity has a copy of an evidence inventory label.
- If for any reason an evidence container is opened, it should be opened at a location other than the sealed edge. If it is opened, it must be repackaged and resealed with the name of the person who handled the evidence, along with the original packaging. The name of the new packager should be written over the new seal. This chain-of-custody information is also located on the evidence inventory label.

Examining the Evidence

Thorough examination of the crime scene will lead to a comprehensive collection of evidence. After examining all of the evidence and interviewing the suspects, investigators will have additional information that will help solve the crime.

Checklist 1: First Responder's Responsibilities

Place a checkmark by each of the following responsibilities as completed:

❑ I approached the scene cautiously (looked, listened, smelled) and determined if the site posed any danger to anyone visiting the scene.

❑ I checked to see if medical attention was needed by anyone injured at the scene.

❑ I called in backup to help the injured.

❑ I secured and separated any witnesses present.

❑ I completed an initial walk-through of the area (scanned the scene) to provide an overview of the crime scene.

❑ I notified superiors of the need for additional police officers and CSI technicians at the crime scene.

❑ I secured the integrity of the scene by establishing the boundaries of the crime scene by setting up a physical barrier (tape) to keep unauthorized personnel (and animals) out of the area.

- ❏ I collected and recorded information, including my name and badge number, case number, address/location of crime scene, time, date, type of call, names of all involved and present parties, as well as the names of everyone present.
- ❏ I documented the entry and exit of all authorized personnel.
- ❏ I provided the next-in-command officer with a brief update of the situation.

Date _____ Signed _____

Checklist 2: Recorder's Checklist

Place a checkmark by each of the following responsibilities as completed:

- ❏ I documented by date, time, location, and name of collector all evidence that was found by completing an evidence inventory label for each piece of evidence recovered.
- ❏ I documented weather conditions, available light, unusual odors, and other environmental conditions.
- ❏ I worked with the sketch artist to measure and document the crime scene.
- ❏ I helped search for evidence.
- ❏ I worked with the photographer to help document the location and direction of the photographed objects and subjects.
- ❏ I worked with the sketch artist to help document the location and direction of the sketched objects and subjects.

Date _____ Signed _____

Checklist 3: Sketch Artist's Checklist

Place a checkmark by each of the following responsibilities as completed:

I will prepare two sketches of the crime scene—a rough sketch and a carefully detailed sketch—each of which includes:

- ❏ All directions of the compass correctly labeled
- ❏ All objects and landmarks within the crime scene labeled in correct position and to scale (each sketch should contain two immovable objects at a measured distance)
- ❏ Carefully measured distances between objects and subjects to add to the accuracy of my sketches
- ❏ Working with the photographer and recorder to document the exact location and direction from which photographs were taken

Date _____ Signed _____

Teaching Tip

After students have processed the crime scene, those who had each role should, as a group, summarize their role for the other students in the class. Next time the class processes a crime scene, make sure all students have different roles, so that each student eventually plays all or most roles.

Checklist 4: Photographer's Checklist

Place a checkmark by each of the following responsibilities as completed:

❑ I worked with the sketch artist, recorder, and evidence collectors to document the crime scene.

❑ I took photos of the crime scene, noting the four points of the compass, the entrance and departure points of the area, any disturbances (damage) at the scene, etc.

❑ I took photographs of any injured persons at the crime scene.

❑ I took close-up photographs of the victim and/or immediate location of the crime.

❑ I took a series of distance photos to give perspective to the crime scene.

❑ I noted and took digital images of any evidence encountered, both with and without a ruler, and had the recorder and sketch artist also record the location of the evidence.

❑ I took a series of at least eight to ten digital images pertinent to the crime scene. These are of sufficient quality that they could be used in a courtroom reconstruction.

Date _____ Signed _____

Checklist 5: Evidence Collector's Checklist

Place a checkmark by each of the following responsibilities as completed:

❑ I marked off the area around the victim and kept out all unnecessary spectators.

❑ I worked within the crime scene, wearing gloves and protective gear while collecting evidence.

❑ I walked an appropriate search pattern in the crime-scene area. The pattern walked was _____.

❑ I properly handled and packaged all materials considered evidence into a bindle.

❑ I properly bindled and packaged all materials considered evidence into a bag or plastic bag and completed the evidence inventory label for each evidence bag.

❑ I properly sealed and labeled all evidence containers.

❑ I wrote my signature across the seals on all evidence I collected.

❑ I completed the chain-of-custody information for each evidence bag.

Date _____ Signed _____

Evidence Inventory Label

Case # _____   Inventory # _____

Item # _____   Item description
                       _____
                       _____
                       _____

Date of recovery _____   Time of recovery _____

Location of recovery _____

Recovered by _____

Suspect _____

Victim _____

Type of offense _____

Chain of Custody

Received from _____   By _____
          Date _____   Time _____ AM or PM
Received from _____   By _____
          Date _____   Time _____ AM or PM
Received from _____   By _____
          Date _____   Time _____ AM or PM
Received from _____   By _____
          Date _____   Time _____ AM or PM

Teaching Tip
Review proper evidence collection, labeling, and chain of custody procedures.

Further Research and Extensions
Have students write a crime story. Have them describe a situation and leave clues as to "whodunit" or how.

Chapter Overview

Hair has been used in forensic analysis since the late 19th century. Hair regulates body temperature, reduces friction, protects the body from light, and is also a sense organ. It is made up of two parts: a follicle and a shaft. Hair varies in length and cross-sectional shape, depending on where on the body it originates. Some hair characteristics allow forensic experts to group hair evidence into categories that reflect ethnic background. Forensic experts examine hair using light and electron microscopy and analyze hair chemically for drugs and toxins. They can also examine the levels of hydrogen and oxygen isotopes in hair for clues as where a person has been living.

The Big Ideas

Hair is an important structure found on mammals, including humans. While all hairs have the same basic structure, differences in the specific characteristics of an individual's hair can help an investigator determine general characteristics of that individual. Forensic investigators rely on their knowledge of hair structure, function, and variation when they use hair from a crime scene as evidence.

CHAPTER 3

Hair Analysis

Analysis of Hair

In 1958, the body of 16-year-old Gaetane Bouchard was discovered in a gravel pit near her home in Edmundston, New Brunswick, across the Canada–U.S. border from Maine. Numerous stab wounds were found on her body. Witnesses reported seeing Bouchard with her boyfriend John Vollman prior to her disappearance. Circumstantial evidence also linked Vollman with Bouchard. Paint flakes from the place where the couple had been seen together were found in Vollman's car. Lipstick that was consistent with the color of Bouchard's lipstick was found on candy in Vollman's glove compartment.

At Bouchard's autopsy, several strands of hair were found in her hand. This hair was tested using a radiological process known as neutron activation analysis (NAA). NAA uses high-energy neutrons to test for the presence and concentration of various elements in a sample. In this case, NAA showed that the hair in Bouchard's hand contained a ratio of sulfur to phosphorus that was much closer to Vollman's hair than to her own. (See Vollman's photo and the headline "Accused of murder" in the newspaper clipping at the right.) At the trial, Vollman confessed to the murder in light of the hair analysis results. This was the first time NAA hair analysis was used to convict a criminal. Today, NAA has been replaced by a combination of chemical, microscopic, and DNA analyses, which are used to analyze hair samples.

Accusé de meurtre

(Tous droits de reproduction réservés)
JOHN JACOB VOLLMAN JR

Newspaper clipping announcing the arrest of John Vollman for the murder of Gaetane Bouchard.

50

SCENARIO

Read the scenario as a class. Then have the class discuss these questions:

What evidence was used in the investigation of Gaetane Bouchard's murder? Was it considered class or individual evidence?

Describe the importance or usefulness of each kind of evidence. For example, would the paint evidence alone have been sufficient to convict John Vollman? Why or why not?

What role did hair play in this investigation?

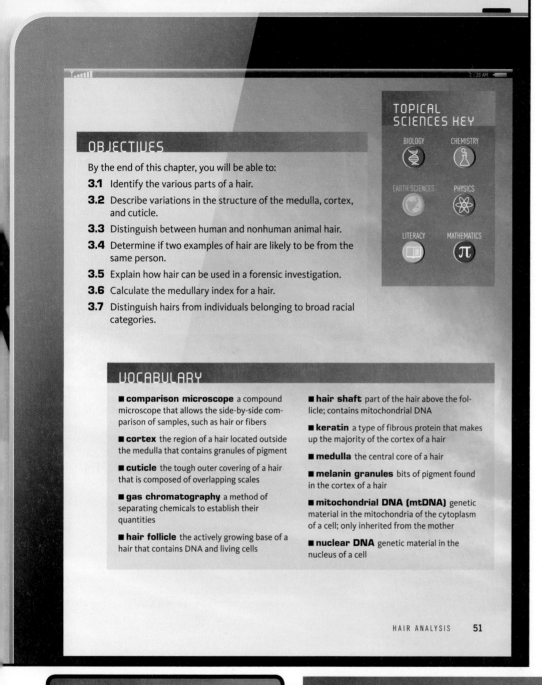

OBJECTIVES

By the end of this chapter, you will be able to:

3.1 Identify the various parts of a hair.

3.2 Describe variations in the structure of the medulla, cortex, and cuticle.

3.3 Distinguish between human and nonhuman animal hair.

3.4 Determine if two examples of hair are likely to be from the same person.

3.5 Explain how hair can be used in a forensic investigation.

3.6 Calculate the medullary index for a hair.

3.7 Distinguish hairs from individuals belonging to broad racial categories.

TOPICAL SCIENCES KEY

BIOLOGY   CHEMISTRY

EARTH SCIENCES   PHYSICS

LITERACY   MATHEMATICS

VOCABULARY

- **comparison microscope** a compound microscope that allows the side-by-side comparison of samples, such as hair or fibers

- **cortex** the region of a hair located outside the medulla that contains granules of pigment

- **cuticle** the tough outer covering of a hair that is composed of overlapping scales

- **gas chromatography** a method of separating chemicals to establish their quantities

- **hair follicle** the actively growing base of a hair that contains DNA and living cells

- **hair shaft** part of the hair above the follicle; contains mitochondrial DNA

- **keratin** a type of fibrous protein that makes up the majority of the cortex of a hair

- **medulla** the central core of a hair

- **melanin granules** bits of pigment found in the cortex of a hair

- **mitochondrial DNA (mtDNA)** genetic material in the mitochondria of the cytoplasm of a cell; only inherited from the mother

- **nuclear DNA** genetic material in the nucleus of a cell

TEACHING RESOURCES

Instructor's Resource CD-ROM includes:
- Activities & Student Handouts
- Alternative Assessments
- Consolidated Bibliography
- Correlations to NGSS and CCSS
- Figure Files
- Lesson Plans with Chapter Outlines
- MST
- Nonfiction Readings
- PowerPoint Presentations
- Student Learning Objectives (SLOs)

CL Testing powered by Cognero

Website: ngl.cengage.com/forensicscience2e

DIFFERENTIATED LEARNING

Teaching English-Language Learners

English-language learners (ELL) will benefit from strategies that make it easier to learn science vocabulary. One strategy is to help ELL students work with terms that are composed of simpler words. Ask students to write each of the following terms on a separate index card: *comparison microscope, nuclear DNA,* and *secondary transfer.* Help students understand the meaning of these terms by discussing the meaning of each of the words that makes up the term. Often, ELL students will know the meaning of the words separately, but will need help understanding how they fit together in the term.

Engage

One of the first cases in which hair was used to help solve a crime was the murder of Germaine Bichon. In 1910, Rosella Rousseau confessed to the murder of Germaine Bichon. Rousseau only confessed after being confronted with hair evidence found at the murder scene.

Organize the class into four groups. Have each group discuss one of the following questions and then share their thoughts with the rest of the class:

• What are the possible *limitations* of using hair as evidence in a crime investigation?

• What are the possible *advantages* of using hair as evidence?

• What limitations might have prevented investigators from using hair in investigations before 1910?

• What kinds of technological advances have made it possible for investigators to use hair as evidence?

Teaching Tip

Students may have a difficult time distinguishing between class evidence and individual evidence. Ask students how the two phrases are different by asking them what other meanings they associate with the words *class* and *individual*. Sample answer: The word *class* is used to describe a group, as in a science class. A class generally has a shared characteristic. For example, all members of a science class are students who are studying the same subject. The word *individual* is used to describe one member of a group or class. An individual has many characteristics that are not shared by the group or class. For example, there may be only one student with green eyes in a science class.

INTRODUCTION

An investigator finds a natural blond hair at a crime scene. She thinks that it might help solve her case. What information could be gained from analysis of that hair (Figure 3-1)? What are the limitations of the information that hair can provide?

A hair without the follicle and its **nuclear DNA**, or genetic material in its nucleus, cannot provide individual evidence. Physical examination of hair *can* yield class evidence. For example, a scientist may exclude people who have entirely Asian or African ancestry as producers of a natural blond hair recovered from a crime scene. Individual evidence could be derived from hair if the follicle were intact and nuclear DNA could be retrieved from it. The investigator could also compare the hair collected with hair from a blond suspect. However, even hairs that share characteristics may not be from the same source.

Hair left behind at a crime scene can adhere to clothes, carpets, and many other surfaces and be transferred to other locations. This is called *secondary* transfer, and it is particularly common with animal hair (Locard's Principle of Exchange).

Because of its tough outer coating, hair does not easily decompose. Hair found at crime scenes or secondary locations can be analyzed. The physical characteristics of hair can offer clues to the predominant ancestry of an individual. Chemical tests performed on hair, such as **gas chromatography**, can identify and quantify drugs, toxins, heavy metals, and even assess nutritional deficiencies. When the follicle or even a portion of the shaft of a hair is present, DNA evidence may be obtained from it, which may lead to individual identification. **Mitochondrial DNA (mtDNA)**, which is present in hair shafts, can reveal some of a suspect's or victim's family relationships. Mitochondrial DNA is inherited from the mother, who inherited it from her mother, and so on.

Figure 3-1 *A forensic scientist prepares a hair for analysis.*

Ldf/Thinkstock/Getty Images

CHEMISTRY

Did you know?

Henri Paul was the driver of the car in which he, Dodi Fayed, and Princess Diana died on August 31, 1997. Henri Paul's history of prescription drug use was determined by analysis of his hair.

HISTORY OF HAIR ANALYSIS

Scientists recognized the importance of hair analysis as trace evidence in criminal investigations in the late 1800s. The case of the murder of the Duchesse de Praeslin in Paris in 1847 is said to have involved the investigation of hairs found at the scene.

A classic 1883 text on forensic science, *The Principles and Practice of Medical Jurisprudence* by Alfred Swaine Taylor and Thomas Stevenson, contains a chapter on using hair in forensic investigations. It includes drawings of human hairs under magnification. The various parts of human hair are identified. The book also references cases in which hair was used as evidence in England.

DIFFERENTIATED LEARNING

Teaching Gifted Students

As a result of a series of *Washington Post* articles beginning in 2012, more than 2,000 criminal cases involving microscopic hair evidence were reviewed due to questionable FBI testimony. The Innocence Project, the FBI, and the Department of Justice partnered to conduct the investigation. Have interested students research the *Washington Post* articles and the investigation at www.innocenceproject .org and report on the following questions: Why were the cases being reviewed? Has anyone been exonerated? What improvements have been recommended by the Organization of Scientific Area Committees (OSAC) to improve hair evidence analysis? How has microscopic hair analysis changed as a result of this controversy?

In 1910, a comprehensive study of hair titled *Le Poil de l'Homme et des Animaux (The Hair of Man and Animals)* was published by the French forensic scientists Victor Balthazard and Marcelle Lambert. This text includes numerous microscopic studies of hairs from most common animals.

The first use of the **comparison microscope** for simultaneous, side-by-side analysis of hairs collected from a crime scene and hairs from a suspect or victim was in 1934 by Dr. Sydney Smith. This method of comparison helped solve the murder of an eight-year-old girl.

Further advances in hair analysis continued throughout the 20th century as technological advances allowed for comparison of hairs through chemical methods. Today, standard procedures of hair analysis include microscopic examination and DNA analysis.

Did you know

All of the hair follicles in a human are formed by the twentieth week of pregnancy.

BIOLOGY

THE FUNCTIONS OF HAIR

All (and only) mammals have hair. Its main purpose is to regulate body temperature—to keep the body warm through insulation. Hair also decreases friction, protects the skin against sunlight, and acts as a sense organ. The very dense hair of some mammals is referred to as fur.

Hair works as a temperature regulator in association with muscles in the skin. If the outside temperature is cold, these muscles pull the hair strands upright, creating pockets that trap air. This trapped air provides a warm, insulating layer next to the skin. If the temperature outside is warm, the muscles relax, and the hair becomes flattened against the body, releasing the trapped air.

In humans, body hair is mostly reduced compared to other mammals; it does not play as large a role in temperature regulation. When humans are born, they have about 5 million hair follicles, only 2 percent of which are on the head. This is the largest number of hair follicles a human will ever have. As a human ages, the density of hair decreases.

THE STRUCTURE OF HUMAN HAIR *Obj. 3.1, 3.2, 3.3, 3.4, 3.5, 3.6, 3.7*

A hair consists of two parts: a follicle (with papilla and capillary blood supply) and a shaft (Figure 3-2). The **hair follicle** is a club-shaped structure in the skin. It contains cells with DNA along with a network of blood vessels that supply nutrients to feed the hair and help it grow. A sebaceous gland secretes oil that helps keep the hair conditioned. Nerve cells wind around the follicle and stimulate the erector muscle in response to changing environmental conditions.

The hair shaft is composed of the protein **keratin**, which is produced in the skin. Keratin makes hair both strong and flexible. Like all proteins, keratin is made up of a chain of amino acids that forms a spiral, or *helix* (plural *helices*). Keratin helices are connected by strong bonds between amino acids. These bonds make

Figure 3-2 *This cross section shows a hair shaft in a hair follicle. If the follicle of the hair is present in evidence, nuclear DNA may be extracted, amplified, and analyzed for use as individual evidence. If no follicle is present, mitochondrial DNA or other characteristics may be analyzed for use as class evidence for comparison with crime-scene evidence.*

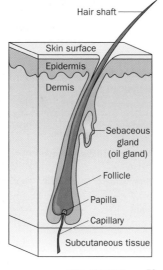

Hair shaft
Skin surface
Epidermis
Dermis
Sebaceous gland (oil gland)
Follicle
Papilla
Capillary
Subcutaneous tissue

HAIR ANALYSIS   53

Explore

Remind students that humans are not the only animals to have structures made of the protein keratin. Tell students that vertebrates—fishes, amphibians such as frogs, birds, reptiles such as turtles, and other mammals—have body structures made of keratin. Ask them what those body parts might be (e.g., scales, skin, fur, feathers, beaks, shells, claws).

Explore

As an inquiry activity, ask students to refute or confirm the claim that it is possible with microscopic analyis to know which end of a whole hair was closer to the scalp. Or, ask students to study the image showing the hair shaft and cuticle in Figure 3-4. Then ask: Which end of the hair shaft shown is closer to the scalp? Cuticle scales always point toward the tips of your hair. Therefore, in Figure 3-4, the top of the photo is closer to the scalp.

Teaching Tip

Students may notice that both fragmented and interrupted medullas are broken in appearance. Explain that interrupted medullas are also known as *intermittent* and are distinguished from fragmented because interrupted and intermittent medullas have breaks that occur at regular intervals, whereas the breaks in the fragmented medullas occur randomly and are of differing lengths.

Figure 3-3 *The cross section of a hair shaft is similar to that of a round, wooden pencil.*

Cuticle   Cortex   Medulla

Pigment granules made of melanin

Figure 3-4 *This scanning electron photomicrograph shows the cuticle of a human hair with the overlapping (imbricate) scales.*

Dee Breger/Science Source

hair strong and resistant to decomposition, making it very useful to forensic scientists.

The hair shaft is made up of three layers: an inner **medulla**, a cortex, and an outer cuticle. A good analogy for the cross section of a hair shaft is the cross section of a round, wooden pencil (Figure 3-3). The painted exterior of the pencil is similar to the cuticle. The graphite in the middle of the pencil is similar to the medulla. The wood of the pencil is analogous to the cortex of a hair. The **cuticle** is a transparent outer layer of the hair shaft. It is made of scales that overlap one another and protect the inner layers of the hair (Figure 3-4). The scales point from the end of the hair closest to the scalp, to the end farthest from the scalp. When examining a hair under a microscope, noticing the direction the scales point reveals the younger and older ends of the hair. This information can be used when an investigator needs to analyze hair for the presence of different toxins, drugs, or metals at specific points in time. Human hair has cuticle scales that are flattened and narrow, also called *imbricate*. Animal hair has different types of cuticles that are described and shown later in the section on animal hair.

Cortex Variation

In humans, the **cortex** is the largest part of the hair shaft. The cortex is the part of the hair that contains most of the **melanin granules** that give the hair its color. The pigment distribution varies from person to person. Some people have larger pigment granules within the cortex, giving the cortex an uneven color distribution when viewed under the compound microscope.

Types of Medulla

The center of the hair is called the medulla. It can be a hollow tube. In some people the medulla is absent, in others it is fragmented, or segmented, and in others it is continuous or even doubled. The medulla can contain pigment granules or be unpigmented. Forensic investigators classify hair into five different groups depending on the appearance of the medulla, as illustrated in Figure 3-5.

Figure 3-5 *Five different patterns of medulla pigmentation pattern are identified in forensic hair analysis.*

Medulla Pattern	Description	Diagram
Continuous	One unbroken line of color	
Interrupted (intermittent)	Pigmented line broken at regular intervals	
Fragmented or Segmented	Pigmented line unevenly spaced	
Solid	Pigmented area filling both the medulla and the cortex	
None	No separate pigmentation in the medulla	

DIFFERENTIATED LEARNING

Teaching At-Risk Students
Engage at-risk students who are tactile or kinetic learners by asking them to create a cross section of a hair using modeling clay. Provide students with three different colors of clay. Ask students to demonstrate one of the following: three parts of hair, different types of medulla (Figures 3-5 and 3-11), or different cuticle patterns (Figure 3-12).

DIFFERENTIATED LEARNING

Teaching Gifted Students
Hair may curl or straighten as a result of natural or artificial causes. Have students research what happens to hair that is artificially curled or straightened. Is naturally curly hair chemically different than naturally straight hair?

Types of Hair

Hair can vary in shape, length, diameter, texture, and color. The cross section of the hair may be circular, triangular, irregular, or flattened, influencing the curl of the hair. The texture of hair can be coarse as it is in whiskers or fine as it is in younger children. Some furs are a mixture, as in dog coats, which often have two layers: one fine and one coarse. Hair color varies depending on the distribution of pigment granules (Figure 3-6) and on hair dyes that might have been used.

In humans, hair varies from person to person, and even varies depending on its location on a particular person. In addition, different hairs from one part of a person's body can vary. Not all hairs on a person's head are exactly the same. For example, a suspect may have a few gray hairs among brown hairs in a sample taken from his head. Because inconsistencies occur within each body region, 50 hairs are usually collected from a suspect's or victim's head.

Hair From Different Parts of the Body

Hair varies from region to region on the body of the same person (Figure 3-7). Forensic scientists distinguish six types of hair on the human body: (1) head hair, (2) eyebrows and eyelashes, (3) beard and mustache hair, (4) underarm hair, (5) body hair, and (6) pubic hair. Each hair type has its own shape and characteristics.

Figure 3-6 *Hairs coming from a single area on one person can vary in characteristics.*

Rick Gomez/Blend Images/Getty Images

Figure 3-7 *The physical characteristics of a hair provide information about which part of the body it came from.*

Courtesy, FBI; photos by Sandra Koch & Douglas W. Deedrick

Pubic hair showing buckling.

Beard hair with double medulla.

Arm or leg hair with blunt, frayed end.

One of the ways hairs from the different parts of the body are distinguished is their cross-sectional shape. Head hair is generally circular or elliptical in cross section. Eyebrows and eyelashes are also circular but often have tapering ends. Beard hairs tend to be thick and triangular. Body hair can be elliptical or triangular, depending on whether the body region has been regularly shaved. Pubic hair tends to be oval or triangular.

Hairs from different parts of the body have other characteristic physical features. Hair from the arms and legs usually has a blunt tip, but may be frayed at the ends from abrasion. Beard hair is usually coarse and may have a double medulla. The diameter of pubic hair may vary greatly, and *buckling*, abrupt changes in the shape of the hair shaft, may be present.

Evaluate

Gray hair is often seen as a sign of aging in humans, but why does hair turn gray? Explain to students that hair has color because melanocytes deposit pigments in the hair as it grows. *Melanocytes* are the same cells responsible for depositing pigment in skin. Although scientists do not know why this happens, the stem cells that produce melanocytes for hair follicles can die. When this happens, hair continues to grow but without pigment.

HAIR ANALYSIS **55**

DIFFERENTIATED LEARNING

Teaching English-Language Learners and At-Risk Students

English-language learners often have little difficulty understanding content once they have mastered the important vocabulary. Help students with reading difficulties use the structure of the chapter to anticipate the important concepts being covered. Before reading, ask students to list the main, dark-green headings and the secondary, red headings below each dark-green heading. Tell them that this gives them a general of the most important topics in a chapter. Then ask students to summarize, in a sentence or two, what they expect to find in each main (dark-green) section. After reading each section, students should evaluate whether their predictions were accurate. Also remind them to refer to the Glossary at the back of the book for the definitions of key terms.

Explore

Hair pulled out of the scalp during the anagen stage is more likely to contain follicle cells than hair pulled out at other stages in the life cycle. Ask students to describe circumstances in which this might be an important fact in a criminal investigation. How might hair that contains follicle cells be used differently than other hair? (Possible answer: Hair with follicle cells may have nuclear DNA, which can be analyzed to provide a DNA fingerprint of the owner of the hair.)

Teaching Tip

Organize the class into three groups. Assign a portion of the hair life cycle to each group, and ask each group to make a short presentation to the class. In their presentations, they should include answers to the following questions:

- What does the hair look like at this stage?
- How long does this stage last?
- Are there any characteristics of a hair at this stage that would be helpful in a criminal investigation?

Explore

Demonstrate the way bleach and hair interact. Before class, prepare a dry mount of a short segment of human hair by placing the hair on a glass slide with a coverslip placed over the hair. In class, use a video microscope to examine the hair with the class. Place a drop of chlorine bleach next to the coverslip. As the bleach wicks across the slide, it will discolor the hair and then, after several minutes, begin to dissolve it. Discuss your observations with students.

Did you know

You lose approximately 100 hairs from your head each day. These end up on your clothes, in your hairbrush, on furniture, and at the places you visit.

CHEMISTRY

Did you know

Hair doesn't "turn gray." The pigment cells stop producing pigment, resulting in hair without pigment.

The Life Cycle of Hair

Hair proceeds through three stages as it develops. The first stage is called the *anagen stage* and lasts approximately 1,000 days. Eighty to ninety percent of all human hair is in the anagen stage. This is the period of active growth when the cells around the follicle are rapidly dividing and depositing materials within the hair. The *catagen stage* follows as the hair stops growing and the follicle recedes as the blood supply is reduced. The catagen stage accounts for about 2 percent of all hair growth and development. The final stage is the *telogen stage*. During this stage, the hair follicle is dormant or resting and hairs are easily lost. About 10 to 18 percent of all hairs are in the telogen stage. At the end of the telogen stage, the blood supply reconnects to the follicle, and another anagen phase begins. There is no pattern as to which hairs on the head are in a particular stage at any time.

Treated Hair

Hair can be treated in many different ways. Bleaching hair oxidizes the natural pigment, lightening it (Figure 3-8). It also makes hair brittle and can disturb the scales on the cuticle. Artificial bleaching shows a sharp demarcation along the hair, while bleaching from the sun leaves a more gradual mark. Peroxide in bleach can also damage mtDNA. Dyeing hair changes the color of the hair shaft and gives it a painted appearance (Figure 3-9) that is easily recognized by an experienced forensic examiner. In addition, the cuticle and cortex both take on the color of the dye.

If an entire hair is recovered in an investigation, it is possible to estimate when the hair was last color-treated. The region near the root of the hair will be colored naturally. Human hair grows at a rate of about 1.3 cm per month (approximately 0.44 mm per day). Measuring the length of hair that is naturally colored and dividing by 1.3 cm provides an estimate of the number of months since the hair was colored. For example, if the unbleached root region measured 2.5 cm, then 2.5 cm divided by 1.3 cm per month equals approximately 1.9 months, or about 7 weeks. This information can be used to identify different-colored hairs from different body locations as belonging to the same individual.

Figure 3-8 *Bleached hair lacks pigment in the cortex and cuticle.*

© Cengage Learning®

Figure 3-9 *Examples of dyed human hair. Notice the dye stains the entire hair, including the cuticle and cortex.*

FBI; photos by Sandra Koch & Douglas W. Deedrick

Ethnic or Ancestral Differences

Hair examiners have identified some key physical characteristics that are associated with hair of different general ancestral groups—European, Asian, and African. These characteristics are only generalities. In addition, a certain hair may be impossible to assign to a particular ancestry, because its characteristics are poorly defined or difficult to measure. The broad characteristics of hairs from different ancestries are compared in Figure 3-10.

DIFFERENTIATED LEARNING

Teaching Gifted Students
There is an even wider diversity of cuticle and medullary structures throughout the animal kingdom than those described in this chapter. Some students may be interested in finding images of these other structures. Direct these students to research the hair structure of deer, dogs, cats, horses, and mice. Ask students to prepare a drawing of their findings to show the class.

Science

MATHEMATICS

MATH
Regardless of their specialty, scientists use mathematics to help describe the world around them. Forensic investigators use average growth rates of various structures in the human body, such as hair and fingernails, to decode clues left at a crime scene. When using average growth rates, it is important to pay close attention to the units of measurement being used.

Figure 3-10 *A comparison of general characteristics of hair from people of different ancestries.*

Ancestry	Appearance	Pigment Granules	Cross Section	Other
European	Generally straight or wavy	Small and evenly distributed	Oval or round of moderate diameter with minimal variation	Color may be blond, red, brown, or black
Asian	Straight	Densely distributed	Round with large diameter	Shaft tends to be coarse and straight; thick cuticle; continuous medulla; color black
African	Kinky, curly, or coiled; shaft may be buckled	Densely distributed, clumped, may differ in size and shape	Flattened with moderate to small diameter and considerable variation	

Courtesy, FBI; photos by Sandra Koch & Douglas W. Deedrick

Animal Hair and Human Hair

Animal hair and human hair have several differences, including the pattern of pigmentation, the medullary index, and the cuticle type. The pattern of pigmentation can vary widely in different animals. While pigmentation in human hair tends to be denser toward the cuticle, in animals it is denser toward the medulla. In animal hair, pigments are often found in solid masses called *ovoid bodies*, especially in dogs and cattle. Human hairs are usually one color along the length.

In other animals, the medulla is proportionally much thicker than it is in humans (Figure 3-11). This air-filled region of a hair aids in providing insulation. The ratio of the diameter of the medulla to the diameter of the entire hair is known as *medullary index*. If the medullary index is 0.5 or greater, the hair came from an animal. If the medullary index is 0.33 or less, the hair is from a human.

MATHEMATICS

Figure 3-11 *The medulla of animal hair is proportionally much thicker than in human hair, and it is always continuous.*

Courtesy, FBI; photos by Sandra Koch & Douglas W. Deedrick

Index = 0.50 or more — Cattle hair

Index = 0.33 or less — Human hair

Evaluate
Ask students to refer to Figure 3-10 when answering the following questions:
- What is the most likely ancestry of a person with dense, straight, black hair? (Asian)
- What is the most likely ancestry of a person with dense, curly, brown hair? (Multiple answers are possible. Use this question to discuss how difficult it is to use hair to define ancestry or ethnic background.)

To avoid fear of racial profiling, make it clear that differences in hair relating to ancestral background can be useful in forensics, but only generally, and only in concert with other types of evidence.

Explore
Remind students that not all crimes have human victims. One example of a forensics lab in the United States that investigates crimes involving or against wildlife, such as poaching or hunting endangered species is the National Fish and Wildlife Forensics Laboratory is located in Ashland, Oregon. Wildlife forensics uses the same techniques and principles as forensic labs that investigate crimes against humans. The University of Florida offers a certificate in Wildlife Forensics and a Master's degree in Veterinarian Forensic Science.

Teaching Tip
Ask students if they think animals other than mammals (such as fuzzy caterpillars) have hair. Explain that these organisms have structures that look like hairs but are not. For example, some caterpillars seem to have thin hairs covering their entire bodies. These structures are actually called *setae* and are structured much differently than hair. Challenge students to investigate how these structures differ from hairs.

Explore

Have students prepare a model (three-dimensional structure, poster, or computer art) of an animal hair and a human hair to compare and contrast the structures.

Evaluate

Tell students that humans and dogs both have hairs with an imbricate cuticle. Ask them to draw a picture of each. Next, ask students what techniques forensic scientists would need to use to distinguish a dog hair from that of a human.

Science

PHYSICS

PHYSICS

Explain to students that light travels at different speeds through different materials. Refraction is the bend, or change in direction of a light ray when it changes speed as it travels from one material to another. For example, when light travels through glass and then it passes into water inside the glass, the light changes speed. As it changes speed, the light ray refracts. The refractive index of a material is an expression of how much light bends as it passes from one medium into that material.

Explore

Inform students that phase contrast microscopy is a technique that produces high-contrast images of transparent objects, such as living cells. Essentially, the technique amplifies small variations in the refraction of light to produce a high-contrast image. This technique has the distinct advantage of allowing living cells to be observed without staining or otherwise damaging or killing the cell.

The cuticle of the hair shaft can also help distinguish human hair from other animal hair. Rodents and bats have a *coronal* cuticle with scales that look like a stack of crowns. Cats, seals, and mink have scales that are called *spinous* and resemble petals. Human hair has cuticle scales that are flattened and narrow, which are called *imbricate* (Figure 3-12).

Figure 3-12 *Imbricate (human), coronal (mouse), and spinous (cat) cuticles.*

Imbricate   Coronal   Spinous

Collecting Hair in an Investigation

As you recall, Locard's Principle of Exchange maintains that two objects in contact will transfer materials. It is the fundamental reasoning behind the use of trace evidence in forensic investigations. One of the major examples of trace evidence is hair. Remember that, as with all trace evidence, the presence of a suspect's hair at a crime scene does not prove his or her guilt because you cannot prove when it was left there.

When investigators enter a crime scene, they collect trace evidence, including hair. Hair can be collected from the crime scene, suspect(s), or the victim by plucking, shaking, and scraping surfaces. It can also be collected by placing tape over a surface so that the hair adheres to it. When surfaces are large, they can be vacuumed. Forensic investigators must search all elements of a crime scene for hair, including vehicles; the fingernails and hands of the victim; on or in the body (during autopsy); blood or other body fluids of the victim or suspect; weapons, tape, or ligatures; abandoned clothing or masks; explosive device mechanisms.

Microscopy

Hair viewed for forensic investigations is studied both macroscopically and microscopically. Length, color, and curliness are macroscopic characteristics. If many hairs are collected, an investigator compares the sample with hair taken from the six major body regions of the victim or suspect(s). An initial analysis is performed using a low-power compound microscope to determine whether the hair is human or nonhuman. Microscopic characteristics include the pattern of the medulla, pigmentation of the cortex, and types of scales on the cuticle (Figure 3-13). Medullary index is calculated. Typical magnification for viewing hair is between 40 and 400 magnification. The comparison microscope is particularly useful for hair analysis.

Figure 3-13 *Using microscopy, investigators might link dog hair to a dog owner or deer hair to a hunter.*

Courtesy, FBI; photos by Sandra Koch & Douglas W. Deedrick

Dog hair 400×

Deer hair 400×

Several microscopic techniques are used in hair analysis. Phase contrast microscopy involves using a special objective lens and special condenser with a compound microscope. This configuration focuses light that passes through objects at different angles. The resulting image shows more contrast, especially when viewing translucent particles. Phase contrast microscopy is useful for observing fine detail in hair structure.

Many dyes and other hair treatments will *fluoresce* (glow) under a certain wavelength of light. In a fluorescence microscope, a beam of light of a certain wavelength is used. If the sample contains particular chemicals, it will absorb some of the light and then re-emit light of a different wavelength. This is called *fluorescence*. A fluorescence microscope is equipped with filters to detect the fluoresced light, indicating the presence of a dye or other treatment.

Instead of using light to view a sample, electron microscopes direct a beam of electrons at a sample. Electron microscopes provide remarkably detailed views of a sample (Figure 3-14), magnifying it 50,000 times or more.

PHYSICS

CHEMICAL TESTING FOR SUBSTANCES IN THE HAIR SHAFT

You are what you eat, and what you eat ends up in your hair. Anything ingested or absorbed through your skin—food, water, drugs, toxic substances (arsenic, lead)—becomes part of your hair.

Hair does not readily decompose, so by testing different parts of the hair, it may be possible to establish a timeline of a suspect's or victim's exposure to toxins or drugs. The math for developing this timeline is similar to that used with hair color discussed earlier in the chapter. Human hair grows at the rate of approximately 1.3 cm per month (or 0.44 mm per day). For example, if a toxin is found 9 cm. from the hair root, dividing this value by 1.3 cm per month provides an estimate of the number of months since the drug or toxin was ingested. In this case, 9 cm divided by 1.3 cm per month equals approximately 7 months.

One method used to identify drugs or toxins involves dissolving the hair in an organic solvent that breaks down the hair protein, thereby releasing any substances incorporated into the hair. Different tests are subsequently performed to identify specific toxins or drugs.

Scientists have devised a sort of tracking system for suspects or victims that uses isotope analysis of a strand of hair. This technique involves determining the ratio of different forms of certain elements in a person's hair and body tissues. Information about where a person lived over several months is useful to crime-scene investigators. Using this method, it is possible to determine where in the United States a person was living by examining the oxygen and hydrogen isotopes in their body tissues. The organic compounds that make up tissues such as hair in animals (including humans), are built using local water (which is made up of hydrogen and oxygen). By using isotope analysis, a single strand of hair can provide a timeline of a person's movements.

Figure 3-14 *A transmission electron microscope produced this extremely detailed image of a long section of human hair. Notice the overlapping cuticle scales on the left side and the pigment granules in the cortex.*

Courtesy, FBI; photos by Sandra Koch & Douglas W. Deedrick

MATHEMATICS

CHEMISTRY

DIGGING DEEPER With Forensic Science eCollection

For more information regarding different isotope levels in tap water, go to the Gale Forensic Science eCollection at **ngl.cengage.com/forensicscience2e.**

Explore

So they can better understand PCR reactions, have students view animations and interactive virtual tutorials on PCR reactions at the following Websites:

http://www.hhmi.org/biointeractive/polymerase-chain-reaction-pcr) and from Learn. Genetics (Genetic Science Learning Center)

http://learn.genetics.utah.edu/content/labs/pcr/

Teaching Tip

Describe the meaning of the term *follicular tag* to students. A follicular tag is tissue from a hair follicle that is still attached to the root end of a hair. Often, this tissue appears colorless and clear. Explain to students that DNA may be extracted from a follicular tag. Ask students why a hair with a follicular tag might be able to be used as individual evidence instead of class evidence.

Did you know

How long colonists lived in England versus their time in America can be determined using carbon isotope analysis of their remains. See *Written in Bone* by Sally Walker.

Through chemical and radiological analysis of a single strand of hair, information that includes a person's travels, their diet, and their drug intake and toxin exposure may be revealed. Knowing this information may provide essential clues to investigators trying to solve a crime.

Hair Examination and Testing

Hair is first examined microscopically to help either include or exclude a suspect. If the hair sample of the suspect appears consistent with those of the crime scene, DNA testing may be done. The hair is cleaned, ground up, added to a sterile solution, and chemically digested by enzymes. The DNA is extracted and amplified (copied) using the polymerase chain reaction (PCR) process. The DNA is profiled using an automated process, about which you will learn more in Chapter 7.

If the hair sample does not contain a follicle, then mitochondrial DNA (mtDNA) can be used to establish a genetic relationship through the mother. The mtDNA will be consistent with the mother and descendants of her mother, descendants of her mother's mother, and so on. Suspects can be excluded if their mtDNA is not consistent with the crime-scene mtDNA. If the root of the hair is present, nuclear DNA can be analyzed and individual evidence can be obtained. Both mitochondrial and nuclear DNA analyses are discussed in Chapter 7.

SUMMARY

LITERACY

www.fbi.gov
Douglas Deedrick,
"Hair Evidence."

- Hair is a form of evidence that has been used in forensic analysis since the late 19th century.

- Hair is a characteristic shared by all mammals and functions in temperature regulation, reducing friction, protection from light, and as a sense organ.

- Hair consists of a follicle embedded in the skin that produces the shaft.

- The shaft is composed of the protein keratin and consists of the outer cuticle, a cortex, and an inner medulla, most of which can vary within and among individuals and among species. The shaft also has pigments and mitochondrial DNA.

- Hair varies in length, medulla type, and cross-sectional shape, depending on where on the body it originates.

- Hair development is divided into three stages: anagen (growth), catagen (resting), and telogen (dormancy).

60   CHAPTER 3

DIFFERENTIATED LEARNING

Gifted students
Ask students to rewrite *Little Red Riding Hood* in a forensic style. Tell them to include information about hair analysis, medullary index, and so forth to identify hair at the crime scene as Red's, Granny's, or the wolf's.

- Various hair treatments produce characteristic effects that are useful to forensic experts, and some hair characteristics allow them to be grouped into ancestral categories.

- Forensic experts examine hair using light microscopy (phase contrast, fluorescence, comparison) and electron microscopy, and analyze hair chemically for drugs and toxins. They also perform DNA analyses.

- The hair shaft can provide mitochondrial DNA for class evidence, and the hair follicle can provide nuclear DNA for sequencing that may result in individual evidence.

LITERACY

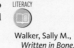

Walker, Sally M.,
Written in Bone.

CASE STUDIES   Obj. 3.4, 3.5

Alma Tirtsche
(1921)

Alma Tirtsche's beaten body was found wrapped in a blanket in what is known as Gun Alley in Melbourne, Australia. Because the body was relatively free of blood, the police deduced that she had been murdered elsewhere and brought to the alley. Her body had been washed before being wrapped in the blanket. A local bar owner, Colin Ross, was questioned. Ross admitted seeing Tirtsche in his bar earlier in the day.

Investigators collected blankets from Ross's home and found several strands of long, reddish-blond hair on them. The length of the hair implied it had come from a female, and the concentration of pigment in the hair indicated a younger woman. Some of the ends of the hair were irregular, implying the hair had been forcibly broken off. The physical similarity of the hair found on the blanket with that of Alma Tirtsche convinced the jury that Ross was the murderer. This was the first time that hair was used to secure a conviction in Australia. Unfortunately, analysis of the hairs 75 years later showed that two of the strands found on the blankets came from different individuals, which throws doubt on Ross's guilt.

Eva Shoen
(1990)

In Telluride, Colorado, Eva Shoen was found dead from a single gunshot to her head. The police recovered the bullet and expected to solve the case using fire-arms evidence. Unfortunately, they did not have any useful leads. Three years later, the police received a phone call from a man who believed that his brother-in-law, Frank Marquis, was responsible for Shoen's death. A gun was found on Marquis, but he had already tampered with its barrel, preventing a comparison.

HAIR ANALYSIS   **61**

DIFFERENTIATED LEARNING

Teaching At-Risk Students
Students may struggle with calculating rates, such as the rate of hair growth. Discuss with these students other rates with which they may be familiar, such as the speed of a moving car measured in miles per hour. Using a time line, ask students to discuss the meaning of the following scenarios:

1. A car traveling at 60 miles per hour: How much time has passed when the car has traveled 60 miles? (1 hour) 120 miles? (2 hours) 90 miles? (1.5 hours)

2. A car traveling at an unknown speed: A car has traveled 30 miles in 1 hour. What is the speed of the car? (30 miles per hour) Another car has traveled 60 miles in 2 hours. What is the speed of this car? (30 miles per hour)

3. A car traveling at an unknown speed: It takes a car 3 hours to travel 90 miles. What is the speed of the car? (30 miles per hour)

Close

Draw an example of a hair on the board or overhead projector. Have students help you label the parts. As they name a part, ask them to explain what information can be gathered from that part. Ask students what value hair can be to a criminal investigation when it is only class evidence?

Digital Vision/Photodisc/Getty Images

From questioning a companion of Marquis's, police learned that Marquis had been in Telluride when Shoen was murdered. They also discovered that Marquis had thrown two bundles out of his car during his drive home from Telluride. Detectives searched the road until they found a bundle of clothing. One of the shirts in the bundle contained a single strand of hair. The color and structure of the hair was similar to that of Eva Shoen's hair. When confronted with the evidence, Marquis confessed to the murder and was sentenced to 24 years imprisonment.

Napoleon's Hair

Napoleon Bonaparte proclaimed himself emperor of France in 1804 after rising swiftly through the ranks of the French army. Following his defeat at Waterloo, he was exiled on the British island of St. Helena in the Atlantic Ocean. History books claim that he died in exile of stomach cancer.

The Gallery Collection/Fine Art/Corbis

In 2001, a Canadian Napoleon enthusiast, Ben Weider, challenged this theory. He had five strands of Napoleon's hair collected in 1805, 1814, and 1821 tested using neutron activation analysis. The results of the analysis showed that Napoleon's hair contained between 7 and 38 times more arsenic than normal, a fatal dose. In 2002, further analysis of Napoleon's hair showed extremely elevated levels of arsenic, leading researchers to joke that Napoleon should have died twice before his actual death, and suggesting that the hair must have been contaminated during storage.

Eventually, the esteemed microscopist Walter McCrone tested a sample of Napoleon's hair. His work contradicted the previous reports, stating that the levels of arsenic that had been incorporated into Napoleon's hair were much too low to have killed him. The story continues to cause controversy. Most chemists believe that McCrone's work is the final story, but Napoleon enthusiasts believe that the emperor's death is surrounded by too many questions to disregard the possibility of murder.

Think Critically Do you consider hair evidence important in solving a crime? Explain your answer.

Careers *in Forensics*

William J. Walsh, Chemical Researcher

With a doctorate in chemical engineering and a research record that includes such illustrious laboratories as the Ames Laboratory in Iowa; Los Alamos National Laboratory in New Mexico; and Argonne National Laboratory in Illinois, William Walsh spent his early career studying chemical processes involved in nuclear fuel production, liquid metal distillation, and electrochemistry.

Dr. Walsh's research in chemistry led to an interest in developing tools and chemical methods for extracting information from hair. Dr. Walsh and his colleagues collected known chemistry information from more than 100,000 people and synthesized it into the world's first standard of known hair composition. Walsh has conducted numerous forensic studies of hair samples in collaboration with medical examiners, coroners, and police groups. Some of the more famous, or infamous, people whose hair chemistry Walsh has studied include Charles Manson (Manson family murders), Henry Lee Lucas (20th-century serial killer), James Hubeity (McDonald's massacre), William Sherrill (Oklahoma post office slayings), and other notorious criminals. In addition, while volunteering at the Stateville Penitentiary in Joliet, Illinois, Walsh became interested in the way that chemicals can affect behavior. These combined interests—hair forensics and the influence of biochemicals on behavior—made Walsh the perfect candidate to head up one of the most famous hair investigations: that of composer Ludwig van Beethoven.

Walsh was the chief scientist on the Beethoven Research Project in 2000. The goal of the project was to understand whether chemical toxins played a role in Beethoven's death. Beethoven developed an illness in his twenties that involved abdominal distress, irritation, and eventually depression. By the age of 31, he began to lose his hearing, and by

Photo courtesy of Walsh Research Institute

Dr. William J. Walsh

42, he was completely deaf. He died of liver and kidney failure. Using highly sensitive techniques—scanning electron microscope energy dispersion spectrometry (SEM/EDS) and scanning ion microscope mass spectrometry (SIMS)—Walsh verified that Beethoven's hair contained extremely high concentrations of lead, which almost certainly contributed to his death.

Dr. Walsh has authored more than 200 scientific articles and reports and made numerous presentations of his research. He is president of the nonprofit Walsh Research Institute. He is recognized as an international expert in nutritional medicine. Dr. Walsh is also a pioneer researcher on the effect of epigenetics (gene expression caused or suppressed by chemical reactions) on mental health.

Learn More About It
▷ To learn more about forensic hair analysis, go to
ngl.cengage.com/forensicscience2e.

Careers

Famous criminologists specialized in many different subject areas when in school. Topics of study that are important for criminologists and forensic scientists include molecular biology, genetics, sociology, psychology, organic chemistry, and biochemistry.

CHAPTER 3 REVIEW

Chapter 3 Review

True or False

1. True
2. False
3. False
4. True

Multiple Choice

5. d
6. d
7. a
8. a
9. b
10. a
11. d
12. b

CHAPTER 3 REVIEW

True or False

1. The shaft of the hair is considered class evidence in a trial. *Obj. 3.5*
2. Hair is composed mostly of a protein called cellulose. *Obj. 3.1, 3.2*
3. All hairs on the head of a person are identical. *Obj. 3.2*
4. Hair can provide clues about someone's ancestry. *Obj. 3.7*

Multiple Choice

5. Hair can be used to determine *Obj. 3.5*
   a) diet
   b) drug habits
   c) geographic history
   d) all of the above

6. Which factors are used to calculate the medullary index of the hair? *Obj. 3.6*
   a) scale diameter of cuticle and the length of the hair
   b) width of cortex and the width of the medulla
   c) length of entire hair and the pattern of pigmentation
   d) width of medulla and the width of the hair

7. Which of the following characteristics is found in typical Asian hair? *Obj. 3.7*
   a) dark medulla
   b) sparsely distributed pigment granules
   c) flattened cross section
   d) curls

8. Human hair has which type of cuticle? *Obj. 3.3*
   a) imbricate
   b) spinous
   c) coronal
   d) pigmented

9. Microscopic hair analysis *Obj. 3.5*
   a) yields individual evidence
   b) is used to exclude a suspect
   c) can prove a suspect's guilt
   d) can determine maternal inheritance

10. Which part(s) of a hair can be analyzed for nuclear DNA? *Obj. 3.5*
    a) follicle
    b) shaft
    c) medulla
    d) all of the above

11. Animal hair can be distinguished from human hair because animal hair *Obj. 3.3*
    a) has a smaller medullary index than human hair and no cortex
    b) does not have a cuticle
    c) always has a continuous medulla pattern
    d) has a greater medullary index and more variation in the cuticle patterns

12. The period when hair is naturally shed is called the _____ stage. *Obj. 3.1*
    a) catagen
    b) telogen
    c) anagen
    d) imagen

13. Although variations can occur, which of the following best describes European hair? *Obj. 3.7*
    a) kinky with dense, unevenly distributed pigment
    b) straight or wavy with evenly distributed granules
    c) round cross section with a large diameter
    d) coarse with a thick cuticle and a continuous medulla

14. Which of the following is most likely a result of hair bleaching? *Obj. 3.5*
    a) increased number of disulfide bonds
    b) oxidized hair and damaged DNA
    c) a more triangular cross section
    d) thickened scales on the cuticle

Short Answer

15. Two different hairs were found at a crime scene. One hair strand only provided class evidence, whereas the other hair strand provided both class and individual evidence. Using what you have learned in this chapter, explain how this is possible. *Obj. 3.5*

16. Describe the structure of hair. Include in your answer the terms *follicle*, *medulla*, *cortex*, and *cuticle*. *Obj. 3.1, 3.2*

17. Crime-scene investigators collected hair from a dead person's body. Is the hair human or nonhuman? Describe two ways that the investigators could distinguish human hair from animal hair. *Obj. 3.3*

18. Calculate the medullary index of a hair whose diameter is 110 microns and whose medulla measures 58 microns. Is this a human or nonhuman animal hair? *Obj. 3.3, 3.6*

19. A woman with long hair is a suspect in a burglary case. At the crime scene, several long hairs were found attached to a broken lock of the safe. The police obtain a warrant and request a sample of 25 to 50 hairs from this woman. They tell the woman it is important that they pull the hairs from her head rather than merely cut the hairs. The police suspect that the woman was stealing to help support a drug habit. *Obj. 3.4, 3.5, 3.7*
    a) Why is it important that the police pull the hairs from her head rather than cut her hair?
    b) Why is it necessary to obtain 25 to 50 hairs from this woman?
    c) The woman denies that she is taking drugs, stating that she stopped using drugs a year ago. Explain how the police can determine if the woman has been off drugs for over one year.
    d) Suppose the hairs of the woman match the hairs found at the crime scene. Does this prove that she was the guilty party? Support your claim with facts from the case.

13. b
14. b

Short Answer

15. Hair is considered class evidence when no source of DNA, such as follicle cells, is attached to the hair. Without DNA, hair can only be used as class evidence, to indicate color of hair and perhaps racial group. The hair providing class and individual evidence must have had follicle cells attached and, therefore, DNA.

16. Sample answer: Hair grows from a follicle found in the skin. It is composed of an inner medulla, surrounded by the cortex, and protected on the outside by the cuticle.

17. Sample answer: Animal hairs have a greater medullary index and can have a different cuticle pattern.

18. Medullary index = diameter of medulla / diameter of hair = 58 microns/110 microns = 0.527 ≈ 0.53. This is most likely animal hair.

19. a. The police need to pull the hair so they will have follicle tags on them, so DNA analysis can be performed that might identify an individual.

    b. Obtaining multiple hairs from the woman will give a more accurate picture of the woman's exposure to drugs and other toxins because the hairs of a single individual vary. This is especially true of hair color that has gray mixed in it.

    c. If the woman has been off drugs for over a year, traces of the drugs will appear in her hair only after roughly 16 cm.

    d. If the hairs at the crime scene do not contain DNA, they cannot be used to determine the identity of an individual. Even if they do contain DNA, they only prove that she was *at* the scene, not that she was there at the time of the crime.

20. a. Any food or drugs absorbed by the body will become part of your hair.
    b. Yes, because over 8 months the hair would grow approximately 10.4 cm.

    8 months x 1.3 cm/month (approximately) = 10.4 cm.

    If the hair measures 14 cm, then there would be a record of drug use in his hair from 8 months earlier.

21. Organic compounds found in tissues and hair are made from what a person ingests, including the local water. When hair is analyzed, the types of hydrogen and oxygen isotopes reflect the water from an area. Through this analysis, scientists can get an indication of where the person lived.

20. A gossip blog published a photo of a famous baseball player using drugs at a party held eight months earlier. The baseball player claims that the photo was manipulated, and he denies any drug use. *Obj. 3.5*
    a) Can drugs injected more than eight months ago be detected in hair?
    b) If his hair measures 14 cm long and hair grows approximately 1.3 cm per month, will there still be evidence of drug use in his hair? Explain.

21. How do forensic scientists use analysis of hydrogen and oxygen isotopes to assist in solving crimes? *Obj. 3.5*

Going Further

Write a short crime-scene story or suggest ideas for a video game that incorporate the use of hair evidence in solving a crime. Be creative in your writing, but also be accurate in your science. Before writing, brainstorm ideas with your classmates listing the different types of evidence that could be found through hair analysis.

a) Describe the crime and the victim(s).
b) Provide evidence found in someone's hair that could link him or her to a particular career, hobby, or sports event.
c) Provide information that could be found in hair that would provide information pertaining either to drug use or exposure to toxins.
d) Provide evidence derived from hair that provides information as to where a person was geographically located.

Bibliography

Books and Journals

Baden, Michael, and Marion Roach. *Dead Reckoning*. London: Arrow Books, 2002.
Gautam, Lata, and Michael D. Cole. Hair Analysis in Forensic Toxicology." *Forensic Magazine*, September 3, 2013.
Hughes, Caroline. "Challenges in DNA Testing and Forensic Analysis of Hair Samples." *Forensic Magazine*, April 2, 2013.
Lee, Henry. *Physical Evidence in Forensic Science*. Tucson, AZ: Lawyers & Judges Publishing, 2000.
Menotti-Raymond, M. et al. "Pet Cat Hair Implicates Murder Suspects." *Nature*, 386, 774 (1997).
Melton, Terry, "Mitochondrial DNA Examination of Cold-Case Crime-Scene Hairs." *Forensic Magazine*, April 1, 2009.
Saferstein, Richard. *Criminalistics: Introduction to Forensic Science*, 9th Edition. Englewood Cliffs, NJ: Prentice Hall, 2006.
Walker, Sally M. *Written in Bone*. Minneapolis, MN: Carolrhoda Books, 2009.

Internet Resources

"Alma Tirtsche." www.history.com/this-day-in-history.do?printable=true&action=tdihArticlePrint&id=982
Deedrick, Douglas W. "Hair, Fibers, Crime and Evidence." Quantico, VA: FBI. www.fbi.gov/hq/lab/fsc/backissu/july2000/deedric1.htm
Deedrick, Douglas W., and Sandra L. Koch. "Microscopy of Hair. Parts 1 and 2: A Practical Guide and Manual for Human Hairs." Quantico, VA: FBI. www.fbi.gov
"Isotope Tutorial on Carbon and Hydrogen." Isoforensics.com
"Mitotyping" www.mitotyping.com
University of Oregon Gas Chromatography and Mass Spectrometry http://www.unsolvedmysteries.oregonstate.edu/MS_03
Shapiro, Ari Daniel. "Strands of Evidence." www.pbs.org/wgbh/nova/sciencenow
"SWGMAT Human Hair Atlas." www.swgmat.org/hair.htm

Trace Evidence: Hair *Obj. 3.1, 3.2, 3.4, 3.5, 3.6, 3.7*

Objectives:

By the end of this activity, you will be able to:

1. Describe the external structure of hair.
2. Distinguish among different hair samples based on color, medulla types, cuticle types, thickness, and length.
3. Compare and contrast a suspect's hair with the hair found at a crime scene.
4. State your claim as to which suspect could have been present at a crime scene and support it with evidence from your investigation.
5. Justify whether or not a suspect's hair sample matches the hair sample left at a crime scene.

Time Required to Complete Activity: 60 minutes

Introduction:

In this laboratory exercise, you will work with hair evidence that was collected at a crime scene. Your task is to try to determine whether the hair evidence collected at the crime scene is consistent with hair collected from any of the four suspects.

Materials:

Act 3-1 SH Data Tables 1 & 2
Act 3-1 SH Student Designed Experiment
plastic microscope slides
clear adhesive, but not "transparent," tape
compound microscope
prepared slides of hair samples
2 plastic slides (made from transparency sheets)
permanent marker
scissors
clear nail polish
glass microscope slide

SAFETY PRECAUTIONS:

Always carry a microscope using both hands.
Do not get nail polish on the eyepiece or objective lenses.

Hair Analysis **67**

Background

Transfer of hair from a suspect to the victim is a good example of Locard's Principle of Exchange. Although hair is not unique to a person, it can be used to identify a class of individuals. (The exception to this rule is if the hair follicle containing DNA is present. DNA is unique to a particular individual.)

Students will examine one of their hairs and a cuticle impression of their hair using a microscope. After reviewing characteristics such as cuticle type and medulla types, students will investigate a crime by trying to link a suspect to a crime scene through microscopic trace evidence analysis of hair.

Safety Precautions

Remind students to always carry a microscope with two hands. This prevents students from dropping an expensive and heavy piece of equipment on their foot. Be sure that students do not place a slide containing wet nail polish under the microscope. To avoid getting nail polish on the lenses, view the cuticle impression under 100X, not 400X.

Teaching Tip

Students can take digital images ("microdigiscoping") through their microscope's eyepiece lens using a digital camera and a film canister with the lid and bottom removed. Focus on the object to be photographed. Put the film canister over the microscope's eyepiece lens. Extend the digital camera lens into the film canister. This setup allows the camera lens to be steadied while excluding outside light. View and zoom using the camera screen as your guide.

Procedures

Prior to the lab, the teacher should complete the following:

1. Print, copy, and distribute Act 3-1 SH Data Tables 1 & 2 and Act 3-1 SH Student-Designed Experiment from the IRCD.

2. Cut overhead transparency (acetate) sheets into pieces approximately 1" × 2½" (about the size of a glass microscope slide). Cut about 100 slides.

3. Obtain hair samples from five students or teachers with different hair color or textures and place them in five separate envelopes.

4. Label four of these hair samples suspect 1, 2, 3, and 4.

5. Label a fifth hair sample as "Victim's Own Hair." Do not allow students to observe which hair you place in which envelope.

6. Choose one of the four suspects' hair to also be used as your crime-scene hair sample. Place some of this hair in an envelope labeled "Crime-Scene Hair."

7. Prepare at least 15 slides of suspects 1, 2, 3, and 4, Victim's Hair, and Crime-Scene Hair.

8. Prepare 15 envelopes containing one slide of 1,2,3,4,crime scene and victim's hair. Students will obtain one of these sets to take to their microscope for analysis to students the importance of taking only one slide at a time to examine.

9. Students should return the one envelope with all six slides upon completion of their analysis.

Teaching Tip

1. Do not use so-called "invisible" tape. It must be clear tape.

Scenario:

A murder was committed. To dispose of the body, the suspect(s) tossed the body from the car into a ditch. When crime-scene investigators arrived, they photographed the crime scene and drew sketches of the body. Hair evidence was found on the victim. Hair samples were collected from the four suspects; a sample of hair also was taken from the victim's head. At the crime lab, a comparison microscope was used to examine each of the hair samples. Your task is to examine all hair samples under the compound microscope and record your observations. After reviewing all samples, determine if any of the suspects' hair is consistent with the hair found at the crime scene. You will then support your claim with evidence from your investigation.

Procedure:

PART 1: CUTICLE IMPRESSION

1. Obtain a clean glass slide.
2. Place the slide along the edge of the desk.
3. Wipe a thin layer of nail polish on the slide the length and width of a cover slip.
4. Either pull out or cut a hair from your head.
5. While holding onto the hair between two fingers in front of the slide, slowly lower the hair onto the slide. Be careful not to wiggle the hair back and forth. Pull the hair down into the nail polish and let go of the hair.
6. Wait 10 minutes to remove the hair.
7. After 10 minutes, grasp the loose end of the hair and pull straight up to completely remove the hair from the nail polish.
8. Observe the slide under 100×. Remember to move the dial on the diaphragm and the fine adjustment *while viewing the slide* in order to see the cuticle. Sketch your cuticle.

PART 2: OBSERVATION OF YOUR OWN HAIR

1. Obtain a plastic slide. Write your initials on the end of the slide with a permanent marker.
2. Remove a hair from your head, preferably a hair that contains a follicle. For a hair with a follicle, you will need to pull it out.
3. Place the hair on your desk.
4. Fold the tape with the sticky side facing the hair on the table. Hold the tape near the hair, but do not touch the hair. The hair should be attracted to the sticky surface of the tape.
5. Place the tape with the attached hair on to the plastic slide. Use your finger to press down on the tape to squeeze out any air pockets. Cut off the excess tape. You now have a permanent slide.

The finished slide.

- Slide
- Tape
- Hair

2. Plastic slides are easy to store but flexible. Students must use stage clips on plastic slides.

3. Remind students to use both the fine adjustment and the diaphragm dial *while* viewing the hair. Cuticles are difficult to see if there is too much light.

Teaching Tip

To stimulate student interest for part 3, use hair samples from faculty members for suspects 1–4 and the victim's hair. Recall that one of your four suspects' hair will also be used as the crime-scene hair. One week prior to this activity, post pictures of the four teachers and your victim. Do not explain why the faculty photos are being displayed. When students ask, tell them you will explain next week. On the day of the lab, describe a crime scene, the victim, and four suspects. Point to the faculty photos and introduce your victim and four suspects. Continue with this scenario for Activity 4-1 (Fibers). Tell students the evidence fibers came from the four suspects' cars.

Data Table 1

Source of Hair	Sketch	Color	Medulla	Cuticle	Straight or Curly	Other Characteristics
Your name						

© 2016 Cengage Learning

6. Focus the hair using 100× magnification. Use stage clips to flatten the slide.

    a. Draw your hair in the space provided on Data Table 1.

    b. Identify the type of medulla, cuticle, color, and any other distinguishing features.

PART 3: COMPARATIVE ANALYSIS OF SUSPECT AND CRIME-SCENE HAIR

1. Obtain a slide of the victim's hair from the envelope prepared by your instructor. Draw a sketch of the victim's hair, and record all of the information in Data Table 2. Return the slide to the envelope as soon as you are finished.

2. Look at each of the four suspects' hair. Draw sketches and record all required information in Data Table 2. Take only one slide at a time.

3. You will need to rule out that the hair found on the victim came from the victim's own head. To do so, you will need to examine the sample entitled "Victim's Own Hair."

4. Compare your results with those of another classmate. If you find you have different answers, it might be necessary to examine more than one hair sample from any individual. Recall that not all head hairs are exactly alike.

5. Is it possible to match any of the suspects' hair with the evidence hair that was found on the victim? Cite evidence from your investigation to support your claim.

Final Analysis:

1. Are any suspects' hair consistent with the crime-scene hair? If yes, which suspect(s)?

2. Cite three different characteristics of hair that can be used to support your answer. Use complete sentences and correct terminology.

Going Further: Inquiry Investigation:

1. Have students bring in hair samples from their pets. Take digital microscope images to share with the class.

    a. Compare and contrast human hair with animal hair.

    b. If the class has several examples of different dog or cat hair, identify any unique features of dog or cat hair.

Answers

Check students' data tables.

Final Analysis

1. Answers may vary.

2. Possible answer: Three characteristics of hair that forensic scientists use in investigations are hair color, texture, and whether or not the hair is curly. Also, scientists examine the structure of the hair's medulla, and they calculate its medullary index.

Teaching Tip

Going Further: Inquiry

2. a. Possible brainstorming questions

    i. Does baby hair differ from adult hair?

    ii. Can hair spray, gels, and other hair treatments be noted under a microscope?

    iii. Does eyebrow hair differ from head hair?

    iv. Is it possible to detect if a person had his or her hair cut with scissors or a razor?

    v. Is it possible to tell if hair was burned or if someone was near a fire?

    vi. Is there a difference in the structure of hair in a dog's winter coat versus its summer coat?

    vii. Do all blondes have the same type of medulla?

    viii. Does bleaching or dyeing one's hair affect the structure of the hair?

    ix. Does using hair conditioner on one's hair make a difference in the appearance of hair under a microscope?

2. b. After a student selects a question to investigate, help him or her organize the experiment by completing the student design experiment form. See IRCD, Activity 3-1 SH Student-Designed Experiment.

2. a. As a class, brainstorm questions about what can be identified in human hair samples when viewed under a microscope. For example, how can you distinguish dyed hair or bleached hair from untreated hair?

    b. In groups of two, select one of the questions from the brainstorming activity. Design and perform an experiment to collect data regarding the question.

Data Table 2

Source of Hair	Sketch	Color	Medulla	Cuticle	Straight or Curly	Other Characteristics
Crime-Scene Hair						
Suspect 1						
Suspect 2						
Suspect 3						
Suspect 4						
Victim's Own Hair						
Final Analysis						

© 2016 Cengage Learning

DIFFERENTIATED LEARNING

Teaching Gifted Students

Allow more motivated students to prepare an expert witness testimony to present to the class based on their Final Analysis and data from this Activity. Use the hair testimony essay support in Activity 3-3 as a model.

Hair Measurement *Obj. 3.2, 3.4, 3.5, 3.6*

Objectives:

By the end of this activity, you will be able to:

1. Describe how to measure the diameter of a hair that is viewed under a compound microscope.
2. Measure and analyze hair samples and determine if the diameter of the hair samples from different sources are the same.
3. Determine if any of the suspects' hair is consistent with the hair evidence found at the crime scene. Cite evidence to support your conclusion.

Time Required to Complete Activity: 60 minutes

Introduction:

Hair is an example of trace evidence that can be left at a crime scene or removed from a crime scene (Locard's Principle of Exchange). Hair examined microscopically is considered class evidence. It can be used to exclude suspects but cannot be used to identify a specific person.

Materials:

Act 3-2 SH Hair Measurement
compound microscope
clear plastic millimeter ruler
clear transparency film cut the size of a microscope slide
clear tape (not "transparent")
pencil
pre-made slide of crime-scene hair
pre-made slide of suspect 1 hair
pre-made slide of suspect 2 hair
pre-made slide of suspect 3 hair
scissors

SAFETY PRECAUTIONS:

Always carry the microscope with both hands.

Scenario:

Not everyone's scalp hair is the same; some is very fine, while some is coarse. Hair diameter provides us with another way to compare a suspect's hair to the crime-scene hair. In this lab activity, examine the crime-scene hair with the three suspects' hair and the victim's hair by examining their medulla, cortex, cuticle types, and hair diameter.

Background

Hair is an important kind of evidence that may be left at a crime scene by any person involved in the crime. In this activity, students will examine their own hair under a microscope and record the following data: color of cortex, type of medulla, type of cuticle, width of hair in micrometers, and whether the hair is straight, curly, or kinky. Then they will use the same techniques to examine hair found at a crime scene and hair from a suspect and try to conclude whether the samples match.

Safety Precautions

It is important for students to carry microscopes with two hands.

Teaching Tips

1. Prior to the lab, select three different sources of hair to represent suspects 1–3. Make at least 15 slides of each, using the same technique as in Activity 3-1, with clear tape and clear transparency film. Be sure to label each slide with a permanent marker as S1, S2, or S3.

2. Note that each student prepares a slide of his or her own hair. This slide will be used as the victim's hair.

3. Select one of the suspects' hair samples to also be the hair used as hair for the crime scene. Prepare at least 15 slides of the crime-scene hair.

4. Each team should obtain in one envelope: Suspect 1 hair, Suspect 2 hair, Suspect 3 hair, and Crime-Scene Hair. (Students will prepare a slide of their own hair to be used as the Victim's Own Hair.)

Procedures

1. Print, copy, and distribute Act 3-2 SH Hair Measurement from the IRCD, Chapter 3.

2. Review what is meant by the term *diameter of the field of view.*

3. Review with students how to measure in millimeters using a metric ruler and how to convert from millimeters to micrometers.

4. Review the different parts of hair found in this chapter.

5. A time-saving alternative to having all students examine all three suspects is to designate one-third of the class to view Suspect 1, one-third to view Suspect 2, and one-third to view Suspect 3. Students will share data.

Teaching Tip

Students should use transparent rules under the low power of their microscopes. Remind them that the lines they see are 1 mm apart. Most microscopes fields of view are 1.2–1.5 mm, or 1,200–1,500 microns in diameter.

Procedure:

1. Measure the size of the diameter of the microscope under 100×.

   a. If an ocular micrometer is available, measure the diameter of the field of view. (Most microscopes have a field of view of approximately 1.2 mm.)

   b. If an ocular micrometer is not available:
      - Place a small, clear plastic ruler under the microscope under 100×.
      - Focus on the metric side of the ruler.
      - Measure the diameter of the field of view to the nearest tenth of a millimeter.
      - Record your answer in Data Table 1.

Plastic ruler viewed under 100×.

© Cengage Learning®

2. Using a hair from your head, make a slide with transparency film and clear tape. Label the slide "victim's hair."

3. View the hair under LOW power (100×). Be sure to use stage clips.

4. Note the following characteristics of your hair and record the information in Data Table 2:
   - Color of cortex
   - Type of medulla (e.g., continuous, interrupted, fragmented, solid, none)
   - Type of cuticle (e.g., spinous, coronal, or imbricate)

5. Measure or estimate the width of the hair using the diameter of your field of view as a reference. Record your answer in Data Table 2. For example: Center your hair in the field of view. Estimate how many hairs would fit across the field of view (100×).

Hair 100× | Number of hairs fitting across the field of view

Hair

It appears that about 10.5 hairs fit across half of the diameter of the field of view (100×). Therefore, it would take about twice as many hairs (or hairs) to fit across the field of view.

The diameter of the single hair is ¹/₂₁ of the diameter of the field of view.

If the diameter is 1.2 mm, or 1200 microns, then the size of a single hair is:

Diameter	$\approx$ ¹/₂₁ of 1.2 mm Diameter	$\approx$ ¹/₂₁ of 1200 microns
	$\approx$ 0.05 × 1.2 mm	$\approx$ 0.05 × 1200 microns
	$\approx$ 0.06 mm	$\approx$ 60 microns

DIFFERENTIATED LEARNING

Teaching At-Risk and Visual Learners

For a further explanation of field of view, teachers could present the example of placing a quarter in a petri dish. The petri dish is the field of view, and the quarter is the specimen to be measured. Ask students to estimate the number of quarters that fit across the dish. From that information and the size of the dish, have them determine the size of one quarter. As a follow-up, provide students with pieces of uncooked spaghetti. Ask them to estimate how many pieces of uncooked spaghetti fit widthwise across the diameter of the field of view (using a petri dish). Then have them test their hypotheses.

6. Focus the victim's hair under 400×. Draw a sketch of the victim's hair in Data Table 2. Examine the hair, and complete the information in Data Table 2.

7. The diameter of the high-power (400×) field of view is ¼ of the diameter of the field of view under 100×, or approximately 300 microns. Calculate the diameter of your field of view under 400× in microns. Record your answer in Data Table 3.

8. Obtain a pre-made slide from your teacher of the crime-scene hair. Focus first on 100×, and then switch to 400×. Make a sketch of the hair in Data Table 4.

9. Measure (or estimate) the diameter of the hair in microns. Record your observations in Data Table 4.

   You will need to record the following information:

   - Sample number
   - Width of the hair in microns
   - Color of cortex
   - Type of medulla
   - Type of cuticle
   - Straight, curly, or kinky

10. Obtain premade slides from your teacher of the hair of suspects 1, 2, and 3. Measure in microns the diameter of each sample. Record all observations and sketches in Data Table 4.

    You will need to record the following information:

    - Sample number
    - Width of the hair in microns
    - Color of cortex
    - Type of medulla
    - Type of cuticle
    - Straight, curly, or kinky

11. Based on the microscopic analysis of hair, did you find any of the suspects' or the victim's hair to be consistent with the crime-scene hair? Justify your answer using the information recorded in your Data Table 4.

12. Check with your classmates regarding the other suspects' hair sample analysis. Did anyone find a hair sample consistent with the hair evidence left at the crime scene?

13. After reviewing both your data and the data from your classmates, record your conclusions in Data Table 4. Prepare a more extensive report or presentation that provides evidence to support your conclusions. Use any of the following formats to report your findings:

    - written report or blog entry
    - PowerPoint presentation
    - poster
    - short video interview
    - oral presentation to the class

Diameter of the field of view at high power = (¼) × diameter at low power.

DIFFERENTIATED LEARNING

Teaching Gifted Students

Allow more motivated students to prepare an expert witness testimony to present to the class based on their Final Analysis and data from this Activity. Use the hair testimony essay support in Activity 3-3 as a model.

Answers

Data Table 1:
1st column: approximately 1.2
2nd column: approximately 1,200

Data Table 2: Answers will vary.

Data Table 3:
1st column: approximately 1,200
2nd column: $1/4 \times 1,200 = 300$
3rd column: approximately 300

Data Table 4: Answers will vary.

Data Table 1: Size of Field of View Under 100×

Diameter of Field of View under 100×	
millimeters	microns (microns = millimeters × 1000)

Data Table 2: Your Own Hair (Victim's Hair)

Victim's Hair	Cuticle Color	Type of Medulla	Type of Cuticle	Straight, Curly, or Kinky	Width (microns)	Sketch

Data Table 3: Size of Field of View under 400×

Diameter of Field of View under 100× (microns)	Calculations 1/4 Diameter of Field of View under 100× (microns)	Diameter of Field of View under 400× (microns)

Data Table 4: Whose Hair Is Consistent With the Crime-Scene Hair?

Hair Sample	Cuticle Color	Type of Medulla	Type of Cuticle	Straight, Curly, or Kinky	Width (microns)	Sketch
Crime Scene						
Suspect 1						
Suspect 2						
Suspect 3						

Conclusion: Is any of the suspects' hair consistent with the crime-scene hair? Justify your answer.

Thought Questions:

Explain each of your answers.

1. Is it possible that none of the hair samples is consistent with the hair found at the crime scene?
2. Is it possible that more than one person's hair is consistent with the hair found at the crime scene?
3. If someone's hair is consistent with the crime-scene evidence, does that mean that he or she committed the crime?
4. If someone's hair was consistent with that at the crime scene, what type of evidence could be obtained to indicate that the DNA at the crime scene was consistent with his or her DNA and not with anyone else's DNA?
5. If class members did not all reach the same conclusions, describe how you would change the lab protocol to ensure more reliable results.

Explore further information at **ngl.cengage.com/forensicscience2e**.

Further Study:

Read the article "Challenges in DNA Testing and Forensic Analysis of Hair Samples" by Caroline Hughes in *Forensic Magazine*, April 2, 2013.
(Search the Internet for the title of the magazine and then search for the article name on the magazine site to view the article.)

After reading the article:

1. Describe the role of keratinocytes in the growth and development of hair.
2. Compare and contrast the role and location of mitochondrial DNA and nuclear DNA.
3. If only the hair shaft from a hair is available, what type of evidence can be derived from DNA analysis of the hair? Cite evidence from the reading to support your answer.
4. Describe the effect of hair bleaching on the DNA found in a hair sample.

Further Research and Extensions

Interested students may be curious about what images of hair from different kinds of microscopes look like. Have these students create a poster or slideshow presentation that shows how the same structure looks using different kinds of microscopes.

Thought Questions

1. Yes, there could easily be a different suspect.

2. Yes, it is possible that more than one person's hair is consistent. Remember that hair is considered to be class evidence, and more than one person can have the same type of hair.

3. No; it would not be possible to tell when that hair was left on the crime-scene victim.

4. If the hair is consistent, then further evidence is needed. If the hair sample has some cells on it from the hair follicle, then a DNA analysis could be conducted. It would then be necessary to get a warrant to request DNA from the suspect. DNA can be obtained from hair, interior cheek cells, blood, semen, or any other cell from the body.

5. a. Repeat the microscopic review.

   b. Check your technique: Did everyone view at 400 magnification? Did each team examine more than one hair from each suspect?

   c. Check the microscope: clean the lens; check for adequate light transmission.

   d. Review proper techniques for evidence collection and storage of hair. Was proper protocol followed by all examiners?

Bonus

Students should measure the medullary index (the diameter of the medulla to the diameter of the hair shaft). If the ratio is 0.5 or greater, it is probably an animal hair. Human hair has a medullary index of 0.33. Besides measuring the medullary index, students should examine the cuticle. Humans generally have an imbricate cuticle, whereas animals have a spinous or coronal cuticle.

Background

When experts testify in court, they must not only address the specific topics relevant to the case, but they must also educate the jury about the subject of their testimony. In this activity, students must prepare a typed, formal presentation to a jury about hair analysis, hair evidence, and why hair from a particular suspect matches hair found at a crime scene. It might be helpful if students know the names of local forensics labs and schools.

Safety Precautions

No safety precautions are necessary for this lab.

Procedures

Emphasize how important it is that students answer each of the questions needed to complete this essay. Also remind them to assume that members of the jury know nothing about hair analysis.

Teaching Tip

Distribute to students the rubric you plan to use in grading their testimony. As students examine your rubric, consider asking them what they consider key points that should be considered in grading their testimonies. A sample rubric, Act 3-3 TN Scoring Rubric, can be found on the IRCD, Chapter 3. Modify it to suit your needs.

Hair Testimony Essay *Obj. 3.1, 3.2, 3.3, 3.4, 3.5, 3.6, 3.7*

Objectives:

By the end of this activity, you will be able to:

1. Write an organized essay, including introductory and concluding paragraphs.
2. Describe the basics of forensic hair analysis.
3. Explain why hair is usually considered only class evidence.
4. Write convincing arguments stating your case that the suspect's hair is or is not consistent with hair found at the crime scene.

Time Required to Complete Activity: 1.5 to 2 hours

Background:

Your task is to write an essay. You are an expert witness called on to testify in a court case. You are asked to prepare a presentation to the jury that will demonstrate that a particular suspect can or cannot be linked to the crime scene based upon the examined evidence. You should assume that the jury knows nothing about hair. Your paper should be typed, with paragraphs separating major ideas. Use spellcheck to correct spelling errors.

Procedure:

You should prepare:

1. An introductory paragraph addressing the following questions:
   a. Who are you?
   b. Why are you there?
   c. Remember: do not cite specific information about hair within your opening statement to the jury.
2. A body paragraph in which you educate the jury about hair.
   a. Include a graphic or visual aid. Cite the source of your picture.
   b. Define all terms.
   c. Describe what characteristics or traits to look for when analyzing hair.
      • Macroscopically
      • Microscopically

DIFFERENTIATED LEARNERS

At-Risk and English-Language Learners
Before assigning a written report, conduct a prewriting activity. Students may have difficulty organizing the report. Provide structure by discussing what should go into the introduction, body paragraph, and conclusion. Brainstorm ideas with the class, list ideas on the board, and have students write one paragraph at a time.

3. Another body paragraph in which you convince the jury why you believe the hair of a particular suspect is consistent or inconsistent with the hair found at the crime scene.
   a. Recall that hair is usually class evidence, and describe how that pertains to your argument.
   b. Recall that the hair could have been left at the crime scene prior to the murder.
   c. Your job is to convince the jury that the crime-scene hair is consistent or not consistent with the hair of a particular suspect.
4. A concluding paragraph in which you:
   a. Summarize your findings.
   b. Remind them you are an expert.
   c. Restate your claim about the suspect hair and the crime-scene hair.
   d. Remember: do not introduce any new information in your conclusion.

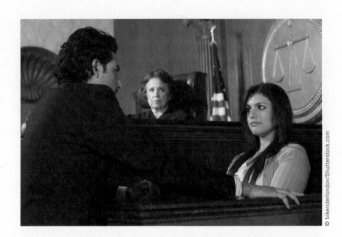

© bikeriderlondon/Shutterstock.com

Teaching Tip

Remind students that as they evaluate testimony, they should consider:

1. Is the evidence scientific?
2. Is the evidence sufficient?
3. Has the evidence been properly handled, documented, and stored?
4. Did the analyst follow established guidelines and standards when examining and analyzing the evidence?
5. Can there be any statistical analysis that would show the probability of someone else having the same characteristics?

Chapter Overview

Fibers from clothing, hair, or the crime scene can be transferred from one person to another or discarded unnoticed at the crime scene. Fiber type and weave pattern are important to forensic investigators. Weave pattern can be discerned by observation under magnification, but further testing is required to determine the fiber composition. Unusual fibers on a suspect's clothing or belongings consistent with fibers belonging to a victim do not prove guilt but can link a suspect and a crime scene or victim.

The Big Ideas

Fibers can be transferred between people and between people and their environments. A close study of these fibers can prove contact between a victim and a suspect, or between a person and a crime scene.

Yarns are made of fibers. Textiles are created by weaving perpendicular yarns. Weave patterns vary depending on the number of threads that wind over and under each other. Weave patterns can be used to identify sources of textiles at crime scenes. Fiber types can be identified by physical and chemical analysis.

Teaching Tip

Show students photos or samples of fibers or hair from cotton, flax, coconuts, silkworms, sheep, alpacas, goats, or rabbits. Ask students to describe what fibers or textiles they think come from each pictured item.

Teaching Tip

Demonstrate how sheep wool is carded and spun into yarn. Display a variety of wool yarns of varying colors and thicknesses. Alternately, show students a video of yarn spinning from the Internet or a DVD.

CHAPTER 4

A Study of Fibers and Textiles

A Thread of Evidence

Wayne Williams

In the 1980s, a string of murders left the African American youth of Atlanta in a state of fear. For 11 months, someone was kidnapping and disposing of murder victims in and around Atlanta's poor neighborhoods. The victims were asphyxiated either by rope or smothering, and the bodies were disposed of in dumpsters or wooded areas. Although the police had no suspects, they were gathering a collection of unusually shaped fibers from the victims. When the fiber evidence hit the news, the bodies began to turn up in the river.

One night, two police officers were staking out a bridge over the Chattahoochee River, where many victims had been found, when a white station wagon stopped on the bridge. The car was seen driving off after something had been tossed over the bridge. The officers followed and stopped the car. The driver was 33-year-old Wayne Williams. Lacking probable cause for a search at the time, the police released him, but later he was arrested on suspicion of murder.

The problem faced by the police was a lack of a pattern and motive. There seemed to be no reason for the killing spree. Williams was an unsuccessful music producer and a pathological liar, but he did not seem like a killer. However, the prosecution's fiber evidence seemed to suggest otherwise.

Fibers of that were consistent with the carpeting in Williams's house were found on many of the victims. What the court did not hear was that no fiber evidence consistent with any of the victims was found in Williams's home, other than a single cotton fiber. Could Williams be guilty and have removed all but one trace of his crimes, or was he innocent? The jury chose guilty. Of the 29 murders, Williams was tried and convicted of two and sentenced to life imprisonment.

Did they get the right man? Some do not think so. After all, there were no witnesses to the crimes and no confession.

78

SCENARIO

In the Atlanta murders, information about fibers found on the victims was released to the press. As a probable result of this, the murderer began disposing the bodies of his victims in the river, where most fibers were lost. Ask students to discuss these questions:

Do you think the press should have free access to information discovered during an investigation? Justify your claims with examples.

Should fiber evidence be sufficient for a conviction when there is no motive or witness testimony?

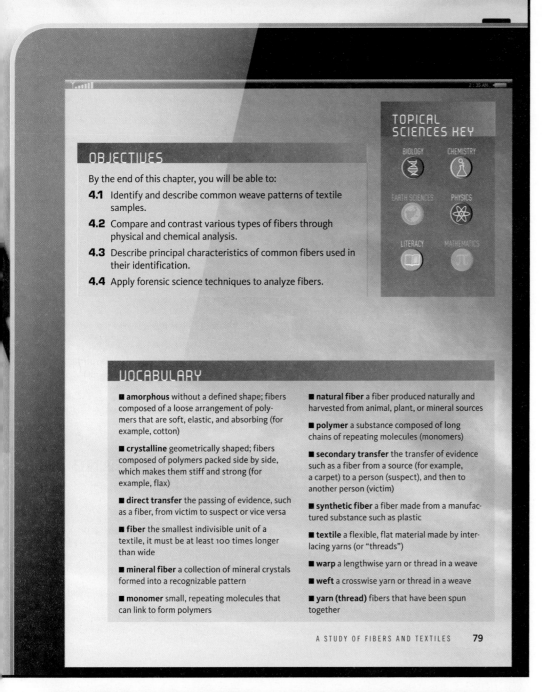

TOPICAL SCIENCES KEY

BIOLOGY   CHEMISTRY

EARTH SCIENCES   PHYSICS

LITERACY   MATHEMATICS

OBJECTIVES

By the end of this chapter, you will be able to:

4.1 Identify and describe common weave patterns of textile samples.

4.2 Compare and contrast various types of fibers through physical and chemical analysis.

4.3 Describe principal characteristics of common fibers used in their identification.

4.4 Apply forensic science techniques to analyze fibers.

VOCABULARY

- **amorphous** without a defined shape; fibers composed of a loose arrangement of polymers that are soft, elastic, and absorbing (for example, cotton)

- **crystalline** geometrically shaped; fibers composed of polymers packed side by side, which makes them stiff and strong (for example, flax)

- **direct transfer** the passing of evidence, such as a fiber, from victim to suspect or vice versa

- **fiber** the smallest indivisible unit of a textile, it must be at least 100 times longer than wide

- **mineral fiber** a collection of mineral crystals formed into a recognizable pattern

- **monomer** small, repeating molecules that can link to form polymers

- **natural fiber** a fiber produced naturally and harvested from animal, plant, or mineral sources

- **polymer** a substance composed of long chains of repeating molecules (monomers)

- **secondary transfer** the transfer of evidence such as a fiber from a source (for example, a carpet) to a person (suspect), and then to another person (victim)

- **synthetic fiber** a fiber made from a manufactured substance such as plastic

- **textile** a flexible, flat material made by interlacing yarns (or "threads")

- **warp** a lengthwise yarn or thread in a weave

- **weft** a crosswise yarn or thread in a weave

- **yarn (thread)** fibers that have been spun together

A STUDY OF FIBERS AND TEXTILES   **79**

TEACHING RESOURCES

Instructor's Resource CD-ROM includes:

- Activities and Student Handouts
- Alternative Assessments
- Consolidated Bibliography
- Correlations to NGSS and CCSS
- Figure Files
- Lesson Plans with Chapter Outlines
- MST

- Nonfiction Readings
- PowerPoint Presentations
- Student Learning Objectives (SLOs)

CL Testing powered by Cognero

Web site: ngl.cengage.com/forensicscience2e

INTRODUCTION

Fibers are used in forensic science to create a link between crime and suspect (Figure 4-1). Since we wear clothes and have hair, we shed fibers. As we walk on carpet, sit on couches, or pull on a sweater, fibers will fall off and may be transferred. Check your clothes: you likely have many fibers from your home, pets, and family on you right now. The crime-scene investigator looks for these small fibers that betray where a suspect has been and with whom he or she has been in contact. When these fibers were shed, however, may be difficult to determine.

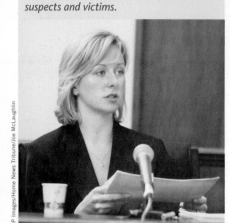

Figure 4-1 *Fiber evidence is used in criminal cases because it shows links between suspects and victims.*

AP Images/Home News Tribune/Joe McLaughlin

Unlike fingerprints and DNA evidence, fibers are not specific to a single person. Criminals aware of investigative methods may wear gloves to avoid leaving evidence at the scene of a crime. However, small fibers shed from most textiles easily go unnoticed, and can therefore provide an important source of evidence.

Fibers are a form of trace evidence. They may originate from carpets, clothing, linens, furniture, insulation, or rope. These fibers may be transferred directly to a victim or to a suspect. This is called **direct transfer**. If a victim has fibers on his person that he picked up and then transferred to a suspect, this is called **secondary transfer**. Secondary transfer also occurs when fibers are transferred from the original source to a suspect and then to a victim. Potential for fiber transfer depends on the duration of contact, type of contact, and the type of fiber.

Early collection of fibers in an investigation is critical. Within 24 hours, an estimated 95 percent of all fibers may have fallen from a victim or been lost from a crime scene. Only fibers you would not expect to find in the area are investigated. If pink fibers were found on the victim's clothes and the victim lived in a house with wall-to-wall pink carpeting, the forensic scientist would not examine these.

Did you know

Police no longer cover dead bodies with cotton sheets because the cotton fibers may contaminate other fiber evidence on the victim.

COLLECTING, SAMPLING, AND TESTING FIBER EVIDENCE *Obj. 4.4*

Depending on the type of crime, fiber evidence may be recovered from rugs, blankets, furniture, clothing, cars, household objects such as screens or windows, or wounds.

Fiber evidence is collected using tape, forceps, a vacuum, or a sticky lint roller (Figure 4-2). Fiber(s) are individually removed, placed on clean paper, and sealed inside evidence bags. The entire article of clothing or other textile from which the fiber was obtained is also rolled inside paper and sealed inside an evidence bag. Large objects such as screens or car fenders from which fiber was removed are also boxed, sealed, and sent to

80   CHAPTER 4

the crime lab for analysis. Great care is taken to avoid packaging evidence from different individuals together. (Refer to Chapter 2). It is important to be very accurate in recording where the fibers are found. Inaccurate or incomplete recording may cause evidence to be inadmissible in court.

The first task is to identify the type of fiber and its characteristics (such as color and shape). The investigator compares the fiber to the fibers found at the crime scene and with fibers associated with the suspect. When you have only one fiber as evidence, you cannot do tests that damage or alter the fiber in any way.

Sometimes the forensic scientist can complete a fiber analysis with a light microscope. Four methods that can analyze fibers in more depth without damaging them are polarizing light microscopy, infrared spectroscopy, microspectrophotometry, and ultraviolet light analysis.

Natural fibers, such as wool or cotton, require only an ordinary light microscope to view characteristic shapes and markings. Polarizing light microscopy uses a microscope with a special filter that allows the scientist to look at the fiber using specific light wavelengths. How the fiber appears can tell the scientist the properties of the fiber. Infrared spectroscopy emits a beam that bounces off the material and returns to the instrument. How the beam of light has changed reveals something of the chemical structure of the fiber, making it easy to tell the difference between fibers that look very much alike. When shining an ultraviolet (black) light on fibers, the light can be re-emitted at a lower, more visible wavelength. Different fibers have a unique, characteristic glow.

Chemical composition and quantities of the chemicals in the fibers are determined using a gas chromatograph and a mass spectrometer. These methods have replaced the burn tests previously performed on fibers.

EVALUATING FIBER EVIDENCE *Obj. 4.4*

Evidence of any kind must be evaluated, and this is especially important for fibers because they are so abundant. The value of fiber evidence in a crime investigation depends on its potential uniqueness. For instance, a white cotton fiber will have less value than an angora fiber because cotton is so common. A forensic scientist will ask questions about the following:

- *Type of fiber.* What is the composition of the fiber? How common or rare is it? What suspects or victims or parts of the crime scene had this type of fiber?
- *Fiber color.* Do the fibers from the suspect's clothes match the color found in the victim's house? Is the type of dye the same? (See the denim in Figure 4-3.)
- *Number of fibers found.* How many fibers were found—one or hundreds? More fibers suggest violence or a longer period of contact.
- *Where the fiber was found.* How close can you place the suspect to the scene of the crime—in the house, or close to a victim's body?

Figure 4-2 *Collecting fiber evidence.*

Mauro Fermariello/Science Source

PHYSICS

CHEMISTRY

Figure 4-3 *By examining denim (jeans fabric) under a microscope, it is easy to distinguish one pair from another. Also, wear patterns can distinguish two samples.*

© Cengage Learning®

© Cengage Learning®

Evaluate

As a class, brainstorm ideas as to how the pattern of contact between perpetrator, victim, and crime scene would be reflected differently in the transfer of fibers in a break-in and in a kidnapping.

Explore

Explain how forensic scientists use microscopy to compare fiber samples. They use a comparison microscope, which allows them to view the two fiber samples simultaneously. A known, or reference, sample is on one microscope stage, and the crime-scene fiber is on the other. The two are separated to prevent contamination of evidence and to allow simultaneous comparison.

Science   PHYSICS

PHYSICS

Different substances absorb different amounts of infrared radiation. The wavelengths of radiation that are absorbed can be used to identify the absorbing substance.

Science   PHYSICS

PHYSICS

To teach students the concept of wavelength, it helps to use a prism to break visible light into its component colors. Each color of light is a different wavelength. Violet light has the shortest wavelength, and red light has the longest. Remind students that infrared light (heat) has a longer wavelength than light that humans can see, and therefore is not visible.

DIFFERENTIATED LEARNING

Teaching English-Language Learners
Remember that language is not the only barrier to learning. An understanding of cultural differences also is also useful. This course involves ethical discussions in which students' opinions may differ. Clarify that respectful disagreement on ethical issues is acceptable. In some cultures, disagreement is considered disrespectful and is discouraged. Girls of many cultures might benefit from being discreetly informed that they do not need to defer to boys in the classroom.

Teaching Tip

In the classroom, observe a variety of fibers and textiles in normal light and then in black (ultraviolet) light. Note how the use of alternative light sources enhances differences between two fibers or textiles that appear similar in visible light.

Explore

Research advances made by the OSAC (Organization of Scientific Area Committees) in developing standards for the collection, analysis and storage of fiber evidence. Forensic fiber analysis is evaluated by the committee on Chemistry and Industrial Analysis under the subcommittee on Materials (trace).

- *Textile from which the fiber originated.* Are these carpet fibers or upholstery from a car?
- *Multiple fiber transfers.* Is there only one type of fiber transferred at the crime scene? Or are there fibers from numerous sources from carpets and clothes and bedding? More sources suggest longer contact or possible violence.
- *Type of crime committed.* Was it a violent crime, a break-and-enter, or a kidnapping? Each type of crime has an expected pattern of contact among suspect, victim, and crime scene that will be reflected in the transfer of fibers.
- *Time between crime and discovery of fiber.* How long ago did the transfer take place—an hour, a day, a week? Unless the fiber location is undisturbed (such as a bagged jacket or locked room), the value of found fiber is greatly reduced with the passage of time because fibers not related to the crime can be picked up.

DIGGING DEEPER

with Forensic Science eCollection

Forensic scientists can solve crimes because fibers adhere to other surfaces, such as a suspect's car seats or a victim's clothes. They also stick to hair. In fact, the nature of violent crime may mean that fibers found in a victim's hair are the only fibers recovered. Research and summarize articles from the Gale Forensic Science eCollection that describe how fiber evidence was used to solve crimes. You can find the Gale Forensic Science eCollection on **ngl.cengage.com/forensicscience2e.**

FIBER AND TEXTILE EVIDENCE

Obj. 4.1, 4.2, 4.3, 4.4

The most common form of fiber transfer to be encountered at a crime scene is fibers shed from a **textile** (fabric or knit). Fibers may be spun with other fibers to form a yarn. To make a textile, the fibers or yarns are either woven or knitted together.

Fiber Classification

Fibers are classified as either natural fibers or synthetic fibers. It is important for a forensic scientist to be able to distinguish among different kinds of fibers because fibers can reveal critical information about suspects and victims and their environments.

NATURAL FIBERS

Natural fibers come from animals, plants, and minerals that are mined from the ground. Fibers are composed of **polymers**, or long, repeating molecules.

Animal fibers Animals provide fibers from three sources: hair, fur, and webbing. All animal fibers are made of proteins. They are used in clothing, carpets, decorative hangings such as curtains, and bedding.

Fur is a good donor of fibers, but it is not a textile. Rather, an animal such as a fox or mink is trapped and the skin removed and treated. This results in a flexible skin that retains the fur. Fur is used almost exclusively for coats and gloves.

Hair fibers are the most popular of animal fibers. Animal hair is brushed out of the animal's coat, shed naturally and collected, or clipped. The most common animal hair used in textiles is wool from sheep (Figure 4-4), but there is also cashmere and mohair from goats, angora from rabbits, as well as hair from members of the camel family—alpacas, llamas, and camels. Hair fibers are used for articles of clothing, bedding, heavy coats, carpets, bags, and furniture upholstery. When animal hair fibers are made into textiles, they are often loosely spun so they will feel more comfortable. These textiles shed fibers easily and provide a good source of trace evidence.

Figure 4-4 *Wool fibers can be spun on spinning wheels like this to make yarns.*

© Cengage Learning®

Figure 4-5 *Silk cocoons.*

© Aldo Gallo/Shutterstock.com

Silk, another natural animal fiber, is collected from the cocoons of the caterpillar *Bombyx mori*. The caterpillars are reared in captivity, and each cocoon (Figure 4-5) must be carefully unwound by hand. The shimmering appearance of silk is caused by the triangular structure of the fiber, which reflects some light back to your eye (Figure 4-6). Fabrics made from silk are commonly used in clothing and some bedding. Because silk fibers are very long, they tend not to shed as easily as hair fibers.

Plant fibers are specialized plant cells. They are grouped by the part of the plant from which they come. Seeds, fruits, stems, and leaves all produce natural plant fibers. Plant fibers vary greatly in their physical characteristics; some are very thick and stiff, whereas others are very smooth, fine, and flexible. Plant fibers are often short, two to five centimeters, and become brittle over time. This means that small pieces of fibers are common as trace evidence at a crime scene. Some fibers are **amorphous**, loosely arranged and soft, elastic, and absorbent. However, all plant fibers share the common polymer cellulose. Cellulose is made up of simple glucose units. Proteins and cellulose have very different chemical and physical properties that allow a forensic scientist to tell animal and plant

Figure 4-6 *Cross-section of cotton and silk fibers.*

Silk   Cotton

© Cengage Learning®

 BIOLOGY

 CHEMISTRY

Science

CHEMISTRY

CHEMISTRY

Discuss the crystalline structure of linen.

DIGGING DEEPER

Scientists working with police agencies and the FBI have burned thousands of types of fibers to study the characteristics of the burned fiber. Investigators use this information to help them identify fiber evidence that has been partially destroyed by fire. To find out more, go to the Gale Forensic Science eCollection at ngl.cengage .com/forensicscience2e.

PHYSICS

fibers apart. For example, cellulose can absorb water but is insoluble (will not dissolve) in water. It is very resistant to damage from harsh chemicals and can only be dissolved by very strong acids, such as sulfuric acid. Cotton is the most common plant fiber used in textiles, making it difficult to link a suspect to a crime scene by means of a cotton fiber. Cotton has an irregular diameter and does not reflect light back to your eye or appear shiny.

Seed fibers Cotton is found in the seedpod of the cotton plant. Because of the ease with which cotton can be woven and dyed, it has been used extensively for clothing and household textiles.

Fruit fibers *Coir* is a coarse fiber obtained from the covering surrounding coconuts. The individual cells of the coir fibers are narrow, with thick walls made of cellulose. When woven together, they are stronger than flax or cotton. Coir fiber is relatively waterproof, which makes it ideal for such things as doormats and baskets (Figure 4-7).

Stem fibers Flax, jute, and hemp are all produced from the thick region of plant stems (Figure 4-8). They do not grow as single, unconnected fibers like cotton, but in bundles. These bundles extend the entire length of a plant. During processing, the bundles are separated from the stem and beaten, rolled, and washed until they separate into single fibers.

Flax is the most common stem fiber and is most commonly found in the textile linen. This material is not as popular as it once was because of its high cost. Linen is a very smooth and often shiny fabric that resists wear and feels

DIGGING DEEPER
With Forensic Science eCollection

Sometimes a murder victim's body is burned to hide the evidence, but rarely are the remains so completely destroyed that no fibers remain. Are burnt fibers of any use forensically? Read articles that describe the effect of heat on fibers in the Gale Forensic Science eCollection. You can find the Gale Forensic Science eCollection on **ngl.cengage.com/forensicscience2e**. Write a one- to two-page essay discussing whether burning a body successfully destroys all evidence. Cite evidence from the reading to support your statements.

Figure 4-7 *Coir fibers are often used in things like floor mats because they are so durable.*

Susan Van Etten

Figure 4-8 *The rough fibers of jute are made into rope and twine.*

© eleana/Shutterstock.com

DIFFERENTIATED LEARNING

Teaching At-Risk Students
Encourage students to search the Internet for pictures of plants used to produce specific types of fibers and share their findings with the class.

cool in hot weather. Pants, jackets, and shirts are the most common garments made from linen. It is also commonly used for tablecloths and bedding. Linen is unique because it is highly **crystalline**, so it is a dense, strong fiber that resists rot and damage from light.

Other stem fibers include jute and hemp. Jute fibers produce a textile that is too coarse for garments and is instead used to make rope, mats, and handbags. Hemp is similar to flax and has been used for a long time in Asia for clothing. It has recently become a popular alternative to cotton in North America.

Leaf fibers Manila is a fiber extracted from the leaves of abaca, a relative of the banana tree. The fiber bundles are taken from the surface of the leaves. A fiber bundle, composed of many fiber cells bound together, can reach a length of ten feet. Sisal, a desert plant with succulent leaves, also provides fibers, which are used for making ropes, twines, and netting. It is commonly seen as green garden twine or on farms as the twine on hay bales. These uses take advantage of the fiber's quick deterioration.

Mineral fibers are neither proteins nor cellulose. They may not even be long, repeating polymers. Fiberglass is a fiber form of glass. Its fibers are very short, very weak, and brittle. Rolls of fiberglass batting (layers or sheets) are used to insulate buildings. The fibers are very fine and easily stick to the skin, often causing an itchy skin rash.

Asbestos (Figure 4-9) is a mineral naturally occurring in different types of rocks. It has a crystalline structure composed of long, thin fibers. Asbestos is very durable. Its many uses once included pipe coverings, brake linings, ceiling tiles, floor tiles, shingles, home siding, and insulation for building materials. Due to its health risks, it is no longer commonly used.

Figure 4-9 *Asbestos fibers.*

Andrew Syred/Science Source

SYNTHETIC (MANUFACTURED) FIBERS

Until the 19th century, only plant or animal fibers were used to make clothing and textiles. Half of the fabrics produced today are **synthetic fibers** (manufactured). They are categorized as regenerated fibers and polymers. In simple terms, the fibers are produced by first joining many **monomers**, or small combining molecules together to form polymers. This is done in large vats. This polymer "soup" is then drained out of the bottom of the vats through tiny holes called *spinnerets* to make fibers that can then be spun into yarns. Manufactured fibers include rayon, acetate, nylon, acrylics, and polyesters. By changing the size and shape of the spinneret, the qualities (for example, shine, softness, feel) of the textile can be altered. Check your classmates' clothing labels: what manufactured fibers are in your classroom?

Regenerated fibers (or modified natural fibers) are derived from cellulose and are mostly plant in origin. The most common of this type is rayon. It is a fiber that can imitate natural fibers and generally is smooth and silky in appearance. Cellulose chemically combined with acetate produces the fiber Celanese® that is used in carpets. When cellulose is combined with three acetate units, it forms polyamide nylon (such as Capron®)—a breathable, lightweight material, used in high-performance clothing.

Synthetic polymer fibers originate with petroleum products and are non-cellulose-based fibers. The fibers are manufactured polymers that serve

Did you know

Inhaled asbestos is known to cause cancer. When broken, the fibers shatter into tiny fragments that float in air. If breathed, they make tiny cuts in the lungs with every breath. The resulting scar tissue easily becomes cancerous.

Science

CHEMISTRY

CHEMISTRY
Monomers are relatively simple molecules made up a few to hundreds of atoms. Polymers are much larger. They are made from repeating monomers and can contain hundreds of thousands of atoms. For example, proteins in silk or wool are made up of chains of amino acids. The amino acids are the monomers, and the silk or wool protein is the polymer.

Teaching Tip
Explain to students that spinnerets, the holes in the bottoms of the vats used to manufacture synthetic polymers, are named after the web-releasing organs of spiders and other web-spinners like silkworms. Liquids turn into polymers when they come out of the openings and dry in the air.

Teaching Tip
Explain to students that a polymer's name tells you the monomer from which it is made. For example, the polymer polyethylene is made from molecules of ethylene. Ask students to identify the monomers in each of these polymers: polypropylene, polystyrene, and polyvinyl chloride.

Explore
Form polymers as a classroom demonstration. For the procedure, go to http://www.reachoutmichigan .org/funexperiments/agesubject/ lessons/polymer.html.

Evaluate

Lead students in a group discussion that asks them to categorize fabric samples or clothing as natural or manufactured. Then have them identify the type of fiber used to make the fabric.

Explore

Pure substances have specific melting points. Scientists can carefully measure the melting point of an unknown solid substance and use that information to help identify the substance. Ask students to research how to calculate the melting point of a fiber.

Teaching Tip

There are many TED Talks with information about fiber innovations. Do an Internet search on "TED Talks and Fiber." You will find talks about fiber and art, technology, fashion, chemistry, etc. Use TED Talks as a resource for student projects.

Teaching Tip

Twisting direction in yarns is easy to demonstrate if you bring a section of rope as a prop.

Figure 4-10 *A polarized light micrograph of nylon fibers.*

Sidney Moulds/Science Source

DIGGING DEEPER with Forensic Science eCollection

Go to the Gale Forensic Science eCollection on **ngl.cengage.com/ forensicscience2e** to research microfibers and their use in clothing, upholstery, and household goods.

no other purpose except to be woven into textiles, ropes, and the like. These fibers can have very different characteristics. They have no definite shape or size, and many, like polyester, may be easily dyed. Distinguishing among the synthetic fibers is easy using either a polarizing microscope or infrared spectroscopy.

Synthetic fibers may be very long or short. Their shape is determined by the shape of the spinneret and may be round, flat, clover-leaf, or even more complex. However, under magnification, all synthetic fibers have very regular diameters. They do not have any internal structures, but may be solid or hollow, twisted, and pitted on the surface. Depending on what is put into the mix, they may be clear or translucent.

Polyester A common synthetic fiber, polyester represents a very large group of fibers with a common chemical makeup. It is found in polar fleece, wrinkle-resistant pants, and is also added to many natural fibers to provide additional strength.

Nylon Nylon has properties similar to polyester, except it is easily broken down by light and concentrated acid. Polyester is resistant to both of these agents. Nylon was first introduced as an artificial silk, and synthetic pantyhose still go by the name *nylons*. Nylon fibers are shown in Figure 4-10.

Acrylic Often found as an artificial wool or imitation fur, acrylic has a light, fluffy feel. However, acrylic clothing tends to ball or pill easily. This is an inexpensive fiber.

Olefins Olefins are used in some clothing such as thermal socks and as fiberfill insulation, and in carpeting, because they are quick drying and resistant to wear.

COMPARISON OF NATURAL AND SYNTHETIC FIBERS

Synthetic fibers are stronger than the strongest natural fibers. Unlike natural fibers, manufactured fibers are not damaged by microorganisms. A disadvantage of manufactured fibers is that they can deteriorate in bright sunlight and melt at a lower temperature than natural fibers. The table shown in Figure 4-11 on the next page shows the characteristics of various fibers.

Yarns

Fibers too short in their natural state to be used to make textiles may be spun together to make **yarns**. (Very thin yarns are often called *threads*.) Short cotton fibers only two centimeters long can be twisted into very strong yarn of any length. Rope is simply a very thick yarn. Depending on their use, yarns may be spun thick or thin, loose or tight. Some may be a blend of fibers, such as wool and polyester, to give desired qualities such as strength or wrinkle resistance. Any given yarn will have a direction of twist. Forensic scientists analyze twist direction as part of their identification.

Figure 4-11 *Descriptions of some common fibers.*

Fiber	Source	Characteristics	Composition	Uses
Descriptions of Fibers				
Cotton	Plant (seed)	Flattened hose appearance; up to 2 inches long, tapers to point; may have frayed root; twist to fiber; hollow core not always visible; smells of burning leaves; helix-shaped fibers	Cellulose polymer; 19 different amino acids, including cysteine; contains double sulfur bonds; absorbs water but not soluble in water	Many types of textiles
Linen	Plant (flax stem)	Short brittle fibers but longer than cotton; smooth, shiny, resists wear	Cellulose polymer; highly crystalline; resists rot and light damage	Clothing; bed linens; tablecloths
Jute and hemp	Plants (stem)	Dense, strong fiber	Cellulose polymer; highly crystalline, resists rot and light damage	Jute: twine, rope, mats; Hemp: clothing
Manila	Plant leaves (abaca plant)	Long fibers; quickly deteriorates	Cellulose polymer	Garden twine
Wool	Animal (sheep)	Helix-shaped; smells of burning hair when burned	Polymer of keratin with 19 different amino acids; includes amino acid cysteine; contains double sulfur bonds; noted for warmth	Clothing, blankets
Silk	Silkworm cocoon	Triangular fibers; reflects light; glossy appearance	Long fiber	Clothing, bedding
Asbestos	Mineral	Short, weak, brittle	Fiber form of glass	Insulation
Manufactured	Regenerated polymers	Melt at lower temperature than natural fibers	Varied; some made with cellulose; some made with petroleum products	Clothing, bedding, towels, carpets

Did you know?

To produce a lightweight polyester fleece pullover, it takes about 12 plastic water bottles.

Evaluate

Review the material in a class discussion. Propose this scenario: A broken window at the scene of a robbery has soft, gray fibers stuck onto the edges of the glass. Police find a suspect nearby wearing a gray wool jacket. What tests should be done to confirm that the fibers on the window glass are consistent with those of the suspect's coat? What results would suggest that the suspect was innocent?

Textiles

Weaving originated with basket-making. Stone Age humans used flax fibers to weave linen cloth. Wool fabrics have been found dating to the Bronze Age. The oldest loom for weaving fabric was found in an Egyptian tomb dating to 4400 B.C. In the early 1700s B.C., the people of China and India developed complicated patterns of weaving fabrics of both silk (China) and cotton (India).

Fibers are woven into textiles in their natural state, if they are long enough, or once they are spun into yarns. Weaving consists of arranging lengthwise threads (the **warp**) side by side and close together. Crosswise threads (the **weft**) are then pushed back and forth in a specific pattern. Ancient weavers used a frame to stretch and anchor the warp and either threaded the weft by hand or used a shuttle to alternate the strands of fibers.

A STUDY OF FIBERS AND TEXTILES   **87**

DIFFERENTIATED LEARNING

Teaching At-Risk Students

Challenge students to demonstrate different type of weave patterns using two different colors of streamer paper. Suggest that they attempt this in a large room, gym, or outside. Students can record a short video of the weaving and photograph the completed weave pattern with a title.

Figure 4-12 *An industrial loom used to weave textiles.*

ImageState/Jupiter Images

Weaving machines were introduced in the early 1700s. Today, enormous industrial looms weave most textiles (Figure 4-12). The pattern in which the weft passes over and under the warp fibers is called the *weave pattern* (Figure 4-13 on the following page). Weave patterns have names like tabby, twill, and satin. Satin is not a type of fiber; it is a type of weave. Look at your shirt, and try to identify the yarns that travel in one direction and those that travel at right angles to them.

The simplest weave pattern is the plain, or tabby, weave. It forms a checkerboard, and each weft passes *over* one warp before going *under* the next one. Patterns can be expressed in numbers. A plain weave is a 1/1 weave. The weft yarn goes *over* one warp yarn, then under one warp yarn, then over one warp, and so on.

Twill weaves are used in rugged clothing such as jeans. Twill is a 3/1 weave. The weft travels *over three* warp yarns, then *under one*, with each successive row shifting over one thread. This creates a diagonal texture on the surface. The two sides of this textile look a little different. Look at the hem of a pair of jeans, and compare the inside to the outside. You will see the difference.

A satin weave is a 3/1, 4/1, 5/1, 6/1, or more weave, with the weft traveling *under three or more* warps and *over one*. This weave results in a glossy appearance. If the warp and weft yarns are different colors, the textile will be different colors on each side. These and other weave patterns are described in Figure 4-13.

Weave pattern is one way that fabrics differ, but it is not the only way. The number of threads that are packed together for any given amount of fabric is another characteristic, which is known as *thread count*. Thread count is the number of horizontal (weft) and vertical (warp) threads in a square inch of fabric. If the weave is *two ply* (two threads twisted together), then the thread count is doubled. Every package of bedsheets includes information on thread count and the type of fiber. Thread count is often written as threads per inch. Typical sheets will have a thread count between 180 and 300 threads per inch, but high-quality sheets can have thread counts of 500 threads per inch. Fiber identification using various microscopes, gas chromatography, and mass spectrometers is possible but provides class evidence only. Fiber evidence alone should not be used to convict someone.

Figure 4-13 *Weave patterns.*

Type of Weave	Diagram	Description	Characteristics
Plain		Alternating warp and weft threads	• Firm and wears well • Snag resistant • Low tear strength • Tends to wrinkle
Basket		Alternating pattern of two weft threads crossing two warp threads	• An open or porous weave • Does not wrinkle • Not very durable • Tends to distort as yarns shift • Shrinks when washed
Satin		One weft crosses over three or more warp threads.	• Not durable • Tends to snag and break during wear • Shiny surface • High light reflectance • Little friction with other garments
Twill		Weft is woven over three or more warps and then under one. In the next row, the pattern is shifted over one to the left or right by one warp thread	• Very strong • Dense and compact • Different faces • Diagonal design on surface • Soft and pliable
Leno		This uses two warp threads and a single weft thread. The two adjacent warp threads cross over each other. The weft travels left to right and is woven between the two warp threads.	• Open weave • Easily distorted with wear and washing • Stretches in one direction only

Teaching Tip

Weave patterns can be difficult for many students to discern. Bring in samples with relatively loose weaves to better illustrate the patterns. The inside of jeans or upholstery usually has an obvious weave pattern with contrasting colors. You could also use a flex camera to magnify and project various weave patterns. For students with vision problems, take a digital photo of the textile weave and enlarge the image.

DIFFERENTIATED LEARNING

Teaching Gifted Students

Present students with open-ended questions that require higher-level thinking. Instruct them to discuss the following:

• What if a woman's roommate borrowed her coat and was then involved in a crime that left textile evidence behind?

• How could investigators distinguish between the woman involved in the crime and the owner of the coat?

• Ask students to investigate how technology has been used to help identify fiber evidence. Research specific cases that used technology to help solve a crime based on fiber analysis.

Evaluate

Review the main points of fiber evidence with the class, using a scenario involving multiple fiber transfers. Have students use what they have learned to discuss the following: How could fiber evidence help police discover that a victim had been moved from a house to a car and then to an outdoor location?

LITERACY

Schiller, Lawrence.
*Perfect Murder,
Perfect Town.*
(JonBenet Ramsey
Case)

SUMMARY

- Fibers are a form of class evidence used by crime-scene investigators; they are a form of trace evidence.

- Fiber evidence may be gathered using tape, forceps, a vacuum, or a sticky lint roller.

- Forensic scientists will try to determine the type of a fiber, its color, how many fibers of each kind were found, where they were found, what textile the fiber came from, and whether there were transfers of multiple types of fibers.

- Fibers may be analyzed using polarized light microscopy, infrared spectroscopy, burn tests, or tests for solubility in different liquids.

- Fibers may be classified as natural or synthetic.

- Natural fibers include animal hair; plant fibers from seeds, fruit, stems, or leaves; and mineral fibers.

- Synthetic fibers include regenerated or modified natural fibers as well as synthetic polymer fibers.

- Fibers are spun into yarns that have specific characteristics.

- Yarns are woven, with different weave patterns, into textiles.

CASE STUDIES

The Murder of George Marsh (1912)

Four bullets were found in millionaire George Marsh's body. Evidence indicated that he had not been robbed. A piece of fabric and an unusual button were found near the corpse. In the rooming house where Marsh lived, an overcoat missing all of the buttons was found in the abandoned room of Willis Dow. The multicolored fibers and weave of the overcoat fabric were consistent with the weave pattern of the piece of fabric found at the crime scene. Based on this fiber evidence, Dow was convicted of the murder and sentenced to death.

Roger Payne (1968)

Bernard Josephs arrived home to find his wife dead. She had been wearing a purplish-red (cerise) woolen dress. On examination, it was determined that Claire Josephs had been choked into unconsciousness and then had her throat cut with a serrated knife. There was no forcible entry, and Claire appeared to have been in the middle of cooking. This indicated to the police that the murderer was probably someone Claire knew.

Suspicion fell to an acquaintance of the Josephses named Roger Payne. On examination of his clothing, more than 60 of the unusual cerise-colored fibers were found. These fibers led to the further examination of Payne's clothing, and fibers from a red scarf similar to Payne's were found under Claire's thumbnail. Additional evidence led to the conviction of Payne and the sentence of life imprisonment.

DIFFERENTIATED LEARNING

Teaching At-Risk Students
Clear communication of expectations, especially for written work and lab reports, is essential. Models of correctly completed projects (such as an "A" lab report with the name omitted) help students visualize your expectations. Review the chapter vocabulary and the Student Learning Objectives (SLOs) with students as you prepare them for the Chapter Review and Activities.

John Joubert
(1983)

The body of 13-year-old newspaper boy Dan Eberle was found bound with a rope. His body showed numerous knife wounds. The FBI Behavioral Science Unit compiled a profile of the killer. The profile included the possibility that the killer was a white, slightly built male, about 20 years of age, neat in appearance. The only other real clue was the rope used to bind the victim. It was very unusual in appearance.

More than two months later, a woman working at a day care center noticed a man watching the children from his car. She wrote down his license number, which led police to John Joubert, a slightly built radar technician at Offutt Air Base. Joubert seemed to fit the profile provided by the FBI. On examination of his possessions, a hunting knife and a length of rope were found. The rope was unusual, having been brought back from Korea. It was consistent with rope found at the crime scene. When confronted by the evidence, Joubert confessed. He was found guilty of Eberle's murder and two others.

© Cengage Learning®

Think Critically

Refer to the murder of George Marsh (1912). How would a defense lawyer today challenge the conviction based on the evidence presented in the case?

Close

Close the chapter with an oral quiz. Organize the class into groups. Ask each group a question and give them a few minutes to prepare their answer. Sample questions include:

- What questions does an investigator ask about a fiber sample? (type, color, number, where found, textile origin)
- What are the two general categories of fiber origins (natural and synthetic), and what are the sources of natural fibers? (animals, plants, minerals)
- Describe textiles and yarn. (Textiles are made by interweaving yarn; yarn is made of fibers spun together.)
- What are the sources for plant fibers? (seed, fruit, stem, and leaf)
- What is a synthetic polymer? (a petroleum-based fiber)

As a final challenge, provide each group with a swath of unusual fiber (canvas, tarpaulin, burlap) to study with the microscope. Ask them to describe and categorize their sample.

Careers

In a technique borrowed from museum conservators, archaeologists use photography in various regions of the electromagnetic spectrum to reveal details about ancient textiles. Photographs in the ultraviolet (UV) range sometimes reveal dyes or patterns on the cloth that are invisible to the unaided eye. Photography has the advantage of leaving valuable relics intact. Ancient cloth is usually degraded, and removing fibers for analysis worsens the damage.

Careers *in Forensics*

Irene Good

Susan Van Etten

Irene Good

Irene Good spends her days with fabrics that come from times and places we can only imagine. She is a textile expert who uses her knowledge of fibers and weaving to understand the lives of people who lived long ago. Just how much can be told from a single fiber might be surprising even to many archaeologists, but not to a forensic scientist.

For example, silk threads found in the hair of a 2,700-year-old corpse buried in Germany were once thought to be evidence of trading with China, whose people were manufacturing silk at that time. Good, however, used her fiber analysis skills to test the hypothesis. Using chemical tests, she looked at the protein of the silk threads very closely. So closely, in fact, that she looked at the building blocks of the protein—the amino acids. This told her that the silk found in Germany was not from *Bombyx mori*—the silkworm—and hence was not from China after all. It was from a wild type of silkworm found in the Mediterranean. At once, Good dispelled this alleged evidence of a trade route between China and Europe hundreds of years ago and revealed new evidence of an ancient European silk industry.

Good has examined ancient textiles of all kinds. On 3,000-year-old mummies from a site in China, she found garments made of cashmere—they were made of the oldest known cashmere threads in the world. She was able to identify the hair by its fiber shape, fineness, and diameter. Not only does the discovery show that the people in China were farming goats to use their hair to make clothes that long ago, but it also reveals that they were highly skilled at spinning.

Good remembers being fascinated by textiles as a child growing up on Long Island. She learned to crochet from her grandmother. Her parents encouraged the fascination by giving her a loom, and Good made her own cloth at home and also spun her own wool. But her career as an archaeologist had nothing to do with textiles. One day, by chance, a colleague showed her a fragment of cloth he had found at an excavation site and asked if she could shed any light on the object. She has used her passion for fibers ever since to solve the mysteries of past cultures.

Good now works at the Peabody Museum at Harvard University. Among other responsibilities, part of her work has been to examine a huge collection of ancient garments and fabrics from Peru. Under Good's keen eye, the fabrics are sure to reveal all kinds of secrets about the people of the Andes, the Incas, and how they lived.

Learn More About It

▷ To learn more about Irene Good and forensic fiber analysis, go to **ngl.cengage.com/forensicscience2e**.

Multiple Choice

1. Natural fibers can be harvested from *Obj. 4.4*
   a) plants and animals
   b) only from plants
   c) only from animals
   d) plants, animals, and minerals

2. The shiny nature of silk can be related to *Obj. 4.3*
   a) its hollow core
   b) its ability to reflect light
   c) its smooth, round fibers
   d) mucus secretions from the silkworm

3. What characteristics of cotton make it a great source of fiber for clothing? *Obj. 4.3*
   a) It is a polymer of keratin.
   b) It is resistant to staining.
   c) The fibers are easily woven and dyed.
   d) The fibers are extremely long.

4. Mineral fibers such as asbestos are very durable. These fibers have been used in all of the following **except** *Obj. 4.3*
   a) rope
   b) shingles
   c) floor tiles
   d) brake linings

5. All of the following are characteristics of a synthetic fiber **except** *Obj. 4.3*
   a) They are formed by combining monomer compounds into polymer molecules.
   b) They are manufactured.
   c) They are used in the production of carpet fibers.
   d) They are produced by plants, animals, or other organisms.

6. A characteristic of natural fibers is that they *Obj. 4.3*
   a) are affected by microscopic organisms
   b) will break down when exposed to bright light
   c) melt at a lower temperature than synthetic fibers
   d) are stronger than synthetic fibers

7. All of the following are generally true about fiber evidence **except** *Obj. 4.4*
   a) It is analyzed using microscopes.
   b) It is possible to determine the composition and quantities of its chemical makeup using gas chromatography and a mass spectrometer.
   c) It can be used to place a person at a crime scene at a specific time.
   d) It is generally considered to be class evidence.

8. The type of weave pattern of a fabric affects all of the following **except**
   a) shiny appearance
   b) stretch of a fabric
   c) solubility in water
   d) strength of a fabric

Chapter 4 Review

Multiple Choice

1. d
2. b
3. c
4. a
5. d
6. a
7. c
8. c

9. a and b
10. a. twill b. plain c. twill

Questions to Research

11. Sample answer: Asbestos fibers lodge in the lungs. The fibers are sharp and make small cuts in lung tissue, leading to chronic inflammation and scar tissue. These conditions in the lungs are often associated with tumor development.

12. Sample answer: Photograph the crime scene first. Next, collect large items and place in separate evidence bags, log items, vacuum floor for trace evidence, use tape to collect trace evidence, and collect examples of known carpet fiber, pet hair, and other items common to the site.

13. Sample answer: In 1988, the Turin Shroud was radiocarbon dated to between A.D. 1260 and 1390. The weave pattern is herringbone (3 over 1 twill). Herringbone patterns date back to Italy, 3rd century B.C. The pattern has existed long enough, but radiocarbon evidence indicates the shroud could not have surrounded the body of Jesus, who died about A.D. 30. Several theories exist as to its production and creator.

9. A fiber is collected at a crime scene. When viewed under a compound microscope, what two traits would indicate that the fiber was a human hair and not a piece of fiber obtained from an article of clothing? (Choose two.) *Obj. 4.3 and 4.4*
   a) the presence of a cuticle
   b) a medullary index of 0.33 or less
   c) a wide diameter
   d) its ability to dissolve in water

10. Describe the weave patterns of each of the fabrics pictured below. Justify your answer for each. *Obj. 4.2*

100% cotton.

Weave pattern:

_____
_____
_____

100% nylon rope.

Weave pattern:

_____
_____
_____

100% spandex nylon.

Weave pattern:

_____
_____
_____

Questions to Research

11. Explain how people working with building products could be at a higher risk of lung cancer from asbestos. *Obj. 4.2*

12. Research and describe proper methods of collecting and storing fiber and textile evidence. *Obj. 4.4*

13. In "Careers in Forensics," Irene Good describes how she works to determine the origins of fibers and textiles and their relationship with a region. Research and discuss the controversy behind the origin and age of the Shroud of Turin. How were weave pattern analysis and radioactive dating used to determine when the Shroud was produced? *Obj. 4.1, 4.4*

© Rob Marmion/Shutterstock.com

14. Silk is a natural fiber produced by the silkworm. Research and summarize how silk is produced by the body of the silkworm. *Obj. 4.2*

15. A crime-scene investigator views two small, red fibers. One fiber was obtained at the crime scene from the victim's body, and the other red fiber was removed from the cuff of the suspect's pants. Although the two fibers appear to be from the same fabric, the crime-scene investigator determines that the two fibers are indeed very different. Describe five characteristics of fibers, other than color, that could have been used to distinguish the two red fibers. *Obj. 4.3 and 4.4*

Further Research and Extensions

Select one of the topics below for further investigation.

- **Variation in Dye Absorption** Use different natural stains on different fibers and note the variation in dye absorption.

- **Fibers and Evidence Reliability** Research the 2009 National Academy of Science Report on Forensics. Outline the many changes that have occurred since the report was published in terms of fiber evidence analysis and expert witness testimony.

Bibliography

Books and Journals

Burnham, Dorothy. *Warp and Weft, A Textile Terminology*. Toronto: Royal Ontario Museum, 1980.
David, Shanntha K. "Classification of Textile Fibres," in J. Robertson and M. Grieve, eds. *Forensic Examination of Fibres, 2nd Edition*. London: Taylor & Francis, 1999.
Gaudette, B. D. "The Forensic Aspects of Textile Fiber Examinations," in R. Saferstein, ed. *Forensic Science Handbook*, Vol. II. Englewood Cliffs, NJ: Prentice Hall, 1988.
Giello, Debbie Ann. *Understanding Fabrics: From Fiber to Finished Cloth*. New York: Fairchild Publications, 1982.
Joseph, Marjory L. *Introductory Textile Science*. New York: Holt, Rinehart and Winston, 1986.
Springer, Faye. "Collection of Fibre Evidence at Crime Scenes," in J. Robertson and M. Grieve, eds. *Forensic Examination of Fibres*, 2nd Edition. London: Taylor & Francis, 1999.

Internet Resources

FBI Trace Evidence and DNA Analysis, http://www.teachingtools.com/HeadJam/index.htm
Gale Forensic Sciences eCollection, ngl.cengage.com/forensicscience2e
Ramsland, Katherine. "Trace Evidence," http://www.crimelibrary.com/criminal_mind/forensics/trace/1.html
https://fril.osu.edu/index.cfm Fiber image library
http://www.naturaldyes.org/instruction.htm dyes
http://swgmat.org SWGMAT hair atlas
http://www.educationworld.com/a_lesson/02/lp259-04.shtml Students dye T-shirts using plants they collect
http://www.fbi.gov/about-us/lab/forensic-science-communications/fsc/july2000/deedric3.htm Hair and fibers from the FBI library
http://www.fabrics.net/natural.asp Fibers
http://www.legalaffairs.org/issues/July-August-2002/review_koerner_julaug2002.msp *Under the Microscope*, by Brendan Koerner
http://www.cnn.com/2012/01/01/opinion/hayashi-spider-silk The secrets of spider silk
www.linenplace.com/product_guide/truth_about_thread_count.html, The truth about thread count
http://www.fiberworld.com
https://new.ted.com TED Talks:
    Fiorenzo Omenetto: Silk, the ancient material of the future
    Cheryl Hayashi: The magnificence of spider silk
    Suzanne Lee: Grow your own clothes

14. Sample answer: Silk is produced in the sericteries of the silkworm. Sericteries are modified salivary glands. The silk is produced as a liquid, which passes through small holes called spinnerets on the larva's mouth. When the liquid hits air, it hardens into a thread. A similar process, where liquid passes through a hole and contacts air, is used to produce manufactured polymers.

15. Sample answer: diameter; cross-sectional appearance; shape; internal structure; melting point, appearance under ultraviolet light.

Background

Students examine carpet samples under a microscope and record and analyze their observations about whether fibers within a sample are the same or multicolored, the number of fibers, the relative thickness of the fibers, and the shape of fibers. Using this information, they must then determine if carpet fibers found on the victim match carpet fibers taken from the cars of four different suspects.

Safety Precautions

Remind students to always carry a microscope using two hands.

Procedures

1. Print, copy, and distribute Activity 4-1 SH Data Table from the IRCD, Chapter 4.

2. Prepare the slides for examination in advance as follows:

   a. Select five different carpet samples.

   b. Prepare carpet samples using "transparency film slides."

   c. Label five slide sets—Suspects 1–4 and victim's body.

   d. Select one of the four suspect samples to be the "evidence" sample from the victim's body.

   e. Place slide sets in envelopes for student use. Each slide set should include: Suspect 1, Suspect 2, Suspect 3, Suspect 4, Victim, Evidence.

3. The teacher should determine which suspect sample(s) is/are consistent with the evidence sample before the exercise begins.

Microscopic Fiber Analysis Obj. 4.2, 4.3, 4.4

Objectives:

By the end of this activity, you will be able to:

1. Distinguish among carpet fibers using microscopic examination.
2. Collect, record, analyze, and evaluate data.
3. Determine if any of the carpet samples on the victim are consistent with carpet fibers found in the suspect's car.
4. Think critically about how well your testing solved the problem, and identify possible sources of ambiguity.

Time Required to Complete Activity: 60 minutes

Materials:

Activity 4-1 SH Data Table
6 microscope slides labeled as follows:
- Fibers from Car of Suspect 1
- Fibers from Car of Suspect 2
- Fibers from Car of Suspect 3
- Fibers from Car of Suspect 4
- Fibers from Car of the Victim
- Fibers found on Victim's Body (Evidence)

colored pencils
microscope
forceps

SAFETY PRECAUTIONS:

Always carry a microscope using two hands.

Scenario:

A murder victim was discovered along a roadside. Police recovered carpet samples from the victim's body. It is speculated that the victim was brought to the location using a car belonging to one of the suspects. Some of the carpet fibers from the floor of the car were transferred to the victim's body. Your task is to determine if the carpet sample found on the victim's body is consistent with one of the carpet samples taken from the cars of four different suspects.

Procedure:

1. View the carpet samples provided by your instructor under the microscope using 100× magnification. Draw sketches of the microscopic view of each carpet fiber sample in the data table.

2. Record the following information:
   Within a sample, are the fibers of a single color or multicolored?
   Color(s) of the fibers
   Relative number of fibers (for example, single, few, numerous)
   Relative thickness of the fibers (for example, thick, thin, or variable)
   Shape of fiber (for example, twisted or straight)

96   **A Study of Fibers and Textiles**

4. Students should read all directions *before* beginning this activity.

5. Instruct students to focus on the textile sample under the microscope by using the low-power lens first and then moving to a higher-power lens. Focusing is faster and easier on low power. The focus will not change much when higher-power objectives are rotated into place.

6. You may wish to organize students into groups for this activity.

Data Table

Source of Fiber	Sketch of Fiber	Single-color or Multi-colored?	Color(s) of Fiber(s)	Relative Number of Fibers (single, few, numerous)	Relative Thickness of Fibers (thin, thick, variable)	Shape of Fiber (twisted or straight)
Car of Suspect 1						
Car of Suspect 2						
Car of Suspect 3						
Car of Suspect 4						
Car of Victim						
Fibers Found on Victim's Body						

Answers

Check students' data tables.

Teaching Tip

On the IRCD, Chapter 4, you can find a teacher handout, Act 4-1 TN, with instructions on how to make a reusable kit of fiber samples.

1. Answers will vary.

2. Answers will vary: color, thickness, shape, smooth or rough, and so forth.

3. a. Fiber evidence is class evidence.

   b. Finding the fiber at the crime scene does not tell when the fiber was left there. The fiber could have been left at the crime scene before the crime.

   c. The fiber could be a very common thread and obtained from a different source.

Questions:

1. Are any of the suspects' carpet samples consistent with the carpet sample found on the victim? If so, which one(s)?

2. Using specific characteristics from the data table, support your claim that a particular suspect's carpet sample is consistent with the carpet sample found on the victim.

3. Suppose you found a carpet fiber from a suspect's car that was consistent with the fiber found on the victim. What arguments could the defense attorney cite to demonstrate that the microscopic comparisons of the car fibers alone does not necessarily prove that his or her client murdered the victim?

Further Research:

1. Research what other tests are performed on fiber samples to evaluate consistency of fiber found at a crime scene with a fiber found on a suspect.

2. Explore whether it is possible to distinguish synthetic fibers from natural fibers using a compound light microscope. Present your findings along with digital images using a poster or PowerPoint presentation.

3. Design a method to view a cross section of fibers under a microscope.

4. **Fibers and Chemistry**

   a. Why do some fibers smell like hair when burned?

   b. Why do some fibers produce black smoke when burned? What chemical reaction is occurring?

   c. What are the differences in structure between animal fibers, plant fibers, and synthetic fibers?

   d. Research and briefly summarize the manufacturing process of a synthetic fiber.

   e. What is the chemistry behind tie-dyeing? Why should clothing first be soaked in sodium carbonate? Why do some tie-dyed clothes fade but not others? Is there a difference in the type of dyes used on different fabrics that affects how well they dye the fibers?

5. **Fiber and Art**
   How are fibers such as silk being used in art? Refer to the TED Talk "Taking Imagination Seriously" by Janet Echelman.

6. **Fibers and Fashion** Investigate why certain fabrics are best suited for different types of clothing.

   a. Why is spandex used in athletic wear?

   b. What makes some fibers wick water?

   c. Why are some fibers better at retaining heat?

   d. How are fibers treated to make them fire-resistant?

7. **Fiber and Biology**
   Research and list some new uses of silk in nanobiology and medicine. Refer to the TED Talk "Silk, the Ancient Material of the Future" by Fiorenzo Omenetto.

8. **Fibers and Going Green**
   Research how plastic water bottles are being used to produce fleece sportswear. Briefly describe the process of how plastic is converted to fibers.

9. **Fibers and Engineering**
   Investigate what type of natural and synthetic fibers are used for their strength and why.

Further Research and Extensions

1. Students should research the range of tests performed on fiber samples to help compare a fiber found at the crime scene with fiber found on a suspect. Ask students to develop a procedure to answer these questions:
   - Do some types of carpet release fibers more or less easily than others?
   - Are there any carpet types that rarely lose fibers?

2. Ask students to examine carpet samples using a UV light. Does this provide any additional data? Ask students to investigate why the sample may appear different under UV light than under normal light.

Bedsheet Thread Count *Obj. 4.1, 4.2, 4.3, 4.4*

Objectives:

By the end of this activity, you will be able to:

1. Determine the thread count of a fabric.
2. Apply knowledge of thread counts, and use critical thinking skills, to solve a forensic problem scenario.

Scenario:

A robbery occurred within a well-to-do neighborhood. The thief grabbed an expensive satin-weave, cream-colored pillowcase to carry out the jewelry that he stole from the jewelry box in the bedroom. The thief immediately took the jewels to a pawnshop to exchange the jewels for money. He then tossed the pillowcase onto the backseat of his car.

Feeling elated at having gotten so much money for the stolen goods, the thief and some of his friends celebrated at the local bar. Having had too much alcohol, the thief was driving erratically on his way home. The police stopped the man to give him a ticket for DWI and noticed the cream-colored pillowcase in the back of his car. The dispatcher at the police headquarters had sent out a message for all patrol officers describing the robbery that occurred that night. No one saw the robber. The only description given was that the robber used a cream-colored satin-weave pillowcase. Later that night, the police located two other suspects with cream-colored pillowcases in their cars.

Was this the pillowcase taken from the home where the robbery occurred? Was it a satin-weave? Was the color the same? Because many people purchase cream-colored pillowcases, what other characteristics would the forensic examiner use to compare this pillowcase with the other pillowcases found on the bed where the incident occurred?

In this activity, you will examine textile samples and use characteristics such as weave pattern and number of threads to help compare a fabric from a crime scene with fabric evidence found on the three suspects.

Background:

The price of sheets varies tremendously. One company advertises a sale on sheets. Included in the package are a fitted sheet, a flat sheet, and two pillowcases. The total price of the package is only $40. Another company is selling a sheet that appears to be the same as the sheets on sale, except the two pillowcases alone cost $40! How is this possible?

The difference between expensive sheets and the bargain brand results from several factors that affect how soft the sheets feel. Factors affecting this could include:

    a. Type of textile:
        Polyester
        Cotton
        Flannel
        Silk

Background

Students will use a magnifying glass or microscope to examine fabric samples and determine the thread count. They will use their knowledge of thread count to determine if fabric found at a crime scene is consistent with fabric found on the suspect.

Teaching Tips

1. Show students examples of a variety of bedsheets having different thread counts. Have them compare and contrast how they look and feel.

2. If bedsheets are not available, show students ads for bedsheets having different thread counts, and have them compare how they are advertised. Do the manufacturers claim a difference in how the bedsheets feel?

3. Ask students to compare the thread counts stated in the ad with thread counts they calculate.

Teaching Tip

Many advertised thread counts are inaccurate. Companies manufacturing sheets outside of the United States may use a different method of counting threads which can make a sheet appear to have a higher thread count. Ask students to research how different manufacturers estimate thread count.

Safety Precautions

Remind students to always carry a microscope using two hands.

Procedures

1. Print, copy, and distribute Activity 4-2 SH Data Table from the IRCD, Chapter 4.

2. All fabrics need to be cream-colored (or all the same color) and satin-weave to fit the scenario. The teacher should select one of the three samples to use as both a sample from the crime scene (before the exercise begins) and one of the three samples provided.

3. Teachers may use fabrics of their choice. Before the lab begins, verify the thread count of each sample.

4. Students should read all directions *before* beginning this activity.

5. Students may use a needle or pin (or other long, thin object as safety dictates) to help keep their place as they count threads.

6. You may wish to organize students into groups for this activity.

7. Provide a magnifying glass for each student or group of students.

8. Taking a high-quality digital image of the sheet along side a ruler and then enlarging the image makes it much easier to count the threads. Or, place the sheet and a ruler under a projecting device to enlarge the image.

Answers

Check students' data tables.

b. Thread count per inch
   The greater the number of threads, the more comfortable the sheet, and thus the higher the price.
   Thread count is often listed as 180 threads per inch, 200 threads per inch, or 400 threads (or higher) per inch.
c. Weave pattern of sheet affects how the sheet feels, resists snagging on other clothes, wrinkles, and wears.

Time Required to Complete Activity: 40 minutes

Materials:

4-2 SH Data Table
Suspect 1: 3 × 3 square-inch sample of pillowcase
Suspect 2: 3 × 3 square-inch sample of pillowcase
Suspect 3: 3 × 3 square-inch sample of pillowcase
3 × 3 square-inch sample from a similar pillowcase found at the crime scene
3 × 5 card with 1 × 1 square-inch cutout to be used as a thread counter
magnifying glass, stereomicroscope, or computer tablet
scissors

SAFETY PRECAUTIONS:

No safety precautions are needed for this lab.

Procedure:

Obtain the three suspect and the evidence samples. For each sample:

1. Place the 3 × 5 card with the 1 × 1 square-inch cutout over the middle of each fabric sample and record your data in your data table.
2. With the aid of a magnifying glass, stereomicroscope, or computer tablet, count the number of warp threads within the square inch. (See the figures on the next page.)
3. With the aid of a magnifying glass, stereomicroscope, or computer tablet count the number of weft threads within a square inch and record in your data table.
4. To determine the thread count, add the number of threads in the warp count to the number of threads in the weft count. Record in your data table.
5. List other distinguishing characteristics of the bedsheet, such as thread color, single or multiple color, relative diameter of the threads, shape, or twisting of fibers.
6. Was the crime-scene evidence consistent with any of the suspect samples?

Data Table

Sample	Warp Thread Count	Weft Thread Count	Total Thread Count (warp + weft)	Characteristics (color, single color, multicolored, relative thickness, flat, tubular, etc.)
Suspect 1				
Suspect 2				
Suspect 3				
Crime Scene				

Teaching Tips

1. Supply the three suspect samples and provide the thread count. Students determine the thread count of the crime-scene sample and compare it to one of the three suspect samples, or students determine the thread counts of all four samples.

2. If cream-colored, satin-weave fabric is unavailable, select a different fabric weave and color and modify your scenario. All samples should be the same color and weave pattern.

Questions:

Compare the fabric samples.

1. Are there any distinguishing characteristics that can help identify one fabric over another?

2. Based on your observations and analysis, would you consider the two pillowcases, the evidence pillowcase from the car and the pillowcase found on the bed, to be a "match"?

3. Suppose the thread count and the color of the pillowcase found in the car were consistent with the thread count and color of the pillowcase found in the burglarized home. Is this sufficient evidence to prosecute the suspect? Prepare arguments and supporting evidence that could be made by

   a. the prosecutor claiming the evidence is sufficient to convict.

   b. the defendant's lawyer claiming that there is insufficient evidence to convict.

   Explain your answer.

Homemade thread counter.

Further Research:

1. The cost of bed linens varies depending on the quality. Do an investigation comparing less expensive bed linens to those that are much higher priced. Include in your comparison:

   • Thread count
   • Type of fabric used
   • Softness of the fabric
   • How well the linens should wear
   • Design of the fabric
   • Ply count

2. Silk satin-weave sheets appear to be very shiny and glossy. Recall that satin is not a type of textile but rather a weave pattern.

   a. Research and describe why silk fibers reflect light.

   b. Research and describe why a satin-weave pattern also produces a shiny appearance.

   c. Compare and contrast the weave patterns of a satin weave and a twill weave. Which weave pattern would probably be better suited for children's clothing? Explain your answer.

Questions

1. Sample answer: The differences among fabrics are caused by several factors that affect how soft the sheets feel. Factors affecting this could include:

   (a) type of textile (e.g., muslin, cotton, flannel);

   (b) thread count per inch (i.e., the greater the number of threads, the more comfortable the sheet and the stronger the fabric); and

   (c) weave pattern.

2. Answers will vary.

3. a. Both thread count and color are consistent. The suspect had the pillowcase in his possession. The prosecutor could claim that it is sufficient evidence to prosecute but would likely look for additional evidence linking the suspect to the home such as fingerprints, hair, and shoe prints.

   b. This is only circumstantial evidence. Possession of a similar pillowcase does not prove that it came from the home where the robbery occurred. Many of these pillowcases could have been sold in this area.

Further Research and Extensions

Pose one or more of the following questions to students. Ask them to form hypotheses, and then have the students design experiments to test their hypotheses. Students may also present their research in the Observation/Claim/Evidence format.

1. Is it possible to tell when a fiber was burned?

2. Is there a difference in the structure of fiber in carpeting in your house and in your (parent's) car?

3. Does using carpet shampoos make a difference in the appearance of carpet fibers under a microscope?

4. Is it possible to tell whether a fiber has been cut or torn?

Background

Weave patterns can help identify a fabric associated with a crime scene. Students will examine fabric samples from each of the suspects' shirts. They will use the weave patterns, stretchability of the fabric, and any other characteristics they observe to determine if any of the suspects' shirts match the fabric found at the crime scene.

Safety Precautions

Remind students to always carry a microscope using two hands.

Procedures

1. Print, copy, and distribute Activity 4-3 SH Data Table from the IRCD, Chapter 4.

2. Attempt to obtain all weave samples of the same color so that students do not rely on a color comparison.

3. The teacher should determine which samples are consistent before the exercise begins.

4. Prepare samples of fabric from various sources. Choices may include: a cotton kitchen towel, blue jeans, a blanket, pantyhose, spandex, silk, nylon, or wool.

5. Obtain samples of fabric representing various weave patterns. You may wish to copy the pictures of weave patterns from the text and hand these out to students to use as a reference as they complete this activity.

6. Students should read all directions *before* beginning this activity.

7. Discuss fabric stretchability with students before beginning this activity. Make sure all students use the same criteria when determining stretchability.

Weave Pattern Analysis Obj. 4.1, 4.4

Objectives:

By the end of this activity, you will be able to:

1. Compare and contrast textiles based on their physical characteristics.
2. Identify the weave patterns of textile samples.
3. Apply comparative data to solve a forensic science problem scenario.

Time Required to Complete Activity: 30 minutes

Materials:

Activity 4-3 SH Data Table
6 different textile samples
textile samples from Suspects 1, 2, 3, 4, and 5
textile sample 6 (crime-scene sample)
magnifying glass, stereomicroscope, or computer tablet

SAFETY PRECAUTIONS:

No safety precautions are needed for this lab.

Scenario:

Weave patterns can help identify a fabric associated with a crime scene. In this lab, you are investigating an assault in which the victim tore off a piece of his attacker's shirt. Five suspects have been taken in for questioning, and a judge has issued a warrant to allow the forensics investigators to look for shirts in the suspects' homes that might be consistent with the torn sleeve obtained during the assault. Your task will be to examine each of the suspects' shirts and determine if any of the fabrics are consistent with the torn piece from the crime scene.

Procedure:

1. Obtain textile samples 1–5 and crime-scene sample 6.
2. Using a magnifying glass, or stereomicroscope, or computer tablet, examine and identify the weave pattern of each fabric. Refer to the weave patterns in Figure 4-13.
3. Gently tug on each fabric. Note any difference in stretchability.
4. Record your answers in the data table.

8. You may wish to organize students into groups for this activity.

9. Provide a magnifying glass for each student or group of students.

Teaching Tip

Prior to the lab, teachers should obtain five different types of fabric with different weave patterns. Try to use fabrics of the same color (all black or white). Cut approximately 5 × 5-inch square pieces of each fabric and label them Suspects 1, 2, 3, 4, and 5. Use one of the fabrics as your crime-scene evidence and label it as such.

Data Table

Six Different Textile Samples	Weave Pattern	Stretchability (No Stretch, Some Stretch, Easily Stretches)	Other Characteristics
Suspect 1			
Suspect 2			
Suspect 3			
Suspect 4			
Suspect 5			
Crime-Scene Sample 6			

Questions:

1. Were any of the weave patterns on the fabric samples 1–5 consistent with the weave pattern of the crime-scene sample 6? Explain the similarities.
2. Refer to the weave pattern table (Figure 4-13) and the textbook information on fiber types and weave patterns to design a textile that would exhibit the following qualities:
   a. strength and durability
   b. comfort
   c. resistance to damage by microorganisms

Justify your answers by citing evidence from the textbook.

Further Research and Extensions:

1. Different types of weaves are used for different purposes. Interested students might research some types of fabrics designed for a specific purpose, such as Spandex designed for athletic wear. They should list the characteristics of the fabric that make it useful for that purpose.
2. Today thread is designed and manufactured to be attractive, comfortable, and much stronger than thread made of 100 percent twisted natural fibers. Research and summarize how various types of thread are produced. Include in your answer:
   a. the number of microfibers per thread
   b. the reasons for the addition of different types of synthetic fibers
   c. other factors that affect the appearance and durability of the product

A Study of Fibers and Textiles   103

Teaching Tip

Review the role of UV light, polarized light, burn testing, and dye testing in the identification of textiles. Microscopic examination of a thread could include a physical description—hollow (or not), flat, oval or spherical, twisted or parallel fibers, or blunt ends.

Answers to Data Table

Check students' data tables.

Questions

1. Students should be able to judge which fibers are consistent.
2. Answers may vary. Sample answer: A twill pattern would be more durable yet comfortable. Textiles made of synthetic fibers would be resistant to microorganism damage and stronger than natural fibers. A blend of natural and synthetic fibers could also be considered.

Further Research and Extensions

Today's threads are manufactured and designed to be attractive, comfortable, and much stronger than the threads made of 100 percent twisted, natural fibers. Research and summarize how threads are produced. Include in your answer:

a. The number of microfibers per thread

b. The addition of different types of synthetic fibers

c. Other factors that affect the appearance, durability, and characteristics of the textile

Background

Students determine if fabric found at a crime scene is consistent with fabric found on one of the suspects by comparing thread counts and weave patterns.

Safety Precautions

Remind students to always carry a microscope using two hands.

Procedures

1. Print Activity 4-4 SH Data Table and Activity 4-4 SH Evidence Label from the IRCD, Chapter 4.

2. Determine which of the three samples are consistent before the exercise begins. Attempt to obtain and prepare all samples of the same color so that students do not rely on a color to make their decisions.

3. Package, seal, and label the evidence inventory labels for all samples.

4. Students should read all directions *before* beginning this activity.

5. Review the correct procedures for packaging evidence before beginning this activity. (See Figure 2-7.)

6. Students may use a needle (or other long, thin object as safety dictates) to help keep their place as they count threads.

7. You may wish to organize students into groups for this activity.

8. Projecting the image of the textile samples or using a flex camera projected image will make it easier for students with vision problems to perform the thread count; or take a digital photo of the textile and enlarge the image.

9. Sample 4 is the evidence textile.

Textile Identification Obj. 4.1, 4.2, 4.3, 4.4

Objectives:

By the end of this activity, you will be able to:

1. Distinguish among textile fibers based on the physical traits of weave patterns and thread counts.
2. Apply knowledge of fabric characteristics to a forensic science problem.
3. Communicate your findings to a lay audience, as though in a court of law.

Time Required to Complete Activity: 45 minutes

Materials:

Activity 4-4 SH Data Table
Activity 4-4 SH Evidence Label
(students work in pairs)
four samples of textiles labeled Suspect 1, 2, 3, and Crime Scene, in plastic bags
masking tape to reseal evidence bags
marking pen to sign evidence bag
3×5-inch card with 1×1 square-inch cutout for each team
magnifying glasses, stereomicroscopes, or computer tablets
set of colored pencils
ruler

SAFETY PRECAUTIONS:

Always carry a microscope using two hands.

Procedure:

1. Obtain the three textile evidence bags (Suspects 1–3) of fabric from your instructor.
2. Correctly open the Sample 1 packaging. (See Figure 2-7.)
3. Examine the sample using a magnifying glass, stereomicroscope, or computer tablet. Note the weave pattern for Sample 1 on your data sheet.
4. Using the colored pencils, sketch the weave pattern in the space provided on your data sheet.
5. If a linen tester is available, measure the number of threads per inch in the sample.
6. If a linen tester is not available, use the 3×5 card with the 1-inch cutout and a stereomicroscope or a magnifying glass to count the number of threads per inch in the fabric sample. Take a digital photo with a ruler beside the textile and enlarge the image to make counting easier.
7. Record the thread count under your sketch.
8. Correctly reseal the evidence in the evidence envelope and write your signature across the label.
9. Complete the Evidence Inventory Labels and correctly reseal the evidence bags. (See Figure 2-7.)

Teaching Tip

In advance of the lab, prepare the following:

1. Three different samples of textiles exhibiting different weave patterns and thread counts. Select textiles of the same solid color.

2. 5×5-inch squares of each textile and label them S1, S2, S3.

3. Select one of the three samples to also represent the crime-scene sample. Cut another 5×5-inch square, and label it "crime scene."

4. Place each sample in a plastic bag. Complete an evidence inventory label for each sample: S1, S2, S3, and crime scene.

5. Cut out a 1-inch square from a 3×5 card for each team to use as a thread counter. (See photo on the next page.)

10. Repeat the process for each of the other two suspect fabric samples.
11. Repeat the process for the crime-scene evidence.
12. Return all samples to your instructor.

Linen tester.

Homemade thread counter.

Data Observations and Measurements

Sample 1
# of Warp threads _____
# of Weft threads _____
Thread count per square inch
_____
Weave pattern _____

Sample 2
# of Warp threads _____
# of Weft threads _____
Thread count per square inch
_____
Weave pattern _____

Sample 3
# of Warp threads _____
# of Weft threads _____
Thread count per square inch
_____
Weave pattern _____

Crime Scene
# of Warp threads _____
# of Weft threads _____
Thread count per square inch
_____
Weave pattern _____

Questions:

1. After examining the textile samples from Suspects 1, 2, 3, and the crime scene, were you able to determine if the fabric found at the crime scene is consistent with the fabric found on any of the suspects? Support your claim with evidence from the activity.

2. Based on your analysis of the textiles:
   a. Can you exclude any of the suspects based on the evidence? Cite evidence for your claim.
   b. Which, if any, of the suspects had textiles consistent with the crime-scene textile? Support your conclusion with evidence from the activity.
   c. Based on this activity, do you feel that the evidence presented is sufficient to convict someone? Support your claim with evidence from the activity.
   d. Describe additional textile and fiber testing that could be done to determine if a textile found at a crime scene and a textile found on a suspect are consistent.

Answers to Data Table
Check students' data observations and measurements.

Questions

1. a., b. Answers will vary.
1. c. Sample answers: Select other areas of the fabric, and do a thread count; have someone else see if he or she gets the same answer; magnify the image so that counting will be more accurate; revise your technique and method of counting.

2. a. Answers will vary.
   b. Answers will vary but should include references to weave pattern, thread count, color, and chain of custody.
   c. The circumstantial evidence provided is probably not sufficient to convict. No time factor can be established. Chain of custody could be an issue.
   d. Burn tests, solubility tests, examination with black light or polarizing filters, and dye analysis could also be useful in matching textiles.

Further Research and Extensions
Form small groups. Each group should select and research one of the following techniques used in textile identification. Each team should prepare a short presentation for the class:

a. Electron microscope imaging
b. Gas chromatography
c. Solubility testing
d. Burn testing
e. Fabric-tear analysis

3. Answers will vary.
4. See Figure 2-7.

3. You have been called to court to appear as an expert witness in textiles. You are to report your findings from this investigation to the jury. Assume the jurors know nothing about textiles. Therefore, you need to define any terms that are not part of normal, everyday conversation. In your discussion, be sure to include the following information:

a. description of fibers

b. thread count

c. weave pattern

d. color of fabric

Remember that your testimony may be used to link a suspect to a crime scene and/or to exclude a witness as a suspect.

4. Outline how to open, view, repackage, and sign the Evidence Inventory Label in order to maintain proper chain of custody.

Burn Analysis of Fibers *Obj. 4.2, 4.3, 4.4*

Objectives:

By the end of this activity, you will be able to:

1. Use a dichotomous key, to identify fibers using a burn test analysis.
2. Make observations, collect, analyze, and record data.
3. Apply your data to solve a forensic science problem.
4. Suggest revisions to the burn testing method to ensure greater evidence validity.

Time Required to Complete Activity: 60 minutes

Materials (for groups of four students):

Activity 4-5 SH Data Table
Activity 4-5 SH Burn Test Dichotomous Key
six different labeled fiber samples:

- fibers from car of Suspect 1
- fibers from car of Suspect 2
- fibers from car of Suspect 3
- fibers from car of Suspect 4
- fibers from Victim's Car—Sample 5
- fibers found on the Victim's Body—Sample 6

alcohol or Bunsen burners
forceps
fire extinguisher
safety goggles

SAFETY PRECAUTIONS:

Handle an open flame source with great care. Fibers will ignite suddenly and burn quickly at a very high temperature. Use metal forceps *only* to hold materials in the flame. Wear protective goggles when flame-testing fabrics. Avoid inhaling fumes from burning. Work in a well-ventilated area. Make sure a nonflammable surface is placed below the fibers to catch drips or sparks.

Background:

Some very simple tests can be used to determine the type of fibers found at a crime scene. Unfortunately, they are destructive to some fibers and consume the evidence. If only a limited number of fibers are recovered from a crime scene, then these tests may not be advisable.

Procedure:

Fiber Burn Test Tips:

1. Use a triangular fabric sample approximately 1.5 inches long.

Background

Students will conduct burn analyses on several fiber samples after observing a teacher demonstration. (The burn test can also be conducted as a teacher demonstration.) They will hold fiber samples in a flame, note observations, such as whether the fiber burns, how it smells when it burns, and the color of the residue left after burning. Using their observations, determine if fibers found on the victim or in the victim's car are consistent with fibers taken from the cars of four different suspects.

Safety Precautions

1. Remind students to tie back their hair and any loose clothing before using any type of open flame.

2. Students should handle open flame sources with great care.

3. Remind students to use forceps and not their fingers to hold samples in the flame.

4. Students and teachers should always wear protective goggles when working with open flames.

5. Inhaling fumes from burning fibers should be avoided. Work in a well-ventilated area or under a hood if possible.

6. Demonstrate the correct procedure for smelling a sample before beginning this activity.

Procedures

1. Print, copy, and distribute Activity 4-5 SH Data Table from the IRCD, Chapter 4.

2. The teacher should determine which samples are consistent with those on the victim's body before the exercise begins. Select fibers that include polyester, rayon, cotton, wool, and silk to match the classification key.

3. Students should read all directions *before* beginning this activity.

4. Review the Burn Analysis Key with the class before beginning the activity.

5. You may wish to organize students into groups for this activity.

6. Candles can be used if burners are not available. Candle smoke may be a source of error.

7. Tell students to hold the fiber samples at right angles to the flame (parallel to the table top).

Teaching Tips

- Prior to doing this activity, review with students how to use a dichotomous key.
- Ask students to analyze your technique after you have performed the burn tests to see if they can think of ways to improve your evidence validity. Deliberately make errors:
- Use the same forceps for each burn test.
- Vary the amount of time you hold the fabric in the flame.
- Hold the fabric parallel to the table for only some of the tests.
- Don't use controls. Remind students that evidence or data obtained without use of proper protocols may be dismissed from a trial.

Questions

Student data tables should show the following:

Wool: Curls, burns slowly, goes out, smells like burning hair, white smoke, forms a hard bead

Rayon: Does not curl; burns quickly; continues to burn; smells like paper; forms small amount of gray, fluffy ash; sputtering flame; black smoke

Silk: Curls, burns slowly, goes out, smells like burning hair, white smoke, forms brittle black residue

Polyester: Curls away from flame and melts, burns slowly and drips, sparkles when it burns, black smoke, goes out, smells like an acrid chemical, forms a hard bead

Cotton: Does not curl; burns quickly; yellow flame, continues to burn; smells like paper; no smoke; forms a light, fluffy, gray ash

Nylon: Shrinks, melts, continues to burn, sputters as it burns, smells like celery, forms a hard residue (not included in the key)

Fibers on victim's body: Should be consistent with one of the suspect fibers

2. Hold the fiber or fabric with the forceps. Try to hold the fabric parallel to the table so that the flames will move across the fabric or fiber. If you hold the fabric so that the fabric droops, the flame will engulf the entire fabric at once. This makes it difficult to determine if the fabric continues to burn after being held in the flame or if the flame dies out.

3. Hold the fabric in the flame for three seconds to ensure that the fabric is ignited.

4. To detect odor of the smoke, it is important to check immediately after the fabric is ignited. You will most likely see a small amount of smoke that disappears quickly. Wave the odor toward your nose with your hand. Do not inhale directly from the source. Describe the odor.

5. Note how the synthetic fibers appear to melt and get a bubbly appearance as they burn.

6. Perform a burn test on each of the fiber samples. Make observations and record your data in the data table provided.

Data Table

Source of Fiber	Flame Test (Does sample curl as it burns?)	Burn Test (Burns or melts? Burns slowly or quickly?)	When Removed from Flame (Goes out or continues to glow?)	Odor while Burning (Tar, burning hair or paper, acrid?)	Color and Texture of Residue (Beads, ash, crusty, fluffy, round?)
Car of Suspect 1					
Car of Suspect 2					
Car of Suspect 3					
Car of Suspect 4					
Car of Victim— Sample 5					
Fibers Found on Victim's Body— Sample 6					

DIFFERENTIATED LEARNING FOR GIFTED STUDENTS

The basic lab is well suited for all students. Students review the use of dichotomous keys and make observations and draw conclusions. However, for more advanced students, challenge them further by doing the following:

1. Revising the key using the same fiber samples.

2. a. Give students four new samples. Ask them to construct a new key after they note different characteristics of each fiber as it burns.

   b. Using their new key and the four new fibers, have them demonstrate to the class how they can identify fibers using their new key.

Questions:

1. Use the information in the data tables along with the Analysis Key to identify the fibers. Obtain Fiber 1 and proceed through each step of the key beginning with Step 1. Choose the correct path to follow until you have identified the fiber. Repeat for Fibers 2 through 6.

Fiber Burn Analysis Key

When fiber is removed from flame,	
1a. Fiber ceases to burn.	Go to Step 2.
1b. Fiber continues to burn.	Go to Step 3.
2a. Fibers have the odor of burning hair.	Go to Step 4.
2b. Fibers do not smell like hair.	polyester
3a. Black smoke is released as fiber burns.	rayon
3b. No black smoke is released as fiber burns.	cotton
4a. A hard, black bead results from burning.	wool
4b. A brittle, black residue results.	silk

2. Which suspect's car had fibers consistent with those found on the victim?

3. Why were fibers from the victim's car examined?

4. Determine another characteristic of burning fibers that could be used to distinguish among fibers when performing a burn test.

5. Discuss ways to improve upon the evidence validity by improving your technique during the burn test.

6. If a fabric was a blend of two different fibers, describe how you could perform a burn test on the fabric so that you could identify the two different fibers.

A Study of Fibers and Textiles 109

Further Research and Extensions

Assign students the following questions for further research:
- Which textiles release toxins or other harmful substances when burned?
- What hazards do these substances pose to firefighters and police officers responding to emergencies?
- Do firefighters have a higher-than-normal chance of developing cancer?
- Ask students to research special health conditions of firefighters and police who were involved with the 2001 World Trade Center rescue.
- Many synthetic fibers are easily ignited. Research what is done to make fibers more fire-resistant.

Questions

1. Answers will vary.

2. Answers will vary.

3. Sample answer: The carpet fibers on the body could have been from the victim's own car.

4. Answers will vary but may include color of flame, fiber pulling away from flame, and flame sputtering.

5. Sample answers
   a. Run controls first. Burn hair first before asking students to note if a fiber smells like burning hair. Burn a known sample of each of the items to be tested (nylon, cotton, wool, etc.).
   b. Repeat the process.
   c. Hold the fabric in the flame for the same amount of time and hold it at the same angle.
   d. Compare and contrast results with another team to see if they got the same results.
   e. Be sure the method of burning is standardized for all tests.
   f. Use a different key for burn-test analysis and see if you get the same results.
   g. Devise a different key to analyze the fibers.
   h. Confirm your test results by conducting other fiber tests such as solubility testing or microscopic analysis.

6. Separate the blended fibers. Perform a burn test separately on each type of fiber.

A STUDY OF FIBERS AND TEXTILES **109**

Chapter Overview

Forensic botany is the application of plant science to crime-scene analysis. Knowledge of plant ecology can establish where and when a crime was committed, who was at the crime scene, the location of a gravesite, and if a body was moved. Botanical evidence such as annual rings in woody plants, pollen and spore analysis, microscopic examination of diatoms, identification of specific plants or plant fragments, gastric contents analysis, and decomposition rates are examples of how the application of forensic botany helps solve crimes. Proper methods of processing an outdoor crime scene are also described in this chapter.

The Big Ideas

Forensic botany was first used in 1932 to help solve the Lindbergh kidnapping case. Botanical evidence can be found both indoors and outdoors and provides a link between a crime scene and people and/or objects. A variety of botanical evidence can be used to solve crimes. Plant fragments such as leaves, roots, stems, flowers, seeds, fruits, and pollen that are recovered from suspects or objects provide insight not only to the location of a crime but also as to the postmortem interval. Proper methods to process a crime scene, and how to collect, document, and analyze botanical evidence are outlined.

CHAPTER 5
Forensic Botany

Season of Death

Pollen is released by different plants at different times of the year, and pollen can survive for many years. Pollen and spore evidence can be important clues in determining a crime's location and time of occurrence. These tiny clues can even unlock murders of the past.

In March 1994 in Magdeburg, Germany, a mass grave of 32 male bodies was uncovered at a construction site. Historical records documented two different mass burials in the area. Nazi secret police might have executed and buried the victims there in the spring of 1945. It was also possible the bodies were Soviet soldiers killed by the Soviet secret police for refusing to break up a revolt in East Germany on June 17, 1953.

The answer was found in the nasal passages of the skeletal remains. The nasal passages contained large quantities of plantain pollen inhaled by the victims shortly before their death. Smaller amounts of pollen from lime trees and rye were found as well. Because all of these plants flower and release pollen in June and July, it was determined that the bodies belonged to the Soviet soldiers killed by the secret police in the summer of 1953 and not the people killed by the Nazi secret police in the spring of 1945.

Skeletal remains with botanical evidence in nasal passages.

110

SCENARIO

Ask students to discuss these questions:
When investigators examined the 32 bodies found in Magdeburg, Germany, why do you think the pollen was still intact after more than 40 years?
Do you think the killers could have removed the pollen evidence from the bodies?

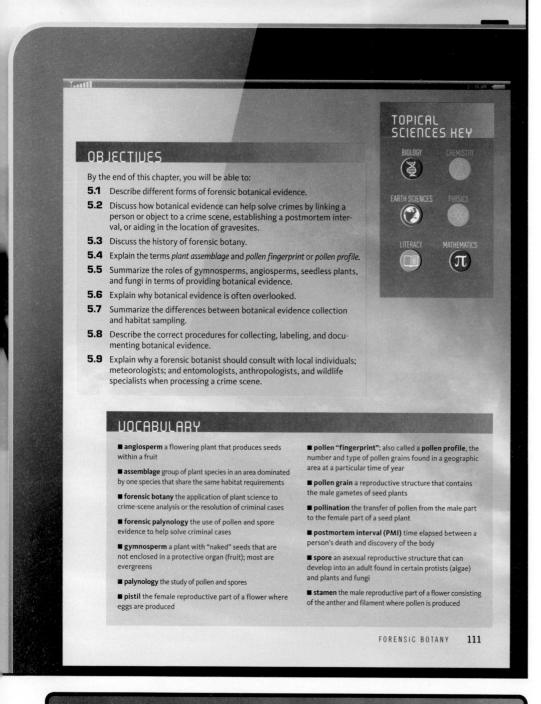

OBJECTIVES

By the end of this chapter, you will be able to:

5.1 Describe different forms of forensic botanical evidence.

5.2 Discuss how botanical evidence can help solve crimes by linking a person or object to a crime scene, establishing a postmortem interval, or aiding in the location of gravesites.

5.3 Discuss the history of forensic botany.

5.4 Explain the terms *plant assemblage* and *pollen fingerprint* or *pollen profile*.

5.5 Summarize the roles of gymnosperms, angiosperms, seedless plants, and fungi in terms of providing botanical evidence.

5.6 Explain why botanical evidence is often overlooked.

5.7 Summarize the differences between botanical evidence collection and habitat sampling.

5.8 Describe the correct procedures for collecting, labeling, and documenting botanical evidence.

5.9 Explain why a forensic botanist should consult with local individuals; meteorologists; and entomologists, anthropologists, and wildlife specialists when processing a crime scene.

TOPICAL SCIENCES KEY

BIOLOGY   CHEMISTRY

EARTH SCIENCES   PHYSICS

LITERACY   MATHEMATICS

VOCABULARY

■ **angiosperm** a flowering plant that produces seeds within a fruit

■ **assemblage** group of plant species in an area dominated by one species that share the same habitat requirements

■ **forensic botany** the application of plant science to crime-scene analysis or the resolution of criminal cases

■ **forensic palynology** the use of pollen and spore evidence to help solve criminal cases

■ **gymnosperm** a plant with "naked" seeds that are not enclosed in a protective organ (fruit); most are evergreens

■ **palynology** the study of pollen and spores

■ **pistil** the female reproductive part of a flower where eggs are produced

■ **pollen "fingerprint"**; also called a **pollen profile**, the number and type of pollen grains found in a geographic area at a particular time of year

■ **pollen grain** a reproductive structure that contains the male gametes of seed plants

■ **pollination** the transfer of pollen from the male part to the female part of a seed plant

■ **postmortem interval (PMI)** time elapsed between a person's death and discovery of the body

■ **spore** an asexual reproductive structure that can develop into an adult found in certain protists (algae) and plants and fungi

■ **stamen** the male reproductive part of a flower consisting of the anther and filament where pollen is produced

FORENSIC BOTANY   **111**

TEACHING RESOURCES

 Instructor's Resource CD-ROM includes:
- Activities and Student Handouts
- Course Pre/Post Assessment
- Consolidated Bibliography
- Lesson Plans
- Nonfiction Suggested Readings

- PowerPoint Presentations
- Student Learning Objectives (SLOs)

CL Testing powered by Cognero

Website: ngl.cengage.com/forensicscience2e

Engage

Ask students who own a dog what type of plant evidence carried in from outside can be found on the dog. Have you seen roots, stems, seeds, or fruits? Is it possible to determine where the dog has been based on the plant evidence?

Engage

Show students a bouquet of flowers and ask them how their lives are affected by flowers and their pollen. (Bees use pollen to make honey; some flowers develop into edible fruits.) Elicit student knowledge about pollen and address their misconceptions. (Contrary to popular misconception, pollen of colorful, fragrant flowers pollinated by insects, such as roses, does not cause allergies.)

Engage

Ask students what an investigator could infer if he or she found grass cuttings on a piece of a victim's clothing that was found in a desert.

Teaching Tip

As a class, brainstorm the types of plant evidence in the area around the school. Then ask how the plant evidence in the area would differ in six months.

CHAPTER

1
2
3
4
5
6
7
8
9
10
11
12
13
14
15
16
17
18

BIOLOGY

British soldier lichen.

iStock.com/Debra Wiseberg

INTRODUCTION Obj. 5.1, 5.2

Seeds and spores attached to clothes, pollen inhaled into nasal cavities, diatoms found in a drowning victim's lungs, vegetables found in the stomach contents of a victim, annual rings in the wood of a ladder, lichen found in the cuff of a suspect's pants, a plant growing out of the eye sockets in a buried skull, and plants recovered from the undercarriage of a car—all are examples of botanical evidence that was used to solve crimes.

Seeds, leaf and grass fragments, pollen, spores, and lichen fragments can easily blend into the background and be overlooked by criminals due to small size. An individual **pollen grain**, the male reproductive structure of a seed plant, is as small as a pinpoint, though you may see collected pollen grains on cars and lawn furniture in the spring. **Spores**, the reproductive structures of algae, some plants, and fungi, are tiny. Many plant structures, such as pollen and seeds, have burrs or hooks with jagged edges that enable them to easily attach to hair, blankets, and clothing. Plant cell walls made of cellulose persist for a long time. Pollen grains, for example, have tough cell walls that can last for decades under some conditions, making them useful in forensic investigations. Forensic botanists use botanical evidence to help locate a crime scene or a gravesite, determine if a body was moved, link a suspect to a crime scene or victim, or to confirm or refute an alibi.

Forensic botany, a relatively new area of forensics, is the application of plant science to crime-scene analysis for use in legal cases. Forensic botany can be used in civil cases to determine who is responsible, for example, for root damage to sewer lines, livestock that have been poisoned by non-native plants, or landscaping contract disputes. However, this chapter focuses on how botanical evidence is used to solve criminal cases.

When crime-scene investigators arrive at a crime scene, their job is to observe and document anything that may help solve a crime. Botanical evidence may help answer the following questions:

- Where did the crime occur? What was the geographical region? Was the crime committed in an open field? Forest? Desert? At a high elevation or in a valley? In fresh water or on a sandy ocean beach?
- When was the crime committed? When was a specific person, vehicle, or article at a crime scene? Did the crime occur within the past few hours, yesterday, last week, or a year ago or longer? Was the crime committed during day or night, spring or fall?
- Who was with the victim, or at the crime scene, at or near the time of death?
- Where was the victim at the time of death?
- What did the victim eat before dying?
- Was the body moved?
- How long has it been since the victim died, the **postmortem interval (PMI)**? How long was a body buried?
- Is it possible to link a suspect or victim to a specific crime scene or to exclude a suspect based on botanical evidence?

112   CHAPTER 5

DIFFERENTIATED LEARNING

Gifted Students

Tree roots are known to grow toward a source of water such as a sewer line. Research the phenomenon known as *hydrotropism*. Do plants have a "brain" that tells them to grow in the direction of a water source? What enables a plant to grow and seemingly bend toward the water?

DIFFERENTIATED LEARNING

Teaching English-Language Learners

Help students create a flash card of each vocabulary word, with the word and pronunciation on one side and the meaning on the other. If time permits, allow students to quiz each other at the end of each class using their flash cards.

- Can you verify or refute a person's alibi?

Forensic botany is usually divided into subdivisions. In this chapter, you explore how the following areas of study have been used to solve crimes:

- Systematics—Classification of plants
- Ecology—Study of how plants are affected by their environment and other living things
- Dendrochronology—Study of tree rings
- Limnology—Study of aquatic environments
- **Palynology**—Study of pollen and spores
- Molecular biology—DNA technology

Teaching Tip

Ask students to think of different crime TV programs or movies in which some type of botanical evidence was used to solve the crime. Describe the evidence and explain how it helped solve the crime.

HISTORY OF FORENSIC BOTANY

Obj. 5.2, 5.3

The first mention in history of forensic botany was in Plato's *Phaedo* of 399 B.C. and describes Socrates' self-administered death sentence of poison hemlock, *Conium macultium*. Legal acceptance of forensic botany evidence first occurred as a result of evidence presented during the trial of the alleged kidnapper of the son of famous aviator and national hero Charles Lindbergh (Figure 5-1). The toddler's body had been found buried in the New Jersey woods 4 miles from the Lindbergh home. In 1935, Richard "Bruno" Hauptmann, an escaped German convict, was arrested after passing a marked bill from the ransom money. The jury convicted Hauptmann after hearing botanical evidence that linked him to the crime scene.

Figure 5-1 *Charles Lindbergh made the first solo flight across the Atlantic Ocean, in 1927.*

NY Daily News Archive/Getty Images

Arthur Koehler, an expert on wood, provided testimony at the January 1935 trial that linked Hauptmann with the ladder found at the crime scene. Koehler claimed that the homemade ladder used in the kidnapping was produced from the wood found in Hauptmann's home. The expert witness identified four different types of wood that were used to construct the ladder. He demonstrated that the wood, microscopic structures of the wood in the ladder, the sawdust, and the planing marks on the ladder were all consistent with the wood found in Hauptmann's home. (A planer is a tool used to shape wood.)

Koehler convinced the jury that the rail of the ladder was made from floorboards found in the attic of Hauptmann's home. He compared the size of the cut wood in the attic to the size of the ladder rail. He discovered the nail marks made by old-fashioned square nails were consistent with the nail marks in the ladder. The annual rings found in the wooden ladder also were consistent with the annual rings found in the floorboards of Hauptmann's home.

The wood expert explained that annual rings in a tree are made of xylem cells (cells that help transport water). The larger spring growth rings are usually lighter than the darker xylem cells produced in the summer.

FORENSIC BOTANY   113

DIFFERENTIATED LEARNING

Teaching At-Risk Students
Show a photo or a model of a car. Challenge the students to describe the type of botanical evidence that could be found on a car that could link the car to different locations. Ask them to describe the evidence and where on the car that evidence might be located.

DIFFERENTIATED LEARNING

Teaching Gifted Learners
The Charles Lindbergh case was the first time that tree-ring evidence was accepted in the courts. Standards for evidence acceptance have become much more rigorous. Have students investigate the Frye and Daubert standards for acceptance of scientific evidence testimony and decide if, based on each, the tree-ring testimony would have been accepted.

Teaching Tip

Encourage students to bring in different fruits and the flowers from which they were derived. Examine pollen from the flower, noting its color, shape, and size.

Teaching Tip

Growth rings (tree rings) can be seen in a horizontal cross section through the trunk of a tree. Growth rings are the result of seasonal growth in the vascular cambium. This layer actively produces xylem and phloem tissue. Xylem tissue carries water up from the roots, while phloem circulates dissolved sugars throughout the plant to nourish it.

Teaching Tip

Before discussing this case, provide tree cross sections for students to view annual rings. (Or project images of tree cross sections.) Ask students to observe and describe what they see. Can they see differences among the sizes of the cells? Ask students what types of cells make up wood. What is the function of those cells? What type of information can be gained by examining tree rings?

Figure 5-2 *Annual rings: Springwood is a lighter-colored wood whose rings alternate with the darker rings of summerwood.*

© artography/Shutterstock.com

Did you know

By chemically analyzing a plant's chlorophyll, it is possible to determine if it grows in a sunny or shady area.

The ring one notices in a tree cross section is a ring formed by the larger spring xylem cells alternating with the smaller, darker, and thicker-walled summer xylem cells. (See Figure 5-2). The size of each annual ring is affected by local weather conditions, the amount of competition from other area plants, and the local soil type. Thus, if two different pieces of wood had the same annual ring markings, it indicates that the wood was cut at the same time in the same area.

As well as examining the growth rings, Koehler was able to trace the origin of the wood in Hauptmann's attic by examining small planing marks in the wood. A mill in McCormick, South Carolina, had a defective planer that produced planing marks consistent with those on the wood in Hauptmann's attic. The wood was traced from the S.C. mill to the National Lumber and Millwork Company in Bronx, N.Y., just 10 miles from Hauptmann's home. The shipment of wood occurred between 1929 and 1932 when Hauptmann was a known customer of the Bronx Mill. This trial was the first time that botanical evidence was accepted in a court in the United States.

Since 1935, the use of botanical evidence to solve crimes has been effective but underutilized due to a lack of training. In Europe in 1959, soil samples containing pollen from the surrounding plants were used to connect a suspect to a crime scene. Max Frei, a Swiss criminalist, was able to link a suspect to a murder weapon when he found pollen consistent with that at the crime scene in the grease of the gun. In the 1960s and early 1970s, few law-enforcement officers were aware of forensic botany. Still today, due to a lack of awareness and training, many crime-scene investigators do not notice or effectively collect botanical evidence. An exception is New Zealand, which has aggressively and effectively used forensic botany for many years.

Use of botanical evidence in the United States is increasing, however, due in part to the work of many botanists turned forensic investigators. Dr. David W. Hall, a renowned forensic botanist at the University of Florida, who is also a consultant, an expert in plant identification and ecology, and author of eight books, and botanist Jane Bock of the University of Colorado have helped solve many crimes. In 1986, Dr. Hall was the first forensic botanist to be admitted to the American Academy of Forensic Sciences, an organization founded by many forensic pioneers. Throughout Dr. Hall's career, he has been actively involved in educating forensic botanists, law-enforcement officers, and lawyers in how to collect and document botanical evidence.

In 1993, Dr. Hall taught forensic botany as part of the training for FBI agents at the National Academy at Quantico, Virginia. Since the late 1990s, many more law-enforcement officers and lawyers are being instructed in forensic botany. With the advent of several crime-related television programs, the general public has gained an awareness of the value of plant evidence.

DIFFERENTIATED LEARNING

Teaching Gifted Students

Ask students to research keystone species of plants from the county in which they live and present their findings to the class.

Ask students to research how the structure of a pollen grain enhances its ability to

a. recognize its correct species of plant.

b. attach itself to a stigma.

c. resist dehydration.

HOW FORENSIC BOTANY IS USED TO SOLVE CASES Obj. 5.1, 5.2, 5.4, 5.9

Understanding plant ecology and how a plant interacts with its environment and other plants is an important job of the forensic botanist. Plants grow in **assemblages**, groups of plants usually dominated by one species (Figure 5-3). Assemblages share the same habitat requirements such as soil type, moisture, sunlight or shade, wind, altitude, and latitude and longitude. A forensic botanist can identify individual plants from tiny fragments found on bodies, automobiles, and other objects. Careful collection of plants, including seeds, fruits, and flowers, along with photos and descriptions of the plants and their environment, facilitate the identification of the plants and their location. Once a plant is identified, the forensic botanist has a better understanding of the type of environment where the plant originated. It is possible to exclude possible crime scenes based on the habitat requirements of the recovered plant. Knowing a crime scene's assemblage of plants can help identify its location.

BIOLOGY

Figure 5-3 *Different environments exhibit different plant assemblages, even in the same region (both photos, Rocky Mountain National Park).*

NATALIE MIRABEL, LEFT HAND CANYON, COLORADO, 1999

EARTH SCIENCES

Dr. Jane Bock, University of Colorado botanist turned forensic scientist, was called to investigate a murder. The body of Natalie Mirabel was found in a canyon off a road leading up into the Rocky Mountains. Her husband, Matthew, had an alibi that he was at home with their daughter. Botanical evidence found in his car's undercarriage, floor mats, and pedals showed that Matthew's car had recently been in an area with plants growing in higher elevations like those found in the canyon, and not the type of plants found growing near his home (Figure 5-4). A combination of motive (a new life insurance policy) and multiple forms of circumstantial evidence (botanical, wife's blood on his gloves, his DNA under the wife's fingernails) led to his conviction for his wife's murder.

Figure 5-4 *Vegetation changes with changes in climate as elevation changes.*

SAMANTHA FORBES FREEPORT, BAHAMAS, 1999

While a tropical storm passed over the city of Freeport, Samantha Forbes was seen leaving a bar with two men. The next morning her body was found on a local golf course. Due to the storm, little evidence

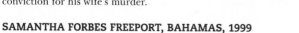

FORENSIC BOTANY   **115**

Teaching Tip

Have students discuss the types of local insects and animals that help disperse pollen. Make a class list of these items.

Explore

In addition to collecting botanical evidence from the crime scene, investigators must also document the main plants in the area around the crime scene through photos and collections *(habitat sampling)*. How would knowing the local plants around a crime scene be useful to the forensic botanist examining the evidence?

Teaching Tip

Ask students to describe the characteristic plants found in their environment (the assemblage). What types of plant evidence could identify their area? What factors determine what type of vegetation is well suited to grow in different areas? Make a list of plants that would be indicators for different biomes.

Teaching Tip

Critical Thinking

What are your students' opinions? Dr. Jane Bock, forensic botanist, testified at the Casey Anthony murder trial on June 11, 2011. Her testimony was controversial. Have students research Dr. Bock's testimony and ask if they agree or disagree with her statements. Students should provide evidence to support their claims.

was recovered at the crime scene. When the two suspects were questioned, the police recovered a tiny fragment of a blade of grass from one of their socks. Could this fragment of grass link the suspect to the crime scene? Dr. Jane Bock was able to identify the grass as Almond Bermuda, a grass that had been specifically selected for that golf course. No other golf course on Grand Bahama Island used this type of grass. This evidence helped convict one of the two suspects.

GOLD HEAD BRANCH MURDER, CLAY COUNTY SHERIFF'S OFFICE, FLORIDA, 1991

A five-inch turkey oak seedling bent to the ground by an isolated human tibia (leg) bone provided the first clue for forensic botanist Dr. David Hall (Figure 5-5). He was trying to estimate how long the human bone had been separated from the rest of the skeletal remains that were recovered by the crime-scene investigators. The bone was found after the detectives called in the National Guard to perform a massive line search to find two missing bones. When Dr. Hall lifted the bone off the seedling, a turkey oak leaf was found. Where the bone had rested on the leaf, a line of dead cells matching the size and shape of the human bone was visible. Without sunlight, leaf cells cannot produce chlorophyll, and they die. Dr. Hall estimated the time it took for the shading to kill the leaves. This provided the *first* time interval.

The leaf was fully formed without any malformations, which indicated to the forensic botanist that the bone was dropped on the leaf *after* the leaf was formed. By speaking to the local park rangers and inhabitants of the area,

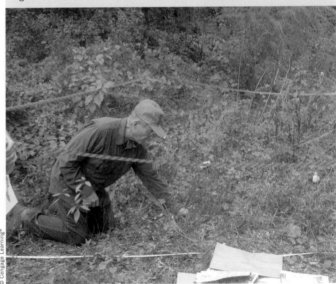

Figure 5-5 *Dr. David Hall examines a collection site.*

Dr. Hall estimated when budding occurred and when the leaf would have reached its full growth. This information provided him with his *second* time interval.

Animals are known to scatter bones and carry them away from the rest of a skeleton. After checking with the University of Florida wildlife and bone experts, Dr. Hall determined that the bite marks found on the tibia were consistent with those of a large dog. Based on information from the local medical examiners, a *third* time interval was estimated from the amount of time required for decomposition to reach a point where a dog of that size could pull a tibia away from the rest of the skeletal remains.

Dr. Hall added the three time intervals together and then subtracted that sum from the time that the skeleton was found. The result placed the deposit of the remains during a rather cold winter, which would slow down the decomposition rate of the body. Dr. Hall adjusted his time interval, factoring in the cold temperature. The detectives checked with the missing persons' bureau and learned there was a report of a missing person a week before Dr. Hall's estimate. The skeletal remains were confirmed to be those of the missing person.

MATHEMATICS

DROWNING VICTIMS *Obj. 5.1, 5.4, 5.5*

When a person drowns, he or she inhales water into the lungs and body tissues. Algae and diatoms are nonvascular photosynthetic organisms, important producers found in fresh water, salt water, and mud. (*Diatoms* are relatives of algae that have cell walls containing silicon dioxide, or silica.) By comparing the number and proportion of algae and diatoms in a drowned person's lungs and body tissues, it is possible in some cases to determine where he or she drowned. A postmortem interval can be estimated based on the number of diatoms found in the body. Fewer than 20 different species indicate a recent drowning; more than 50 species indicate a longer postmortem interval.

An assemblage of algae and diatoms can help identify a specific body of water as a crime scene, just as an assemblage of plants can identify specific woods or a field. Diatoms have distinctive shapes that are easily identified under a light microscope. Unique refractive patterns are produced by their silica cell walls (Figure 5-6). Because they are resistant to decay, they provide a long-lasting source of evidence.

Figure 5-6 *In this micrograph of diatoms, you can see the beauty and symmetry of some of the thousands of species.*

Scenics & Science/Alamy

POND ATTACK CASE STUDY

Two young boys were attacked while fishing in a pond in Connecticut. The assailant beat both boys with a baseball bat, bound them with duct tape, and left them to drown. One boy escaped and helped his friend. Mud found on the boys' sneakers contained the same diatoms and algae that were found in the pond. When a suspect was apprehended, police collected mud from his sneakers and found that they, too, had algae

Explore

Have students compare algae from a pond and a fish tank by observing them microscopically. Have students draw or describe as many different types of algae from the two sources as they can. What environmental influences would affect the type of algae found in a location? How would this relate to forensics?

Science

BIOLOGY

BIOLOGY

Since the 1950s, scientists have noted that lichens require clean air to survive. In the Los Angeles area, for example, rising smog levels have been linked to the disappearance of lichens. For this reason, scientists now use lichens to monitor air quality.

Explore

Encourage students to examine samples of diatomaceous earth under a microscope so they can see the various sizes and shapes of diatoms.

Teaching Tip

Discuss the cellular structure of diatoms with their silica cell walls. Because the silica cell walls do not decompose, it is possible to view them under a microscope long after the organism has died. Students may not be aware of the many uses of diatoms or diatomaceous earth, such as in toothpaste (abrasion), as an insecticide, or the diatomaceous filters used in beverages, syrups, insulation, and sandpaper. If possible, bring in samples of these items, or project images of these products.

Evaluate

Lead students in a discussion of the following questions:

- Finding pollen on a suspect that is consistent with pollen found on a victim may aid in a conviction of the suspect, but can it be the sole evidence in a conviction? Why?
- Can you think of any situations where pollen could be the sole evidence?

Explore

Have the students take a brisk walk through a field of grass or wildflowers. (You should inspect the area first for debris, ticks, or poisonous plants like poison ivy.) After the walk, have students use adhesive tape to remove trace evidence from their shoes, socks, or even their hair. Discuss what they found.

Teaching Tip

Review with students the organs of the alimentary canal using a model, projected image, or photos.

Science

BIOLOGY

BIOLOGY

The time food remains in the stomach varies depending on the amount of food, the type of food, the temperature of the food, and one's activity level. The following ranges of time food is in each digestive organ are approximate:

Stomach	2–6 hours
Small Intestine	12 hours or less
Large Intestine	~ 10 hours
Total	24 hours or less

Science

CHEMISTRY

CHEMISTRY

The cell walls of plants are composed of cellulose, which is not digested by humans, and as a result, it passes out of the digestive tract. Dr. Jane Bock and Dr. David Norris published *A Handbook of Forensic Botany*, a reference book of images of

Figure 5-7 Eunotia *is a large, diverse genus of diatoms.*

Michael Abbey/Science Source

and diatoms similar to those found at the crime scene.

All three samples contained 14 of the 15 different species of algae and diatoms common to that pond. All samples contained the most numerous alga *Mallomonas caudata*. Freshwater diatoms of the genus *Eunotia* (Figure 5-7) were found in all samples. However, the convincing evidence that linked the suspect to the crime scene was that the proportion of different forms of algae and diatoms was consistent in all three samples. Nevertheless, because diatoms can be present in living tissues and in the bodies of people whose cause of death is not drowning, forensic analysis of diatoms is controversial in the United States.

INFORMATION FROM GASTRIC CONTENTS Obj. 5.1, 5.2, 5.5, 5.6

Many of you have watched TV crime programs in which the stomach contents (gastric contents) are emptied and examined as part of an autopsy. What are the examiners looking for? What part of a meal can withstand the action of digestive juices? How will gastric contents help solve a crime?

Dr. Jane Bock, forensic botanist, understood that plant cells with their cellulose cell walls could easily withstand digestion. She and her graduate students created a lab manual to assist in the identification of plant cells in a person's last meal and to estimate postmortem intervals based on the degree of digestion. The graduate students' job was to chew onions, olives, spinach, okra, lettuce, and tomatoes (separately) and prepare microscopic images of the chewed cells that could be used for comparison with the plant cells found in a victim's stomach or intestines.

Suppose the victim's last meal consisted of tomatoes, chili beans, black olives, onions, and hot peppers; or perhaps the meal was burgers, fries, and a shake. The meal could be traced to the local Mexican restaurant or to a fast-food restaurant. If some of the meal was still in the victim's stomach when the body was recovered, the police could use that information to estimate the postmortem interval. Knowing where the victim had been prior to death helps the investigators because they know where to start questioning people who last saw the victim.

THE BODY COVERED BY WILTED SUNFLOWERS Obj. 5.1, 5.2, 5.5, 5.7

Who is the victim whose decomposing body was left abandoned on the roadside, covered by wilted, uprooted sunflowers? How long has the body been in that area? The only clues seem to be the wilted sunflowers. The question to ask: How long would it take for sunflowers, such as those

118   CHAPTER 5

digested plant matter to help forensic scientists identify the type of food found in the digestive tract or feces of a deceased person. Once the plant matter is identified, it may lead to clues as to a postmortem interval.

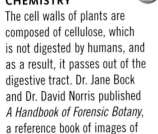

DIFFERENTIATED LEARNING

Help students visualize how long the entire alimentary canal is by using a string. Tie knots at different locations to indicate the length of the esophagus, the stomach, small intestine, and large intestine. Stretch out the string to help students visualize the overall length of the digestive tract. Remind students that the only way anything enters the alimentary canal is via the throat, and the only way anything leaves is via the anus, once digestion is complete.

Figure 5-8 *Dr. Bock's PMI estimate was based in part on her experiments with wilting sunflowers in which she tried to replicate the same degree of wilting shown by sunflowers on the body.*

© Maxim Petrichuk/Shutterstock.com

in Figure 5-8, to wilt in that environment? The answer could help estimate the postmortem interval.

To find out, pick more sunflowers from the same area, put them in a similar environment, and observe the number of days required to reach the same state of wilting as the flowers found covering the body. This was the procedure performed by Dr. Jane Bock of University of Colorado. Based on her experiment, she estimated that the body had been abandoned for seven days, which was consistent with the insect evidence. Using missing person information, the identity of the victim was determined.

SECRETS FROM A GRAVE *Obj. 5.1, 5.2, 5.9*

A series of kidnappings has occurred. Several victims' remains have been recovered from a shallow grave. When another person in the area goes missing, the police search for the missing person and for evidence of a recent grave.

How do you recognize a gravesite? If it is an old one, then the actual site sinks into and fills the grave as the ground settles. If the gravesite is new, a mound of soil will be visible near the grave, perhaps totally devoid of any plants. Broken branches may indicate recent activity.

When ground has been dug for a grave, existing vegetation is removed. Because of changes resulting from the new gravesite, the type of plants that inhabit that particular area will be different from the established

EARTH SCIENCES

FORENSIC BOTANY **119**

Figure 5-9 *A crime-scene investigator examines a potential gravesite.*

© Cengage Learning®

dominant plants around the area. The disturbed soil is aerated by digging, thus allowing more oxygen to the roots and more water to flow into the area. Due to the turning of the topsoil, the soil becomes enriched. Different plants will grow in the area, and the gravesite will look different from the area around it. (See Figure 5-9.)

Other clues can be spotted at the gravesite. If the grave was dug using a shovel, tool marks may be visible along the edge of the gravesite, along with broken tree or plant roots. Bright green leaves in the soil would indicate that the ground was recently overturned. If new growth has started, estimates can be made of how long ago the gravesite was disturbed based on annual rings of roots or the development of new growth. In 1960, anthropologist Clyde Snow estimated the time of death of a victim as late June or July based on the size of the soybean seeds found on the dead plants under the skeleton. (Snow's evidence was admissible in court in 1960, but because he was testifying outside his field of expertise (anthropology), this botanical testimony would be inadmissible today.) Smaller botanical evidence such as pollen, spores, seeds, and lichen fragments are also useful. Often, these smaller items are easily transferred to a suspect and can be used to link the suspect to the crime scene. Their presence could also indicate that a body was moved from a different site.

BOTANICAL CRIME-SCENE ANALYSIS *Obj. 5.6, 5.7, 5.8, 5.9*

The crime scene for a forensic botanist can be anywhere a crime was committed: forest, desert, tropical rain forest, pond, lake, street, or inside a car or home. Recall that Locard's Principle of Exchange states that evidence from one area can be transferred to another.

A forensic botanist follows all the procedures for evidence collection, documentation, photographing, recording, and maintaining chain of custody discussed in Chapter 2. In this section, you will study special concerns of the rest of the crime-scene processing team in terms of processing a crime scene for botanical evidence.

After the examiner has scanned and walked through the scene, photographs are taken of the crime scene both from a distance and close up. A crime-scene artist prepares a preliminary sketch of the crime scene. Both the photographer and the recorder are responsible for documenting each photo. The recorder documents information about the crime scene such as the following:

• Case number

• Name of the agency processing the crime scene

• Names of investigators at the crime scene

• Crime-scene location, including longitude and latitude, compass readings of the crime scene, and distance from fixed locations or datum points such as trees or buildings

- Description of the crime scene
- Descriptions of any biological materials at the crime scene
- Habitat assessment (deciduous forest, desert, open field, lake, pond, building, etc.). The description should include both the crime-scene and the areas around the crime scene.

A general description of the dominant plants should be included, along with notations on the presence of broken branches or disturbed plants. Environmental conditions such as temperature, cloud cover, sun, humidity level, type of soil, wind speed, and so forth should be noted.

In addition to the usual photos of the crime scene noted in Chapter 2, the crime-scene photographer (Figure 5-10) should take images of the following:

- Dominant plants and other plants found both at the crime scene and in the area around the crime scene
- Possible entrances or exits from the crime scene as evidenced by depressed grasses
- Broken branches or disturbed plants with both micro and macro lenses
- Plants that seem to be unusual for the area

Figure 5-10 *A crime-scene photographer.*

Engage
To calculate the probability that a specific event will occur, divide the number of favorable outcomes by the number of possible outcomes. For example, if you toss a coin, the probability of the coin landing on heads is 1 in 2.

DIFFERENTIATED LEARNING

Teaching At-Risk Students

Broken branches and damaged plants provide clues of activity in an area. These types of botanical evidence may indicate a path used by a suspect. If possible, have several students walk through an area that has many types of plants. Students should leave some type of token at the end of their path. Challenge other class members to locate disturbed or broken plants and find their way to the token. This activity is a good indicator of students' observational skills.

- Plants that are found in the following locations:
  - Plants covering a body, vehicle, or object
  - Plants on a body, vehicle, or object
  - Plants under a body, vehicle, or object
  - Plants between objects and a body

SEARCHING FOR AND MAPPING BOTANICAL EVIDENCE *Obj.* 5.8

Figure 5-11 *Even a broken branch at a crime scene may be documented, photographed, and labeled as botanical evidence.*

© Cengage Learning®

When evidence of any kind is discovered, whether it is botanical, such as the broken branch in Figure 5-11, or another type, it is important to know what and how much to sample and how to package and label it. Failure could result in contamination or destruction of the evidence or inadmissibility of the evidence in court. As you recall from Chapter 2, when evidence is discovered, it is marked with a flag that is then numbered. A recorder documents the evidence items in number sequence, while a photographer photographs the items. The recorder documents the exact location of each evidence item. Each item gets its own properly completed Evidence Inventory Label. In the case of botanical evidence, the recorder should enter the following information on the label:

- Description of plant (tree, shrub, vine, pollen, flower, woody or herbaceous, algae, etc.)
- Height of plant if the entire plant was not collected
- Color and shape of flowers, fruits, seeds, stems, leaves, and so forth

All evidence should be mapped by establishing a datum point. Measurements and directions are taken from the datum point to a corner stake of the crime scene, marking the subdatum point. (Refer to the Chapter 2 section Mapping the Crime Scene.)

BOTANICAL EVIDENCE COLLECTION *Obj.* 5.6, 5.8

More than one person can search for botanical evidence, but only one person should do the actual collecting to avoid duplication of specimens. Several people can assist with the labeling and packaging of the evidence. Besides collecting evidence, it is important to collect at least 10 different types of plants from the area's assemblage, called a *habitat sample*, including any unusual plants. This sample helps the forensic botanist determine if any botanical samples on a body could have been transferred from a primary crime scene. Samples should never be stored in plastic, nor should they be frozen. Botanical evidence is best placed in paper. Using a pencil, label the paper with the case number and evidence number. Note what part of the plant was collected and indicate color and shape of the plant part, especially for flowers and fruits. Photographs of the evidence are taken before collection in situ and again in the paper showing the case and evidence number.

Plants can also be temporarily stored using a plant press (Figure 5-12). Place blotter paper on the plant press, followed by newsprint, plant, newsprint, blotter paper, and the plant press. More layers of blotter paper and newsprint should be used for herbaceous plants that contain more water. General guidelines for collection of different types of plants include the following:

Figure 5-12 *Wooden plant press.*

© Cengage Learning®

- Woody plants: collect at least eight to twelve inches of the plant showing several leaves with variation in size, color, and leaf arrangement.
- Tall plants or vines should be zigzagged, and not coiled, in paper.
- Small plants or plant fragments should be stored in large pieces of newsprint.
- Broken branches should be cut at least an inch above and below the broken area.
- Collect roots when possible.
- Fruits can be sliced and placed in thick newsprint or between sheets of wax paper if the fruit has a high sugar content.
- Larger dry items such as pinecones can be placed in a box or large paper bag (with the bottom flap closed).

POLLEN AND SPORES IN FORENSICS *Obj. 5.1*

Pollen and spores provide clues as to when and where a crime occurred and whether the body was moved from the scene of the crime. The victim's clothes may actually hold evidence that provides information about the crime scene. Trace evidence, such as plant material, can provide clues about a crime's location, such as whether the crime was committed in the city or country. It can also provide clues that the crime occurred during a particular season of the year. In some instances, the evidence can even help determine when the crime occurred, such as during the day or night.

Several specialized forensic fields are devoted to studying biological evidence at a crime scene. One of these fields is **forensic palynology,** the study of pollen and spore evidence to help solve criminal cases. Pollen (Figure 5-13) and spores have different functions, but they have similar characteristics, such as being microscopic and having a resistant cell wall. These characteristics make them very useful for crime-scene investigations.

Did you know

Pollen grains can be extracted safely from rocks that are millions of years old. This is a valuable characteristic not only for palynologists, but also for oil companies and archaeologists.

Figure 5-13 *A false-color scanning electron microscope (SEM) photograph of pollen grains.*

Scott Camazine/Science Source

FORENSIC BOTANY **123**

Teaching Tip

Packaging plant evidence: If possible, have students go outside to photograph, document, and collect botanical evidence using the methods described in this chapter. If students cannot go outside, bring botanical samples to class. Include a variety of plants, seeds, fruits, flowers, stems, and roots. Before students collect plants, review the information in the text concerning what parts of the plant to collect.

Teaching Tip

Explain to students that scientists use many different types of microscopes. Other than the light microscopes students may be familiar with, more sophisticated microscopes use lasers or electron beams to produce an image.

Teaching Tip

Find images of various types of microscopes, particularly some of the large electron microscopes, to show students. Show of different levels of magnification different types of microscopes are capable of producing.

Teaching Tip

Explain to students that light microscopes use light to pass through a specimen in order to see the object. Because pollen and spores are not transparent, other types of microscopes, such as a scanning electron microscope (SEM), are required for clear, detailed images. The SEM produces a stream of electrons that interact with the surface of an object and produce an image that has a three-dimensional appearance.

Teaching Tip

Bring in both male and female evergreen cones. The larger, woody, female cone may release many seeds if you strike it against the desk. Many students don't realize that the cones contain seed. Explain that the smaller, softer cones are the male cones, which contain pollen. Gently tap the male cone on your desk to release some pollen. (Be aware that some students are likely to have pine pollen allergies.) Discuss with students the forensic value of each cone.

Teaching Tip

Have students develop a digital image database of the gymnosperms and angiosperms located on your school property. Photograph the plants in situ and take digital images of the pollen viewed under 400×.

Teaching Tip

Pollen finger prints, or profiles, can be used to trace drug shipments and explosives. A pollen finger print can identify a specific geographic region. The route and origin of shipments can be determined by a pollen analysis of the drugs, explosives, weapons, or packaging in which they were shipped.

The use of pollen and spores in forensic investigations is based on Locard's Principle of Exchange, which you studied in Chapter 2. Recall that every contact between two objects or persons leaves a trace. Suspects pick up microscopic evidence that helps investigators link them to a crime scene.

POLLEN PRODUCERS *Obj. 5.4, 5.5*

Knowledge of pollen (and spore) production is an important factor in the study of forensic palynology. By understanding pollen production patterns for plants in a given location, one can better predict the type of pollen "fingerprint" to expect in samples that come from that area. A **pollen fingerprint** or **pollen profile,** is the number and type of pollen grains found in a geographic area at a particular time of year.

The plant kingdom can be classified into two groups based on how they reproduce: nonseed plants and seed plants. The earliest plants were nonseed plants. They reproduce by dispersing, or spreading, spores. Nonseed plants existing today include ferns, mosses, liverworts, horsetails, and club mosses. Some of the more recently evolved seed plants also produce spores, but their primary means of reproduction and dispersal is by seeds. During their life cycles, seed plants produce cones or flowers that make pollen to disperse male gametes. Seed plants existing today include the gymnosperms and the angiosperms. Seed plants are the predominant land plants, so they are the most likely plants to leave evidence at a crime scene.

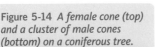

BIOLOGY

Figure 5-14 *A female cone (top) and a cluster of male cones (bottom) on a coniferous tree.*

Paul Whitten/Science Source

© Cengage Learning®

Gymnosperms

The seeds of **gymnosperms**, the oldest seed plants, are exposed and are not enclosed in a protective organ (fruit). Gymnosperms include cycads, ginkgoes, and the conifers. Conifers (cone-bearing plants) are the largest, most familiar group of gymnosperms (Figure 5-14). They include pines, spruces, firs, junipers, and other evergreen plants.

Many conifers produce their seeds within a hard, scaly structure called a *cone*. There are female cones and male cones (Figure 5-14). Female cones, which are typically larger than male cones, contain eggs inside structures called *ovules*. The male cones of conifers release large amounts of pollen grains, which are spread by wind currents to the female cones. This process is called **pollination**. Sperm cells from pollen grains fertilize the eggs inside the ovules on the female cones. A seed develops from a fertilized ovule. The vast amounts of pollen released by male cones is a great benefit to forensic palynology.

Angiosperms

Angiosperms are the flowering plants, and they produce seeds within an organ called a fruit. Angiosperms are very diverse and include corn, oaks, maples, and the grasses. There are about 300,000 angiosperm species known, and they are found in almost all habitats. Because angiosperm plants are found in so many places, most crime scenes contain angiosperm pollen.

The basic reproductive unit of an angiosperm is the flower (Figure 5-15). The **pistil** is the female part of a flower that produces eggs. The stigma is the part of the pistil where pollen lands. A pollen tube produced by a pollen grain grows down the long, thin style until it reaches the ovary.

The male part of the flower, or **stamen,** is responsible for pollen production. The long, thin filament of the stamen elevates the anther that produces pollen sacs. Following pollination, one of the released sperm cells successfully fuses with an egg, the ovule becomes a seed, and the ovary develops into a fruit. Figure 5-16 shows an avocado seed encased within the fruit.

Types of Pollination

Pollen (and spore) dispersion patterns are important in forensic studies for analyzing palynological samples that come from the crime scene.

In all seed plants, before a sperm can fuse with an egg during fertilization of a seed plant, pollination must occur. Pollination can involve one or more flowers. In flowering plants, pollination that involves the transfer of pollen from an anther to a stigma within the same flower is known as *self-pollination*, as found in pea plants. If pollination involves two distinct plants, it is known as *cross-pollination*. Note that some plants can both self- and cross-pollinate. Strict self-pollinating plants generally produce less pollen than cross-pollinating ones because of the efficiency of self-pollination. Thus, the pollen of self-pollinating plants is generally less useful in forensic studies because it exists in a relatively small volume and does not travel far. Of course, pollen transfer onto clothing or skin is possible from brushing up against a self-pollinating plant.

Methods of Pollination

Pollen can be carried by wind, animals, or water. Wind-pollinated plants release large amounts of pollen from small and nonfragrant flowers, or cones. Producing large amounts of pollen increases the chance of the pollen reaching a female reproductive part. As a result, wind-pollinated plants are often dominant in the pollen profile of a crime scene. However, for the same reason, wind-pollinated plants may actually be overrepresented in collection samples. They may be less effective for determining direct links between individuals and places.

Other flowering plants are pollinated by animals, such as insects, birds, bats, and even monkeys. These plants have fragrant or showy flowers to

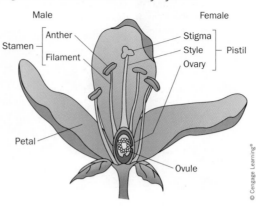

Figure 5-15 *The basic structure of a flower.*

Figure 5-16 *Following pollination, one of the released sperm cells successfully fuses with an egg, the ovule becomes a seed, and the ovary develops into a fruit.*

Science

BIOLOGY

BIOLOGY

Students may not understand how plants disperse seeds. Explain that some plants have built-in dispersal methods, whereas others need help from wind, water, or other organisms.

Science

BIOLOGY

BIOLOGY

The structure of the fruit of a plant often provides clues to the method of pollen dispersal. Burdocks have hooks that attach to animal fur or a person's clothing. Animals eat sweet fruit and the seeds are deposited in the animal waste. Insects disperse the pollen from flowers with petals. Wind can transport pollen from flowers without petals.

Teaching Tip

Use grains of pepper to help students visualize dispersal. Have a volunteer touch a finger to a small pile of pepper and then look at the finger. He or she will note a few grains stuck to the finger. Ask what will happen to the pepper as the student walks away. (Some will fall to the ground.) Explain that this is one method of dispersal. Have another volunteer blow lightly on a pile of salt. Tell students that this is how wind helps disperse pollen.

Explore

Show a time-lapse film of the development of a flower from a seed or a fungus from a spore, or have students search the Internet for a video of the same. Many students will be amazed at the transformation.

Figure 5-17 *Insects are important pollinators of flowering plants.*

Susan Van Etten

attract the animals (Figure 5-17). Animal-pollinated plants also make adhesive and durable pollen because it must adhere to the animals. Durable pollen grains are more likely to be collected during evidence collection. Moreover, this kind of pollen can provide strong evidence of contact because pollen may be transferred only by direct connection with the plant or the surface on which the plant has made contact. However, animal-pollinated plants tend to produce less pollen than wind-pollinated plants because animal carriers directly transfer the pollen more efficiently. Thus, animal-dispersed pollen may be underrepresented in the pollen profile of a crime scene.

BIOLOGY

Seed Dispersal

Seed development occurs after pollination. Plants have evolved diverse ways to disperse their seeds. Animals eat seeds that are surrounded by fleshy fruits. The seeds pass through the digestive tract of the animals and are distributed via their feces. In contrast, dandelion seeds are dispersed by the wind and take flight. Other seeds are surrounded by dry fruits with burrs that stick to animal hair or people's clothing. By examining a victim or suspect for unusual seed evidence, it is sometimes possible to link a person to a crime scene.

SPORE PRODUCERS *Obj. 5.5, 5.6*

Spores are asexually reproductive structures produced by a variety of organisms, including algae, fungi, and plants (Figure 5-18). Like pollen and seeds, spores are very small, produced in large quantities, easily transferred, and easily overlooked by perpetrators, making them useful for forensic work. Identification of individual spores and recognition of a spore profile (spore fingerprint of a specific area) help to identify specific locations and provide clues that can link a person to a crime scene.

Spore Dispersal

Spores are dispersed in a variety of ways. Algae release spores directly into the water or into the air. Fungi such as mold grow in moist, dark areas and may depend on wind or water dispersal, depending on species. Mushroom spores scattered by wind are released under their caps from structures known as *gills*, shown in Figure 5-18. Seedless land plants such as ferns and mosses release their spores in structures known as *sori* or *sporangia* (Figure 5-19).

Some fungi have evolved mechanisms to enhance spore dispersal, such as spore ejection and animal dispersal. *Pilobolus* fungi eject

Figure 5-18 *Note the different parts of a mushroom and how spores are released into the wind.*

Cap

Gills

Spores

Stalk

126   CHAPTER 5

Figure 5-19 *Examine the fern. Note the round, spore-producing sori on the underside of the fronds.*

Sporangia

Frond

Susan Van Etten

Figure 5-20 *Puffball fungus ejecting spores.*

Kenneth H. Thomas/Science Source

Teaching Tip

Students might not be as familiar with fungi as they are with plants. Mushrooms and molds are common types of fungi. Have students discuss what they know about these organisms.

Science

BIOLOGY

BIOLOGY

The stalk and cap of a mushroom are not green like the stem and leaves of a plant. Plants appear green because they contain chlorophyll, the pigment that aids in photosynthesis. Fungi do not contain chlorophyll. Instead, they get energy by breaking down organic materials and absorbing nutrients.

masses of spores, while puffball fungi, such as the one you see in Figure 5-20, release spores when disturbed. Edible truffle fungi are eaten by foraging animals, though humans have to pay for the pleasure. Fungi spores pass through animal digestive tracts and are distributed to a new area in feces.

Bacterial Spores: An Exception

Some bacteria produce spores. When environmental conditions are unfavorable, some bacteria form thick-walled, resistant spores, called *endospores*. Endospores are different from the spores produced by fungi, algae, and plants because endospores are not used in reproduction, and a bacterium can produce only one endospore at a time. Endospores are of interest in forensics because several types of bacteria that make endospores can cause diseases, such as anthrax and botulism. But bacterial endospores are a topic of *forensic microbiology*, so even though they are sometimes called spores, they are not covered in this chapter.

POLLEN AND SPORE IDENTIFICATION IN SOLVING CRIMES *Obj. 5.2*

BIOLOGY

Pollen and spore identification can provide important trace evidence in solving crimes, but it can be challenging. However, viewed under a microscope, the hard outer layer of a pollen grain or spore has a unique and complex structure.

DIGGING DEEPER

With Forensic Science eCollection

Go to the Gale Forensic Science eCollection at **ngl.cengage.com/ forensicscience2e** to research methods used to identify various pollen and spore types.

DIFFERENTIATED LEARNING

Teaching At-Risk Students
Bring in examples of gymnosperms, angiosperms, and fungi. Ask students to classify them as such. If you can find examples of seeds, pollen, and spores, let students classify them also.

Help students prepare a spore demonstration by turning over a mushroom cap onto a piece of paper, or find a fern sorus with sporangia and examine it.

DIFFERENTIATED LEARNING

Teaching English-Language Learners
Organize students into a group. To help them practice writing and pronouncing the terms in this chapter, have students create and label a poster of a gymnosperm, an angiosperm, and a spore producer to post in the classroom.

Teaching Tip

Activity 5-1
Pollen Examination involves comparing microscopic examination of pollen on suspects to the pollen on a victim.

Teaching Tip

In *Activity 5-3 Botanical Evidence Case Studies Presentation*, different student teams research how pollen was used forensically in a variety of criminal cases. Student teams research and present case studies.

Figure 5-21 *Lily pollen (top) and mushroom spores (bottom, with probe in view) magnified 400 times.*

© Cengage Learning®

© Cengage Learning®

Distinguishing features include size, shape, wall thickness, and surface textures, such as spines. For example, larger pollen grains such as that of corn cannot travel far and can only drift with the wind about one-half mile. So someone with corn pollen on him or her has probably been close to a cornfield or a corn flower.

Wind-dispersed pollen grains are relatively simple, with thin cell walls, and are easily preserved for identification. In contrast, animal-dispersed pollen is usually large, sticky, highly ornamented, thick-walled, and also easily preserved for identification.

Pollen and spores differ in other ways important to forensic scientists. Most important, spores are much smaller and more difficult to identify than pollen grains and spores are produced in far greater numbers than pollen (Figure 5-21). An advantage of spore analysis over pollen is that it is possible to grow a new organism from a spore and thus identify the species.

Pollen and spore production is seasonally and geographically specific. Thus, pollen and spore evidence from a crime scene can lead to useful information about the crime. Also, if pollen, spores, or both found on the victim are not native to the crime scene, it may indicate that the body was moved.

Pollen and spores also play an important role in solving crimes because they are very small, or even microscopic, and difficult for a perpetrator to eliminate at a crime scene. The resistant nature of most pollen and some spores allows them to avoid dehydration and degradation. In fact, they can be found in dry sediment from millions of years ago. Pollen, especially from animal-pollinated angiosperms, usually has sharp edges that enable it to better adhere to its animal pollinator, and thus, a perpetrator can easily pick up evidence on his or her shoes and clothes that cannot be seen and that will not go away.

Pollen and Spore Evidence at Crime Scenes

Pollen and spore collection should be done by a forensic palynologist if possible. It is critical that forensic palynologists carefully and methodically collect and store samples while avoiding contamination. Contamination is a major problem and can result in the evidence being judged inadmissible in court.

FINDING POLLEN AND SPORES

Pollen and spores are all around us. The following list identifies some places crime-scene investigators look for pollen and spore evidence:

- Living and decaying plant material
- Soil, dirt, mud, and dust
- Hair, fur, and feathers
- Clothing, shoes, blankets, rugs, baskets, carpet, and rope
- Victim's skin, hair, nails, respiratory tract, digestive tract, fecal matter, and wounds

- Paper, money, and packaging material
- Vehicles, including tires, windshield, air filter, and undercarriage
- Furniture
- Air filters of homes and airplanes
- Cracks and crevices in floors, walls, roofs, and fences
- Drug wrappings or containers
- Honey and other food

It is especially important to sample soil, dirt, and dust because they are usually abundant at crime scenes, and they often contain abundant pollen and spores. Dirt collected from a victim's body or belongings might help identify the location of the crime. Some unusual materials that can contain pollen and spores include enamel-painted wood, painted works of art, grease on guns, stuffed animals, and foot impressions.

EARTH SCIENCES

COLLECTING POLLEN AND SPORES

Ideally, the forensic palynologist should be called to the crime scene(s) immediately to minimize contamination and destruction of the evidence. He or she collects evidence samples as well as control samples at all potential crime scenes during the investigation. Control samples are specimens of surface dirt from the region where a crime was committed. Control samples document the pollen and spore profile of the area so there is a comparison for evidence samples.

All samples are collected by a forensic palynologist wearing gloves and using clean tools, such as paintbrushes and cellophane tape. Each sampling instrument is cleaned after each sample is taken, or a new one is used each time. All samples should be placed into new, dry, sterile (if possible) containers, such as paper bags or paper envelopes, and then dried to prevent decomposition. Plant presses with blotter paper and newsprint temporarily store plant evidence in the field. Site and vegetation surveys, as well as photographs, should also be taken to help analyze samples, explain how samples were collected in court if necessary, and determine the processing techniques to be used in extracting pollen and spores from the samples. And as you learned in Chapter 2, it is always vital to secure the evidence and maintain an accurate chain of custody.

ANALYZING POLLEN AND SPORES

After pollen and spores are processed and chemically extracted from samples in the laboratory, forensic palynologists examine them using microscopes (Figure 5-22). Pollen and spores are best viewed with transmitted light or phase contrast microscopes.

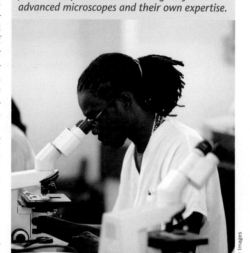

Figure 5-22 *Forensic palynologists identify pollen and spores with technologically advanced microscopes and their own expertise.*

Joe Raedle/Getty Images

DIFFERENTIATED LEARNING

Teaching At-Risk Students
Many students think that being a crime-scene investigator means that you're only working in the field or laboratory. However, analysts sometimes called upon to present their findings during trial. *Activity 5-2 Pollen Expert Witness Presentation* provides a pre-writing activity to assist students in preparing an expert witness testimony on pollen analysis. Written and oral communication are essential components of forensics.

Additional details of surface features may require the use of a scanning electron microscope (SEM). To identify pollen and spores, specialists use pollen and spore reference collections that represent native species and species from other geographic regions. Preliminary identifications may be made by reference to drawings and photographs in atlases, journal articles, Websites, and books. After scientists narrow their search with illustrations, they refer to herbariums to compare actual plant material, pollen, and spores.

Once the pollen evidence has been collected, processed, analyzed, and interpreted, it is presented in court so that a jury can assess the value of the evidence. Palynology is best used to confirm certain aspects of the crime; that is, pollen and spore evidence is unlikely to be the primary or only evidence in a crime.

LITERACY

David W. Hall and Jason Byrd.
Forensic Botany: A Practical Guide.

Maryalice Walker.
Entomology and Palynology: Evidence for the Natural World.

Did you know?

New Zealand is the world leader in forensic palynology and in the acceptance of pollen and spore evidence in court cases. Palynological evidence is underutilized in many parts of the world, including the United States.

SUMMARY

- Forensic botany and forensic palynology can provide information about the geographic origin of a crime and the time or season when it took place.

- Knowing a crime-scene's assemblage of plants can help narrow down its location.

- Forensic botany can help solve crimes based on plant evidence found on or in a victim, on the suspect(s), or at the crime scene(s).

- Pollen is a reproductive structure containing male gametes that is produced by seed plants. Spores are reproductive cells produced by algae, fungi, and nonseed plants such as ferns and mosses.

- Seed plants including gymnosperms (cone-bearing plants) and angiosperms (flowering plants) produce pollen.

- Plants may disperse pollen in the wind or by the movements of animals.

- Pollen from wind-pollinated plants is more common in forensic samples, but pollen from insect-pollinated plants tends to provide more specific information about location.

- Pollen evidence collected at a crime scene must be compared with baseline samples from the area.

- Collection of all botanical evidence must be performed carefully to avoid contamination.

CASE STUDIES

Dr. Max Frei
(1960s)

Dr. Max Frei, a noted Swiss criminalist, often used pollen as a forensic tool to link suspects to events or to crime scenes. In one case, pollen found in the gun oil of a weapon linked the firearm to the murder scene. Frei also used pollen analysis to document forgery. He found fall-pollinating cedar pollen stuck to the ink used to sign a document. The document was dated during the month of June. Because the document contained pollen only visible in the fall, the document could not have been signed in June. Frei examined the Shroud of Turin, a garment believed to have wrapped the body of Jesus after his crucifixion. Frei's pollen analysis did link the shroud to pollen unique to Israel.

Do additional research on the Shroud of Turin, the cloth that is believed to have covered the body of Jesus. Go to the Gale Forensic Science eCollection on **ngl.cengage.com/forensicscience2e** and research the case. Much controversy continues regarding the origin of the shroud. Cite some of the arguments used by those who believe that there is not enough evidence to indicate that the Shroud of Turin is authentic.

"Otzi the Iceman"
(1991)

Two hikers in the mountains on the border between Italy and Austria found the frozen remains of a man who has come to be known as Otzi. Otzi was estimated to be 5,300 years old and probably died in his 40s. To date, Otzi is the oldest frozen mummy ever found. Upon thawing, Otzi's intestine was examined and hop hornbeam pollen was found in it. Hop hornbeam flowers only in May and June, so Otzi's death must have occurred in the spring.

Dr. Dallas Mildenhall (1997)

A Colin McCahon painting valued at $1.25 million was stolen from the Visitor's Center, Lake Waikaremoana, New Zealand. A year later, the painting was returned. Dr. Dallas Mildenhall, a New Zealand pollen expert, used pollen evidence collected from the artwork to provide clues to where the painting had been stored. A typical pollen signature, or fingerprint, taken from an area includes pollen from the dominant plant and five or six secondary species of plant and as many as several hundred trace pollen species. Dr. Mildenhall compared the pollen signature from the stolen art to known pollen signatures from other areas to determine where the painting had been stored.

DIGGING DEEPER

Forensic palynology is a new area of forensics that is being used to help solve criminal cases. Today, using pollen and spore evidence is in its pioneering stages. Interested students may want to research forensic palynology further by going to ngl.cengage.com/forensicscience2e or by reading the book *Corpse* by Jessica Snyder Sachs.

Close

As students progress through the chapter, have them help you collect pictures of plants from magazines and Websites. Make sure to include gymnosperms, angiosperms, ferns, mosses, and fungi. As a closing activity, hold up (or post) the pictures and have students tell you what they know about pollen and spore evidence from each organism. Encourage a collaborative, cumulative discussion.

Dr. Tony Brown
(2004)

EARTH SCIENCES

On September 9, 2004, the BBC News headline read: "Pollen helps war crime forensics." Forensic experts working in Bosnia had used pollen to help convict Bosnian war criminals. Professor Tony Brown used pollen analysis to link mass graves in Bosnia to support the claim of mass genocide. Bosnian war criminals tried disguising their acts of genocide by exhuming mass graves and reburying bodies in smaller graves, claiming they were the result of minor battles. Soil samples were taken from skeletal cavities, inside the graves, and from around the suspected primary and secondary burial sites. Pollen from the soil samples was cleaned with powerful chemicals before being analyzed, and the mineralogy of the soil was examined. Once complete, comparisons could be made between different samples, and this ultimately led to links between primary and secondary burial sites.

Professor Brown noted one primary execution and burial site was in a field of wheat. When bodies were found in secondary burial sites, they were linked to the primary location through the presence of distinctive wheat pollen and soil recovered from the victims.

Think Critically

Imagine you are a reporter accompanying either Dr. Frei or Dr. Tony Brown during their investigations. Write a news story about their work.

Careers *in Forensics*

Dr. Lynne Milne, Forensic Palynologist

Dr. Lynne Milne is a palynologist who spends most of her time working in the field of forensics. She is a lecturer in the Centre for Forensic Science at The University of Western Australia (UWA). There, she supervises Master's and Ph.D. students in the field of forensic palynology. Her work also involves teaching police about forensic palynology, as well as conducting casework for state and federal police.

Dr. Milne has spent a great deal of time promoting the field of forensic palynology in the media. She has published a book describing her forensic palynology murder and rape cases. In the book, she also includes other criminal cases and mysteries that palynology has helped solve. Milne states, "like DNA and fingerprinting, palynology can link a person to a crime—but it can also help in investigations for which DNA and fingerprinting are not applicable. For example, palynology can help direct police to an area where a person who committed a crime may live and work, and can determine where illicit drugs and illegally imported goods have come from."

Her typical workweek may include meeting with police; attending a crime scene; working with other forensic scientists such as soil and fiber experts; collecting samples and doing a vegetation survey at a crime scene; collecting reference pollen samples from the herbarium; processing pollen, soil, and other samples; analyzing prepared pollen samples; writing a police report; and teaching and helping students with their projects in the field or laboratory.

Dr. Lynne Milne enjoys her job because it is never boring and can be extremely rewarding to help

Courtesy, Dr. Lynne Milne, Centre for Forensic Science, University of Western Australia.

Dr. Lynne Milne

solve crimes and other mysteries. She says, "Pollen is often very beautiful, and it always has a story to tell. I enjoy the supersleuth aspects—working out past vegetation, patterns in evolution, and helping to solve crimes."

Dr. Milne's advice to those wishing to pursue a career in forensic palynology is to obtain an undergraduate degree in botany, geology, geography, or archaeology. Several colleges and universities in the United States and Canada offer courses in forensic palynology. A science degree would allow a person to work under the supervision of an experienced palynologist. Much of the real training will be on the job. A Master's or Ph.D. degree in a related area of study would be the next step for eventually conducting one's own forensic cases.

Careers

Palynology is one of many areas of biology. Palynologists study contemporary and fossilized pollen. Botany, microbiology, and molecular biology are biological disciplines that are important to the field of forensic palynology.

Learn More About It

▶ Go to **ngl.cengage.com/forensicscience2e** to learn more about the work of a forensic botanist or forensic palynologist.

True or False

1. T
2. F
3. F
4. T
5. T
6. T
7. T
8. F
9. F
10. T

Multiple Choice

11. d
12. c
13. a
14. b
15. An assemblage is group of plant species in an area dominated by one species that share the same habitat requirements; a pollen fingerprint is the number and type of pollen grains found in a geographic area at a particular time of year.
16. a. Called in to help with a line search to locate two bones missing from human skeletal remains
    b. Based on the loss of chlorophyll in the leaf and an estimate of how long it would take for the chlorophyll to break down, Dr. Hall established the first time interval. Because the leaf had reached full growth without any distortion, he knew the leaf had developed before the bone landed on the turkey oak seedling. After checking with local people and the park rangers as to when the trees started to bud, Dr. Hall derived a second time interval. A third time interval was established after taking into consideration other evidence (weather conditions affecting rate of decomposition, time it

---

True or False

1. A skilled botanist may be able to identify a type of habitat from a fragment of a plant. *Obj. 5.7*
2. Plant cells found in the gastric juices cannot be identified after 3 hours. *Obj. 5.1, 5.2*
3. A limitation of forensic botany is that all living matter decomposes quickly. *Obj. 5.1, 5.2*
4. A forensic botanist must look not only at the different species in an area, but must also calculate the percentages of each species when comparing two locations. *Obj. 5.7*
5. Annual rings are formed as a result of differences in color of the lighter springwood and the darker winterwood. *Obj. 5.1*
6. The datum point in a crime scene is a reference point from an immovable object. *Obj. 5.8*
7. The photographer should take distant and close-up images of the crime scene as well as photos of the habitat and all botanical evidence. *Obj. 5.8*
8. Information obtained from weather-reporting stations and people living in the immediate area are not factored into a forensic botanist's report. *Obj. 5.9*
9. Pollen present on the victim that is consistent with pollen from a suspect provides strong evidence that the suspect is guilty. *Obj. 5.2, 5.5*
10. Botanical evidence should not be stored in a plastic bag. *Obj. 5.8*

Multiple Choice

11. Botanical evidence is a valuable source of evidence because *Obj. 5.2, 5.6, 5.8*
    a) it is easily overlooked by perpetrators
    b) many plants have adaptations that make them easily transferred
    c) the collection of plants in an area can help identify an area
    d) all the above
12. Diatoms *Obj. 5.1*
    a) are visible to the naked eye
    b) have a cell wall composed of rigid cellulose
    c) are found attached to rocks and plants in bodies of water
    d) are used to assist in crime scenes involving insects
13. All of the following should appear on an evidence label *except* *Obj. 5.8*
    a) postmorten interval
    b) date, time
    c) name of collector
    d) case number

---

would take for a large dog to remove a leg bone from the skeleton).

Being able to identify the plant, understand how plants grow and are affected by the environment, and to factor in all the evidence obtained though all of the investigators, Dr. Hall was able to estimate when the body had been left in the area. He added all the intervals and subtracted the time when the body was found and was able approximate the postmortem interval.

c. They were able to tell Dr. Hall when the leaves started to bud that season in the park. Local weather conditions can vary, so information had to come from people living and working in the area.

d. Examined the bone and determined that the bite marks came from a large dog. Knowing this, it was possible to better estimate when a large dog would be able to pull the leg bone off the skeletal remains.

14. Which procedure is incorrect when collecting botanical evidence? *Obj. 5.8*
    a) zigzag long vines as opposed to rolling them
    b) collect broken stems by cutting one inch above and below the broken area
    c) include roots of plants as part of botanical evidence
    d) include the color of any flowers or fruits

15. Compare and contrast an assemblage and a pollen fingerprint by defining both and giving examples of each from the chapter.

16. Refer to the Gold Head Branch Murder in Clay County, Florida, cited in the textbook. The victim was ultimately identified using missing person's records, but only after a time interval was established. Cite specific evidence from the case study that explains the role of each of the following: *Obj. 5.9*
    a) National Guard
    b) Dr. David Hall, forensic botanist
    c) Local park rangers and inhabitants of the area
    d) Wildlife expert
    e) Medical examiner
    f) Detectives
    g) Office of Missing Persons

17. "Plants provide a biological clock that provides evidence as to when a person died, or the postmortem interval." Using two different case studies from the textbook (other than the Gold Head Branch Murder) provide specific evidence that supports this claim. Include in your answer a description of the botanical evidence and how it was used to help estimate the postmortem interval. *Obj. 5.2*

18. It seems that it would be an impossible task to find the location of a gravesite in the middle of an overgrown field or forest. However, many botanical clues help reduce the size of search sites. Describe ways to locate both a recent and an older gravesite based on botanical evidence cited in the chapter. *Obj. 5.2*

19. a) How would a forensic botanist use habitat sampling to help solve a crime? What type of information will this sampling provide? *Obj. 5.7*

    b) Provide a list of botanical evidence that you might collect from an area near either your home or school.

      i) Include the type of evidence (algae, seaweed, cactus, shrub, tree, corn, flowers, palm tree, pine trees, maple trees, vines, ground cover, weeds, lichen, moss, fern, fungus).

      ii) Identify the dominant species, if possible.

      iii) Include the colors of flowers, seeds, or fruits.

e. Based on information from the local medical examiners, a third time interval was established based on the amount of time required for decomposition to reach a point where a dog of that size could pull a tibia away from the rest of the skeletal remains.

f. The detectives are the ones who investigate the case and examine the evidence. The detectives requested the assistance of the National Guard. They also were able to identify the name of a person who was reported missing from that area around the time that Dr. Hall estimated to be the time of death.

g. The office had the name of a person who was missing around the time that Dr. Hall estimated the time of death. It was easier to confirm the skeletal remains belonged to the known missing person than to try to identify a totally unknown person from decomposed skeletal remains.

17. Answers will vary but could include the following:
   - Annual rings found in roots surrounding a skeleton
   - Estimating how long it takes sunflower plants to arrive at the same stage of wilting as those found at a gravesite
   - Time it took to digest different plant cells found in the gastric contents of a deceased body
   - The type and variety of diatoms found in the lungs of a drowned victim
   - The stage of succession in plant development over a gravesite

18. The area around a newer gravesite will be altered due to digging up the dirt. The environmental conditions are altered due to moving the dirt, turning over the soil, creating greater soil aeration and drainage, and reducing competition of plants by removing some. In other words, the environment created by a new gravesite is very different from the surrounding established ecosystem. Different types of plants will be better suited for that changed environment. In time, those plants modify the environment, resulting in a secondary succession of plants.

An older gravesite will have different types of plants growing on it than those in the surrounding area. It also may be sunken because the ground settles over time.

19. a. Plants grow in association with each other because they require the same or shared

habitat. Since the habitat is the same, if a botanist knows the dominant plants, he or she might be able to suggest a possible crime-scene location from the collection of plants in the habitat sampling.

b. Answers will vary depending on location.

20. Students should refer to the evidence obtained:

- From the wood analysis, both macroscopic and microscopic
- The identification of four different types of wood found in the homemade ladder and the floorboards
- Planer marks on the lumber
- Alignment of the square nail holes, marks on the wood, in the floorboards, and on the ladder

Students can present questions regarding the validity of the expert witness testimony, including the following:

- Did any other wood expert examine the evidence?
- How common were the planer marks on the wood? Could other lumberyards also produce wood with similar planer marks?
- Was there ever any direct evidence linking Hauptmann to the crime scene, or was it all circumstantial?
- Did anyone check where Hauptmann was the night of the murder? In other words, did he have an alibi?

Explore

Suggest students explore TED talks on botany, such as "Every Pollen Grain Has a Story" by Jonathan Drori. He shows SEMs of flowers and pollen and explores the forensic value of pollen in solving cases involving drugs, bank notes, antique furniture, and Bosnian war crimes. See it at https://www.ted.com/talks/jonathan_drori_every_pollen_grain_has_a_story#t-417028

20. Do you feel that there was sufficient evidence to convict Hauptmann based on the wood expert's testimony in the Lindbergh kidnapping case? Use specific evidence from the case study to support your claim.
Obj. 5.2, 5.3

Going Further

Research one of the following topics

1. Pollen allergies
2. Why diatom evidence is not generally accepted in the United States as evidence of drowning
3. Decline in pollinators and the potential effect on the world food supply
4. The use of diatomaceous earth as a nontoxic pesticide
5. Develop a dichotomous key to help identify local pollen types.
6. Design a method to collect pollen or diatoms.
7. Produce a digital database of local pollen, algae, or diatoms.
8. Explore the role of diatoms in toothpaste or various kinds of filters (such as water filters).
9. Design a procedure to determine the effectiveness of diatomaceous earth as an abrasive to polish dull pennies.
10. Search the Internet for cases in which the DNA of botanical evidence was used to link a suspect to a crime scene.

Bibliography

Books and Journals

Berg, Linda. *Introductory Botany: Plants, People, and the Environment.* Belmont, CA: Thomson Higher Learning, 2008.

Bock, J. H., M. A. Lane, and D. O. Norris. *Identifying Plant Food Cells in Gastric Contents for Use in Forensic Investigations: A Laboratory Manual.* U.S. Dept. of Justice, National Institute of Justice Research Report, January 1988.

Botanical Society of America, "Plant Talking Points," *Plant Science Bulletin* 52–53.

Clary, Rennee, and James Wandersee. "MicroWorld: Interdisciplinary Investigations of Scale." *The Science Teacher*, Vol. 81, No. 1, pp. 53–60, January 2014.

Graham, S. "Anatomy of the Lindbergh Kidnapping." *Journal of Forensic Sciences* 42: 391–393, 1997.

Hall, David W. and Jason Byrd. *Forensic Botany: A Practical Guide.* Chichester, UK: John Wiley and Sons, 2012.

Milne, Lynn. "A Grain of Truth: How Pollen Brought a Murderer to Justice." New Holland Publishers, 2005.

Nickell, Joe, and John Fischer. *Crime Science: Methods of Forensic Detection.* Lexington, KY: The University Press of Kentucky, 1999.

Sachs, Jessica Synder. *Corpse: Nature, Forensics, and the Struggle to Pinpoint Time of Death.* New York: Basic Books, 2001.

Silver, P. A., W. D. Lord, and D. J. McCarthy. "Forensic Limnology: The Use of Freshwater Algal Community Ecology to Link Suspects to an Aquatic Crime Scene in Southern New England." *Journal of Forensic Sciences*, Vol. 39, Issue 3 (May 1994): 847–853.

Internet Resources

ngl.cengage.com/forensicscience2e (Gale Forensic Science eCollection)

sierra.org/sierra/200705/profile.asp (Nijhuis, Michelle. "Profile: Of Murder and Microscopes: How Jane Bock Became a Crime Fighter." Sierra Club, May–June 2007.)

Pollen Examination: Matching a Suspect to a Crime Scene *Obj. 5.2, 5.4, 5.6, 5.8*

Scenario:

A burglary had taken place at the Huxton's home. Footprints were found throughout the recently watered flower garden and leading to the window of a bedroom located at the back of the expensive home. Just as the burglar was leaving the house, the owner returned home and caught a glimpse of a teenage boy dressed in a T-shirt and blue jeans running through the garden.

The police questioned four neighbor teens. All four young men denied that they had been anywhere near the Huxton property and stated that they did not burglarize the home. After obtaining a warrant, the police searched the home of each of the four young men looking for blue jeans that could have been worn during the burglary. Four pairs of jeans were confiscated and taken in evidence bags to the crime lab to be examined for pollen evidence that could link the suspect to the Huxton garden.

Objectives:

By the end of this activity, you will be able to:

1. Prepare wet-mount slides of flower pollen.
2. View pollen under a compound microscope at 100× and 400× magnification.
3. View, observe, and analyze pollen grains.
4. Determine if pollen evidence from any of the suspects is consistent with pollen from the crime scene.

Time Required to Complete the Activity: 40 to 60 minutes

Materials:

Act 5-1 SH
Act 5-1 SH Student Design Ex
(for each group of two students)
1 microtube labeled "crime scene (CS)" containing pollen from the crime scene
4 evidence microtubes containing pollen from Suspect 1, Suspect 2, Suspect 3, Suspect 4
microtube or minitube sponge rack or small beaker to hold the tubes of pollen
1 compound microscope
5 microscope slides
5 flat wooden toothpicks
1 small beaker of tap water
dropper or pipette
5 coverslips
forceps
marker pen

Background

Students will prepare and examine microscope slides of pollen grains. From their observations, they will determine whether pollen obtained from any of the four suspects was consistent with pollen from the crime scene.

Materials

Print and distribute Act 5-1 SH Data Table: Pollen Comparison and Act 5-1 SH Student-Designed Experiment from the IRCD, Chapter 5.

Teaching Tip

Copy and distribute Act 5-1 SH and Act 5-1 SH Student-Designed Ex from the IRCD, Chapter 5. Refer to IRCD, Chapter 5, Act 5-1 TN Pollen Collection Tips and Act 5-1 TN.

Teaching Tip

Before students perform this activity, ask if anyone is allergic to pollen. (Pollen from colorful, fragrant, insect-pollinated flowers such as lilies or roses is less likely to cause allergies.)

Teaching Tip

The teacher will need to prepare four different microtubes of pollen from four different flowers in advance of the activity. One of the suspect's pollen samples should be the same as the crime scene pollen.

Safety Precautions

Identify students with allergies. These students may need to use prepared slides rather than being exposed to circulating pollen. They may also need to wear gloves and masks.

Students must handle sharp instruments carefully. Remind students to always carry a microscope with two hands.

Procedures

You may want to demonstrate how to make a wet-mount slide before beginning this activity.

Answers

Check students' data tables to make sure they are thorough and use correct terms.

Questions

1. Answers may vary.

Teaching Tip

Have students use a very small amount of pollen in preparing their slides.

Teaching Tip

When viewing pollen under 400×, remind students that they may need additional light and to adjust the diaphragm on the microscope. Students should use the fine-adjustment knob as they view the pollen. Look for areas of non-clumped pollen to view individual pollen structure.

---

colored pencils (optional)

digital camera (optional)

empty film canister with ends removed (optional)

SAFETY PRECAUTIONS:

Any student who has pollen allergies should inform the instructor of the type and severity of the allergy. If any students are allergic, they should prepare the microscope and have their partner handle any flowers and pollen. Handle pollen samples carefully, using a clean toothpick in each microtube. Do not contaminate one pollen sample with another by using the same toothpick in different tubes.

Procedure:

PART A: PREPARATION OF POLLEN WET-MOUNT SLIDES

1. Obtain the tube containing pollen from the crime scene.
2. Prepare a wet-mount slide of the pollen:
   a. Obtain a clean slide and label it "CS" for crime scene.
   b. Add one or two drops of fresh water to the slide.
   c. Using the flat end of the toothpick, touch the anthers of the crime-scene flower or if using tubes of pollen, place the moist end of the toothpick into the crime-scene tube of pollen and remove a very small amount of pollen.
   d. Swirl the toothpick with the crime-scene pollen in the drop of water and apply a coverslip.
3. Observe the pollen under 100x of the microscope.
4. Switch the microscope lens to 400x and observe the pollen grain.
5. Complete the data table for the crime-scene pollen sample. Include a sketch of the pollen viewed under 400x and provide a description of the pollen grain.
6. (Optional) Using a digital camera and a cut-out film canister as an interface, take a digital photo of the view of the pollen under the microscope.

PART B: OBSERVATION OF POLLEN COLLECTED FROM THE FOUR SUSPECTS

Evidence samples of pollen have already been collected from the four suspects. The pollen evidence is contained in four different microtubes.

7. Using a marker pen, label four different slides: Suspect 1, Suspect 2, Suspect 3, Suspect 4.
8. Using the same procedure described in Steps 2 through 6, prepare and examine a wet-mount slide of pollen from each of the four samples (suspects).
9. After reviewing the crime-scene pollen and the pollen obtained from the four suspects, analyze your data. Are any of the suspect pollen samples consistent with pollen from the crime scene?

Questions:

1. Are any of the pollen samples consistent with pollen collected from the crime scene? If so, which one(s)?

2. Using the information gained from your microscopic examination of the pollen, justify your answer to question 1.
3. Suppose the pollen from one of the suspects did match the pollen found at the crime scene. What arguments could the defense attorney present to discredit the evidence?
4. What could you do to improve the reliability of your analysis? Include in your answer any other instruments that you would like to use to compare the pollen samples.

Data Table: Pollen Comparison

Sample	Color	Shape	Relative Size	Sketch
Crime Scene				
Suspect 1				
Suspect 2				
Suspect 3				
Suspect 4				

Further Study 1

MICROSCOPIC MEASUREMENT OF POLLEN

Several different methods can be utilized to measure the size of an individual pollen grain. If your school has a digital microscope, record the size of the pollen grain. However, if you do not have a digital microscope, it is still possible to estimate the size of each individual pollen grain.

1. Place a clear plastic mm ruler under the field of view at 100×. While looking through the ocular lens, estimate the measurement of the diameter of the field of view at 100×. Estimate this measurement to the nearest ¹⁄₁₀ mm. Record your answer. (Most microscopes have a field of view of 1.2 mm to 1.4 mm at 100×.)

2. To determine the size of the field of view under 400×, take ¼ of the diameter of your field of view under 100×. For example, if the diameter of the field of view under 100× equals 1.6 mm, then the diameter of the field of view under 400× equals ¼ (1.6 mm), or about 0.4 mm.

3. Record your answer to the nearest ¹⁄₁₀ mm.

1 mm   0.6 mm

Diameter of field of view under 100× is 1.6 mm.

© Cengage Learning®

Questions

2. Answers may vary.

3. a. pollen is class evidence (unless it is analyzed using DNA)

   b. it is not possible to know when the pollen evidence was transferred

4. Sample answer:
   - examine many samples of pollen
   - confer with other students to compare results
   - use sterile slides to ensure that the pollen came only from the source flower
   - prevent cross contamination by separating flowers -greater magnification would result using SEM
   - individual ID of pollen could be done using DNA analysis

Teaching Tip

Make sure students are familiar with the abbreviations of metric units of measure.

Teaching Tip

Further Study 1: Remind students that their rulers are marked in centimeters. When a ruler is viewed at 100X, the markings seen under the microscope are the lines between millimeters, *not* centimeters. The ruler's image will appear upside-down.

Further Study 2 Refers Act 5-1 SH Student-Designed Experiment on the IRCD, Chapter 5. Refer to the IRCD, Chapter 5, Act 5-1 TN for a sample experiment.

Pollen is a great source of trace evidence because it is easily transferred to clothing. Ask students to examine their clothes for any evidence of pollen after handling flowers. Some types of pollen can adhere to clothing even after the clothing is washed.

4. To determine the size of one pollen grain, align one pollen grain along the diameter of the field of view under 400×. Estimate how many pollen grains could fit across the diameter of your field of view under 400×.

5. Using the following formula, determine the size of a single pollen grain when viewed under 400× (e.g., if the size of the 100× field of view is 1.6 mm). To determine the size of one pollen grain, estimate the number of pollen grains that fit across the diameter of the field of view under 400× while looking through the ocular lens.

Approximately 11 pollen grains fit across the diameter under 400×. If x is equal to the size of one pollen grain, then:

$$11x = 0.4 \text{ mm}$$
$$x = 0.4 \text{ mm}/11$$
$$x \approx 0.04 \text{ mm}$$

Diameter of field of view under 400×

One pollen grain

Field of view under 400× is 0.4 mm.

One pollen grain

Further Study 2

DESIGN YOUR OWN EXPERIMENT

Choose one of the following statements. Form a hypothesis and design an experiment to test your hypothesis. Be sure to include a data table, analysis, and conclusion.

1. Is there any similarity between the pollen of two flowers of the same type (e.g., a red tulip and a yellow tulip)?
2. Is there any relationship between the size of the pollen grain and the size of a flower?
3. Is the pollen from gymnosperms larger than the pollen from angiosperms?
4. Does the pollen produced by plants that depend on animals or wind for pollination have a sharper appearance than the pollen produced by flowers that self-pollinate?

Further Study 3

Design an experiment to gather and analyze the pollen assemblage (sample of all the pollen from a particular location collected at a specific time) from one of the following:

1. Two different areas collected at the same time
2. From the same area but collected a week apart
3. From the same area but collected before and after a rainfall

Determine if there is any difference in the pollen assemblage. Form a hypothesis and design an experiment to test your hypothesis. Be sure to include a data table that describes the different types and amount of pollen collected. Your report should also include an analysis and conclusion for your experiment.

Further Research and Extensions

Interested students may want to try dissolving the pollen grains in various solvents to see if they behave in the same way. Some solvents to consider using are vinegar, alcohol, and vegetable oil.

Pollen Expert Witness Presentation *Obj. 5.2, 5.4, 5.6, 5.8*

Scenario:

Neighbors long suspected that the college students living in an adjacent apartment were growing their own marijuana. Why else would they need so many artificial lights set up in their basement? The parade of people coming and going into their apartment in the late evening hours also made the neighbors suspicious that the students were not only growing marijuana but selling it, too! The police were notified. The police were going to make a surprise visit to the home, arrest the occupants, and confiscate the drugs.

Just before the police arrived, the students got a call from one of their friends telling them what was about to happen. They quickly bagged all of the plants and got rid of the indoor lights an hour before the police arrived. The police had a warrant to search the premises. No plants or grow lights were visible. The occupants denied growing marijuana. With no visible evidence of the plants, the police decided to look for trace evidence of pollen.

Marijuana plants are known to release large quantities of pollen. Although the occupants of the house had removed the plants, they did not eliminate all of the pollen that was left on the floor and tabletops. The occupants just assumed it was dust from a lack of cleaning. The police sent the trace evidence of pollen to the crime lab. As expected, the dust was identified as marijuana pollen. The amount of pollen in the room indicated that many plants had been present.

Procedure and Pre-writing Assignment:

As the expert in pollen analysis, you are called as an expert witness for the prosecutor's office. You are asked to testify at the hearing. Because many jurors lack a scientific background, you need to begin your presentation with background information. It is important to incorporate photographs, pictures, charts, and other visual aids to help the jury understand your presentation. Your task will be to do the following:

1. Introduce yourself and list your credentials as an expert witness in pollen. (Your report should include what qualifies someone as an expert in pollen identification.)
2. Educate the jurors about pollen:
   a. What is pollen?
   b. Where is it produced?
   c. What does it look like?
   d. How big is pollen?
   e. When is it produced?
   f. What is its function?
   g. How is pollen transferred?
   h. How does pollen differ from plant to plant?

Background

Students will prepare a presentation, either in essay or PowerPoint form, as if they were an expert witness testifying before a jury. In the presentation, the student has to educate jurors about pollen, marijuana and pollen, how pollen can be used to solve a crime, the pollen evidence in this particular case, and the expert's conclusion about the identity of the pollen found in the apartment. Students should include visual aids, such as charts, photographs, and pictures in their presentations.

Safety Precautions

There are no safety precautions for this activity.

Materials

Print and distribute Act 5-2 SH from the IRCD, Chapter 5.

Procedures

1. Print, copy, and pass out to your students the rubric from the IRCD, which you will use to grade the presentations, before beginning this activity. Thus, students will understand what is expected of them.

2. Prior to this activity, consider:
   - Are students going to present to the class?
   - About how long should the presentations be?
   - Will students have time to do research in class?

3. Make sure students are familiar with PowerPoint and the equipment they will need to show their presentation.

Answers

Use the scoring rubric to evaluate students' presentations.

Teaching Tip

Peer Review: Students should have at least one other student review their presentations. Following peer review, students should record any modifications suggested by the peer reviewers.

3. Background information about marijuana pollen
   a. Describe the structure of marijuana pollen as viewed under the microscope.
   b. Describe how to prepare a microscope slide of marijuana pollen.
4. Pollen and crime-solving background
   a. Review Locard's Principle of Exchange.
   b. How can pollen link a person or object to a crime scene?
5. Pollen evidence and this case
   a. What is the evidence that marijuana pollen was collected from this apartment?
   b. Describe where in the room the marijuana pollen evidence was obtained.
   c. Describe when and how the evidence was collected, labeled, documented, and stored.
   d. Describe how this pollen evidence was examined and verified to be marijuana.
   e. Discuss the reliability of the evidence.
6. Conclusion

   Based on the evidence observed and your expertise, can you testify that evidence collected from this apartment at the time of the search was indeed marijuana pollen?

Objectives:

By the end of this activity, you will be able to:

1. Research information on pollen.
2. Prepare expert witness testimony.
3. Complete either an essay or a PowerPoint presentation.

Materials:

Activity 5-2 SH

Choice 1: Essay Presentation

Essay of at least 250 words

Paragraph format

Introduction, several body paragraphs, and a conclusion

Complete sentences and correct spelling

Typed, double-spaced

Avoid terms such as *it, that, them,* or *they.*

Properly credit any photos or pictures by writing the source of the picture or photo.

Choice 2: PowerPoint Presentation

Your presentation will be submitted electronically.

You must credit any drawing or photo by copying the address of the source or citing where you obtained the drawing or photo.

Avoid using sentences. Use short statements or bullets.

Include graphics and photos (either from the Internet or from your own camera).

Do not include any sounds as you transition from frame to frame.

Scoring Rubric: A maximum of 40 points will be credited for this assignment.

	Excellent 5 points	Good 3 points	Needs Improvement 1 point	Total Points
Scientific clarity and accuracy in oral presentation	Material highly accurate and clearly presented; includes several supporting examples and details	Material mostly accurate with some supporting examples and details	Material lacking accuracy or presented in a confusing way	
Speaks clearly and with sufficient volume	Speaks clearly and with sufficient volume for entire presentation; all terms correctly pronounced	Speaks clearly but is difficult to hear at times; may have some mispronunciations	Is difficult to hear through most of the presentation	
Covered all required topics	Thoroughly covered all required material	Covered all material	Incomplete coverage of required topics	
Length of presentation	Thoroughly covered material within the 5 minutes	Covered most of the material within the designated time	Inadequate coverage of material; too brief or too long	
Visuals (PowerPoint, poster, report with projected images)	Extremely well presented; exceptionally attractive in size, design, layout, and neatness; supports the text	Well presented; most visuals attractive and support the text	Confusing or not well presented; size may be inappropriate; some visuals did not support the text.	
Background information research	Very complete; in-depth background	Completed all required portions of the research	Incomplete research; needed more information	
Scientific references used in presentation	Used more than three reputable scientific sources all correctly cited	Used at least three sources; most were scientific sources and correctly cited.	Most are either not scientific sources or not properly cited; used fewer than three scientific sources.	
Courtesy	Listens politely to all other presenters, maintains good eye contact, asks pertinent questions	Listens but shows some restlessness; no questions asked of the presenter	Appears not to be listening or may express a lack of interest	

Further Research and Extensions

Interested students may want to prepare a presentation that argues against the validity of the pollen evidence.

Expert witnesses should be prepared to address the following concerns in their presentations:

1. How reliable is the evidence?

2. What were the credentials of the expert witness?

3. Was chain of custody maintained?

4. Is it possible pollen evidence was in the apartment months before the crime?

Background

Student pairs will research past cases involving either pollen or spore evidence. They will then prepare presentation.

Safety Precautions

There are no safety precautions for this activity.

Materials

Print and distribute Act 5-3 SH Botanical Topics, Act 5-3 SH Botanical Planning, and Act 5-3 SH Rubric from the IRCD, Chapter 5.

Procedures

1. Discuss with the class what databases and resources are available to students other than the Internet.

2. Print, copy, and distribute to your students the Act 5-3 Student Handouts from the IRCD, Teacher Resources.

3. Students should be familiar with PowerPoint and the equipment they will need to show their presentation.

4. Describe the process and purpose of a peer review to students. Encourage them to find something positive to say. Encourage them to suggest areas that need improvement. Consider modeling how to conduct a peer review.

Teaching Tip

Encourage students to use appropriate three-dimensional objects to enhance their presentation.

Botanical Evidence Case Studies Presentation Obj. 5.2, 5.4, 5.8

Objectives:

The purpose of this activity is for you and a partner to research an actual court case that involved botanical evidence to help solve the crime. After completing the research, you and your partner will prepare an oral presentation.

Time Required to Complete the Activity:

Time required to complete this activity varies depending if students complete parts of the research and planning outside class time. Time will be needed for the students to do the following:

1. Research information.
2. Organize and discuss the information.
3. Complete the botanical planning sheet.
4. Prepare the PowerPoint presentation or the poster.
5. Present the information to the class for peer review.
6. Present the final project to the class.

Materials:

reference textbooks or articles
computer with Internet connectivity
Act 5-3 SH Botanical Topics
Act 5-3 SH Botanical Planning
Act 5-3 SH Rubric

SAFETY PRECAUTIONS:

There are no safety concerns with this activity.

Procedure:

1. Student teams register for one of the following topics. Choose a specific court case that used either pollen or spore evidence or some other type of botanical evidence to solve a crime.

   Pollen or Spore Evidence
   a. Found in hair
   b. Found in mud or sediment
   c. Found in clothing
   d. Found in animal hair or fur
   e. Found in honey
   f. Found in antique furniture
   g. Found on money
   h. Found in cocaine

i.   Found in marijuana

j.   Found on paper (other than money)

Other Forms of Botanical Evidence

k.   diatoms

l.   algae

m.   lichen

n.   mushrooms

o.   mold or mildew

p.   herbaceous plants

q.   woody plants

r.   seeds

s.   flowers

t.   roots

u.   stems

v.   leaves

w.   annual rings

2. Research Sources:

To begin your research, start with the Internet. Perform an Internet search for "pollen" and the name of your topic (e.g., honey, mud) and "forensics" and find numerous references. Include books and current articles from reputable periodicals from the last four years (your teacher can give you suggestions).

3. What information do you need to investigate?

a.   Explain the case to the class:

| Who? | When? | Why? |
| What? | Where? | How? |

b.   Describe how the case was solved using botanical evidence.

c.   Describe the proper method to collect and preserve botanical evidence.

d.   Describe anything in your case that is not common knowledge. For example, explain what the Shroud of Turin is or describe sheep shearing, how honey is produced, or how cocaine is imported into the United States.

4. Submit the Botanical Planning Sheet one week before your presentation.

5. Each group will have its presentation peer-reviewed prior to the final presentation.

6. Each team delivers an oral presentation of its research findings. Your presentation should include the following:

a.   PowerPoint presentation or a poster

b.   Three-dimensional object that pertains to your topic (e.g., rope, muddy boot, air filter)

Planning the Oral Presentation:

Your presentation should be equally divided among your team members.

Answers

Use the scoring rubric, Act 5-3 SH Rubric, on the IRCD, Chapter 5, to evaluate students' presentations.

Future Research and Extensions

Ask students to compare the cases they chose and construct a timeline of when the cases were heard by the court. Ask them if they saw a pattern for the court dates, or if the dates were sporadic.

Teaching Tip

Encourage students to practice their presentations before a group, either of students or their family.

Guidelines for Your Presentation:

1. Be prepared: Practice, rehearse, and time your presentation in advance.
2. Block out what each person will do for the presentation and when they will do their part of the presentation.
3. Special equipment: If you are showing a PowerPoint presentation, be sure that you are familiar with the equipment before your presentation. If you are using a flex camera, practice setting up your visuals and focusing the camera before your presentation.
4. *Do not read from your PowerPoint slides or your report!* You can refer to the PowerPoint or notecards, but do not read it word for word.
5. Make eye contact with your audience. Do not turn your back on the audience.
6. Scan the group and speak to the entire group.
7. Speak slowly and with enough volume that the people in the back row can easily hear you! Try to relax and smile!

Extra Credit:

If you provide a handout that pertains to your topic, you will be given extra credit. The handout should contain both information and graphics. It should *not* merely be a script of your presentation or copies of your PowerPoint slides.

Processing a Crime Scene for Botanical Evidence Obj. 5.8

Objective:

The purpose of this activity is to familiarize you with the proper procedures for processing a botanical crime scene.

By the end of this activity, you will be able to:

1. Process a crime scene for botanical evidence.
2. Complete the Botanical Evidence and Site Information Sheet for the crime scene.
3. Establish datum and subdatum points.
4. Stake out the collection limits of your collection site.
5. Identify, flag, and document all botanical evidence.
6. Measure and record the location of the evidence on the Botanical Evidence and Site Information Sheet.
7. Properly photograph the botanical evidence and crime scene.
8. Collect the evidence and complete the evidence label for each source of evidence.

Safety:

There are no safety issues with this activity.

Time Required to Complete the Activity:

If students complete the activity, it should take 2½ hours.

Materials:

Act 5-4 SH Botanical Evidence and Site Form (1 per team)
Act 5-4 SH Evidence Inventory Labels (10 per team)
Act 5-4 SH Evidence Markers (10 per team)

Optional checklists:
Act 5-4 SH First Responder
Act 5-4 SH Evidence Collector
Act 5-4 SH Recorder
Act 5-4 SH Photographer
Act 5-4 SH Artist
Act 5-4 CSI Investigator

compass
measuring tape or meter sticks
string
4 wooden stakes (one foot tall × 1 inch × 2 inches)
hammer or other object to pound stakes into ground
trowel or shovel

Teaching Tip

- Demonstrate how to mark evidence with either a flag or evidence marker.
- Do not remove evidence until photographs are taken.
- Collect habitat samples after evidence has been processed.

Safety Precautions

There are no safety issues with this activity.

Materials

Print and distribute Act 5-4 SH Botanical Evidence and Site Form (1 per team); Act 5-4 SH Evidence Inventory Labels (10 per team); and Act 5-4 SH Evidence Markers (10 per team) from the IRCD, Chapter 5.

Teaching Tip

Before students collect and document botanical evidence, you might demonstrate or explain how to do the following:

- Use a compass.
- Identify possible datum sites.
- Set up collection site limits.
- Document evidence locations using a compass and perpendicular measurements from two sides of the collection site.
- Record information in the data table.
- Distinguish between botanical evidence and habitat sampling.

Teaching Tip

Refer to Act 5-4 TN CS Botanical on the IRCD, Chapter 5, for information on how to set up a botanical evidence crime scene.

Teaching Tip

- Review Chapter 2 (Crime-Scene Investigation and Evidence Collection) with your students.
- Remind students that each evidence item must be packaged separately with an individual evidence label.
- Review the section in this chapter on How to Collect Botanical Samples

evidence flags or evidence markers
newspapers
blotter papers
plant press (optional)
pencil
large and small brown paper bags
camera

Background:

Proper procedure to process a crime scene and collect evidence is found in both Chapter 2, Crime-Scene Investigation and in Chapter 5, Forensic Botany. Chapter 5 contains specific information for botanical collection identification, photography, documentation, and collection.

Procedure:

1. First responder secures scene and does a walk-through to scan the area.
2. Crime-scene examiner appoints and distributes checklists for each of the following jobs:
   - Photographer
   - Recorder
   - Botanical-evidence collector
   - Sketch artist
   - Three crime-scene investigators (CSIs) to set up and stake out the collecting limits for crime-scene processing
3. Each person processing the crime scene needs to review the proper procedures by referring to Chapter 2 and to Chapter 5 for information specific to crime-scene processing of botanical evidence.
4. Each person conducting the crime-scene investigation should use the checklist student handouts to ensure that all steps are followed.
5. The recorder works with other investigators to complete the first page of the Botanical Evidence Site Form, noting the following:
   - Case number
   - Date
   - Time
   - Name of agency processing the crime scene
   - Name of investigator(s)
   - Location of scene: general description and compass reading and distance from datum point
   - General description of the scene
   - Description of the biological conditions at the scene
   - Habitat assessment (e.g., field, pond, hardwood forest, desert, beach, open field)

   The recorder also works with the evidence collector and photographer recording each piece of evidence and photograph number.

Teaching Tip

Assign specific duties for the various jobs. Use the checklists in the IRCD, Act 5-4 SH.

6. **Photographer**
   - Photographs the crime scene from a distance; takes photos from the crime scene facing north, east, south, and west, as well as close-ups.
   - Photographs evidence close up and farther away.
   - Photographs evidence in the collection newspaper (at the site) alongside an evidence label.
   - Documents and numbers each photo.

7. **The Crime-Scene Investigators and Location of the Crime Scene**
   a. Locate a datum point, a permanent fixed point of reference such as a corner of a building or a telephone pole. If inside a building, you can use fixed items such as a fireplace, refrigerator, etc. A marker can be placed at the datum point to ensure accuracy when measuring.
   b. Standing at the datum point, use a compass to measure the direction from the datum point to the crime scene, and record this information on the botanical evidence sheet.
   c. Distance measurements should be taken from the datum point to the closest two corners of your collecting limits (subdatum points refer to Step 8). Record this information on the botanical evidence sheet.

8. **Crime-Scene Investigators and Establishing Collecting Limits and Subdatum Points**
   a. Using a compass, find north. Pound a stake into the ground at the northwest corner of your crime scene at least one meter away from any evidence. This marks the first corner (subdatum point) of your crime scene.
   b. Establish a north–south baseline from this first corner and drive a second stake in one meter beyond your crime scene.
   c. Run a measuring tape from the stake located in the northwest corner along this north–south baseline, extending the tape at least one meter beyond any evidence. Put in a stake at this second corner (subdatum) (located along the south end of your north–south base line). Record the distance of this north–south baseline to stake 2.
   d. From the first stake, *use a compass* to form a second line directly east from the first corner. Extend the measuring tape at least 1 meter beyond your evidence. Put in a stake into corner 3 (subdatum). Record the length of this second line. Position stake 4 so that a rectangle (or square) is formed around the evidence. *Be sure all corners are right angles.*
   e. Once you have established your four corners, enclose the entire area with string by securing the string around all four stakes.

Teaching Tip

Be sure students understand the difference between a datum point and a subdatum point before performing this activity. You may refer students to the explanation in Chapter 2.

Teacher Tip

- Botanical evidence should be placed in newspaper or a paper bag, never in plastic.
- Collect flowers, seeds, fruits, and roots, noting color and shape.
- Large items should be placed in brown paper bags or cardboard boxes.
- Collect a broken branch at least 6" above and below the break.
- If available, use a plant press or blotter paper.

Teaching Tip

Reminders: Take several photos of the crime scene from various angles with and without reference markers and rulers.

Photos should be taken at close range from the north, east, south and west. Other photos should be taken at some distance from the crime scene. Include photos of the dominant plant life as well as of other plants in that region.

Evidence should be photographed in situ alongside a ruler.

9. **Evidence Collector and Recorder:** Evidence collection, documentation, and packaging

a. The location of any evidence is measured as the perpendicular distances from the evidence to two reference lines along the perimeter of your rectangle. For example, the location can be the perpendicular distance from the north–south baseline and the perpendicular distance from your second east–west line. You can also cite the compass heading of the evidence taken from a stake or subdatum point in corner 1 to validate the position of the evidence. Each piece of evidence must be measured and recorded on the Botanical Evidence Collection Data Table found in the Botanical Evidence and Site Form. (Refer to the following diagram.)

The location of the green evidence spot in the following diagram is measured from the north line and from the west line. A compass reading of the evidence location is taken from corner 1. The evidence could be cited as 2 meters from the north side and 2 meters from the west side at a compass setting of 135 degrees.

b. To measure evidence found *above or below* the ground, use the ground as your baseline and measure the distances as above ground (positive numbers) or below ground (negative numbers).

c. Only one person should collect the evidence and hand it over to crime-scene investigators, who are responsible for properly wrapping it in newspaper. Each botanical evidence item is packaged separately. The case number, date, and name of the collector should be written in pencil on the inside of the newspaper next to the botanical evidence.

d. The photographer photographs the evidence in situ and in the newspaper with the information written on the newspaper next to the evidence.

e. An evidence inventory label should be completed for each piece of evidence. The recorder documents the evidence in the Botanical Evidence Collection Data Table.

10. **Habitat Sampling:** For the area, 10 different representative types of botanical samples should be identified, photographed, documented, and properly collected. *Note: This is not the same as evidence collection.* Habitat samples provide a sampling of the dominant plants found at the crime scene.

   a. One person should collect the plants.

   b. Several people work with the collector and package the evidence in newspaper. Each sample should have the item number and the case number recorded next to the botanical sample in the newspaper.

   c. The photographer photographs each sample in place with both close-up and distance shots and photographs the sampled plant in the newspaper with the case number visible in the photograph.

   d. The recorder records each habitat sample in the Botanical Habitat Sampling Data Table found in the Botanical Evidence and Site Information form.

11. **Discussion:** After completing the Botanical Evidence and Site Information form and after all evidence is photographed, documented, and packaged, discuss the activity and any problems that you encountered. As a group, brainstorm ideas on how to improve on processing a botanical crime scene that would make the procedure easier and would help to ensure evidence reliability.

© iStockphoto.com/Kali Nine LLC

Safety Precautions
None

Materials
Print and distribute one copy of the Act 5-5 SH Data Table from the IRCD, Chapter 5, for each team of two students.

Teacher Note
When comparing the pollen fingerprint from one area with another, a botanist examines the following:

A. total pollen count per sample, the *pollen index*

B. different types of pollen found in the sample

C. the percentage of each pollen grain found within a sample

If students prepare a larger sketch, or if they take a digital image of their field of view, have them calculate the percentages of the three dominant forms of pollen in each sample.

Teaching Tip
Instead of making pollen sketches, have students take digital images of their field of view. Using an old film canister (with the lid and bottom removed) and a digital camera, take a photo. Place the cut-out film canister over the ocular lens and place the lens of the digital camera on top of the film canister. To reduce external light, it may be necessary to wrap a hand around the connection between the film canister and the lens of the digital camera. Go to ngl.cengage .com/forensicscience2e and find the link to the authors' Website for a webinar on how to make a comparison microscope.

Pollen Index *Obj. 5.8, 5.9*

Background:
In the spring, as the temperature warms, male pinecones are among the first to release pollen into the air. Pollen is produced in large amounts to compensate for the inefficiency of wind pollination. Pollen grains have evolved special adaptations that enable them to stick to a surface so they can be carried from place to place. The type and number of pollen grains found at a crime scene can be a valuable source of trace evidence linking a victim and suspect.

Pollen rain on roof of car.

In this activity, you will compare the pollen index (pollen rain), amount, and types of pollen released in an area over a period of time.

Objectives:
At the end of this activity, you will be able to do the following:

1. Describe how to collect, stain, and view pollen under a microscope.
2. Perform a pollen count over a five-day period.
3. Collect and analyze pollen data for a five-day period.
4. Suggest a possible explanation for variations in the average pollen index over a five-day period, citing evidence from the data.

Time required: About 20 minutes a day for 5 consecutive school days

Materials:
(per two students)
Activity 5-5 SH data table
1 glass microscope slide/day
petroleum jelly
1 cover slip/day
QuICK® Cure Stain
compound microscope (shared use)
1 piece graph paper to serve as a counting chamber

SAFETY PRECAUTIONS:
None

Procedure:

1. Spread a thin layer of petroleum jelly about the size of a cover slip on the center of a microscope slide.
2. Place the slide on a windowsill or outdoors at a site selected by your teacher for 30 minutes.

3. Bring the slide indoors and stain with a QuICK® Cure solution prepared by your teacher.
4. Add a drop of stain to the center of the slide and cover with a cover slip.
5. Place the "graph paper counting chamber" under the stained pollen slide and view under 400×. Count the number of pollen grains in four different random squares by counting all pollen touching or included in each square.
6. Record your results in the data table provided by your teacher.
7. Sketch the appearance of each type of pollen in the data table.
8. Repeat Steps 1–7 for the next 4 days.
9. Complete the questions at the end of the activity.

Day	Count Sample 1	Count Sample 2	Count Sample 3	Count Sample 4	Average Count/day (1+2+3+4)/4	Sketch of Pollen Types	Environmental Conditions			
							Temp	Sun Shade	Wind Speed	Humidity
1										
2										
3										
4										
5										

Questions:

1. Refer to your data table to answer the following questions. Which day had
   a. The highest pollen index?
   b. The lowest pollen index?
   c. The greatest variety of pollen types?
2. Prepare a bar graph comparing the average pollen count per day. Include a title and label both axes.
3. Referring to your data on the average pollen count/day and weather conditions, can you correlate the weather conditions to the pollen index? Cite evidence to support your claim.
4. Compare your data on the average pollen index with your classmates who did their own pollen counts.
   a. Were their results similar?
   b. Brainstorm ideas with your classmates on how to improve on your techniques for pollen collection and counting to make your results more accurate.
5. Pollen evidence found on a suspect is being used to link the suspect to a crime scene. Present arguments cited by both the prosecution and the defense regarding whether or not pollen evidence is sufficient to convict a suspect of the crime.
   a. Prosecutor arguments
   b. Defense arguments

Teaching Tip

Distribute half pieces of graph paper to students to serve as counting grids. When students examine their stained slides, have them place the graph paper under the slide so that students will be able to count the number of pollen grains per square. Have them double-check that the average count is the total of pollen grains in four randomly chosen squares divided by four.

Explore

Have students research the effect of the seasons or weather conditions on pollen count. Have them explain why input from a meteorologist would be important when evaluation pollen evidence.

Questions

1-4. Answers will vary with location and season.

5. a. Pollen evidence was found on the suspect; the color, size and shape of pollen was consistent with the crime-scene pollen.

   b. Pollen is considered class evidence (unless there was a DNA analysis performed on the pollen, which was not likely); pollen evidence provides no time frame for when the pollen was transferred to the suspect;

The types of pollen dispersed by wind and insects differ in appearance and can be distinguished with scanning electron microscope (SEM) images.

Going Further:

1. Explore cases where pollen evidence has been used to place a suspect at a crime scene.

2. People suffering from allergies, asthma, and other respiratory conditions use the pollen index to avoid going outside on days when the pollen count is high. Research what happens to a person who suffers from allergies related to pollen. Include in your answer
   a. How pollen causes your immune system to respond
   b. What causes a person's eyes and nose to run
   c. What allergic reactions could result in lung difficulties

3. Using small collaborative groups,
   a. Interview a local meteorologist to investigate
      - How a pollen index is measured in your area
      - What are the major pollen allergens in your area during different times of the year
   b. Research and obtain digital images of the main types of pollen found in your area.
   c. Prepare a class presentation (poster, PowerPoint, or video) that summarizes your findings.

4. Design a 3-D model of a pollen grain that would easily adhere to a person's clothing.

5. When examining a pollen fingerprint for one area, a botanist examines:
   a. The total number of pollen grains (pollen index)
   b. The different types of pollen grains
   c. The percentage of each type of pollen grain in each sample

Refer to your data table. Select one day from your sample. Using your sketch of pollen, determine the dominant form of pollen and calculate the percentage of pollen for that type of pollen compared to the total pollen sample.

Reference: www.pollenlibrary.com

Isolation of Pollen from Honey Obj 5.8

Background:

When bees search flowers for nectar, they pick up and carry pollen back to the hive. Pollen and nectar are used to produce honey. From a study of the pollen found in the honey, beekeepers can determine the plants visited by the bees.

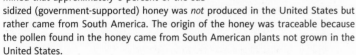

© Cengage Learning®

In the 1970s, a U.S. government study determined that approximately 6 percent of the subsidized (government-supported) honey was *not* produced in the United States but rather came from South America. The origin of the honey was traceable because the pollen found in the honey came from South American plants not grown in the United States.

In this activity, you will examine stained pollen extracted from honey samples. Based on your observations and research, you will make a claim as to whether the product label stating the source of the honey is consistent with your findings.

Objectives:

At the end of this activity, you will be able to:

1. Summarize the procedure for extracting pollen from honey
2. Prepare and examine a stained slide of pollen extracted from honey
3. Based on your observations and research, determine if the product label stating the source of the honey is accurate
4. Support that claim by citing evidence from your observations and research

Time required to Complete the Activity: 30–45 minutes

Materials:

(per two students)
Activity 5-6 SH
graduated cylinder
beaker (50 mL)
centrifuge (to share with other groups)
2 centrifuge tubes
2 pipettes or droppers
QuICK® Cure stain or another suitable stain
4 microscope slides
4 cover slips
marking pen for slides
250-mL beaker (use as a test-tube holder)

© Cengage Learning®

Teacher Note

Check honey jars and select one with a "Product of USA" label and the other with a label of either a mixed source or one outside the United States.

Safety Precautions

Glassware is extremely fragile. Make sure students are careful in handling it. The instructor should clean up any broken pieces.

Materials

Print and distribute one copy of Act 5-6 SH from the IRCD, Chapter 5, to each team of students.

Teacher Note

Prepare QuICK® Cure with hand sanitizer in a ratio of five drops of QuICK® Cure to one mL of hand sanitizer. Try other suitable stains. (QuICK® Cure is a fish antifungal used in fish tanks.)

Teaching Tip

Instead of making pollen sketches, have students take digital images of their field of view. Using an old film canister (with the lid and bottom removed) and a digital camera, take a photo. Place the cut-out film canister over the ocular lens and place the lens of the digital camera on top of the film canister. To reduce external light, it may be necessary to wrap a hand around the interface of the film canister and the lens of the digital camera. Go to ngl.cengage.com/forensicscience2e and find the link to the authors' Website for a webinar on how to make a comparison microscope.

Questions

1. Answers will vary depending on honey used.

2. Either the honey contained the correct type of pollen or it did not. The test could be inconclusive because no pollen was found.

3. Pollen differs in structure and size. If it was all the same type of pollen, the pollen would look exactly the same.

hot or warm water
microscope
cover slips
2 jars of honey from different sources (labeled A and B)

Procedure:

1. Add 6 mL of honey to 12 mL of hot or warm water and then add to a 50-mL beaker.
2. Divide the honey-and-water solution equally between two centrifuge tubes.
3. Label the tubes A1 and A2 and centrifuge for five minutes.
4. Pipette off and discard all but the last drop of liquid. This last drop contains the pollen concentrate.
5. Label two microscope slides A1 and A2.
6. Using a pipette, remove one drop of the pollen concentrate from A1 onto slide A1.
7. Add 1 drop of stain and a cover slip to slide A1.
8. View slide A1 under high power (400×).
9. Sketch the pollen. Be sure to sketch all pollen types observed.
10. Repeat Steps 7–9 with slide A2.
11. Complete the data table for samples A1 and A2.
12. Record in your data table the source of the honey, according to the product label.
13. Research the microscopic structure of the pollen used to produce the honey. Based on your observations and research, determine if the honey source cited on the jar is correctly labeled.
14. Repeat the procedure using honey from source B.

Act 5-6 Data Table

Sample	Sketch of Pollen (Circle the Dominant Form)	Observations (Shape, Relative Size, Color)	Number of Pollen Types	Honey Source From Product Label
A1				
A2				
B1				
B2				

Questions:

1. Based on your observations and research, state your claim regarding whether the honey jars are correctly labeled.
2. Cite evidence from your observations and research to support your claim.
3. Describe how you were able to determine if more than one type of pollen was found in the honey-and-water solution examined.

4. Describe any problems you encountered in extracting and viewing the pollen grains in the honey-and-water extract.

5. Propose a revised technique that might correct any problems you encountered with the procedure and that would make your results more accurate.

Going Further:

1. Research why the U.S. government was willing to subsidize honey production.

2. Investigate the hypotheses for a sudden decrease in the honeybee population and the effect of the decrease on honey and fruit production. Research "Colony Collapse Disorder" in bee populations.

3. Research the reason for the warning on the honey label—"Warning: Do not feed honey to infants under one year of age."

Product of USA
Warning: Do not feed honey to infants under one year of age.

© Cengage Learning®

Teacher Note

Clostridium bacteria, the cause of infant botulism, can be found in honey.

4. Honey was not completely dissolved, water was not hot enough, pollen was strained from the sample (check honey jar), not centrifuged long enough, too much fluid on slide.

5. See answer to Question 4 for suggestions.

Chapter Overview

If a standard DNA analysis were done on identical twins, it would show that they have identical DNA. How would a forensic investigator determine which of the twins committed a crime? Today, forensic science depends heavily on DNA analysis. However, in the case of twins, the forensic investigation team might need to use a technique that began in the mid-1800s to identify the suspect—fingerprinting. Every individual, even an identical twin, has a unique fingerprint made up of whorls, loops, or arches. Today, fingerprint analysis using scanners and computers allows examiners to quickly search interconnected local, state, and national databases. This automated system improves speed, accuracy, and efficiency of fingerprint identification, helping to solve both current and cold cases.

The Big Ideas

Fingerprinting has a long history of forensic use. A person's fingerprints develop long before birth. The ridges on our fingers in the shapes of loops, arches, and whorls are different from anyone else's. Fingerprint examiners look for unique characteristics, such as a core and deltas. Computer algorithms based on location of minutiae help to quickly sort fingerprints. There are three types of prints that might be found at a crime scene: patent, plastic, or latent. The IAFIS database, developed by the FBI, is used to compare prints. Fingerprints can be collected by using tape, powders, or other chemicals; or they can be photographed and compared with criminal fingerprint cards on file.

CHAPTER 6
Fingerprints

Technology Catches Up to Crime: FBI Latent Hit Award 2013

By September 2001, the 1999 San Bernardino, California, murder and robbery of 74-year-old Marshall Adams was a "cold case." All leads had been exhausted. But a new lead had just come to light. The San Bernardino County Sheriff's Department had submitted latent prints from the case to the FBI's *Integrated Automated Fingerprint Identification System* (*IAFIS*), a national fingerprint and criminal history database, and several possible fingerprint matches had been identified. One was about to lead to an arrest and guilty plea.

The crime In December 1999, a call to San Bernardino's Police Department reported an unresponsive male on the floor of a jewelry store. Detective John Munoz headed the investigation and found the victim, Marshall Adams, brutally beaten and stabbed. His wallet, along with jewelry from the store, had been taken.

Crime-scene evidence Randy Beasley, a fingerprint identification technician from the San Bernardino County Sheriff's Department, collected latent (hidden) fingerprints, palm prints, and blood evidence from a knife, store doors, and a store catalog. A bloody palm print was recovered from the face of the victim.

1999 investigation In 1999, the Sheriff's department searched the latent prints against their local databases without any success. All the evidence from the case was stored in their cold case unit.

2001 evidence and arrest In 2001, IAFIS returned several possible matches to the latent print from the crime scene. James Nursall, a fingerprint examiner with the San Bernardino County Sheriff's Department, concluded that the print belonged to Jad Salem. Through IAFIS, it was discovered that Salem had been arrested and fingerprinted in Texas about two weeks after the 1999 murder. Salem was initially stopped for a traffic violation but was later arrested on a drug charge.

Detective Munoz located Salem in San Bernardino and told him about the fingerprint evidence from the 1999 murder. At first Salem denied being there. Later in the interrogation, Salem admitted being there, but only as a witness. However, after Salem was shown the bloody palm print on the victim's face, along with all the other evidence, he admitted he was the murderer. He was sentenced to 32 years in prison for the murder and robbery.

An FBI technician compares prints on IAFIS with handprints from a crime scene.

Ulrich Baumgarten/Getty Images

158

SCENARIO

Use the case in the scenario to introduce fingerprinting in a class discussion.

1. Discuss the crime and the type of evidence left at the crime scene.
2. Have students describe the role played by each of the various crime-scene investigators.
3. Discuss the cooperation required among different law-enforcement agencies in one area and among agencies.
4. Discuss the changes in fingerprint technology over the past 20 years.
5. Have students describe IAFIS and how it helped solve the case.

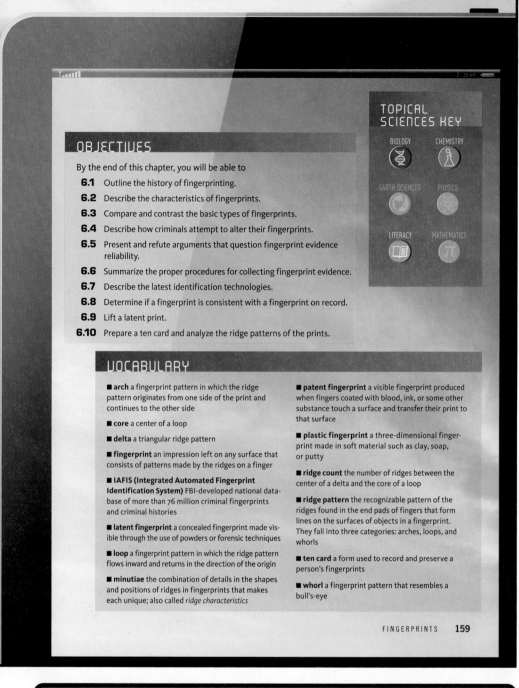

KEY SCIENCE CONCEPTS

Biology: the skin; fingerprints are formed in utero; fingerprints are different in identical twins

Chemistry: powders and other chemicals used to recover fingerprints; skin oil can leave a fingerprint on a surface; chemical reactions can help lift latent fingerprints

Technology: scanners and computers are used to collect and sort fingerprints; biometric technology

OBJECTIVES

By the end of this chapter, you will be able to

6.1 Outline the history of fingerprinting.

6.2 Describe the characteristics of fingerprints.

6.3 Compare and contrast the basic types of fingerprints.

6.4 Describe how criminals attempt to alter their fingerprints.

6.5 Present and refute arguments that question fingerprint evidence reliability.

6.6 Summarize the proper procedures for collecting fingerprint evidence.

6.7 Describe the latest identification technologies.

6.8 Determine if a fingerprint is consistent with a fingerprint on record.

6.9 Lift a latent print.

6.10 Prepare a ten card and analyze the ridge patterns of the prints.

TOPICAL SCIENCES KEY

BIOLOGY   CHEMISTRY

EARTH SCIENCES   PHYSICS

LITERACY   MATHEMATICS

VOCABULARY

- **arch** a fingerprint pattern in which the ridge pattern originates from one side of the print and continues to the other side

- **core** a center of a loop

- **delta** a triangular ridge pattern

- **fingerprint** an impression left on any surface that consists of patterns made by the ridges on a finger

- **IAFIS (Integrated Automated Fingerprint Identification System)** FBI-developed national database of more than 76 million criminal fingerprints and criminal histories

- **latent fingerprint** a concealed fingerprint made visible through the use of powders or forensic techniques

- **loop** a fingerprint pattern in which the ridge pattern flows inward and returns in the direction of the origin

- **minutiae** the combination of details in the shapes and positions of ridges in fingerprints that makes each unique; also called *ridge characteristics*

- **patent fingerprint** a visible fingerprint produced when fingers coated with blood, ink, or some other substance touch a surface and transfer their print to that surface

- **plastic fingerprint** a three-dimensional fingerprint made in soft material such as clay, soap, or putty

- **ridge count** the number of ridges between the center of a delta and the core of a loop

- **ridge pattern** the recognizable pattern of the ridges found in the end pads of fingers that form lines on the surfaces of objects in a fingerprint. They fall into three categories: arches, loops, and whorls

- **ten card** a form used to record and preserve a person's fingerprints

- **whorl** a fingerprint pattern that resembles a bull's-eye

FINGERPRINTS   **159**

TEACHING RESOURCES

Instructor's Resource CD-ROM includes:
- Activities and Student Handouts
- Alternative Assessments
- Consolidated Bibliography
- Correlations to NGSS and CCSS
- Figure Files
- Lesson Plans
- Nonfiction Readings
- PowerPoint Presentations
- Student Learning Objectives (SLOs)

CL Testing powered by Cognero

Website: ngl.cengage.com/forensicscience2e

Engage

Organize students into groups of two or three to read the Introduction. Read them the following scenario. Then have them discuss it in their groups. It is your first year at college and there is a break-in at the dorm. Fingerprints have been left at the crime scene. Based on this evidence, you are brought in for questioning. If the police are accusing you of stealing the missing items from the dorm based on the presence of your fingerprints, what arguments could you present to support your innocence?

Explore

Have students research the relevant work of Jan Evangelista Purkinje, who was a professor of physiology and pathology at the University of Prague. In 1823, he recognized fingerprints as a way of making identifications.

Figure 6-1 *Early, though fictional, fingerprint cards from Twain's* Pudd'nhead Wilson.

THUMB PRINTS

From Pudd'nhead Wilson's Collection
"Every human being carries with him from his cradle to his grave certain physical marks which do not change their character."

INTRODUCTION

Pudd'nhead Wilson is a lawyer created by Mark Twain in the novel of the same name, published in November 1894. In his final address to a jury, Lawyer Wilson exhibits his knowledge of the cutting-edge technology of the day:

> Every human being carries with him from his cradle to his grave, certain physical marks which do not change their character, and by which he can always be identified—and that without shade of doubt or question. These marks are his signature, his physiological autograph, so to speak, and this autograph cannot be counterfeited, nor can he disguise it or hide it away, nor can it become illegible by the wear and mutations of time.

No one is sure how Mark Twain learned that fingerprints made good forensic evidence, but he used them in his book to dramatically solve a case in which identical twins were falsely accused of murder. Using fingerprints as a means to identify individuals was a major breakthrough in forensic science in real life, as well as in novels, and it gave law enforcement around the world a new tool to solve crimes, clear the innocent, and convict the guilty. Fingerprint cards from *Pudd'nhead Wilson* are shown in Figure 6-1.

HISTORICAL DEVELOPMENT *Obj. 6.1*

For thousands of years, humans have been fascinated by the patterns found on the skin of their fingers. But exactly how long ago humans realized that these patterns could identify individuals is not clear. Several ancient cultures used fingerprints as personal markings (Figure 6-2). Archaeologists discovered fingerprints pressed into clay tablet contracts dating back to 1792–1750 B.C. in Babylon. In ancient China, it was common practice to use inked fingerprints on all official documents, such as contracts and loans. The oldest known document showing fingerprints dates from the third century B.C. Chinese historians have found fingerprints and palm prints pressed into clay writing surfaces and surmise that they were used to authenticate official seals and legal documents.

In Western culture, the earliest record of the study of the patterns on human hands comes from 1684. Dr. Nehemiah Grew wrote a paper describing the patterns that he saw on human hands under the microscope, including the presence of ridges. Johann Christoph Andreas Mayer (1788) described that "the arrangement of skin ridges is never duplicated in two persons." He was probably the first scientist to

Figure 6-2 *This ancient seal shows the fingerprint of a person who lived hundreds of years ago.*

160   CHAPTER 6

recognize this fact. In 1823, Jan Evangelist Purkyn described nine distinct fingerprint patterns, including loops, spirals, circles, and double whorls. Sir William Herschel began the collecting of fingerprints in 1856. He noted the patterns were unique to each person and were not altered by age.

In 1879, Alphonse Bertillon, an assistant clerk in the records office at the police station in Paris, created a way to identify criminals using a list of physical measurements taken from prisoners. The system, sometimes called Bertillonage, was first used in 1883 to identify repeat offenders. In 1902, he was credited with solving the first murder using fingerprints.

Sir Francis Galton (1822–1911) verified that fingerprints do not change with age. In 1888, Galton, along with Sir E. R. Henry, developed the classification system for fingerprints that is still in use today in the United States and Europe.

Beginning in 1896, Sir Edmund Richard Henry, with the help of two colleagues, created a system that divided fingerprint records into groups based on whether they have an arch, whorl, or loop pattern. Each fingerprint card in the system was imprinted with all 10 fingerprints of a person and marked with individual characteristics. This set of fingerprints has come to be called a **ten card** (Figure 6-3).

Fingerprints are now taken digitally, providing clearer reference prints. By 2012, the FBI-maintained IAFIS system had more than 76 million computerized fingerprints, mug shots, scars, tattoo photos, and other identification records. IAFIS contains information on criminals; known and suspected terrorists; military personnel; and civilians seeking employment, who have had background checks, or who have applied for licenses to purchase firearms. When trying to identify an unknown latent print, crime-scene investigators submit the fingerprint to IAFIS. IAFIS quickly searches its database of fingerprints and selects possible matches. A fingerprint examiner makes the final decision concerning consistency. This system has improved speed and accuracy of identifying matches for both current and cold cases. The IAFIS system will soon be enhanced by Advanced Fingerprint Identification Technology (AFIT).

By 2013, the FBI was integrating the ability to compare crime-scene palm prints with prints collected at the time of arrest. About 20–30 percent of latent prints at a crime scene come from the palm or side of the hand from the little finger to the wrist. These prints may be left on the back of a chair, on a window, or when a suspect pushes off a surface or uses a handle or a doorknob.

Did you know

Alphonse Bertillon was the first person to document incoming prisoners with a photograph, the forerunner of the modern mug shot.

Figure 6-3 *An early example of a ten card.*

© Cengage Learning®

Explore

Alphonse Bertillon created anthropometry, which records the measurements of humans. Physical anthropology is the study of the measurements of living humans to understand physical variations. Anthropometry was the first scientific system police used to help solve crimes. Have interested students research whether it is still being used today.

Teaching Tip

Before discussing fingerprint patterns, ask students to view fingerprints and have them devise their own method of classification.

Teaching Tip

Ask students if they are aware of what jobs require fingerprinting as a requirement for employment. (The list varies by state, but always includes jobs that involve care of the elderly, children, and the disabled, such as school teachers, nursing home administrators, and V.A. Center workers.)

Teaching Tip

Have students research Internet photos of finger pads on apes and chimpanzees and compare them to human fingerprint patterns.

Explore

Have students write a short story or draw a short graphic feature involving a crime committed by one of two identical twins. Eyewitnesses provided a detailed description of the suspect. Which twin committed the crime? The conclusion should explain how the case was solved through the use of fingerprinting.

Science

BIOLOGY

The skin has three layers, each with different functions. The surface of the skin is called the *epidermis*. The epidermis is a relatively thin layer where the outermost cells are shed. The newer cells grow from the lowest layer of the epidermis, called the basal layer. The epidermis, when undamaged, is mostly waterproof, prevents bacteria and viruses from entering the body, and contains melanin that filters out UV rays from the sun. The next layer is called the *dermis*. This layer provides the skin with strength and flexibility, and contains nerve endings, sweat glands, oil glands, hair follicles, and blood vessels. The *subcutaneous layer* is the most internal layer of the skin. This layer provides the body with insulation from the cold and heat, offers protective padding, and stores energy.

WHAT ARE FINGERPRINTS?

Look at the surface of your fingers. Are they smooth and shiny? No. All fingers, toes, feet, and palms are covered in small ridges. These are raised portions of skin, arranged in connected units called dermal, or friction, ridges. They help us with our grip on objects that we touch. When these ridges press against things, they leave marks. A finger leaves an impression called a **fingerprint.**

The imprint of a fingerprint consists of natural secretions of the sweat glands that are present in the friction ridge of the skin (Figure 6-4). These secretions are a mixture mainly of water, oils, and salts. Dirt from everyday activities is also mixed into these secretions. Anytime you touch something, you leave behind traces of these substances in the unique pattern of your dermal ridges.

Figure 6-4 *Our fingertips are covered with hundreds of microscopic sweat pores, which make our fingers moist and able to grip better.*

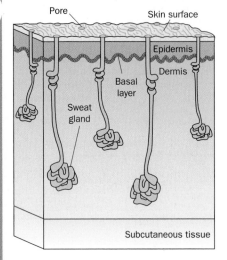

Formation of Fingerprints *Obj. 6.2*

The individual nature of fingerprints has been known for about 2,000 years, but scientists only recently discovered how fingerprints form in the womb. The latest information suggests that the patterns are formed at the beginning of the 10th week of *gestation* (time since conception). Similar prints are formed in many other areas of the body, such as the palms of the hands, the soles of the feet, and the lips. (Note that although identical twins have the same DNA, they do not have the same fingerprints because of alterations during gestation.)

The development of fingerprints happens in the basal layer of skin, where new skin cells are produced. As the basal layer grows, unique ridge patterns form, influenced by the environment surrounding the fetus. The pattern cannot be altered or destroyed permanently by skin injuries, because the outer layer of epidermis protects it.

Characteristics of Fingerprints *Obj. 6.2*

Fingerprint characteristics are named for their general visual appearance and **ridge patterns.** Major ridge patterns are **loops, whorls,** and **arches** (Figure 6-5). About 65 percent of the total population has loops, 30 percent has whorls, and 5 percent has arches.

Arches have ridges that enter from one side of the fingerprint and leave from the other side with a rise in the center. Whorls look like a bull's-eye. Loops enter and exit from the same direction. The **core** is the center of a loop. Loops can be further classified as *ulnar* or *radial* depending on the direction of the *opening* of the loop. A radial loop opens toward the thumb (toward the radius bone), and an ulnar loop opens toward the little finger (toward the ulna bone).

A ridge count may help distinguish one fingerprint from another. To take a ridge count for a loop pattern, an imaginary line is drawn from the

Figure 6-5 *Three basic fingerprint ridge patterns occur at different frequencies in humans.*

Arches 5%   *Whorls* 30%   *Loops* 65%

© Cengage Learning® (all)

center of the core to the middle of the delta. Count the number of ridges between the core and the center of the delta. In Figure 6-6, the yellow line shows the area used in the ridge count.

Some fingerprints have a triangular ridge pattern called a **delta**. A delta has ridges that run in different directions above and below it. Note in Figure 6-7 that arches lack deltas, whorls have at least two deltas (print lower left and lower right), and loops have one delta (print lower right).

The basic fingerprint patterns can be further classified. Whorl patterns may be plain whorl (24%), central pocket loop whorl (2%), double loop whorl (4%), or accidental whorl (0.01%). The plain whorl (Figure 6-7A) has one or more ridges that make a complete spiral. There are two deltas, and if a line is drawn between them, at least one of the concentric circles crosses that line. The central pocket loop whorl (Figure 6-7B) has one or more ridges that make a complete circle. There are two deltas, and if a line is drawn between the two deltas, then at least one of the concentric circles crosses that line. The double loop whorl (Figure 6-7C) has two separate loop formations and two deltas. The accidental whorl (Figure 6-7D) has two or more deltas and is a combination of two of the other patterns (other than a plain arch).

Figure 6-6 *The red patch is called the core, and it is located at the center of a loop or whorl.*

— Core

— Delta

The ridge count is the number of ridges between the core and the center of the delta.

© Cengage Learning®

Figure 6-7 *Types of whorl pattern.*

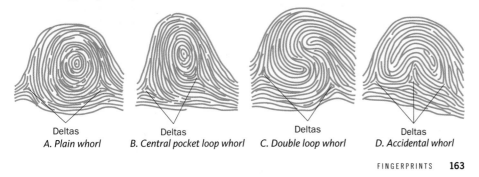

Deltas   Deltas   Deltas   Deltas
A. Plain whorl   B. Central pocket loop whorl   C. Double loop whorl   D. Accidental whorl

Explore

Explain how the prints on a ten card are made. For the upper ten impressions, each digit is individually rolled nail-edge to nail-edge on the card. This is done to obtain all available ridge detail. The prints at the bottom of the ten card are taken simultaneously without rolling. All of the fingers of each hand—except the thumb, which is printed separately—are set down at a 45-degree angle. These are referred to as plain or flat impressions. The bottom prints are taken in this manner to verify the sequence and accuracy of the rolled impressions at the top of the card.

Explore

Plastic prints found at a crime scene can be preserved by taking photographs of the prints or making casts of the prints to be analyzed later in a lab.

Evaluate

Read students the following scenario and then ask them to explain where fingerprints may be found and what type—patent, plastic, or latent—they would be: A local pottery studio was robbed while the potter was out. The thieves broke a window on the studio's front door and then reached inside, turning the doorknob to get in. (Patent and latent prints might be left on the doorknob as well as on whatever was used to break the window.) Designs (latent print) the potter had drawn were strewn about the room. A fresh clay platter (plastic print) was torn in half. A cash register (a possible latent print on the register or whatever tool was used to force the drawer) was forcibly opened, and all of the cash (partial latent prints on individual slots) was taken. The criminals left by opening the back door (latent print on the knob; could be patent if they had dirty hands).

Figure 6-8 *Types of arch pattern.*

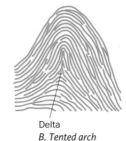

A. Plain arch

Delta
B. Tented arch

Did you know

Fingerprints can be taken from dead bodies by chemically treating the fingertips to help them puff out. Another method involves removing the finger skin and placing it like a glove onto the (gloved) finger of someone else, who can then roll the print.

Arches may be divided into plain arches (4%) and tented arches (1%). The plain arch (Figure 6-8A) has ridges entering one side, rising in the center, and exiting the other side. It does not have a delta. The tented arch (Figure 6-8B) has ridge patterns entering one side, rising in the center, and exiting out the other side. However, the ridge pattern has a sharp rise in the center of the arch.

While looking at the basic fingerprint patterns can quickly help exclude a suspect, in order to consider a print found at a crime scene consistent with that of an individual, more information is needed. An examiner needs to know if he is viewing a partial print, multiple prints, or prints from a right or left hand. (Left and right fingerprints are not, however, mirror images.) Every individual, including identical twins, has unique ridge characteristic details called **minutiae** (because the details are so small). Recognizing minutiae in the differences between ridges, their relative number, and their location on a specific fingerprint is called *fingerprint identification*. There are about 150 individual ridge characteristics on the average full fingerprint. When forensic examiners identify a fingerprint, they are, in theory, identifying the unique signature of a person.

Prior to the use of computers and scanners, fingerprints were identified by people comparing ridge patterns and minutiae points, a slow, tedious process often resulting in inaccuracies. Today scanners are used to identify minutiae points. Software calculates the distances and angles between key minutiae points and defines a unique pattern. A computer rapidly searches the database for possible matches to that unique pattern. The use of computers and scanners helps the fingerprint examiner quickly narrow the search to a small number of individuals. The final identification is done by a fingerprint examiner. As a result, many more fingerprints can be examined with fewer mistakes.

In Figure 6-9 on the next page, you can see descriptions of some fingerprint minutiae. In the lab activities, you will practice the techniques necessary to identify and compare fingerprints, including analyzing these ridge characteristics.

Types of Fingerprints   *Obj. 6.3*

There are three types of prints that can be left at a crime scene. **Patent fingerprints**, or visible prints, are left on a smooth surface when blood, ink, or some other liquid comes in contact with the hands and is transferred to that surface. **Plastic fingerprints** are actual indentations left in some soft material such as clay, putty, or wax. **Latent fingerprints**, or prints not visible to the unaided eye, are caused by the transfer of oils and other body secretions onto a surface. They can be made visible, or *lifted*, by dusting with powders or by using a chemical reaction.

Fingerprints of suspects are taken by rolling each of the 10 fingers in ink and then rolling them onto a ten card that presents the 10 fingerprints in a standard format. In Activity 6-4, you will learn how to take your own fingerprints. You can see some lifted latent prints in Figure 6-10.

LEARNING

Teaching English-Language Learners

Students may have difficulty distinguishing between the terms *latent* and *patent* because they only differ by one letter. Try to come up with a clever way for them to remember these terms. For example, because latent begins with an L, that L could refer to investigators having to LOOK for these kinds of prints, because latent prints are invisible prints.

Figure 6-9 *Some minutiae patterns used to analyze fingerprints.*

Name	Visual Appearance
1. Ridge ending (including broken ridge)	1.
2. Fork (or bifurcation)	2.
3. Island ridge (or short ridge)	3.
4. Dot (or very short ridge)	4.
5. Bridge	5.
6. Spur (or hook)	6.
7. Eye (enclosure or island)	7.
8. Double bifurcation	8.
9. Delta	9.
10. Trifurcation	10.

Figure 6-10 *Lifted latent prints: on a soft drink can (top); on a quarter (bottom).*

© Cengage Learning®

© Cengage Learning®

Fingerprint Forensic FAQs *Obj. 6.4*

CAN FINGERPRINTS BE ALTERED OR DISGUISED?

As soon as fingerprints were discovered to be a means of identification, criminals began to devise ways to alter them so they could avoid being identified. American Public Enemy Number One in the 1930s, John Dillinger put acid on his fingertips to change their appearance, something he likely learned from stories of workers in the pineapple fields in Cuba who did not have readily visible fingerprints. This is because chemical substances found in the pineapple plant, when combined with the pressure of handling the plants, dissolved the workers' fingertip skin. What Dillinger did not learn is that when these workers ended their contact with the pineapples, their fingerprints grew back! Fingerprints taken from Dillinger's body in the morgue were compared to known examples he left behind during his life of crime. Despite his efforts to destroy his fingerprints, they still allowed him to be identified. Sometimes the scars formed by trying to remove fingerprints even makes fingerprint identification easier!

FINGERPRINTS **165**

Teaching Tip

The IAFIS is a database and search engine, but it does not initially evaluate or scan prints. Other software must do this. A police department buys the software and uses it to scan, evaluate, and upload the image to the IAFIS.

Teaching Tip

Refer to the Capstone Project 3 "How Reliable Is the Evidence?"

Teaching Tip

Help students learn the information in Figure 6-13 by enlarging the figure and making several copies of it. Then, cut out the squares of information and place each set of pieces into a separate envelope. Working in groups of two, have students recreate the figure from the pieces. Make this exercise into a game by assigning a point value for each piece placed in the correct position.

Science

CHEMISTRY

CHEMISTRY

Collecting latent fingerprints requires chemicals that will help investigators see and remove the prints for analysis without damaging them. The method used depends on the surface material. For example, ninhydrin reacts with traces of amino acids left on porous surfaces. Cyanoacrylate fumes adhere to latent prints on nonporous surfaces, such as plastic bags or electrical tape.

Science

CHEMISTRY

CHEMISTRY

When crime-scene investigators work with metal dusting powders, they typically use a Magna Brush. The Magna Brush is a specially designed magnet that picks up finely divided metal powder. This method is far less messy, and the metal powder can be swept up and reused.

HOW RELIABLE IS FINGERPRINTING AS A MEANS OF IDENTIFICATION? *Obj. 6.5*

Some experts claim that fingerprint identification is almost flawless. However, humans make mistakes. In 1995, 156 fingerprint examiners were given a test. One in five examiners made at least one false identification. In 2004, the FBI arrested and jailed Oregon lawyer Brandon Mayfield based on fingerprint evidence that linked him to the Madrid train bombings, which killed 170 people. Mayfield, who had not traveled out of the United States for 10 years, claimed the fingerprint was inconsistent with his. Mayfield was held in custody for two weeks, until the Spanish authorities told the FBI that the fingerprint was, in fact, that of an Algerian citizen.

In light of human fallibility, it is important that fingerprint examiners be held to a high standard of performance. Results need to be double-checked to prevent false convictions and to maintain the integrity of the science. In 2009, the U. S. National Academy of Sciences requested a federal board to research and access reliable methods in forensic science. This resulted in the creation of Scientific Working Groups (SWG). In 2014, the Organization of Scientific Area Committees (OSAC) was also created to ensure high standards of evidence evaluation.

HOW ARE FINGERPRINTS ANALYZED? *Obj. 6.7*

Contrary to what we see on television, fingerprint comparisons are not carried out by a computer in a matter of seconds. By 1987, the FBI had 23 million criminal fingerprint cards on file, and getting a comparison with a fingerprint found at a crime scene and one stored on file required manual searching. It could take as long as three months to do a thorough search.

In 1999, that all changed with IAFIS, which provides digital, automated fingerprint searches, latent print searches, electronic storage of fingerprint photo files, and electronic exchange of fingerprints and test results (Figure 6-11). It operates 24 hours a day, 365 days a year. The FBI Next Generation Identification program (NGI) is enhancing IAFIS by adding physical characteristics such as facial scans of known and suspected terrorists to the system. Today, local, state, and federal agencies submit fingerprints to IAFIS, where fingerprints can be quickly and efficiently searched. In most instances, a fingerprint examiner scans the fingerprints, identifying the print pattern and marking minutiae. Then he or she inputs the information into IAFIS, which identifies any possible candidates, often within 2 hours. A fingerprint examiner then analyzes all candidates identified by IAFIS. If a print is consistent with a suspect, then the examiner must obtain a copy of the original fingerprint record for a final confirmation and verification. Because a person initially identified the print pattern, it is essential that the fingerprint be re-examined for accuracy.

Figure 6-11 *A technician compares fingerprints in the AFIS system.*

Peter Foerster/dpa/Landov

DIFFERENTIATED LEARNING

Teaching Gifted Students

Allow students to research court cases that have been reopened or thrown out because of faulty identification of fingerprints.

Ask students to investigate when fingerprint evidence was first recognized by the courts. Ask students to research the newest methods of fingerprint identification used today.

Figure 6-12 *A crime-scene specialist lifting a print.*

Kayte M. Deioma/PhotoEdit

Teaching Tip
Ask a fingerprint technician to visit
your class and demonstrate the
correct procedure in preparing a
ten card.

HOW ARE LATENT FINGERPRINTS COLLECTED? *Obj. 6.6*

CHEMISTRY

As mentioned earlier, latent fingerprints are not visible, but techniques can
"lift" them. Dusting surfaces such as drinking glasses, the faucets on sinks,
telephones, and the like with a fine carbon powder can make a fingerprint
more visible. Metal or magnetic powders may also be used. They are easier
to clean up than carbon powders. Tape is used to lift and preserve the fingerprint. The tape with the fingerprint is then placed on an evidence card
on which the date, time, location, and collector of the print are logged.
Proper evidence collection techniques involve photographing the fingerprints before they are lifted (Figure 6-12).

To recover a print from a surface that is not smooth and hard requires
the use of different chemicals. When the fingerprint residue combines with
these chemicals, the fingerprint image becomes visible. Figure 6-13 summarizes some of the more common chemicals used to recover a latent print.

Figure 6-13 *Other methods used for visualizing latent fingerprints.*

Chemical	Uses	Application	Safety	Chemical Reaction	Latent Print
Ninhydrin	Paper	Object is dipped or sprayed in ninhydrin; wait 24 hours	Do not inhale or get on your skin	Reacts with amino acids (from proteins) found in sweat	Purplish-blue print
Cyanoacrylate Vapor	Household items: plastic, metal, glass; and skin	Sample is heated in a vapor tent	Do not inhale or get on your skin: irritating to mucous membranes	Reacts with amino acids	White print
Silver Nitrate	Wood; styrofoam	Object is dipped or sprayed in silver nitrate	Wear gloves to avoid contact with skin	Chloride from salt in perspiration on the print combines with silver nitrate to form silver chloride	Black or reddish-brown print under UV light
Iodine Fuming	Paper; cardboard ; unpainted surfaces	In a vapor tent, heat solid iodine crystals	Toxic to inhale or ingest	Iodine combines with carbohydrates in latent print	Brownish print fades quickly; must be photographed or sprayed with a starch solution

FINGERPRINTS **167**

DIFFERENTIATED LEARNING

Teaching Gifted Students
Have students research the chemical reactions involved in fingerprint recovery using ninhydrin and
cyanoacrylate.

CHAPTER

1 2 3 4 5 **6** 7 8 9 10 11 12 13 14 15 16 17 18

Did you know ?

Biometric finger and hand scanners can use fingerprint ridge patterns, the length of your fingers, and your body temperature to help identify you.

Did you know ?

► DNA can be collected from your fingerprint.
► Some mobile fingerprint scanners can produce an image of sweat produced in the pores of your finger.
► It has been estimated that at least 40 percent of latent prints collected are unusable.

The Future of Fingerprinting

Obj. 6.7

Fingerprinting is as much a part of the future of forensics as it has been a part of its past. With new scanning technology, such as that being used in Figure 6-12, and digital systems of identifying patterns, fingerprints can be scanned at a resolution of 500 to 1,000 dots per inch. This provides an image that reveals minute pore patterns on the fingerprint ridges, allowing for more precise pattern comparisons (Figure 6-14). Nanoparticles have now been added to fingerprint powders, making pore patterns appear even sharper. Perhaps with time, the chances of mistakes being made will be virtually eliminated.

Entirely new uses for fingerprints are also being developed. Scientific studies have shown that much of the material we touch in our daily lives leaves trace evidence on our fingers and hands, which is in turn left behind on the objects that we touch. Dr. Sue Jickells is doing research to learn how things criminals may touch, such as explosives, cigarettes, and drugs, can leave behind traces on the skin. When identified and studied, these trace substances could tell us much more about the lives of fingerprint donors than just their identities.

Figure 6-14 *This high-resolution fingerprint is a digital image that shows the pores along the ridges, which appear as bumps in the print.*

©Hans van den Nieuwendijk

DIGGING DEEPER With Forensic Science eCollection

Are fingerprints really unique? How much of the interpretation of fingerprints is subjective on the part of the fingerprint analyst? Search the Gale Forensic Science eCollection for answers at **ngl.cengage.com/forensicscience2e.**

SUMMARY

- Humans have noticed the patterns on their hands for thousands of years, but it was not until 1684 that these patterns were described in detail. In the mid-1800s, the idea of a fingerprint's uniqueness was studied, and the application of fingerprints to an identification system began. By the late 1800s, two effective systems were being used to identify criminals, and fingerprints were being collected as evidence in crimes.

- The elevated regions in a fingerprint are called friction ridges. Fingerprints consist of several main ridge patterns, including whorls, loops, and arches. They have a core, which is an area where ridges separate or unite after running in a parallel direction. The triangular region located near a loop pattern, or whorl, is called a delta.

- Fingerprints are formed in the womb at about week 10 of gestation. They are formed between two layers of skin, and their shape does not change during a person's lifetime. They are unique to an individual. Not even identical twins have identical fingerprints.

- Fingerprints left on an object are created by the naturally occurring ridges in the skin of fingertips and secretions from sweat glands that leave small amounts of oils and salts when the ridges are pressed against an object. The residues leave an impression of the ridges found on the finger of the donor.

- The basic types of fingerprints are patent (visible) fingerprints, plastic (indentation) fingerprints, and latent (not visible to the unaided eye) fingerprints. They are characterized as loops, whorls, or arches, and compared on the basis of their minutiae.

- Criminals have sought to alter their fingerprints with chemicals, surgery, and superficial destruction. Some fingerprints can temporarily be altered by long-term contact with rough surfaces. Attempts at permanent fingerprint alteration have not been successful.

- Mistakes in fingerprint analysis have led to wrongful convictions, mostly because of human error. New forensic standards are being developed through the Scientific Working Groups and the Organization of Scientific Area Committees.

- The Integrated Automated Fingerprint Identification System (IAFIS) is a national database that holds more than 76 million fingerprint, identifying mark, and criminal history records.

- Fingerprints can be collected from surfaces by dusting them with certain powders and impressing them on tape, or putting them into contact with certain chemicals that help reveal the fingerprints.

LITERACY

Search the Internet for "FBI-Latent Print of the Year 2012," and read how a cold case was solved using IAFIS.

Did you know

Digital fingerprint images can be enhanced. Characteristics like ridge endings and bifurcations are assigned coded mathematical values. Corrupted regions on the fingerprint file can be blended with distinct regions to produce an enhanced composite print.

Evaluate

Research OSAC, the Organization of Scientific Area Committees, to learn about the new standards and guidelines being developed to help improve the accuracy and reliability of fingerprint analysis.

Teaching Tip

Have students discuss how a fingerprint examiner might incorrectly match two fingerprints as happened in the Stephen Cowans case. Ask: How does the case affect the confidence in fingerprint evidence?

Close

Point out to students that they have learned much technical vocabulary in the chapter. Ask them to call out key words from the chapter. As you write each word on the board or overhead, have them tell you what it means and why it is significant.

CASE STUDIES

Francisca Rojas (1892)

On June 29, 1892, in the village of Necochea, Argentina, two children, Ponciano Carballo Rojas, age six, and his sister Teresa, age four, were found murdered in their home. Their mother, Francisca, age 27, was found with a superficial knife wound to the throat.

Francisca told police that her neighbor, Pedro Ramón Velásquez, had committed the crime. Velásquez, a one-time boyfriend of Francisca's, did not confess, even after being tortured.

Inspector Commissioner Alvárez went to the crime scene to reexamine it, searching for any trace evidence that might have been overlooked. He spotted bloody fingerprints on the doorpost of the house. Because Francisca had denied touching the bodies of her children, Alvárez believed he had found an important clue.

He took the bloody doorpost and fingerprint samples of Pedro Velásquez to Juan Vucetich, who in late 1891 had opened the first fingerprint bureau in South America in Buenos Aires. Vucetich examined the fingerprints and found they were not consistent with those of Velásquez. Alvárez became suspicious of Francisca, who had been so insistent that Velásquez had committed the crime. He took a sample of her fingerprints and discovered that they matched the bloody prints found on the doorpost of the house.

When Francisca was confronted with the evidence against her, she confessed. She had murdered her own children, faked an attack on herself, and cast blame on an innocent man, intending him to die for the crime. Her reasons for the murder and for blaming Velásquez were that he had interfered in a romance between her and another man and she felt she would be more appealing to the other man if she did not have children. Francisca Rojas was the first person in the Americas to be convicted of a crime based on fingerprint evidence.

Stephen Cowans (1997)

On the afternoon of May 30, 1997, Boston police officer Gregory Gallagher was shot with his own gun in a backyard in Roxbury, Massachusetts. Still carrying the gun, the assailant ran to a nearby residence, where he received a glass of water as he wiped off the gun. Investigators found a print on the glass used by the individual. The print was considered to be consistent with the prints of Stephen Cowans by two fingerprint examiners with the Boston Police Department. Cowans maintained his innocence. With the compelling fingerprint evidence, Cowans was convicted of the shooting and sentenced to 30 to 45 years in the state prison.

In 2004, Cowan's defense team requested DNA testing of the glass and a baseball cap dropped at the scene of the shooting. Neither DNA sample was consistent with Cowan's DNA. The original verdict was overturned. As Suffolk County reexamined the fingerprints in preparing to retry Cowans, the assistant district attorney discovered "conclusively and unequivocally that...the purported match was a mistake." Cowans was released from prison after 6½ years. As a result, Boston police and the Suffolk County District Attorney's office established new guidelines for identification and evidence handling.

Think Critically

"To get a conviction, I would rather have one good fingerprint than a pound of hair and fiber evidence." Do you agree or disagree? Support your answer.

Careers *in Forensics*

Peter Paul Biro

A Hungarian immigrant currently living and working in Canada, Peter Paul Biro is an art conservator who, in 1984, was the first to study the fingerprints left behind on paintings by artists. After years of careful study, he began using these marks as a means of identifying artists.

Biro's job is to discover, by the use of fingerprint comparison, who painted a work of art and to support the claim with strong evidence. No two fingerprints are alike, so Biro's evidence is extremely valuable to those who buy and sell art because a painting that can be attributed to a specific artist rises in value.

Biro only uses fingerprints on artworks that were clearly made during the original creation of the work. These include imprints left in the paint while it was still wet, or prints left as a result of the use of a fingertip to apply paint (Leonardo da Vinci often used his fingertips as paintbrushes), or a palm print that might have resulted from applying varnish by hand. The print used for comparison should come from an unquestioned work of art by the artist.

In 1993, Biro examined a painting discovered in the early 1980s entitled *Landscape with Rainbow* that was thought to be painted by J. M. W. Turner. During the restoration of this painting, fingerprints were discovered in the paint. Even though fingerprints on *Landscape with Rainbow* and fingerprints photographed on another Turner painting, *Chichester Canal* were consistent, art experts and scholars alike discounted the evidence. Turner, who was known to work alone with no assistants, had used his fingertip on both paintings to model the still-wet paint and was the only possible donor for both prints. When an independent fingerprint examination by John Manners of the West Yorkshire Police confirmed the conclusions that the fingerprints on both paintings were consistent,

Courtesy, Peter Paul Biro, Forensic Studies in Art, Montreal, QC, Canada.

Peter Paul Biro

the unbelievers changed their minds. This case was the first successful use of fingerprints to authenticate artwork. The newly authenticated Turner painting sold for much more money than it would have otherwise.

The fingerprint circled in Figure 6-15 is that of Leonardo da Vinci. Although not visible in this photograph, nine distinct characteristics were found by Biro and other experts to identify Leonardo's prints.

Figure 6-15 *Leonardo da Vinci's fingerprint is in the right center of this document.*

AP Images/Courtesy of Piero Lucco, Chieti University, HO

Learn More About It
▷ To learn more about the work of a fingerprinting expert, go to
ngl.cengage.com/forensicscience2e.

Chapter 6 Review

True or False

1. True
2. False
3. False
4. False
5. True
6. False
7. True
8. False
9. False
10. True

Multiple Choice

11. c
12. a
13. a
14. b

Short Answer

15. To take a ridge count, an imaginary line is drawn from the center of the core to the center of the delta.

16. Sample answer: Fingerprints are formed in the womb at about the 10th week of pregnancy in the basal layer of skin. These cells grow fast and fold and bend on top of each other. In the womb, fingerprints are exposed to the uterine wall and amniotic fluid, which shape the individualized prints.

17. Possible answer: It is possible to temporarily alter fingerprints superficially. Eventually, when the skin is repaired, the fingerprint will return with the same pattern. Scars may make the fingerprints even more distinctive if permanent damage occurred.

18. Ninhydrin and cyanoacrylate: reacts with amino acids. Silver nitrate: Chlorine from salt in perspiration on the print combines with silver nitrate to form silver chloride. Iodine fuming: Iodine combines with carbohydrates in latent prints.

CHAPTER 6 REVIEW

True or False

1. Fingerprints are a result of oil and secretions from skin mixing with dirt. *Obj. 6.2*

2. Fingerprints are generally considered to be a form of class evidence. *Obj. 6.5*

3. It is necessary to obtain a full print from a suspect in order to compare his fingerprint with a fingerprint found at the crime scene. *Obj. 6.5, 6.6, 6.7*

4. Plastic prints must be dusted or treated in order to identify the ridge patterns. *Obj. 6.6, 6.7*

5. It is important to always photograph a fingerprint before you attempt to lift it. *Obj. 6.6*

6. Fingerprints are formed deep within the dermis layer of the skin. *Obj. 6.2*

7. IAFIS improves the speed and accuracy of fingerprint searches because it electronically accesses fingerprints from local, state, and national agencies. *Obj. 6.7*

8. The type of powder used to dust prints will vary depending upon the weather conditions when the print is lifted. *Obj. 6.6*

9. Fingerprints of the left hand are mirror images of the fingerprints on the right hand. *Obj. 6.2*

10. Similar print or ridge patterns can also be found on the toes. *Obj. 6.2, 6.3*

Multiple Choice

11. Fingerprints are formed *Obj. 6.2*
    a) shortly after birth
    b) at about two years of age
    c) at 10 weeks' gestation (pregnancy)
    d) at conception

12. Fingerprints that are actual indentations left in some soft material such as clay or putty are referred to as *Obj. 6.3*
    a) plastic fingerprints
    b) patent fingerprints
    c) latent fingerprints
    d) indented fingerprints

13. The use of fingerprints in identification is not perfect because *Obj. 6.5, 6.6, 6.7*
    a) The current technology depends on humans to analyze the information, and humans make mistakes.
    b) Many people have the same exact fingerprints.
    c) People can easily change their fingerprints.
    d) All of the above

19. a. Latent fingerprints; palm prints; and blood evidence on a knife, doors, and a store catalog. Bloody palm print was found on the face of the victim.

19. b. Patent fingerprints were found on the victim's face.

19. c. (i) Detective John Munoz: Homicide detective with the San Bernardino Police Department. He headed the investigation of the murder and arrested Jad Salem in San Bernardino.

(ii) Randy Beasley: Fingerprint identification technician with the San Bernardino Police Department who collected the prints and blood evidence at the crime scene.

(iii) James Nursall: Fingerprint examiner with San Bernardino County Sheriff's Department reviewed the possible fingerprint "matches" from IAFIS and concluded that Salem's prints were consistent.

14. The presence of two deltas in a fingerprint indicate *Obj. 6.2*
    a) scar tissue
    b) a print is a whorl pattern
    c) a print is a loop pattern
    d) a print has a core

Short Answer

15. Outline the steps in taking a ridge count from a fingerprint. *Obj. 6.2*

16. Summarize how fingerprints are formed. *Obj. 6.2*

17. Is it possible to alter fingerprints? Defend your opinion, citing evidence from the chapter. *Obj. 6.2, 6.4*

18. Another way to make prints visible is to apply certain chemicals. What component of a fingerprint chemically reacts with each of the following? *Obj. 6.6*
    a) ninhydrin
    b) cyanoacrylate
    c) silver nitrate
    d) iodine fuming

19. Refer to the scenario at the beginning of the chapter entitled Technology Catches Up to Crime, and answer the following questions: *Obj. 6.7*
    a) List the evidence recovered from the December 1999 murder case.
    b) Describe the patent fingerprints found at the crime scene. Define *patent fingerprints* in your answer.
    c) Several investigators were involved with the May 1999 murder case. List each investigator's name, the name of his agency, and the description of his role in the investigation.
    d) Compare and contrast fingerprint searches today using IAFIS with fingerprint searches that might have occurred 25 years ago.
    e) When the San Bernardino County Sheriff's Department submitted the latent print recovered at the 1999 murder scene to IAFIS, it was compared to Jad Salem's prints, which were already in the IAFIS system. Describe the circumstances that resulted in Salem's fingerprints being entered into IAFIS.
    f) What is the significance of the title Technology Catches Up to Crime?

20. Design a procedure to demonstrate how to produce a plastic fingerprint impression of one of your fingers. Compare the plastic fingerprint with an inked or graphite impression of the same fingerprint. Contrast your plastic fingerprint with a graphite or inked fingerprint impression of your partner's fingerprint.
    a) List the materials you will need.
    b) Describe how to
        i. Make a plastic fingerprint impression of one of your fingertips.
        ii. Take a digital image of the plastic fingerprint.
        iii. Make an inked or graphite fingerprint impression of the same fingertip.

(iv) Traffic officer: Texas police stopped Jad Salem for a traffic violation but arrested him for a drug charge. Salem's fingerprints were entered in IAFIS about two weeks after the murder. When the San Bernardino County Sheriff's office submitted the unknown latent print from the 1999 murder, they were able to get a "hit," with Salem's fingerprints.

19. d. Similar: Both methods still examine fingerprint ridges and minutiae. The final analysis is still done by a person today as it was 25 years ago.

Different: Fingerprints were taken manually using ink. At that time, there was no integrated system that combined all criminal fingerprints at a national level. As a result, searching was slow and limited, and the quality of the prints was not always good. Today most criminal fingerprints are digitally scanned and entered into IAFIS. The quality of the scanned prints is much better.

19. e. Salem's fingerprints were entered into IAFIS two weeks after the 1999 murder.

19. f. Because of improved technology, computers and scanners, cold cases are now being solved more rapidly. Because of digital scanners and computers, it is now possible to identify previously unknown latent prints by comparing them to criminal fingerprints that are entered into IAFIS.

20. a. Answers will vary. Possible answers include putty, Mikrosil, soap
    (i) Gently press a finger into soft putty, Mikrosil, or gum to create a plastic print impression.
    (ii) Students can take a digital photograph of the plastic print.
    (iii) Using an inkpad or graphite pencil, create a fingerprint impression of a fingertip, ensuring that the ink or graphite extends below the first digit and goes from nail edge to nail edge.
    (iv) and (v) In both cases, students should describe the basic ridge pattern. Then they should compare and contrast minutiae patterns. Included in their study should be any scars unique to the fingerprint.

Connections

Sample answer: Both prints have whorl ridge patterns with two deltas. (Students should do a ridge count on each print.) Students are also encouraged to note the presence of ridge endings, and to sort ridges, islands, and bifurcations. The FBI file print has two deltas found at the base of the whorl pattern, while the suspect print only has one. They are not consistent.

Teaching Tip

Have students use transparency film to mark minutiae on the crime-scene fingerprint and check to see if the same minutiae appear on the FBI fingerprint at the same locations.

iv. Compare both images of the plastic fingerprint with the inked or graphite fingertip impression. Cite evidence that demonstrates that the two fingerprints are consistent.

v. Contrast your plastic fingerprint impression with your partner's inked or graphite fingerprint impression. Defend your claim citing evidence from the two impressions that the two fingerprints are not consistent.

Going Further

1. Repeat Question 20, creating a patent fingerprint impression instead of a plastic fingerprint impression.

2. Do you agree or disagree with the following statement? "At birth, all children should be fingerprinted and photographed so that in the future it will be easier to identify them." Explain your reasoning.

Connections

Refer to the two prints below. The first print is taken from the FBI files of a suspect. The second print has been lifted off a glass taken from a crime scene. Determine if the prints are consistent with those of the suspect. Justify your answer.

- Identify the type of ridge pattern found in both prints.

- Describe similarities or differences.

Bibliography

Books and Journals

Cole, Simon A. *Suspect Identities: A History of Fingerprinting and Criminal Identification.* Cambridge, MA: Harvard University Press, 2001.

Cummins, Harold, and Charles Midlo. *Finger Prints, Palms, and Soles: An Introduction to Dermatoglyphics.* Philadelphia, PA: The Blakiston Company, 1943; reprinted 1976.

Garfinkel, Simson. *Database Nation: The Death of Privacy in the 21st Century.* O'Reilly Media, 2001.

Jones, T. "Inherited Characteristics in Fingerprints (or Theory of Relativity)." *The Print,* 4(5), 1991.

Lafontaine, Ryan. "Man Found Without Fingerprints." *The Sun Herald,* Biloxi, Mississippi, May 31, 2006.

Matera, Dary. *John Dillinger: The Life and Death of America's First Celebrity Criminal.* New York: Carroll & Graf, 2004.

McCann, J. S. "A Family Fingerprint Project." *Identification News,* May 1975, 7–11.

Shahan, Gaye. "Heredity in Fingerprints." *Identification News,* XX(4): 1, 10–14, April 1970.

Internet Resources

ngl.cengage.com/forensicscience2e (Gale Forensic Science eCollection)

http://www.shirleymckie.com "Wrongly Charged with Perjury on Fingerprint 'Evidence'"

http://www.fbi.gov/about-us/cjis/fingerprints_biometrics/ngi

http://www.fbi.gov/hq/cjisd/iafis.htm

http://www.fbi.gov/hq/cjisd/takingfps.htm

http://www.fbi.gov/news/stories/2010/october/latent_102510/latent_102510

http://www.fbi.gov/news/stories/2013/july/2013-latent-hit-of-the-year-award

http://www.truthinjustice.org/fingerprints.htm

http://www.livescience.com/30-lasting-impression-fingerprints-created.html

http://www.nist.gov/forensics/osac.cfm NIST Forensic Sciences

http://galton.org/fingerprints/books/henry/henry-classification.pdf

Study Your Fingerprints *Obj. 6.2, 6.3*

Objectives:

By the end of this activity, you will be able to:

1. Lift your fingerprint using tape and a graphite pencil.
2. Identify the ridge pattern of your finger.
3. Compare and contrast your fingerprints to your classmates' fingerprints.
4. Find two other students with the same basic ridge pattern as your own.
5. Calculate the percentage of students having each of the three different ridge patterns.

Time Required to Complete Activity: 40 minutes

Materials:

Act 6-1 SH
clear, adhesive tape ¾ inch in width or wider (not "transparent" tape)
pencil
two 3" × 5" cards or Act 6-1 SH
magnifying glass

SAFETY PRECAUTIONS:
No special precautions

Procedure:

1. On a lined 3" × 5" card, rub the end of a graphite pencil in a back-and-forth motion, creating a dark patch of graphite about 2 by 3 inches.
2. Rub your right index finger across the graphite patch so that the fingertip becomes coated with graphite from the first joint in the finger to the tip, and from fingernail edge to fingernail edge.
3. Tear off a piece of clear adhesive tape about 2 inches long. Carefully press the sticky side of the tape onto your finger pad from the edge of your fingernail across your finger pad to the other side of your fingernail.
4. Gently peel off the tape.
5. Press the tape, sticky side down, on the clean 3" × 5" card.
6. Examine your fingerprint using a magnifying glass.
7. Compare your fingerprint to the pictured samples.
8. Identify whether your fingerprint pattern is a loop, arch, or whorl.
9. Find two other students who have the same ridge pattern as yours.

Background

This activity gives students an opportunity to examine their own fingerprints and compare them with their classmates' prints. Students use tape to make an impression of their fingerprints and determine what type of pattern they have.

Safety Precautions

Students should wash their hands after using the graphite pencils.

Teaching Tip

Demonstrate how to cover a fingertip with graphite. The graphite should extend from nail to nail across the pad of the finger. The graphite should cover the crease of the first joint.

Procedures

1. Print, copy, and distribute Act 6-1 SH from the IRCD, Chapter 6.
2. Clear, 3/4-inch-wide adhesive tape will not be wide enough for a thumbprint. If you take a thumbprint, use a wider tape.
3. Reminder: Students should not be rolling their fingers across the graphite; they are vigorously rubbing them back and forth across the graphite.

1. Answers will vary. (Tips: Be prepared to address averages that greatly deviate from the percentages given by the experts (small sample size). Pool the data with other class periods and save them from year to year so students can see the power of having more data when drawing conclusions.

2. Possible answer: The larger your sample size, the closer to the national averages the data will be.

Teaching Tip

If the fingerprint impression does not look like a square (or rectangle), it is likely that the student did not spread graphite from nail edge to nail edge as directed.

---

10. Find two other students who have the other two types of ridge patterns.
11. Calculate the percentage of loops, whorls, and arches found in your class.

© Cengage Learning® (all)

Arches 5%   Whorls 30%   Loops 65%

Data Collection From Class:

Record the number of students showing each of the three types of fingerprint patterns and place those numbers in the data table. Complete the rest of the data table.

Data Table

	Loop	Whorl	Arch
Number of students showing trait			
Total students in class (This will be the same total for each column.)			
Percentage of class showing the trait (Divide the number of students with the trait by the total number in the class, and then multiply by 100.)			
National averages	65%	30%	5%

Questions:

1. Did the class percentage agree with the national averages? Support your claim using data from the data table.
2. Describe how to improve this data-collecting activity so that your results might be more reliable.

Going Further:

Research chi-squared statistical analyses. Then run chi-squared statistical analyses to determine if the differences between your data and the national averages were significant.

Further Research and Extensions

In this activity, students examine one of their fingerprints. If time permits, have students make prints of each of their fingers and describe the pattern of each. They can also compare and contrast their two index fingers or their two thumbs. Have them identify other classmates' fingerprints for more practice.

ACTIVITY 6-2

Giant Balloon Fingerprint *Obj. 6.3*

Objectives:

By the end of this activity, you will be able to:

1. Create a giant balloon fingerprint for use in studying various ridge patterns.
2. Identify the three basic ridge patterns among your classmates' fingerprints.

Introduction:

Ridge patterns on fingerprints are unique and identifiable. In this activity, you will be comparing and contrasting your own thumbprint and those of your classmates to identify these patterns.

Time Required to Complete Activity: 20 minutes

Materials:

1 large white balloon
fingerprinting inkpad
hand soap or moist wipes
paper towels
Act 6-2 SH
ballpoint pen

What you will need to do this experiment: a white balloon and an inkpad.

© Cengage Learning®

SAFETY PRECAUTIONS:

Before doing this activity, if you are allergic to latex, ask your teacher for a nitrile glove instead of a balloon.

Procedures:

1. Slightly inflate a large balloon.
2. Ink your thumb from thumbnail to thumbnail and past the first joint.
3. Position your thumb so that your print will be about a quarter of the way from the top of the balloon and two thirds of the way from the bottom. Gently press your thumb into the semi-inflated balloon. Do not roll your thumb. Pull your thumb from the balloon.
4. Fully inflate the balloon and examine your thumbprint.
5. Identify your thumb pattern as a loop, whorl, or arch.
6. Examine the balloons of your classmates and identify the ridge types.
7. Deflate your balloon and save it, unless you plan to do the Going Further activity below.

Going Further:

Refer to Figure 6-9, which describes minutiae patterns. Use a ballpoint pen to identify and circle the minutiae patterns on the balloon. Then deflate your balloon and save it.

Further Research and Extensions

This activity does not take much time. To extend the activity, ask each student to examine the balloons of every student in the class. Remind students to write their initials on their balloon to keep track of the balloons. Give students two minutes to observe a balloon print. For each print they examine, they should record the fingerprint pattern and the initials written on the balloon. After two minutes, have students switch balloons until all students have examined every balloon. Compile the class data and determine the percentage of students with arches, whorls, or loops.

ACTIVITY 6-2

Background

In this activity, students use a balloon to enlarge their thumbprint so the ridge lines will be easier to see and identify. Instead of looking under a microscope, students enlarge the image of their fingerprint by inflating the balloon.

Safety Precautions

Some students may be allergic to latex. You may want to have students sign a waiver stating that they are not allergic to latex. Local hospitals or clinics might be willing to donate latex-free gloves.

Procedures

Placement of the print on the balloon is critical to enlarging the print. It should be placed about one-quarter of the way from the top and two-thirds of the way from the bottom of the balloon for optimal results. Semi-inflate the balloon to about one-third capacity before applying the fingerprint. Then inflate it fully to magnify the fingerprint. Allow students to experiment with placement of the print on the balloon.

Answers

At the end of this activity, collect all balloons from the students. Students should staple a piece of paper to the end of the balloon before turning it in. The piece of paper should have their name, which finger they printed, the fingerprint pattern, and any other identifying marks. Turning in the balloon will allow the teacher time to enter grades for this activity based on completeness and participation. Balloons should be cut up after grading, for privacy protection.

Background

In this activity, students touch a piece of glassware and dust the glass to reveal the latent fingerprint.

Safety Precautions

1. Make sure to cover the work area with newspapers.

2. Emphasize that students must handle the dusting powder with care, because it can be very messy.

3. Be prepared. Dust will settle on everything in the room no matter how careful the students are.

4. Emphasize to students how important it is to be careful blowing off the excess dust.

5. Have dusting cloths and a broom ready for cleanup at the end of the lab.

6. Set up one area of the room for fingerprint powders.

Procedures

Print and distribute Act 6-3 SH from the IRCD, Chapter 6.

Teaching Tip

Fingerprinting tape purchased from a forensic supply house really works the best. If you don't have the budget for this special tape, a wide, clear tape works well.

Studying Latent and Plastic Fingerprints

Obj. 6.2, 6.3, 6.6, 6.9

Objectives:

By the end of this activity, you will be able to:
1. Distinguish between a latent and plastic fingerprint.
2. Summarize how to dust and lift a latent fingerprint.
3. Lift latent fingerprints from a glass surface.
4. Design an experiment to demonstrate plastic fingerprint impressions.
5. Identify ridge patterns from lifted and plastic fingerprints.

Introduction:

Every person has a unique set of fingerprints, even an identical twin. Whenever you touch a surface without gloves or other protection, you leave behind an invisible (latent) fingerprint. Law enforcement agencies use various fingerprint powders and chemicals to help visualize these telltale prints. Plastic fingerprints are those impressions left in soft material, such as wax.

Time Required to Complete Activity:

Part 1: Latent Fingerprints: 40 minutes
Part 2: Plastic Fingerprints: 40 minutes

Materials:

newspaper
black dusting powder or brush and magnetic powder
adhesive tape ¾ inch wide
dusting brush
cloth
magnifying glass
drinking glass, glass petri dish, beaker, other pieces of glass or Plexiglas®
soap or moist hand wipes
paper towels
3" × 5" card per student or Act 6-3 SH
digital camera (for plastic print procedure)

SAFETY PRECAUTIONS:

Cover the work area with newspapers.
Remember that the dusting powder can be very messy.

Procedure:

PART 1: LATENT FINGERPRINTS

1. Cover the work table with newspaper.
2. Wipe off your glass or Plexiglas® with a clean cloth.
3. Take your thumb and run it along the side of your nose or the back of your neck. These areas of your body are rich in oils and will help lubricate the ridges of the thumb to produce a clearer print.
4. Choose an area on the glass object and touch the glass with your thumb. Use a paper towel or other type of cloth in your other hand to prevent leaving other fingerprints. Avoid placing any other fingerprints in this area.
5. Dip the dusting brush lightly into the fingerprint powder. Place the brush between your hands and gently twist the brush back and forth, so that the bristles spin off excess powder near the surface of the object you are dusting. A latent (hidden) fingerprint should begin to appear. Continue to dust lightly, touching the surface until you have exposed as much of the latent print as possible. Gently blow off the excess powder. (Be prepared for dust to settle on everything in the area.)
6. Tear off a 3-inch piece of adhesive tape and place it over the fingerprint and press down.
7. Peel off the tape and place it on a 3" × 5" card. This process is called lifting the print.
8. On the 3" × 5" card, identify and record the ridge pattern.

The three types of fingerprints.

© Cengage Learning® (all)

Loop   Arch   Whorl

Procedure:

PART 2: PLASTIC FINGERPRINTS

1. Design an experiment to demonstrate how plastic fingerprint impressions are formed. Include in your design:
   a. Materials list
   b. Procedure

Teaching Tip

If dusting powder is unavailable, you can dust with carbon powder on a light surface or talcum powder on a dark surface.

Teaching Tip

Using magnetic powder and a wand is a much cleaner way to dust for latent prints.

Answers

Check students' data tables.

Teaching Tip

Ask students to watch episodes of *CSI* or movies that show a variety of surfaces from which fingerprint evidence was collected and then compare the differences in the techniques and materials used to collect them.

Teaching Tip

Suggested items for plastic fingerprints: silicone putty, poster putty, moist (not wet) soap.

Teaching Tip

Pores along fingerprint ridges can be made visible using tincture of iodine and good-quality stationery cut into pieces about the size of a glass microscope slide. Have students swab some iodine on a thumb and let it almost dry. Press the "iodined" thumb onto the paper and hold for about a minute. The pores, if present, will produce tiny dark blue dots on the paper.

Further Research and Extensions

This activity can be extended by having four students leave thumbprints on a piece of glassware. Lift these prints yourself. Then ask students to match each print with the person who made it by comparing the prints to those collected earlier in the activity.

2. Have another student create a plastic fingerprint impression using your procedure.
3. Take a digital image of the plastic fingerprint.
4. Discuss with your partner ways to improve your procedure.
5. (Optional) Create a PowerPoint presentation of the digital images of the class's plastic fingerprint impressions. Ask students in the class to identify the ridge patterns seen in the presentations.

Further Study:

1. If time permits, clean the glass and place additional fingerprints on the surface and repeat the technique; then exchange your glass for a classmate's. Dust, lift, and identify his or her print.
2. Fingerprints are not the only latent prints left at a crime scene. Sometimes, if someone is trying to look into a window from the outside, they will cup their hands around their eyes to shield the light and lean against a window this way. Try creating and lifting a latent print from side of your hand (nearest the little finger). Can you identify ridge patterns in the latent print?

© iStock.com/mediaphotos

ACTIVITY 6-4

How to Print a Ten Card *Obj. 6.6, 6.10*

Objectives:

By the end of this activity, you will be able to:

1. Properly ink a finger for a fingerprint impression.
2. Roll a fingerprint for a thumb and a finger.
3. Prepare a ten card.
4. Analyze fingerprints to diagnose errors in the fingerprinting process.

Background:

In this activity, students produce a ten card of their fingerprints. At the end of the activity, students should take their ten cards home.

Introduction:

Digitally recording fingerprints.

© Cengage Learning®

Law-enforcement officials prepare and use fingerprint cards, or ten cards, to identify criminals, security workers, teachers, bus drivers, and individuals licensed to carry firearms, as well as to register children's personal identification for parents. Today most police departments prepare digital scanned fingerprints. In this activity, you will prepare and ink a ten card.

Time Required to Complete Activity: 45 minutes

Materials:

Act 6-4 SH
blank ten card
inking strips and inkpad or non-ink pads and paper
magnifying glass
moist cleansing wipes, soap, and paper towels

SAFETY PRECAUTIONS:

There are no safety issues with this lab.

ACTIVITY 6-4

Background

In this activity, students produce a ten card of their fingerprints. At the end of the activity, each student should take home his or her fingerprints.

Safety Precautions

1. Cover the work area with newspaper.

2. Be sensitive to the fact that some students may already have had their fingerprints taken by the police. Send a letter home with students explaining the activity before doing this activity. Include in the letter that all student fingerprints will be kept by the students and not the school.

Teaching Tip

Inkless pads and papers are available from catalogs. These use a yellow inkless pad and a special paper. These are generally easier and cleaner to use than ink pads.

Procedures

1. Print and distribute Act 6-4 SH from the IRCD, Chapter 6.

2. Sirchie Fingerprint Laboratories (www.sirchie .com) may have a demo video that shows students the proper way to print a ten card or how to dust for prints. The company lists videos available on its Website, so check it out before beginning the lab.

3. Washable markers will also work instead of inking strips or an ink pad. They are cheaper than ink pads, and when capped, they will resist drying out much better than ink pads. Simply paint the surface of the skin with a dark-colored marker and proceed as usual.

4. Explain to students that the best parts of the print (such as a delta) are usually closer to the knuckle crease than to the fingertip. Knowing this in advance, students may be able to roll their fingerprints more carefully and get more of the print to appear, making it easier to assess.

Procedure:

PART 1: PRACTICE BEFORE USING INK

Prior to inking the fingers, have students practice the technique of how to ink a finger and how to roll a finger to get good fingerprint impressions.

1. How to ink a finger
   - Ask students to hold up their right index finger. Bend the finger. The ink should be applied below the first joint.
   - Ask students to look at the edges of the fingernail. Ink should be applied nail edge to nail edge. If properly inked and rolled, the fingerprint should appear square.

2. How to roll a print
   a. Students should stand sideways to the fingerprinting table (right side closest to the table to roll the right fingers).
   b. Students should extend one arm so that their fingers extend over the table. If the student is too close to the table, his or her own body and elbow will get in the way of rolling a print.
   c. Students should relax their arms and shoulders.
   d. The direction that a finger is rolled depends on if you are rolling a thumb or a finger.
      - Think of the expression **TIFO** (*thumbs inside, fingers outside*).
      - *Thumbs* roll toward the *inside* of the body.
      - *Fingers* roll toward the *outside* of the body.

3. Practice rolling the right index finger.
   Once in the correct body position, students should extend their right index finger above the table:
   - Turn the finger so that the right side edge of the finger is just above the table. Remember that you roll nail edge to nail edge!
   - Hold fingers, hand, and wrist parallel to the table.
   - Extend the arm fully with relaxed shoulders and arm.
   - Once in the proper position, practice rolling the finger from nail edge to nail edge by placing the finger onto the table and rolling the finger using a smooth, continuous motion. Do not hesitate or reverse direction.
   - Some students may find that taking a step forward or backward might be more comfortable.
   - Repeat the practice maneuver using different fingers.
   - Repeat the practice using your thumb (remember the thumb will roll to the inside of your body (TIFO). Place the right edge of the right thumb onto the table and roll the thumb toward the center of the body.

Procedure:

PART 2: INKING AND ROLLING A TEN CARD

1. Align the card so that the right-hand fingerprints on the card are located on the edge of the fingerprint table.
2. Ink the right index finger and roll the finger from nail edge to nail edge.
3. Continue inking and rolling each fingerprint.
4. After completing the right hand, turn the fingerprint card so that the left side prints are closest to the table edge.
5. Repeat the process for the left hand.
6. Re-ink the fingers of the right hand and press them gently into the box labeled "first four" for the right hand.
7. Re-ink the right thumb, placing the print in the box labeled right thumb.
8. Repeat the process for the left hand.
9. Using a magnifying lens, examine each fingerprint, labeling each as a loop, whorl, or arch.
10. Examine other students' ten cards. Provide suggestions to them on how to improve upon their technique based on their ten card fingerprint impressions.

Questions:

It takes practice to be able to roll good fingerprints. Diagnose what error occurred to produce fingerprints that

1. Looked more like a circle than a square
2. Appeared very faint
3. Had a smudge in the middle of the print
4. Had a smudge at the end of the print
5. Had a square edge only on one side
6. Were totally smudged

Answers

1. Student did not ink to both nail edges and/or just inked the finger pad.
2. Students used too little ink or used too a light a touch when rolling the print.
3. Student paused in the middle of making the print.
4. Student paused at the end of the print instead of lifting the finger.
5. Square edge on one side indicates that the student did not ink to nail edge; square edge on neither side indicates student either did not ink to the nail edge or did not roll the finger to the nail edge.
6. Student rolled finger back and forth.

Background

In this activity, students study pictures of latent prints and examine ridge pattern minutiae.

Safety Precautions

There are no safety precautions for this activity.

Procedures

1. Print and distribute Act 6-5 SH from the IRCD, Chapter 6.

2. Refer to the fingerprint minutiae chart in the text.

3. Project an image of the suspect's prints and the latent crime-scene print shown in Step 1 in the text. Identify the minutiae patterns in each.

4. You may wish to project images of the fingerprints found in Step 3.

Teaching Tip

To create a new analysis of the suspects' and the crime-scene prints, place the crime-scene print in the center of the paper. Arrange the suspects' prints around the border of the paper.

Teaching Tip

An alternative way to compare prints uses transparency film. Circle the minutiae patterns on the first fingerprint and then the second fingerprint. Along the side of each print, label the minutiae by type. Then place the transparency film over the first fingerprint and trace over the minutiae. Move the transparency over the second fingerprint and see if they are consistent. Discuss how many minutiae are consistent. Discuss if there is sufficient, scientific, reliable evidence to consider the evidence latent print consistent with the suspect's fingerprint.

Is It Consistent? Obj. 6.2, 6.3, 6.8

Objectives:

By the end of this activity, you will be able to:

1. Describe different types of fingerprint minutiae patterns.
2. Identify different minutiae patterns found in fingerprints.

Time Required to Complete Activity: 30 minutes

Introduction:

Latent fingerprints found at crime scenes are usually incomplete (partial) prints. Investigators need to examine the characteristics of a fingerprint very carefully. The simple identification of a whorl, loop, or arch is not sufficient. Other markers (minutiae) are used in distinguishing one fingerprint from another.

Materials:

red pen
Act 6-5 SH
ruler or straight edge
magnifying glasses

Procedure:

1. Study the following picture. It shows fingerprints obtained from a suspect (left) and a fingerprint lifted from the crime scene (right). Notice how the investigator has labeled the points of comparison with the same letter on the rolled ink print and the latent print from the crime scene. Use the table of minutiae patterns (Figure 6-9) in your text to identify the specific types of minutiae.

© Cengage Learning®

Suspect print.   *Latent print from crime scene.*

Fingerprint Ridge Patterns:

2. Identify each of the patterns labeled in the ridge pattern diagram. Refer to the table on minutiae (Figure 6-9) in the text.

A. _____

B. _____

C. _____

D. _____

E. _____

3. Examine each of the fingerprints below. On your student handout, using a red pen and referring to Figure 6-9 in your text, circle the minutiae pattern and then label it with the appropriate number.

Arthur

1. Bifurcation
2. Island ridge
3. Ridge ending

Doris

4. Eye
5. Spur or hook
6. Ridge ending

Alice

7. Double bifurcation
8. Island ridge

Suspect

What patterns can you find in this print?

Further Research and Extensions

Allow interested students to research Daubert criteria and then explain either through a PowerPoint presentation, poster, or research paper what these criteria are and how they are used in forensic science and the courts.

Background

In this activity, students match a latent print to a selection of prints and label reference points.

Safety Precautions

There are no safety precautions for this activity.

Procedures

Print and distribute Act 6-6 SH from the IRCD, Chapter 6. You may wish to make an overhead of the suspect print (or project the suspect's print using a flex camera) and identify the reference points together as a class. You may want to enlarge the fingerprint first.

Teaching Tip

Students should first determine the major type of ridge pattern in the crime-scene print. Try to exclude suspects who do not have the same major type of ridge pattern. Further analysis is required to determine if any of the remaining suspects has a print consistent with the crime-scene print.

Answers

Suspect H is consistent with the crime-scent print. Note that the crime-scene print is only a partial print.

Fingerprint Analysis *Obj. 6.3, 6.8*

Objectives:

By the end of this activity, you will be able to:

1. Analyze the fingerprints to determine if any of the suspects' prints are consistent with the crime-scene print.
2. Support your claim by identifying the ridge pattern and fingerprint minutiae found in both the crime-scene print and the suspect's fingerprint.
3. Circle common minutiae on the crime scene and suspect's fingerprints.

Procedure:

Using a red pen, circle and identify as many minutiae reference points as you can shared by the crime-scene fingerprint and the suspect's fingerprint.

Materials:

Act 6-6 SH
red pencil

Crime-scene print

Time Required to Complete Activity:

30 minutes

Suspect A	Suspect B	Suspect C	Suspect D

Suspect E	Suspect F	Suspect G	Suspect H

© Cengage Learning® (all)

Analysis:

Prepare a written report or PowerPoint or poster presentation demonstrating which suspect's print is consistent with the crime-scene print. Include as evidence ridge patterns, minutiae, any deltas or ridge count, and any scars.

Further Research and Extensions

Collect thumbprints from three or four teachers from your school. Make copies of these prints and pass them out to each student. Have them identify the reference points of each print and the print characteristics.

Using Cyanoacrylate to Recover Latent Fingerprints

Obj. 6.3, 6.6, 6.9

Objectives:

1. Outline the procedure for using cyanoacrylate (Super Glue®) on a latent fingerprint to produce a visible print.
2. Given a latent fingerprint, use cyanoacrylate on the fingerprint to produce a visible fingerprint.
3. Photograph the cyanoacrylate fingerprint and print a copy of the digital image.
4. Identify the ridge pattern and minutiae patterns on the latent print.

Introduction:

This procedure is an inexpensive method of developing a fingerprint using cyanoacrylate. The chemical bonds to the fatty acids, amino acids, and proteins in a fingerprint and produces a permanent white product of that chemical reaction on the ridges of the print. Factors that affect how quickly the product forms include the amount of heat and water vapor. You will do a basic experiment using cyanoacrylate to reveal a print on a glass side. Then your group will redesign the procedure by altering variables in an effort to produce more reliable results.

Time Required to Complete Activity: Part 1: 45 minutes; Part 2: 1 hour

Materials:

Act 6-7 SH
resealable plastic bags (quart or gallon-sized)
glass slide
fume hood if performed inside
camera or phone or computer tablet that takes high-quality photos
plastic beverage-bottle caps
cyanoacrylate
desk lamps, drying lamps, or other nonfluorescent light sources
3" × 5" cards (not white; darkest cards possible)
safety goggles
nitrile or latex gloves

SAFETY PRECAUTIONS:

Because cyanoacrylate and its fumes are toxic, this experiment should be done inside a fume hood or outdoors. Students should wear safety goggles and gloves when handling cyanoacrylate. Students wearing contact lenses should not be exposed to cyanoacrylate or its fumes.

Safety Precautions

Cyanoacrylate, or Super Glue®, is toxic in both the glue form and vapor form. As such, it should *not* be handled with bare skin or inhaled. Students doing this lab should only do the lab under a vented fume hood or outside. Students wearing contact lenses should not be exposed to the fumes of cyanoacrylate. All students should wear goggles and gloves.

Procedures

1. Print and distribute Act 6-7 SH from the IRCD, Chapter 6.
2. Students will follow the step-by-step procedures in Part 1 and then redesign (ideally, *improve*) the protocol in Part 2.

Teaching Tip

Cyanoacrylate will leave a white permanent print on glass, metal, or plastic. It bonds to the amino acids, fatty acids, and proteins found in a fingerprint. To enhance the fingerprint, have students rub the fingers back and forth across the nose or the back of the neck before leaving the print. Students should blow into the bag to add more moisture to the bag. For better results, enclose a beaker of hot water in the bag. The more moisture, the faster the reaction.

Teaching Tip

Remind students that in research, the scientist may continually redesign an existing protocol to produce more reliable results. In Part 2 of the lab, students identify different variables that affect how the fingerprints are produced. Brainstorm the variables.

1. Moisture: Source, placement, amount

2. Cyanoacrylate: Quantity used, brand name, time of exposure, specific placement

3. Heat source: Type, temperature range, placement of heat source, duration

4. Chamber: Type, size, composition

5. Surface from which the print was taken: Does cyanoacrylate work better on plastic, metal, or glass?

Divide students into small groups. Each group selects a different variable to investigate. Have them redesign the protocol using their revised protocol. Teams will photograph their results and present their observations to the class. The class should evaluate which variables seemed to improve the quality of the prints.

Procedure:

PART 1: USING CYANOACRYLATE TO RECOVER LATENT FINGERPRINTS

1. Work with the glue should only be done in a fume hood or outdoors on a flat surface.
2. Fold a 3" × 5" card in half by folding the top down to the bottom (creating a 1½" × 5" folded card).
3. Rub your finger on your nose or the back of your neck to pick up additional skin oil on your fingertip. Use this finger to leave a latent fingerprint on a clean glass slide.
4. Insert the slide with the latent fingerprint into your folded 3" × 5" card. Be sure the fingerprint is on the top of the slide in the folded 3" × 5" card.
5. Insert the folded 3" × 5" card with the latent fingerprint into an opened, resealable plastic bag. The folded card will prevent the plastic bag from touching the latent fingerprint.
6. Blow into the bag to add moisture, and seal the bag.
7. Place 3–5 drops of cyanoacrylate into the beverage cap. (Be sure you are working under a fume hood or outdoors.)
8. Unseal the bag and quickly slide the bottle cap containing the cyanoacrylate into the plastic bag so it is positioned next to the microscope slide. Quickly reseal the bag.
9. Position a lamp above the fingerprint to provide warmth to vaporize the cyanoacrylate.
10. Examine the slide approximately every 5 minutes until a fingerprint is clearly visible.
11. Open the plastic bag (inside a fume hood or outdoors). Remove the 3" × 5" folded card containing the slide from the bag.
12. Photograph the cyanoacrylate fingerprint. Print a copy of the fingerprint photo. (You may want to enlarge the image prior to printing to make for easier viewing. If the fingerprint is difficult to see, you can dust the fingerprint with a powder.)
13. Identify the ridge pattern and minutiae patterns on the fingerprint.
14. Instead of using a glass slide, try working with other objects such as a soda can, paper, or plastic items such as a water bottle.

Procedure:

PART 2: CYANOACRYLATE PROTOCOL REDESIGN

1. Discuss the different variables that affect the development of latent cyanoacrylate fingerprints, and record the information on Act 6-7 SH.

2. Working in small collaborative groups, develop a more reliable procedure for developing cyanoacrylate fingerprints. Each team will work with changing *one* of the variables, observing the results, and subsequently revising the lab procedures. Each team should demonstrate its results showing a cyanoacrylate fingerprint made using the original protocol (control group) and a cyanoacrylate fingerprint produced after altering one variable (experimental group). The class will evaluate which procedural change(s) improved the quality of the print.

Questions:

1. List the different variables that affect the development of latent cyanoacrylate fingerprints.
2. State which variable your team will alter to try to produce better cyanoacrylate fingerprints.
3. Describe how you will alter this variable compared to the original Activity 6-7 lab protocol.
4. Compare and contrast the cyanoacrylate fingerprint made using the original protocol (control group) with the cyanoacrylate fingerprint made using your revised protocol (experimental group).
5. What claims can you make regarding which procedure is more reliable: the original (control group) or your revised protocol (experimental group)? Cite evidence from your experiments to support your claim.
6. Review the experiments of your classmates. What changes made to the original protocol by your classmates seemed to have the greatest effect on the quality of the cyanoacrylate fingerprints? Justify your claim citing evidence from their presentations.

Further Study:

1. Investigate other methods of revealing latent prints, such as iodine fuming and ninhydrin. Prepare a table comparing cyanoacrylate fuming, iodine fuming, and ninhydrin. Include the following:
   - Procedure for each method
   - What the chemical is reacting to in the fingerprint
   - Advantages of each method
   - Disadvantages of each method, including safety concerns (if any)
2. Research why cyanoacrylate bonds to a fingerprint. Describe the chemical reactions that result in formation of the white precipitate.
3. Research how cyanoacrylate fuming became a method used to reveal a latent fingerprint.

1. Answers will vary but should include

   Moisture: Amount, source, location

   Heat: Amount, the source, the duration the slide was exposed to the heat, location

   Cyanoacrylate: Brand name, amount, duration of slide's exposure, its container

   Chamber: Type of chamber, size, composition

   Surface: Glass, metal, plastic

2. Answers will vary. Each group selects one variable to alter.

3. Answers will vary. However, there should only be a single change from the original protocol.

4. Students should consider clarity of the print, visibility of the print, and quality of the print.

5. Answers will vary, but students should compare and contrast results from the original protocol and the redesigned protocol with the altered variable, citing specific evidence. Evidence cited should refer to the actual cyanoacrylate fingerprints, comparing the two photos.

6. Answers will vary depending on what variables the groups altered. In comparing the control group to the altered experimental group, students should make sure that one and only one variable was altered.

Chapter Overview

DNA is an important form of evidence in forensics. Scientists can analyze DNA samples to prove a suspect committed a crime, did not commit a crime, or to determine identity or parentage. This is possible because no two people have exactly the same DNA, except for identical twins. DNA is found in the nucleus of most human cells and carries the genetic information of an individual. One half of a person's DNA is contributed by the mother and the other half is contributed by the father. Crime-scene investigators must be very careful when collecting and preserving DNA evidence, because it can be easily contaminated or degraded. When nuclear DNA is analyzed, a DNA profile is usually obtained by analyzing noncoding parts of DNA called short-tandem repeats (STRs). Mitochondrial DNA and Y STRs can be analyzed to trace maternal or paternal relatives, respectively, of a suspect or victim.

The Big Ideas

DNA is an important form of evidence that is used in criminal and civil investigations. From biological evidence such as saliva, blood, urine, or human remains, DNA can be isolated, amplified using PCR, and analyzed. (Mitochondrial DNA and Y STRs can be analyzed to trace maternal or paternal relatives, respectively). Since the advent of DNA fingerprinting with restriction fragments in the mid-1980s, DNA analysis has advanced. With advances in biotechnology and computer science, a more automated method of DNA analysis using STRs has improved both the accuracy and speed of analyzing DNA. Using population studies, the probability of someone else's DNA profile being consistent can be calculated. CODIS, a DNA database managed by the FBI, has advanced the application of DNA profiling by improving communication among local, state,

CHAPTER 7
DNA Profiling

DNA and Family Relationships

Andrew was a teenage boy living in England with his mother Christiana and her other three children. The family was from Ghana. On his way back from a family visit to Ghana in 1984, immigration authorities stopped Andrew at Heathrow Airport near London. They suspected that his passport had been altered or forged and that Andrew was not its true owner. Andrew was not allowed to enter the country. Because his father's whereabouts were unknown, no blood specimen could be collected from the father. Traditional biological evidence, such as blood typing, could only be used to prove that Andrew was related to Christiana, but could not prove he was her son.

In 1985, lawyers sought help with Andrew's case from Dr. Alec Jeffreys, a famous British geneticist. Dr. Jeffreys had developed the DNA fingerprinting technique in 1984. In this technique, DNA fingerprints appear as a pattern of bands on X-ray film. Except for identical twins, no two humans have identical DNA or DNA fingerprints. Because half of a child's DNA is inherited from the mother and the other half is inherited from the father, DNA fingerprints (or profiles) can be used to prove family relationships. Any bands in a child's DNA fingerprint that are not from the mother must be from the father.

Dr. Jeffreys collected blood samples from Andrew, Christiana, and her other three children. He isolated the DNA and ran DNA fingerprints. He used the DNA fingerprints of Christiana and her three children to reconstruct the DNA fingerprint of the missing father. Each of the bands in Andrew's DNA fingerprint could be found in the DNA fingerprints of Christiana or her three children. About half of the bands in Andrew's DNA fingerprint was consistent with Christiana's fingerprint. The remaining bands were consistent with the reconstructed bands of the DNA fingerprint of the father of Christiana's children.

DNA fingerprinting provided evidence that Andrew was indeed a member of the family. The case against Andrew was dropped. He was allowed to enter the country and was finally reunited with his family.

Dr. Alec Jeffreys

AP Images/Rui Vieira/PA

SCENARIO

In the case described in this scenario, Andrew's DNA would not be perfectly consistent with that of his mother Christiana. Because each person inherits half of his or her nuclear DNA from each parent, only half of Andrew's nuclear DNA fingerprint would be consistent with Christiana's DNA. Ask students: Is sharing half of his nuclear DNA with his mother enough to prove, beyond a doubt, that Andrew is Christiana's son? Ask them to explain their answers.

and national law-enforcement agencies. The creation of a National DNA Index System with more than 10 million DNA profiles of convicted offenders enables law enforcement to identify unknown DNA of repeat offenders.

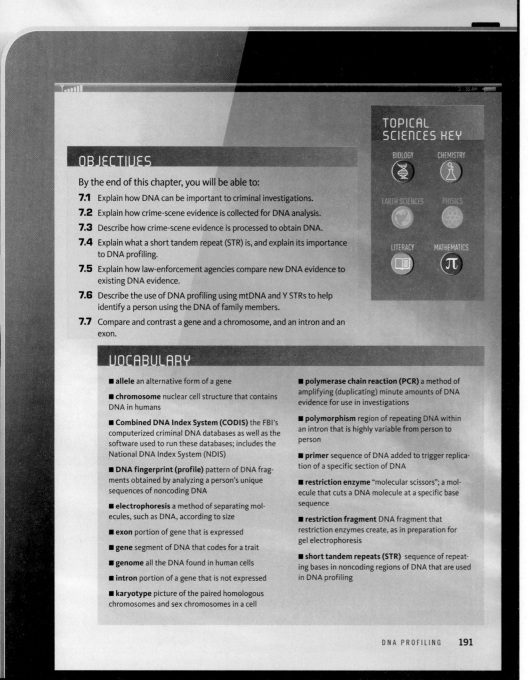

OBJECTIVES

By the end of this chapter, you will be able to:

7.1 Explain how DNA can be important to criminal investigations.

7.2 Explain how crime-scene evidence is collected for DNA analysis.

7.3 Describe how crime-scene evidence is processed to obtain DNA.

7.4 Explain what a short tandem repeat (STR) is, and explain its importance to DNA profiling.

7.5 Explain how law-enforcement agencies compare new DNA evidence to existing DNA evidence.

7.6 Describe the use of DNA profiling using mtDNA and Y STRs to help identify a person using the DNA of family members.

7.7 Compare and contrast a gene and a chromosome, and an intron and an exon.

TOPICAL SCIENCES KEY

BIOLOGY CHEMISTRY

EARTH SCIENCES PHYSICS

LITERACY MATHEMATICS

VOCABULARY

- **allele** an alternative form of a gene
- **chromosome** nuclear cell structure that contains DNA in humans
- **Combined DNA Index System (CODIS)** the FBI's computerized criminal DNA databases as well as the software used to run these databases; includes the National DNA Index System (NDIS)
- **DNA fingerprint (profile)** pattern of DNA fragments obtained by analyzing a person's unique sequences of noncoding DNA
- **electrophoresis** a method of separating molecules, such as DNA, according to size
- **exon** portion of gene that is expressed
- **gene** segment of DNA that codes for a trait
- **genome** all the DNA found in human cells
- **intron** portion of a gene that is not expressed
- **karyotype** picture of the paired homologous chromosomes and sex chromosomes in a cell

- **polymerase chain reaction (PCR)** a method of amplifying (duplicating) minute amounts of DNA evidence for use in investigations
- **polymorphism** region of repeating DNA within an intron that is highly variable from person to person
- **primer** sequence of DNA added to trigger replication of a specific section of DNA
- **restriction enzyme** "molecular scissors"; a molecule that cuts a DNA molecule at a specific base sequence
- **restriction fragment** DNA fragment that restriction enzymes create, as in preparation for gel electrophoresis
- **short tandem repeats (STR)** sequence of repeating bases in noncoding regions of DNA that are used in DNA profiling

DNA PROFILING **191**

KEY SCIENCE CONCEPTS

Biology: function and structure of DNA

Math: calculating probability

Chemistry: chemical composition of DNA and STRs, PCR reactions, restriction enzymes

Teaching Tip

For instructors with less background in genetics or DNA profiling, or for those who wish to give motivated students research opportunities, see the tutorials and multimedia resources from the National Institute of Justice (NIJ) on DNA structure, introns and exons, PCR, mtDNA, STRs, electropherograms, Y-STRs, and familial inheritance. Go to http://www.nij.gov/nij/training/dna-multimedia.htm

TEACHING RESOURCES

Instructor's Resource CD-ROM includes:

- Activities and Student Handouts
- Alternative Assessments
- Consolidated Bibliography
- Correlations to NGSS and CCSS
- Figure Files

- Nonfiction Readings
- PowerPoint Presentations
- Student Learning Objectives (SLOs)

CL Testing powered by Cognero

Website: ngl.cengage.com/forensicscience2e

Engage

Lead the class in a discussion of the following topics:

- Why do children often look like their parents?
- Why do you think brothers and sisters often look alike?

Did you know

If the DNA in one human chromosome were unwound, it would reach a length of 6 feet.

INTRODUCTION

DNA (deoxyribonucleic acid) fingerprinting, first introduced in the mid-1980s, and the improved DNA profiling, have dramatically changed forensic science and the ability of law enforcement to link perpetrators with crime scenes. DNA analysis has resulted in greater certainty of the guilty being punished and the exclusion of innocent individuals as suspects. It has also been used to exonerate the innocent, including those imprisoned prior to the use of DNA technology. Cold cases have been solved by analyzing DNA evidence that may have been stored for decades.

DNA profiling for personal identity purposes has been used in cases involving parentage, identification of disaster and war victims, and resolution of historical and recent missing persons cases. Since the early 1990s, the U.S. military has collected and stored blood samples of soldiers in the event they are killed in action and the remains need to be identified.

In 1994, Congress passed the *DNA Identification Act*, which provided funds to improve forensic labs and communication among law-enforcement organizations. In 1998, the FBI launched the *National DNA Index System (NDIS)*, a database of DNA profiles of individuals who were either arrested or were convicted of a serious crime (depending on the laws of the state). Crime investigators at the local, state, and national levels compare the unknown DNA found at a crime scene with the DNA already entered into the DNA database in an effort to establish the identity of the unknown DNA. **CODIS (the Combined DNA Index System)**, collects, analyzes, and communicates criminal DNA information. (NDIS is now part of CODIS.) By 2014, CODIS had 11.1 million offenders' DNA profiles and 1.9 million arrestee DNA profiles with more than 257,000 hits (successful searches for consistent DNA profiles), assisting in more than 246,000 investigations.

The basis for DNA profiling is that no two people share the same DNA, with the exception of identical twins. Half a person's DNA comes from his or her mother and the other half comes from his or her father. When DNA evidence is left at a crime scene in the form of hair, blood, saliva, semen, bone, or other body tissue, it can establish the identity of the person at the crime scene. The science behind DNA technology is sound. But proper collection, documentation, storage, and processing of DNA must follow precise protocols in order to be accepted as reliable evidence in court.

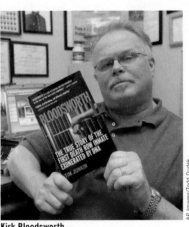

Kirk Bloodsworth

AP Images/Todd Dudek

One benefit of DNA profiling is that innocent suspects, falsely imprisoned before or without the benefits of DNA technology, can be exonerated. In 1992, lawyers Barry C. Scheck and Peter J. Neufeld at the Benjamin N. Cardozo School of Law at Yeshiva University started the Innocence Project. Together with their law students, they used DNA technology to investigate cases and exonerate innocent people falsely convicted of crimes. As of 2014, 318 people, such as Kirk Bloodsworth, left, had been exonerated and released from prison after serving an average of 13 years. Because evidence is stored by law enforcement, it is often possible to perform DNA tests years after collecting the evidence.

DIFFERENTIATED LEARNING

Teaching At-Risk Students

DNA is often a difficult topic for at-risk students because it is abstract; students cannot see or manipulate DNA. Help at-risk students understand DNA and its relationship to chromosomes and cells by using models. After discussing DNA structure, prepare 10 sheets of paper or index cards. On three pieces, write an "A," on three write a "T," on two a "G," and on the last two write a "C." (You can also use different colors of paper for this activity.) Ask students to create a section of DNA with the correct base pairing.

DIFFERENTIATED LEARNING

Teaching English-Language Learners

Many English-language learners may already be familiar with DNA, but by a different acronym. Research some of the terms that have to do with DNA used by non-native speakers, so that you might reference them when an English-language learner is struggling with concepts related to DNA.

WHAT IS DNA? *Obj. 7.7*

DNA (deoxyribonucleic acid) is the genetic material of all living things. Except for red blood cells, all human cells contain DNA in the cell's nucleus (nuclear DNA) or inside the organelles called mitochondria (mtDNA). (Red blood cells have no nuclei or mitochondria.) DNA contains a genetic code for the production of proteins that enable a cell to *replicate* its DNA (make an exact copy) and carry on all life functions. All the DNA found in human cells makes up the human **genome**.

DNA is composed of long repeating units (polymers) known as nucleotides. Each nucleotide consists of a sugar molecule (deoxyribose), a nitrogen-containing (nitrogenous) base, and a phosphate group (Figure 7-1). The four nitrogenous bases in DNA are adenine, thymine, cytosine, and guanine (A, C, T, and G). The order of these bases makes up the genetic code that specifies what proteins a cell produces, when they are produced, and how much of the protein is produced. The reason for variation among people is that the sequence of nitrogen bases in our DNA differs (except in identical twins), making our physical characteristics, and us, unique. The DNA of every organism on Earth is made of the same four nitrogenous bases.

James Watson and Francis Crick received the Nobel Prize (1953) for their work in describing the structure of DNA as a double helix, a sort of twisted ladder (Figure 7-2). The sides of the double helix consist of alternating sugar and phosphate molecules. The steps, or rungs of the ladder, are made up of pairs of *complementary* (paired) nitrogen base pairs with adenine bonding to thymine (A-T) and cytosine bonding to guanine (C-G). If the order of nitrogen bases of one strand of DNA is CGTCTA, then the order of bases in the complementary section of DNA in the other strand must be GCAGAT. There are approximately 6 billion base pairs in human body cells.

Figure 7-1 *A DNA nucleotide consists of a deoxyribose sugar, a phosphate group, and one of four nitrogenous bases.*

Phosphate

Base

Deoxyribose sugar

BIOLOGY

CHEMISTRY

Figure 7-2 *Base pairs on the double helix of DNA.*

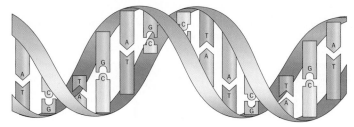

Chromosomes

Nuclear DNA is stored in organelles known as chromosomes. The 46 chromosomes found in human body cells are composed of tightly coiled DNA. Two chromosomes, an X and a Y, are known as the sex chromosomes because

Students may need help understanding what is meant by a double helix and complementary strands of DNA. You might use the analogy of a spiral staircase to help students visualize the double-helix configuration. Tell students that forensic investigators always work with double-stranded DNA, even when they use restriction enzymes to cut DNA into shorter segments.

DIFFERENTIATED LEARNING

Teaching Gifted Students

Gifted students could research genetic recombination. During meiosis, the genes in a pair of chromosomes may be mixed randomly during a process called recombination.

Ask students to investigate how the structure of DNA was discovered. Suggest that they read the book *The Double Helix,* by James D. Watson, one of the discoverers. After reading the book, ask students to explain why Watson and Crick's backgrounds in physics and chemistry were so important to the discovery of the shape of a DNA molecule. Students could also view Watson's TED talk "How We Discovered DNA" at http://www.ted.com/talks\james_watson_on_how_he_discovered_dna

Students can also explore the role of X-ray diffraction in determining the shape of DNA. Have the students research and report on the role of Rosalind Franklin in the discovery of DNA.

Science

BIOLOGY

BIOLOGY

Begin by asking: How is the sex of a fetus determined? Explain that a karyotype is also a tool used by genetic counselors to determine whether a person has a genetic condition caused by chromosomal aberrations, such as Down syndrome.

Explore

Students may find the work of genetic counselors an interesting extension of this material. Invite a local genetic counselor to speak to the class. Ask interested students to research one of the disorders or conditions that the genetic counselor mentions.

Teaching Tip

Portions of DNA that do not have a known purpose are called noncoding DNA, or introns. They are often composed of a sequence of DNA bases that repeat a random number of times per person. This sequence is used for DNA profiles in forensic DNA analysis.

Evaluate

As a review for the information presented in this section, ask students the following questions:

- Where is genetic informa- tion located in a human cell? (Answer: In the nucleus, on chromosomes, which are com- posed of DNA, and in the cyto- plasm as mitochondrial DNA.)
- Why is DNA important? (Answer: It contains the instructions that cells use to build proteins and build new cells and regulate proper functioning of the cell.)

Teaching Tip

For more genetics background, see the multimedia resources at http://learn.genetics.utah.edu

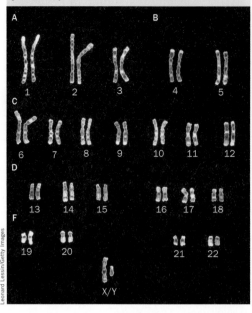

Figure 7-3 *In this karyotype of human chromo-somes, note the 22 homologous pairs of autosomes followed by the two sex chromosomes.*

Leonard Lessin/Getty Images

they determine the sex of the child. Most males have one X and one Y sex chromo-somes (XY), while most females have two X chromosomes (XX). The other 44 chromo-somes, known as *autosomes*, appear in *homol-ogous* pairs (which have the same shape and contain the same genes). Refer to Figure 7-3 for a typical **karyotype**, or picture of homol-ogous pairs of human chromosomes.

In the formation of human sperm and egg cells, the chromosome number (46) is halved. One chromosome of each pair is inherited from the mother along with one of her sex chromosomes. The other chro-mosome of each pair is inherited from the father along with one his sex chromo-somes. So half of your DNA is inherited from your mother and the other half is inherited from your father.

Genes

A **gene** is a segment of DNA that serves in the production or regulation of proteins. Genes average about 3,000 base pairs, but they can be composed of many thousands of base pairs. DNA in a chromosome con-sists of both coding regions and noncoding regions. Approximately 5 percent of human DNA consists of coding regions of DNA, **exons**, that contain blueprints for proteins. The other 95 percent, *noncoding* DNA or **introns**, do not code for proteins, but some may be involved in cell regulation or act as genetic "on-and-off switches." (See Figure 7-4.) After a cell transcribes, or reads the DNA, the introns are deleted.

Figure 7-4 *The coding region of DNA known as a gene includes both exons and introns. Only the exons will be expressed. The introns will be deleted.*

EXON	INTRON	EXON	INTRON	EXON

Alternative forms of a gene are referred to as **alleles**. For example, one per-son may have an allele for the production of normal hemoglobin molecules, but someone else may have a different allele for that gene and produce abnor-mal hemoglobin. The location, or "street address," of a gene on the chromo-some is referred to as its *locus* (plural *loci*).

DIFFERENTIATED LEARNING

Teaching Gifted Students and Visual Learners
The following image may help visual learners comprehend DNA. If each nucleotide were 1 inch long, the nuclear DNA in a single human cell would be more than 100,000 miles long. The DNA in the highly variable regions (polymorphisms) would be only 300 feet long.

DIGGING DEEPER
With Forensic Science eCollection

Go to the Gale Forensic Science eCollection at **ngl.cengage.com/forensicscience2e** to research how polymerase chain reactions (PCR) amplify DNA. If possible, view an animation of the PCR process. Explore the role of enzymes, complementary bases, and promoters. Then outline the steps of a PCR.

COLLECTION AND PRESERVATION OF DNA EVIDENCE *Obj. 7.2*

Critical Thinking

Are the privacy issues involved in the collection of DNA different from those involved in the collection of fingerprints? Consider the differences between the information in fingerprints and the information in DNA.

Because DNA is found in human cells and because people are always shedding cells, it's easy to find samples of DNA. Today, DNA can be recovered from white blood cells, skin cells, semen, saliva, and hair. Criminal cases can use DNA evidence to link a suspect to the crime scene. With the use of **polymerase chain reactions (PCR)**, trace samples of DNA evidence can be *amplified* (copied) so that adequate amounts of DNA evidence are available for testing. Because often only extremely small samples of DNA are available, avoiding contamination is critical when collecting, preserving, and identifying DNA evidence. (Amplifying will amplify contamination as well.) Contamination of DNA evidence can occur when DNA from another source is accidentally mixed with DNA that is relevant to the case. To avoid contamination of DNA evidence, the following precautions must be taken (many can be seen in Figure 7-5):

- Wear disposable gloves and change them often.
- Use disposable instruments for handling each sample.
- Avoid touching the area where DNA may exist.
- Avoid talking, sneezing, and coughing on evidence.
- Avoid touching your face when collecting and packaging evidence.
- Air-dry evidence thoroughly before packaging.
- If wet evidence cannot be dried, it may be frozen, refrigerated, or placed in a paper bag.
- Put evidence into new paper bags or envelopes.

It is important to keep DNA evidence dry and cool during transportation and storage. Moisture may compromise DNA evidence because humidity encourages mold growth, which may damage DNA. Prolonged direct sunlight and warm conditions are also harmful to DNA.

Figure 7-5 *A law-enforcement officer taking precautions to avoid contaminating the DNA evidence he is collecting.*

Marmaduke St. John/Alamy

Teaching Tip

To help make the idea of PCR more accessible, Play the following for students:
A sing-along video about PCR reactions:
GTCA So Fast (song about PCR) sung by Bio-Rad staff http://practicality.wordpress.com/2009/09/11/video-bio-rad-gtca-song/
The PCR Song
bio~rad.cnpg.com/lsca/videos/ScientistsForBetterPCR/
In a class discussion, ask students to explain the lyrics.

Explore

DNA evidence is often preserved for long periods of time, even after its use at trial. Encourage interested students to research the methods of DNA evidence preservation.

Teaching Tip

From 1989 and 2014, there were more than 325 post-conviction DNA exonerations in the United States. If DNA were not properly stored in these case, none of these exonerations would have been possible. Suggest that students read the book *Picking Cotton* by Jennifer Thompson Cannino and Ronald Cotton. It describes how a convicted but innocent man was eventually exonerated on the basis of DNA evidence.

1
2
3
4
5
6
7
8
9
10
11
12
13
14
15
16
17
18

Teaching Tip

Explain to students that in an individual, exactly the same DNA is located in each somatic cell throughout that person's body, with the exception of certain specialized cells (such as red blood cells, which have no DNA). This is why DNA profiling is possible, because the DNA found in the nucleus of a cheek skin cell is identical to the DNA in a white blood cell.

LITERACY

The process of DNA fingerprinting was first proposed by Dr. Alec Jeffreys in England in the 1980s in an effort to solve the rape and murder of two girls. A fictionalized account of this true story can be found in the Joseph Wambaugh novel *The Blooding*.

Did you know

"-phoresis" is based on a Greek word meaning *migration*.

FORENSIC DNA AND PERSONAL IDENTIFICATION *Obj. 7.1*

It may seem to you that personal computers, the Internet, cell phones, and DNA analysis have been around forever. But it wasn't until the 1980s that all these technologies became available. In 1987, Dr. Alec Jeffreys (University of Leicester, U.K.) conducted the first forensic personal identification of a suspect based on a technique he called DNA fingerprinting. We now call an improved technique DNA profiling. In the words of John Butler, Special Assistant to the Director for Forensic Science at National Institute of Standards and Technology (NIST) and author of *Fundamentals of DNA Typing*, "DNA typing (profiling) is the most useful tool to law enforcement since the development of fingerprinting more than 100 years ago." But how is DNA used to establish someone's identity?

When using DNA analysis to identify a person, we do not consider what the person looks like: height, eye or skin color, facial features, or any other physical characteristic that might describe him or her. What scientists use to distinguish one person from another are regions of high variability called *polymorphisms*. These variable regions are located within the noncoding regions of DNA and consist of repeating base sequences of DNA that repeat one after the other, or in tandem. The number of polymorphisms differs among individuals and results in a different DNA pattern, or profile, for each individual. Because 99 percent of all human DNA is the same, scientists only need to examine that 1 percent region of variability instead of analyzing the entire DNA. DNA profiles can help forensic scientists decide if two or more DNA samples are from the same individual, related individuals, or unrelated individuals.

EARLY DNA FINGERPRINTING USING GEL ELECTROPHORESIS *Obj. 7.3*

DNA fingerprinting and profiling examine regions of high variability within the noncoding regions of DNA to establish the identity of a person. In DNA fingerprinting, DNA is isolated and cut using **restriction enzymes**, creating fragments of DNA called **restriction fragments**. Because each person's DNA is different, each person's length and number of DNA restriction fragments differs. Restriction fragments are separated by size on a gel when an electric field is applied. Radioactive probes bond to the highly variable regions. This creates a unique band pattern that can be used to identify a person.

Here is a brief summary of the procedure used by Dr. Alec Jeffreys:

- Collected and extracted DNA from a mouth swab from male villagers
- Added restriction enzymes to cut DNA into fragments
- Performed gel electrophoresis (described above) to identify DNA sequences
- Compared DNA sequences of crime-scene evidence to suspect from village population

Gel electrophoresis has been replaced by the use of STR analysis, which analyzes shorter pieces of DNA.

DIFFERENTIATED LEARNING

Teaching Visual and At-Risk Learners
Students can use an interactive tutorial on gel electrophoresis

SHORT TANDEM REPEATS (STRs) *Obj. 7.4*

In 1991, a new and improved method of analyzing variable regions of DNA was introduced using **short tandem repeats**, or **STRs**. Unlike the repeating bases used by Dr. Alec Jeffreys in DNA fingerprinting, these repeating bases were shorter, consisting of fewer than 50 bases. STRs could be more easily recovered from the often-degraded and limited quantities of DNA typically found in evidence. STR, or an allele of that STR, variable regions of DNA consist of two to six bases of DNA that repeat. For example, one person could have a repeat of GAAT that occurs six times: (GAAT) (GAAT) (GAAT) (GAAT) (GAAT) (GAAT). A different form of that STR, or an allele of that STR, could be four repeats in a different person: (GAAT) (GAAT) (GAAT) (GAAT).

The FBI and the 13 Core STRs

The FBI uses 13 core STRs for identification of Americans. In Figure 7-6, you can locate each of the 13 core STRs on the chromosomes. Some chromosomes have more than one core STR locus (chromosome 5, for example), while others do not have any of the core STR loci (chromosomes 1 and 10). The sex chromosomes X and Y have a non-STR locus (AMEL) that is used to identify the DNA source as belonging to a male or female. One of the more highly variable core STR markers is D18S51 with a repeat of four bases AGAA. The number of repeats found among its alleles varies from 7 repeats to 40 repeats.

Figure 7-6 You can locate each of the 13 core STRs used by the FBI in this image. AMEL on the X and Y chromosomes is not an STR but an indicator of sex.

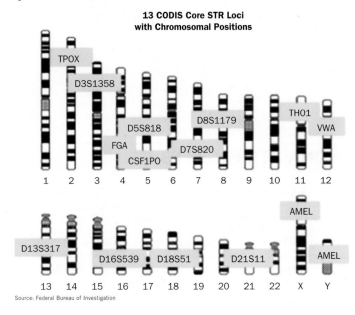

**13 CODIS Core STR Loci
with Chromosomal Positions**

Source: Federal Bureau of Investigation

bar

Explore

For more information on STR analysis, interested students can go to the National Institute of Justice (NIJ) Multimedia Resources for DNA or search the Internet for "NIJ Multimedia Resources DNA."

Teaching Tip

The amelogenin (AMEL) gene is found on the X and Y chromosomes. It can be used to identify gender from a DNA sample. The gene's function is to regulate the formation of enamel in the teeth. The AMELX (female) gene has a 6 base-pair deletion that distinguishes it from the AMELY (male) gene. However, the test is not 100 percent accurate because of mutations in AMELY, so other Y-chromosome markers are often used to confirm.

CHAPTER

1
2
3
4
5
6
7
8
9
10
11
12
13
14
15
16
17
18

Explore

Have students research "touch DNA." The DNA from as few as 30 skin cells recovered from an object or crime scene can be forensically useful when analyzed.

Teaching Tip

Focus on helping students understand STR analysis, since this is the most common practice used in forensic labs. STR analysis does not require pristine DNA for an accurate analysis.

Inheritance of STRs

STRs are inherited when alleles for different traits are assorted independently as sex cells are developed during meiosis. A child inherits one allele from each parent for each STR locus. In the example in Figure 7-7, note that the mother inherited a repeat of 9 from one parent and a repeat of 12 from her other parent (9, 12). When the mother develops an egg cell, only one allele for this STR will appear in that cell. Half of her egg cells will contain the allele with 9 repeats, while the other half will contain the allele with 12 repeats.

In a similar fashion, the father has inherited an allele of 14 from one parent and an allele of 15 from his other parent (14, 15). Half of the father's sperm contains the allele with 14 repeats, while the other half contains the allele with 15 repeats. Through independent assortment, four different allele combinations are found in their offspring: (9, 14), (9, 15), (12, 14), and (12, 15). If one individual has two alleles that are the same for a specific STR, then that individual is considered to have a *homozygous genotype* (for example, (5, 5)). If a person has two different alleles for a particular STR, then that individual is said to have a *heterozygous genotype* (for instance, (9, 14)).

Figure 7-7 *Inheritance of STRs through independent assortment.*

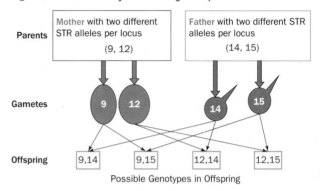

Possible Genotypes in Offspring

DNA STR PROFILES   *Obj. 7.1, 7.4, 7.5*

Because of the great variability of STRs in the human genome, an individual's DNA STR profile is unique. The DNA profile usually includes the alleles for all 13 core STR loci plus the non-STR indicator for the sex chromosomes (AMEL). For example, a person's alleles for one STR locus are expressed as (6, 9), and his or her alleles for a different STR locus are expressed as (5, 5). Gender is indicated by (X, X) for females or (X, Y) for males. The more loci used, the greater the probability that the DNA profile came from the individual identified and not someone else.

DIFFERENTIATED LEARNING

Teaching Gifted Students
Research the role of primers and electropherograms in DNA STR profiles.

STR Analysis

Today, DNA STR analysis is performed using automated machines and computers. Commercial kits and analyzers are used that can amplify multiple STR markers simultaneously. By adding fluorescent dyes to the PCR reaction, it is possible to identify different STR markers (Figure 7-8).

1. DNA is extracted from body tissues.
2. Fluorescent primers are added to amplify the STRs using PCR.
3. DNA STR alleles are separated by size within capillary electrophoresis tubes.
4. DNA samples pass through a laser. Fluorescent dyes on DNA absorb and emit light.
5. A prism separates different colors of light so that they strike an electronic detector at different locations.
6. A signal is recorded as peaks in the graphic display (electropherogram).
7. STR alleles are identified by size and color on the graphic display (such as that in Figure 7-9).

Explore

Have students research the use of nanoparticles in DNA analysis.

Explore

Refer interested students (or a group) to the animated electropherogram tutorials at the Nation Institute of Justice site http://www.nij.gov/nij/training/dna-multimedia.htm. The tutorials are found at "From the Course: Forensic DNA for Officers of the Court." Encourage students to construct a visual presentation of what they learned and to share it with the class.

Figure 7-8 *Steps in STR typing.*

Source: John M. Butler, *Fundamentals of Forensic DNA Typing*. New York: Academic Press, 2010.

Teaching Tip

Refer to the NIJ Web site to view an animation on how the product rule is used to estimate STR frequencies: http://www.nij.gov/nij/training/dna-multimedia.htm

Figure 7-9 *Crime-scene STR profile comparing evidence DNA to the DNA of two suspects. Three different STR markers are analyzed: D3S158, VWA, and FGA. Note that Suspect 1 was excluded, while Suspect 2's STR profile was consistent with the STR profile of the evidence DNA.*

Source: Dr. John M. Butler and Dr. Bruce R. McCord, "Capillary Electrophoresis in DNA Analysis." September 29–30, 2004.

STR Allele Frequencies

MATHEMATICS

BIOLOGY

An *allele frequency* is a calculation of how often a particular allele appears within a given population. Allele frequency equals the number of times an allele is observed in a given population divided by the total alleles observed in the population. Because allele frequencies differ among different populations, it's important that the data for allele frequencies be taken from the correct population. Calculations using STR allele frequencies are made to determine the probability that a random person in the population would have the same DNA profile as the suspect in a crime. For example, refer to Figure 7-10, which compares the STR allele frequencies for a population in North Portugal. The data were derived from 427 Europeans, 414 blacks, and 414 Hispanics. Note that an allele with eight repeats for the STR marker TH01 is more common among blacks and least common among the Hispanic population. This knowledge could provide important clues to that country's law-enforcement agencies when they are searching for suspects whose DNA they've analyzed.

Figure 7-10 *STR allele frequencies differ among ancestries. Allele frequencies for STR TH01 marker for three different ancestries are noted. Note the most common and least common allele for each group.*

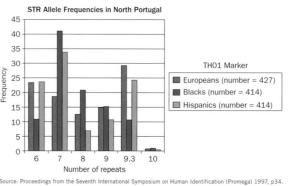

Source: Proceedings from the Seventh International Symposium on Human Identification (Promega) 1997, p34.

DIFFERENTIATED LEARNING

Teaching Gifted Students

Have students view and perform the interactive from NIJ on Analyzing the Parts of a Sample DNA Lab Report. Upon completion, discuss with students:

1. What information is required on the lab report
2. Examples of samples used to obtain DNA
3. Techniques used to analyze the DNA
4. How the DNA analysis is reported.
5. What information is contained in the DNA analysis interpretation section?
6. What is evidence disposition?

http://www.nij.gov/nij/training/dna-multimedia.htm. or go directly to the interactive at https://static.dna.gov/flash/DNACD_mod06-1-01.swf

To better understand how STR analysis is performed, search for information on DNA profiling and STR analysis in the Gale Forensic Science eCollection at **ngl.cengage.com/forensicscience2e**.

Y STR AND MTDNA ANALYSES

Obj. 7.5, 7.6

Many STR markers are being used for identification besides the FBI's 13 core STRs. Many STRs located on the Y chromosome (Y STRs) are used to trace ancestry through the male line because only males carry a Y chromosome. Ancestry traced through the *maternal line* uses *mtDNA* (mitochondrial DNA) because only mothers pass on mitochondrial DNA.

When nuclear DNA is not present or is degraded, scientists will analyze mtDNA. Each cell has thousands of copies of mtDNA. Analysis of mtDNA does not examine STRs. Instead, base sequences within two noncoding, hypervariable regions are compared. Unlike the individual evidence provided by nuclear DNA, mtDNA (and Y STRs) can only yield class evidence, since they can only link evidence to a maternal or paternal line of a family.

Did you know?

The cytoplasm of the human egg cell contains mitochondria with DNA. Human sperm cells contribute no mitochondria to an embryo, so no mitochondrial DNA from the father is inherited by the child.

Kinship or Familial Studies

In 2003, Saddam Hussein was found hiding in a small underground chamber near Tikrit. Scientists did not have a sample of Saddam's DNA, so they compared DNA collected from him with known DNA of his two sons, Uday and Qusay Hussein (Figure 7-11). His identity was confirmed using a rapid DNA test that compared his Y STRs to his sons'. (Recall that an identical Y chromosome is passed from father to son.)

Figure 7-11 *Saddam Hussein and his sons Uday and Qusay.*

Reuters/CORBIS

Civil Liberty Concerns

Erin Murphy, professor of law at the New York University School of Law, raises the concern that the civil liberties of innocent people are being threatened because of familial testing. (Fifty percent of a child's nuclear DNA is consistent with 50 percent of the nuclear DNA found in his or her parents' cells.) Solely because of their DNA, people who have done nothing wrong but are related to a criminal suspect can be investigated. As DNA technology advances, she believes that eventually scientists will be able to determine physical traits and ethnic backgrounds from DNA. Some people think that this is a violation of the Fourth Amendment right that protects the individual from improper search and seizure.

DNA PROFILING **201**

Teaching Tip

Mitochondrial DNA is important because it can be used to identify a person's mother; mitochondria are inherited through the cytoplasm of the egg. The sperm does not contain any of the father's cytoplasm and therefore it will not contain any of the paternal mitochondria. However, it is important to remind students that DNA fingerprints are derived from the DNA that is located in the nucleus and not the mitochondria.

Teaching Tip

In a class discussion, have students compare and contrast nuclear DNA and mitochondrial DNA. What does analysis of each yield? Which is more plentiful? Which can be used to identify an individual?

Explore

Research the case of the Unabomber and find out how his brother's DNA profile was used to determine the identity of the Unabomber.

Teaching Tip

Read the Fourth Amendment to students. (See Teaching Tip p. 210 for the text.) Discuss with the class how it pertains to privacy in familial DNA cases.

Teaching Tip

In 2006, a second gravesite was discovered near the original Romanov gravesite. Because some of the skeletal remains from the 1991 site were still available, more DNA testing was done on them. More advanced methods available in 2006, such as autosomal STR, Y-STR, and mtDNA analysis, along with vast improvements in computers, helped to confirm the identity of the two youngest children. Anastasia and Alexei had been buried in the new gravesite.

Teaching Tip

Use Cross-Cutting Concepts by integrating biology, forensics, history, political science, and literacy in the story of the Romanovs. Coordinate a lesson with the history teacher who can provide background on the Russian political environment in 1917, World War I, the Romanov dynasty, and/or the genealogy of the Romanovs as pertains to Queen Victoria of England. Consider reading excerpts form Robert K. Massie's book *The Romanovs: The Final Chapter*.

Figure 7-12 *Top: Princess Anastasia; bottom: Anna Anderson.*

Pictorial Press Ltd/Alamy

INTERFOTO/Alamy

ROMANOV FAMILY CASE STUDY LINKING HISTORY AND FORENSICS *Obj. 7.6*

The Romanov family ruled Russia for 300 years. Tsar Nicholas II ruled 180 million people and was reported to be worth more than 45 billion (1918) dollars. In 1918, the Bolsheviks captured, held hostage, and ultimately brutally executed the tsar and his family and secretly buried them in mass graves in Siberia.

In the late 1970s, a local geologist, Dr. Alexander Avdonin, located a mass grave containing the remains of nine people believed to be five of the seven members of the Romanov family and their four servants. The location of the grave was kept a secret until 1991, after the fall of the Soviet Union.

In 1991, the nine skeletons were exhumed from a shallow grave near Yekaterinburg in Siberia. A forensic team of experts included Dr. Peter Gill, former member of the Forensic Science Service; Dr. William Maples, anthropologist; Michael Baden, pathologist and New York medical examiner; Dr. Lowell Levine, forensic odontologist; and a Russian forensics team led by Dr. Pavel Ivanov. They assembled to identify the skeletal and dental remains using DNA testing and forensic analysis of bones and teeth.

Using STR analysis, scientists identified the skeletal remains belonging to Tsar Nicholas II, Tsarina Alexandra, and three of the Romanov daughters. The four other skeletal remains belonged to their servants and physician. The remains of the youngest children, Alexei and Princess Anastasia, were not in the grave.

Over the years, many women claimed that they were Anastasia. For more than 60 years, Anna Anderson (Figure 7-12, bottom), because of her extensive knowledge of life at the palace along with her many physical similarities to Anastasia, had many people convinced that she was Anastasia.

In 2006, a second gravesite was discovered. More-advanced methods of autosomal STR, Y-STR, and DNA analysis, along with vast improvements in computers, helped confirm that Anastasia and Alexei were buried in the new gravesite. (An mtDNA analysis had also confirmed that Anna Anderson was not Anastasia.)

DIGGING DEEPER With Forensic Science eCollection

Read the original paper that describes the identification of the remains found in the mass gravesite in 1991. Peter Gill et. al. "Identification of the Remains of the Romanov Family by DNA Analysis." *Nature Genetics*, 1994: Feb 6(2):130–135. Also search the Gale Forensic Science eCollection at **ngl.cengage.com/ forensicscience2e**.

DNA AND FORENSIC SCIENCE Obj. 7.1, 7.4

The following table (Figure 7-13) summarizes some advances in DNA micro-biology and related forensic science.

Figure 7-13

Notable Advances in DNA Forensics and Genetic Technology	
1983	Dr. Kary Mullis invents PCR.
1985	Dr. Alec Jeffreys develops DNA fingerprinting.
1986	Automated DNA sequencing developed
1988	FBI begins DNA casework; Andrews v. Florida is first American case to convict a suspect based on DNA evidence.
1990	Population statistics used with DNA fingerprinting; Human Genome Project begins mapping of human genes.
1991	Fluorescent STR first described
1992	Barry Scheck and Peter Neufeld launch The Innocence Project.
1993	First STR kit available; DNA sex typing developed; first DNA exoneration—Kirk Bloodsworth
1994	DNA Identification Act of 1994 allowed for the establishment of a national DNA database.
1995	O. J. Simpson murder trial raises public awareness of DNA and importance of proper crime-scene processing.
1996	FBI starts mtDNA testing.
1997	13 Core STR loci and Y-chromosome STR loci defined
1998	FBI initiates National Combined DNA Index System (CODIS).
2000	FBI develops National Missing Person DNA Database (NMPDD) to help identify missing persons using STR, Y-STR, and mtDNA.
2002	Improved STR analysis of 16 loci in an easy-to-read graphic display
2003	U.S. DNA database exceeds 1 million convicted offender profiles; Human Genome Project completed.
2004	Justice for All Act grants federal inmates the right to DNA testing.
2007	James Watson and Craig Venter release fully sequenced genomes.
2013	Supreme Court decision: Police can with probable cause take a DNA swab from an arrestee for serious offenses.
2014	National Commission on Forensic Science appointed to standardize and set requirements for certification and training

Source: John M. Butler, *Fundamentals of Forensic DNA Typing*. New York: Academic Press, 2010.

Teaching Tip

"Create a DNA Fingerprint" is an interactive where students create a DNA fingerprint and solve a crime. A tutorial for the interactive describes the role of enzymes, gel, nylon membrane, and X-ray film. It makes a great homework assignment. It can be found at http://www.pbs.org/wgbh/nova/education/body/create-dna-fingerprint.html

Explore

Have students discuss invasion-of-privacy issues in the DNA manhunt described in the first Case Study.

LITERACY

Jennifer Thompson Cannino. *Picking Cotton.*

SUMMARY

- DNA is a nucleic acid that contains the genetic information necessary for a cell to replicate and make proteins. The code of DNA is found within the sequence of nitrogenous bases.

- DNA sequences are unique to each individual (except an identical twin). The variations within noncoding parts of the DNA molecule are the basis for forensic identification.

- DNA analysis can help solve crimes and exonerate the falsely accused.

- Using PCR amplification, minute amounts of DNA evidence can be used to solve crimes.

- DNA contains within its noncoding regions many repeated sequences, including STRs, which vary in number among individuals; these differences are used to produce a DNA profile of a person.

- DNA profiling has dramatically improved over the past 25 years due to improvements in biotechnology, computers, and automated processing of DNA. STR analysis has replaced gel electrophoresis in forensics work.

- DNA profiling enables us to determine whether DNA samples came from the same person or different persons, or to establish kinship.

- Analyses of hypervariable base sequences of mtDNA in noncoding regions can help identify people through their maternal relatives.

- CODIS and the NDIS have helped to prevent and solve crimes by improving communication among law enforcement agencies at the local, state, and national levels.

CASE STUDIES

Colin Pitchfork (1987)

Two schoolgirls in the small town of Narborough in Leicestershire, United Kingdom, had been raped and murdered three years apart along an isolated country lane. The methods used were the same for both cases. Blood-type testing revealed that semen samples collected from both victims were from a person with type A blood. This blood type matched 10 percent of the adult male population in the area, but without further information, no suspects could be identified. The noted geneticist Dr. Alec Jeffreys, developer of the DNA fingerprinting technique, was consulted.

© Cengage Learning®

To compare the DNA of a suspect to the DNA found in the semen, Dr. Jeffreys suggested that police launch the first-ever DNA-based manhunt. Every young man in the entire community was asked to submit a blood or saliva sample. Blood group testing was performed and DNA fingerprinting

DIFFERENTIATED LEARNING

Teaching Gifted Students

Invite students to debate the rights of the individual when asked to provide a DNA sample. Under what conditions might it seem appropriate?

was carried out on the 10 percent of men with type A blood. At first, none of the 5,000 samples of DNA collected was consistent with the crime-scene DNA. Then it was discovered that Colin Pitchfork, a bakery worker, had asked a friend to give a blood sample on his behalf. The police forced Pitchfork to give a blood sample. His DNA was consistent with the DNA evidence found on both victims. He confessed to the crimes and was sentenced to life in prison. This was the first time DNA fingerprinting was ever used to solve a crime. Joseph Wambaugh's book *The Blooding* is based on this case.

Tommie Lee Andrews (1986)

Nancy Hodge, 27, worked at Disney World in Florida. She was raped at knifepoint in her apartment. Her attacker's face was covered. A series of rapes followed, and police suspected that as many as 27 attacks could be attributed to the same man. Tommie Lee Andrews was apprehended and linked to the rapes by fingerprint and DNA profile evidence. He was sentenced to more than 100 years in prison. This was the first time DNA evidence was used in the United States to convict a criminal.

Ian Simms (1988)

Helen McCourt was last seen alive as she boarded a bus on her way home from work in Liverpool, England. Evidence found in the apartment of Ian Simms, a local pub owner, linked him to McCourt's disappearance. His apartment was covered with blood, and part of McCourt's earring was found there. The rest of her earring was found in the trunk of his car. Bloody clothing belonging to McCourt was found on the banks of a nearby river. Her body was never recovered. Dr. Alec Jeffreys analyzed the blood found in Simms's apartment and compared it to blood from McCourt's parents. Dr. Jeffreys determined that there was a high probability that the blood found in Simms's apartment was consistent with that of Helen McCourt. Simms was found guilty of murder, and sentenced to life imprisonment. This was the first time DNA evidence was used to convict a murderer in a case where the victim's body was not found.

Kirk Bloodsworth (1984)

Dawn Hamilton, age nine, was found raped and beaten to death in a wooded area near her home in 1984. In 1985, Kirk Bloodsworth was accused and convicted of the crime, despite evidence supporting his alibi. Because of a legal technicality, his case was retried, and he was again found guilty in 1986. He was sentenced to three terms of lifetime imprisonment. Bloodsworth continued to maintain his innocence. In 1992, a semen sample from the victim's clothing was analyzed by both a private laboratory and the FBI laboratory. Using PCR and DNA fingerprinting, both laboratories determined that Bloodsworth's DNA was not consistent with the DNA evidence from the crime scene. He was pardoned after spending nine years in prison.

Kirk Bloodsworth was the first death-row inmate to be exonerated by post-conviction DNA testing.

ALEXIS C. GLENN/UPI/Landov

Close

Write the following uses of DNA evidence on the board or overhead projector: investigate crimes, establish paternity, identify victims of war and mass fatalities from disasters and accidents, and exonerate the falsely convicted. Organize students into four groups and assign each group one of the topics. Have the group explain how DNA is analyzed to determine identity in that context?

Grim Sleeper

Nicknamed the Grim Sleeper, a Los Angeles serial killer managed to hide from the police for more than 25 years. He acquired the nickname because his crimes were committed interspersed with long periods of inactivity. In 2008, California became the first state to authorize familial searching of the DNA database. An initial search of the evidence DNA did not turn up a hit. A second search in 2010 of a suspect in another crime provided a connection. The markers on the Y chromosome of the suspect's DNA were consistent with those on the Y chromosome of the Grim Sleeper and provided investigators new leads in their search. A police officer posed as a waiter at a pizza restaurant and obtained DNA evidence from the suspect's father, leading to the father's arrest.

DIGGING DEEPER with Forensic Science eCollection

Go to the Gale Forensic Science eCollection at **ngl.cengage .com/forensicscience2e** to research the Grim Sleeper case or other cases in which the use of DNA evidence reopened cold murder cases. Did any of the other cases involve familial DNA? Write a short summary of another murder case in which familial DNA evidence led to a conviction.

Think Critically

Should DNA evidence alone be sufficient to convict when there is no corroborating evidence? State your opinion and provide support for it.

Careers *in Forensics*

Kary Banks Mullis, Nobel Prize–Winning Biochemist

In 1983, Dr. Kary Mullis developed the polymerase chain reaction (PCR) technique for amplifying DNA. The PCR technique is now used throughout the world in medical and biological research laboratories to detect hereditary diseases, diagnose infectious diseases, and clone human genes. Both commercial and forensics laboratories use the PCR technique in paternity testing and DNA profiling.

Dr. Mullis received a Bachelor of Science degree in chemistry from the Georgia Institute of Technology in 1966 and earned a Ph.D. in biochemistry from the University of California at Berkeley in 1972. After several years of postdoctoral work, Dr. Mullis joined Cetus Corporation, a biotechnology company in Emeryville, California, as a DNA chemist in 1979. During his seven years there, Dr. Mullis developed the PCR method. In 1983, Dr. Mullis had the idea of using a DNA polymerase to "bracket" and help amplify small segments of DNA. Unfortunately, the polymerases were destroyed by the heat of the process and could only be used once. In 1986, another scientist in that lab, Randall Saiki, started to use *Taq* DNA polymerase, isolated from the bacterium *Thermophilus aquaticus*, a strain of bacteria that lives in hot springs. *Taq* polymerase is heat resistant and, when added once, can be used repeatedly, making the technique much simpler and less expensive.

In 1993, Dr. Mullis received the Nobel Prize in chemistry for inventing the PCR technique. The

AP Images/Rhonda Birndorf

Dr. Kary Banks Mullis developed the PCR technique.

process is hailed as one of the monumental scientific breakthroughs of the 20th century. A method of amplifying DNA, PCR multiplies a single, microscopic strand of the genetic material billions of times within hours. The process has multiple applications in medicine, genetics, biotechnology, and forensics.

Learn More About It

▶ To learn more about the work of a DNA microbiology researcher, go to **ngl.cengage.com/forensicscience2e**.

Chapter 7 Review

True or False

1. F
2. F
3. T
4. F
5. T
6. T
7. F
8. T
9. F
10. F

Multiple Choice

11. c
12. d
13. a

CHAPTER 7 REVIEW

True or False

1. No two persons can have the same DNA profile. *Obj. 7.1*
2. DNA analysis for criminal conviction was first used in 1980. *Obj. 7.1*
3. Most of our DNA consists of regions that do not code for any proteins. *Obj. 7.4*
4. To confirm someone's identity using DNA analysis, it is necessary to have a preexisting sample of his or her DNA. *Obj. 7.3, 7.6, 7.7*
5. Short tandem repeats are found in highly variable areas of noncoding DNA. *Obj. 7.4*
6. The sex of an individual can be determined using karyotyping or DNA profiling. *Obj. 7.1, Obj. 7.4*
7. Both nuclear and mtDNA analyses are based on the number of repeats of short, tandem repeating bases. *Obj. 7.4*
8. Maternal DNA can be traced using mitochondrial DNA, while paternal DNA can be traced using the STRs on the Y chromosome. *Obj. 7.6*
9. The National DNA Index System is a database of DNA from all people arrested in the United States that is available to law-enforcement agencies at the local, state, and national level. *Obj. 7.5*
10. A DNA profile of a person describes the person's sex, eye color, skin color, and facial characteristics. *Obj. 7.4*

Multiple Choice

11. DNA restriction enzymes *Obj. 7.3*
    a) are used to produce STR fragments.
    b) determine sex in a karyotype.
    c) cut DNA into restriction fragments for gel electrophoresis.
    d) are the same in all humans.

12. Which is true regarding DNA collection? *Obj. 7.2*
    a) DNA is only collected from suspects in murders and rapes.
    b) DNA must be collected in a plastic bag to prevent contamination.
    c) DNA evidence is destroyed after five years to reduce storage problems faced by law-enforcement organizations.
    d) DNA evidence found in trace amounts can be used to solve crimes.

13. Where within the DNA molecule is the genetic code? *Obj. 7.1*
    a) order of the nitrogen bases
    b) sugar-phosphate groups
    c) introns
    d) STRs

14. Describe the relationships between the following pairs of terms: *Obj. 7.1*
    a) gene and chromosome
    b) gene and allele
    c) intron and exon

15. What are the four nitrogenous bases of DNA, and what is their importance? *Obj. 7.1*

16. Advances in technology have improved forensic science and the ability to solve crimes. State the significance of each of the following: PCR, automated STR analysis, CODIS.

17. What is the significance of Dr. Kary Mullis to the history of DNA in forensics? *Obj. 7.3*

18. Refer to the following DNA sequence to answer the questions. *Obj. 7.4*

    CTAGAAGCTTAAAGCTTCATCATCATCATCATCATCATTTAAGCTTCAAAGCTT
    a) What is the STR found within this DNA sequence?
    b) How many repeats are there for this STR?

19. Refer to Figure 7-10, STR allele frequencies. Suppose a witness of a murder in North Portugal reported that a suspect was black, but the DNA profile of the crime-scene evidence came back with 9.3 STR repeats. Using the data in the graph and information in the text, could you draw the conclusion that the perpetrator was black? Explain your reasoning. *Obj. 7.4, 7.5*

20. Refer to the following description of the collection of DNA evidence at a crime scene. Identify errors made during the collection of DNA evidence and provide suggestions as to how those errors could have been avoided.

    A break-in occurred at a jewelry store. The suspect was seen on security cameras breaking a window and entering the shop. A piece of glass from the broken window cut the suspect's arm. A small piece of the suspect's torn shirt and some of his DNA were found at the crime scene. Two cigarette butts were also found outside of the jewelry store near the broken window. Before the crime-scene investigators arrived, the police officer used the empty zip-top bag from his sandwich to collect the torn piece of the bloody shirt along with the two cigarette butts, hoping to retain DNA evidence that could be used to identify the suspect. *Obj. 7.2*

Going Further

1. Form small groups of students to create a model of a DNA concept discussed in this chapter. Present your completed model to another group for peer review and revision before presenting it to the whole class. The model can be a poster; a PowerPoint presentation; a 3-dimensional object; a song, poem, or short story; or a kinesthetic model involving other students.

   Suggested topics

   - A model of PCR reactions, showing how several replications can be produced from DNA molecules

DNA PROFILING **209**

Short Answer

14. a. Chromosomes consist of many genes.
    b. Alleles are variations of a particular gene.
    c. Exons are the parts of the gene that express and code for a protein. The introns are the parts of a gene that are noncoding and not expressed.

15. Adenine (A), thymine (T), guanine (G), cytosine (C); the order of these bases makes up the genetic code that determines the protein produced.

16. PCR: polymerase chain reaction is able to copy DNA evidence so that a DNA profile can be generated from limited sources.
    STR automated analysis: Using computers and technology, it is possible to generate a DNA profile more quickly and more accurately than with previous methods.
    CODIS: Combined DNA Information System of the FBI has created a shared DNA database of convicted persons. This database is shared with law enforcement at the national and state level. It has significantly improved upon the ability to solve cases.

17. Dr. Kary Mullis invented the polymerase chain reaction (PCR) in 1983, which enabled minute amounts of DNA to be duplicated, or *amplified*, so they could be tested for multiple matches in the crime lab.

18. a. CAT b. 7 repeats of CAT

19. Answers may vary. Sample answers: Since 9.3 repeats are much less common in blacks of that population than in the Caucasians or Hispanics, the suspect (if black) has an unusual genome; if the suspect has left DNA anywhere else, that could make him/her easier to find. Since the ID of "black" is based on witness ID, it could be unreliable.

(continues at left)

---

19. *(continued)* Or if the suspect is of mixed ethnicity, he/she may look "black" but have much Caucasian and Hispanic DNA, which can explain the unusual DNA results.

20. • DNA should never be placed in a plastic bag because of concerns with contamination by mold. DNA evidence should be collected in a paper bag.
    • A used plastic bag may be contaminated with other people's DNA, in this case, the police officer's DNA. Only clean paper bags should be used to collect DNA evidence.

• The officer should have used gloves and protective gear to avoid getting his DNA mixed with the DNA of the suspect. Or he should have just secured the area and waited for the CSIs to come and collect the evidence.
• The blood on the shirt should have been allowed to dry before the shirt was put into any collection bag.
• One bag should not have been used to collect both the bloodied shirt evidence and the cigarette butt evidence. Different DNA samples could contaminate each other and ruin both evidence samples.

Teaching Tip

- Be careful not to provide precise suggestions as to how students should do the modeling DNA exercise. Allow students time to come up with their own creative ideas.
- Prior to the activity, each group should review its knowledge of what it will be modeling. Make sure all students have the basic understanding. Direct students to first brainstorm ideas and then select the best of the brainstormed ideas.
- Students will feel more comfortable if they can demonstrate their model to a small peer-review team first. This also allows for improvements.
- Provide some type of award for the best presentation as voted on by the class or a team of outside judges to increase student interest and motivation.

Teaching Tip

The Fourth Amendment states
   "The right of the people to be secure in their persons, houses, papers, and effects, against unreasonable searches and seizures, shall not be violated, and no warrants shall issue, but upon probable cause, supported by oath or affirmation, and particularly describing the place to be searched, and the persons or things to be seized."

   People have a right not to be searched and not to have their possessions searched without a warrant. People also have the right to not have their possessions taken unless the court deems that there is probable cause and has issued a warrant for that seizure.

   The Supreme Court has allowed that DNA be collected as "reasonable" evidence from suspects. But there is no similar ruling regarding DNA collection from *relatives* of suspects. Accept positions backed up by well-supported arguments.

- A model of independent assortment of STRs during meiosis. Show some different combinations of offspring that could be produced from the same parents. (Students may choose to work with only one, two, or three different STR loci.)
- A demonstration showing how to establish relationships with DNA when given the STR loci from the mother, child, and father

2. a) Research the U.S. Constitution's Fourth Amendment. Summarize the main ideas of the Fourth Amendment. (Refer to the text section on civil liberties.)

   b) Form debate teams in which one side presents arguments supporting the collection of DNA from relatives of arrested suspects, while the opposing side presents arguments against the collection of such DNA. Other members of the class can serve as judges and determine which side provided stronger support for their argument.

   Each team needs to:

   1. Prepare a clearly-stated argument that relates to the question of whether or not the arrested suspects' relatives' DNA should be collected.

   2. Provide references to important facts, science, and studies that justify their position.

   3. Avoid justifications that rely on "feelings" or that are not supported by facts or science.

   4. Consider how other people may be affected by their position.

   5. Consider the strengths and weaknesses of the opposite point of view.

   6. Provide a logical explanation showing how your argument is supported by your evidence.

3. Research the 2004 *Justice for All* Act.
   a) Outline the main provisions of this law.
   b) How does this law affect how DNA evidence is used in a federal case?
   c) How does this law provide for better training of lawyers and evidence handlers?

4. Investigate cases that used human DNA collected from animals to help solve crimes. Examples of the variety of cases range from human blood collected from the fur of dogs to human blood found in the digestive tract of mosquitoes that were used to establish personal identity.

Connections

Use colored pencils to draw and color a strand of DNA with at least eight pairs of bases. Make sure that the bases are paired correctly. Explain how your sketch illustrates how DNA can be unique.

Bibliography

Books and Journals

Bhattacharya, Shaoni. "Fast-Track DNA Tests Confirm Saddam's Identity." *New Scientist*, December 16, 2003.

Butler, John M. *Fundamentals of Forensic DNA Typing*. New York: Academic Press, 2010.

Coble, Michael D. "The Identification of the Romanovs: Can We (Finally) Put the Controversies to Rest?" *Investigative Genetics*, 2011: 2:20.

Gill, Peter, et al. "Identification of the Remains of the Romanov family by DNA Analysis." *Nature Genetics*, 1994: Feb: 6(2): 130–135.

Grever, Louis E. "Rapid DNA Technology to Revolutionize Arrestee Screening," *Evidence Technology Magazine*, Jan–Feb 2014.

Hughes, Caroline. "Challenges in DNA Testing and Forensic Analysis of Hair Analysis." *Forensic Magazine*, April 2, 2013.

Massie, Robert. *The Romanovs: The Final Chapter*. New York: Ballantine Books, 1995.

Melton, Terry. "Mitochondrial DNA Examination of Cold-Case Crime-Scene Hairs." *Forensic Magazine*, April 1, 2009.

Murphy, Erin, "The Government Wants Your DNA." *Scientific American*, March 2013, 72–77.

Stoneking, Mark et al. "Establishing the Identity of Anna Anderson Manahan." *Nature Genetics* (1995), 9: 9–10.

Wambaugh, Joseph. *The Blooding*. New York: William Morrow & Company, 1989.

Internet Resources

http://www.innocenceproject.org (The Innocence Project)

http://science.howstuffworks.com/forensic-science-channel.htm (Podcast—How DNA Profiling Works)

http://www.biology.arizona.edu/human_bio/activities/blackett2/overview.html (human ID and probability) or http://www.biology.arizona.edu/default.html (DNA Activity or DNA Profiling link)

www.cstl.nist.gov/strbase/training/NewYork-Apr2012Workshop.html (John M. Butler and Michael Coble. "Topics and Techniques in Forensic DNA Analysis." National Institute of Science and Technology, April 2012. Refer to 3:15–4:45 presentation on Y-STRs, mtDNA, and Romanovs.)

http://www.cstl.nist.gov/strbase/training.htm (or search Internet for "NIST Training Resources" (National Institute of Standards and Technology) or for "Multimedia Resources DNA from NIJ" (National Institute of Justice))

http://www.plosone.org/article/info%3Adoi%2F10.1371%2Fjournal.pone.0004838 (M. D. Coble et al. (2009). *Mystery Solved: The Identification of the Two Missing Romanov Children Using DNA Analysis*)

https://www.fbi.gov/about-us/lab/biometric-analysis/codis/codis-and-ndis-fact-sheet (CODIS) www.ncbi.nlm.nih.gov/pmc/articles/PMC3205009/

http://cibt.bio.cornell.edu/labs/dl/STAT.PDF

© iStock.com/Snowleopard1

Teaching Tip

Additional instructor support and/or material to share with students:

Journals

Coble, M. D., et al, (2009) "Mystery Solved: The Identification of the Two Missing Romanov Children Using DNA Analysis." PLoS ONE 4(3): e4838. doi:10.1371/journal.pone.0004838

Harris, Dennis "New Advances Make DNA Even More Powerful as a Crime-Fighting Tool." *Evidence Technology Magazine*, Jan-Feb. 2013, pp. 6 -10.

Internet Resources

NIJ (National Institute of Justice) Multi-Media Resources http://www.nij.gov/nij/training/dna-multimedia.htm

HHMI (Howard Hughes Medical Institute)

http://www.hhmi.org/biointeractive/double-helix

http://www.hhmi.org/biointeractive/polymerase-chain-reaction-pcr

TED TALKS "How We Discovered DNA," James Watson, 2005

http://www.ted.com/talks/james_watson_on_how_he_discovered_dna

Analyzing the Parts of a Sample DNA Lab report (NIJ)

http://www.nij.gov/nij/training/dna-multimedia.htm

mtDNA Sequencing

http://www.dnajunction.com/technology/mtdna.php

http://learn.genetics.utah.edu

See the IRCD for Activity 7-6 Design and Build a Human DNA Structure

ACTIVITY 7-1

Background

In this project, students have the opportunity to extract and view DNA from living cells of plant tissue. The source of DNA will be wheat germ, the part of a seed that germinates into a wheat plant. Raw wheat germ was chosen because it is inexpensive and can be stored for long periods of time without odor or decomposition.

Procedures

1. Make sure students follow the steps outlined in the text.
2. Print, copy, and distribute Act 7-1 SH Data Table.

You can simplify the procedures and reduce the amount of time to complete the project by premeasuring the materials. It is not necessary to be exact in your measurements. You can assemble all lab materials for students in advance so all they need to do is mix as directed.

Prepare sets in lab "buckets." Each set would contain two plastic foam (hot) cups prepared as described below.

1. Add one rounded teaspoon of wheat germ to one cup.
2. Place a second (empty) cup in the first cup on top of the wheat germ.
3. Add ½ teaspoon of meat tenderizer to the cup on top.
4. Add 3 mL of detergent to the 10-mL pipette.
5. Add 4 mL of alcohol to a second 10-mL pipette.
6. Place both pipettes (ready to use) in the top cup with a stirring rod and test tube.

Students add warm water to the wheat germ in the first cup. The second cup becomes the "test tube holder" for all the other reagents. Instruct students to follow the procedures in the text for mixing and extracting the DNA.

ACTIVITY 7-1

Simple DNA Extraction Obj. 7.3

Objectives:

By the end of this activity, you will be able to:

1. Extract DNA from raw (unprocessed) wheat germ.
2. Describe the role of detergent, meat tenderizer, and alcohol in the extraction.
3. Compare and contrast the solubility of DNA in the soapy solution and the alcohol.
4. Describe how to extract DNA from other cell types.

Introduction:

In this activity, you will extract and view DNA from cells of plant tissue. The source of the DNA is wheat germ. The germ is the part of a seed that *germ*inates into a plant. To extract DNA, you first rupture or break down both the cellular and nuclear membranes that surround DNA. Because they are made mostly of lipids or fats, it is possible to dissolve the membranes by adding detergents. Stirring the wheat germ with the detergents will increase their contact with the detergent and, thus, rupture the membranes.

Once the DNA is free from the membranes and is floating freely within the test tube, it is necessary to deactivate the cytoplasmic enzymes that can shred the long, thin fibers of DNA. Recall that enzymes are proteins. By adding meat tenderizer to the wheat germ mixture, you will deactivate the enzymes and the other proteins, leaving the DNA threads intact.

Because alcohol and DNA are not soluble, you will be able to separate the DNA from the rest of the mixture by layering alcohol on top of the wheat germ and detergent mixture. The alcohol and wheat germ mixture between the DNA strands will collect and can then be removed.

Time Required to Complete Activity:

40 minutes

Materials:

Act 7-1 SH Data Table
Act 7-1 SH Student Design
250-mL beaker
50 mL of warm water
0.8 grams raw wheat germ
2.5 mL dish detergent
1.5 grams of meat tenderizer, such as Adolph's
4 mL of chilled ethanol (ethyl alcohol)
1 test tube (15 mm × 125 mm)
1 stirring rod
10-mL syringes (2)
thermometer
balance

DIFFERENTIATED LEARNING

Teaching At-Risk Students

1. Review the following terms with students:
   - Dependent variable versus independent variable
   - Control group versus experimental group
   - Hypothesis versus theory
   - Diploid number versus octoploid number
2. Discuss with students the use of meat tenderizer in cooking and the role of adding detergent to grease spots on clothing as a pre-wash.

(continued)

SAFETY PRECAUTIONS:

All students must wear safety glasses throughout the project.

Procedure:

1. Add 50 mL of approximately 37° water to the 250-mL beaker.
2. Add 0.8 grams raw wheat germ to the warm water and gently stir.
3. With the 10-mL syringe, add 3 mL of detergent to the wheat germ mixture. Stir.
4. Add 1.5 grams of meat tenderizer to the mixture and continue to gently stir.
5. Wait 10 minutes, gently stirring with the stirring rod at intervals of about three minutes. This helps to hydrate the wheat germ and mix it thoroughly with the detergent.
6. Wait 5 minutes.
7. Fill a test tube half full of the wheat germ and detergent mixture.
8. Tilt the test tube to a 45° angle and gently add 2 mL of cold ethanol. Pour slowly and carefully down the inside edge so it forms a layer on top of the wheat germ mixture.
9. Gently rotate the test tube for at least 3 minutes holding the test tube at eye level. Notice the white strands of DNA forming between the bottom of the alcohol and the top of the wheat germ mixture.
10. Complete Act 7-1 SH Data Table provided by your instructor.

Data Table

Substance added	Describe the function
Detergent	
Meat tenderizer	
Ethanol (Ethyl alcohol)	

Further Study:

1. After completing the wheat germ DNA extraction, work in teams to "perfect" the lab directions. Each team will alter the lab procedures by modifying one aspect of the lab protocol. For example, you might change the type of detergent used; alter the amount of wheat germ, tenderizer, detergent, or alcohol; or modify the stirring time or temperature of the water or alcohol. Complete the Act 7-1 SH Student Design provided by your instructor.
2. This project can be done with any living cells. In teams, set up DNA extractions using strawberries, bananas, liver, hamburger, lettuce, or green peppers. Each team should develop and perfect a lab protocol for its extraction method. All teams should present their DNA extraction method, provide recommendations, and discuss the pros and cons of each technique.
3. Research the genome of strawberries known to be octoploid. Explain why octoploid strawberries yield more DNA than diploid strawberries.

DNA Profiling   213

DIFFERENTIATED LEARNING (continued)

3. Create a model of a cell in the classroom using two long pieces of string to represent a nuclear (inner) membrane and a cell (outer) membrane. Arrange string to form an outer circle and an inner circle. Have a student hold a poster labeled "DNA" stand within the inner circle (nuclear membrane). Have three other students representing DNA-degrading enzymes (*Dnases*) stand in the outer (cytoplasmic) circle. Use this model to discuss and demonstrate the role of the detergent and meat tenderizer in extracting DNA.

Background

A DNA sample is collected from a soda can at a crime scene. Students will work to compare the profile of the DNA from the soda can with that of DNA taken from the suspects. The purpose of this activity is to compare the DNA from a crime scene to available DNA samples.

Safety Precautions

There are no safety precautions for this lab.

The Break-In Obj. 7.2, 7.3

Scenario:

At a high school one day, a break-in occurred that involved the theft of several computers. At the time of the break-in, the building was empty. A motion detector in one of the hallways alerted police. When the police arrived to investigate, they found that one of the doors leading into the school had been propped open with paper wedged into the doorjamb. The door appeared to be locked, but it was not, and it could be pushed open. Near the door, police found a cold soft-drink can. Because of the cool temperature of the drink, police suspected that the can was recently left by one of the intruders.

The can was bagged as evidence, and in the forensics laboratory, a DNA sample was obtained from the lip of the can. A clerk at a nearby convenience store remembered selling canned soft drinks to two young men just before the break-in occurred. The surveillance video in the convenience store was examined, and the clerk was able to provide the police with the names of all three young men who were in the store just prior to the break-in. The three young men were later fingerprinted and each provided a DNA mouth swab sample.

Introduction:

In this activity, you will look for clues from the scenario that provide information about the identity of the thieves or about the theft. Review the DNA fingerprints created using gel electrophoresis. Then compare the DNA from the crime scene with the DNA evidence obtained from the suspects. Determine if any of the suspects were present at the crime scene.

Objectives:

By the end of this activity, you will be able to:

1. Summarize how DNA profiling can be used to help identify a suspect.
2. Analyze the DNA profiles on the gel and determine if any of the suspects' DNA is consistent with the DNA left at the crime scene.
3. Evaluate the evidence and determine if there is sufficient evidence to convict any or all of these suspects.
4. Prepare a table identifying other possible clues left at the crime scene, and describe what tests should be done to analyze those clues to help establish who committed the crime.

Materials:

Act 7-2 SH
colored pencil or marker
ruler

SAFETY PRECAUTIONS:
None

Time Required to Complete Activity:
Analysis of the DNA profiling can be completed in one period.

Procedure:

1. Refer to the DNA profiles comparing the DNA obtained from the three suspects with the crime-scene DNA.
2. Use a ruler to align the bands found under the crime-scene DNA with any of the bands found in the suspects' DNA. Place the ruler at the bottom of the bands. Take notes on whether any of the suspects' DNA shares the same bands as the crime-scene DNA.
3. Analyze your notes on each suspect's DNA profile. Do any suspects share all the DNA bands found in the evidence DNA?

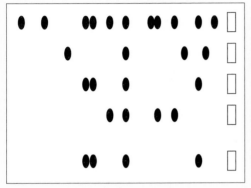

Ladder

DNA from suspect #1

DNA from suspect #2

DNA from suspect #3

Crime-scene DNA

Questions:

1. Did any suspect share all four bands of DNA with the crime-scene DNA? If so, which suspect or suspects?
2. Note that one band of the evidence DNA was found in all four suspects. Explain.
3. If any of the suspects did not share any of the bands found in the evidence DNA, can they be excluded as suspects?
4. What arguments could a defense lawyer present to support his claim that even though his client's DNA was consistent with the evidence DNA, his client did not commit the crime?
5. Refer to the scenario presented at the beginning of this activity and your knowledge of DNA profiling. List the many ways that DNA technology has improved the ability of law enforcement to solve crimes.

Procedures
From the IRCD, Chapter 7, copy and distribute Act 7-2 SH.

Answers
Check students' DNA samples.

Questions

1. Suspect 2 shared all four bands found in the evidence DNA.
2. This could be a very common gene.
3. No. They could still have been at the crime scene. The evidence DNA came from one soda can. Investigators need to look for other clues left at the crime scene that may link those suspects to the crime.
4. Answers may vary. Sample answers: The DNA evidence on the soda can links him to the crime scene, but there is no direct evidence that he committed the crime; it's not clear when the soda can was left at the crime scene—it could have been left before or after the crime occurred; could someone else's DNA match this profile?
5. Answers may vary. Sample answers: DNA is direct, individual evidence; PCR can amplify trace DNA evidence; STRs can create DNA profiles of suspects.

7. Answers will vary. Some may argue that this is not a serious crime and does not jeopardize the safety of others, so none of the suspects should have their DNA entered. Since the suspects were arrested but not yet convicted, they may all be innocent.

Others may argue that there is sufficient evidence to link them to the crime scene, even if they aren't convicted, so one is likely guilty, and therefore their DNA evidence needs to be entered into the system. Students may cite that most crimes are committed by repeat offenders. Although this crime did not endanger the lives of others, perhaps the next crime will. Their DNA should be entered into NDIS.

6. Refer to the scenario and identify the clues that could help the police identify who was recently at the crime scene. Prepare a table listing the evidence and describe what type of testing should be done on that evidence.

7. Do you think DNA from the three suspects arrested for the break-in should have their DNA entered into the National DNA Index System before any are convicted? What rational arguments could be used to support your claim?

Going Further:

1. Research cases heard by the Supreme Court or current articles regarding whether or not states have the right to take DNA evidence from an arrestee.

216   DNA Profiling

6.

Evidence at Crime Scene	Testing
Soda in can	ID DNA on can or in soda; measure temperature of soda to indicate time since purchase; lift fingerprints from can.
Paper wedged in door	Lift fingerprints from paper.
Surveillance video	Identify suspect; see if the soda can was the same brand as that left at crime scene.
Footprints	Compare to footwear of suspects.

Anna Anderson or Anastasia? STR Analysis *Obj. 7.6*

Background:

Anna Anderson claimed for more than 60 years that she was Princess Anastasia. In addition, Anna Anderson knew a great deal about life in the Russian palace and she could speak very knowledgably about family members. Anna had many people convinced that she was Anastasia. Does the DNA evidence support her claim?

In this activity, you will examine the STR profiles of Anna Anderson, along with those of Tsar Nicholas and Tsarina Alexandra. In this way, you will determine if the DNA evidence supports the claim that Anna Anderson was the child of the tsar and tsarina. Recall that each parent must contribute one STR allele at each STR locus.

SAFETY PRECAUTIONS:

Time Required to Complete the Activity:

30 minutes

Materials:

Act 7-3 SH
red pencil
blue pencil

Objectives:

At the completion of this activity, the student should be able to:

1. Analyze STR profiles of the tsar, tsarina, and Anna Anderson.
2. Determine if Anna Anderson was the biological daughter of the tsar and tsarina based on STR analysis.
3. Describe the number and types of different STR loci used in this analysis.
4. Summarize how to analyze STR profiles to determine if Anna Anderson was the daughter of the tsar and tsarina.
5. Describe other applications of STR analysis besides establishing maternity and paternity.

Procedure:

1. Refer to the data table entitled Short Tandem Repeats STR Results Tsar-Tsarina—Anna Anderson at the end of this activity. The data table shows the STRs of the tsar, tsarina, and Anna Anderson. Note that there are five STR loci: VWA, TH01, F13A1, FES/FPS, ACTBP2, and a test for amelogenin (AMEL), which indicates sex (X, X or X, Y).

Procedures

From the IRCD, Chapter 7, copy and distribute Act 7-3 SH.

Questions

1. a. There were five different loci analyzed.
    b. VWA, TH01, F13A1, FES/FPS, and ACTBP2
    c. The AMEL or AMELOGENIN STR is used to determine sex, male or female.
2. Both the tsar's and tsarina's DNA came from skeletal remains. Anderson's DNA came from an intestinal tissue sample.
3. DNA samples could be retrieved from hair on hairbrushes or combs; hair on clothing; saliva on toothbrushes or cigarette butts; sweat, saliva, or blood found on clothing.
4. a. Locus F13A1 shows Anderson with a combination of 3.2 and 7. She could have inherited the 3.2 from the tsarina and the 7 from the tsar.
    b. ACT BP2 shows that Anderson inherited the (15, 18) combination. Neither the tsar nor tsarina had a 15 or an 18.

DNA Profiling   **217**

DIFFERENTIATED LEARNING

Gifted Students

Have students research the normal function of the amelogenin gene. What are the gene's loci? How does it distinguish the gender of the person? How does the DNA for amelogenin differ in males and females?

5. a. Anderson's allele for the first STR (VWA) is (14, 16)

   b. Disagree. It is not possible to tell if Anderson inherited the 16 from the tsar or tsarina because both the tsar and tsarina have an allele of 16.

6. Based on the DNA profiles, Anna Anderson was not the biological daughter of the tsar and tsarina. To be the daughter of these two people, she would have had to inherit one STR allele from the tsarina and one STR allele from the tsar for every locus. This is only true for one STR locus out of the five STR loci shown.

7. a. Three out of six alleles have a repeat of 16. The allele frequency is 3/6 or .500.

   b. Two of the six alleles have a repeat of 15. The allele frequency is 2/6 or .333.

   c. Only 1 of six alleles has a repeat of 14. The allele frequency is 1/6 or .166.

8. The allele with 15 repeats

2. If Anna Anderson's claim of being Anastasia were true, then Anna Anderson must have had one allele from the tsar and one allele from the tsarina for *each* STR locus.
   - If Anderson did have one allele from the tsar and one allele from the tsarina for *each* STR locus, then it was likely that she was the biological daughter of the tsar and tsarina.
   - If she did *not* have at one allele from the tsar and one allele from the tsarina for *each* STR locus, then it is unlikely that she was their biological daughter.

3. Examine the third STR locus F13A1. Compare Anderson's STR alleles to those of the tsar and the tsarina. Did Anna Anderson inherit one STR allele from each of them?
   - Note on both Anderson's and the tsar's STR genotypes below the allele they have in common. (Circle them in blue on Act 7-3 SH.)
   - Note on both Anderson's STR and the tsarina's STR genotypes below the allele they have in common. (Circle them in red on Act 7-3 SH.)

Tsar	(7) 7
Tsarina	(3.2) 5
Anna Anderson	(3.2) (7)

4. Repeat the process for the remaining STRs.

5. Analyze your data to determine if Anna Anderson was the daughter of the tsar and tsarina. Discuss and compare your finding with another student. Did you both reach the same conclusion?

Short Tandem Repeats Results: Tsar, Tsarina, Anna Anderson

Name	VWA	TH01	F13A1	FES/FPS	ACTBP2	AMELOGENIN
Tsar (Skeleton 4)	15,16	7, 9.3	7,7	12,12	11,32	X,Y
Tsarina (Skeleton 7)	15,16	8,8	3.2, 5	12,13	32,36	X,X
Anna Anderson (Intestinal Sample)	14,16	7, 9.3	3.2, 7	11,12	15,18	X,X

Source: Gill, Peter, et al. "Establishing the Identity of Anna Anderson Manahan." *Nature Genetics* 9 (9–10), 1994.

Questions:

1. Refer to the DNA profile. Recall that this analysis was completed in 1995.
   a. How many different STR loci were analyzed (besides the AMEL test)?
   b. List the abbreviations for each of the STR loci analyzed.
   c. What does the AMEL STR reveal?

2. Refer to the data table. What tissues were used to obtain DNA from the tsar, the tsarina, and Anna Anderson?

3. Although Anna Anderson was cremated when she died in 1984, a tissue sample from surgery she'd had was stored in a hospital. It was from this tissue sample that scientists were able to extract her DNA and perform the STR profile. Suppose this tissue sample hadn't been available. What are other ways to obtain someone's DNA after they have already died and have been buried?

Further Research and Extensions

- View the presentation by the National Institute of Standards and Technology (NIST) entitled "Brief History of Forensic DNA Typing" to learn more about how DNA is used in personal identification. How is DNA analyzed? What are STRs? http://www.cstl.nist.gov/strbase/ppt/intro.pdf

- View the presentation by Michael D. Coble of the National Institute of Standards and Technology entitled "Y-STRs, mtDNA, and the Romanov Case." http://www.cstl.nist.gov/strbase/training/NY-Apr2012-Y-mtDNA-Romanovs.pdf (frames 75-140, earlier slides contain more advanced information.)

- Read the original paper describing the findings of the first sets of skeletal remains found in Russia. Peter Gill et al. "Identification of the remains of the Romanov family by DNA analysis." *Nature Genetics* (1994) 6 (2): 130–135.

(continued)

4. Refer to the data table.
   a. Which STR locus or loci in Anderson's DNA profile show(s) one allele coming from the tsar and the other allele coming from the tsarina?
   b. Which STR locus or loci show(s) that Anderson did not inherit either of her alleles from either the tsar or tsarina?
5. Refer to the data table. Examine the first STR locus called VWA.
   a. What are the two alleles in Anderson's DNA?
   b. Do you agree or disagree with the following statement?

Based on this first STR locus, Anderson would have had to have inherited one allele from the tsar but no alleles from the tsarina.

6. Based on your DNA STR profile analysis, was Anna Anderson the daughter of the tsar and tsarina? Support your claim.
7. Refer to the STR locus VWA. Notice that among the tsar, tsarina, and Anderson there are a total of 6 alleles. Recall that allele frequency equals number of alleles observed in a population divided by the total number of alleles observed in a population. In this very limited population of 3, calculate the allele frequency at this locus for
   a. the allele having 16 repeats.
   b. the allele having 15 repeats.
   c. the allele having 14 repeats.
8. For the alleles of the VWA locus, which one has a frequency of about 0.333? (Convert the fraction to a decimal.)

Going Further:

1. Discuss with your classmates and record ways that you could you apply STR analysis techniques other than establishing family relationships.
2. Read the article describing the discovery of the second Romanov gravesite discovered in 2006: "Mystery Solved: The Identification of the Two Missing Romanov Children Using DNA Analysis" by Michael D. Coble, and Odile M. Loreille, et al. http://www.plosone.org/article/info:doi/10.1371/journal.pone.0004838
   a. What new information was learned about Alexei and Anastasia from the recovery of skeletal remains from this second gravesite?
   b. DNA technology advanced between the years 1991 and 2006. Compare and contrast the STR analysis done in 1991 with the STR analysis completed in 2006. Why were the results of the STR analysis more accurate in 2006?
   c. Additional testing was done on some of the skeletal remains that were recovered in 1991. Did these additional tests support the original findings?
3. Research the life of Anna Anderson. Did she marry? Where did she live most of her life? What was her real name? Why did she have a tissue sample in Virginia? Why did so many people believe that she was Anastasia?
4. Notice that some STRs are written in the form of a decimal. Research these STRs. They are known as microvariants. Explain what it means when an STR is written in a decimal form.

Going Further

For more information about the Romanovs refer to (and refer students to)

- www.DNAi.org/d/index.html
  Click on Applications and then on Recovering the Romanovs.
- DNA learning center tutorial: Romanovs DNA Learning Center, Media and Animation, "Solving the Mystery of the Romanovs". Mitochondrial DNA http://www.geneticorigins.org/mito/media3.html
- YouTube video http://www.youtube.com/watch? V=AL-Uytazezy "Forensic Investigation of Remains" (7 min 42 s) or search "YouTube Romanovs" on the Internet

Teaching Tip

1. Once you know how common a specific STR allele is for a given population, you can determine the probability or likelihood that the STRs found in a particular individual could also be found in someone else. As a class, discuss how to use the product rule and population studies of allele frequencies to calculate the probability of any particular STR profile being found in more than one person.

- Read the original paper describing the discovery of skeletal remains in 2006 and the identification of the last two Romanov children. Open access PLOS one. "Mystery Solved: The Identification of the Two Missing Romanov Children Using DNA Analysis," by Michael D. Coble, Odile M. Loreille, et al. http://www.plosone.org/article/info:doi/10.1371/journal.pone.0004838
- Read *The Romanovs: the Final Chapter* by Robert K. Massie (Ballantine Books, NY,) 1995.
- Read the original document that compared Anna Anderson's STRs to those of the tsar and tsarina. Mark Stoneking et al. "Establishing the Identity of Anna Anderson Manahan," *Nature Genetics* (1995) 9: 9-10.

Background

During this activity, students will examine STR loci to hypothesize whether remains found at the World Trade Center site could belong to the father of two boys based upon STR data presented in a table.

Time Required to Complete the Activity

40 minutes

Safety Precautions

There are no safety precautions for this lab.

Teaching Tip

Prior to doing this lab, lead students in a carousel brainstorming activity as a preassessment of their knowledge of the September 11 attacks. Post at least eight large posters throughout the room. On each of the posters, write a question about September 11 and its impact on society. Refer to Act 7-4 TN Carousel (IRCD, Chapter 7) for a list of suggested questions. Ask students to count out in eights. All number 1s move to poster 1, all number 2s go to poster 2, etc. Provide each group of students with a different-colored marker. Students brainstorm ideas to answer the questions at each poster before rotating to the next poster. One student is the recorder. When students have completed the rotation, one person summarizes the brainstorming list and presents the information to the class. This is a good preassessment activity with small-group collaboration that identifies misconceptions. Students who may be hesitant about speaking in a large group feel more comfortable expressing their ideas in small groups.

STR Identification of a September 11 Victim *Obj. 7.6*

Scenario: Author's Personal Recollection of September 11

A warm breeze flowed into my sunny biology classroom on the early morning of September 11, 2001. Shortly after 8:46 AM, a frantic fellow teacher ran into my classroom stating that the North Tower of the World Trade Center, the tallest building in New York City, had been struck by an airplane. I turned on the television and my class and I watched in horror as the black, billowing smoke and intense heat spewed out of the upper-story windows. At 9:03, we witnessed a second plane crash into the South Tower of the World Trade Center.

We later learned that four different commercial airplanes had been hijacked by 19 members of al Qaeda. This was an act of terrorism directed toward the United States. Initially, approximately 3,000 people died as a result of the attacks—people working at the World Trade Center and the Pentagon, first responders, airline passengers, and the hijackers. Later estimates attribute more than 6,000 deaths to the initial attack or subsequent illnesses.

Because of the intense heat and the ultimate collapse of the World Trade Center buildings, identification of remains has been very difficult. Only 1,634 remains have been identified by DNA analysis (as of 2013).

A student whose father died in the World Trade Center bombings brought to school the printed DNA STR profiles used to determine if remains found near the World Trade Center could have been his father's remains. The student had no idea what the graph represented and asked for help in understanding the information.

The student asked if I could explain how this test was done and to determine if the results of the test confirmed the identity of his father. The names have been removed and the numbers were changed to protect his and his family's privacy. The student requested that I keep the graph and use it to educate others to show how some of the victims of September 11 were identified using DNA.

In this activity, you will review the STR profiles of the DNA remains thought to be the young man's father along with the STR profiles of his wife and their two sons. Based on this analysis, determine if the remains are indeed the remains of this young man's father.

Background:

To establish paternity and maternity of a child, each parent must contribute one of the two STRs for any given STR locus. Recall that a *genotype* is made up of the allele combinations for a trait. If a person has one allele with 14 repeats and another allele with 15 repeats for a specific STR, then their genotype is written as (14, 15).

Objectives:

At the end of this activity, you will be able to:

1. Analyze the results of the STR profiles of the two boys, their mother, and remains from the World Trade Center site (thought to be the boys' father).

Teaching Tip

This activity is an opportunity to team teach with the biology, history, math, and English teachers.

- History: Effect and consequences of September 11.
- Math: Calculating probability of someone matching alleles at all 13 loci using allele frequencies from population databases

- English: Assist in writing about September 11.
- Biology: What is DNA? What are STRs?

If it isn't possible to involve different teachers in this lesson, divide the class into four teams. Each team will be the specialist or the "teachers" for each discipline. Have student teams develop "lessons" about September 11 and present them to the class.

2. Determine if the unknown DNA belonged to the father of these two boys.

3. Summarize how kinship can be established using STR profile analysis.

Time Required to Complete This Activity:

40 minutes

SAFETY PRECAUTIONS:

Materials:

Act 7-4 SH STR Profile
blank sheet of 8-1/2" × 11" paper
red pencil
blue pencil

Procedure Part 1: Understanding the STR Profiles

Refer to the data sheet Act 7-4 SH STR Profiles

1. The STR profiles of the four people appear in a line from left to right. Each one appears as a series of peaks. Locate all four persons' STR profiles on the Act 7-4 SH STR Profiles. Hold a blank sheet of paper under each person's profile to make it easier to read.

   • Mother's profile is the top line beginning with (14, 16) (11, 13) (17, 18), etc.
   • Unknown DNA from World Trade Center site (thought to be the father) is the second line.
   • Son 1 is the third line
   • Son 2 is the fourth line

2. Notice that the 13 different STRs are listed at the top of the page. The amelogenin test for gender is abbreviated as AMEL. To simplify the reading of the STR loci, the different STRs are identified as numbers 1–13 and not by names of the STR. Find the column on the profile sheet for the AMEL test. Note the mother's AMEL test is XX, and all the other AMEL tests are XY (for the unknown DNA and the two sons).

3. Examine the first STR, STR 1, on the top left side of the paper. Place the blank sheet of paper so that only STR 1 is visible. You should be looking at the first vertical columns of numbers.

   Examine the STR allele combinations for the STR Locus 1 for each of the four people.

Mother	14, 18
Unknown DNA	15, 16
Son 1	15, 18
Son 2	14, 15

   Recall that each person has two alleles for any STR locus. You inherit one allele from your mother and the other from your father.

Teaching Tip

Review how different STRs are inherited through independent assortment, which results in different gene combinations, or *genotypes,* in offspring.

Teaching Tip

Act 7-4 SH STR Profile is found on the IRCD. The Act 7-4 TN Carousel, also on the IRCD, is a list of suggested questions for the teacher to use for the September 11 carousel brainstorming activity that can be done prior to Activity 7-4.

Teaching Tip

Have students use a blank sheet of paper to cover the part of the STR profiles not in use. For example, when viewing the STR profile of the mother, cover all the other STR profiles for the other persons. (STR profiles are read from left to right.)

When examining the genotypes for STR 1, use the blank sheet of paper to cover all the other STR loci (STR 1 is read from top to bottom).

Teaching Tip

Review that sex determination depends on the inherited sex chromosomes. Males are XY and females are XX.

Explore

To simplify the activity, the actual names of each of the 13 CODIS STRs are not used in this activity. Rather, they are numbered. For more advanced classes, refer students to Figure 7-6 for the actual names of the STRs.

Examine the STR allele combinations for STR 2. Slide your paper to the right so that you are not looking at the other STR profiles, just the STR 2 loci.

Mother	11, 13
Unknown DNA	12
Son 1	12, 13
Son 2	11, 12

Can you think of a reason the "Unknown DNA" has only one number, *12*? In this instance, the unknown DNA sample has inherited *two* alleles for a repeat of 12. On the graph, it appears only as one number 12. In actuality, it is (12, 12), or a homozygous genotype. Look for other examples on the printout that show a homozygous genotype.

5. Continue to examine the STR profiles for STR 2. Notice that the peaks on the profiles for the mother are much higher than the peaks for Son 1. The height of the peak is not affected by the number of repeats of the STR. The height of the peak is a reflection of the quantity of DNA in the sample. If there was not a sufficient amount of DNA, then the DNA would have to be amplified.

6. Slide your blank sheet of paper to the right and examine STR 5. Notice the mother has a genotype of (6, 9.3). One allele has a repeat of 6, while the other allele is listed as 9.3. An allele of 9.3 indicates there are 9 complete repeats and a partial repeat consisting of only 3 bases. For example, GATA is one example of a repeating STR. If the allele is written as 9.3, that means that there are 9 full repeats of GATA followed by GAT.

9.3 means GATA GATA GATA GATA GATA GATA GATA GATA GATA GAT, or 9 full repeats [GATA], followed bya partial repeat of [GATA], with only 3 of the 4 bases.

Procedure Part 2: Analysis of Four STR Profiles to Establish Kinship

To establish the kinship and identification of the unknown DNA recovered from September 11, you will determine if

- The man supplied one STR allele for each STR locus to each child
- The mother provided one allele for each STR

7. Examine each STR locus individually. Cover your STR profiles so that only the STR 1 profiles are visible. (STRs run from top to bottom.)

a. Notice Son 2 has a (14, 15) genotype for STR 1. Which person contributed the 14? Check the mother first. Since she has a (14, 18) genotype, it was possible for her to contribute the 14 to Son 2. Draw a red circle around the 14 on the mother's STR and a red circle around the son's 14 as shown below:

Son 2 (14), 15   Mother (14), 18

Teaching Tip

Review the word *genotype* with your students. Remind them that each parent contributes one allele for any STR. If the data table shows a person with only one number (as in STR 2 for the unknown DNA), that is because the person is homozygous for an allele (has two of the same alleles at that locus).

b. The son's other allele, 15, had to come from the father. Check the unknown DNA for STR 1. Note that unknown DNA has a (15, 16). Using your blue pen, draw a circle around the 15 in the son's genotype and a 15 around the unknown DNA genotype as shown below:

Son 2 ⑭, ⑮   Unknown DNA ⑮, 16
       OK

c. For STR 1, you have shown that Son 2's (14, 15) could have been inherited from these two people. Under the 14, 15 of Son 2 write the word "OK" as indicated above.

d. However, having one STR "match" could be a coincidence. Therefore, it is necessary to check each of the 13 STR loci to ensure that this mother and the unknown DNA from September 11 were actually the parents of Son 2.

8. Using the same procedure, examine the 12 remaining STR profiles for Son 2 with the mother's DNA and the unknown DNA.

9. Repeat this process for all 13 STR loci for Son 1, mother, and unknown DNA.

10. Based on your examination of all the STRs and the evidence found on the STR profile, could the unknown DNA recovered at the World Trade Center site be the father of Son 1 and Son 2?

Questions:

1. Based on your observations and your analysis of the STR profiles, would you consider the unknown DNA from the World Trade Center site to be the father of Son 1 and Son 2 and the husband of this woman? Support your claim.

2. Refer to the Act 7-4 SH.
   a. Which STR had the largest number of repeats?
   b. Which STR had the smallest number of repeats?

3. The peaks on the STR profile sheet refer to the quantity of the DNA sample. If there was insufficient DNA evidence recovered,
   a. What would the graph look like?
   b. What process could amplify the amount of DNA?

Further Study:

1. A database called CODIS uses 13 core STRs for personal identification for Americans. Search the Internet for CODIS and the 13 core STRs. What are the names of the 13 STRs? On which chromosomes would you find these 13 STRs? Why would different STRs be used in Europe?

2. Refer to the Blacket Family DNA Activity at the University of Arizona Biology Project for more information about STRs and human identification and probability: http://www.biology.arizona.edu/human_bio/activities/blackett2/overview.html or search the Internet for "Biology Project Arizona."

Questions

1. It appears that the DNA recovered from the World Trade Center is from the father of these two sons and that the woman is the mother of these two sons. Both children have at least one STR for each allele contributed by each parent.

2. a. STR 9 with a repeat of 31.2
   b. STR 5 had a repeat of 6

3. a. There would not be a visible peak on the graph.
   b. PCR reactions can amplify the DNA.

Teaching Tip

Refer to these sites for additional information.

Frequently Asked Questions (FAQs) on the CODIS (Combined DNA Index System) Program and the National DNA Index System http://www.fbi.gov/about-us/lab/biomertic-analysis/codis/codis-and-ndis-fact-sheet

National Institute of Justice, Multimedia Resources from DNA.gov http://www.nij.gov/nij/training/dna-multimedia.htm

The Biology Project, University of Arizona

http://www.biology.arizona.edu/default.html (home page)
Go to DNA Activity and DNA Profiling links
Or go to Biology Project Activity 2 Blackett Family
http://www.biology.arizona.edu/human_bio/activities/blackett2/overview.html

3. Using population studies produced by the National Institute of Standards and Technology, allele frequencies are calculated for each of the CODIS 13 STRs. Research how to calculate the odds that someone else could have inherited the same STRs. You will need to use the product rule and the Hardy Weinberg principle in your calculation.

4. To understand how a DNA Profile is derived or interpreted, refer to the interactive animations on the Multimedia Resources page of the National Institute of Justice's Website. http://www.nij.gov/nij/training/dna-multimedia.htm

Identification of the Romanovs Using STR Profiling   *Obj. 7.6*

Scenario:

In 1991, the skeletal remains of Tsar Nicolas II and his wife Tsarina Alexandra were identified among the nine sets of remains recovered from a mass gravesite in Russia. Evidence from the bone fragments indicated the sex and age, but the dental work and DNA evidence provided a more definite identification.

The Russians labeled the skeletons numerically. Skeletal remains 7 were of a middle-aged woman whose ribs showed possible signs of damage from bayonet thrusts. Dr. Lowell Levine, forensic odontologist, noted elaborate and beautiful dental work. Two crowns were made of platinum and other crowns were made from porcelain with gold fillings. This type of dental work was practiced in Germany, Alexandra's homeland. None of the servants would have been able to afford such expensive dental work. Therefore, skeletal remains 7 were identified as belonging to the tsarina, Alexandra.

Skeletal remains 4 were identified as Tsar Nicholas II. The skeleton was of a fairly short middle-aged man with signs of wear and deformation in the hipbones, probably a result of years of riding on horseback. The skull was wide with a sloping forehead and a flat palate resembling Tsar Nicholas II. The teeth had evidence of periodontal disease.

The forensic team's next concern was to determine if any of the remaining seven skeletons belonged to the Romanov children. One method used, along with the skeletal and dental analyses, was STR analysis. The American scientists were able to identify three of the Romanov daughters, Olga, Maria, and Tatiana. The four other skeletal remains in the mass gravesite belonged to three servants and a physician. The remains of the youngest children, Alexei the Crown Prince and Anastasia, were not found in this gravesite. Their remains were discovered in 2006 in a second gravesite.

In this activity, students will examine the data obtained from the nine STR profile analyses of the skeletal remains of the bodies found in the 1991 mass gravesite and determine which of the nine skeletal remains belong to the Romanov children.

Objectives:

At the conclusion of this activity, students will be able to do the following:

1. Analyze the STR profiles of the nine skeletal remains found at the Romanov gravesite.
2. Given the STR profiles of Tsar Nicholas, Tsarina Alexandra, and the STR profiles obtained from the other skeletal remains in the gravesite, determine which remains belonged to the tsar and tsarina's children and which belonged to the nonfamily members (servants and the family doctor).
3. Determine which allele in each child was inherited from the mother (tsarina) and which allele was inherited from the father (tsar) based on STR profiles.
4. Summarize how kinship or lack of kinship is established using STR profiles.

Background

In this activity, students will examine the data from the nine STR profiles of the skeletal remains found in the 1991 mass gravesite and determine which of the nine skeletal remains belong to the Romanov children.

Safety Precautions

There are no safety precautions for this lab.

Time Required to Complete the Activity

The analysis of the nine skeletal remains can be completed within one class period of 40 minutes.

Procedure

Print and distribute Act 7-5 SH Genotypes and Act 7-5 SH STR Profile 2006 (for Further Study) from the IRCD, Chapter 7.

Teaching Tip

For support during this activity: At DNAi.org, click on Applications and then click on Recovering the Romanovs.

Teaching Tip

Before doing this activity, refer to the more detailed directions for establishing kinship described in Act 7-3 "Anna Anderson or Anastasia." It is suggested that students complete Act 7-3 prior to this activity. Act 7-5 expands on determining kinship using more STRs.

SAFETY PRECAUTIONS:
none

Time Required to Complete This Activity:

The analysis of the nine skeletal remains can be completed within one class period of 40 minutes.

Materials for Each Team of Students:

Act 7-5 SH STR Genotypes
Act 7-5 SH STR Profile 2006
1 red pencil or pen
1 blue pencil or pen
8-1/2" × 11" sheet of blank paper or a ruler

Background:

To establish kinship, each child's genotype must show one STR allele from the mother (tsarina) and one STR allele from the father (tsar). Recall that *genotype* refers to the combination of alleles.

Procedure:

1. Refer to the data table labeled STR Genotypes for the Nine Skeletal Remains, at the end of this activity. This data table provides the STR Profiles for five STR markers used in the identification of nine skeletal remains found in the first gravesite in 1991. The skeletal remains are identified by numbers 1 through 9 in the left column.

2. Skeletal remains 4 were identified as belonging to Tsar Nicholas II (blue) and skeletal remains 7 were identified as Tsarina Alexandra (pink), based on bone, tooth, and DNA analysis.

3. Each person's STR profile is read from left to right. When examining a person's STR profile, place either a ruler or a blank sheet of paper under the name to make it easier to see the STR profile and not confuse it with another line.

4. The heading refer to the five STR markers used in the analysis. The "HUM" prefix refers to *human*.

   Five different STR markers are used in the DNA analysis of the skeletal remains are

   HUMVWA/31
   HUMTH01
   HUMF13A1
   HUMFES/FPS
   HUMACTBPE

5. Your task is to analyze the STR profiles from the remains of the nine people buried in the mass gravesite. Determine if any of the skeletal remains could be the Romanov children based on STR alleles inherited from the tsar (skeletal remains 4) and from STR alleles inherited from the tsarina (skeletal remains 7).

DIFFERENTIATED LEARNING

Teaching Gifted Students

Print and distribute Act 7-5 Y STR Analysis and Act 7-5 SH Romanov Paternal for students who wish to pursue more in-depth study of the Romanov family.

a. For each of the skeletal remains from remains 1, 2, 3, 5, 6, 8, and 9,
   - Circle with a **red** pencil the allele that could have been inherited from the tsarina.
   - Circle with a **blue** pencil the allele that could have been inherited from the tsar.

For example, locate STR marker HUMTH01 on Data Table 1. Locate the STR profile for remains 3. The genotype for STR marker HUMTH01 is (8, 10). The 8 allele could have been inherited from the tsarina, and the 10 could have been inherited from the tsar. On the data table, for skeletal remains 3 under HUMTH01, circle the 8 in red and the 10 in blue. If the allele does not come from either the tsar or tsarina, do not circle the allele.

b. Repeat this process for the STR marker HUMTH01 for remains 1, 2, 5, 6, 8, and 9.

c. Repeat the process for the other 4 STRs (HUMVWA/31, HUMF13A1, HUMFES/FPS, and HUMACTBP2) and circle the allele inherited from the tsarina in **red** and circle the allele inherited from the tsar in **blue**.

d. To determine if the skeletal remains could have been one of the Romanov children, verify if they have inherited one allele from the tsar and one allele from the tsarina for each of the five STRs. (Note that it may be easier to view data for individual skeletal remains if you place a blank sheet of paper under the number of the remains and view the data from left to right.)

e. Compare your answers with the answers of another student. Do you agree? If not, check both of your answers for any errors.

f. In the table "STR Genotypes for Nine Skeletal Remains," circle the number of the skeletal remains that you have identified as a child of the tsar and tsarina.

STR Genotypes for Nine Skeletal Remains

Skeletal Remains	HUMVWA/31	HUMTH01	HUMF13A1	HUMFES/ FPS	HUMACTBPE
1	14,20	9,10	6,16	10,11	Not Determined
2	17,17	6,10	5,7	10,11	11,30
3	15,16	8,10	5,7	12,13	11,32
4 (tsar)	15,16	7,10	7,7	12,12	11,32
5	15,16	7,8	5,7	12,13	11,36
6	15,16	8,10	3,7	12,13	32,36
7 (tsarina)	15,16	8,8	3,5	12,13	32,36
8	15,17	6,9	5,7	8,10	Not Determined
9	16,17	6,6	6,7	11,12	Not Determined

Source: Peter Gill, et al. "Identification of the Remains of the Romanov family by DNA Analysis." *Nature Genetics*, 1994: Feb: 6(2): 130–135.

Questions

1. No; only one STR marker (HUMF13A1) for remains 2 and 8 showed an allele for both the tsar and tsarina. These remains could not be children of the tsar and tsarina; they did not have an allele from both the tsar and tsarina for each marker.

2. Skeletal remains 2, 3, 5, 6, and 8 all have one allele consistent with the tsar and tsarina for each marker.

3. The Romanov children were skeletal remains 3, 5, and 6. Nonrelated remains were skeletal remains 1, 2, 8, and 9 (servants and physician).

Teaching Tip

See IRCD, Act 7-5 SH STR Y Analysis, Act 7-5 Romanov Paternal for information on the Romanov Y chromosome and paternal pedigree.

LITERACY

References

M. D. Coble, O. M. Loreille, M. J. Wadhams, S. M. Edson, K. Maynard, et al. (2009). "Mystery Solved: The Identification of the Two Missing Romanov Children Using DNA Analysis." PLoS ONE 4(3): e4838. doi:10.1371/journal.pone.0004838

Michael D. Coble "The identification of the Romanovs: Can we (finally) put the controversies to rest?" *Investigative Genetics.* 2011; 2: 20. Published online 2011 September 26. doi: 10.1186/2041-2223-2-20 PMCID: PMC3205009

Robert K. Massie. *The Romanovs: The Final Chapter.* New York: Ballantine, 1995.

John M. Butler and Michael Coble. "Topics and Techniques in Forensic DNA Analysis," National Institute of Science and Technology, April 2012, www.cstl.nist.gov/strbase/training/NewYork-Apr2012-Workshop.htm

Questions:

1. Refer to skeletal remains 2 and 8. Could those skeletal remains be children of the tsar and tsarina? Support your answer using evidence from the STR analysis.

2. Refer to your analysis of STR marker HUMF13A1. Which skeletal remains could have inherited one allele from the tsar and one allele from the tsarina for this particular marker?

3. Based on your analysis of all five STRs, which skeletal remains are those belonging to the Romanov children, and which skeletal remains are those that belong to the nonrelated individuals? Cite evidence from your study to justify your conclusion.

Further Study:

1. Research the pedigree of Tsarina Alexandra, and explain how maternal inheritance of mitochondrial DNA was used to analyze the skeletal remains from the gravesites.

2. Research the pedigree of Tsar Nicholas II, and describe how paternal inheritance is traced using the Y chromosome.

3. When the second gravesite was found in 2006, many advances had occurred in DNA STR analysis. Refer to the 2009 article by Coble et. al., "Mystery Solved: The Identification of the Two Missing Romanov Children Using DNA Analysis," and read how new information about STR analysis had improved the reliability of using DNA to identify individuals.

4. When the first gravesite was examined in 1991, only five STRs were used to help identify the skeletal remains. In 2006, skeletal remains from both gravesites were examined or reexamined using additional STRs. Refer to Act 7-5 SH STR Profile 2006 (the Further Study Data Table on the following page), and note that 16 STR markers were examined and that the AMEL test were performed on the skeletal remains of the entire Romanov family.

   a. The left column shows the list of markers used in the DNA study. Notice that the DNA was taken from different bone samples identified as 4.3, 7.4, 3.46, 5.21, 6.14, 147, and 146.1 (listed on the top line).

   b. Check all alleles for Olga, Tatiana, Anastasia, Maria, and Alexei to confirm that they have inherited one allele from each parent. Use the same method you used earlier, circling the maternal allele in red and the paternal allele in blue.

   c. Compare and contrast the forensic tools used by the scientists in 1991 to the forensic tools used by the forensic scientists in 2007. Include in your answer the following:

      1. How many STR markers were used in 1991 compared to 2007?

      2. What other STR markers were used in 2007 that were not available in 1991?

   d. Dr. Michael Coble states in the 2009 article "Mystery Solved . . ." that there now exists "irrefutable evidence these are the (Romanov) children." Cite evidence from the article to support this statement.

DIFFERENTIATED LEARNING

Teaching Gifted Students

There are many opportunities for extension for advanced students in the ideas listed in the further study section.

e. Data in the following table came from Michael D. Coble's article "The identification of the Romanovs: Can we (finally) put the controversies to rest?" *Investigative Genetics*, 2011; 2: 20. It was published online, 2011 September 26. doi: 10.1186/2041-2223-2-20 PMCID: PMC3205009. Reading the original article will help explain the results in the table.

P. Gill, P. L. Ivanov, C. Kimpton, R. Piercy, N. Benson, G. Tully, I. Evett, E. Hagelberg, and K. Sullivan. "Identification of the Remains of the Romanov Family by DNA analysis." *Nature Genetics,* 1994 Feb: 6(2):130–5.

Further Study Data

Marker	Sample 4.3 Tsar Nicholas II	Sample 7.4 Tsarina Alexandra	Sample 3.46 Olga	Sample 5.21 Tatiana	Sample 6.14 Maria or Anastasia	Sample 147 Anastasia or Maria	Sample 146.1 Alexei
Amelog	X, Y	X, X	X, X	X, X	X, X	X, X	X, Y
D3S1358	14, 17	16, 18	17, 18	17, 18	16, 17	17, 18	14, 18
TH01	7, 9.3	8, 8	8, 9.3	7, 8	8, 9.3	7, 8	8, 9.3
D21S11	32.2, 33.2	30, 32.2	30, 33.2	32.2, 33.2	30, 33.2	30, 33.2	32.2, 33.2
D18S51	12, 17	12, 13	12, 12	12, 12	13, 17	12, 17	12, 17
D5S818	12, 12	12, 12	12, 12	12, 12	12, 12	12, 12	12, 12
D13S317	11, 12	11, 11	11, 11	11, 11	11, 11	11, 11	11, 12
D7S820	12, 12	10, 12	12, 12	10, 12	12, 12	10, 12	12, 12
D16S539	11, 14	9, 11	11, 11	11, 11	11, 14	9, 11	11, 14
CSF1PO	10, 12	11, 12	11, 12	11, 12	10, 11	10, 12	10, 12
D2S1338	17, 25	19, 23	17, 19	23, 25	17, 19	17, 23	23, 25
vWA	15, 16	15, 16	15, 16	15, 16	15, 16	15, 16	15, 16
D8S1179	13, 15	16, 16	13, 16	15, 16	13, 16	15, 16	15, 16
TPOX	8, 8	8, 8	8, 8	8, 8	8, 8	8, 8	8, 8
FGA	20, 22	20, 20	20, 22	20, 20	20, 22	20, 22	20, 22
D19S433	13, 13.2	13, 16.2	13.2, 16.2	13.2, 16.2	13, 16.2	13, 13	13, 13.2

Source: Coble MD et al. Mystery Solved: The Identification of the Two Missing Romanov Children Using DNA Analysis. March 22, 2009.

Chapter Overview

Blood consists mainly of three components suspended in a fluid called plasma. Blood is one of the most important kinds of biological evidence. Blood typing and DNA profiling of bloodstains help to identify persons that were at a crime scene. Blood type, a form of class evidence, is determined by testing a sample for the presence of antigens. It can exclude a suspect. DNA profiling from white blood cells provides individual evidence. Blood-spatter patterns at crime scenes help investigators understand what happened at a crime scene. The size and shape of bloodstains, or blood spatter, provide clues as to how injuries occurred as well as what weapon was used to produce those injures. Blood spatter also reveals the directionality of blood, angle of impact, and area of origin of the blood. Investigators must answer an important question from blood-stain evidence: "Is the evidence consistent with the suspects' (and perhaps witnesses') description of the crime?"

The Big Ideas

Blood is composed of red blood cells, white blood cells, and platelets. Red blood cells transport oxygen to, and transport carbon dioxide away from, all parts of the body; white blood cells fight diseases; and platelets help blood clot. Scientists have been analyzing blood-spatter patterns since the late 1800s. When investigators find dark stains at a crime scene, they first test whether the stains are blood. Investigators can detect blood even after a scene has been cleaned. Once the presence of blood is confirmed, investigators test to see if the blood is human. Tests can determine the blood type and the DNA profile of the person who lost the blood. By studying

CHAPTER 8

Blood and Blood Spatter

Blood Paints a Picture

Concerned neighbors called the police after hearing a woman screaming in the upstairs apartment. When the police arrived, they found the woman with a split lip, bruised cheek, and several facial cuts. Her left eye was swollen shut, and it looked like her right eye was turning black. Both of her upper arms were bruised. Behind the woman's chair, blood spatter was evident.

When questioned, the woman said she had been climbing the stairs and had fallen on the last step, striking her head as she fell. Her husband had a small cut on his fist and some blood on the cuff of his shirt sleeve. He told the police that the blood on his shirt was his wife's blood. He explained that the blood must have gotten on his sleeve as he helped her wipe the blood from her head.

The police photographed and noted all of the evidence. Was the description of the accident consistent with the blood evidence? Did the woman fall on the steps? Why wasn't any blood found on the steps? The blood-spatter evidence found behind the chair where the woman was sitting indicated that the blood originated from the area of the chair and moved toward the wall. Was the blood on the man's shirt his wife's blood or his own? Were the woman's injuries of the type that would occur by falling or were they more consistent with a beating from her husband? These are the types of questions a blood-spatter expert can answer.

Collecting blood evidence at a crime scene.

230

blood-spatter patterns, investigators can tell the direction in which the blood was traveling, the angle of impact of the weapon, and the point of origin of the blood. Bloodstain-pattern analysis provides quantitative evidence as to what occurred at a crime scene. These procedures can help investigators recreate the sequence of events at a crime scene.

SCENARIO

After reading the scenario, have students discuss these questions:
Why did the police suspect that the wife did not fall and injure herself?
What would they need to determine about the bloodstain on the husband's sleeve to support their suspicions?
Was there other evidence the police could use to support or refute the husband's story?

OBJECTIVES

By the end of this chapter, you will be able to:

8.1 Describe the forensic significance of the different types of blood cells.

8.2 Summarize the history of the use of blood and blood-spatter analysis in forensics.

8.3 Outline the procedure used to determine blood type.

8.4 Describe how to screen for the presence of human blood.

8.5 Calculate the probability of a person having a specific blood type, using data from population studies.

8.6 Describe the proper procedures for handling blood evidence.

8.7 Analyze blood-spatter evidence using angle of impact, area of convergence, and area of origin.

8.8 Compare and contrast different types of blood-spatter patterns.

8.9 Describe how different types of blood-spatter patterns are formed.

TOPICAL SCIENCES KEY

BIOLOGY

CHEMISTRY

EARTH SCIENCES

PHYSICS

LITERACY

MATHEMATICS

VOCABULARY

- **agglutination** clumping of cells caused by an antigen–antibody response

- **angle of impact** angle at which blood strikes a target surface relative to the horizontal plane of the target surface

- **antibodies** proteins secreted by white blood cells that attach to specific antigens

- **antigen** substance that provokes an immune response in the body

- **antigen–antibody response** reaction in which antibodies attach to specific antigens; causes agglutination in cross blood-type transfusions

- **area of convergence** two-dimensional view of the intersection of lines formed by drawing a line through the main axis of at least two drops of blood that indicates the general area of the source of the blood spatter

- **area of origin** the location of a blood source viewed in three dimensions as determined by projecting angles of impact of individual bloodstains

- **cast-off pattern** blood projected onto a surface as a result of being flung from an object in motion

- **passive drop** blood drop created solely as a result of gravity

- **satellite** smaller droplets of blood projected from larger drops of blood upon impact with a surface

- **spine** elongated blood streaks radiating away from the center of a bloodstain

- **swipe** blood pattern resulting from a lateral transfer from a moving source onto another surface

- **wipe** smeared blood pattern created when an object moves through blood that is not completely dried

KEY SCIENCE CONCEPTS

Biology: antigen–antibody reactions, blood types

Chemistry: chemical reactions used to discover blood evidence that may not otherwise be visible

Physics: effects of forces on blood—gravity, adhesion, cohesion, surface tension

Math: calculating probability; using trigonometry to calculate origin of blood

Teaching Tip

This chapter provides many opportunities for students to use math skills in the real-life application of analyzing blood at a crime scene. Probability calculations involving blood types and trigonometry calculations are performed. In the activities, students have the opportunity to practice these skills. Activities are organized to allow students to master easier math before attempting more challenging skills. Given the high interest of blood spatter, some students who think they can't do math may realize they can.

TEACHING RESOURCES

Instructor's Resource CD-ROM includes:
- Activities and Student Handouts
- Alternative Assessments
- Consolidated Bibliography
- Correlations to NGSS and CCSS
- Figure Files

- Nonfiction Readings
- PowerPoint Presentations
- Student Learning Objectives (SLOs)

CL Testing powered by Cognero

Website: ngl.cengage.com/forensicscience2e

DIFFERENTIATED LEARNING

Teaching English-Language Learners
Reinforce the vocabulary used in this chapter by asking students to create flash cards with a vocabulary word on one side and its meaning on the other. Have students write the meaning in both their native language and in English. Encourage students to review their flash cards before each class.

Engage

Ask students the following questions:

- What are the functions of blood in the human body?
- What are the major components of blood?
- Do you think all human blood is the same? Explain. Have students view a short segment of *CSI* dealing with blood at a crime scene.
- Do you think you could determine where blood at a crime scene originated based upon the blood-spatter stains? (You might show students a picture of blood spatter from a crime scene as you ask the question.)
- Can blood-typing be used to individually identify a suspect?

Explore

Discuss the medical history of bloodletting and the use of leeches. Ask students why they think blood has been studied much longer than DNA.

In 1937, Dr. Bernard Fantus established the first blood bank.

INTRODUCTION

The truth of what actually happened at a crime scene is written in the blood evidence; sometimes even in "invisible" blood evidence. Crime-scene investigators locate blood evidence and analyze it to determine if the evidence is consistent with the accounts of the suspect(s). If inconsistencies exist, the investigators realize that more investigation is needed—either more interrogation or more evidence analysis.

Blood typing provides only class evidence because many people have the same blood type. However, individual evidence from DNA STR analysis of white blood cells provides a high degree of certainty regarding whether blood left at a crime scene is consistent or inconsistent with the blood of a particular suspect (or victim).

Using blood-spatter pattern evidence, it is possible to determine the area of origin of the blood, the direction the blood was traveling, and the angle of impact when the blood struck an object. The type of weapon used to cause an injury is indicated by the size of the blood droplets found in the blood spatter.

In this chapter, you will explore how to make blood evidence visible, how to determine if the evidence is blood, and how to analyze blood-spatter patterns found at a crime to recreate what happened at the crime scene.

HISTORY OF THE STUDY OF BLOOD *Obj. 8.2*

The table in Figure 8-1 provides a brief history of the study of blood.

Figure 8-1 *A chronological history of the study of blood.*

Date	Who	Contribution
2500 B.C.	Egyptians' bloodletting	Effort to cure disease
500 B.C.	Greeks	Distinguished between arteries and veins
175 A.D.	Galen	Established that circulatory paths exist
1628	Sir William Harvey	Noted continuous circulation within body
1659	Antony van Leeuwenhoek	Viewed blood cells with microscope
1874	Sir William Osler	Discovered platelets
1901	Karl Landsteiner	Discovered three blood types: A, B, O
1935	Mayo Clinic	Developed a method to store blood for transfusions
1940	Karl Landsteiner	Discovered Rh antigen
1971	Dr. Blumberg	Developed method of antibody detection
1984	Dr. Robert Gallo	Demonstrated that HIV causes AIDS
1987–2002	Various	Development of blood-screening tests for infectious diseases

232   CHAPTER 8

DIFFERENTIATED LEARNING

Teaching English-Language Learners
Make sure students understand "blood:" what it is, and what its function in the human body is. Ask volunteers to explain how the circulatory system works and to list some functions of blood.

DIFFERENTIATED LEARNING

Teaching At-Risk Students
At-risk students will benefit from a brief review of the importance and function of blood. While students may be familiar with the concept of tissue, they may have a difficult time believing that a tissue can be a fluid. Explain to students that blood is a tissue made of different kinds of specialized cells and that blood is an important tissue in the cardiovascular system. Blood analysis can also provide an overview of the health of a person.

COMPOSITION OF BLOOD
Obj. 8.1

 Blood is a circulating tissue consisting of three components: red blood cells, white blood cells, and platelets (Figure 8-2). These components are carried throughout the body suspended in a liquid known as plasma. Plasma carries antibodies, hormones, clotting factors; nutrients such as glucose, amino acids, salts, and minerals throughout the body.

Figure 8-2 *Circle graph showing proportions of the components of blood.*

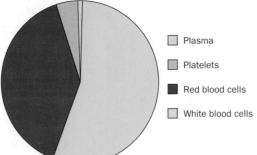

- ☐ Plasma
- ☐ Platelets
- ■ Red blood cells
- ☐ White blood cells

Blood Cells *Obj. 8.1*

Each blood component performs a different function. Red blood cells carry respiratory gases, mainly oxygen and carbon dioxide. The hemoglobin in red blood cells is an iron-containing protein that binds to oxygen in the lungs and transports the oxygen to cells in all the tissues in the body. Hemoglobin in red blood cells is also responsible for the red color in blood. White blood cells fight disease and foreign elements. Platelets aid in blood clotting and are involved in repairing damaged blood vessels.

Our bodies have the ability to discriminate between their own cells and molecules (self) and foreign elements (non-self). The immune system functions to protect our bodies by identifying cells or molecules that are foreign, such as viruses, bacteria, fungi, and parasites. When the immune system recognizes the presence of foreign elements, white blood cells converge in the location of the invading material. Some white blood cells engulf and digest foreign elements. Other types of white blood cells secrete proteins, known as **antibodies**, which assist in the immune response by "labeling" foreign materials. White blood cells are the only blood components that have nuclei and can be used as sources of DNA for profiling. Figure 8-3 shows various types of white blood cells. Figure 8-4 shows the quantities of major blood components in a microliter sample.

Blood Types and Forensics *Obj. 8.1, 8.3*

 Prior to DNA profiling, blood-type analysis was used to help identify an individual or link a person to a crime scene. Because many people share the same blood type, this type of evidence is only class evidence. Blood-type evidence is used to exclude a person as a suspect when the person's blood type is different from the blood type at the crime scene. In this section, we will examine different blood types and how blood type is determined.

Figure 8-3 *Types of white blood cells.*

Basophil   Eosinophil   Neutrophil   B cell (Lymphocyte)

T cell (Lymphocyte)   Monocyte

BLOOD AND BLOOD SPATTER   **233**

Science

BIOLOGY

Blood is an important tissue that is responsible for transporting nutrients, water, and oxygen to all of the cells in the body, and for transporting carbon dioxide and wastes away from all of the cells in the body. The immune system depends upon circulating white blood cells to identify and destroy pathogens.

This might also be a good time to discuss the overall importance of blood banks.

Science

BIOLOGY

In addition to transporting nutrients, water, and oxygen to the cells, blood carries hormones, vitamins, and minerals to nourish and regulate certain bodily functions.

Science

BIOLOGY

The movement of hormones through the blood enables one organ to control the function of another organ, even though the two organs might be located far apart. In this way, blood acts not just as a means of transportation, but also as a communication system.

Science

BIOLOGY

Blood is responsible for delivering all of the body's wastes to the appropriate location for disposal. Waste gases, such as carbon dioxide, are delivered to the lungs, where they are exhaled. Other wastes are filtered from the blood in the kidneys, where they are dissolved in water and excreted as urine. Many foreign substances are identified and destroyed through the action of the circulating blood.

Evaluate

To assess students' understanding of the relationship between blood and DNA, ask them the following questions:

- What component of blood can be used for DNA analysis?
- How long has DNA analysis been possible?
- Why is DNA an important tool for forensic scientists?

Teaching Tip

For additional information on genes and blood type, refer to http://learn.genetics.utah.edu/content/inheritance/blood/

Science

BIOLOGY

BIOLOGY

- A person with A antigens is type A and can produce antibodies to B antigens.
- A person with B antigens is type B and can produce antibodies to A antigens.
- A person with both antigens is type AB and will not produce any antibodies against the A or B antigen.
- A person with none of the antigens is type O and can produce antibodies to both A and B antigens.

Did you know

The adult human body contains 5.5 liters (about 6 quarts) of blood. The heart pumps nearly 300 liters every hour.

Figure 8-4 *The components of blood.*

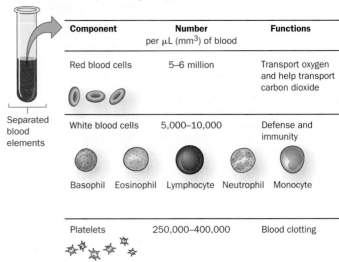

Component	Number per μL (mm^3) of blood	Functions
Red blood cells	5–6 million	Transport oxygen and help transport carbon dioxide
White blood cells	5,000–10,000	Defense and immunity
Platelets	250,000–400,000	Blood clotting

Basophil   Eosinophil   Lymphocyte   Neutrophil   Monocyte

Separated blood elements

DISCOVERY OF BLOOD TYPES

In 1900, Karl Landsteiner found that blood from one person did not always freely mix with blood from another person. Instead, clumping of red blood cells, or **agglutination**, might occur, resulting in death. The presence or absence of **antigens**, substances that trigger an immune response, on red blood cells determines a person's blood type. In 1901, Landsteiner described the A and B antigens. Other antigens, such as the Rh factor, were later identified.

A AND B ANTIGENS

As Landsteiner discovered, reactions to a blood antigen other than a person's own can have fatal consequences during a blood transfusion. Like other antigens, foreign antigens on blood cells can cause an immune reaction. A and B antigens are found on the surface of some red blood cells (Figure 8-5). An antibody reaction test is used to identify the antigens on a person's red blood cells. If a person's blood contains only antigen A, then he or she has type A blood. If the blood has only antigen B, then the person has type B blood. If the person's blood has both the A and the B antigens, then he or she has type AB blood. The blood of some people lacks both the A and the B antigens. This blood is designated type O blood.

Figure 8-5 *A diagrammatic representation of the antigens for the human ABO blood types.*

Type A   Type B   Type AB   Type O

DIFFERENTIATED LEARNING

Teaching At-Risk Students and Visual Learners

To help student visualize the quantity of blood in an average adult, show them 6 liters of water with red food coloring.

The percentages of the U.S. population with each of the four ABO blood types:

    Type O (43%)
    Type A (42%)
    Type B (12%)
    Type AB (3%)

Rh FACTOR

In 1940, Alexander Weiner, working with *Rhesus* monkeys, noticed another type of red cell antigen. Eighty-five percent of the human population has a protein called Rh factor on their red blood cells. This factor is independent of the A and B antigens. Blood that has the Rh factor is designated Rh+ (positive), while blood that does not have this factor is designated Rh– (negative) (Figure 8-6).

Figure 8-6 *Rh factor and ABO blood type examples.*

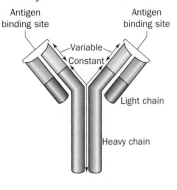

Antigen A present
Rh factor present
Type A+

Antigen A present
Rh factor absent
Type A−

Antigen–Antibody Response

To help white blood cells identify foreign elements, B-lymphocytes, specialized white blood cells, secrete antibodies. An antibody is a Y-shaped protein molecule that binds to the molecular shape of specific antigens, fitting like jigsaw puzzle pieces. The binding sites of the antibody are located on each tip of the Y-shaped molecule (Figures 8-7 and 8-8).

Figure 8-7 *The general structure of an antibody.*

Antigen binding site

Antigen binding site

Variable
Constant

Light chain

Heavy chain

Figure 8-8 *The shape of the antigen fits the binding site on the antibody.*

Antigens

Antigen
Antigen-binding site

Antibody

Teaching Tip

Many students may not know their own blood types. Encourage students to find out their blood types. Emphasize the importance of knowing your blood type by describing the consequences of receiving a transfusion of the wrong kind of blood. As a class, determine the percentages of students who have each of the four main blood types. How do these percentages compare with the U.S. population?

Evaluate

Help students understand how blood typing is used as evidence by discussing these questions:

- What kind of evidence is a blood type?
- How can a blood type be used to rule out a suspect in a case?
- Compare and contrast the use of blood typing to DNA profiling as a forensic tool to identify suspects and victims.

Science

BIOLOGY

BIOLOGY

Each biological parent contributes one of his or her two ABO alleles to the child. These genotypes produce these phenotypes (blood types).

Genotype	Blood Type
AA or AO	A
BB or BO	B
AB	AB
OO	O

Science

MATHEMATICS

MATH

To illustrate how blood types are inherited, show (using a Punnet square) a cross between a mother who has blood type O and a father who has type AB. The mother can contribute only an O allele. The father can contribute either an A or a B allele. So this couple could have children of either blood type A (O from the mother and A from the father) or B (O from the mother and B from the father). Point out that the child would have a probability of 1 in 2 of having type A blood. Emphasize that there is no chance of these parents producing a type O baby.

Explore

Ask several students to help model antibodies. Have students stand and raise their arms above their head in a Y position to represent an antibody. Ask students to show you their bonding sites (located at the tips of the Y/student hands).

Ask another student to enter the room wearing a red cap. This student is considered to be an antigen. As the student with the red cap enters the room, instruct the Y-shaped antibodies to surround him or her. Have the antibodies "label" the antigen by placing their hands on the red cap.

Have another student represent an engulfing white blood cell (phagocyte). Have this student wander around the room. Have the white blood cell notice the antigen surrounded by antibodies. Have it engulf the antigen by putting its arms around the student in the red hat. Explain that the white blood cell (phagocyte) would digest the antigen. Have the white blood cell display the red cap. Tell students it does this to alert the other immune cells of the nature of the antigen.

You might want to replay the preceding scenario. However, this time when the antibodies have identified the red-hatted antigen, have another white blood cell, known as a killer or cytotoxic killer T-cell, approach the antigen surrounded with antibodies. The role of the killer T-cell is to secrete digestive enzymes on the antigen.

Teaching Tip

Explain to students that there are thousands of binding sites on the surface of a red blood cell.

When a foreign element is recognized by the immune system, the immune system responds. This is called the **antigen–antibody response**. White blood cells recognize a substance as foreign and try to destroy it. The foreign substance may be viruses, bacteria, fungi, or even red blood cell antigens from a person with a different blood type.

AGGLUTINATION

There are many antigens on the surface of the red blood cell membrane. When one arm of a Y-shaped antibody attaches to the red blood cell, the second arm of the antibody can attach to another red blood cell. The result is **a**gglutination (Figure 8-9).

Figure 8-9 *An antibody reaction to surface antigens on red blood cells causes agglutination, or clumping, of the cells. Agglutination can be fatal.*

If agglutination occurs within the circulatory system of a person receiving a blood transfusion, blood could cease to flow. The blood vessels become obstructed by clumped red blood cells. Without blood circulation, the cells of the body cannot receive oxygen or eliminate carbon dioxide, and the person dies.

BLOOD-TYPING TESTS

When a patient needs a blood transfusion, his or her blood needs to be typed to ensure that the blood to be transfused does not contain any blood antigens that will cause agglutination. The person's blood is tested for the presence of three antigens: A, B, and Rh.

Three separate tests are performed. First, the patient's blood is mixed with antibodies that bind to the A antigen. If the patient's blood clumps, or agglutinates, that means that the person's blood contains antigen A. If the blood does not agglutinate, then that person's blood does not contain antigen A.

Similar tests are performed with antibodies to antigen B and the Rh factor. If the blood agglutinates in the presence of these antibodies, it means that those antigens are present in the blood. In the absence of these antigens, no clumping will occur (Figure 8-10). If a blood sample is not available, blood type can often be determined from body fluids. Eighty percent of people are known as secretors and release their blood proteins in body fluids such as saliva, tears, sweat, and milk.

Figure 8-10 *Notice that agglutination occurs in only two of the blood tests, indicating that the person has blood type B+ (clumping with anti-B and with anti-Rh antibodies).*

Antibodies A   Antibodies B   Rh Factor

Probability and Blood Types *Obj. 8.1, 8.5*

MATHEMATICS
π

Given the frequency of different genes within a population, it is possible to determine the probability or chance that a particular blood type will appear within a particular population. To determine the probability of two simultaneous events, it is necessary to multiply their individual probabilities. In Figure 8-11, you can see the percentages of Americans who have the A and B antigens and the Rh factor.

Science   BIOLOGY

BIOLOGY

The level of antibodies in the blood ebbs and flows with need. They naturally decline over time but rapidly increase following renewed contact with a specific antigen. Viral infections lead to antibody level increases in an infected person.

Science   BIOLOGY

BIOLOGY

Scientists note that antibodies are normally absent at birth. In time, they begin to appear in response to antigens. Nursing mothers introduce antibodies in their breast milk, providing breast-fed babies with short-term immunity. They are also introduced by immunization with vaccines, or following normal infections.

Figure 8-11 *A summary of the population percentages with different blood antigens in the United States.*

BIOLOGY

ABO

Type	Percent	Fraction
A	42%	42/100
B	12%	12/100
AB	3%	3/100
O	43%	43/100

Rh

Type	Percent	Fraction
Rh +	85%	85/100
Rh−	15%	15/100

Example 1: What are the chances of throwing dice and getting two sixes?

The probability of one die showing a six is $\frac{1}{6}$ (one side out of six).

The probability of the other die showing a six is $\frac{1}{6}$ (one side out of six).

The chance of throwing two dice and getting both showing a six is calculated by multiplying the individual probabilities, or $\frac{1}{6} \times \frac{1}{6} = \frac{1}{36}$.

Using the percentages in Figure 8-11, Examples 2 and 3 show you how to estimate the percentage of the population with a specific blood type.

Example 2: What percentage of the population would have A+ blood?

Type A blood = 42% of the population
Rh+ = 85% of the population
Step 1. Convert the percentages to decimals.
Type A blood = 42% = 0.42 of the population
Rh+ = 85% = 0.85 of the population
Step 2. Multiply the decimals.
0.42 × 0.85 = 0.357 (357 out of 1,000) of the population should be both A and Rh+.
Step 3. Multiply by 100 to convert the decimal to a percentage.
0.357 × 100% ≃ 35.7% of the population should be both A and Rh+.
Therefore, about 36 out of every 100 people would have Type A+ blood.

Example 3: What percentage of the population would have the following combination of blood-type antigens? Type O−

Step 1. Convert the percentages to decimals.
Type O = 43% = 0.43
Rh− = 15% = 0.15
Step 2. Multiply the decimals.
0.43 × 0.15 = 0.0645
Step 3. Multiply by 100 to convert the decimal to a percentage.
0.0645 × 100% ~ 6.4% of the population are O−. Therefore, only about 6 out of every 100 people would have Type O−blood. This would make the suspect population small.

There are other blood antigens used to type blood in addition to the AB and RH antigens. However, DNA profiling using STR markers has largely replaced blood typing as a way to establish the identity of criminal suspects.

Teaching Tip

In addition to A, B, and Rh antigens, people can have M and N antigens. Approximately 30 percent of the population are MM, inheriting a gene for the M antigen from each parent. Twenty-two percent of the population are NN, inheriting a gene for the N antigen from each parent. The remaining 48 percent of the population are MN, inheriting a gene for M from one parent and a gene for N from the other parent.

Science

BIOLOGY

BIOLOGY

The M protein is a derivative of an antibody found in unusually large amounts in the blood or urine of patients with multiple myeloma, a form of cancer that arises in plasma cells.

Blood Substance	Probability	Probability	Probability
Phosphoglucomutase (PGM)	PGM-1 58%	PGM-2 6%	PGM-3 36%
Adenylate kinase (AK)	AK 1 93%	AK 2-1 7 %	
Adenosine deaminase (ADA)	ADA 1 88%	ADA 2-1 10%	ADA 2 2%
Esterase D (EsD)	EsD 1 79%	EsD 2-1 19%	EsD 2 2 %
Glucose-6-phosphate Dehydrogenase G-6-PD	G-6-PD G 62%	G-6-PD BA 25%	G-6-PD A 13%
Haptoglobins (Hp)	Hp1 14%	Hp2-1 53%	Hp2 33%

Teaching Tip

Additional enzymes and proteins in the blood, including those in the following table, are also used for forensic identification purposes.

Science

PHYSICS

Surface tension is the result of the attraction between like or similar molecules in a substance, such as water molecules being attracted to other water molecules. You can see surface tension in a drop of blood. Because of the strong cohesive forces of blood, the blood molecules at the interface between blood and air will bond tightly to other blood molecules, creating a strong, elastic connection.

Science

PHYSICS

Blood also exhibits the forces of cohesion (Figures 8-13 and 8-14), adhesion, and surface tension. As a droplet of blood is released from an eyedropper, it will be teardrop shaped because of adhesive forces (Figure 8-12), but as it falls, the droplet's shape becomes spherical because of internal cohesion and surface tension.

Teaching Tip

For animations of blood spatter, refer to "A Simplified Guide to Blood Spatter Analysis" at the following URL. Scroll down to *Animations. http://www .forensicsciencesimplified.org/blood/ principles.html*. The material is not presented at the student level.

BLOOD-SPATTER PATTERNS

Obj. 8.2, 8.7, 8.8, 8.9

When a wound is inflicted and blood leaves the body, a blood-spatter pattern may be created. A single stain or drop of blood does not constitute a spatter. Instead, a grouping of bloodstains composes a blood-spatter pattern. This pattern can help reconstruct the series of events surrounding a shooting, stabbing, or beating.

History of Blood-Spatter Analysis

In 1895, Edward Piotrowski wrote the earliest reference to blood-spatter analysis. In 1939, Dr. Victor Balthazard was the first researcher to analyze the meaning of the spatter pattern. In 1955, blood-spatter evidence used by the defense in the Sam Shepard case helped to exonerate him. In 1971, investigators began to use the physics of blood-spatter analysis as a tool in modern forensic examinations. Today, blood-spatter evidence is an integral part of crime-scene analysis.

Blood-Spatter Pattern Analysis

In the laboratory activities in this chapter, you will study how blood-spatter patterns can be used to recreate the events that occurred at a crime scene. Given blood-spatter patterns, it is possible to determine the direction the blood was traveling, the angle of impact of each blood droplet, and the area of origin and general velocity of the blood. Blood-spatter patterns may help resolve whether a victim died from a suicide or homicide. Instructions on blood-spatter analysis are provided within each activity.

Did you ever wonder why blood forms droplets as it falls from a wound? If blood is a mixture, then why doesn't it separate in the air before it hits the ground or an object? Why does a drop of blood have a domed surface when it lands on a flat surface instead of spreading out flat? The answers to these questions relate to how the forces of gravity, cohesion, adhesion, and surface tension act on blood.

Recall that blood is a suspension of blood components in plasma. When blood is dripping, gravity acts on it, pulling it downward (Figure 8-12). Blood has *cohesion*. This means that its molecules are attracted to each other, so blood tends to stick together as it falls. The cohesion of the falling blood droplets results in a spherical shape (Figure 8-13).

When a droplet of blood strikes a surface, it flattens out, but the cohesive forces still act to give it a domed shape (Figure 8-14). If any of the blood overcomes cohesion and separates from the main droplet of blood,

Figure 8-12 *A falling droplet of blood.*

Figure 8-13 *Cohesive forces in a blood droplet.*

Figure 8-14 *Cohesive forces resist droplet flattening.*

it will form small secondary droplets known as **satellites** (Figure 8-15).

Besides gravity and cohesion, another force, adhesion, affects the shape of a blood droplet. *Adhesion* is the attraction between molecules of unlike substances (for example, adhesive tape and paper). When blood directly strikes a porous surface, such as wood, ceiling tile, or clothing, then the edge of the drop of blood may form **spines,** or elongated extensions, due to the adhesion of the blood to the uneven, porous surface (Figure 8-15). Note that spines are connected to the main blood droplet, whereas satellites are separated from it.

Figure 8-15 *Satellites and spines in a blood droplet pattern.*

Satellite

Spine

Directionality of Blood

 The shape of an individual drop of blood provides clues to the direction from where the blood originated. Blood droplet shape varies from round to elliptical (longer than wide). The directionality of the blood is easily determined since the pointed or elongated end of the blood indicates the direction of travel (Figure 8-16).

If blood is dropped straight down (90-degree drop), the shape of the blood droplet is circular. This is typical if the blood was passively produced (without any force other than gravity), as when blood drips from a wound.

If blood is released from an angle other than 90 degrees, then the shape of the blood droplet will be more elliptical (longer than wide). The droplet tends to become less rounded and more elongated as the angle changes from a 90-degree drop toward a 10-degree drop.

What causes blood droplets to have varying shapes? When blood comes into contact with another surface, the blood tends to adhere to the surface. As a result, less blood continues to move, and the point of impact of the blood droplet is wider than the forward traveling edge of the blood (Figure 8-17).

Cohesion causes most of the blood to remain in a single drop. Smaller satellite droplets may break away from the main drop of blood and will appear in front of it in a spatter pattern.

Figure 8-16 *Blood droplets moving left to right away from source.*

© Cengage Learning®

Figure 8-17 *Point of impact (left) to traveling edge (right).*

Direction blood is traveling

Bloodstain Patterns

Careful observation of bloodstain patterns resulting from falling, projected, or smeared blood at crime scenes helps investigators interpret and reconstruct what happened. Refer to Figure 8-18, which illustrates some of the common patterns.

The importance of blood-spatter analysis is that it helps to recreate the crime scene based on scientifically analyzing the blood-spatter patterns. If blood-spatter analysis isn't consistent with the eyewitness account(s) of the crime, police will realize that the truth is not being told and further investigation is needed.

Teaching Tip

Ask students to investigate cohesion and adhesion by using water droplets and a glass surface such as a glass slide. A water drop will move slowly across a tilted glass slide because of adhesion as the water sticks to the glass. Water will form a domed drop on a flat surface because of cohesion due to water molecules being attracted to other water molecules. Use a flex cam to project an image of water drops sticking together.

Science

PHYSICS

PHYSICS

The spatter pattern can give two pieces of information: the direction in which the droplets were traveling and the angle of impact on the surface.

Science

PHYSICS

PHYSICS

To discover the direction of the path of the blood droplet at the instant of impact, investigators recreate the elliptical pattern by dropping "blood" drops from various angles. The direction can be detected by noting which side of the blood droplet seems to taper, creating a spine. Blood is moving in the direction of the elongated spine. When the blood first strikes a surface, the spatter tends to be wider and darker than the thinner, lighter spine.

Teaching Tip

Use a water gun filled with colored water or nontoxic, washable paints to recreate blood-spatter patterns. As a class, analyze the patterns left by the water gun. Use a large cardboard refrigerator box to create a corner spatter.

Teaching Tip

Artificial Blood Recipe:

12–16 oz corn syrup
1 oz liquid detergent
1 oz water (if necessary, to thin)
1 oz red food coloring
3 drops blue food coloring
Condensed milk as needed for opacity

Mixing directions:

Mix syrup, food coloring, liquid detergent, and water. Add condensed milk as needed to make blood more opaque.

Figure 8-18 *Bloodstain patterns.*

Bloodstain Patterns			
Type	Photo or Diagram	Description	What Likely Happened
Trail of Circular Drops of Blood (Passive Drops)	● ● ● ●	Linear pattern of round droplets of blood	Person walking while bleeding
Cast-off Pattern		Seen on walls or ceilings: pattern of lines with blood direction changing as arm moves up and back; blood flung off weapon; change in direction of blood drops	Person repeatedly striking someone with a weapon, raising and lowering his or her arm with each blow; second blow creates the first blood spatter
Transfer Pattern		Wet, bloody surface contacts a second surface; minimal lateral motion	Person steps in blood or presses hand onto bloody surface and transfers blood
Wipe		Object moves through partly dried blood with lateral motion, altering appearance	Trying to remove blood from a surface with a cloth
Swipe		Lateral transfer of wet blood from a moving source onto a surface; feathered edge indicates direction from source	Bloody hair dragged across floor
Arterial Gush		Blood exiting under pressure from an artery and striking a surface; peaks indicate heart contraction	Severed artery due to injury or attack
Expired Blood		Blood blown out of nose or mouth as a result of air pressure, similar to high-velocity blood spatter, often with bubbles	Injury causing internal bleeding; body trying to expel blood
Shadowing or Void		Area devoid of blood spatter	Object was in front of the wall during injury but object has since been moved

© Cengage Learning®

240   CHAPTER 8

Area of Convergence

The approximate location of a blood source can be determined if there are at least two drops of blood. Draw straight lines down the center of the long axis of the blood spatter and, noting where the lines intersect, you will find the **area of convergence** (Figure 8-19). You can use this information to calculate the height above the floor at which the injury took place.

Figure 8-19 *Area of convergence is estimated by drawing the smallest circle around the area where all lines through long axes of blood-spatter drops intersect.*

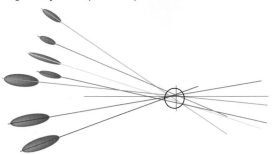

Angle of Impact Calculations

The angle of impact of blood relative to a surface that it strikes can establish the area of origin of the blood. The **area of origin** is the location of the blood source as viewed in three dimensions. It is determined by projecting angles of impact of individual bloodstains. When blood is cast onto a surface at an acute angle, the droplet will not be round. Blood droplets tend to become more elliptical as they are released from a body at angles increasingly more acute than 90 degrees. (Figure 8-20).

Figure 8-20 *The shape of a blood droplet from a circular 90-degree drop to a very elongated 10-degree drop, based on angle of release from the body.*

© 2016 Cengage Learning®

Science PHYSICS

PHYSICS

Convergence is the point at which all lines come together. Imagine drawing lines from each blood droplet and viewing your work from above. As you look down on your work, you will see the area where all of the lines come together—the area of convergence.

Science PHYSICS

PHYSICS

Investigators once laid out lengths of string from each stain found at the crime scene. The point where the strings intersected was the area of convergence—the location of the blood source. Now investigators use lasers to help locate the area of convergence and point (area) of origin.

DIFFERENTIATED LEARNING

Visual Learners
Visual learners might better comprehend blood-spatter patterns if you practice with simpler patterns first. Use the images in the text as guides to draw larger pictures. Have students determine the direction that blood was moving when it created the blood-spatter pattern.

Evaluate

Ask students the following questions:

- What four properties of a crime scene can be identified from blood spatter?
- Can blood spatter be used to identify a victim or suspect? Explain your answer.
- Compare and contrast spines and satellites.
- Distinguish between area of convergence and area of origin.

Teaching Tip

Bloodstain pattern analysis terminology has been reviewed by experts in the Scientific Working Group SWGSTAIN, and they discovered it has been classified by different experts in different ways. Visit the SWGSTAIN Website to review the terminology.

Science

PHYSICS

PHYSICS

The term *velocity*, when used in analyzing blood spatter, does not refer to how fast the blood droplets are traveling. It is a reference to the speed of the object (weapon) striking the body (the source of the blood).

CALCULATING THE ANGLE OF IMPACT

1. Measure the width and length of each droplet of blood in millimeters. Do not include any extensions of the blood droplet such as spines. The top and the bottom of the main droplet of blood should be symmetrical. Refer to Figure 8-21.

Figure 8-21 *Measuring bloodstain droplets.*

2. Divide the width by the length (this gives you a decimal value, a number less than 1).
3. Take the arcsine, or inverse sine, of the ratio width : length to determine the angle of impact. You can find this decimal value by using a sine table, a calculator, or a computer.

Determine the angle of impact for a blood droplet 5 millimeters wide and 14 millimeters long. Use Figure 8-22.

Example:

1. width = 5 mm   length = 14 mm
2. width/length = 5 mm/14 mm
3. 5/14 = 0.3571
4. inverse sine of 0.3571 ≈ 21 degrees

Once the area of convergence and impact angles are determined, it is possible to estimate the area of origin. This can be calculated either using a string method, protractor, or laser pointer method, or you can use basic trigonometry to estimate the area of origin. The process and associated calculations are described fully in Activity 8-6.

Blood Velocity and Spatter Size

Blood-spatter size is indicative of the weapon and type of injury. Spatter patterns can help the investigator determine the type of wound and the type of weapon used to produce the spatter. A fine-mist spatter pattern (less than 1 mm) is produced by high-velocity impact, such as a gunshot wound. Beatings or stabbings will produce medium-velocity-sized blood spatter (1–4 mm). However, a beating with a pipe or bat will produce low-velocity-sized blood spatter (4–6 mm), as shown in Figure 8-23.

Figure 8-22 *For a blood droplet 5 mm wide by 14 mm long, the angle of impact is about 21 degrees.*

Figure 8-23 *Blood velocity and spatter size (not to scale).*

Velocity	Size of Droplets (mm)	Visual Image	Velocity of Blood	Examples of Injuries
High	Less than 1		100 ft/sec	Gunshot wounds
Medium	1–4		25 ft/sec	Beating, stabbing
Low	more than 4		5 ft/sec	Blunt object impact or dripping

All photos © Cengage Learning®

CRIME-SCENE INVESTIGATION OF BLOOD *Obj. 8.4, 8.6*

PHYSICS In an attempt to hide evidence, a perpetrator may try to remove blood evidence by cleaning the area. Although a room may look perfectly clean and completely free of blood after washing, blood evidence remains. To detect blood, investigators spray the area with Luminol, which reacts with the hemoglobin found in red blood cells. This chemical reaction produces light for approximately 30 seconds. Photos are taken of the illuminated blood and can be used for later reference.

Confirmation of Human Blood

At a crime scene, clothing is found with a red stain. Is it animal blood? Could ketchup, ink, or some other red substance cause the red stain? Before deciding to collect the sample, it is necessary to confirm the stain is blood. A variety of test kits have been developed for rapid identification. Former testing methods yielded many false positives. The Kastle-Meyer test detects hemoglobin but can also detect nonblood compounds containing nickel or copper.

Confirmation of the presence of human blood requires detecting human antibodies in a sample.

An ELISA test (Enzyme-Linked Immunosorbent Assay) involves an antibody–protein reaction. This test is similar to one used in blood typing but uses different antibodies. Human blood is injected into a rabbit to

Did you know

Perpetrators often try to wash blood evidence from a crime scene. But even if a surface has been washed many times, blood can still be revealed using Luminol.

CHEMISTRY

Science CHEMISTRY

CHEMISTRY

Luminol is a compound that has important uses in forensic field investigations. It is extremely sensitive and can detect bloodstains diluted as much as 300,000 times.

Science CHEMISTRY

CHEMISTRY

Investigators mix Luminol ($C_8H_7O_3N_3$) with hydrogen peroxide (H_2O_2) to detect blood. If blood is present, the hemoglobin and Luminol mixture come into contact. The iron in the hemoglobin accelerates a chemical reaction (oxidation) between the Luminol and the hydrogen peroxide. The Luminol loses nitrogen and hydrogen atoms, and is left in an energized state. As the electrons fall back to a lower energy state, they emit a faint blue light, which is only visible in a darkened room.

Science CHEMISTRY

CHEMISTRY

The Kastle-Meyer test is a presumptive test that can confirm the presence of blood. It relies on the oxidation of reduced phenolphthalein (colorless) changing to oxidized phenolphthalein (pink). Reduced phenolphthalein becomes oxidized in the presence of blood. The test does not discriminate between human and other hemoglobin-based blood.

Teaching Tip

Review proper handling and labeling of evidence in Chapter 2.

Teaching Tip

Videotaping a crime scene is preferable to photography because it helps demonstrate the relationship among various areas of spatter, the position of the victim, and other datum points in the room. Images should be taken perpendicular to the spattered surface. When taking images of blood spatter, the following items are useful:

- Tripod to steady the camera
- Tape measure to record spatter positions and to show distances in the photograph
- Additional light sources (if necessary) at oblique angles to the spatter surface

Evaluate

Have students answer these questions:

- What steps should be taken when blood is found at a crime scene?
- If the crime scene appears clean, can blood evidence still be found? Explain.

Teaching Tip

Ask students to shoot a 5-minute video (similar to a YouTube clip) where they explain one aspect of how to analyze blood-spatter patterns. Students can either use artificial blood and create a "crime scene" or they can use paper cutouts to represent the bloodstains. Remind students that they can shoot the video in shorter sequences rather than all at one time. This will help students feel more confident in their presentation knowing that they don't have to remember everything all at one time.

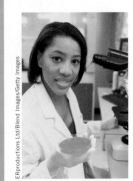

ERproductions Ltd/Blend Images/Getty Images

produce rabbit antibodies against human blood. These antibodies are isolated and stored. When a sample of human blood is mixed with some of these anti-human antibodies produced by the rabbit, a positive reaction occurs, and the presence of human blood is confirmed.

Collection of Blood Evidence

If crime-scene blood is in liquid pools, it should be picked up in gloved hands with gauze pads or sterile cotton cloths. Allow cloths to dry thoroughly at room temperature before packaging. Do not place bloody cloth of any type in a plastic container. Cloth should be delivered to a lab, refrigerated or frozen as soon as possible. Include only one bloodstained item in each package. Keep bloodstained evidence away from heat and direct sunlight.

If blood is dried on cloth or clothing, place the entire item into a paper bag. Do not attempt to wash off dried blood. Always follow the procedures outlined in Chapter 2 for proper evidence labeling.

LITERACY

Stuart H. James, Paul E. Kish, T. Paulette Sutton, and William G. Eckert. *Principles of Bloodstain Pattern Analysis.*

SUMMARY

- Blood consists of cellular components and plasma containing dissolved ions, proteins, and other substances.

- Blood types result from the presence of antigens on the surface of red blood cells and vary among individuals. Although considered class evidence, blood type is used today to exclude suspects.

- Blood-spatter analysis can be used to help recreate a crime scene.

- The size and shape of bloodstains provide clues to the directionality, speed, and angle of impact.

- The angle of impact is calculated as the inverse sine of (width/length).

- Lines of convergence are used to determine the source of blood in a two-dimensional view.

- The characteristics of blood drops on surfaces can show the direction of blood movement and the location of the source of blood and indicate the nature of the wound producing the blood.

- Investigators can use Luminol to reveal hidden blood spatter. Chemical tests can confirm that the blood found is human.

- Characteristic blood-spatter patterns provide clues to the type of injury incurred, along with a possible weapon used to deliver the injury.

- Blood-spatter analysis provides scientific evidence used to confirm or refute a person's description of what happened at a crime scene.

244   CHAPTER 8

DIFFERENTIATED LEARNERS

Teaching At-Risk Students

Discuss with the students how it's possible to get bloodstains on shoes at a crime scene. Brainstorm different ideas such as stepping into a pool of blood, running through blood, having blood projected onto them from an injured person, transferring blood from clothing onto shoes, etc. Divide the class into separate teams and ask them to demonstrate one of the methods discussed, using artificial blood and old shoes, boots, or sneakers. Each group should analyze the bloodstains and present its findings to the class.

CASE STUDIES

Ludwig Tessnow
(1901)

The bodies of eight-year-old Hermann and his six-year-old brother, Peter, were found in the woods on Rugen Island, off the coast of Germany. Ludwig Tessnow, a local carpenter, was a suspect. Both his clothing and boots had dark stains on them. Tessnow told officials the stains were from wood dye, which he used in his carpentry work.

Three years earlier in Osnabruck, similar murders had taken place. Two young girls, ages seven and eight, had been murdered in a similar manner. Their remains had been found in a nearby wooded area. Ludwig Tessnow had been detained for questioning in that murder as well.

A German biologist, Paul Uhlenhuth, developed a test that could be used to differentiate between blood and other types of stains. His test could also discriminate between human and animal blood. The test he developed used an antigen–antibody reaction to test for the presence of human blood. Uhlenhuth examined the boots and clothing belonging to Tessnow and concluded that the clothing did contain wood dye as Tessnow had claimed. Seventeen spots of human blood were also identified, as well as several stains of sheep's blood. Based on this evidence, Tessnow was found guilty and executed at Griefswald Prison.

Graham Backhouse
(1985)

Graham Backhouse was accused of killing his neighbor and attempting to kill his wife to collect his wife's life insurance. Backhouse's wife had been injured in an explosion of a homemade car bomb. Backhouse claimed his neighbor had a grudge against him, and the bomb was really intended for him.

When police arrived at the Backhouse home, the neighbor, Colyn Bedale-Taylor, was found dead from shotgun wounds. Backhouse had sustained wounds to his chest and face. He claimed self-defense. The blood-spatter evidence contradicted Backhouse's statement. The blood spots on the kitchen floor were those made by dripping blood, circular in appearance and not what would have been produced by a violent encounter as Backhouse related. His wounds appeared to be self-inflicted. Chairs and furniture had been overturned on top of the blood spots, indicating a staged crime scene. Backhouse was convicted of the murder of his neighbor and the attempted murder of his own wife.

Think Critically

Select one of the Case Studies and imagine you could interview the forensic scientist who studied the blood evidence. Write the questions and answers from the interview. Be sure your questions demonstrate what you have learned about blood and blood-spatter evidence.

Close

Write the following topics on the board or on poster paper. Organize students into groups and assign each group a topic. Have each group prepare a 3- to 5-minute presentation that reviews one topic from the following list for the class:

1. Blood types
2. Blood-spatter patterns
3. Blood directionality and area of convergence
4. Angle of impact
5. Area of origin

Careers

Forensic bloodstain specialists investigate sudden or unexpected deaths that involve bloodstains or spatter. Because of the specialized math and physics involved, if blood spatter turns out to be important to a case, they are often called as expert witnesses.

Look up other forensic investigators and their roles in analyzing high-profile crime scenes, for example, Dr. Henry Lee or Dr. Thomas Noguchi.

Teaching Tip

Invite a crime-scene investigator, law-enforcement officer, or criminal-case lawyer to visit your class and describe how blood evidence from a crime scene is analyzed in court. If possible, have him or her describe two types of cases:

1. Where the blood evidence supports the suspect's description of what happened at the crime scene

2. Where the blood evidence does not support the suspect's description of what happened at the crime scene

Careers *in Forensics*

Bloodstain Pattern Analyst

Photo courtesy of T. Paulette Sutton

"There's nothing I love more than feeding questions to investigators."—T. Paulette Sutton

T. Paulette Sutton, one of the world's leading experts on bloodstains, is the former Assistant Director of Forensic Services and Director of Investigations at the University of Tennessee, Memphis. She has been involved in nationally known murder cases, and has worked hard during a long career to make a positive contribution to the legal system. "It's best for my fellow man that we get killers off the street," she says. Since her official retirement in 2006, she has continued to teach, consult, and testify about her area of expertise.

Sutton began her career by training as a medical equipment technician at the University of Tennessee. She looked forward to traveling throughout the country. Before she started, though, she took what she thought was a temporary job in a medical examiner's office. Her supervisors recognized that her technical training, her patience, and her precision in collecting and analyzing evidence made her an excellent crime-scene technician. They sent her for training in bloodstain analysis, a fairly new field in the 1970s.

As Sutton describes bloodstain analysis, it is "one part math (measuring stains and calculating angles), one part physics (fluid behavior), and one part common sense (applying science to everyday life)." If properly done and carefully used, bloodstain analysis can distinguish what is impossible from what is possible.

As well as an ability to get at the truth, Sutton has a talent for explaining her techniques and

conclusions in court. In one of her earliest cases, her testimony about the origin of bloodstains on a defendant's shirt convinced the defendant to change his plea. He admitted that he had, in fact, stabbed and killed his mother.

Sutton's analysis sometimes finds truth rather than a lie. She did extensive research to check the account of one of the three defendants in the 1998 dragging murder of James Byrd, Jr., in Texas. The defendant claimed that bloodstains on his clothing came from cleaning the bloody truck at a carwash, and that he had not taken part in the dragging itself. Dr. Sutton's results supported this story, and the defendant was given a lesser sentence than the other two murderers.

Sutton is qualified as an expert witness in 12 states and in federal courts, and she has consulted for the Royal Canadian Mounted Police. Along with two other criminalists she is an author of *Bloodstain Pattern Analysis: Theory and Practice.* Sutton is a member of the Scientific Working Group on Bloodstain Pattern Analysis (SWGSTAIN) and the Forensic Science Editorial Review board for CRC Press. Among other honors, she is a Distinguished Member of the International Association of Bloodstain Pattern Analysts, and she received the Lecturer of Merit Award and Distinguished Faculty Award from the National College of District Attorneys. She also earned the Outstanding Service Award from the FBI.

CHAPTER 8 REVIEW

True or False

1. To determine blood type, Luminol is added to blood. *Obj. 8.3*

2. Blood-typing evidence is now used more to exclude a suspect than to identify a suspect. *Obj. 8.5*

3. Blood spatter on a wall in a series of rising and falling arcs is often caused by a severed artery. *Obj. 8.7, 8.8, 8.9*

4. Analyze the results of typing blood below. The blood type is A-. (*Hint:* The clumped red blood cells indicate agglutination.) *Obj. 8.3*

Antibodies to A   Antibodies to B   Anti-Rh antibodies

Short Answer

5. Compare and contrast the following pairs of terms:
   a) adhesion and cohesion
   b) spine and satellite *Obj. 8.8*
   c) swipe and wipe blood-spatter stains *Obj. 8.8*
   d) type AB+ and type O− blood *Obj. 8.3*

6. Refer to the following photos of blood-spatter patterns. Based on the relative size of the blood spatter and on images in Figure 8-23, Blood Velocity and Spatter Size, determine which pattern could have been produced as a result of a gunshot wound and which one could have resulted from a blow to the head. Cite evidence from the chapter to support your claim. *Obj. 8.7, 8.8, 8.9*

Sample A   *Sample B*

7. Refer to the two drops of blood below. What evidence can be obtained by viewing a single drop of blood? Describe as much about each drop as you can. Include evidence from the text to support your claims. *Obj. 8.7, 8.8, 8.9*

BLOOD AND BLOOD SPATTER   **247**

---

7. Round blood drop
   - It is apparent that this is a passive blood drop with no force other than gravity acting on it.
   - Given the roundness, it appears that this blood struck the surface at 90 degrees.
   - Given lack of spines, it appears that the surface on which it landed is very smooth, such as glass or marble. If the surface had more texture, then adhesion between the blood drop and the surface would have resulted in elongated spines.

- Elliptical bloodstain
   - Blood struck the surface at an angle as evidenced by the spine.
   - Blood was traveling from right to left as evidenced by the spine appearing on the left side.
   - The angle of impact could be measured by taking length/width and finding the inverse sine of that decimal. The angle of impact is approximately 19 degrees.

Chapter 8 Review

True or False
1. F   3. T
2. T   4. F

Short Answer

5. a. Both involve forces of attraction; they differ in that adhesion is the attraction between unlike molecules, whereas cohesion is the attraction between like molecules.

   b. Both are extensions of the main drop of blood; they differ in that a spine is an elongation of the main drop that is still connected to the main drop, whereas a satellite is a drop of blood that has separated from the main drop of blood.

   c. Both involve the disruption of the original bloodstain. They differ in that a wipe occurs when a dry surface moves in a lateral direction through a bloodstain, whereas a swipe involves the movement of a wet, bloody object in a lateral motion.

   d. Both refer to the presence or absence of antigens on the red blood cells; they differ in that type AB+ blood has three antigens, A and B, whereas Type O− blood has neither the A, B, nor the Rh antigen.

6. The photo lacks a ruler for scale, so definitive answers cannot be made. However, Sample A appears to be from a blow to the head, due to the larger bloodstains. Sample B appears to be the type of bloodstain and spatter one would expect to see as a result of a gunshot wound. It is a higher-velocity blood spatter.

8. a. Examine each drop; if a spine is present, that indicates forward movement of blood. If no spine is present and the drop is circular, that indicates a 90-degree-angle drop.

b. Examination of the size and shape of each blood drop provides a clue as to the type of injury that occurred. Refer to Figure 8-23. Besides examining drops of blood, view the spatter pattern. A series of straight lines of blood droplets can indicate castoff spatter produced by a strike with a blunt object. Gunshot wounds result in very fine droplets that fan out (both in front and behind a person if the gunshot wound was through and through). Arterial spurts result when an artery was severed.

c. The direction from which the victim was wounded can be determined by the location of the bloodstains. If the person was wounded on the right side, then the spatter would appear on the right. If the person was wounded from the back, then there would be blood-spatter projected away from the back.

d. The victim's location can be determined by calculating the area of convergence and then the area of origin. The perpetrator's position can be determined from blood-spatter evidence found on the perpetrator or from a void where the perpetrator was standing. Other indicators could be transfer evidence from the perpetrator walking through the victim's blood.

e. Movements made after the bloodshed can be inferred from evidence such as transfer patterns, swipes and wipes, a trail of passive

8. Discuss with a partner how each of the following questions can be answered by observation of blood-spatter patterns. After answering the questions, discuss your answers with another pair of students. *Obj. 8.7, 8.8, 8.9*
   a) Where did the blood come from?
   b) What caused the wounds?
   c) From what direction was the victim wounded?
   d) How were the victim(s) and perpetrator(s) positioned?
   e) What movements were made after the bloodshed?
   f) How many perpetrators were present?
   g) Does the bloodstain evidence support or refute witness statements?

9. Read the following case study regarding a hit-and-run accident. *Obj. 8.1, 8.3, 8.4, 8.6*

   On a dark, rainy night, a high school student was walking home after a basketball game and was struck by a car. Injuries to the young man included a broken leg and cuts and bruises that occurred when the young man was hit by the front of the car and bounced off the hood. The driver of the car drove away from the scene. The police were called by another driver who witnessed the accident.

   The witness provided a description of the car and partial license plate number. The next day, the police found and interviewed the alleged driver of the hit-and-run. They asked to see the man's car to look for any evidence of recently hitting a person. The car owner said that he'd recently hit a small deer.

   a) What type of testing could achieve the following?
      i. Reveal the presence of blood.
      ii. Determine whether any blood found was animal or human.
      iii. Exclude this driver as being the driver who struck the young man.
   b) The police officer noticed a dried reddish stain on the front of the car and along the hood. He took out a sealed moist hand wipe and wiped the stain with it. He placed the wipe with the evidence in a plastic ziptop bag and then put it into an evidence bag.
      i. Identify the numerous errors made by this police officer in collecting the evidence.
      ii. Summarize the proper method of collecting dry evidence that could be blood.
      iii. Do police have the right to demand see your car if they suspect that you were involved in a hit-and-run accident? Research your rights in that situation. Support your answer with evidence from your research.

blood drops from an injured person, and a void indicating someone left the area.

f. The number of perpetrators may be indicated by evidence such as different shoeprints or fingerprints found in transfer patterns and multiple areas of origin of blood.

g. To determine if a witness's description of the crime is consistent with blood-spatter analysis, check the following:
   • Whether the size of the blood droplets is consistent with the type of injury.

   • Whether the directionality and arrangement of the bloodstains are consistent with the descriptions.
   • The area of origin based on calculations made from the blood spatter and compared to what the person is telling you about where an injury occurred.
   • Whether the person is sitting or standing when they bled can be verified by the height of the area of origin.

Going Further

1. Research and describe what happens when fluids such as blood strike a surface. On the Internet, go to forensicsciencesimplified.org, click on the Bloodstains link, then the Principles link, and then go to the Interpreting the Patterns section. Include the terms *contact and collapse*, *displacement*, *dispersal*, and *withdrawal* in your response.

2. Research the different forces acting on a drop of blood as it falls to the ground. Describe each force and its effect on the drop as it is falling and on the resulting bloodstain when the drop strikes a surface. Include in your answer gravity, friction, momentum, surface tension, and cohesion.

3. Research and describe the chemical reactions that occur using the following tests and substances: Kastle-Meyer test, leukomalachite green, Hemastix®, and Luminol.

Bibliography

Books and Journals

Bevel, Tom and Ross M. Gardner. *Bloodstain Pattern Analysis*, 2nd ed. Boca Raton, FL: CRC Press, 2002.

James, Stuart H., and William G. Eckert. *Interpretation of Bloodstain Evidence at Crime Scenes*, 2nd ed. Boca Raton, FL: CRC Press, 1999.

James, Stuart H., Paul E. Kish, T. Paulette Sutton, and William G. Eckert. *Principles of Bloodstain Pattern Analysis*. Boca Raton, FL: CRC Press, 2015.

Laber, Terry L. and Barton P. Epstein. *Bloodstain Pattern Analysis*. Minneapolis, MN: Callan Publishing, 1983.

Lewis, Alfred Allen. *The Evidence Never Lies*. New York: Dell Publishing, 1989.

Russell, Peter J., Stephen L. Wolfe, Paul E. Hertz, and Cecie Starr. *Biology: The Dynamic Science*. Belmont, CA: Thomson Higher Education, 2008.

Solomon, Eldra, Linda Berg, and Diana W. Martin. *Biology*, 8th ed. Belmont, CA: Thomson Higher Education, 2008.

Wonder, A. Y. *Blood Dynamics*. New York: Academic Press, 2002.

Internet Resources

ngl.cengage.com/forensicscience2e (Gale Forensic Science eCollection)

http://www.crime-scene-investigator.net/blood.html (Schiro, George. "Collection and Preservation of Blood Evidence from Crime Scenes")

http://www.crimelibrary.com/criminal_mind/forensics/serology/8.html

http://www.youtube.com/watch?v=9XVJ2xBZV2c&feature=youtube (YouTube Blood Spatter Analysis)

http://www.bloodspatter.com/bloodstain-resources

http://www.forensicsciencesimplified.org/blood/principles.html (National Forensic Science Technology Center (NFSTC), Bureau of Justice)

https://www.ameslab.gov/mfrc/bpa_videos (Bloodstain Pattern Video Collection, slow-motion video clips, Ames Laboratory, U.S. Dept. of Energy)

9. a. i. Apply Luminol to the car to illuminate any blood evidence and perform a presumptive blood test like the Kastle-Meyer reagent test;

   ii. ELISA blood tests can be done to determine if blood is human or animal blood,

   iii. blood typing could be done to possibly exclude the suspect if the blood type found on the car was not consistent with the blood type of the victim, but then it seems the car was involved in another hit-and-run, which would need to be investigated.

   b. i. He didn't get a warrant before searching; he assumed it was blood; he wiped dried blood with liquid; chemicals in the wipe could have damaged DNA in the blood; he placed potential DNA evidence in plastic; he put wet blood evidence in a plastic bag.

   ii. • Photograph the blood evidence in situ, and document the evidence in writing.
   • Swab the dried blood off the car.
   • Be sure the blood is dry before packaging.
   • Put the blood evidence into paper packaging.
   • Place the paper packaging into an evidence bag.
   • Label and document the evidence.

   iii. Answers will vary. Individual state laws vary. Police usually need a warrant issued by a judge to allow them to search the car. That warrant is only granted if there is probable cause.

Background

See the IRCD for additional Activity 8-8 Antigens and Antibodies: Kinesthetic Activity

Background

This activity gives students an opportunity to determine the presence of blood in a stain. Students use reagents to test a bloodstain, a non-blood stain, and an unknown stain.

Time Required to Complete Activity

45 minutes

Safety Precautions

1. Emphasize to students that all procedures should be done while wearing protective gloves and goggles.

2. Dispose of all samples in the biohazard container provided.

Teaching Tip

Prepare in advance three small dropper bottles containing the reduced phenolphthalein (or Kastle-Meyer reagent), alcohol, and hydrogen peroxide (20 mL in each). (*Note:* Preparation of Kastle-Meyer reagent is not recommended because of the difficulty and the caustic and corrosive nature of materials.) Use fresh hydrogen peroxide. Each team needs only a few drops of each substance for each test, so two teams can share a set of bottles. It may be useful to number the dropper bottles to ensure that they are used in the correct sequence: #1 alcohol, #2 reduced phenolphthalein (or Kastle-Meyer reagent), and #3 Hydrogen Peroxide. Cloth samples containing dried animal blood (positive control) and dried ketchup (negative control) should be prepared in advance. (Animal blood can be ordered from a biological supply house.) You should prepare cloth samples containing two different dried unknowns. You can use a variety of unknowns, including beet juice, cranberry juice, tomato sauce, or food coloring, that look like blood.

ACTIVITY 8-1

A Presumptive Test for Blood *Obj. 8.4*

Objective:

By the end of this activity, you will be able to:
Use the Kastle-Meyer presumptive blood test to determine if a given stain contains blood.

Scenario:

Dried drops of red fluid found on a murder weapon, clothing, or automobile are noted, photographed, and analyzed. Did blood cause the red stain? If the red stain is not blood, then valuable time and money can be saved by not sending the red stain in to the laboratory for further testing. If it is determined that the red stain is blood, then further testing needs to be ordered to identify the source of the blood as human or animal.

A sample of the stain can be tested at the crime scene using a presumptive chemical reagent in what is known as the Kastle-Meyer test. The test will tell that a red stain is likely blood. This test *does not* confirm that the stain is human blood. That can be done with a later confirmatory test. It is also possible to determine with the Kastle-Meyer test that the stain is *not* blood. The Kastle-Meyer test uses hydrogen peroxide and a chemical, reduced phenolphthalein solution, which turns pink in the presence of the substance hemoglobin in animal blood.

When exposed to light, hydrogen peroxide breaks down into water and oxygen. This breakdown can be sped up in the presence of a *catalyst*, a substance that regulates the speed of a chemical reaction. In the Kastle-Meyer test, the hemoglobin of the blood contains an iron compound (*heme*) that acts as an enzyme (*peroxidase*), catalyzing a rapid breakdown of hydrogen peroxide into water and oxygen. In the presence of oxygen, the colorless phenolphthalein turns pink.

reduced phenolphthalein + hydrogen peroxide $\longrightarrow$ no reaction without blood

reduced phenolphthalein + hydrogen peroxide + Blood $\longrightarrow$ oxidized phenolphthalein (colorless) (pink)

Because other animal blood also contains heme molecules and enzymes, it will also give a positive result. If other animal blood could be present, then additional tests should be performed to determine if the blood is human.

Time Required to Complete Activity: 45 minutes

Science

BIOLOGY

BIOLOGY

Remind students how enzymes (organic catalysts) and substrates work together in biochemical reactions. Peroxidases are enzymes, many of which act on the substrate hydrogen peroxide. Living cells naturally contain peroxidase. If you put hydrogen peroxide on a cut to disinfect it, the peroxide bubbles. The bubbles are oxygen released as the hydrogen peroxide decomposes rapidly in the presence of the peroxidase in the red blood cells. This is related to the reaction seen in the Kastle-Meyer test.

Materials:

Act 8-1 SH

goggles

ketchup (1 oz or 10 ml)

blood from animal source (1 oz or 10 ml)

cloth or shirt with dime-sized bloodstain (positive control)

cloth or shirt with dime-sized ketchup stain (negative control)

cloth or shirt with unknown sample 1

cloth or shirt with unknown sample 2

20 mL 3% hydrogen peroxide solution in dropper bottle labeled 3

20 mL 95% ethyl alcohol in dropper bottle labeled 1

20 mL 2% reduced phenolphthalein solution in dropper bottle (or commercially purchased Kastle-Meyer reagent) labeled 2

biohazard container

latex or nitrile gloves

4 cotton swabs or 4 sterile cotton gauze pads per team

4 plastic knives

SAFETY PRECAUTIONS:

Wear protective gloves during all procedures.

Dispose of all samples in a biohazard container provided.

Assume that all red solutions are blood and handle according to safety regulations.

Be careful not to contaminate any of the reagents.

Be sure to drop the solutions onto the cotton swab without touching the dropper to the cotton swab.

Return the caps of all reagent bottles to the correct reagent bottle. Do not switch the caps from one bottle to the other.

Procedure:

1. Obtain a section of cloth that contains a known bloodstain (positive control). Before testing any unknown stains, it is important to check all reagents on a known sample of blood. If you do not get the expected results on a known sample, then you know that your reagents are malfunctioning and you need to replace them. This also allows you to see positive test results.

2. Remove the dried blood from the cloth by either scraping the blood off with a plastic knife, rubbing the dried blood off with sterile cotton gauze, or using a cotton swab to rub the dried stain.

3. Drop two drops of ethyl alcohol onto the swab or cotton gauze (don't allow the dropper to touch the swab).

4. Drop two drops of the reduced phenolphthalein solution or Kastle-Meyer reagent onto the swab (don't allow the dropper to touch the swab). Wait 5 seconds.

5. Drop two drops of the hydrogen peroxide solution onto the swab (don't allow the dropper to touch the swab).

Procedures

1. Print, copy, and distribute Act 8-1 SH from the IRCD, Chapter 8. Instructional support is available on the IRCD in Act 8-1 TN.

2. Make sure there are no state or county regulations prohibiting the use of animal blood in high school laboratories.

3. Make sure animal blood is obtained from a reputable supply company and the blood is sterile.

4. Before beginning the activity, demonstrate the correct procedure for testing a reagent without contaminating the solution.

5. Use universal precautions—treat all blood as if it is a source of blood-borne pathogens.

6. Use cotton swabs to test stains with reagents.

7. Have the students put their initials on stains so they can identify theirs.

8. Record observations in the table.

Teaching Tip

Phenolphthalein is the colorless, reduced form of phenolphthalein. To avoid confusion, in this activity we will discuss reduced phenolphthalein (colorless) and oxidized phenolphthalein (pink).

Teaching Tip

Colorless phenolphthalein is oxidized to form pink phenolphthalein in the presence of blood.

reduced phenolphthalein + blood (iron and peroxidase) + hydrogen peroxide → oxidized phenolphthalein
(colorless)   (pink)

If blood is not present, then the reaction will not occur, and reduced phenolphthalein will remain colorless. Note that you are looking for an immediate reaction of a deep pink color. If you wait more than 30 seconds, even a negative test will turn pink because of oxygen in the air. Therefore, evaluations of the Kastle-Meyer test must be done within 10 seconds after adding all the reagents.

Answers

Check students' Data Table 1.

1. Sample answers (Data Table 2):

   a. Ethyl alcohol breaches (disrupts) cell membranes so that hemoglobin is more exposed.

   b. Reduced phenolphthalein is a color indicator. In the presence of blood, it oxidizes, turning from its original clear color to pink.

   c. Hydrogen peroxide—Substrate for the perioxidase in hemoglobin.

2. Sample answers:

   a. A positive control is used to verify that all reagents are functioning in the expected manner. If the expected color change does not occur using the positive control, then new reagents are needed before testing any unknowns.

   b. A negative control is used to verify that a pink color will not result when using these reagents. If a pink color is produced with the negative control, you need to get new reagents or reexamine your technique. There could be some contamination of your reagents.

3. a. A pink color should not occur until after the hydrogen peroxide is added. If it does, there might be other chemicals on the swab that are oxidizing the reagent.

   b. If no reaction occurred on the positive control, check the reagents. The hydrogen peroxide may have broken down, and you will need a fresh supply.

---

6. A pink color (positive result) will appear within seconds if blood is present. Record your results in Data Table 1. (This is your positive control demonstrating the appearance when blood is present.)

7. Using a permanent marker, record your initials next to the stain that was just tested.

8. Dispose of all used cotton swabs and bloodstain samples into the biohazard waste container.

9. Using clean cotton swabs, repeat Steps 1 to 8 using the shirt containing the ketchup stain. (This is your negative control, since ketchup is not blood.)

10. Record the appearance of the ketchup test in Data Table 1.

11. With fresh cotton swabs or gauze pads, repeat Steps 1 to 8 on the section of the shirt containing the unknown stain 1.

12. Using fresh cotton swabs or gauze pads, repeat Steps 1 to 8 on the section of the shirt containing the unknown stain 2.

Data Table 1: Test Results

Stain	Color (Pink or not pink)	Describe Your Observations (Blood or not blood)
Bloodstain (positive control)		
Ketchup (negative control)		
Unknown 1		
Unknown 2		

Questions:

1. Complete the following data table, indicating the function of each of the chemical reagents used in this experiment.

Data Table 2: The Role of Chemical Reagents in Blood Sample Analysis

Chemical	Function
a. Ethyl alcohol	
b. Reduced phenolphthalein	
c. Hydrogen peroxide	

2. Explain why you need to use both a positive and negative control before testing the unknown stains.

   a. Positive control

   b. Negative control

3. Suggest a possible explanation for the following results:

   a. A pink color was produced *before* the hydrogen peroxide was added to the testing swab or cotton gauze.

   b. No color reaction occurred for the positive control.

Teaching Tip

The Kastle-Meyer test can produce false positives. Remind students that the Kastle-Meyer test is a presumptive test. If a positive reaction occurs with the Kastle-Meyer reagent test, it does not confirm that the substance being tested is blood. Confirmatory testing is required.

4. If nonhuman animal blood is different from human blood, how is it possible to get a positive reaction with the Kastle-Meyer test using dog blood?

5. If you performed the Kastle-Meyer test on potatoes, beets, or horseradish, you would also get a positive pink reaction although no blood is present. How would you account for these vegetables producing a positive reaction when no blood was present?

6. Why is it important to use a cotton swab when doing this test?

7. Why aren't the reagents applied directly to the original bloodstain?

8. Suppose that a red stain was found in a bathtub along with some bathwater. Would it be possible to detect the blood since it might have been diluted? Research and state the concentration of blood needed for a positive Kastle-Meyer blood test.

© iStock.com/Jani Bryson

Further Research:

1. Research the history of using this method as a presumptive blood test. Investigate the role of each of these scientists:
   a. Louis-Jacques Thenard
   b. Christian Freidrich Schonbein
   c. Joseph H. Kastle
   d. Erich Meyer

2. Research how to distinguish dog blood from human blood.

3. Research each of the following cases. Explain the role of blood analysis in helping to solve the crime.
   a. Peter Porco case, Albany, New York (2006)
   b. O. J. Simpson criminal case (1994)

4. Sample answer: The Kastle-Meyer test detects the presence of heme (or iron) found in hemoglobin of the blood. Both dogs and humans have hemoglobin in their blood. Therefore, both dog and human blood will produce a positive reaction using the Kastle-Meyer test.

5. These vegetables also contain the enzyme peroxidase that is found in human blood.

6. Sample answer: It is important to use a sterile cotton swab to preserve the evidence and avoid contamination of the original piece of evidence. The bloody fabric may need to be reexamined at a later date. Therefore, avoid adding anything to the original stained fabric.

7. Sample answer: Adding reagents directly to the original bloodstain will cause a chemical reaction that would permanently change the composition of the stain, making further testing impossible.

8. Sample answer: The Kastle-Meyer blood test is sensitive to dilutions of one part blood to 10,000 parts water. If the dilution of the blood does not exceed this level, then the blood could indicate a positive reaction. The more diluted the blood, the lighter the reaction color.

Further Research and Extensions

1. Louis-Jacques Thenard discovered hydrogen peroxide in 1818. Christian Freidrich Schonbein developed one of the first presumptive tests in 1863. Dr. Kastle developed a presumptive test for hemoglobin using reduced (phenolphthalein) in the early 1900s. Dr. Meyer later refined and improved on Dr. Kastle's test.

2. To determine if blood is human or from some other animal, a precipitin test is performed. Essentially, this test uses an antigen–antibody response. This test was developed in Germany in 1901 by Paul Uhlenhuth. To determine if the blood is human, it is necessary to produce antihuman antibodies. Injecting some human blood into an animal (e.g., a rabbit) does this. When human blood is injected into the rabbit, the rabbit produces antihuman antibodies or antiserum. Have students study these scientists and their contributions.

Time Required to Complete the Activity

If the activity is to be done during class time, then three class periods are needed:

- Brainstorm ideas and gather materials.
- Produce the model and create the simulated blood spatter.
- Have each team present its model and expert witness testimony to another team.
- Prepare a list of suggested improvements from the peer review.

Safety Precautions

Using artificial blood avoids exposure to human blood.

Warn students to avoid getting blood in their eyes, clothing, and areas other than the target area.

Procedures

1. Print, copy, and distribute Act 8-2 SH and Act 8-2 Peer Review to students from the IRCD, Chapter 8.
2. Divide the class into groups of 3–4 students. Students select from the Act 8-2 SH list a type of blood-spatter pattern that they will investigate. Each team will do the following:

- Research and brainstorm ideas on how to simulate their chosen blood-spatter pattern.
- Create the model and prepare their expert witness testimony.
- Present expert witness testimony with the model to a different team for peer review.
- Summarize a list of improvements and recommendations from the peer review.

Teaching Tip

Discuss with students the importance of crime-scene investigators recognizing different blood-spatter patterns. Review the various types of blood-spatter patterns in the text.

Creating and Modeling Blood-Spatter Patterns

Obj. 8.7, 8.8, 8.9

Objectives:

At the end of this activity, you will be able to:

1. Recognize and describe different blood-spatter patterns.
2. Design a technique to simulate and model various blood-spatter patterns.
3. Prepare expert witness testimony analyzing a blood-spatter pattern. Include in the testimony a possible scenario of how that blood-spatter pattern resulted, as well as evidence to support the scenario.
4. Working with one other team, conduct a peer review of each other's models and presentations.
5. Summarize any revisions or improvements that resulted from the peer reviews.

Time Required to Complete the Activity:

If the entire activity is to be done during class time, then four class periods are needed.

- Brainstorm ideas and gather materials.
- Produce the model and create the simulated blood-spatter pattern.
- Present models and expert witness testimony.
- Prepare a list of suggested improvements from the peer review.

Materials:

Act 8-2 SH Blood-Spatter Patterns

Act 8-2 SH Peer Review

Students prepare a list of materials used to create a blood-spatter model, including:

- source of artificial blood
- means of dispensing the blood to create the desired blood-spatter image
- target surface for the blood

SAFETY PRECAUTIONS:

Using artificial blood avoids exposure to human blood.

Warn students to avoid getting blood in their eyes, clothing, and areas other than the target area.

Background Information:

Crime-scene investigators use blood-spatter patterns to help them understand what happened at a crime scene. Is a person's description of the crime consistent with the blood-spatter analysis?

Challenge students with the task of designing a simulation of blood-spatter patterns using artificial blood. Divide students into groups of 3–4. Each team selects one of the blood-spatter patterns from the activity sheet.

In this activity, each team designs and builds a model of a blood spatter pattern. Following a peer review of the model and the presentation, each team submits a summary of the revisions and modifications suggested.

Review the information in the figures Blood Velocity and Spatter, and Bloodstain Patterns in Chapter 8 to assist in your design. For additional ideas, view the "Blood Stain Pattern Video Collection" from Ames Laboratory and the U.S. Department of Justice at https://www.ameslab.gov/mfrc/bpa_videos.

Procedure:

1. The instructor creates groups of 3–4 students.
2. Each group selects one type of blood-spatter pattern from Act 8-2 SH Blood-Spatter Patterns.

Research-Review:

3. Each team should review bloodstain patterns and research additional information.
   - Chapter 8, Figure 8-23 (Blood Velocity and Spatter Size) and Figure 8-21 (Blood-Spatter Patterns); note the shape of the blood spatter.
   - View slow-motion videos of blood-spatter. Google "Bloodstain Pattern Video Collection (Ames Lab)" or www.ameslab.gov/mfrc/bpa_videos.
   - Research additional sources from books or the Internet.
4. Brainstorm ideas of how to create your blood-spatter model.
   - What type of artificial blood will you use?
   - What type of surface will be your target surface?
   - What instruments will you need to produce the blood spatter?
   - What procedure will you use to produce the blood-spatter stain?
5. Your model should represent the blood-spatter pattern selected by your team.
6. Upon completion, each team will present its model to another team. The presentation should model the expert witness testimony that might be given at a trial. Include the following in your presentation:
   a. Your description and analysis of the blood-spatter pattern.
   b. Relate this particular blood-spatter pattern to events at the crime scene that could have produced this type of pattern.
   c. Support your claims using evidence from scientific sources.
7. Listen to another team's presentation, and view its model of a blood-spatter pattern. Prepare a list of suggestions or modifications of the team's testimony that would enhance its model and presentation.

Procedures

3. Using artificial blood, students design a method to produce a model of the blood-spatter pattern. Students prepare the simulated blood-spatter pattern and present their model and expert witness testimony to another team who will offer suggestions or modifications during a peer review.

   To stimulate more interest, students can present their revised presentations and models to a different class, to parents, and to other teachers. Or, students can prepare a video clip of their presentation and model.

Teaching Tip

Avoid providing all the information about how to create the blood-spatter patterns. Allow students time to develop their own ideas before sharing these suggestions:

   Target surface: poster paper, cardboard, large cardboard box such as from an appliance, Plexiglas, window glass, clothing, floor, ceiling tiles, floor tiles

   Instruments: turkey baster, pipettes, toothbrush, droppers, mousetraps, or blunt-force object on a blood-soaked sponge

Teaching Tip

Discuss with students the protocol for peer review. Refer to Act 8-2 SH Peer Review.

Going Further:

1. a. Modify your presentation and design incorporating the changes suggested during peer review.

   b. Present your revised model and presentation to another team, panel of teachers, or parents.

   c. Create a video of your presentation that can be viewed by other students, teachers, and parents.

2. a. Each team should post its blood-spatter patterns in the classroom.

   b. Class members should review and identify all the teams' blood-spatter patterns.

   c. Write a crime-scene scenario that could be applied to your team's blood-spatter pattern.

ACTIVITY 8-3

Blood-Spatter Analysis: Effect of Height on Blood Drops *Obj. 8.7, 8.9*

Objectives:

By the end of this activity, you will be able to:

1. Prepare reference cards of blood spatter dropped from varying heights.
2. Compare and contrast the blood spatter produced from different heights with regard to size, shape, and number of satellites.
3. Distinguish between the parent drop and satellites.
4. Distinguish between satellites and spines.
5. Analyze the results of your experiment, and prepare a summary of the effect of height on blood-spatter stains.

Background:

A blood-spatter pattern is created when a wound is inflicted and blood leaves the body. This pattern can help reconstruct the series of crime-scene events surrounding a shooting, stabbing, or beating. Recall that blood forms droplets as it falls from a wound. A drop of blood that falls on a flat surface will not totally flatten out—the blood drop will have a domed surface. The reason for this shape is the internal cohesive nature of blood. Blood tends to pull together because of cohesion and resists flattening out on a surface. The result is that the surface of the blood is elastic, giving the top of the blood spatter a rounded appearance.

Cohesive forces give a domed shape to a blood droplet.

If any of the blood does overcome cohesion and separates from the main droplet of blood, it will form small secondary droplets known as satellites.

Time Required to Complete Activity:

Two 45-minute class periods (one period to prepare and observe the blood drops, the second period to measure and analyze the blood drops)

Materials:

(per group of two students)
2 copies Act 8-3 SH
2 dropper bottles of simulated blood
6 5-by-8-inch index cards, not glossy
3 meter sticks
3 12-inch rulers with centimeter markings, or calipers
newspapers

SAFETY PRECAUTIONS:

Cover the floor in the work area with newspaper.
Simulated blood may stain clothing and surfaces.

ACTIVITY 8-3

Background

In this activity, students will study the effect of height on blood-spatter patterns.

Safety Precautions

1. Cover the floor in the work area with newspaper. Simulated blood may stain clothing.
2. Treat all waste as biological and dispose of it accordingly.

Time Required to Complete Activity

Two 45-minute class periods (one period to do the blood drop, the second period to measure the blood drops)

Teaching Tip

Be sure that the 5 × 8-inch index cards are not glossy.

Artificial blood can be purchased or you can prepare artificial blood.

Groups of three work well for this activity. One student holds the meter stick, another drops the blood, and a third helps to measure the diameter.

Procedures

1. Print, copy, and distribute Act 8-3 SH from the IRCD, Chapter 8.

2. Recipe for simulated blood: red food coloring, glycerin (or corn syrup), and water. Also, adding a little melted chocolate and white glue makes it appear more realistic.

3. Groups of three work well. One student holds the meter stick, another drops the blood, and the third ensures the proper height. After all blood is dropped, each student is responsible for measuring two of the six cards and recording the information in the data table.

4. Using a disposable pipette, dispense two drops of blood from various heights: 25, 50, 100, 150, 200, and 250 cm. Make sure students avoid dropping one drop of blood on top of another drop of blood.

5. Use separate cards for each height.

6. Students label cards with their initials and height before dropping blood on them. Let them dry for at least 30 minutes (overnight if possible). The cards must be dry before moving them, otherwise the blood will run.

7. Use plenty of newspaper. The floor may become stained if not enough paper is used to cover it. If weather permits, this is a good activity to do outside, but not on a windy day.

8. Make sure each team designates a team member to oversee that drops are dispensed from the correct height.

9. Do not rush students—provide extra cards as necessary.

10. Droplets of simulated blood will probably not dry for several days. Do not stack the spatter cards.

Procedure:

PART A: PREPARATION OF BLOOD-SPATTER REFERENCE CARDS FOR BLOOD DROPPED FROM DIFFERENT HEIGHTS

1. Spread newspaper on the floor of the work area. Be sure the newspaper is flat on the floor.
2. You will prepare 5 × 8-inch cards for each height used in the blood drop.
3. Label the top-right corner of each card with the height of the blood drop and your initials.
4. Place the labeled 5 × 8-inch index cards on the newspaper.
5. Use the rulers/meter sticks to measure the distance above the card.
6. One of the partners holds a meter stick vertically over the top of the card. The other partner holds the dropper of blood 30 cm above the card, and aiming toward the top of the card, releases one drop of blood.
7. Add a second drop on the same card from the same height. Avoid dropping the blood in the same location.
8. Repeat this process, dropping blood from heights of 50, 100, 150, 200, and 250 cm. Remember to prepare a new card for each height.
9. Do not pick up the cards until the blood is dry.
10. Measure the diameter of each of the spatter patterns to the nearest millimeter and record the data in the Data Table. Measure at the widest part of the main drop. Do not include any satellites or spines in your measurement.

Your initials and height of blood drop.

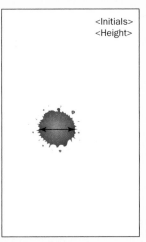

Blood dropped from various heights.

11. Determine the average diameter for the blood spatter for each height, and record it in the Data Table.
12. Prepare a bar graph comparing the effect of height on the average diameter of the blood drop. Your graph should have a title, labeled x-axis and y-axis, and an appropriate scale.

Data Table: Effect of Height on Diameter of Blood Drop

Height of Drop (cm)	Diameter of Drop (mm)	Diameter of Drop (mm)	Average Diameter (mm)
30			
50			
100			
150			
200			
250			

Questions:

1. Is there a relationship between the height from which the blood is dropped and the size of the blood-spatter droplets? Support your conclusion with data from your experimentation.
2. True or False: As the height from which the blood is dropped increases, the size of the blood spatter continues to increase. Support your answer with data from your experimentation.
3. Blood is dropped from heights of 25 cm and 250 cm. Compare and contrast the outer edges of blood droplets produced from these two heights.
4. Examine the blood spatter produced by dropping blood from the six different heights. Is there a relationship between the height from which the blood is dropped and the number of satellites produced? Support your answer with data from your experimentation.
5. Compare your results with those of your classmates.
   a. Were your results similar to those of your classmates? If not, how did they differ?
   b. If someone accidentally dropped two or more drops of blood in the same location, what effect would it have on the blood-spatter pattern?
6. If blood were dropped from a roof, would the diameter of the bloodstain be larger than the diameter of the bloodstain dropped from 250 centimeters? Support your claim with data from your experimentation or from research.

Teaching Tip

Students should not immediately pick up the cards because the blood will not be dry. Leaving the cards on the floor, the team members can measure the diameter of the blood drops.

Or, allow the cards to air dry and have them measure the cards the next day.

Answers

Check students' data tables.

1. Yes. See data table. Blood droplets increase diameter until the blood reaches terminal velocity, and the size no longer increases (around 200 cm).
2. False. See data table.
3. The outer edges of the blood dropped from 250 cm have more spines and more satellites.
4. Yes, the greater the height from which the blood was dropped, the larger the number of satellites. However, the size of the blood drop will not enlarge after a distance of 7 feet or 200 cm.
5. Answers will vary depending on the results of the class.
6. The bloodstain formed when blood drops from the rooftop will not be larger than the bloodstain when blood drops from 250 cm because blood reaches its terminal velocity after 7 feet, or approximately 200 cm. The size of the bloodstain does not increase after a blood drop reaches terminal velocity.

DIFFERENTIATED LEARNING

Teaching At-Risk Students

Encourage interested students to design an experiment investigating the relationship between the shape of a blood droplet and the smoothness of the surface upon which it is dropped. You may wish to suggest cloth and glass as possibilities for the independent variables. Consider running the best experiment as a class demonstration.

Further Study:

1. A drop of blood will continue to pick up speed until it reaches its terminal velocity.
   a. What is terminal velocity?
   b. What factors affect the terminal velocity of a substance?
   c. What is the terminal velocity of blood?
   d. How far does blood need to fall until it reaches its terminal velocity?

2. a. What effect does the surface of a target have on the shape of the blood-spatter stain? Design an experiment to test the effect of the target surface on the shape of the bloodstain. Your experiment should investigate four different types of surfaces.
   b. Using the terms adhesion and cohesion, provide an explanation for the variety of shapes of bloodstains found on different target surfaces.

Further Research and Extensions

Students may want to find out if terminal velocity varies from substance to substance. Encourage interested students to design and perform an experiment to verify the information.

Area of Convergence *Obj. 8.7, 8.9*

Objectives:

By the end of this activity, you will be able to:

1. Distinguish between passive blood spatter and blood spatter that was produced by some type of force, based on the shape of the bloodstain.
2. Determine the forward direction of the bloodstain based on its shape.
3. Use blood spatter to draw lines of convergence to locate the area of convergence.
4. Based on your blood-spatter analysis, describe a scenario that could have produced the blood spatter.

Background:

When the police arrived at a crime scene, both the victim and the attackers had already fled. Two areas of blood spatter were the only evidence that an assault had occurred. After drawing lines from the blood spatter, the crime-scene investigator determined not only the direction the blood was traveling and the approximate speed the blood was traveling but also the approximate location where the victim was standing when the injury occurred.

The shape of an individual drop of blood provides clues to the origin of the blood. A passive drop of blood with a spherical shape (equal width and length) indicates that the blood fell straight down with an impact angle of 90 degrees. When a drop of blood is elongated (longer than it is wide), it is possible to determine the direction the blood was traveling when it struck a surface.

The location of the source of blood can be determined if there are at least two drops of blood spatter. Draw a *line (of convergence)* down the long axis of each droplet of blood and note and circle the area where the lines intersect. This circle, known as the area of convergence, shows in a two-dimensional view where the victim was injured.

In this activity, you will analyze blood spatter and locate the area of convergence.

Time Required to Complete Activity: 45 minutes

Materials per Student:

Act 8-4 SH
1 ruler
1 pencil with sharp point and eraser

SAFETY PRECAUTIONS:

None

ACTIVITY 8-4

Background

This activity provides students with the opportunity to draw lines of convergence from blood spatter to determine the location of a person when he or she lost blood.

Safety Precautions

There are no safety precautions for this activity.

Time Required to Complete Activity

45 minutes

Procedures

1. Print, copy, and distribute Act 8-4 SH from the IRCD, Chapter 8.

2. Have students use very sharp pencils to draw the lines of convergence.

3. Encourage students to erase and redraw lines if necessary.

4. Remind students to draw through the middle of the droplet.

5. Lines of convergence start at the "tail" end (spine) of the blood droplet and extend towards the source of the blood.

6. Lines should only be drawn to the point where the lines intersect, not beyond.

7. The smallest circle should be around the area of convergence where ALL lines intersect.

Teaching Tip

Model for students the correct way to draw lines of convergence before they begin the activity.

Answers

Use the diagram as a guide to check students' diagrams.

Sample A

Procedure:

1. Refer to blood-spatter Sample A. Based on the shape of the bloodstains, determine the forward direction of each.

2. Draw a line of convergence for each group of blood stains.
   - Do not include any spines.
   - Draw a line through the center axis of each stains.
   - Your line should move toward the origin of the blood.
   - Continue the lines toward the origin until the lines intersect.
   - Draw the smallest circle you can around *all* of the intersecting lines to determine the area of convergence.

3. Determine how many incidents occurred based on the number of areas of convergence.

4. Repeat Steps 1–3 for Samples B, C, and D.

5. Select one of the blood-spatter patterns. Write a short narrative to explain how the blood-spatter pattern could have been produced.

Example

Drawn correctly!
Lines are started near the leading edge of the droplets and continue until they intersect.

Areas of Convergence
Sample A

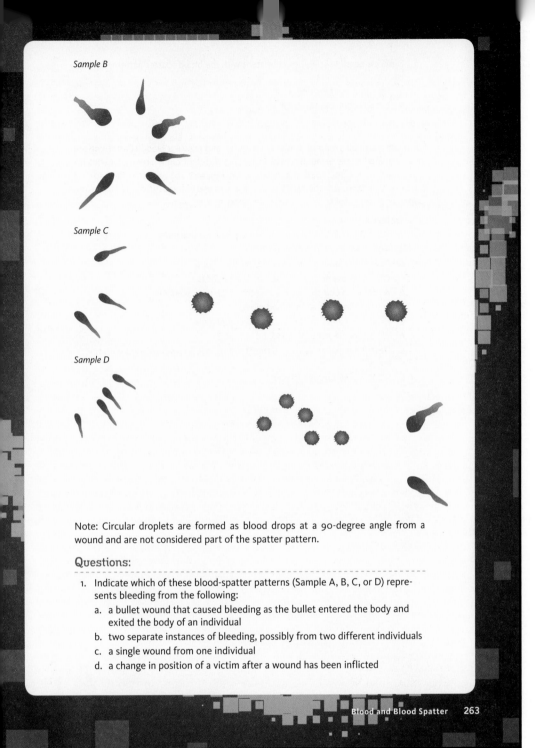

Sample B

Sample C

Sample D

Note: Circular droplets are formed as blood drops at a 90-degree angle from a wound and are not considered part of the spatter pattern.

Questions:

1. Indicate which of these blood-spatter patterns (Sample A, B, C, or D) represents bleeding from the following:
    a. a bullet wound that caused bleeding as the bullet entered the body and exited the body of an individual
    b. two separate instances of bleeding, possibly from two different individuals
    c. a single wound from one individual
    d. a change in position of a victim after a wound has been inflicted

Answers

Refer to Act 8-4 TN in the IRCD, Chapter 8 for answers to Samples A, B, C, and D.

1. a. Sample B shows the entry wound on the left, and the exit wound on the right.
    b. Samples A and D
    c. Sample C
    d. Samples C and D both indicate movement.

Answers

2. Sample the number of individuals and their direction of movement.
   a. could be one incident with entrance and exit wound or two people injured
   b. one incident with entrance and exit wound
   c. one incident, followed by passive bleeding as person walked away
   d. two incidents with passive drops from each

Teaching Tip

Suggested blood-spatter patterns for students to use include the following:
   a. an injured person running
   b. an injured person walking
   c. a simulation of blunt force trauma injury
   d. a simulation of a stabbing
   e. a simulation of a gunshot wound
   f. a combination of injuries such as a stabbing followed by the person moving to a different part of the room

2. Describe possible scenarios consistent with the blood-spatter patterns for each sample. Include:
   a. the number of incidents
   b. the direction of movement

Going Further:

Work with a small group of students to design and create a blood-spatter pattern of a simulated crime scene. Brainstorm ideas of different crime-scene scenarios (or use a crime scene described in a movie or TV program) and produce blood-spatter patterns that represent the crime scene. You can use either artificial blood, ink on paper, or paper cutouts to represent the blood-spatter stains.

Consider the following:
   a. What type of crime is depicted by your blood spatter?
   b. How many people are injured?
   c. Does the injured person move after the injury?
   d. Where on the body or bodies are the injuries?
   e. What size blood spatter is consistent with your scenario?
   f. In what direction is the blood moving?
   g. How many areas of convergence are depicted?
   h. What type of artificial blood did you use?
   i. Describe how you spattered the blood so that it was consistent with the injury.
   j. What is your target surface?

Further Research and Extensions

Area of convergence can help an investigator find the source of any liquid left at the scene of a crime, not just blood. Have interested students research how area of convergence has helped investigators solve other crimes, such as burglary.

Blood-Droplet Impact Angle *Obj. 8.7, 8.8, 8.9*

Scenario:

Two police officers walk into a neighborhood convenience store. They discover blood-spatter patterns on the walls and ceiling. "What happened here?" says one officer as she walks around the store. The officers call in the situation, and a forensics team is dispatched to the scene. Investigators will examine the crime scene and seek answers to the following questions:

- Whose blood is this?
- Does it belong to just one or to several people?
- How many people were injured?
- If more than one person was injured, is it possible to tell who was injured first?
- What type of injury caused the blood loss?
- What type of weapon caused the injury?
- If the weapon was a gun, from which direction was the bullet fired? Did the shooter point the gun upward, downward, or straight ahead?
- In what direction(s) did the injured person(s) move?

Objectives:

By the end of this activity, you will be able to:

1. Create blood-spatter patterns from different angles of impact.
2. Examine the relationship between angle of impact and blood-spatter patterns.
3. Calculate the angle of impact from blood-spatter patterns.

Time Required to Complete Activity:

Two 45-minute class periods
First period: Create blood-spatter patterns from different angles.
Second period: Measure blood spatter and calculate angle of impact.

Materials:

(per group of two students)
Act 8-5 SH
1 dropper bottle of simulated blood (per two groups)
2 5-by-8-inch index cards
2 metric rulers
newspapers
2 cardboard apparatuses (with dental floss)
1 protractor with 0-degree line along bottom edge
1 roll masking or drafting tape

SAFETY PRECAUTIONS:

Cover the floor in the work area with newspaper.
Simulated blood can stain clothing and furniture, so care should be taken to avoid spills.

Safety Precautions

Cover the floor in the work area with newspaper. Simulated blood may also stain clothing.

Time Required to Complete Activity

Two 45-minute class periods
First period: create blood-spatter patterns from different angles
Second period: measure blood spatter and calculate angle of impact

Teaching Tip

Blood-spatter cards should not be moved until they have dried. If the cards are moved before they dry, then the blood-spatter pattern can change. Drop the blood onto the cards in an area where they can be left undisturbed until they have dried (ideally, overnight).

Teaching Tip

Option: To save time, assign groups two different angles of impact and have groups share results. For example:

Group 1: 10 degrees and 50 degrees
Group 2: 20 degrees and 60 degrees
Group 3: 30 degrees and 70 degrees
Group 4: 40 degrees and 80 degrees

Teaching Tip

Refer to the Act 8-5 TN in the IRCD, Chapter 8, for tips on the cardboard apparatus construction. Most activities of this type use clipboards for mounting the spatter cards. Clipboard design is cumbersome and makes results extremely inaccurate. Instead, use cardboard cut from the side and bottom of a box for copier paper or similar-sized box. Cut a 36-inch length of dental floss to secure the apparatus. Cardboard dimensions are approximate:

11-inch total width
8-inch side height to bottom fold in box
11-inch bottom length from fold outward

Cut a 36-inch length of dental floss to secure the apparatus. Punch a hole in the upper-left corner for the dental floss to be tied. Cut a notch on each side of the bottom panel to anchor the floss. See the photos on the following student page. Each setup will hold two 5 × 8-inch cards. When the angle is set and locked with floss (at eye level), there is a dramatic increase in the accuracy of student results. See photo in Act 8-5 TN. The base of the cardboard is the larger section, 11 inches square.

Procedures

1. Print, copy, and distribute Act 8-5 SH from the IRCD, Chapter 8.

2. 30 cm is the distance from the blood source to the impact point on the card.

3. Try not to hit the same place twice.

4. Use a new card for each new angle.

5. Use two cardboard setups (if available) so one card can be drying while placing drops on the next.

6. Obtain a paper towel and wipe the bottle mouth before dropping liquid.

7. Be sure to allow each card to dry at least 30 minutes before removing it from the cardboard setup.

8. Label each card with an arrow pointing in the direction the drop is falling. If unsure, turn the card over and notice where bleeding through has occurred. This is the bottom of the drop.

Teaching Tip

Remind students that a 12-inch ruler is approximately 30 centimeters long and can be used to judge the distance between the blood dropper and the card.

Background:

Blood-spatter analysis is a powerful forensic tool that helps investigators reconstruct what happened at a crime scene. In this activity, you will drop blood from different angles and observe how the shape of the blood droplet provides clues to what happened at a crime scene.

Procedure:

PART 1: PRACTICE DETERMINING ANGLE OF IMPACT

Using the measurements in Data Table 1 and a calculator, determine the angle of impact for the five bloodstain measurements given.

Data Table 1: Calculation of Impact Angle From Bloodstains

Stain	Width (mm)	Length (mm)	Width/Length (sine)	Decimal	Impact Angle (inverse sine)
1	8	10			
2	3	4			
3	5	9			
4	2	10			
5	8	9			

PART 2 In this activity, each group drops artificial blood from two different angles of impact determined by your instructor. Measure each bloodstain and calculate the angle of impact based on the length and width of each blood drop. Blood will be dropped 30 cm above the target. Share and record the results from all groups so data represent impacts from 10, 20, 30, 40, 50, 60, 70, and 80 degrees.

Group 1: 10 degrees and 50 degrees

Group 2: 20 degrees and 60 degrees

Group 3: 30 degrees and 70 degrees

Group 4: 40 degrees and 80 degrees

A. Labeling the Cards and Setting Up the Cardboard

Note: You will have one 5 × 8-inch card on the same cardboard set for each angle of impact.

1. Obtain two 5 × 8-inch index cards; turn the cards over so that no lines are visible.

2. Label each card with your initials and angle of impact on the top-right corner with small letters and numbers.

3. Obtain two cardboard apparatuses. Note that one side of the cardboard apparatus is shorter than the other side. Tape the 5 × 8-inch index cards on the shorter side of one of the cardboard apparatus as shown in the photo, and align the top of the card to the top of the cardboard.

4. Place your cardboard setup with your 5 × 8-inch card in a location where you can leave it undisturbed while the blood droplets dry for at least 30 minutes. (Refer to the cardboard apparatus photo.) The longer end of the cardboard should be on your desk or floor, and the shorter piece of cardboard with the 5 × 8-inch card should be elevated.

Blood drop cardboard apparatus.

5. Repeat Steps 3 and 4 for your other angle of impact. You should have two cardboard setups with one card on each.

B. Using a Protractor to Establish the Desired Angle of Impact

1. Place the protractor so that the center zero mark is located at the bend of the cardboard apparatus. The protractor setting is the *outside* angle of the cardboard.

Example 1

Desired impact angle is 20 degrees. Protractor reading is 90 minus the angle of impact, or 90 minus 20 = 70 degrees.

Cardboard

Example 2

Desired impact angle is 30 degrees. Protractor reading is 90 minus the angle of impact, or 90 − 30 = 60 degrees.

2. After setting the protractor for the desired impact angle:

a. Use the dental floss to anchor the cardboard in position. Secure the dental floss to the bottom cardboard by inserting the dental floss in the notch in the bottom cardboard and passing the floss under the bottom cardboard and into the opposite notch. This will lock the cardboard in the proper position. Recheck the angle in case the card slipped, and adjust it if necessary.

b. Use masking tape to secure the cardboard in place by taping the bottom of the cardboard to the desk or floor.

c. Repeat Steps a and b on your second angle of impact cardboard apparatus.

3. a. One partner holds a ruler 30 cm above the 5 × 8 card that is taped to your cardboard apparatus.

b. A different student drops one drop of artificial blood from a height of 30 cm above the target 5 × 8-inch card. Aim towards the top one-third of the card.

Teaching Tip

Use protractors that have the 0-180-degree line *along the bottom edge of the protractor*. Most protractors have this line raised, and this will lead to errors in measurement.

Teaching Tip

The activities in this chapter may be a good opportunity to review metric measurements and abbreviations.

Teaching Tip

If students have a difficult time understanding why they subtract the desired angle of impact from 90 degrees when positioning the cards on the cardboard, show them that the desired angle of impact is actually measured from the vertical. To obtain a 20-degree angle of impact, your protractor is set at 70 degrees.

(90 − 20 = 70) It is not possible to throw blood at an exact angle (gravity pulls it down). Therefore we change the position of the cardboard to use gravity to produce the desired angle.

Teaching Tip

A common source of error is that students set their protractor reading for the same number of degrees as their desired impact setting. For example, an impact angle of 20 degrees should have a protractor setting of 70 degrees. Many students set their protractor at 20 degrees. You may choose to alert students to this mistake before they do the activity.

Teaching Tip

Prepare your own set of blood spatter cards. Laminate the cards to preserve them for reuse.

c. The student dropping the blood should move his or her hand slightly and drop a second drop of blood onto the same card, avoiding both drops striking the same place.

d. Do not remove the cards from the cardboard setups until the blood has dried, at least 30 minutes.

e. While the first card is drying, prepare the second cardboard apparatus at a different impact angle. Repeat Steps a–d.

Blood-spatter angles, 90- to 100-degree angles of impact.

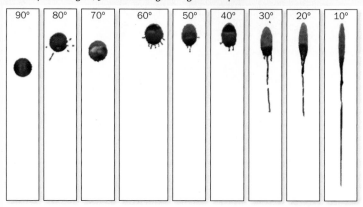

4. For each drop of blood on your cards:

a. Measure in millimeters the width and length of each blood drop (do not include any spines).

b. Divide the width by the length.

c. Using a calculator, determine the angle of impact for each drop.

d. Record the information in Data Table 2.

Data Table 2: Angle of Impact and Bloodstains

Expected Impact Angle (degrees)	First Blood Drop				Second Blood Drop			
	Width (mm)	Length (mm)	Width/ Length *(sine)*	Calculated Angle of Impact (degrees)	Width (mm)	Length (mm)	Width/ Length	Calculated Angle of Impact (degrees)
10								
20								
30								
40								
50								
60								
70								
80								

Calculation of Impact Angle From Bloodstains

Stain	Width	Length	Width/Length	Decimal	Impact Angle
1	8	10	8/10	0.8000	53
2	3	4	3/4	0.7500	49
3	5	9	5/9	0.5555	34
4	2	10	2/10	0.2000	12
5	8	9	8/9	0.8889	63

5. Observe your data, another team's data with the same impact angles, and class data for all angles of impact.

   a. Compare the two drops of blood for the same angle of impact (on the same card). Do they have the same shape?

   b. Compare and contrast the blood drops for the two *different* angles of impact. Do they have the same shape?

   c. Confer with a different team who used the same two angles of impact. How do your bloodstains compare with the bloodstains of the other team?

   d. Refer to Data Table 2. Was the calculated angle of impact consistent with the angle of impact you built your cardboard apparatus for?

   e. If your calculated angles of impact differed from those you anticipated with your cardboard setup, brainstorm ideas to account for the discrepancy. Then suggest ways to improve upon your technique.

   f. As a class, discuss your data for all the different angles of impact. Then record the data for the other angles of impact in Data Table 2.

Questions:

1. How accurate were you in obtaining the desired angles of impact?

2. How would you account for any differences between your measured angle of impact and the angle of impact you anticipated from the construction of your cardboard setup?

3. Describe how you could modify this activity to ensure more reliable results.

4. Elaborate on how the calculation of the angle of impact of blood spatter is of forensic value.

Going Further:

1. A brief review of right triangles and trigonometry demonstrates why angle of impact is calculated by taking the inverse sine of the width/length of blood drops. A right triangle has a 90-degree angle. The side opposite the right angle is called the *hypotenuse*, the side across from the angle of interest is known as the *opposite side*, and the side next to the angle of interest is known as the *adjacent side*.

The sine function shows the relationship between two sides of a right triangle. The sine of an angle is equal to the length of the side opposite an angle of interest divided by the length of the hypotenuse.

$$\text{sine of an angle} = \text{opposite side/hypotenuse}$$

Answers

Check students' data tables.

1. Answers will vary.

2. Sample answer: Incorrect placement of protractor in determining angle.

3. Answers will vary. Sample modifications: Use larger protractors; use thinner cardboard; standardize where measurements are taken: top of cardboard or the bottom; use actual (sterile supply-house) blood instead of artificial; replicate the activity and take the average.

4. Sample answer: The determination of the actual position of individuals involved in a conflict can be used to corroborate stories or point out discrepancies.

Teaching Tip

If students need additional practice measuring and calculating angle of impact before doing the wet lab, use these images. These were produced by students and are not very accurate. Ask students to analyze the blood-spatter angles and determine the actual angle of impact.

Refer to the following diagram showing a blood drop about to strike a surface. Note the right triangle and the angle of impact. It is possible to calculate the angle of impact by measuring the width of the blood droplet (*AB*) divided by the length of the blood droplet (*BC*).

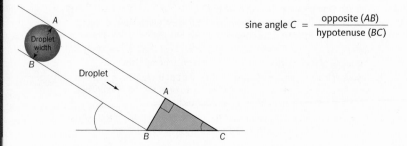

$$\text{sine angle } C = \frac{\text{opposite } (AB)}{\text{hypotenuse } (BC)}$$

Note that the opposite side AB is the width of the blood-stain, and the hypotenuse BC is the length of the bloodstain.

$$\text{sine angle } C = \frac{\text{opposite } (AB)}{\text{hypotenuse } (BC)}$$

$$\text{sine angle } C = \frac{\text{opposite } (AB)}{\text{hypotenuse } (BC)} = \frac{\text{width (1.5 cm)}}{\text{length (3.0 cm)}}$$

$$\text{sine angle } C = 0.5000$$

inverse sine 0.5000 = 30 degrees

2. Refer to the photos of blood-spatter angles above. The drops were produced by students using the cardboards setups used in this activity. Measure each of the droplets and calculate the *actual* angle of impact for each of the droplets using their width and length. Compare the calculated angle of impact with the labeled angle of impact. If they differ, suggest possible sources of error and how they could be avoided to ensure more reliable results.

Further Research and Extensions

Assign students to research the following topic: Can blood spatter alone be used to solve a difficult criminal case? Look for instances where evidence about the sequence of events in a crime led to someone's conviction. How might blood-spatter analysis help establish the sequence of events?

Area of Origin *Obj. 8.7, 8.9*

Objectives:

By the end of this activity, you will be able to:

1. Determine the direction of blood flow based on the shape of the droplet.
2. Use lines of convergence to help determine the position of the victim when the wound was inflicted.
3. Calculate the angle of impact for individual drops of blood spatter.
4. Use the law of tangents to calculate the height above floor level where the wound was inflicted.

Time Required to Complete Activity: 45 minutes

Materials:

Act 8-6 SH
1 metric ruler
1 colored pencil or marker
1 graphite pencil
calculator with sine and tangent functions or sine table (Appendix A) and tangent table (Appendix B)

SAFETY PRECAUTIONS:
None

Introduction:

In previous activities, you determined the angle of impact and area of convergence for blood spatter. Now you will apply that knowledge and the law of tangents to estimate the height (position) of the wound, the area of origin, or the source of the blood spatter.

Background:

Blood-spatter analysis helps crime-scene investigators reconstruct what happened at the crime scene. By estimating the angle of impact along with the area of origin of the blood spatter, investigators can determine if the physical evidence left by the blood spatter is consistent or inconsistent with the events as described by witnesses.

For example, in domestic abuse cases, the victim may lie to protect the abusing partner. A victim may state that a head injury occurred as a result of a fall rather than abuse. However, if the blood-spatter patterns are inconsistent with this type of injury, then the question becomes what type of injury did cause the blood spatter? What actually happened? Is a witness lying? Further investigation is required when the blood-spatter evidence reveals a different account of the incident than that described by the eyewitness.

Blood and Blood Spatter 271

ACTIVITY 8-6

Background

In this activity, students will have the opportunity to determine area of origin for blood spatter. Students use pencils, markers, calculators, and tangent tables for their calculations.

Time Required to Complete Activity

45 minutes

Safety Precautions

There are no safety precautions for this activity.

DIFFERENTIATED LEARNING

Teaching Visual Learners

To help students visualize blood-spatter analysis: have students cut out three paper droplets of blood (with spines to indicate direction of movement) and place them on the floor. Position a student behind the drops of blood. Use meter sticks to show the area of convergence for the three drops. For each drop of blood, measure the width and length to indicate angle of impact. With a protractor at the beginning of the drop of blood, set a string at the origin of the protractor (0,0) for the correct angle of impact. Continue the string at that angle until it meets the person, the area of origin. Do this for all three blood droplets.

Procedures

1. Print, copy, and distribute Act 8-6 SH from the IRCD, Chapter 8. (You can find instructional support on Act 8-6 TN on the IRCD.)

2. Students might need some help with the tangent function on the calculator or the tables.

In this activity, you analyze blood spatter by noting (or calculating) the following:

- Shape of the droplet of blood, indicating direction
- Diameter of the blood spatter, indicating velocity of the blood
- Length and width of blood droplets to calculate angle of impact using the sine function
- Lines of convergence, indicating area of convergence
- Distance from the center of convergence to the edge of the blood spatter
- Area of origin by applying the law of tangents

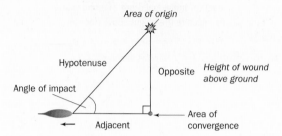

Horizontal distance from center of area of convergence to the leading edge of the blood

Math Review:

Right triangle

- Contains one 90-degree angle.
- The hypotenuse is the longest side of a right triangle, opposite the 90-degree angle (right angle).
- The opposite side to an angle is the side directly across from the angle of interest.
- The adjacent side to an angle is the side closest to the angle that is not the hypotenuse.

Review: Blood-Spatter Analysis and Area of Origin:

1. Examine blood-spatter stains, and note the forward direction of the bloodstains. Circular bloodstains indicate the blood fell at a 90-degree angle of impact. Bloodstains longer than they are wide indicate blood falling at an angle other than 90 degrees. The presence of a spine or satellites in front of the bloodstain indicates forward direction.

2. Using several drops of blood, determine the area of convergence.
   - Draw a line along the main axis of each droplet.
   - Start the line from the edge of the droplet of blood and draw a line in the opposite direction of the forward motion of the blood. Do not include any spines or satellites.
   - Draw the smallest circle possible around the area where *all* lines intersect.

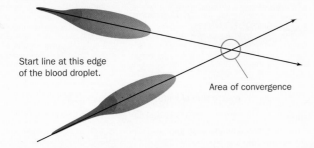

Start line at this edge of the blood droplet.

Area of convergence

3. Once you have determined the area of convergence, you will measure the distance from the area of convergence to the edge of the drop of blood where it first struck a surface. This distance is indicated in green.

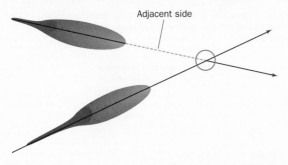

Adjacent side

Recall the diagram of a right triangle. This dotted green line next to the angle of impact is the adjacent side. It is the line extending from the center of the area of convergence to the leading edge of the blood droplet.

Area of origin of blood spatter

Opposite

Angle of impact

Adjacent

Teaching Tip
Sine and tangent tables are in the appendices.

4. Determine the angle of impact for *each* droplet of blood.
   - Measure the width and length of each blood droplet.
   - Divide width by length.
   - Find the inverse sine of width/length to get the impact angle.

angle of impact = inverse sine of width/length

Example
width = 14 mm and length = 45 mm
14/45 = 0.3111 (sine value)
The inverse sine of 0.3111 is 18 degrees.

5. Once you have calculated the impact angle for a specific droplet of blood (Step 4) and you have measured the distance from the center of the area of convergence to the leading edge of the blood droplet (the adjacent side of the right triangle; Step 3), you can solve for the opposite side, or height, or location of the source of blood using the law of tangents.

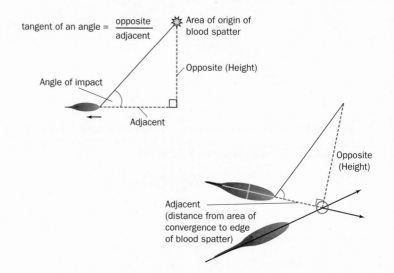

tangent of impact angle = opposite side/adjacent side (solving for opposite side)
tangent of impact angle × adjacent side = opposite side

The opposite side is really the height and the adjacent side is the distance measured from the area of convergence to the bloodstain. You are solving for one unknown: height.

tangent = opposite/adjacent or
tangent = height/distance (solving for height)
tangent × distance = height

Example:

Crime-scene investigators detected blood spatter on the floor of the kitchen. The investigators drew lines of convergence and measured the distance from the center of the area of convergence to the leading edge of a drop of blood. That distance was recorded as 5.75 feet. After measuring the length and width of the blood droplet and using the law of sines, it was determined that the angle of impact was 27 degrees. The police wanted to determine the area of origin, or the height from the floor to where the person was bleeding.

Height

27°

Distance to area of convergence = 5.75 ft

Solution:

tan = opposite/adjacent = height/distance
tangent of the blood-spatter angle = height of the wound/distance from blood to area of convergence

Substituting values in the equation:

tan 27° = height of wound/distance
tan 27° = height/5.75 ft

Consult your calculator or tangent table to find the tangent of 27°.

tan 27° = h/5.75 feet
0.5095 = h/5.75 feet

Solving for h ∼ 0.5095 × 5.75 feet

h ≈ 2.9 feet is the distance above the ground where the wound began bleeding.

Problems: Blood-Spatter Analysis and Area of Origin

Refer to the blood-spatter patterns to estimate the area of origin for each of the problems.

Answers

Problem 1

The answers for Problems 1, 2, and 3 are approximate and depend on the width of the pencil lines, size of the circle drawn, and accuracy of measurement.

Distance from the center of the area of convergence to the edge where blood first strikes the target is 17 mm on the scaled diagram.

If scale of diagram is 1 mm : 0.2 feet, then 17 mm in the diagram is actually 3.4 ft.

$$0.2 \text{ ft}/1 \text{ mm} = x \text{ ft}/17 \text{ mm}$$

solving for x

$$0.2 \text{ ft}/1 \text{ mm} \times 17 \text{ mm} = x \text{ ft}$$
$$3.4 \text{ ft} = x$$

Blood droplet 1 width = 3.5 mm
and length = 7 mm

width/length = 3.5 mm/7 mm
= 0.5000
Inverse sine of 0.5000 is 30 degrees.
Angle of impact is 30 degrees.

Area of Origin
tangent of impact angle = opposite/adjacent or
tangent of impact angle = height/distance from area of convergence
tangent of 30 degrees = height/3.4 ft
0.5774 = height/3.4 ft
0.5774 × 3.4 ft = height
1.9 ft is the approximate height of area of origin.

PROBLEM 1

Refer to Blood-spatter Sketch 1. From these drops of blood, determine the area of origin of the blood by completing the following steps. Record your answers in the data table on Act 8-6 SH.

1. Determine the direction in which the blood was traveling.
2. On Act 8-6 SH, draw lines of convergence using the three droplets of blood.
3. On Act 8-6 SH, draw a small circle around the intersection of the lines of convergence to indicate the area of convergence.
4. On Act 8-6 SH, measure the distance in millimeters from the center of the area of convergence to the leading edge of the blood where it first strikes the surface.
5. Using the scale of 1 millimeter : 0.2 feet, convert the distance in millimeters to the distance in feet.
6. Using blood droplet 1, determine the angle of impact:
   a) On Act 8-6 SH, measure the width and the length of the blood droplet.
   b) Find the width/length ratio for the blood droplet (the sine).
   c) Using a calculator and the inverse sine function or a sine table, determine the angle of impact for blood droplet 1.

Blood-spatter Sketch 1. (Blood droplets are drawn to scale.)

Blood droplet 1

7. Using the law of tangents, determine the area of origin, or height, of the source of blood for blood droplet 1.

PROBLEM 2

Refer to the following Blood-spatter Sketch 2. From those drops of blood, determine the area of origin of the blood by completing the following steps. Record your answers in the data table on Act 8-6 SH.

1. Determine the direction in which the blood was traveling.
2. On Act 8-6 SH, draw lines of convergence.
3. On Act 8-6 SH, draw a small circle around the intersection of the lines of convergence to indicate the area of convergence.
4. On Act 8-6 SH, measure the distance in millimeters from the area of convergence to the leading edge of the blood where it first strikes the surface.

Problem 2

The distance from the center of area of convergence to the edge where blood first strikes the target is 10 mm on the scaled diagram.

If scale of diagram is 1 mm : 0.3 feet, then 10 mm in the diagram is actually 3.0 ft.

$$0.3 \text{ ft}/1 \text{ mm} = x \text{ ft}/10 \text{ mm}$$

solving for x

$$0.3 \text{ ft}/1 \text{ mm} \times 10 \text{ mm} = x \text{ ft}$$
$$3.0 \text{ ft} = x$$

blood droplet 2 width = 4 mm and length = 18 mm

width/length = 4 mm/18 mm = 0.2222
Inverse sine of 0.2222 is approximately 13 degrees.
Angle of impact is approximately 13 degrees.

Area of Origin

tangent of impact angle = opposite/adjacent or
tangent of impact angle = height/distance (distance from area of convergence)
tangent 13 degrees = height/3.0 ft

5. Use the scale of 1 millimeter : 0.3 feet to convert the distance in millimeters to the distance in feet.
6. Use blood droplet 2 to determine the angle of impact:
   a. On Act 8-6 SH, measure the width and the length of the blood droplet.
   b. Find the width/length ratio for the blood droplet.
   c. Using a calculator and the inverse sine function or a sine table, determine the angle of impact for blood droplet 2.
7. Use the law of tangents to determine the area of origin, or the height, of the source for blood droplet 2.

Blood-spatter Sketch 2. (Blood droplets are drawn to scale.)

 Blood droplet 2

PROBLEM 3

Refer to the following blood-spatter sketch. From the drops of blood, determine the area of origin of the blood by completing the following steps. Record your answers in the data table on Act 8-6 SH.

1. Determine the direction in which the blood was traveling.
2. On Act 8-6 SH, draw lines of convergence.
3. On Act 8-6 SH, draw a small circle around the intersection of the lines of convergence to indicate the area of convergence.
4. On Act 8-6 SH, measure the distance in millimeters from the area of convergence to the leading edge of the blood spatter (droplet 3) where it first strikes the surface.
5. Use the scale of 1 millimeter : 1.5 feet to convert the distance in millimeters to the distance in feet.

(Blood droplets are drawn to scale.)

$0.2279 = \text{height}/3.0 \text{ ft}$
$0.2279 \times 3.0 \text{ ft} = \text{height}$
0.7 ft is the approximate height or area of origin.

Note that the origin of the blood was less than a foot from the ground; it appears that the man was on the ground when he was shot. The suspect claimed that he shot the man in self-defense. That doesn't seem likely.

Problem 3

Distance from center of area of convergence to the edge where blood first strikes the target is 12 mm on the scaled diagram.

If scale of diagram is 1 mm : 1.5 ft, then 12 mm in the diagram is actually 18 ft.

$1.5 \text{ ft}/1 \text{ mm} = x \text{ ft}/12 \text{ mm}$

solving for x

$1.5 \text{ ft}/1 \text{ mm} \times 12 \text{ mm} = x \text{ ft}$
$18 \text{ ft} = x$

blood droplet 3 width = 4 mm and length = 9 mm

width/length = 4 mm/9 mm = 0.4444

Inverse sine of 0.4444 is approximately 26 degrees.

Angle of impact is approximately 26 degrees (continued below).

Area of Origin
Tangent of impact angle = opposite/adjacent   or
Tangent of impact angle = height/distance from area of convergence
Tangent of 26 degrees   = height/18 ft
0.4961 = height/18 ft
0.4961 × 18 ft = height
9 ft ~ height

6. Use blood droplet 3 to determine the angle of impact.
   a. On Act 8-6 SH, measure the width and the length of the blood droplet.
   b. Find the width/length for the blood droplet (the sine).
   c. Using a calculator and the inverse sine function or a sine table, determine the angle of impact for blood droplet 3.
7. Use the law of tangents to determine the area of origin, or the height, of the source of blood for blood droplet 3.

Data Table

Example	Distance (mm)	Actual Distance (ft)	Width of Blood Droplet (mm)	Length of Blood Droplet (mm)	Width/ Length (sine)	Angle of Impact (inverse sine; degrees)	Tangent of Angle of Impact (degrees)	Height (ft)
1								
2								
3								

Further Research and Extensions

Encourage students to investigate other uses for the geometry and trigonometry used in this activity.

Crime-Scene Investigation <small>Obj. 8.7, 8.8, 8.9</small>

Scenario:

A woman calls the police and says she heard gunshots fired in the apartment next door. When the police arrive, they discover two deceased men, two handguns, and bloodstains. Man 1 was shot through the forehead and probably died immediately. Man 2 was shot in the abdomen and later died. The neighbor was the only witness. Can the blood spatter "tell the story"? Where were the men standing? Who shot first? In this activity, you will analyze the crime scene by examining the blood-spatter evidence and any other evidence at the crime scene to determine what happened.

Objective:

By the end of this activity, you will be able to:

1. Analyze the blood-spatter patterns from the following crime-scene diagram.
2. Determine the area of convergence and the area of origin based on the blood-spatter evidence at the crime scene.
3. Based on your blood-spatter analysis and other evidence found at the crime scene, make a claim as to which person was shot first, and support your claim with evidence.

Time Required to Complete Activity: 40 minutes

Materials:

Act 8-7 SH Data Table
Act 8-7 SH Crime Scene
ruler
pencil
calculator with trigonometric functions or sine table (Appendix A) and tangent table (Appendix B)

SAFETY PRECAUTIONS:
None

Procedure:

1. Examine the following crime-scene diagram. Look for blood-spatter, along with other evidence that may help solve the crime.
2. Determine lines of convergence for all blood-spatter patterns using the crime-scene diagram. Draw a circle around the area of convergence. Determine how many incidents occurred to produce the blood-spatter pattern.
3. Using the width and length measurements of the blood-spatter stains found in the Data Table, calculate the angle of impact for each droplet of blood. Record your results in the Data Table.

   Recall that the sine of the angle of impact = the inverse sine of the width/length of the blood droplet. (Find the angle of impact with a calculator or sine table.)

Blood and Blood Spatter   279

Background

This activity gives students the opportunity to use various skills to gather information from blood spatter. Students use crime-scene diagrams to determine direction, height, and angle of impact.

Safety Precautions

There are no safety precautions for this activity.

Time Required to Complete Activity

40 minutes

Procedure

Print, copy, and distribute Act 8-7 SH and Act 8-7 Crime Scene from the IRCD, Chapter 8.

Teaching Tip

In this activity, the length and width of each blood droplet as well as the distance from the area of convergence to the area where the blood drop first hits the floor are provided in the data table. By providing these measurements, you give the students more time to practice the math to determine impact angles using the inverse sine function and to determine the area of origin using the tangent function.

After doing this activity, students should analyze a crime scene set up in the room where they will do all the measurements.

Answers

1. Man 1 was most likely standing because his area of origin for bloodstains was more than 5 ft high.

2. In Position 1, there are bloodstains both in front of and behind the area of convergence. This is most likely due to more blood being released in front of the man than behind him. The bullet could have exited the body and created a bloodstain behind him.

3. There were two areas of bleeding; Man 1 was shot at a height above 5 ft, consistent with a head wound. Man 2's area of origin was about 2.5 ft. He walked to Position 3 (evidenced by passive drops) after being shot. It appears likely that Man 1 fired his gun first because with a head injury, he would not have been able to fire it after being shot; the head injury would likely incapacitate him.

   See student data tables for evidence.

4. Using a calculator or a tangent table, find the tangent for the angle of impact for each blood droplet. Record the tangent value for each blood droplet in the Data Table.

5. Using the angle of impact and the distance from the nearest edge of the bloodstain to the area of convergence (found in the Data Table), calculate the area of origin for all bloodstains.

   Recall that the height of the injury = (tan of angle of impact) × (distance from the center of area of convergence to the leading edge of the blood).

6. Complete the Data Table.

Questions:

1. Based on your calculations, which man was most likely standing when he was shot? Support your answer with evidence from the crime scene.

2. In Position 2, there are four bloodstains in front and one bloodstain behind the victim. How do you account for this?

3. Based on the blood-spatter evidence, describe the series of events resulting in the deaths of these two men. Support your claim with evidence obtained from the blood-spatter analysis.

Data Table

Stain	Width of Stain (W) (mm)	Length of Stain (L) (mm)	Width/ Length (4 Decimal Places) (Sine Value)	Angle of Impact (Nearest Degree)	Tangent of Angle of Impact (4 Decimal Places)	Distance From Near Edge of Stain to Center of Area of Convergence (feet)	Height (h) of Wound = Tangent × Distance (Area of Origin)
1	9.6	18.1				4.0	
2	9.0	18.6				4.4	
3	13.2	17.8				2.2	
4	12.8	18.9				2.8	
5	13.2	19.2				2.5	
6	4.5	9.0				10.1	
7	5.1	10.6				10.3	
8	3.9	8.4				10.4	
9	3.6	8.1				10.3	

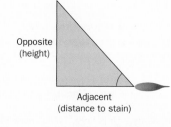

Opposite (height)

Adjacent (distance to stain)

tan = opposite/adjacent

Stain	Width of Stain (W) (mm)	Length of Stain (L) (mm)	Width/ Length (4 Decimal Places) (Sine Value)	Angle of Impact (Nearest Degree)	Tangent of Angle of Impact (4 Decimal Places)	Distance From Near Edge of Stain to Center of Area of Convergence (ft)	Height (h) of Wound = Tangent × Distance (Area of Origin)
1	9.6	18.1	0.5304	32	0.6256	4.0	2.5
2	9.0	18.6	0.4839	29	0.5529	4.4	2.4
3	13.2	17.8	0.7416	48	1.1054	2.2	2.4
4	12.8	18.9	0.6772	43	0.9205	2.8	2.6
5	13.2	19.2	0.6875	43	0.9467	2.5	2.4
6	4.5	9.0	0.5000	30	0.5773	10.1	5.8
7	5.1	10.6	0.4811	29	0.5488	10.3	5.7
8	3.9	8.4	0.4643	28	0.5242	10.4	5.5
9	3.6	8.1	0.4444	26	0.4961	10.3	5.1

Crime-Scene Diagram (Scale 1/4 inch = 1 foot).

Further Research and Extensions

Ask students to research whether guns of different calibers leave different blood-spatter patterns.

Chapter Overview

Toxicology is the study of poisons, toxins, drugs, and other substances people use for medical, recreational, or criminal purposes. Identification of these substances has improved due to advances in technology. When substance evidence is recovered, it is processed, weighed, separated, and identified. The use, sale, and distribution of illegal drugs are major areas of crime in the United States today. Exposure to poisons and toxins can occur naturally or as a result of crime or suicide attempts. Forensic toxicology helps determine the relationship between exposure to a substance and the toxic or lethal effects of that exposure on humans.

The Big Ideas

Toxic substances include poisons, toxins, illegal drugs, and controlled drugs. Toxicity depends on dose, duration, nature of exposure, interactions with other substances, and by-products of metabolism. Exposure to poisonous and toxic substances, including arsenic, mercury, lead, toxic gases, pesticides, herbicides, and radiation, may occur naturally or deliberately. Drugs can affect a person's health, mood, metabolism, perception of reality, and awareness. Extended drug use can lead to drug tolerance, dependence, addiction, health issues, brain damage, criminal behavior, and even death. Lethal gases can damage the nervous system and interfere with breathing. Substance evidence collection, processing, and handling must follow established guidelines. Because of improved technology and other scientific breakthroughs, toxicologists and medical examiners are better able to determine how a person died when exposed to drugs, toxins, or poisons.

CHAPTER 9

CHAPTER 9
Forensic Toxicology

Another Famous Overdose

Cory Monteith, 31-year-old co-star of the popular American musical-drama television series *Glee*, was found dead in a Vancouver, British Columbia, hotel on July 13, 2013. The Coroner Service stated that evidence found in his room was consistent with a drug overdose. It appeared that the death was accidental. The autopsy and toxicology tests confirmed that Cory died due to a combination of alcohol and heroin.

Cory was raised in Canada by a single mother and had a troubled adolescence involving abuse of alcohol and marijuana from age 12. After attending 16 different schools, he dropped out at age 16 but eventually received his high-school diploma. To support his alcohol and drug dependency, Cory resorted to petty crime and stealing from his family. When he was 19, his family staged an intervention, and he began attending a rehabilitation program.

After rehab, Cory played in a band, drove a taxi, and was eventually discovered by an agent who helped him start an acting career. On *Glee*, Cory was cast as Finn Hudson, the good-looking quarterback with a boyish charm who dazzled audiences with his smooth voice. After four seasons on *Glee*, Cory's onstage romance with character Rachel turned into a real-life romance with actress Lea Michele. It seemed that Cory had everything: a rising career, money, and a beautiful and talented girlfriend. He was voted one of the Sexiest Men in America. But he also still had his addictions.

In April 2013, Cory went to rehab again. No one claims to know what went wrong. Close friends of Cory agreed with the medical examiner that Cory's death was likely accidental and not intended to be suicide. Combining drugs doesn't just double the effect of the drugs. The effect is often exponential—and it's frequently deadly.

SCENARIO

How do drugs affect the body? How can different drugs act as stimulants, depressants, or hallucinogens? Drugs affect the transmission of nerve impulses in the brain. Neurons (nerve cells) have spaces between them called *synapses*. In order to transmit a message between neurons, the body uses chemical messengers called *neurotransmitters*. Drugs interfere with nerve transmission by either blocking or mimicking neurotransmitters. When drugs are combined, as in Cory Monteith's case, the effects can be especially lethal. Go to www.learn.genetics.utah and search for the *Science of Addiction, How Drugs Can Kill* for information on the danger of alcohol and heroin combinations.

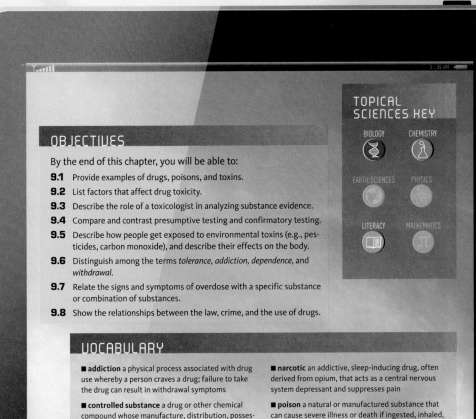

OBJECTIVES

By the end of this chapter, you will be able to:

9.1 Provide examples of drugs, poisons, and toxins.

9.2 List factors that affect drug toxicity.

9.3 Describe the role of a toxicologist in analyzing substance evidence.

9.4 Compare and contrast presumptive testing and confirmatory testing.

9.5 Describe how people get exposed to environmental toxins (e.g., pesticides, carbon monoxide), and describe their effects on the body.

9.6 Distinguish among the terms *tolerance, addiction, dependence*, and *withdrawal*.

9.7 Relate the signs and symptoms of overdose with a specific substance or combination of substances.

9.8 Show the relationships between the law, crime, and the use of drugs.

TOPICAL SCIENCES KEY

BIOLOGY   CHEMISTRY

EARTH SCIENCES   PHYSICS

LITERACY   MATHEMATICS

VOCABULARY

- **addiction** a physical process associated with drug use whereby a person craves a drug; failure to take the drug can result in withdrawal symptoms

- **controlled substance** a drug or other chemical compound whose manufacture, distribution, possession, and use are regulated by the legal system

- **Controlled Substances Act** law that established penalties for possession, use, or distribution of illegal drugs and established five schedules for classifying drugs

- **dependency** powerful craving for a drug; unlike addiction, dependency does not result in physical withdrawal symptoms upon discontinuation of the drug.

- **depressant** a substance that decreases or inhibits the nervous system, reducing alertness

- **hallucinogen** a drug that changes a person's perceptions and thinking during intoxication

- **illegal drug** a drug that causes addiction, habituation, or a marked change in consciousness, has limited or no medical use, and is listed in Schedule I of the U.S. Controlled Substances Act

- **narcotic** an addictive, sleep-inducing drug, often derived from opium, that acts as a central nervous system depressant and suppresses pain

- **poison** a natural or manufactured substance that can cause severe illness or death if ingested, inhaled, or absorbed through the skin

- **stimulant** a substance affecting the nervous system by increasing alertness, attention, and energy, as well as elevating blood pressure, heart rate, and respiration

- **tolerance** a condition occurring with consistent use of one drug whereby a person needs more and more of the drug to produce the same effect

- **toxicity** the degree to which a substance is poisonous or can cause illness

- **toxicology** the study of drugs, poisons, toxins, and other substances that harm a person when used for medical, recreational, or criminal purposes

- **toxin** a substance naturally produced by a living thing that can cause illness or death in humans

TEACHING RESOURCES

Instructor's Resource CD-ROM includes:

- Activities and Student Handouts
- Alternative Assessments
- Consolidated Bibliography
- Correlations to NGSS and CCSS
- Figure Files
- Lesson Plans

- Nonfiction Readings
- PowerPoint Presentations
- Student Learning Objectives (SLOs)

CL Testing powered by Cognero

Website: ngl.cengage.com/forensicscience2e

Teaching Tip

This chapter is devoted to examination of many drug-related topics. Your school's health education department can provide you with more specific information relating to drug and alcohol abuse.

Teaching Tip

If you used the first edition of this text, you will notice that bioterror content is no longer in this chapter. It has been deleted for content adherence reasons. You can find information on bioterror issues at www.fbi.gov or www.dhs.gov (the Department of Homeland Security).

Teaching Tip

Students have many misconceptions and varied backgrounds regarding drugs. As a pre-assessment, consider a carousel brainstorming activity. Write 8 questions about drugs or drug abuse on poster paper and post the questions around the classroom. Have students count off 1-8. All number 1s go to poster 1, all number twos go to poster 2, and so on. Students brainstorm answers to the questions and write them on the posters. After two minutes, they rotate to the next poster. Upon completion, each group has a spokesperson summarize the comments on each poster.

Figure 9-1 *Forensic toxicologist.*

© Darren Baker/Shutterstock.com

Did you know

Intelligent fingerprint testing may soon revolutionize drug testing. Metabolites detected from fingerprints could indicate the use of cannabis, opiates, benzodiazepines, amphetamines, and cocaine.

INTRODUCTION *Obj. 9.1, 9.2, 9.3*

Toxicology is the study of drugs, poisons, toxins, their metabolites, and other substances that can harm a person when used for medical, recreational, or criminal purposes. **Poisons** are natural or manufactured chemicals, such as arsenic or rat poison, that can cause severe harm. **Toxins** are naturally occurring poisonous substances living things produce, such as ricin or rattlesnake venom. *Toxicologists* (Figure 9-1) examine the effects of these harmful substances on the body, establish a cause and effect from the exposure, and develop treatments and techniques for detection. Substances of interest to toxicologists vary from misused legal drugs, to illegal and controlled drugs, to environmental toxins such as heavy metals, solvents, vapors, radioactive materials, pesticides, and herbicides.

Most people are exposed to drugs or harmful substances by (1) ingesting them into the digestive tract, (2) inhaling them, (3) injecting them, or (4) absorbing them through the skin. How a person is exposed to a substance is described as follows:

- **Intentionally** Taken as a drug to treat illness or to relieve pain
- **Accidentally** Unintentionally taken
- **Deliberately** Taken as in suicide

Toxicologists and chemists have developed specific tests and technologies to determine if someone has been exposed to a harmful substance. Body fluids such as blood, sweat, stomach contents, or fluids from the vitreous humor of the eye are used to detect substances in both living people and dead bodies. The toxicologist isolates the *metabolites* (products of cellular reactions) of the substances to verify their presence in the body.

The **toxicity** of a substance, the degree to which a substance is harmful to a given person at a given time, depends on many factors, such as

- Dose (how much was taken in or absorbed)
- Duration (the frequency and length of the exposure)
- Nature of the exposure (whether it was ingested, inhaled, or absorbed through the skin)
- Interactions with medications, alcohol, or other substances
- By-products when broken down or metabolized by the body; for example, wood alcohol or methanol is chemically converted to toxic substances when metabolized in the body, forming formaldehyde and formic acid.

In this chapter, you will examine some of the many substances studied by toxicologists and the effects of those substances on both the individual and society. In the activities, you will perform simulated drug testing and drug identification.

Brief History of Forensic Toxicology

"All substances are poisons; there is none which is not a poison. The right dose differentiates a poison and a remedy." Paracelsus (1493–1541)

The Greek philosopher Socrates was one of the earliest reported victims of poisoning (hemlock, 399 B.C.). By the 1600s, poisoning had become a profession. The rich, and even the royal families, of Europe paid people to poison their enemies as a means of settling disputes. The use of arsenic as a poison was widespread and became known as "inheritance powder." Arsenic is extremely toxic in small amounts; it is tasteless, odorless, and mimics the symptoms of natural disease, making it an "ideal" drug for poisoning someone. It was not until the 1800s that methods of chemical analysis were developed to identify arsenic and other poisons in human tissue. The first forensic toxicologists to popularize these new methods were physicians Mathieu Orfila (1787–1853) and Robert Christison (1797–1882). In 1855, Karl Friedrich Mohr, along with Carl Fresenius, pioneered improvements in qualitative analytical chemistry. In 1918, Charles Norris, New York City's first medical examiner, along with the director of the first toxicology lab, Alexander Gettler, developed standardized techniques and testing to help determine the cause of death. Together they transformed how scientists investigated death. The Food and Drug Administration (1959) was formed to protect people from any food, drug, or cosmetic that could contain toxic components. In 1970, Congress passed the Controlled Substances Act, which established penalties for possession, use, and distribution of illegal drugs.

Although poisoning is still popular in murder mysteries, it is not a common form of murder today. Less than one-half of 1 percent of all homicides results from poisoning. In recent history, only a few notable individuals have been murdered by poison. Bulgarian dissident Georgi Markov was stabbed in the leg with an umbrella armed with a ricin toxin capsule in 1978. (Ricin is derived from castor bean seeds. See Figure 9-2.) More recently, Russian ex-spy Alexander Litvinenko was poisoned by exposure to the radioactive element polonium in 2006.

Figure 9-2 *Castor bean plant (above) and seeds (below), from which ricin is derived.*

CHEMISTRY

Evidence Detection, Collection, and Storage

Drugs, poisons, and toxins can be transported inside luggage, boxes, or large shipping containers. Drug-sniffing dogs trained to detect the smell of different drugs are used to locate drugs in airports and schools. People paid to smuggle drugs ("mules") have been known to hide drugs in their bodies by packaging the drugs and swallowing them or putting them into body cavities. Unfortunately, a number of deaths have occurred when the

Teaching Tip

Integrate history, toxicology, and forensics using excerpts from *The Poisoner's Handbook* by Deborah Blum. Blum explores cause of death in four historical poisoning case studies. (The PBS Website has an interactive graphic novel based on this book at www.pbs .org ; search for *Tales From the Poisoner's Handbook*.)

DIFFERENTIATED LEARNING

Teaching At-Risk Students

To connect academic concepts to real-world situations, ask at-risk students to collect reports of drug overdoses and/or poisoning from television, newspapers, magazines, and the Internet. Have them discuss the reports in class. Help them connect the concepts of drug class and effects on the body to these real-world situations.

drug bag breaks open, releasing large quantities of drugs into the bodies of such mules.

Proper documentation, photography, and collection of anything related to drugs, poisons, or toxins are essential if the evidence is to be presented in court. (Refer to Chapter 2 to review proper methods of evidence collection and handling.) The evidence may be in the form of pills, powders, liquids, botanical matter (seeds, leaves, mushrooms), crystals (methamphetamine), or imbedded in food, paper, or candy. Other evidence can be found on clothing, objects, or liquid-soaked fabrics. Biological evidence from suspects can include urine, blood, sweat, or saliva.

Correct packaging of the evidence is important to preserve the evidence and protect those individuals working with the evidence. To prevent mold and contamination, all plant matter (marijuana) or any wet items (blood-stained clothing) should be dried and placed in paper bags (not plastic). Syringes with needles should be placed in a glass container labeled "biohazard." Many agencies have their own specific protocol for proper collection of manufacturing goods from drug labs. These materials are hazardous and volatile and should be handled with extreme caution. Typically, small quantities are seized as evidence to protect those handling the evidence.

Evidence Testing and Reporting of Drugs, Poisons, and Toxins *Obj. 9.4*

The type of toxicological testing depends on the amount of substance recovered. When evidence is recovered, three basic questions need to be answered by the toxicologist:

1. What substances are there? (qualitative testing)
2. Might there be any illegal components?
3. How much of each substance is present? (quantitative testing)

At the crime scene, a presumptive test may be performed by first-responding law-enforcement officers: Presumptive tests are preliminary and do not provide positive identification. Most presumptive testing is colorimetric testing, which produces a color change. Other presumptive testing may include the following:

- Microscopic examination of plant matter
- Microcrystalline test using a small amount of the evidence put into solution. Upon drying, the material is examined for an identifying crystalline shape when viewed under ultraviolet spectroscopy, in which evidence is exposed to ultraviolet light. A measurement is made based on the way the material absorbs light.
- Gas chromatography–mass spectrometry (Figure 9-3), which is used to visually distinguish components prior to confirmatory testing

Confirmatory testing is usually a multistep process to provide a positive identification of the substance. Toxicologists must also distinguish between acute poisoning and chronic poisoning.

Figure 9-3 *Gas chromatography–mass spectrometry separates a substance into its individual components.*

ZUMA Press, Inc/Alamy

Acute poisoning is caused by a high dose over a short period of time, such as cyanide ingestion or inhalation, which immediately produces symptoms. *Chronic poisoning* is caused by lower doses over long periods of time, which produces symptoms gradually. Mercury and lead poisoning are examples of chronic poisoning, in which symptoms develop as the metal concentrations slowly rise and accumulate to toxic levels in the victims' bodies over a long period of exposure. The types of tests can include the following:

The National Institute of Standards and Technology (NIST) is developing the Organization of Scientific Area Committees (OSAC) to coordinate standards and guidelines for quality and consistency of work in the forensic science community. Toxicology and controlled substances are part of the OSAC on Chemistry/Instrumental Analysis. Go to the Gale Forensic Science eCollection at **ngl.cengage.com/forensicscience2e** and look up the NIST for more information about the OSAC.

- Gas or liquid chromatography: separates samples visually into individual components
- Mass spectrometry: converts molecules to ions, which are moved by electric and magnetic fields separating each substance, and displaying each substance graphically.
- Capillary electrophoresis: separates ions based on charge
- Wet chemistry: uses liquid solvents to separate compounds

When a forensic toxicologist testifies in court he or she must be able to explain what type of test was done and state his or her degree of confidence in the test results. Strict adherence to regulations regarding instrument calibration and maintenance must be maintained.

HEAVY METALS, GASES, POISONS, AND TOXINS *Obj. 9.1*

Suicides, homicides, and accidental deaths have occurred due to exposure to heavy metals such as arsenic, lead, and mercury. Heavy metals enter the body by ingestion, inhalation, or absorption through the skin or mucous membranes. Heavy metals are stored in the soft tissues and can damage organs throughout the body. Many deaths are due to environmental exposure. Arsenic contaminates the drinking water of millions of people throughout the world. Mercury poisoning has occurred due to industrial wastes being dumped into bodies of water. Lead once was an ingredient of paint. Children suffer from lead poisoning when they eat old, lead paint chips. Figure 9-4 on the next page lists heavy metals and typical symptoms of an overdose.

Lethal Gases and Lethal Injections *Obj. 9.5*

The use of lethal gas chambers by the Nazis during World War II resulted in the death of millions of Jews, dissidents, and the disabled. Many Nazi gas chambers used carbon monoxide from engine exhaust, but many also used

BIOLOGY

Science

BIOLOGY

BIOLOGY

How does inhaling chemicals into the lungs affect the body? Because the lungs have large beds of capillaries, which are tiny blood vessels, inhaled chemicals are capable of entering the blood fairly rapidly. The blood then travels through the circulatory system to the heart, which pumps it out through the arteries to cells in the body tissues.

Figure 9-4 *Heavy metals with typical symptoms of overexposure.*

Heavy Metal	Source	Symptoms of Overexposure
Lead	Naturally occurring element, additive to gas and older paints, weights, bullets	Nausea, abdominal pain, insomnia, headache, weight loss, constipation, anemia, kidney problems, vomiting, seizure, coma, and death. Blue discoloration appears along the gum line in the mouth.
Mercury	Ingested in fish, coal-fired power plant pollutant	Mad Hatter's Disease (hat makers in England used a mercury compound), a progressive disorder; acute poisoning from inhalation causes flu-like symptoms such as muscle aches and stomach upset. Chronic poisoning causes irritability, personality changes, headache, memory and balance problems, abdominal pain, nausea, and vomiting; excessive salivation and damage to the gums, mouth, and teeth. Long-term exposure can cause death.
Arsenic	Naturally occurring element In groundwater	Profound acute exposure quickly produces severe gastro-intestinal symptoms, difficulty speaking, muscle cramps, convulsions, kidney failure, delirium, and death. Lesser chronic exposure produces skin lesions and changes in pigment, headache, personality changes, and eventually coma.

hydrogen cyanide. Hydrogen cyanide was also used in the American penal system as a form of capital punishment, especially for murderers, during the 1900s. Cyanide is naturally present in a variety of seeds and nuts and is inhaled in cigarette smoke.

Thousands of suicides and accidental deaths have been caused by the inhalation of carbon monoxide gas fumes from car exhaust or defective heating units. The gas causes death by interfering with the ability of the body to absorb oxygen.

Death can also result from injections of potassium chloride or sodium pentothal, usually as a result of capital punishment. Potassium chloride injections affect the heart's ability to send electrical signals. Sodium pentothal acts as a depressant and slows down the central nervous system. Homicides caused by lethal injections may be confused with death by natural causes if there isn't obvious evidence of an injection. This is why a toxicologist's job is so important.

Two Cases:
1. The Cuyahoga River, in Ohio, was once described as the most polluted river in America. An oil slick on the river actually caught fire and burned in 1969. Research the components of the oil slick that caught fire.
2. A West Virginia chemical spill deposited an estimated 7,500 gallons of MCHM, a chemical used to wash coal, into the Elk River in 2014. Drinking water for 300,000 West Virginia residents was affected.
   Research the effects of this spill on the residents and the legislation that resulted.
   Go to the Gale Forensic Science eCollection at **ngl.cengage.com/forensicscience2e** to learn more about these incidents and other polluted bodies of water.

Pesticides and Herbicides

Herbicides that control weeds, and pesticides that control insects and rodents, are poisons designed to kill. If ingested or absorbed by humans, some can lead to serious illness or death. Many of these poisons are stored in fatty tissue in the body. The longer the exposure, the more severe the symptoms (Figure 9-5).

Figure 9-5 *Common pesticides with symptoms of overexposure*

Pesticides or Herbicides	Symptoms of Overexposure
Aldrin, Dieldrin (Pesticides)	Anxiety, seizures, twitching, rapid heartbeat, muscle weakness, sweating, excessive salivation, diarrhea, coma, death
Glyphosate Mixture (Herbicide)	Ranges from gastrointestinal problems, skin and eye irritation, kidney malfunction, to death

Toxins

Toxins of interest to forensic toxicologists are substances produced by plants or animals that are poisonous to humans. Examples include rattlesnake venom (Figure 9-6) and ricin. Ricin (Figure 9-2 above) is a waste product of the manufacture of castor oil from castor beans. It is lethal to humans in quantities as small as 500 micrograms—a dose the size of a pinhead! Ricin can be inhaled as a mist or a powder, ingested in food or drink, or even injected into the body. Depending on how ricin is encountered, death results within six to eight hours. Toxins are rarely used in crimes, but ricin has been used in at least one successful assassination and one unsuccessful attempt.

Figure 9-6 *Some snake venoms are deadly toxins.*

Tom McHugh/Science Source

Drugs and Crime *Obj. 9.6, 9.7, 9.8*

Drugs are intended to prevent and treat illness and reduce pain. However, abuse of legal and illegal drugs is costly to our nation in loss of lives, health, and the economy. Abuse of drugs has led to many deaths. According to the National Bureau of Justice, almost half of the individuals in federal prisons are there because of drug-related offenses such as the following:

- Possession or distribution of illegal drugs
- Drug-related offenses where the effects of the drugs contributed to the crime
- Drug-using lifestyle where the frequency of involvement in illegal activity is increased

According to the National Institute on Drug Abuse 2013 survey, more than $600 billion is spent annually in costs related to crime, lost work productivity,

Science

BIOLOGY

People react differently to toxins found in nature. Some people go into shock or die from a bee sting or insect bite, while others merely experience skin irritation. Unfortunately, there is no sure way to know how someone will react except experience.

Teaching Tip

Ask a local or state law-enforcement officer to visit the class or join via a Webcam to discuss the relationship between drugs (including alcohol) and the local crime rate. Also ask what percentage of motor vehicle accidents are caused locally by impaired drivers (those intoxicated by drugs and/or alcohol).

Evaluate

Organize students into small groups. Instruct each group to gather and graph data on the number of drug abuse violations in the United States (or a select state) for one year, from 2000 to the present. Have each group share its results with the class. Then, compare the graphs, and discuss any trends students detect and how they might be explained.

DIFFERENTIATED LEARNING

Teaching Gifted Students

Will random drug searches help reduce drug-related problems among students, or are random drug searches an invasion of privacy? What is your opinion? Prepare a debate on this issue based on constitutional freedom.

DIGGING DEEPER With Forensic Science eCollection

Should drug-testing labs be liable for faulty results? A mishandled drug test result could mean a prison sentence for a convicted individual. Research recent court decisions based on improper analysis of drug tests. Go to the Gale Forensic Science eCollection at **ngl.cengage.com/forensicscience2e** and enter the search term "drug testing" for more information.

and health care because of drug abuse. Arrests for drug-abuse violations and possession have steadily increased since the early 1990s. Drug-abuse violations are on the list of the seven leading arrest offenses in the United States.

Drugs are divided into five classes based on the reactions they produce. These classes include narcotics, depressants, stimulants, hallucinogens, and anabolic steroids. An individual's reaction to a drug can't always be predicted because everyone's body chemistry is different; also, drugs may interact with foods, medications, or alcohol in a person's system. Also, with continued use of some drugs, **tolerance** may build up so that more of the drug is needed to produce the same effect. Drug use can lead to abuse, criminal behavior, serious health problems, and even death. Continued use of a drug can lead to a physiological need called **addiction**. Sudden discontinuation of a drug one is addicted to can result in physical withdrawal symptoms such as illness or even death. Drug **dependency** results when there is an intense craving for the drug. Dependency, unlike addiction, does not result in physical withdrawal upon discontinuation of the drug.

Did you know?

All drugs are not controlled substances, and all controlled substances are not illegal. Narcotics are controlled substances that are legal with prescriptions but illegal without prescriptions.

Five Schedules of Drugs

Drugs categorized as **illegal drugs** are those with no current medical use, such as heroin and LSD. A second category includes **controlled substances**, legal drugs whose sale, possession, and use are restricted because of the effects of the drug, the potential for abuse, and how easily someone may become dependent on the drug. Examples of controlled drugs include stimulants, depressants, anabolic steroids, and some narcotics. The federal **Controlled Substances Act** of 1970 (CSA) recognizes five schedules of drugs. (These are different from the five classes of drugs mentioned earlier). The drugs are grouped based on any accepted medical use of the drugs and their abuse or dependency potential. Those in Schedule I are considered most dangerous have the highest potential for abuse.

Schedule I: no medical use, high potential for abuse; for example, heroin, LSD, peyote, MDMA, bath salts; also marijuana (see Figure 9-7)
Schedule II: severely restricted medical use, high potential for abuse; for example, cocaine, methamphetamine, methadone, oxycodone
Schedule III: accepted medical use, moderate potential for abuse, moderate to low risk of dependence; for example, barbiturates, steroids, ketamine
Schedule IV: medical use, low potential for abuse and low risk of dependency; for example, Xanax, Valium, sleeping pills, other tranquilizers
Schedule V: widely used for medical purposes, very low potential for abuse, contains limited quantities of narcotics; for example, Robitussin® AC, Tylenol® with codeine

Figure 9-7
Marijuana is a Schedule I substance, although its medical use is legal in several states, and its recreational use is no longer a crime in a few others.

© Africa Studio/Shutterstock.com

Teaching Tip

For more detailed information on abused drugs, refer to the IRCD, Chapter 9, for Ch09 TN Drug Schedules, Ch09 DEA ref (lists of drugs in each schedule), and Ch09 NIH Drug Ref (links to commonly abused drugs and health effects Websites).

Figure 9-8 *Table of hallucinogenic drugs and characteristic symptoms of overdose*

Drug	Source	Characteristics of Overdose
Mescaline	Cactus Peyote	Dizziness, vomiting, diarrhea, headaches, anxiety, irrational thoughts
LSD	Rye fungus	Dilated pupils, loss of appetite, sleeplessness, increase in body temperature, sweating, confusion
Psilocybin	Mushroom	Altered perceptions, panic, paranoia, confusion
Marijuana	Plant	Heightened sensory perceptions, impaired memory, judgment
Synthetic Marijuana (Spice)	Herbs sprayed with synthetic THC	Similar to marijuana but variable because of variable levels of active ingredient
PCP (Angel Dust)	Synthetic	Feelings of invulnerability and exaggerated strength, seizures, coma, hyperthermia
MDMA (Ecstasy)	Synthetic	Euphoria, increased energy, empathy, sweating, impaired cognition and motor function, irritability, anxiety

Illegal Drugs

Illegal drugs include hallucinogens and heroin. **Hallucinogens** (Figure 9-8) affect the perception, thinking, self-awareness, and emotions. People hear and see things that aren't there. These effects can vary with the dose, setting, and mood. Physical reactions to hallucinogens increase heart rate and blood pressure and cause dilated pupils. Visual effects caused by hallucinogens can recur long after the drugs wear off in the form of flashbacks. Hallucinogens are classified as Schedule I drugs.

Heroin is a narcotic. **Narcotics** are addictive, sleep-inducing drugs, often derived from opium, that act as central nervous system depressants and suppress pain. Narcotics are highly addictive and can lead to withdrawal. The drug opium comes from the dried resin found in poppy plant seedpods. There are many derivatives of opium, or *opiates*, of which heroin is the strongest. Heroin is not prescribed as medication and is considered an illegal drug (Schedule I). Other opiates are legal controlled substances.

When combining drugs such as heroin and alcohol, the effects are amplified. Both drugs depress the central nervous system, but they affect different areas of the brain. Together, the combination can be fatal. The opening scenario of the drug overdose of Cory Monteith in 2013 is just one of many tragic examples of how a combination of drugs can result in an untimely death. When singer Whitney Houston and actor Phillip Seymour Hoffman died from drug overdoses, there was widespread news coverage. We seldom hear about the many accidental deaths of those who are not so famous.

Controlled Substances

Controlled substances include stimulants, narcotics, depressants, and anabolic steroids. These drugs are on Schedules II through V of the DEA Drug Schedule.

Did you know?

Emergency responders are beginning to carry Narcan (naloxone) routinely in their vehicles. This opiate antagonist counteracts the effects of heroin or morphine overdoses.

Explore

In 2012, The United States Army Criminal Investigation Command (CID) conducted investigations on bath salts, spice (a synthetic marijuana), and other synthetic drugs used by soldiers. In 2013, biotechnologists began developing a biosensor to detect synthetic drugs. Research the advancements made toward development of this technology.

Teaching Tip

Download copies of the online publication *Methamphetamine Labs, Neighborhood Resource Guide*, http://adaiclearinghouse .org/downloads/Methamphetamine -Labs-Neighborhood-Resource -Guide-21.pdf

Explore

Share interactives at www.learn .genetics.utah with students. Search on the *Science of Addiction*, with students or view in class:

1. Drugs of Abuse
2. Mouse Party (brains of animated mice intoxicated on various drugs)
3. Meth Mouse

Science

BIOLOGY

Why are certain drugs controlled? Controlled substances such as hallucinogens and narcotics have a powerful effect on the human body. They increase or decrease blood flow to the brain and major organs. They affect liver functions and, depending on how they are taken into the body, can affect the lungs, throat, and other areas of contact.

DIFFERENTIATED LEARNING

Teaching At-Risk Students
Cooperative learning allows students of varying abilities to share responsibility for learning. Assign students to work together as a group to research recent accidental—and fatal—drug overdoses of musicians, actors, and/or athletes. Students should then organize and present their findings to the class.

DIFFERENTIATED LEARNING

Teaching English-Language Learners
Ask students to tell you what the words "accidental" and "overdose" mean. They might first use words in their native language before learning the English word. Have them look in the chapter for some of the words they might need. The use of visual aids can help illustrate concepts.

Did you know

Hair analysis can be used in compliance testing and drug-abstinence monitoring. Hair analysis is becoming an alternative to urinalysis because urine samples provide only short-term information about drug use. Hair samples span a longer history of use. Head hair grows at an average rate of 1 centimeter per month, and therefore preserves a longer timeline of drug use.

BIOLOGY

CHEMISTRY

Teaching Tip

Ask students to introduce news items about traffic accidents involving drugs and/or alcohol. As a class, discuss these accidents.

Explore

Students can perform a fermentation lab using yeast and molasses to show the production of alcohol.

Explore

Have students research how breathalyzers and alcosensors work at http://electronics .howstuffworks.com/gadgets/ automotive/breathalyzer.htm

STIMULANTS

Stimulants are highly addictive drugs that increase feelings of energy and alertness while suppressing appetite. Examples include amphetamines, methamphetamines, and cocaine. They are used and sometimes abused to boost endurance and productivity. Users may develop a tolerance to some stimulants and need more to produce the same effect. Side effects include high blood pressure, rapid heart rate, and in extreme cases, bleeding into the brain. Depression often results when the effect of the drug wears off.

Methamphetamines ("meth") are synthetic drugs often made in small, illegal home laboratories. The chemicals used in the process of making meth are very dangerous and frequently result in explosions endangering workers in the laboratories, neighbors, and the environment. The physical effects of methamphetamines include major weight loss, severe dental problems, cardiac damage, and neurological damage.

NARCOTICS

Legal opiates include morphine, prescribed for extreme pain, and codeine, a cough suppressant and mild painkiller. Hydromorphone is a synthetic opiate prescribed for severe pain. People requiring long-term painkillers are in danger of becoming addicted to other prescribed narcotics such as hydrocodone and oxycodone. Symptoms of abuse include difficulty breathing, low blood pressure, weakness, dizziness, confusion, loss of consciousness, coma, cold clammy skin, and permanently contracted pupils.

DEPRESSANTS

Depressants are drugs such as barbiturates and benzodiazepines that relieve anxiety and produce sleep but are typically highly addictive. Depressants slow down body functions, including heart and breathing rate. Many accidental and suicidal deaths have resulted from people taking a combination of depressants and alcohol. An abrupt withdrawal from some depressants can be fatal. Overdose of depressants can cause slurred speech, loss of coordination, coma, or death.

Alcohol

Alcohol is a central nervous system depressant. It is a legal, but very potent, drug. In overdose amounts, it can destroy nerve cells, and even kill you. Alcohol's effects on the body depend on how quickly alcohol is absorbed into the blood. The amount of food in the stomach, body weight, and individual tolerance to alcohol influence how quickly alcohol gets to the brain. A person not accustomed to drinking may exhibit intoxication after one drink, while someone with a higher tolerance may not. All effects of alcohol are increased when it is used with other medications or drugs.

The amount of alcohol in a beverage is expressed as a percentage by volume or in proof, which is twice the percentage. A liquor that is 80 proof contains 40 percent alcohol. Beer and wine alcoholic content is expressed by percentage of volume. Generally, one serving of an alcoholic beverage contains about the same amount of alcohol: a 5-ounce glass of wine (12 percent), a 12-ounce beer (5 percent), and 1.5 ounces of 80 proof liquor (40 percent) contain about the same amount of alcohol.

Recall that alcohol can be fatal. The liver metabolizes alcohol by converting it into acetaldehyde and then to acetic acid. (Acetaldehyde is toxic, and is responsible for some hangover symptoms experienced by a binge drinker.) Liver problems are common among alcoholics, whose livers must work harder to convert the acetaldehyde than those of nonalcoholics do. The rate of alcohol metabolism is no more than one serving an hour, and often less. If more alcohol is consumed, the level of alcohol circulating in the blood increases, along with its effects on the brain. Someone with a blood-alcohol concentration (BAC) of 0.15 percent will retain alcohol in his or her body for approximately 10 hours.

Because alcohol is exhaled, it's possible to detect alcohol in someone's breath. In most states, blood alcohol concentration is expressed as the number of grams of alcohol (weight) found in 0.1 L (100 mL or 1 deciliter) of blood. A breathalyzer test measures the alcohol in a person's breath and calculates BAC. If the BAC is greater than or equal to 0.08 percent, then that person is considered to be driving under the influence of alcohol in most states. (In some states, the legal limit is lower.)

The cost of driving while impaired is high in terms of loss of lives and in penalties and legal fees. The fines differ based on the age of the driver, the type of drug, whether there is a combination of drugs, and how many times that person has been arrested. A person found driving while impaired more than once can lose his or her driver's license for life *and* end up in jail.

ANABOLIC STEROIDS

Anabolic steroids promote cell and tissue growth and division. These drugs have a chemical structure similar to testosterone, the male sex hormone. Anabolic steroids were originally used to treat hypogonadism, a condition in which the testes produce abnormally low levels of testosterone. Today, they are used to treat some cases of delayed puberty, impotence, and muscle wasting caused by HIV infection. In the 1930s, they gained popularity with weight lifters and bodybuilders because they increase muscle and bone mass. The negative side effects of anabolic steroids range from mild ones, such as acne, increased body hair, and baldness, to severe ones such as increased aggression, high blood pressure and cholesterol levels, impaired fertility in males, blood clotting, kidney and liver cancers, and heart attacks. These drugs are classified as Schedule III drugs.

Doping is the use of substances to enhance athletic performance. It has been banned by most organized sports, because many feel it violates the "spirit of competition" by providing an advantage to doping participants. Nevertheless, competitors who feel desperate to win find ways to dope. Because of doping controversies, many fans have lost their faith in the integrity of competition in many sports (cycling, weight lifting, running, hurdling, baseball, etc.).

Did you know

Ethyl alcohol, or ethanol, is a product of fermentation, and the type of alcohol found in beer, wine, and liquor. When yeast break down the sugars in grapes, apples, rice, or potatoes, ethyl alcohol and carbon dioxide are released as waste products. The process of distillation collects and concentrates alcohol from the fermented mixtures.

DIGGING DEEPER
With Forensic Science eCollection

Research the relationship of anabolic steroid use to crime. Has the use of anabolic steroids ever been given as someone's reason for committing a crime? Go to the Gale Forensic Science eCollection at **ngl.cengage.com/forensicscience2e** and enter the search term "steroid use" for more information.

Science

BIOLOGY

The liver metabolizes alcohol and many drugs. This function causes the liver to be directly affected by substance abuse and some toxic exposures.

Evaluate

Conduct a student debate:
- Should student athletes be tested routinely for drugs?
- Should all students be tested routinely for drugs?

Explore

Have students research anabolic steroids. How are they used? What effects do they have on the body? Why is taking anabolic steroids dangerous? Then have students create posters illustrating their findings.

Explore

Have students research the story of the detection of Lance Armstrong's doping. Two journalists who helped break the story tell it in Albergotti, Reed, and Vanessa O'Connell. *Wheelmen*. New York: Gotham, 2013.

DIFFERENTIATED LEARNING

Teaching English-Language Learners
Form small collaborative student groups to create graphic organizers (concept maps, Venn diagrams) that classify all of the drugs, poisons, and toxins described in this chapter.

Explore

Tell students that before taking any prescription, they should read the prescription information. What is the purpose of the drug? How much should they be taking? Are there any side effects? Are there any precautions? Assign students one of the following to research: aspirin, Actifed, Allegra, Aleve, ampicillin, amoxicillin, AZT, Celebrex, Coumadin, Coricidin, cyclosporine, Dimetapp, erythromycin, Heparin, Imitrex, Lipitor, Lotrel, Nexium, prednisone, Ritalin, Robitussin, Valium, Xanax, Zyrtec. Have them report the following information:

- Brand name of the drug
- Generic or common name of the drug
- Is this drug prescribed or is it an over-the-counter (OTC) drug?
- Major uses of this drug
- Possible side effects
- How is the drug administered?
- Suggested dosages for different age groups
- Any drug interactions?
- Special warnings or precautions
- Is there any controversy over the use of this drug?

LITERACY

To learn more about drug analysis and the work of Charles Norris and Alexander Gettler, read *The Poisoner's Handbook*, by Deborah Blum.

Rubberball/Getty Images

SUMMARY

- Toxicology is the study of poisons, toxins, drugs, and other substances a person may use for medical, recreational, or criminal purposes. Forensic toxicologists study the harmful effects of these substances on the body, typically after a death.

- The toxicity of a substance depends on the dose, the duration of exposure, the nature of exposure, interactions with other substances, and the byproducts formed when metabolized.

- Exposure to heavy metals, poison gases, other poisons, toxins, or radiation may occur accidentally or as a result of a crime (or punishment) and have harmful or lethal effects on the body.

- Drugs are classified by their effect on the body as stimulants, depressants, narcotics, hallucinogens, or anabolic steroids; drugs are classified under five schedules created by the 1970 Controlled Substances Act.

- Use of drugs can affect a person's health, mood, awareness, metabolism, and/or perception of reality.

- Extended exposure to drugs can lead to tolerance, dependence, addiction, and illness.

- Drug combinations can have compounding effects and result in accidental death.

CASE STUDIES

Mary Ansell
(1899)

Mary Ansell, an English housemaid, poisoned her sister Caroline to obtain an insurance settlement. Mary sent Caroline a cake tainted with phosphorus. Caroline died after eating the poisoned cake. Evidence of Mary's recent purchases of phosphorus and a life insurance policy in her sister's name were provided at her trial. Based on this evidence, Mary was quickly convicted and executed.

Radium Poisoning
(1924)

In 1918, Charles Norris became the first Chief Medical Examiner for the city of New York, the first chief medical examiner of any city in the United States. Working with chemist Alexander Gettler, he established the first toxicology lab that would study and certify cause of death in medico-legal proceedings. The cases examined helped to establish a system of standardized testing for the detection of a number of lethal substances. Deborah Blum's book *The Poisoner's Handbook* describes several cases reviewed by Charles Norris.

Radium had been shown to have therapeutic importance in shrinking tumors and was used in body lotions and health drinks. The U.S. Radium Corporation opened a factory near Newark, New Jersey, in 1917, to produce radium-based products. World War I demonstrated the need for a watch that would be visible at night, for soldiers. The pocket watch was replaced by a watch strapped to the wrist, with a dial and glowing numbers. U.S. Radium produced these watches,

DIFFERENTIATED LEARNING

Teaching At-Risk Students and English-Language Learners
Students can view an interactive graphic novel depicting the radium poisoning described in the case studies on www.pbs.org. Search on *Tales From The Poisoner's Handbook, The Poison Paint*.

and women in the factory painted the watch faces, which contained radium and glowed in the dark. They shaped their brush tips to a fine point in their mouths and then dipped the brushes into the paint for precise application.

Unfortunately, many of the women working in the factory fell ill. They suffered from tooth loss, bone-density loss, mouth sores, deteriorating jaw bones, anemia, and cancers. Examiners found that the women were exhaling radon, a byproduct of the radioactive decay of radium. By 1924, nine previously healthy women in their twenties were dead. A body exhumed after five years still showed the presence of radium. The company did not stop the hand painting of the watch dials until 1947.

The Death of Georgi Markov and the Attack on Vladimir Kostov (1978)

After defecting from Bulgaria, Georgi Markov moved to London and worked as a news reporter. While walking one day, he was injected in the leg with ricin. The delivery method was a specially constructed umbrella with a modified tip for injection. He became gravely ill, and on the third day after the attack was vomiting blood. He suffered a heart blockage and died. The autopsy revealed a platinum-iridium pellet the size of a pinhead in his leg. It had been drilled with tiny holes to contain the toxin. The pellet contained only two milligrams of ricin, but that was enough to kill him.

Ten days earlier, a similar assassination attempt was made against Vladimir Kostov in Paris. Kostov's heavy clothing prevented an identical projectile from entering a major blood vessel. Instead, the pellet lodged in muscle tissue, preventing the poison from circulating as it had in Markov's body. This saved Kostov's life. On hearing of Markov's death, Kostov underwent a surgical examination, and the pellet was found before sufficient toxin could be absorbed to cause his death.

The ricin-laced pellet that killed Georgi Markov.

Keystone-France/Getty Images

Tylenol Tampering (1982)

In 1982, Extra-Strength Tylenol capsules laced with cyanide claimed seven lives. The person(s) responsible have never been caught. It is believed that cyanide was added to the Tylenol and that the tainted bottles were placed on the shelves of several supermarkets and pharmacies in the Chicago area. In addition to the five bottles responsible for the seven deaths, three poisoned bottles were found on the shelves. Because they were from different production locations, investigators believed the tampering occurred after the product was shipped, rather than in the factory. This was the first documented example of random drug poisoning. The $100,000 reward posted by the drug manufacturer, Johnson & Johnson, has never been claimed. This incident led to the development of tamper-resistant packaging and caplets designed to protect the public.

In 1986, Stella Nickell, a Seattle woman, laced some Excedrin with cyanide and killed her husband for his life insurance. She placed three other poisoned bottles of Excedrin in the store to make it look like a random killing and killed another woman, Susan Snow, in the process. In 1988, Nickell was sentenced to 99 years in prison.

Think Critically

Suppose you were an advertising executive. Select a category of illegal drug. Using your expertise, create a message to communicate the dangers of that substance to the public.

Close
Organize students into groups and assign each group one of the following chapter topics: hallucinogens, narcotics, and stimulants; anabolic steroids; organic toxins, including ricin; alcohol; heavy metals; pesticides; and drug testing. Have each group summarize the key information about their topic. You might use the following Website as background: http://www.drugabuse.gov/drugs-abuse/commonly-abused-drugs/health-effects.

DIFFERENTIATED LEARNING

Teaching English-Language Learners
With early and intermediate English learners, make content more understandable by providing many nonverbal clues such as pictures, objects, and demonstrations. For example, you may want to show various OTC drugs and their containers to students and discuss their names and uses. As competency develops, build from language that is already understood, and use graphic organizers and hands-on learning techniques, especially with the activities.

Careers

Some pharmacologists research drug addiction. They focus on drugs, both legal and illegal, that cause dependence. Those pharmacologists who study drug dependence focus on the mechanisms and risk factors that alter drug-taking behavior, as well as the consequences of drug exposure. Their long-term goals are to increase our ability to prevent and treat drug dependencies and reduce the harm associated with drug-taking behavior.

Careers *in Forensics*

Dr. Don Catlin, Pharmacologist and Founder of Sports Drug Testing

For 25 years, Dr. Don Catlin was the director of the UCLA Olympic Analytical Laboratory. The UCLA laboratory, with more than 40 researchers, was the world's first anti-doping laboratory. It helped expose many drug-related sports scandals by identifying players who were using performance-enhancing drugs. Catlin is one of the most respected sports and anti-doping drug testers in the world, and he is still involved in anti-doping research in private companies.

Dr. Don Catlin, sports drug tester.

Christian Science Monitor/Getty Images

Catlin became a professor in the Department of Pharmacology of the UCLA School of Medicine in 1972. In 1982, his interest in substance abuse led him to open the UCLA Olympic Analytical Laboratory to do the drug tests for the 1984 Los Angeles Summer Olympics. He also provided the drug testing for the 1996 Atlanta Summer Olympics and the 2002 Salt Lake City Winter Games. His work has included testifying and defending his drug-testing methods in court.

The UCLA laboratory has provided drug education and urine tests to a growing number of sports organizations, including the U.S. Olympic Committee, NCAA, NFL, and Minor League Baseball. The lab has developed novel drug tests, such as the one used to distinguish between naturally produced and pharmaceutical testosterone. The laboratory is one of the world's premier places for analyzing samples from athletes to detect the use of illegal substances such as anabolic steroids, illegal levels of the blood-oxygen booster erythropoetin, and many other performance-enhancing substances. It is the busiest lab of its kind in the world, with about 40,000 samples analyzed each year. What kept Don Catlin so dedicated to the field of sports drug testing? Catlin says, "You should care about preserving something natural and beautiful. I can't think of anything more exciting than the Olympic model, where 220 countries in the world participate, and every four years they send their best to compete against the best from other countries and the best man or woman wins."

To be in the field of pharmacology, one needs a science education with graduate studies that include courses in analytical chemistry, drug metabolism, and drug pharmacokinetics. The drug-testing field requires special knowledge of legal and ethical issues. Pharmacologists can work in universities, hospitals, governmental organizations, nonprofit organizations, or pharmaceutical or related industries.

Learn More About It
▷ To learn more about a career as a forensic toxicologist, go to **ngl.cengage.com/ forensicscience2e**.

True or False

1. Drug or toxin exposure can be established only if exposure occurred within the past six months. *Obj. 9.3, 9.5*

2. All death by lethal gases or in lethal injections interferes with the body's ability to use oxygen. *Obj. 9.2, 9.5, 9.7*

3. The effects of some hallucinogens can recur in the form of flashbacks long after the drugs wear off. *Obj. 9.7*

4. All controlled drugs are illegal. *Obj. 9.8*

5. A side effect of using anabolic steroids can be increased levels of aggression. *Obj. 9.8*

6. A person who builds up a tolerance to a drug no longer experiences any side effects. *Obj. 9.2, 9.6*

7. The type of testing done to identify a substance will vary depending on the quantity of the substance expected. *Obj. 9.3, 9.4*

8. Accidental deaths can result from exposure to poisons such as arsenic, mercury, and herbicides found in drinking water. *Obj. 9.5*

9. The federal Controlled Substances Act of 1970 characterized drugs into five schedules. The schedules are organized based only on the substances' effects on the body. *Obj. 9.8*

10. Improvements in technology such as mass spectroscopy have improved the ability of toxicologist to separate and identify the components of different drugs and toxins. *Obj. 9.3, 9.4*

Short Answer

11. List five factors that influence the degree to which a substance is harmful or toxic. *Obj. 9.2*

12. Many of the crimes committed in the United States are related to the use, possession, and distribution of drugs. *Obj. 9.8*
    a) List four types of crimes related to drug use.
    b) What do you think can be done to reduce the number of drug-related crimes in the United States?

13. Research the 18th Amendment and the 21st Amendment. *Obj. 9.8*
    a) Summarize the main idea of each of these amendments.
    b) Research and describe how prohibition laws led to more crime and fraud. Provide specific examples to support your statements.

14. Refer to Figure 9-4 (Heavy metals with typical symptoms of overexposure). Briefly summarize the source of and symptoms of overexposure to the following: *Obj. 9.1, 9.5, 9.7*
    a) lead
    b) mercury
    c) arsenic

FORENSIC TOXICOLOGY   **297**

Chapter 9 Review

True or False

1. False
2. False
3. True
4. False
5. True
6. False
7. True
8. True
9. False
10. True

Short Answer

11. Dose, duration, nature of exposure, interactions with other drugs or medications, and by-products of metabolism

12. a. Answers may vary, but include traffic accidents, theft, burglary, assault, fraud, rape, domestic and child abuse, abductions, human trafficking, and manufacturing of illegal drugs.

    b. Answers will vary; accept reasonable answers.

13. a. The 18th Amendment prohibited the manufacture, sale, and transport of alcoholic beverages. Ratified in 1920, the period the 18th Amendment was in effect was known as Prohibition. The 21st Amendment repealed the 18th Amendment in 1933.

    b. Producing and distributing illegal alcohol led to more crime and corruption. Individuals distilled alcohol in their homes and garages. Doctors wrote prescriptions for alcohol-based medications. Gangsters smuggled and distributed illegal alcohol. Law enforcement and politicians accepted bribes to not arrest those guilty of distributing alcohol.

14. See the table in Figure 9-4 for answers.

15. Answers will vary. Accept answers that are well supported by evidence.

16. a. Presumptive testing is not positive identification of a drug. Many presumptive tests are inexpensive and based on color reactions. Confirmatory testing is done by trained analysts and will provide a positive identification of the substance.

b. Qualitative analysis identifies the components. Quantitative analysis determines the amount of each component.

c. Addiction is extreme craving leading to compulsive use of a drug. Failure to take the drug can result in physical reactions known as withdrawal. Dependence is a craving but is a psychological phenomenon that does not lead to withdrawal.

d. Concentration of alcohol is the percentage of alcohol measured by volume. Proof is equal to double the concentration of alcohol.

e. Acute poisoning is caused by a high dose of poison over a short period of time. Chronic poisoning is caused by a low dose of poison over a long period of time.

Teaching Tip

The University of Utah's Learn Genetics Website has extensive interactive activities and tutorials regarding different types of drugs and how they affect nerve transmission in the brain. Have students view the site at home and use one of the links to prepare a presentation. For the topic of medical marijuana use, try "flipping" the classroom, so that students in favor of federal legalization have

15. Your neighbor is very proud of his garden and lawn. He brags that there's not a weed or insect to be found in his yard because he treats his yard with pesticides and herbicides (weed killers). Another neighbor feels that no chemicals should be used in a yard because they are poisons. *Obj. 9.1, 9.5*

a) What is your opinion? Support your claims with scientific evidence.

b) Do you think that there should be any local laws regarding use of pesticides and herbicides?

16. Compare and contrast the following:

a) presumptive testing and confirmatory testing *Obj. 9.4*

b) qualitative analysis of drugs and quantitative analysis of drugs *Obj. 9.3*

c) addiction and dependence *Obj. 9.6*

d) alcohol proof and concentration of alcohol *Obj. 9.2*

e) acute and chronic poisoning *Obj. 9.2, 9.5, 9.7*

- -

Going Further

1. In many states, a BAC (blood alcohol concentration) of 0.08% g/dL is considered driving under the influence of alcohol. However, in New York State, a person under the age of 21 is considered to be driving impaired when he or she has a BAC of only 0.02%.

It is possible to estimate the quantity of alcohol consumed to give someone a BAC of 0.02% by using the following formulas. It is assumed that the person is drinking on an empty stomach and drinking 100-proof liquor. (One serving is slightly over an ounce.)

Males $\text{volume of alcohol (oz)} = \dfrac{\text{weight} \times \text{BAC}}{3.78}$ (weight in lb and BAC in g/dL)

Females $\text{volume of alcohol (oz)} = \dfrac{\text{weight} \times \text{BAC}}{4.67}$

a) Calculate the volume of alcohol consumed to give a 150-lb male a BAC of 0.02%.

b) Calculate the volume of alcohol consumed to give a 120-lb female a BAC of 0.02%.

c) What other factors would affect BAC besides weight?

2. Laws regulating driving under the influence of alcohol vary from state to state. Research the laws in your state: *Obj. 9.8*

a) Is there a distinction between driving while ability-impaired and driving while intoxicated?

b) Describe if the laws differ for someone under the age of 21 versus over the age of 21.

c) List the penalties for the first offense.

d) List the penalties for the second offense.

e) Estimate the costs of getting a ticket for driving under the influence, combining fines, penalties, court costs, legal fees, and increases in the cost of insurance.

298   CHAPTER 9

to argue against their view and vice versa. Of particular interest are these links:

1. Brain Reward Pathway: Neurons Transmit Messages and Crossing the Divide

2. Drug Reward Pathway: Drugs of Abuse, Mouse Party, Drug Use Changes Your Brain

3. Challenges and Issues: Medical Marijuana Debate

3. Many drugs affect the brain by altering nerve impulses in the brain. Neurons or nerve cells have gaps between them called synapses. In order for messages to be conveyed from one neuron to another, the neurons secrete neurotransmitters. Drugs alter the activity of neurotransmitters and therefore affect brain functioning. Select one of the following drugs and research how the drug affects the activity of the selected neurotransmitter. Summarize your findings, concentrating on the behavioral changes of the intoxicated person.

   a) methamphetamines and dopamine
   b) cocaine and dopamine
   c) LSD and serotonin

4. In the opening scenario about the overdose death of Cory Monteith, the medical examiner ruled the death accidental due to a combination of alcohol and heroin. Research why these two drugs in combination are a deadly mixture. Read "Science of Addiction Genetics and the Brain" (http://learn.genetics.utah.edu/content/addiction/) from Learn Genetics University at Utah. Click on "Crossing the Divide Interactive: Crossing the Great Divide." Click on "Drugs and the Reward Pathway, How Drugs Kill." Describe how alcohol and heroin have different effects on the neurons and brain, but both slow down breathing rate.

Bibliography

Books and Journals

Baden, Dr. Michael. *Unnatural Death: Confessions of a Medical Examiner*. New York: Ballantine Books, 1989

Blum, Deborah. *The Poisoner's Handbook: Murder and the Birth of Forensic Medicine in Jazz Age New York*. Penguin Press, 2010.

Benjamin, D. "Forensic Pharmacology," in *Forensic Science Handbook*, R. Saferstein ed. Upper Saddle River, NJ: Prentice Hall, 1993.

Chen, Albert. "A Scary Little Pill: A powerful medicine for pain, Oxycontin has quickly become a dangerous street drug." *Sports Illustrated* 101.24 (Dec 20, 2004).

Gnant, Jackie. "Chemistry, Toxicology... What's the Difference?" *The Forensic Teacher*, Spring 2012, pp. 16–24.

Lyle, D. P., M.D. *Forensics: A Guide for Writers*. Cincinnati: Writer's Digest Books, 2008.

Internet Resources

ngl.cengage.com/forensicscience2e (Gale Forensic Science eCollection)
Search the Internet for Lance Armstrong and doping controversies.
http://www.pbs.org and search for *Tales From the Poisoner's Handbook*.
http://www.forensicsciencesimplified.org/drugs/
http://www.chemistryexplained.com/Fe-Ge/Forensic-Chemistry.html
http://www.drugabuse.gov/drugs-abuse/commonly-abused-drugs/commonly-abused-drugs-chart
http://www.drugabuse.gov/drugs-abuse/commonly-abused-drugs/
   commonly-abused-prescription-drugs-chart
http://www.drugabuse.gov/drugs-abuse/commonly-abused-drugs/health-effects
http://learn.genetics.utah.edu
www.bjs.gov/index.cfm Bureau of Justice Statistics
www.DEA.gov, Drug Enforcement Administration
www.drugabuse/gov/related-topics/trends-statistics National Institute on Drug Abuse, 2013
http://www.washingtonpost.com/wp-dyn/content/article/2007/03/12/AR2007031200804.html
www.tiaft.org

DIFFERENTIATED LEARNING

Teaching Gifted Students

Allow motivated students to take Going Further item 3 a step further and create a physical model that shows the effects of a drug on neurotransmitter activity.

This chapter has a number of additional activities on the IRCD, Chapter 9.

All directions, student activity forms, and teacher notes are included on the IRCD.

Additional activities:

Act 9-4 Urine Presumptive Drug Test

Act 9-5 Drug Research and Presentation

Act 9-6 Analyzing Drug Residue on Paper Money

Act 9-7 Drug Testing Debate

Each activity has instructional support (TN). Ch09 reference sheets are also provided.

ACTIVITY 9-1

Background

Students conduct a presumptive test on a simulated drug. A chemical indicator is used that changes color in the presence of the drug. Bertinol (a fictitious drug) is phenolphthalein powder (positive control). The negative control is powdered sugar. The Bertinol test solution is 3 M NaOH. Phenolphthalein turns pink in the presence of a base.

Safety Precautions

1. Review the safety precautions with the students before the start of the activity.

2. Post the procedure for disposal of materials in a prominent place.

3. Check that all students wear goggles.

4. Students should also wash their hands after handling the substances.

Teaching Tip

This is an introductory lab that introduces students to the concept of presumptive color tests used in drug testing. It demonstrates the importance of using positive and negative controls.

ACTIVITY 9-1

Drug Analysis *Ch. Obj. 9.4*

Objectives:

Upon completion of Procedure Parts A and B, you will be able to do the following:

1. Conduct a positive and negative control for this presumptive drug test.
2. Discuss the role of positive and negative controls for presumptive drug tests.
3. Perform a presumptive test on an unknown drug.
4. Analyze the results of the presumptive drug test and determine if there was a positive or negative result.

Introduction:

Presumptive drug tests use reagent(s) with which a particular drug will produce a color change. These tests do not confirm the presence of a specific drug because other substances can also give a positive test. The results of a presumptive test help an analyst decide what, if any, additional testing is needed. For positive identification, you need a confirmatory test, which is more involved, more expensive, and is conducted in a certified lab.

In this activity, students will be working with a (fictitious) powdered drug called Bertinol. It is classified as a Schedule I drug because it has no known medical use and a high potential for abuse. To perform the presumptive test, students will prepare a positive control (with Bertinol) and a negative control (without Bertinol). After testing the unknown powder with the reagents, the results will be compared to the controls to determine if the presumptive test results were positive or negative.

Scenario:

Police received an anonymous call stating that drugs were being used at the high school. Dogs trained to locate drugs identified four different lockers. When the lockers were opened, the police confiscated small bags of white powder in each. Your task is to perform presumptive drug tests on the white powder bags.

SAFETY PRECAUTIONS:

A carefully maintained clean area should be set aside for testing of drugs. All materials used in this activity are harmless, but it is essential to maintain appropriate techniques in handling all samples. *Treat all samples as if they were actual samples of the drug.* Maintain the chain of custody. Wear safety goggles and dispose of all materials in the manner described by your instructor.

Time Required to Complete Activity:

45 minutes to complete both Activities A and B if working in groups of two

In Going Further, higher-level students research other chemicals that can be used to produce color changes. Students then design a new activity using a different color indicator of their choice and unknown "drugs" (over-the-counter drugs or powders or solutions of powders).

Teaching Tip

If your students are already familiar with positive and negative controls, consider using Activity 9-3 to teach presumptive drug testing instead.

Materials:

(per group of two students)

Act SH 9-1

6 empty clean vials with caps for testing

marking pen and labeling tape

positive control envelope containing the drug Bertinol

negative control envelope containing a white powder that does not contain Bertinol

4 evidence envelopes containing white powder obtained from each of the four lockers

50 mL rubbing alcohol (70 percent isopropyl alcohol by volume) or ethyl alcohol

10-mL graduated cylinder or 5-mL pipette

flat wooden toothpicks

25 mL of Bertinol drug test solution in dropper bottles

tape

Procedure:

PART A: CREATING THE POSITIVE AND NEGATIVE CONTROLS

1. Label one empty vial Negative Control.
2. Label the second vial Positive Control.
3. Into each vial, add 5 mL of rubbing alcohol.
4. Using the broad, flat side of a clean toothpick, remove a pinhead-sized amount of Bertinol from the envelope labeled Positive Control. Add this pinhead-sized amount of Bertinol to the vial labeled Positive Control.
5. Using the broad, flat side of a toothpick, remove a pinhead-sized amount of the white powder from the envelope labeled Negative Control. Add this pinhead-sized amount of white powder to the vial labeled Negative Control.
6. Add three drops of Bertinol drug test solution to the Negative Control vial.
7. Add three drops of Bertinol drug test solution to the Positive Control vial.
8. Observe and record the color changes in the Data Table.
9. Save these vials for comparison with the suspects' samples in Procedure B.

PART B: COMPARING SAMPLES

1. Label the four vials as follows: Locker 1, Locker 2, Locker 3, and Locker 4.
2. Using the graduated cylinder or pipette, add 5 mL of rubbing alcohol to each vial.
3. Using a clean, flat toothpick, transfer a pinhead-sized amount of the white powder from Evidence Envelope 1 to your vial labeled Locker 1. Leave the toothpick in the Locker 1 vial. It will be used later for stirring.
4. Reseal the Evidence Envelope properly, and sign your name to maintain the chain of custody.
5. Repeat the procedure for each of the other Evidence Envelopes (i.e., Lockers 2, 3, and 4).
6. Leave the toothpicks in the locker vials to stir the contents of each vial until dissolved. Be careful not to mix up the toothpicks.

Procedures

1. Print, copy, and distribute Act 9-1 SH Drug Test from the IRCD, Chapter 9. For instructional support, refer to Act 9-1 TN Drug Test in the IRCD, Chapter 9.
2. Make sure students read all directions *before* beginning the activity.
3. Demonstrate the use of a graduated cylinder or pipette, and the toothpick transfer process, before beginning the activity.
4. Remind students of the need for positive and negative controls.
5. A new toothpick should be used with each new sample.

Teaching Tip

Prepare in advance individual labeled envelopes for each team of two students. (Find the label on the IRCD, Chapter 9, in Act 9-1 TN Evidence Inv Label.) Each envelope must contain the following:

- Positive control powder (phenolphthalein)
- Negative control powder (powdered sugar)
- 4 separate envelopes with powders labeled Locker 1, 2, 3, and 4. (One of the four envelopes should contain phenolphthalein powder, which produces a positive reaction. The other three envelopes contain confectionery sugar, which will not produce a positive reaction.)
- dropper bottle containing 25 mL of Bertinol reagent
- dropper bottle containing 50 mL of 70 percent isopropyl alcohol or ethyl alcohol

Teaching Tip

To reinforce the procedure outlined in Chapter 2 on how to open and reseal evidence envelopes, have students cut open the evidence bag in a new area, remove some of the evidence, and then reseal, tape, and sign their name over the tape. Students should also complete an Evidence Inventory Label. If no contamination occurs, the teacher can reuse these sample evidence bags. Be sure to add enough powders to use for several different activities so that you don't need to restock every time.

Answers

Check students' data tables.

Questions

1. Answers vary depending on which envelopes contain the "Bertinol."

2. Results should be consistent. Different results may occur if students contaminated their samples or recorded the information in the wrong column. Depending on the amount of drug in each vial, the color intensity will vary.

3. Measuring with a toothpick is not precise. The amount of drug in the vial will affect the color intensity of the results.

4. a. Quantify the exact amount of drug used for each test.

   b. Use a better tool for measuring the drug; a toothpick is not an accurate tool for measurement.

   c. Designate the amount of time after adding the Bertinol testing solution that one should wait before recording the results.

   d. Use larger samples of the drug to do the testing. Because many drugs contain "fillers" like sucrose, you may not have enough of the drug present in the test to produce a color change.

5. Presumptive tests do not positively identify a specific drug; confirmatory tests do that. Many different substances may test positive in a presumptive test.

6. If the positive control did not produce a positive reaction, then it may indicate that your testing solutions are contaminated. You cannot use a reagent if the positive test does not produce a positive reaction.

7. Add three drops of Bertinol drug test solution to each of the four vials and stir with the individual toothpicks.

8. Observe any color changes. Record your results in the Data Table.

9. Compare test vials with the Positive Control and Negative Control vials. Do any of the evidence powders obtained from the four lockers contain the drug Bertinol?

10. Discard all liquids as described by your instructor except the two control vials.

Data Table 1: Drug Analysis

Sample	Appearance of Solution
Positive Control	
Negative Control	
Locker 1	
Locker 2	
Locker 3	
Locker 4	

Questions:

1. Based on your results, did any of the drug evidence in the lockers test positive in this presumptive drug test? Support your claim with your data from the activity.

2. Were the results consistent in all groups? Brainstorm possible sources of error to account for inconsistent results.

3. Different teams may have seen a difference in the intensity of the color. How would you account for the variation in color intensity?

4. Describe three ways to improve the activity protocol to ensure more reliable results.

5. Suppose one student concluded that his group confirmed the presence of Bertinol in one of the samples. Explain why this is not a valid conclusion based on this test.

6. Suppose your positive control did not produce any color. What would this indicate about your experiment?

Going Further:

1. Design an activity that uses a different color indicator to detect the presence of different powders or solutions. Include in your design the name of the indicator and describe conditions under which the indicator turns colors. Describe specific powders (simulated drugs or over-the-counter drugs or solutions) that can be tested with your indicator.

2. Research and describe types of presumptive tests other than those utilizing a color change. (Microcrystalline tests are one example.)

302   Forensic Toxicology

Sample	Appearance of Solution
Positive Control	Pink color
Negative Control	No color
Locker 1	Color will vary based on instructor design.
Locker 2	Color will vary based on instructor design.
Locker 3	Color will vary based on instructor design.
Locker 4	Color will vary based on instructor design.

Should Medical Marijuana Be Legalized? *Ch. Obj. 9.6, 9.8*

Objectives:

Upon completion of this activity, you will be able to:
1. Better understand the status of legalized marijuana in the United States
2. Defend positions on both sides of the issue

SAFETY PRECAUTIONS:

There are no special safety precautions for this activity.

Materials:

Act 9-2 SH Debate Strategy
Act 9-2 SH Debate Planning
sheet of paper
pen

Time Required to Complete Activity:

This activity will be completed over several class periods depending on whether student research is done in class or outside of class.

Introduction: Should Medical Marijuana Use Be Legal in All States of the United States?

As of October 2014, 20 states and the District of Columbia had enacted laws to approve medical use of marijuana. Marijuana, or *Cannabis sativa*, is prescribed to help treat symptoms of a variety of conditions, including cancer, AIDS, nerve pain, multiple sclerosis, seizures, long-term pain, and autoimmune disorders.

Legalization of medical use of marijuana is regulated by each state. However, in June 2005, the Supreme Court ruled that individuals in all states can be prosecuted under federal law under the Controlled Substance Abuse Act of 1970. Marijuana was classified as a schedule 1 drug, one without medical applications and one that puts the individual at a high risk of abuse. People using marijuana in states that have legalized marijuana are technically breaking a federal law.

During this activity, students will be asked to consider if medical use of marijuana should be legalized in all states. Instead of answering with an emotional response, students are asked to justify their claims with supporting scientific evidence. Students will debate the issue of whether or not medical marijuana should be legalized, taking into account ethical and stakeholder (those who are affected) considerations.

Scenarios:

Because medical marijuana is legal in Colorado, Charlotte Figi was able to reduce the number of epileptic seizures she experienced from three or four an hour to only three or four in six months. She is one of 400,000 American children suffering from medication-resistant epilepsy.

Forensic Toxicology   303

Procedures

1. Students read the introduction and the scenarios of individuals regarding the medical use of marijuana.

2. Students record their reflections about the scenarios on a sheet of paper. On the back of the paper, students add additional questions they have regarding whether or not medical marijuana should be legalized. Collect the papers (with or without names).

3. Pose the questions to the class: Should the people in the scenarios be allowed to use medical marijuana without fear of being arrested? Personalize the case studies by asking students what they would do if the person in need were a family member. Ask students if anyone they know has ever been prescribed medicinal marijuana. What is their feeling about the woman who sees any form of marijuana as a gateway to using and abusing drugs? Do students know friends or acquaintances who have used marijuana and progressed to using other drugs? Conduct a brief discussion on the topic to allow students to voice their opinions and ask questions.

4. The next day, read some of their reflections and address some of their questions at the beginning of class.

Teaching Tip

Following the BSCS (Biological Science Curriculum Study) 5E model (Engage, Explore, Explain, Elaborate, and Evaluate), guide students through an information-gathering process that will help them make a claim based on scientific justifications and not emotions. Research teams are assigned to specific topics. Each team will summarize and present its research. Students use the information from the research to prepare justifications that support their claims in a debate about the legalization of medical use of marijuana.

5. Have student teams select what topic they would like to research. Students should obtain several different reputable and scientific resources for their research. One site that would be particularly useful is Learn Genetics at the University of Utah Web site. Students can search the site for *Science of Addiction* and click on *Cannabis in the Clinic: The Medical Marijuana Debate.* http://learn.genetics.utah.edu/content/addiction/cannabis/

6. To obtain more information on the topic, divide the class into small research teams who will investigate one of the five research questions described in the lab or a topic of their choice.

7. Each of the research groups summarizes and presents their findings to the class. Students select a format of their own choice for their group presentation (poster, PowerPoint, video, interview, etc.).

8. Print, copy, and distribute Act 9-2 SH Debate Planning and Act 9-2 SH Debate Strategy from the IRCD, Chapter 9. Form debate teams, one in favor of medical marijuana legalization and one against medical marijuana legalization. Students use the information derived from the student research of the various teams to develop justifications for their claim, based on scientific evidence. In preparing for their debate, students complete the Act 9-2 SH Debate Planning table that includes ethics, stakeholder considerations, alternative options, rebuttals, and explanations

Hector has suffered from chronic pain for years. Doctors prescribed morphine, but Hector experienced side effects and developed an addiction to morphine. Hector's doctors have told him that marijuana might help his pain, but medical use of marijuana is not legal in his state.

Zoe's father has lost a great deal of weight due to chemotherapy to treat his cancer. The doctors told him if he used medical marijuana, his appetite would be stimulated and he would be able to gain back some of the weight. He is debating whether to move to one of the states where medical marijuana is legal so he can try the therapy.

Maria's mother thinks her daughter's drug habit started when her daughter starting using marijuana in high school. She hears the news about legalizing marijuana and she shudders. If medical marijuana is legalized throughout the United States, she believes the increased availability will lead more young people to abuse drugs and commit crimes to get money to buy drugs.

Procedure:

PART A: INTRODUCTION AND DISCUSSION

1. Read the introduction and scenarios regarding the medical use of marijuana.
2. Record your thoughts regarding the introduction and scenarios on the front of a sheet of paper. On the back, record any questions you have regarding medical marijuana use. Submit the form to the teacher.
3. As a class, discuss the following questions with the scenarios in mind.
   - Is medical use of marijuana legal in your state?
   - What kinds of conditions are treated with medical marijuana?
   - Do you know of anyone who has been prescribed medical marijuana?
   - Do you know of anyone who started using marijuana and then started using other illegal drugs?
   - What kind of questions should be considered when forming an opinion about legalizing medical marijuana?
   - What are some of the reasons why people are opposed to legalizing medical marijuana?
   - What are some of the reasons people want medical marijuana to be legalized?

PART B: EXPLORE

4. The class will be divided into small collaborative groups to research information regarding legalizing medical marijuana. Each group will research and prepare a brief presentation for the class.

Research Topics: (One per Team)

a. What are the medical uses of marijuana? What conditions are treated with marijuana? How does marijuana help to improve a person's symptoms? Are there negative side effects of medical marijuana use?
b. Investigate at least two ways that medical marijuana is administered besides smoking. Prepare a table of the benefits and disadvantages of each delivery system.

that connect their evidence to their claims. Students also should complete the Act 9-2 SH Debate Strategy form from the IRCD prior to the debate. A suggested time frame for each component of the debate is included.

c. Drugs affect the brain because they are similar to the body's own chemicals. Research endocannaboids and determine how they affect both nerve cells in the brain and immune cells in the body. (Search the Internet for "Science of Addiction Learn Genetics," and click on "Cannabis in the Clinic.")

d. Prepare a list of reasons people feel that laws permitting medical marijuana should be passed.

e. Prepare a list of reasons people feel that laws permitting medical marijuana use should not be passed.

PART C: EXPLAIN

5. Each team summarizes its research and prepares a brief presentation to the class. The presentation can utilize whatever format the team chooses: poster, PowerPoint, expert panel, interview, etc. Members of teams not presenting should take notes.

PART D: ELABORATE AND DEBATE

6. The class will be divided into two teams: those who will argue that medical marijuana use should be legalized and those who will argue that medical marijuana should not be legalized. Review the table Elements of a Strong Justification.

Elements of a Strong Justification

Element	Which means ...
Decision	Your position or **claim is clearly stated** and relates to the question.
Facts	The facts and science content can be confirmed or refuted regardless of personal or cultural views. **These can be used to support the claim.**
Ethical considerations	These include respect for persons, maximizing benefits, and minimizing harm and justice. These can serve as **evidence to support the claim.**
Stakeholder views	There are a variety of views and interests in the decision, and more than one individual or group will be affected by the outcome.
Alternative options and rebuttals	No one decision will satisfy all parties. **A thorough justification considers strengths and weakness of various positions.**
Reasoning and logic	A logical explanation **connects the evidence to the claim.**

Adapted from: Copyright © 2014, National Science Teachers Association (NSTA). Reprinted with permission from *The Science Teacher*, Vol. 81, No. 1, January 2014.

PART E: EVALUATE

7. During your debate planning session, work with your team and complete the Debate Planning table. (You may need additional sheets to record your answers.) Present your claim and specific justifications. Include facts, ethical considerations, and stakeholder views. Be prepared to offer alternative options and rebuttals. Be sure to connect the evidence to your claim to prepare logical and reasonable justifications. Prior to the debate, each team completes Act 9-2 SH Debate Strategy.

Time Frame for the Debate:

Opening Statements (both sides)	3 minutes each
Arguments (both sides)	3 minutes each
Rebuttal Conference	3 minutes
Rebuttals (both sides)	3 minutes each
Closing Statements (both sides)	3 minutes each

Avoid:

1. Using the following words: *never, always, all, most.* They are inaccurate.
2. Exaggeration
3. Trying to deceive your opponents by representing opinion as fact
4. Becoming hostile or raising your voice
5. Attacking the debater

Consider the Following:

When you justify your claim, you are providing reasons you support a position or claim.

1. *Weak justifications* are based on emotions or feelings and not substantiated with facts or science.
2. *Strong justifications* include
   a. science or facts
   b. ethical considerations (what is morally right)
   c. consideration for all those people affected by the claim
   d. all supporting evidence

How to Enhance Your Presentation:

1. Attack the idea and not the debater.
2. Stress the positive in your argument.
3. Quote reliable sources and provide data.
4. Smile.
5. Don't lose a friend over a debate. Remember—everyone is entitled to an opinion.

Debate Planning: Should Medical Marijuana Be Legalized?

Reason	Yes	No
Facts Support your claim with scientific evidence.		
Ethical Considerations Doing what is morally right, trying to do the best for all persons while minimizing harm		
Stakeholders Who else will be affected? How will they be affected?		
Rebuttals and Alternative Options Weaknesses in opposing argument? Strengths in opposing argument? Can you propose an alternative?		

Debate Strategy:

1. Opening Statement (3 minutes):
   State your team's position and main arguments. Do not provide supporting details at this time.
2. Main arguments supporting your position (3 minutes):
   For each argument, provide supporting details.
3. 10 questions to be asked of your opponents:
   Anticipate what their main arguments are so that you are ready with questions.
4. Note taking during opponent's presentation:
   List your opponents' main arguments and list your rebuttals to those arguments.
5. Rebuttal (3 minutes):
   Anticipate the opposing team's rebuttals to your rebuttals and prepare responses.
6. Closing Statements (3 minutes):
   Repeat your main argument and restate the details used to support your arguments.

Background

In this activity, students conduct presumptive spot tests on drugs. Small quantities of both the drugs and reagents are used in this activity because the reagents are caustic.

Teaching Tip

For teachers working with 45-minute class periods:

- Have students dispense the drugs into the well tray the day before the lab.
- Cover the trays to prevent any contamination of the drugs. If you do not have covers for the trays, cover them with aluminum foil.
- The following day, students add the reagents, conduct the test, and analyze their results.

Teaching Tip

In advance:

1. Use a mortar and pestle to grind up the drugs into a fine powder. Be sure to remove any traces of color from the coating on the pills. Store in plastic containers. To save time, prepare enough drugs for several classes.

2. Set up four microtubes or small containers of the four drugs that will be used in the lab as the positive controls. These should be labeled with the name of the drug: aspirin, Tylenol, Motrin, Aleve. Students will take a "toothpick scoop" of the drug when running controls for each reagent. Have a toothpick next to each of the drugs.

3. Set up and label another four microtubes or small containers for each of your unknowns with labels Unknown 1, 2, 3, and 4. Record what drug is used for each of the unknowns. Divide the class into four groups with each group getting a different unknown.

ACTIVITY 9-3

Drug Spot Test Obj. 9.3

Objectives:

By the end of this activity, you will be able to:

1. Conduct a preliminary drug spot test.
2. Compare and contrast the reactions of the reagents on the positive controls with the reactions on the unknown drug.
3. Analyze the results of the drug spot test to determine if the results of the tests on the unknown drug are consistent with any of the reactions of the reagents on the positive controls.

Scenario:

Neighbors at the College Apartments complained that the person in room 202 had his television continually running with the volume turned up too loud. The people in rooms 200 and 204 said the sound kept them awake all night. When the neighbors tried knocking on the door of room 202, no one answered. They became concerned and called the police.

When the police arrived, they discovered that the young man had apparently died sitting in front of the television. While working the crime scene, the police discovered 15 identical white pills on the table next to the victim. There was evidence that the victim had consumed many of the pills. Did a doctor prescribe the drugs? Are these over-the-counter drugs? Did the person use illegal drugs?

Before performing more complex confirmatory testing to identify the components of any drug, forensic technicians perform presumptive color spot testing. In this activity, you will be testing aspirin, acetaminophen (Tylenol), naproxen (Aleve), and ibuprofen (Motrin).

Background:

When a sample is suspected of being an illegal drug, spot tests are often performed. Spot tests rapidly show results and are used as preliminary, presumptive tests to indicate the possibility that certain drugs are present. The test used to confirm the identify of the drug depends on the results of the spot test. The confirmatory tests include:

Name of Reagent	Drug Identified	Positive Reaction
Marquis	Opium alkaloids such as heroin, morphine, codeine, or ecstasy Amphetamines Speed Oxycontin	Purple Orange Orange-brown Gray
Cobalt thiocyanate	Cocaine	Blue flaky precipitate
p-Dimethylaminobenzaldehyde (P-DMAB)	LSD	Blue
Duquenois	Marijuana	Purple
Cobalt acetate/isopropylamine	Barbiturates	Red-violet

4. Prepare drug-testing solutions. (Note that the Marquis solution needs to be fresh, made no more than a week in advance of the lab.)

5. Prepare four small containers for the chemical reagents (glass, not plastic). Label each of these containers with the name of the reagent.

Because most of these drugs to be tested are controlled substances, we will substitute similar tests, which parallel real testing situations. The drugs in question for this case include aspirin, acetaminophen (Tylenol), naproxen (Aleve), and ibuprofen (Motrin).

SAFETY PRECAUTIONS:

1. Anyone working at or near the testing station *must* wear safety goggles and gloves. The chemicals used are hazardous. They will be used in minute amounts.
2. Place newspapers on the desktops where testing is to be conducted.
3. Wash your hands thoroughly after testing is complete.
4. Discard all chemicals as directed by your instructor.
5. Thoroughly clean all counters and desk surfaces where testing has been completed.
6. Plastic well trays with covers reduce student exposure to the reagents.

Materials:

(per group of three to four students)
Act 9-3 SH Drug Identification
2 plastic well trays (24 wells per tray)
drug-testing reagents in dropper bottles labeled Marquis, tannic acid, ferric chloride, nitric acid
samples of aspirin, Tylenol, Motrin, and Aleve (ground into powder)
colored pencils
2 (5×8-inch) index cards
1 pair of scissors
1 pair of safety goggles per person
1 pair gloves per person
flat wooden toothpicks
paper towels

Time to Complete the Activity:

60 minutes (Drugs can be dispensed in the wells one day, and the chemical reagents can be added on a second day.)

Procedure:

PART A: PREPARING THE WELLS

1. Obtain a 5×8-inch card. Turn it so that the blank side is up. Place a mini 24-well tray on top of the card.
   a. Trace an outline of the mini tray on top of the 5×8-inch card.
   b. On the four-row side of the plastic mini tray, write the first letter (M, T, F, and N) for each of the chemical reagents.
   c. On the six-row side of the plastic mini tray, write the name of the "drug" to be tested in the first four rows: aspirin, Tylenol, Motrin, Aleve.
   d. Leave the fifth row blank.
   e. Write "unknown" in the sixth row
   f. Record your initials in the lower-right corner of the 5×8-inch card.

Procedures (continued)

3. To produce samples of the drugs to be tested, it is suggested that you use a mortar and pestle to finely grind all of the pills. Try to find drugs that do not contain any color. If any pills are coated with a colored substance, remove all traces of color from the drug.

4. Use empty film canisters or small microtubes to store the drugs. Be sure to label each of the drugs.

5. You can either provide each team with separate containers of the drugs in film canisters or microtubes, or set up one location in the lab where students can obtain their drug samples.

6. Select one of the drugs to be your unknown. It is more interesting if different groups have a different unknown so they can later review the class results.

Safety Precautions

1. Review the safety precautions with the students before the start of the activity.
2. Post the procedure for disposal of materials in a prominent place.
3. Check that all students wear goggles and gloves.
4. After this activity, it is important that students wash their hands and clean all counters and desk surfaces thoroughly.
5. The reagents used in this activity are caustic! The teacher should clean the lab dishes used by flooding with water and then washing and allowing them to air dry.

Materials

mortar and pestle
5 small covered plastic containers (film canisters) or microtubes wooden toothpicks
aspirin, Tylenol, Motrin, and Alleve
Marquis solution, tannic acid, nitric acid, and ferric chloride

Teaching Tip

Before beginning, demonstrate for students

- How much drug should go into each well
- How to use the slotted 5×8-inch card to prevent contamination
- How much reagent should be added (one to two drops, enough that there is a solution in the well and no dry powder)

Remind students to

- Keep the cover on the plastic well tray when not dispensing reagents
- Keep the cover on the plastic well tray after all reagents are dispensed

Procedures

1. Print, copy, and distribute Act 9-3 SH from the IRCD, Chapter 9.
2. Make sure students read all directions before beginning the activity.

Preparation of Drug Testing Solutions

Except for Marquis solution, prepare enough solution to last for the year. (Marquis solution must always be fresh.) At the end of the school year, dispose of any unused solutions. Old solutions will discolor and interfere with readings.

Marquis solution: 5 mL H_2SO_4 + 5 drops of formaldehyde—turns pink

Tannic acid solution: dissolve 10 g tannic acid in 90 mL water.

Ferric chloride solution: 2 g ferric chloride dissolved in 100 mL water

Nitric acid: diluted 1 : 1 with water

Teaching Tip

To save lab time, prepare the slotted cards in advance for students

Teaching Tip

The protocol is intentionally imprecise. At the end of this activity, students are asked to analyze the results of the color testing obtained by different groups and consider why all the colors are not exactly alike. Challenge the students to identify sources of error in this protocol and to redesign the lab for more reliable testing.

2. On the second 5 × 8-inch card, cut out a horizontal section the width of four rows of wells as indicated in the following diagram to form a slotted card. This 5 × 8-inch card will be used to prevent contamination of one drug with the other while filling your wells. Put the slotted card aside for later use when adding your drugs to the mini tray.

PART B: ADDING THE DRUGS TO THE TEST WELLS

1. The four known drug samples have been placed at different stations in the room. Take your plastic mini tray with its lid and your labeled 5 × 8-inch card to each of the four stations. Place the labeled 5 × 8-inch card under the plastic plate to ensure that you add the correct drug to the correct well.

Slotted card

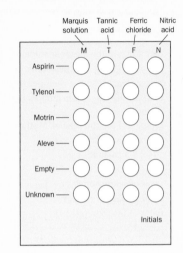

2. Each station will have one of the known drugs and a toothpick for dispensing the drug. For example, Tylenol will be added in the first row under Marquis, under tannic acid, under ferric chloride, and under nitric acid. There should be four wells in a row containing aspirin, as indicated by the diagram. To avoid contamination, use your cut-out slotted 5 × 8-inch card. Place the card over the plastic wells so that the cut-out row is correctly positioned for the drug being added. This way, the other rows are covered and will not become contaminated.

All groups add the controls: aspirin, Tylenol, Motrin and Aleve. Each team will be assigned one unknown. Be sure to record the number of the unknown drug your team is testing.

3. Using the flat end of the toothpick, place a pinhead-sized amount of aspirin powder into the four wells as indicated by the diagrams. Wipe off the 5 × 8-inch slotted card with a clean paper towel after adding each row of drugs.

4. Different groups will be assigned different unknown drugs. Be sure to record the number of your unknown drug. The unknown drugs will be set up in a different part of the room. Using the same procedure as before, add your assigned unknown drug in the last row on your well tray.

(If the lab needs to be completed during a different lab period, cover your mini trays with the plastic lid. You can add the chemical reagents during your next lab period.)

PART C: ADDITION OF CHEMICAL REACTIONS

1. Place the plastic well plate on top of the 5 × 8-inch labeled card. In column M, add two drops of Marquis solution to each of the five different drugs. Use the slotted card to shield the other rows to avoid contamination. You will need to rotate the slotted card in a vertical position to align with the columns.

2. In column T, add two drops of tannic acid solution to each of the five different samples. Use the slotted card to shield adjacent wells from contamination.

3. In column F, add two drops of ferric chloride solution to each of the five different samples. Use the slotted card to shield adjacent wells from contamination.

4. In column N, add two drops of nitric acid solution to each of the five different samples. Use the slotted card to shield adjacent wells from contamination.

5. Place the cover on the well tray and do not open the cover. Gently agitate.

6. Observe any changes that occur in the wells after adding the reagents. Record the changes in Data Table 1. Write "NR" if no reaction occurred.

Teaching Tip

Students may notice that different groups testing the same unknown had slightly different results with some colors more intense than others. Ask students to discuss what could account for different results obtained by groups performing the same procedure using the same unknown and the same reagents. Possible answers:

- If there was a smaller quantity of the drug, they may not get a strong reaction.
- If there was a smaller quantity of the reagent, the powder may not have dissolved. As students are reviewing the results, ask them what could be done to get more accurate and consistent results.
- Discuss the importance of standardized lab procedures and protocols.
- Describe how lawyers will cross-examine toxicologists and chemists at a trial, asking very specific questions that pertain to whether or not the lab procedures were followed and whether the equipment used was working properly. Improperly tested evidence will result in the evidence being "thrown out of court."

Teaching Tip

Invite a crime-scene investigator to visit the class either in person or via Webcam to explain how drug evidence is collected and documented. Ask if he or she can show an actual drug evidence form and review the information required on the form.

Photograph the lab results using a white paper under the dish for contrast. With a photo, if class time runs short, the results can be analyzed the next day using the photo.

Do not store the dishes with the chemicals. You (not the students) should clean them after the class, and they should not be left overnight.

Data Table 1: Drug Testing Results

Row	Drug Tested	Marquis (Column M)	Tannic Acid (Column T)	Ferric Chloride (Column F)	Nitric Acid (Column N)
Row 1	Aspirin				
Row 2	Tylenol				
Row 3	Motrin				
Row 4	Aleve				
Row 5	Empty				
Row 6	Unknown				

7. Sketch the appearance of your results in Data Table 2. Use colored pencils to indicate any color changes.
8. Examine your unknown drug. Compare the reactions of the unknown drug with the four known drugs. Are the color changes of the unknown consistent with any of the color changes of the known drugs? Support your claim with evidence from this presumptive test.
9. If possible, take a digital photo of your results.

PART D: COMPARING YOUR RESULTS

1. After you have recorded your results, bring your well plate (covers on) to a designated area for each of the unknowns. Place your labeled 5 × 8-inch card underneath the plastic well plate.
2. Compare and contrast your results with other students who tested the same unknown.
3. Discuss why the results of testing the same unknown may not be exactly alike.
4. Examine the results of the other unknown drugs. As a class, determine what unknowns were being tested based on the color result of this presumptive testing.
5. Identify possible sources of error using this lab procedure.
6. Discuss how the lab procedures should be modified to ensure more accurate and more reliable results.

Questions:

1. Refer to the opening scenario. Suppose your unknown sample was consistent with the evidence from that crime scene. Assume your unknown drug was the drug from this scenario. Could you claim that you were able to positively identify the substance as aspirin, Tylenol, Motrin, or Aleve based on your results? Support your claim with evidence from your experiment and information from your text.
2. Prepare a table identifying possible sources of error in this procedure in one column, and suggest a modification of the procedure in the next column.

Answers

1. The results are not conclusive. If you got a reaction consistent with one of the controlled tests, it may indicate that one of those drugs was in the evidence. However, presumptive tests may test positive for several different drugs; they do not identify just one drug. Further, confirmatory testing must be done.

2. Table of errors

   Row 1. Volume of drug measured by a toothpick "scoop." Weigh the drug and use an exact amount of the drug.

   Row 2. Use a precise volume of the indicator. Measure in mL, not drops.

Row 3. Color change noted. Be more precise as to how long to allow the change to occur before checking for a color change.

Row 4. Using the 5 × 8-inch slotted card over and over. Use a clean card each time you add a drug.

Row 5. Rotate the dish to mix the powder and reagents. Stir the mixture with a toothpick.

Row 6. Companies add filler ingredients to pills that may alter test results. Check each of the unknowns for its purity.

3. Recall that a toxicologist needs to determine if the victim actually took these drugs or if the drugs were just found next to the victim.

   a. Refer to the chapter and describe what type of samples would be taken from the victim to determine if the he or she actually was exposed to this drug. Include in your answer what the toxicologist would be looking for in those samples.

   b. Give three questions that must be answered regarding any substance evidence obtained from the crime scene.

4. Suppose that all four control drugs got no reaction when tested with Marquis solution. Suggest possible reasons for getting no reaction. If this occurred when you were doing your lab, describe what course of action you would take.

Data Table 2: Sketch Your Results.
Use colored pencils to indicate color changes.
Write NR to indicate no reaction.

	Marquis solution	Tannic acid	Ferric chloride	Nitric acid
	M	T	F	N
Aspirin	○	○	○	○
Tylenol	○	○	○	○
Motrin	○	○	○	○
Aleve	○	○	○	○
Empty	○	○	○	○
Unknown	○	○	○	○

Initials

Further Study:

If a person is found unconscious as a result of an overdose of pills, he or she may be taken to a hospital to have his or her stomach "pumped."

   a. What is this procedure?

   b. Is there any danger in having this procedure done?

   c. Would a stomach pump be of value if someone had injected the drug into his or her system? Explain your answer.

Answers (continued)

3. a. Blood sample, urine sample, stomach contents, and a liver sample. The toxicologist would not be looking necessarily for the drug itself. He or she might also look for a metabolite of the drug.

   b. i. How much does it weigh? (quantitative analysis)

      ii. Is the sample composed of more than one substance?

      iii. What is found in the substance? (qualitative analysis)

4. Check your reagents.

Teaching Tip

Check students' data tables. For Data Table 2, students should shade in each test area with the appropriate color. See Act 9-3 TN on the Instructor Resources CD, Chapter 9, for a photograph of test results.

DIFFERENTIATED LEARNING

Teaching Gifted Students
Investigate the chemical reactions that result in the color changes. Ask students to design a revised activity that uses different powders or solutions and different chemical reagents to simulate a presumptive color test for drug identification.

Further Research and Extensions
Students might be interested in researching controversial drug-related deaths in history. Ask them to research the question, How did Napoleon die? Information available from multiple data sources provides conflicting conclusions about whether Napoleon died from natural causes or was poisoned. Biographies by Alan Schom (1998) and Frank McLynn (2003) also support different theories.

Chapter Overview

Document analysis is an important area of forensics. Experts can tell if a document is authentic by examining not only the handwriting but also other components such as paper, ink, and glue. Checks, historical documents, wills, passports, and money are a few of the items document examiners analyze to determine their authenticity. Computer-enhanced techniques have increased the accuracy of the analyses. The United States has gone to great lengths to produce currency that is difficult to counterfeit.

The Big Ideas

Document analysis is an area of forensics that compares questioned documents with authentic ones, which are called exemplars. One element that document experts examine is the handwriting in a document. These experts use many major categories of handwriting characteristics when examining a sample. These include shape of letters, angle or slant of letters, size of letters, and use of connecting lines between letters. Besides their expertise, document experts also use techniques such as infrared spectrometry and computerized handwriting analysis to determine the authenticity of a sample. Check forgery and counterfeit currency are always problems. To prevent check forgery, banks are changing how they print checks, and some are trying to eliminate paper checks all together. The U.S. government has changed printing and paper-making techniques to try to stop counterfeiting.

CHAPTER 10

Handwriting Analysis, Forgery, and Counterfeiting

Master Forger

Frank W. Abagnale, a reformed master forger, describes in his book *The Art of the Steal* how a visitor from Argentina was issued a parking ticket on a rental car in Florida. Although the fine was $20, he placed $22 in an envelope and mailed it to the Miami city clerk. On receipt of the money, the clerk issued a $2 refund. On receiving the check, the man scanned it into his computer, changed the amount to $1.45 million, and deposited the check into his account in a bank in Argentina. The check was cashed, and the money was transferred. He was never arrested, and the money was not recovered.

According to Abagnale, the Argentinian example is not uncommon. Stolen money is often not recovered, and thieves are not caught. Abagnale tells of his own life of forgery and fraudulence in the book *Catch Me If You Can*. He began his life of crime as a teenager, when he changed a number on his driver's license to make himself appear 10 years older. After acquiring a small amount of money, he opened a bank account. He printed his account number on deposit slips and returned them to the bank counter. By the time the bank discovered his fraudulent scheme, he had received deposits of over $40,000, and had already changed his identity. Working with eight different identities, he passed more than $2.5 million in fraudulent checks in 26 countries and throughout the United States. For his offenses, Abagnale served prison time in France, Sweden, and the United States.

Today, Frank Abagnale is a consultant in the detection of forgery and fraudulence, and in the securing of documents. For more than 35 years, he has consulted with financial institutions, corporations, and government agencies, including the Federal Bureau of Investigation (FBI). Abagnale teaches and lectures on how to detect forgery, avoid consumer fraud, and prevent crime. Abagnale says that the best way to deal with fraud is to prevent it in the first place.

Frank Abagnale, a convicted forger, is now a leading consultant in the area of document forgery and fraudulence.

314

SCENARIO

Lead the class in a discussion by asking these questions:
Do you think you can tell the difference between an authentic $10 bill and a counterfeit?
With all of the available technology, would you expect forgery to be an increasing problem?
Why or why not?

Students may wish to read the book or view the film *Catch Me If You Can*, which is based upon the life of Frank Abagnale.

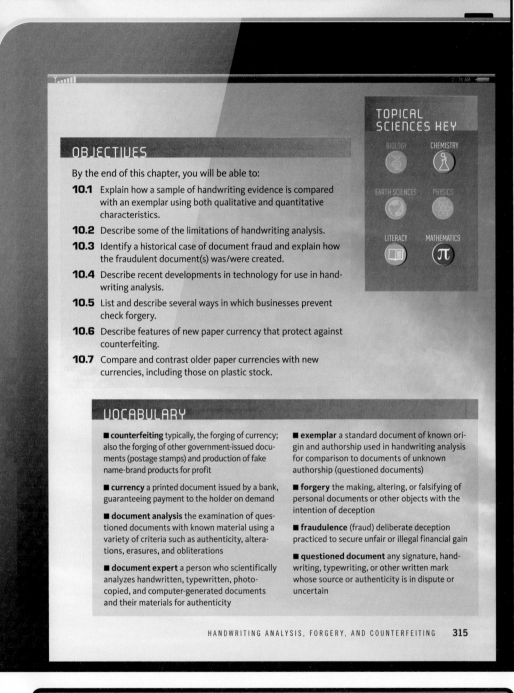

OBJECTIVES

By the end of this chapter, you will be able to:

10.1 Explain how a sample of handwriting evidence is compared with an exemplar using both qualitative and quantitative characteristics.

10.2 Describe some of the limitations of handwriting analysis.

10.3 Identify a historical case of document fraud and explain how the fraudulent document(s) was/were created.

10.4 Describe recent developments in technology for use in handwriting analysis.

10.5 List and describe several ways in which businesses prevent check forgery.

10.6 Describe features of new paper currency that protect against counterfeiting.

10.7 Compare and contrast older paper currencies with new currencies, including those on plastic stock.

TOPICAL SCIENCES KEY

BIOLOGY

CHEMISTRY

EARTH SCIENCES

PHYSICS

LITERACY

MATHEMATICS

VOCABULARY

- **counterfeiting** typically, the forging of currency; also the forging of other government-issued documents (postage stamps) and production of fake name-brand products for profit

- **currency** a printed document issued by a bank, guaranteeing payment to the holder on demand

- **document analysis** the examination of questioned documents with known material using a variety of criteria such as authenticity, alterations, erasures, and obliterations

- **document expert** a person who scientifically analyzes handwritten, typewritten, photocopied, and computer-generated documents and their materials for authenticity

- **exemplar** a standard document of known origin and authorship used in handwriting analysis for comparison to documents of unknown authorship (questioned documents)

- **forgery** the making, altering, or falsifying of personal documents or other objects with the intention of deception

- **fraudulence** (fraud) deliberate deception practiced to secure unfair or illegal financial gain

- **questioned document** any signature, handwriting, typewriting, or other written mark whose source or authenticity is in dispute or uncertain

HANDWRITING ANALYSIS, FORGERY, AND COUNTERFEITING **315**

TEACHING RESOURCES

 Instructor's Resource CD-ROM includes:
- Activities and Student Handouts
- Alternative Assessments
- Consolidated Bibliography
- Correlations to NGSS and CCSS
- Figure Files
- Lesson Plans
- Nonfiction Readings
- PowerPoint Presentations
- Student Learning Objectives (SLOs)

CL Testing powered by Cognero

Website: ngl.cengage.com/forensicscience2e

Engage

Ask for a volunteer to write a statement on the board without the other students' knowledge. Then, ask the class if they can identify the person who wrote the statement from his or her handwriting. What clues gave it away?

Teaching Tip

Graphology is a tool used to interpret personality from clues in a person's handwriting. While not accepted as a science, it sometimes can provide background for investigators.

Explore

Have students research whether billionaire Howard Hughes actually signed a will giving 1/16 of his fortune to gas station attendant Melvin Dummar, or whether the will was a forgery.

DIGGING DEEPER

Refer students to the Gale Forensic Science eCollection for more information about the *Daubert* factors or the role of Hauptmann's handwriting in the Lindbergh handwriting case.

Did you know

A subcommittee of OSAC, (Organization of Scientific Area Committees) is being developed to establish standards and guidelines for reviewing questioned documents.

INTRODUCTION

Is a document signature authentic, or has it been faked? This is a question teachers ask as they view hall passes or papers apparently signed by teachers or parents. Any document that has handwriting, a written mark, type, or any paper and ink with uncertain authenticity may be a **questioned document**. Checks, wills, passports, driver's licenses, currency, letters, contracts, suicide notes, and receipts are questioned documents that may undergo **document analysis**.

All **document experts** (document analysts) must first work as apprentices of experienced analysts. Certification by The American Board of Forensic Document Examiners (ABFDE) or the Board of Forensic Document Examiners (BFDE) is voluntary, but having certification helps to demonstrate training in the field. A college degree in a related field is encouraged, since it is a requirement for certification. Document analysts look for any changes, erasures, or obliterations in a document. They also analyze the paper, ink, and glue if those components can provide clues to authenticity (the age of the document, for example). By examining and comparing questioned documents to known material, experts attempt to establish the authorship and authenticity of documents.

A document analyst is different from a graphologist, who interprets the personality of a writer based on his or her handwriting. Graphology is not accepted in forensic science. The scientific analysis of handwriting is the focus of this chapter.

EARLY FORENSIC HANDWRITING ANALYSIS

Like fingerprints, every person's handwriting is unique. Once learned, handwriting becomes automatic. Individual handwriting characteristics take on a unique style over time. If a forgery of a person's handwriting is suspected, questioned samples are compared to an **exemplar** of that person's writing, a document of known origin and authorship, to determine if the two documents are consistent. Exemplars are often documents that were written or signed with trusted witnesses, such as legal documents.

DIGGING DEEPER

With Forensic Science eCollection

According to the *Daubert* ruling in 1993, what additional factors must be met in determining admissibility of expert witness testimony? Find more information about admissibility of expert witness testimony at the Gale Forensic Science eCollection at **ngl.cengage.com/forensicscience2e**.

Handwriting evidence was first used in an American court around 1868, when a forged will was exposed in the case of Robinson *v.* Mandell. In the 1930s, handwriting analysis played an important forensic role during the trial of Richard "Bruno" Hauptmann for the kidnapping and murder of the son of world-famous aviator Charles Lindbergh. Handwriting analysis of the many ransom notes, along with known handwriting samples and other evidence, led to Hauptmann's conviction and execution (Figure 10-1).

Courts have not consistently admitted expert handwriting analysis as evidence. This changed in 1999, when the U.S. Court of Appeals determined that handwriting analysis qualified as a form of expert testimony. Handwriting evidence is admissible in court, provided that scientifically accepted guidelines are followed. Scientific analysis of handwriting has always been an important tool for forensic document examiners. Today, some statistical and quantitative analysis is done using computers.

HANDWRITING CHARACTERISTICS

Obj. 10.1, 10.2

Handwriting is a learned complex skill involving the neurological coordination of visual and muscular impulses. The use of different types of writing instruments, such as a pen, pencil, marker, or crayon, can affect our handwriting. Our mood may contribute to differences we notice in our own handwriting. The use of drugs, alcohol, and medications may have a temporary effect on handwriting due to loss of coordination. Handwriting may change somewhat as we age because of arthritis or illness. Despite these minor variations in handwriting, each person develops and maintains a unique handwriting style. Characteristics such as the slant and curl of the letters, the height of the letters, or even how a person fills the page with text can determine our identity.

A person's handwriting exhibits characteristics that make it distinguishable from other samples. Handwriting experts examine at least 12 characteristics, including letter form, line form, and formatting.

Letter form includes the shape of letters, curve of letters, the angle or slant of letters, the proportional size of letters, and the use and appearance of connecting lines between letters. It also includes whether letters are shown correctly, such as a dotted "i" and a crossed "t."

Line form includes the smoothness of letters and the darkness of the lines on the upward compared to the downward stroke. Line form is influenced by the speed of writing and the pressure exerted while writing. The choice of writing instrument can also influence line form.

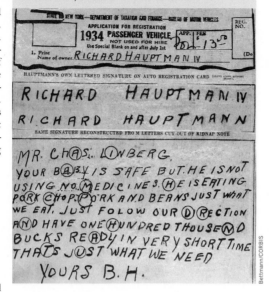

Figure 10-1 *Top: Hauptmann's printed signature from his automobile registration (exemplar); middle: enlargement of exemplar signature compared to signature made up of letters from ransom note; bottom: ransom note.*

Bettmann/CORBIS

Explore

Hauptmann's involvement in the Lindbergh crime has come into question because of the manner in which samples were collected and how the evidence was handled. Have students investigate the evidence against Hauptmann.

a. How many ransom notes were received?

b. What was used as an exemplar of Hauptmann's writing?

c. Was the sample long enough that it could be properly analyzed for handwriting analysis?

d. Was the handwriting analysis properly performed?

e. Have students review the Chapter 5 account of the case against Hauptmann. What other evidence was used to convict him?

f. Interested students may wish to investigate the case evidence further with sources listed in Chapter 5 or in the Gale Forensic Science eCollection.

Explore

Encourage interested students to research the Organization of Scientific Area Committees' (OSAC) subcommittee on questioned documents and their guidelines for handwriting analysis. Recommend that students report their findings to the class.

Evaluate

Ask students to review Figure 10-2 and then tell you which characteristics they think might be the most significant to forensic document investigators. Ask students which of the characteristics in the table could be measured or quantified to increase evidence reliability.

Formatting includes the spacing between letters, the spacing between words and lines, the placement of words on a line, and the margins a writer leaves empty on a page. Some characteristics studied by handwriting experts are shown in Figure 10-2.

Figure 10-2 *Characteristics of handwriting (continued on following page).*

Characteristic	Description	Example
Line quality	Do the letters flow, or are they erratic or shaky?	*forensic science* *forensic science*
Spacing	Are letters equally spaced or crowded?	*The right of the people to be* *The right of the people to be secure in their* *The right of the people to be secure in their*
Size consistency	Is the ratio of height to width consistent?	*The Right of the People* *The Right of the People* *The Right of the People*
Continuous	Is the writing continuous or does the writer lift the pen?	*forensic science* *forensic science*
Connecting letters	Are uppercase and lowercase letters connected and continuous?	*The Right of the* *The Right of the*

Characteristic	Description	Example
Letters complete	Are letters completely formed? Or is part of the letter missing?	*the right of the people* *the right of the people*
Cursive and printed letters	Are there printed letters, cursive letters, or both?	*Forensic Science* *Forensic Science* *Forensic Science*
Pen pressure	Is pressure equal when applied to upward and downward strokes?	*forensic science* *forensic science* *forensic science*
Slant	Left, right, or variable?	*forensic science* *forensic science* *forensic science*
Line habits	Is the text on the line, above the line, or below the line?	*forensic science* *forensic science* *forensic science*
Fancy curls or loops	Are there fancy curls?	*Forensic Science*
Placement of crosses on t's and dots on i's	Correct or misplaced? Are t's crossed, crossed in the middle, toward the top, or toward the bottom? Are i's dotted, dotted toward the right, left, or centered?	*right right right right*

Explore
Ask students to share times they wrote their signature or other writing differently than they normally do. Why did they do it?

DIFFERENTIATED LEARNING

Teaching At-Risk Students
Some at-risk students have handwriting problems. During discussions of handwriting and activities using samples, encourage students to accept differences among handwriting styles.

HANDWRITING ANALYSIS *Obj. 10.1*

The goal of forensic handwriting analysis is to answer questions about a suspicious document and determine authorship. Analysis is based on the principle of identification in that "two writings are the product of one person if the similarities…are… [unique] and there are no fundamental unexplainable differences." (See Figure 10-3.)

Analyzing a Handwriting Sample

Forensic analysis of handwriting may be done either to solve a crime or to evaluate a suspected forgery. A **forgery** is a document made or altered with the intent to deceive. There are four basic steps in the process of analyzing a handwriting sample.

If no exemplar of a person's writing exists, then a writing sample of a person that can be used as an exemplar may be requested. The writer should always be supervised during the production of an exemplar so that there is no doubt as to who wrote it. Do not inform the suspect that the sample will be analyzed or he or she may try to disguise the writing. Note that exemplars that are dictated are often more natural than those obtained from copying a document.

Control as many variables as possible when requesting an exemplar to compare with a questioned item. For example, try to supply the same paper type, writing implement, and/or ink type; request the same letters and numbers; and dictate similar passages to the writer.

The characteristics of the questioned item are compared with the new exemplar. Then, experts determine which characteristics are valuable for drawing a conclusion about the authenticity and authorship of the questioned document (Figure 10-4). Finally, the case is peer reviewed by another expert.

Highly trained document experts must consider many factors in their analyses. Experts even have ways of determining whether a person has tried to disguise his or her handwriting or to copy someone else's handwriting, known as a *conscious writing effort*. Many things can be done to minimize this conscious writing effort: (1) do not show the suspect the questioned or evidence document and (2) do not provide the suspect guidance in punctuation or spelling.

Figure 10-3 *Four signatures written by the same individual, demonstrating variation within an individual's handwriting.*

Courtesy of FBI

Figure 10-4 *A document expert analyzes the handwriting in a document.*

Michael Karison/Alamy

DIGGING DEEPER

With Forensic Science eCollection

Find out more about the future of handwriting analysis at the Gale Forensic Science eCollection at **ngl.cengage.com/forensicscience2e**.

Technology of Handwriting Analysis *Obj. 10.4*

Initial comparisons of documents are done with the unaided eye, a hand-held lens, or a microscope. Today, faster and more objective analysis is also available using technology that includes more statistical and quantitative analyses. Such technology includes infrared spectroscopes, biometric signature pads, and computerized analysis.

INFRARED SPECTROSCOPE

An infrared spectroscope can reveal if more than one kind of ink was used on a document because different inks absorb and reflect different wavelengths of light.

BIOMETRIC SIGNATURE PADS

The biometric pad, a new research tool, has been designed for identity authentification. The computerized pad records signature data based on the speed, pressure, and rhythm of signing your name (Figure 10-5), which are then analyzed by an expert. Forgeries can be recognized by slight differences that are detected by the pad.

COMPUTERIZED ANALYSIS

Computerized analysis of handwriting samples enables handwriting analysis to be faster and more objective. If the pen pressure is being reviewed, an examiner looking at the sample uses his or her subjective opinion.

The Forensic Information System for Handwriting (FISH) is a computerized handwriting database used and maintained by the Secret Service. Investigators scan in handwritten documents for a comparative analysis against other existing handwriting in the database. This system has verified that every writer is unique.

Figure 10-5 *Technology such as biometric signature pads allows for more accurate analyses of handwriting samples, such as at the grocery checkout line.*

ePad-i.d., Handwritten electronic capture device by Interlink Electronics, Inc.

MATHEMATICS

Handwriting Evidence in the Courtroom

After handwriting samples are analyzed and compared, the expert handwriting witness prepares a written report of the analysis to present to the court. Both the defense and prosecuting attorneys ask the handwriting experts questions about the analyses. The expert witness demonstrates how document comparisons are made and how he or she reached conclusions about the authorship of the questioned documents. The expert witness validates comparisons by showing the court examples of similarities or differences between the evidence and exemplar documents. In court, the expert must be able to defend his or her claims with strong factual evidence, because the defense will likely hire its own document examiner to try to refute the prosecution's expert witness.

Shortcomings of Handwriting Analysis *Obj. 10.2*

Although an experienced document expert detects many cases of forgery, he or she may occasionally fail to identify one. But the quality of the exemplar(s) often determines the quality of an analysis, and good exemplars may be difficult to obtain. For example, analysis errors have occurred

---

---

when the exemplar documents that experts used in their comparisons also turned out to be forgeries. Another limitation is the effects of mood, age, drugs, fatigue, and illness on a person's handwriting.

Handwriting analysis is ultimately subjective, relying on the expertise of the examiner. Its use in document analysis has become accepted in foren-sics alongside other evidence types. Programs have evolved to certify the training. The Board of Forensic Document Examiners (BFDE) offers such a training program. Although it is still important that handwriting evidence be used in combination with other sources of evidence, handwriting analy-sis is considered a reproducible and peer-reviewed process.

FORGERY   *Obj. 10.5, 10.6*

Forged documents might include checks, employment records, legal agreements, licenses, and wills. When expectation of financial gain accom-panies a forgery, it is called **fraudulence, or fraud.**

Forgery can be accomplished by altering documents in a number of ways.

- Erasure (removal): Mechanical erasures (e.g., a pencil eraser) alter paper fibers. Placed under a stereomicroscope, changes to paper fibers are evident where an erasure was made. Chemical erasure (e.g., bleach) is evident when the paper is exposed to ultraviolet or infrared light.
- Cross-outs: The use of solvents may expose writing that was crossed out.
- Additions: Exposure to ultraviolet or infrared light can distinguish between different inks that look the same to the unaided eye.
- Burning: Some inks and pencil leads burn more slowly than paper. Marks may be revealed if the burned document is exposed to oblique (angled) light.

Check Forgery

Americans write more than 70 billion checks a year. Approximately $27 million in illegitimate checks are cashed each day. Criminals can alter or acquire checks in many ways, including:

- Ordering someone else's checks from a deposit slip
- Directly altering a check
- Intercepting someone's check, altering it, and cashing it
- Creating forged checks from scratch

Reformed forger Frank Abagnale once said that the best way to deal with fraud is to prevent it from happening in the first place. How do companies protect themselves against forgeries? Several techniques are used to protect businesses, banks, and the public from forged and altered checks, as shown in Figure 10-6. However, these are all aspects of the document, and they require someone to be knowledgeable about these security features and to be willing to look for them. In their attempts to prevent check fraud, many banks hope to eventually eliminate checks altogether. In fact, many banks and credit unions encourage the use of debit or check cards and electronic bill payments for this very reason.

Did you know?

Indented paper is produced when someone writes on a pad and tears off the top document. Oblique light (held at an angle) may help make the writing vis-ible. Another method is the electrostatic detection appa-ratus (ESDA). The document is covered with plastic and is held tightly with a vacuum. A static charge is applied to the plastic. Toner is applied to the charged plastic and accumulates in the indentations, which can then be read and photographed.

Figure 10-6 *Methods used by banks to prevent check forgery.*

Print checks on chemically sensitive paper.
Use a large font size that requires more ink and makes alterations more difficult.
Use high-resolution borders on the checks that are difficult to copy.
Print checks in multiple color patterns.
Embed fibers in checks that glow under different types of lights.
Use chemical-wash detection systems that change color when a check is altered.

Literary Forgery

A literary forgery is a forged piece of historical writing, such as a letter from a famous person or a manuscript of an important work. Letters are often valuable if the writer was an important political figure, scientist, or literary figure. For example, a letter written by Abraham Lincoln, Albert Einstein, or Charles Darwin would be valuable because it might provide insight into the thinking of the writer (Figure 10-7).

The best literary forgers try to duplicate the original document, so the materials used are similar to those used in the original document. They do this by collecting old paper or old books, from which they can cut out properly aged paper for their forgeries. Because the process of papermaking has changed, it is essential for forgers to use aged paper to pass the microscopic examination tests. Inks have also changed, so careful forgers must mix their own inks from materials that were used at the time. Old watermarks (Figure 10-8) impressed in new paper may make paper seem as old as the document being forged. Handwriting tools and styles of penmanship popular in the historical era of the document being forged are used.

Documents are sometimes chemically treated to make them look older. Chemicals may be added to the paper to age both the paper and the ink. In the early 1980s, Mark Hofmann, a document dealer and forger, created several hundred forged documents using this method. One of Hofmann's most significant

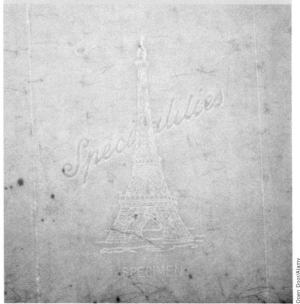

Figure 10-7 *Martin Coneely forged Lincoln's writing and signature, but was caught in 1937 and sent to prison for three years. His forgeries are collectors' items today! (This signature is a forgery.)*

Shawn Thew/epa/Corbis

Figure 10-8 *The Eiffel Tower image on this antique paper is a watermark impressed during the manufacturing process.*

Open Door/Alamy

HANDWRITING ANALYSIS, FORGERY, AND COUNTERFEITING **323**

Science

CHEMISTRY

CHEMISTRY

Model chromatography in class to illustrate that ink is a mixture of different colors. You will need a large test tube, saltwater solution (½ tsp of table salt in 100 mL of water), and a length of filter paper ½" by 5". Draw a line across the filter paper with a black transparency pen about an inch from the narrow edge. Add about ½" of salt water to the test tube and position the filter paper so the inked line is about ½" above the top of the salt water. In about 15 minutes, the black ink will separate into a series of color bands. The bands will always be the same sequence of colors for the same ink. This is analogous to the way document examiners distinguish different inks on altered documents, such as checks.

Explore

Have students research some of Martin Coneely's other forgeries.

Science

CHEMISTRY

CHEMISTRY

Investigators use several instruments to help them analyze the components of paper and ink. Have students research the instrumentation involved.

Evaluate

Show students several examples of watermarks. Ask them why they think companies use them. *(They are a type of trademark.)*

DIFFERENTIATED LEARNING

Teaching Gifted Students

Challenge students to design investigation protocols to investigate the effects on documents of

1. mechanical erasures (under a stereomicroscope or hand lens)

2. the effects of chemical erasures (using ultraviolet light)

3. other types of erasures (using different inks and ultraviolet light).

Consider running the best protocols as class demonstrations.

DIGGING DEEPER
With Forensic Science eCollection

Research the 1875 Shakespeare forgeries by Englishman William Henry Ireland using the Gale Forensic Science eCollection at **ngl.cengage.com/forensicscience2e**. Ireland claimed that he had acquired an authentic handwritten manuscript of Shakespeare's known as *Kynge Leare*. Cite some of the evidence discovered by scholarly investigators that showed that this and other documents presented by Ireland were forgeries. Discuss how Ireland obtained the antique paper and ink to create the manuscript. Discover how he evaluated the credibility of the paper and writings he produced.

CHEMISTRY

forgeries was his creation of 116 pages of a supposedly lost Mormon document. He sold this document to a Mormon collector. Hofmann also forged works attributed to Emily Dickinson, Abraham Lincoln, and Mark Twain. In 1985, Hofmann devised a plan to forge another collection of Mormon documents. Unable to produce the forgeries in time, he used a bomb to buy time and escape detection. His bombs killed Mormon business leader Steven Christensen and Kathy Sheets. A third bomb exploded unexpectedly in Hofmann's car, injuring him. Hofmann was tried and convicted of forgery and murder and is currently serving his life sentence. Figure 10-9 shows Hofmann after his arrest, with injured hands.

Figure 10-9 *An injured Mark Hofmann is arrested for murder.*

AP Images/The Desert News

Did you know

U.S. law enforcement agencies estimate that companies lose approximately $400 billion to $450 billion annually to counterfeiters.

COUNTERFEITING

Obj. 10.6, 10.7

Counterfeiting is typically the forging of **currency** (bills or coins), but it can also be the production of fake name-brand products for the purpose of deception and profit. Other examples of counterfeited items include coins and postage stamps. Counterfeiting of money is one of the oldest crimes. Under U.S. law, counterfeiting is a federal felony punishable with up to 15 years in prison. The U.S. Secret Service is the federal agency in charge of investigating counterfeit U.S. currency.

324   CHAPTER 10

Counterfeit Currency

In the past, with access to a scanner and color printer, it was not very difficult to create counterfeit currency. Scanning could pick up the intricate lines and details found on currency. The Secret Service, with the aid of technology, has added features to paper currency that, when scanned, prevent the currency from being copied. If the currency was successfully scanned, a counterfeiter would still encounter difficulty printing it, even with the most sophisticated printers (Figures 10-10 and 10-11). Counterfeit money also feels different because real money is printed on special paper. In fact, the most common characteristic that leads people to suspect fakes and scrutinize money is because it doesn't feel right. The paper itself is therefore the most important security feature.

The government continues to change the design of paper money to make currency more difficult to copy and to prevent counterfeiting. A series of currency changes began with a revision to the $20 bill (2003) followed by the $50 bill, $10 bill, $5 bill, and finally the $100 bill (2013). The safeguards built into the design of the $100 bill make it the most costly to produce. In Activity 10-3, you will make observations about the redesigned bills.

Detecting Counterfeit Currency

It is relatively easy to detect counterfeit currency. Counterfeit-detecting pens are inexpensive special pens and markers containing the element iodine. When they come in contact with a counterfeit bill, the paper marked with the pen will change to a bluish-black color. The color change is caused by a chemical reaction involving starch, a compound found in regular paper. By contrast, real currency does not contain starch because it is printed on stock made of plant fibers such as cotton and linen. When real money is marked with the counterfeit-detecting pen, the pen will leave a pale yellow color on the bill, which fades within a very short time. Figure 10-12 shows features found in authentic currency.

The pen manufacturers claim the counterfeit-detecting pen is 98% effective. However, the U.S. government does not concede this level of effectiveness and uses additional criteria for judging whether currency is counterfeit. These criteria are important, because some counterfeiters actually bleach small bills to provide the correct paper for use. For example, a counterfeiter might bleach a $1 bill for reprinting into a $50 or $100 denomination. This bill will pass the counterfeit-pen test, but will not duplicate some of the other safety measures found in real U.S. currency.

There is currently a global movement to change to stock made of polymer, a type of plastic. Currency made of plastic is much more difficult to counterfeit, less expensive to produce, and more durable. Canada, Australia, and Great Britain (2016) have begun producing plastic (polymer) money to replace paper bills. The United States has chosen to continue to produce money on paper and cloth stock.

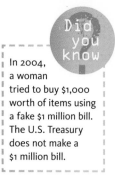

Did you know

In 2004, a woman tried to buy $1,000 worth of items using a fake $1 million bill. The U.S. Treasury does not make a $1 million bill.

CHEMISTRY

Did you know

Newer photocopiers will not copy paper money actual size. If money is legally copied, it must be either larger (150%) or smaller (75%) than the actual bill size, copied in black and white, and one-sided only.

Science
CHEMISTRY

CHEMISTRY
When starch is mixed with iodine and water, iodine ions move into the structure of the larger starch molecule, producing a blue-black color. This reaction is very useful as an indicator in certain redox titrations, because the color change happens quickly and is easy to identify.

Teaching Tip
Show the History Channel *Modern Marvels* video *Making Money*, which traces the production path of our currency from old blue jeans to printed bills: www.history.com

Explore
Ask students if they have ever seen a cashier hold currency up to the light or use a pen on a $50 bill. Ask students to explain what they were checking.

DIFFERENTIATED LEARNING

Teaching Gifted Students
Ask students to design a new $10 bill that would be difficult to duplicate. What safeguards do they think the bill should include?

Explore

Have students discover for themselves the many "hidden" images and security features of redesigned U. S. currency. Provide students with ultraviolet lights so they can examine currency from their own wallets. Alternately, have students view the Website tutorial www.newmoney.gov individually, or as a class.

Figure 10-10 *AUTHENTIC BILL: Different parts of paper money contain tiny, intricate lines and details that may scan but will not print well.*

Figure 10-11 *FORGED BILL: As you can see, the tiny, intricate lines and details on paper money do not print well on counterfeit bills printed from scanned images.*

Figure 10-12 *Features found in authentic currency that make counterfeiting money difficult.*

Number	Some Features Found in Authentic Currency
1	Portrait stands out from the background and appears raised off the paper
2	There is minute microprinting on the security threads, as well as around the portrait.
3	Serial number is evenly spaced and the same color as the Treasury seal
4	Check Letter and Quadrant Number
5, 6	Federal Reserve seal (5) no sharp points, and Treasury seal (6) with clear, sharp sawtooth points
7	Clear red and blue fibers are woven throughout the bill. The security thread is evident when exposed to a UV light. It consists of a thin, embedded vertical line or strip with the denomination of the bill written in it.
8	Federal Reserve Number and Letter
9	Series
10	Check Letter and Face Plate Number
11	Watermark appears on the right side of the portrait of the bill in the light
12	When a new series bill is tilted, the number in the lower-right corner makes a color shift from copper to green resulting from color-shifting ink.
13	Clear, distinct background details and lines
14	Clear, distinct border edge

DIFFERENTIATED LEARNING

Teaching English-Language Learners and At-Risk Students
Before proceeding, clarify the following terms for students:
1. watermark
2. serial number
3. Federal Reserve
4. U. S. Treasury seal

DIFFERENTIATED LEARNING

Teaching Gifted Students
Encourage motivated students to research the production of U. S. paper currency, including the following questions: Who makes the stock? What is it made of? Who prints the currency? When is more currency printed? What is the Federal Reserve's role in the printing of currency?

Teaching Tip

In December 2013, Great Britain joined Canada and Australia in the production of currency on plastic (polymer) stock. More than 20 other countries already use plastic currency.

Improvements:
- More difficult to counterfeit
- Bill lasts longer
- Bill appears cleaner

Drawbacks:
- Bills have unfamiliar texture
- Difficult to fold
- Bill is slippery and falls out of pockets
- Bills "jump" out of cash registers
- Bills stick together

Close

Ask students how forensic analysis of questioned documents and counterfeiting has improved over the past 100 years. What role has technology played in this improvement?

SUMMARY

Plastic money from Canada.

© iStock.com/powerofforever

LITERACY

Robert K. Wittman's book *Priceless* describes his work as founder of the FBI's Art Crime Team.

- Fraudulence, or fraud, is attempting to get financial or other gain from forgery.

- Handwriting analysis by document experts is the examination of questioned documents compared with exemplars to establish the authenticity and/or authorship of the documents.

- Document experts use their expertise along with scientific methods and technology to compare handwriting characteristics of a questioned document to those of an exemplar to help identify authors and detect any alterations, erasures, and obliterations.

- Handwriting analysis has always been an important tool, especially for forensic scientists. Handwriting experts help financial, legal, and governmental institutions, as well as the general public, detect and prevent forgery, counterfeiting, and other fraudulent crimes.

- Technological advances, such as biometric signature pads and the infrared spectroscope, have improved objectivity, increased quantitative analysis, and enhanced the detection of forged documents.

- Countries, including the United States, continue to refine methods to protect their currency from counterfeiters, changing designs and experimenting with different stocks.

CASE STUDIES

John Magnuson
(1922)

A package mailed to the rural home of James Chapman exploded as he unwrapped it. Chapman's wife, Clementine, was killed, and James was injured. John Magnuson, a neighbor, was a suspect because he had recently quarreled with Chapman over property drainage rights. Handwriting analyst John Tyrell was called in to analyze the handwriting on the package. He concluded that Magnuson's handwriting was consistent with the handwriting on the package. In addition, many of the misspellings were phonetic spellings a person of Swedish ancestry might use. John Magnuson was the only person of Swedish ancestry in the area and lived less than four miles from Chapman's home. The pen point and ink mixture used on the bomb's label also matched supplies found at Magnuson's house. Magnuson was sentenced to life imprisonment.

The Hitler Diaries
(1981)

In February 1981, three diaries supposedly written by Adolf Hitler appeared. Document experts compared them with exemplars (that later proved to be forged) and declared them to be authentic. A bidding war followed, with the price of some of the supposed "Hitler Diaries" reaching $3.75 million. Eventually, the inauthentic paper, ink, and glue exposed the hoax. A paper whitener found in many of the pages of the documents had not been developed until nine years after the war ended, long after Hitler committed suicide. The inks used were also from the postwar era. It was determined that the documents had been written less than a year before their discovery. Konrad Kujau, the West German memorabilia dealer who had written and forged the diaries, was located and imprisoned for four years. The hoax was said to have cost more than $16 million in lost revenues to those who had purchased the alleged diaries.

The fake "Hitler Diaries" of the early 1980s set the standard for literary hoaxes. The diaries were at best an amateur job by forger Konrad Kujau. So, how did they acquire such world-wide fame? Go to the Gale Forensic Science eCollection on **ngl.cengage .com/forensicscience2e** and research the Hitler Diaries. Make your own investigation by examining the primary sources available online. Write a summary of the case that covers (1) the motives of the forger, (2) the involvement of the German magazine *Stern*, (3) the forgery errors that were uncovered during the analysis of the diaries, and (4) the information that was unveiled at the trial.

Explore
Ask a lawyer to come to class and discuss legal issues that arise over questioned documents. What type of documents are questioned? How are the documents analyzed? What changes has the lawyer seen during his/her career regarding the court acceptance of document analysis?

DIGGING DEEPER
In Digging Deeper, students were asked to research the forged diaries of Adolf Hitler. Interested students may want to do further research to see if diaries of other famous people have been forged.

Explore
Invite a bank teller to class to explain what training is given and what measures are taken to ensure that tellers recognize and reject counterfeit bills.

Careers *in Forensics*

Lloyd Cunningham, Document Expert

Lloyd Cunningham is the world's leading handwriting expert of San Francisco's famous fugitive killer known as the Zodiac. The Zodiac, a serial killer who has never been identified, mocked the police with handwritten notes describing his crimes. For more than 25 years, Cunningham has analyzed documents from potential suspects that are submitted by police officers, news reporters, and detectives, hoping to identify the elusive Zodiac killer. Cunningham carefully analyzes the handwriting of each submitted sample and compares it to Zodiac's original documents with hopes of finding clues and answers.

Lloyd Cunningham first became interested in the Zodiac case as a San Francisco police officer. In 1969, he was among the many police officers who came to Presidio Park following the shooting of cab driver Paul Stine, the last of the Zodiac's verified victims. Cunningham eventually trained with the U.S. Secret Service. In 1980, he became the U.S. Secret Service's first forensic document examiner. He began investigating Zodiac soon after he finished his forensic training. Since then, Cunningham has analyzed hundreds of famous documents, including the ransom letter in the JonBenet Ramsey case. He retired in

A Zodiac letter.

1991, but has continued to work on the Zodiac case as a private consultant.

Over the years, Cunningham has memorized Zodiac's handwriting, including his unique letter formations and style of formatting. So, how does Lloyd Cunningham determine if a newly submitted Zodiac sample is just another hoax? Cunningham says, "There's a rhythm in writing; when people jot notes or sign documents, they write quickly and confidently. But if someone tries to copy or disguise their handwriting, it's no longer spontaneous, and an expert can see signs of the effort in the script." Cunningham explains his lack of frustration in the never-ending supply of new samples because "Who knows? Maybe one of them is right."

There is no college degree in forensic document examination. Although a degree is not required, many investigators earn a degree in science and acquire training in technological document analysis. Many skills in document analysis must be acquired through job experience. With a college degree, a candidate is eligible for a certified training program in a government crime laboratory.

Learn More About It
▶ To learn more about the work of a document expert or handwriting analyst, go to **ngl.cengage.com/forensicscience2e**.

APPS

UV Lamp Money Scans currency, searching for the security thread embedded in a bill

Careers

Being a document expert requires many skills. Patience and skill in identifying patterns are extremely important when analyzing a document. Ask students to do an Internet search on the term "document expert" to find out the kind of training it requires and possible salaries.

For more information on the work of document experts, go to http://www.fbi.gov/about-us/lab/scientific-analysis/qdu

True or False

1. There are only 10 major categories of handwriting characteristics. *Obj. 10.1*

2. To prevent forgery, some checks have embedded fibers that glow under special lights. *Obj. 10.5*

3. Evidence handwriting may be compared to pre-existing exemplars of someone's handwriting or requested exemplars of their writing. *Obj. 10.1*

4. Only advanced age can affect someone's handwriting. *Obj. 10.1, 10.2*

5. Some forgers apply chemicals to paper to make a document look older than it is. *Obj. 10.3*

6. A biometric pad measures the speed, rhythm, and pressure of handwriting. *Obj. 10.4*

7. The Secret Service is charged with the security of U.S. currency. *Obj. 10.6*

8. Document experts analyze paper and ink as well as the writing to determine authenticity. *Obj. 10.2, 10.3, 10.5, 10.6*

Short Answer

9. Describe three different characteristics of handwriting that experts analyze during a forensic investigation. *Obj. 10.1*

10. List five suggestions as to how requested handwriting exemplars should be taken to ensure reliable and authentic samples. *Obj. 10.1*

11. Describe some of the technologies used by document experts to analyze handwriting. *Obj. 10.4*

12. Suppose you found a new $100 bill on the street. List the characteristics you would check to determine if the bill was real. *Obj. 10.6*

13. Refer to the handwriting samples on the right, written by two different people. *Obj. 10.1*

    Sample 1   Sample 2

    Courtesy, FBI

    - Make a table describing the similarities and differences between sample 1 and sample 2.

    - Describe the handwriting characteristics shown that could be quantified (measured).

    - Do you have sufficient evidence to determine if the handwriting samples are consistent? Explain.

Further Research and Extensions

Have students investigate each of the following court decisions and summarize how each affected the admission of handwriting evidence (expert witness testimony).

a. 1923 *Frye vs. United States*

b. 1975 Federal Rules of Evidence

c. 1993 *Daubert vs. Merrell Dow Pharmaceutical*

d. 1999 *U.S. Supreme Court: Kumho Tire Company vs. Carmichael*

Chapter 10 Review

True or False

1. False
2. True
3. True
4. False
5. True
6. True
7. True
8. True

Short Answer

9. Sample answer: spacing between letters, whether letters flow or are erratic, and if the ratio of letter height to width is consistent.

10. Answers will vary; samples: the writer should not realize an exemplar is being taken; it should be at least one page long; dictate the words, do not allow the writer to copy them; supply ink and paper similar to the evidence documents; include common letters and numbers similar to ones used in the questioned document; take more than one sample.

11. Sample answer: Biometric signature pads help authenticate signatures. Computerized handwriting analysis helps identify individual samples by using pen pressure comparisons.

12. Answers will vary. Consult Figure 10-12 for a list of features.
    - Answers will vary, but should include characteristics in Figure 10-2.
    - Answers will vary; samples: ratio of uppercase letters to lowercase letters; spaces between letters; angle of slant—right, left, or straight; how far away from the line the letters are.
    - No; there is insufficient evidence.

Going Further

1. Evidence reliability of handwriting analysis is sometimes debated. Find and read one article from a scholarly source that claims handwriting analysis is not reliable and another that says handwriting analysis is reliable. For each article do the following: *Obj. 10.1, 10.2*

   a. State the claim made by the author of the article regarding handwriting reliability.

   b. Cite at least two different sources of evidence in the article.

   c. Outline the reasoning used in each source.

   d. Choose one of the articles to evaluate how strongly the evidence supported the author's claim.

2. Research and report on the recent advances in biometric signature pads. *Obj. 10.4*

Bibliography

Books and Journals

Abagnale, Frank W. *The Art of the Steal: How to Protect Yourself and Your Business from Fraud, America's #1 Crime*. New York: Broadway, 2002.

Abagnale, Frank W. *Real U Guide to Identity Theft*. Real U Guides, 2004.

Deaver, Jeffrey. *The Devil's Teardrop*. New York, NY: Pocket Books, 2000.

Dolnick, Edward. *Stealing the Scream*. UK: Icon Books, 2005.

Grebanier, Bernard. *The Great Shakespeare Forgery*. Portsmouth, NH: Heinemann, 1966.

Haring J. Vreeland. *Hand of Hauptmann: The Handwriting Expert Tells the Story of the Lindbergh Case*. Montclair, NJ: Patterson Smith (reprint), 1937.

Harrison, Diana, et al. "Handwriting Examination: Meeting the Challenges of Science and the Law." *Forensic Science Communications*. 2009:11(4).

Magnuson, Ed. "Hitler's Forged Diaries." *Time*, May 16, 1983, 36–47.

Perenyi, Ken. *Caveat Emptor: The Secret Life of an American Art Forger*. New York, NY: Pegasus Books, 2012.

Sillitoe, Linda, and Allen D. Roberts, *Salamander: The Story of the Mormon Forgery Murders*. Salt Lake City: Signature, 1988.

Wittman, Robert. *Priceless*. New York, NY: Crown Publishers, 2010.

Internet Resources

ngl.cengage.com/forensicscience2e (Gale Forensic Science eCollection)

http://www.lib.udel.edu/ud/spec/exhibits/forgery/wise.htm

http://www.crimelibrary.com/criminal_mind/scams/shakespeare/6.html

http://www.secretservice.gov/money_detect.shtml

http://www.myhandwriting.com/celebs/ransom1.html

http://www.csad.ox.ac.uk/CSAD/newsletters/newsletter10/newsletter10c.html

http://www.celebritymorgue.com/lindbergh-baby/

http://www.pbs.org/wgbh/nova/vinland/fakes.html

http://www.nytimes.com/2013/12/19/business/international/britain-to-join-ranks-of-nations-using-plastic-currency.html?_r=0

http://www.telegraph.co.uk/finance/currency/10299039/Plastic-fantastic-six-countries-that-use-polymer-banknotes.html

http://www.nist.gov/forensics/upload/The_Future_State_of_Handwriting_Examinations.pdf-64k-2014-03-05

http://www.history.com/showsmodern-marvels/videos/making-money

http://www.fbi.gov/about-us/lab/scientific-analysis/qdu (Questioned Documents Unit)

http://www.newmoney.gov

http://forensic-evidence.com/site/ID/handwrtg_prime_ID.html

Further Research and Extensions

Review the proceedings of the NIST 2013 conference on the Future of Handwriting Analysis.

- What new automated technologies are being considered for use in handwriting analysis?
- What new quantitative measurements can be taken when analyzing handwriting samples?

Handwriting Analysis *Obj. 10.1, 10.2*

Objectives:

By the end of this activity, you will be able to:

1. Describe 12 different characteristics used in handwriting analysis.
2. Analyze your own handwriting sample and that of a classmate using 12 characteristics.

Time Required to Complete Activity: 45 minutes

Materials:

(per student)
Act 10-1 SH
pencils and lined paper
colored pencils or highlighters
ruler (mm) or calipers
protractor
one handwriting sample provided by student
one sample of another student's handwriting

SAFETY PRECAUTIONS:
None

Procedure:

PART 1: ANALYSIS OF YOUR OWN HANDWRITING

1. Obtain a copy of your handwriting exemplar from your instructor.
2. Review the descriptions and examples of 12 handwriting characteristics found in Data Table 1.
3. Use Figure 10-2 as a guide to analyze your own handwriting, and complete Data Table 1.
   a. Use highlighters or colored pencils to circle letters, words, or lines that demonstrate unusual characteristics or traits.
   b. For some characteristics, it is important that you use a ruler or a caliper to measure the letters or spacing. For example, for characteristic 2, you will need to measure the spacing between words. Include your measurements under the description heading.
   c. You will need to complete all of Data Table 1 as you analyze the handwriting using the different characteristics.

Additional activities for this chapter can be found in the IRCD, Chapter 10.

Background

Students will familiarize themselves with exemplars and use handwriting characteristics to evaluate their own handwriting and that of a classmate.

Time Required to Complete Activity
40 minutes

Safety Precautions
There are no safety precautions for this activity.

Procedures

1. Print, copy, and distribute Act 10-1 SH from the IRCD, Chapter 10.

2. Make sure students read all directions *before* beginning the activity.

3. The handwriting samples should be obtained in advance of this activity without the students' knowledge of how they will be used.

4. Have each student sign his or her name on the back of each copy.

   This writing sample can also be photocopied and saved for use in Activity 10-2.

Remind students to measure the characteristics whenever possible and note the measurements in the data tables.

Teaching Tip

Avoid using handwriting samples from students in the same class. Inform students that this is the case, as well, avoiding students disrupting the activity to inquire who has their writing sample.

Teaching Tip
Remember to

obtain writing samples that are at least one full page long. Include in the writing sample upper- and lowercase letters and numerals The Fourth Amendment can be used, but longer samples with more numerals would be better for analysis. Students should not be aware that they are supplying a writing sample that will be analyzed. Printing or cursive will work.

Data Table 1: Analysis of Your Own Handwriting

Characteristic	Yes	No	Comments (and measurements in mm) if Required
1. Is line quality smooth?			
2. Are words and margins evenly spaced?			Margins: Words:
3. Is the ratio of lowercase to uppercase letters consistent? What is the ratio?			
4. Is the writing continuous?			
5. Are uppercase and lowercase letters connected?			
6. Are letters complete?			(If not, specify which letters.)
7. Is all of the writing cursive?			(If not, specify which words.)
8. Is the pen pressure the same throughout?			
9. Do all letters slant to the right?			
10. Are all letters written on the line?			
11. Are there fancy curls or loops?			(Which letters?)
12. Are all i's and t's dotted and crossed? (top, middle, or not)			i's t's

Procedure:

PART 2: ANALYSIS OF A CLASSMATE'S HANDWRITING

1. After completing the analysis of your own handwriting, exchange a second, unmarked handwriting sample with a classmate.
2. Analyze a classmate's handwriting by completing Data Table 2. Be sure to use highlighters or colored pencils to mark any unusual characteristics. Include measurements where necessary.
3. After completing the analysis, answer the questions on the following page.

Data Table 2: Analysis of Your Partner's Handwriting

Characteristic	Yes	No	Comments (and measurements in mm) if Required
1. Is line quality smooth?			
2. Are words and margins evenly spaced?			Margins: Words:
3. Is the ratio of lowercase to uppercase letters consistent?			
4. Is the writing continuous?			
5. Are uppercase and lowercase letters connected?			
6. Are letters complete?			(If not, specify which letters.)
7. Is all of the writing cursive?			(If not, specify which words.)
8. Is the pen pressure the same throughout?			
9. Do all letters slant to the right?			
10. Are all letters written on the line?			
11. Are there fancy curls or loops?			(Which letters?)
12. Are all i's and t's dotted and crossed?			i's t's

Questions:

1. Were the handwriting samples of you and your partner similar, or could you easily tell that the two samples were from different people by simply glancing at them? Explain.
2. Review your data tables of the two handwriting analyses. Did the two handwriting samples have any characteristics that were consistent? Explain your answer.
3. Review your data tables and state which characteristics of your own handwriting were very different from your partner's handwriting.
4. Did any handwriting characteristics found in either of the samples seem to be very unusual and perhaps able to help easily identify any other handwriting samples written by either you or your classmate? If so, describe the characteristic.
5. Unique letter combinations are another characteristic that could be added to the list of characteristics used for handwriting analysis. For example, many people have distinctive ways of writing double Ls, as in the word *galloping*. Other people may have a unique way of writing the letters "th," such as in the words *the, them,* or *their.* Describe a different example of characteristics that you would like to see added to the 12 used in this activity.

Answer

Check students' data tables.

Questions

1. Answers will vary, but students should refer to the characteristics.
2. Answers will vary, but students should refer to the characteristics.
3. Answers will vary.
4. Answers will vary.
5. Answers will vary. Sample answer: the way different people write numbers.

Further Research and Extensions

Interested students may want to try doing this activity with a brother, sister, or parent. Afterward, ask them to answer these questions:

- How does your handwriting compare to that of your family member?
- Do you think handwriting patterns are inherited or learned? Explain your answer.

Background

In this activity, students take part in a real-life scenario in which handwriting analysis of a document is crucial. They are required to document their conclusions in a written report to a jury.

Time Required to Complete Activity

Two 40-minute periods are required to analyze the ransom note and the six suspect handwriting samples. Additional time is required to prepare the written report.

Safety Precautions

There are no safety precautions for this activity.

Teaching Tips

- Provide the class with identical lined paper, and have them write their names on the back.
- Obtain the writing samples from students well before you plan to introduce handwriting analysis. Be prepared with a cover story as to why you are asking students to copy the amendment. (The amendment is available on the IRCD, Chapter 10.) If students know you will be analyzing their handwriting, they will not use their normal, spontaneous handwriting!
- Do not give the handwriting samples from one class back to the same class. Use those from a different class.
- From the class set of handwriting samples, you will need to select six. Be sure to have two samples that look somewhat similar. Label each sample with a suspect number, 1 through 6. Be sure you keep a record of whose handwriting sample was used for each of the suspects.
- You will need to quietly inform one of the students that you are using his or her writing sample, because that person will need to copy the ransom note (in the IRCD).

Analysis Of Ransom Note and Report to Jury

Obj. 10.1, 10.2

Objectives:

By the end of this activity, you will be able to:

1. Analyze the six suspects' requested exemplars and compare them to the handwriting on the ransom note.
2. Make a claim supported by evidence as to whether you found any of the suspect's handwriting samples consistent with the ransom note.
3. Present your analysis in a written report that could be submitted to a jury.

Scenario:

Someone abducted a 10-year-old child from a well-to-do, private, residential school. His wealthy and famous parents received a ransom note requesting a large sum of money in exchange for the safe return of their son. They immediately contacted the police and provided the ransom note.

The police received a lead implicating a group of six young men, who were taken to the police station for questioning. The six men were separated so that they could not collaborate on their story. Police asked them to write down their whereabouts for the past 48 hours. The police needed a handwriting exemplar from each of the men.

When the police obtained the six handwriting exemplars, they called in a renowned handwriting expert (you!) to analyze the ransom notes and the six suspect exemplars. Were any of the exemplars consistent with the handwriting in the ransom note?

Time Required to Complete Activity:

Two 40-minute periods are required to analyze the ransom note and the six suspects' exemplars. Additional time is required to prepare the written report.

Materials:

(per teams of 2 students)
Act 10-2 SH
6 different handwriting samples
1 ransom note
protractor
1 six-inch ruler (with millimeter markings) or calipers
several colored pencils or highlighters

SAFETY PRECAUTIONS:
None

Be sure to choose a student you can trust, because the student will need to keep this secret.
- In advance, you will need to photocopy class sets of the ransom note for each team. Also, after the samples are taken, you will need to photocopy the packets of the six suspects' writing samples and staple them together. One packet can be handed to each team.
- Each student should prepare his or her findings in a written report. The handwriting packets with the circled or highlighted findings should be included with the written report.

- You may also have one or more teams present their findings to the "jury" (the rest of the class). The students presenting their findings should be prepared with visuals in the form of projected images with an overhead projector, flex camera, PowerPoint presentation, or poster and/or charts that demonstrate their analysis. You could appoint three other students to act as the prosecuting attorney, the defendant's attorney, and the judge.
- Have multiple blank copies of Data Tables 1 and 2 and the Visual Elimination Form available for student use.

Procedure:

1. Study the ransom note provided by your instructor. Perform an analysis of the handwriting sample using the 12 characteristics in Figure 10-2. Record your findings in Act 10-2 SH Data Table 1.

2. Examine the six suspects' exemplars. Exclude any exemplars that are obviously dissimilar to the ransom note. For those exemplars that are not obviously different from to the ransom note, perform a handwriting analysis using the 12 different handwriting characteristics in the data tables. Record your results in a separate data table for each suspect's exemplar.

3. After analyzing the ransom note and the six suspects' handwriting samples, determine which suspect's handwriting, if any, is consistent with the handwriting of the ransom note. Support your claims with data from your analysis. You will need to present your findings in a written report to be submitted to the jury.

Written Report

1. The purpose of the written report is to convince members of a jury that you have used reliable analytical techniques and arrived at valid conclusions.

2. Citing evidence from your analysis, you will explain to the jury how the handwriting samples are consistent or inconsistent with the ransom note.

3. Keep in mind that most juries have no knowledge of handwriting analysis. They may be highly educated, or they may have very little formal education. Therefore, any terms you use must be clearly defined.

4. Your report should be typed and spell-checked.

5. Print a rough draft. Ask a partner to proofread your rough draft and help you correct and edit it. Your editor should sign the bottom of your rough draft after editing.

6. Submit both the edited rough draft and your final copy.

The format for your written report to the jury is outlined as follows:

I. Introduction (10 points)
   a. State the purpose of your report.
   b. No detailed information should be in the introduction.
   c. State how you analyzed the handwriting.
     • State how many different characteristics you used.
     • State if you concluded that any of the exemplars was consistent with the handwriting on the ransom note.

II. Body paragraphs (at least six) (60 points)
   a. One main idea or characteristic in each paragraph (at least six)
   b. For each characteristic, you need to do the following:
     • Describe the characteristic.
     • Compare and contrast the characteristic of the handwriting on the ransom note with the handwriting of the suspect's exemplar.
     • Convince the jury that your comparisons are valid and well-supported by evidence.

Procedures

1. Print, copy, and distribute Act 10-2 SH from the IRCD, Chapter 10.

2. Make sure students read all directions *before* beginning the activity.

3. Review the lab report outline with students, and explain what you will be looking for when you grade their reports.

4. If time permits, students may want to do a mock trial using their testimony.

5. Remind students to use colored pencils or a highlighting pen to mark any consistent characteristics shared by a suspect's sample and the ransom note.

Teaching Tip

Print Act 10-2 SH, the ransom note analysis table, on colored paper.

Invite a lawyer or judge to speak to the class about courtroom testimony of expert witnesses.

Example: Characteristic 3
- State the ratio of lowercase letters to uppercase (capital) letters.
- State whether the ratio is consistent throughout the document.

III. Conclusion (10 points)
  a. Summarize your findings.
  b. Do not repeat detailed information.
  c. How reliable is your conclusion?
  d. Is handwriting evidence enough to convict someone?
  e. Is this an important piece of evidence?

Data Table 1: Ransom Note Analysis

Characteristic	Yes	No	Comments (and measurements in mm) if Required
1. Is line quality smooth?			
2. Are words and margins evenly spaced?			Margins: Words:
3. Is the ratio of lowercase to uppercase letters consistent?			
4. Is the writing continuous?			
5. Are uppercase and lowercase letters connected?			
6. Are letters complete?			(If not, specify which letters.)
7. Is all of the writing cursive?			(If not, specify which words.)
8. Is the pen pressure the same throughout?			
9. Do all letters slant to the right?			
10. Are all letters written on the line?			
11. Are there fancy curls or loops?			(Which letters?)
12. Are all i's and t's dotted and crossed?			i's t's

Further Investigation and Extensions

Ask a social studies teacher to work with you in preparing students for a trial. If any students have been involved with mock trials, elicit their expertise.

Data Table 2: Suspect ___ Note Analysis

Characteristic	Yes	No	Comments (and measurements in mm) If Required
1. Is line quality smooth?			
2. Are words and margins evenly spaced?			Margins: Words:
3. Is the ratio of lowercase to uppercase letters consistent? What is the ratio?			
4. Is the writing continuous?			
5. Are uppercase and lowercase letters connected?			
6. Are letters complete?			(If not, specify which letters.)
7. Is all of the writing cursive?			(If not, specify which words.)
8. Is the pen pressure the same throughout?			
9. Do all letters slant to the right?			
10. Are all letters written on the line?			
11. Are there fancy curls or loops?			(Which letters?)
12. Are all i's and t's dotted and crossed? (top, middle, or not)			i's t's

Visual Elimination Format

If any of the suspects' exemplars can be quickly eliminated without performing a 12-characteristic analysis, you will need to justify your elimination with a brief statement explaining why the handwriting is obviously not the same as the handwriting found in the ransom note. Use the following format, which you can find on the Act 10-2 Elimination Form.

Suspect _____

Reasons for quickly eliminating this suspect:

1. _____
2. _____
3. _____

Going Further:

1. If five suspects' exemplars are inconsistent with the handwriting of the ransom note, does that mean that those five suspects can be excluded? Explain.
2. Several famous cases other than the Lindbergh baby kidnapping have involved handwriting analysis evidence. Research the impact of handwriting analysis evidence on the JonBenet Ramsey case or another famous case.

Answers

Check students' data tables, visual elimination forms, and written reports. Lab reports should follow the outline given. See the rubric in the IRCD, Chapter 10.

Teaching Tip

See the ransom note, the Fourth Amendment text, and a grading rubric on the IRCD, Chapter 10.

Teaching Tip

If possible, project an image of the ransom note. Ask students which handwriting samples they excluded visually. Ask students which handwriting sample seems to be consistent with the evidence. With the ransom note projected, call on different students to come forward and point to the letter(s) in the ransom note that were consistent with the suspect exemplar. If it is possible to project both the ransom note and the suspect's exemplar, have students show where the consistencies were between the two samples.

Teaching Tip

Remind students that it's important to demonstrate why some suspects were excluded by citing specific inconsistencies between their exemplars and the ransom note. Excluding suspects early in an investigation saves time, money, and the stress of innocent people.

Further Research and Extensions

Interested students may want to research and report their findings on court trials in which handwriting analysis was used as part of a prosecuting or defense attorney's strategy.

Background

Students investigate real currency and outline characteristics that help identify counterfeit bills.

Time Required to Complete Activity

Part A: Pre-test (5 minutes)
Part B: $1 bill examination (30 minutes)
Part C: Hidden feature exploration (30 minutes)
Part D: $10 bill analysis (30 minutes; optional)
Part E: Internet tutorial (30 minutes; optional)

Safety Precautions

Remind students to use both hands when carrying a microscope.

Teaching Tip

If this activity is performed while students view the tutorial at www .newmoney.gov, then no actual currency is necessary.

ACTIVITY 10-3

Examination of U.S. Currency: Is It Authentic or Counterfeit? *Obj. 10.6, 10.7*

Objectives:

By the end of this activity, you will be able to:

1. Identify who is on the front of $1, $5, $10, and $20 bills.
2. Describe what images appear on the back of the bills.
3. Describe the seals, signatures, and images that appear on American currency.
4. With a counterfeit-detecting pen, determine if a bill is genuine or a forgery.
5. Given U.S. currency, describe methods to determine if the currency is counterfeit or authentic.
6. Summarize the features of redesigned U.S. currency that make counterfeiting it more difficult.

Scenario:

Camille handed the cashier her $50 bill. The cashier held it up to the light and looked at it. Perplexed, Camille asked the cashier why he held the $50 bill up to the light. He told her that cashiers were required to examine all $50 bills to be sure that they were authentic and not counterfeit. Camille couldn't imagine how holding the bill up to the light could help him distinguish between an authentic and counterfeit bill. What was he looking for?

Time Required to Complete Activity:

Part A: Pre-test (5 minutes)
Part B: $1 examination (30 minutes)
Part C: Hidden feature exploration (30 minutes)
Part D: $10 bill analysis (30 minutes)
Part E: Internet tutorial (30 minutes)

Materials:

(per each team of two)
Act 10-3 SH
compound microscope or stereomicroscope or hand lens
projecting device (optional, if projecting a bill)
UV light source
counterfeit-detecting pen (to share with other groups)
redesigned U.S. currency ($1, $10 bill (image could be projected))
computer with Internet access (optional)
digital camera (optional)

SAFETY PRECAUTIONS:

Use both hands when carrying a microscope.

Procedure:

1. Complete the pre-test questions in Part A
2. Complete Part B: $1 bill examination
3. Complete Part C: Hidden feature exploration
4. Complete Part D: $10 bill analysis
5. Complete Part E: Internet tutorial

If computers are available, examine the following Website:
http://www.newmoney.gov

Part A

Take the pre-test before starting the lab to determine how much you know about our paper currency. For this part of the lab, you should not be looking at any money but answering the questions from memory. Record your answers on Act 10-3 SH Data Table 1.

Procedure:

Take the pre-test before starting the lab.

Pre-test:

1. Whose face appears on the front of a $1 bill?
2. Whose face appears on the front of a $5 bill?
3. Whose face appears on the front of a $20 bill?
4. What building is pictured on the back of a $5 bill?
5. What building is pictured on the back of a $10 bill?
6. What building is pictured on the back of a $20 bill?
7. What pictures appear on the back of a $1 bill?
8. Are the words *United States of America* written on the front of a $1 bill?
9. Are the words *United State of America* written on the back of a $1 bill?
10. Is the date the bill was issued printed on the front or back of the bill?
11. What seals appear on the front of a bill?

True or False:

12. The Secretary of the Treasury and the U.S. Treasurer are the same.
13. The serial number is printed in two places on the front of a bill.
14. Newer bills contain more colors than the older bills.
15. There is only one signature located on the front of a bill.
16. There is a picture of a building located on the back of $1, $5, $10, and $20 bills.

Handwriting Analysis, Forgery, and Counterfeiting   341

Procedures

1. Print, copy, and distribute Act 10-3 SH from the IRCD, Chapter 10.
2. Make sure students read all directions before beginning the activity.
3. Remember that currency cannot legally be copied at actual size. It must be enlarged or reduced to indicate it is obviously a copy.
4. It may be helpful for students to visit the following Website: www.moneyfactory.gov/section.cfm/4. They may also view the tutorial at www.newmoney.gov during the activity, if they have not already done so.

Pretest

Answers

1. Washington
2. Lincoln
3. Jackson
4. Lincoln Memorial
5. U.S. Treasury
6. The White House
7. The Great Seal (pyramid with eye) and the Presidential Seal (with eagle)
8. Yes
9. Yes
10. Front
11. Department of Treasury Seal, Federal Reserve Seal
12. False
13. True
14. True
15. False
16. False $5, $10, and $20 only

17. True

18. False

19. True

20. True

17. The White House appears on the back of the $20 bill.

18. Because of the separation of church and state, no mention of a higher being or deity can be printed on the bills.

19. There are "hidden images" on the front side of a bill that can only be seen if you hold the bill up to the light.

20. On the back of $10 and $20 bills, small yellow numbers indicating the denominations are stamped in the area surrounding the picture.

Data Table 1: Pre-test

Question	Answer
1	
2	
3	
4	
5	
6	
7	
8	
9	
10	
11	
12	
13	
14	
15	
16	
17	
18	
19	
20	

Part B: Observation of $1 Bills

After reviewing your answers to the pre-test, you will be given some time to study a $1 bill. To help guide you in your observations, answer the following questions and enter your answers in Act 10-3 SH Data Table 2. You will need to look at the bill using a hand lens or a stereomicroscope.

Front of the $1 bill

1. Whose picture is on the front of the $1 bill?
2. What is written across the very top of the front of the $1 bill?
3. What is printed on the very bottom of the front of the $1 bill?
4. What seal appears on the front, left side?
5. What seal appears on the front, right side?
6. What is the date you find on the bill?
7. Who was the Secretary of Treasury at the time this bill was issued?
8. Who was the U.S. Treasurer at the time the bill was issued?
9. Record the serial number for this bill.
10. How many places on the bill is the serial number printed?

Back of the $1 bill

11. What words are printed on the top line?
12. What words are printed on the bottom line?
13. What image appears on the back on the left side?
14. What image appears on the right side?
15. What reference to God appears on the back of the bill?

Data Table 2: $1 Bill Examination

Question	Answer
Front	
1	
2	
3	
4	
5	
6	
7	
8	
9	
10	
Back	
11	
12	
13	
14	
15	

Answers
Front

1. Washington
2. Federal Reserve Note
3. One Dollar
4. Federal Reserve Seal
5. Treasury Seal
6. Answers will vary.
7. Answers will vary.
8. Answers will vary.
9. Answers will vary.
10. 2

Back

11. The United States of America
12. One Dollar
13. Pyramid
14. Eagle with arrows
15. In God We Trust

Teaching Tip

Using various camera and projection devices, create enlarged images so students may view characteristics of bills of higher denominations.

Part C

1. a. Light examination: Front
        of bill:
        Images from the bill's oppo-
        site side can be seen.
        Watermark images of Grant
        ($50), Jackson ($20), and
        Hamilton ($10) can be
        seen in the lower-right
        corner of the bill. The
        $5 bill has three numeral
        5 watermarks to the left of
        Lincoln's image and a large
        numeral 5 to the right.
    b. The front of the bill shows
        no additional miniature
        writing. The back of the
        bill shows: $5: The states'
        names across the front of
        the Lincoln Memorial; all
        denominations: denomi-
        nation amount in yellow
        numerals across the back
        of the bill;
2. Under UV light, a band in each
    denomination—$5 and $10 to
    the right of image, $20 to the
    left of the image

Part C: How Many Hidden Images Can You Find? (Optional)

For this part of the activity, locate some "hidden" features on redesigned U.S. currency. Or view an interactive tutorial on money: http://www.newmoney.gov/newmoney/flash/interactivebill/10_InteractiveNote.html
Record your observations on Act 10-3 SH Data Table 3.

1. Hidden images can be revealed by
    a. Holding the bill up to a bright light
    b. Viewing the bill with a hand lens or stereomicroscope
2. Viewing under UV light.

Data Table 3: Hidden Images on the $10, $20, or $50 Bill

Location	Images	Numbers
Front of the Bill		
Back of the Bill		

Part D: Analysis of a Higher-Denomination Bill (Optional)

Photos are of a $10 bill, but other higher denominations have similar characteristics. Using a camera and projection system, your teacher will check bills for the following:

1. The portrait appears flat on the genuine bills, but appears raised on counter-feit bills.

2. For newer, larger-denomination bills, the oval around the portrait is gone.
3. The background details of the portrait are clear and distinct on genuine bills.
4. The border edge of the genuine bill is clear and distinct.
5. Note the hidden numbers and words embedded in fine print.
6. On genuine bills, the Treasury seals have clear, sharp, sawtooth points.

Hidden numbers and letters

Written above Hamilton's name

7. On genuine bills, the numerals in the serial number are evenly spaced and the same color as the Treasury seal.

8. Genuine paper currency has red and blue fibers woven throughout the bill. You may not be able to see these red and blue fibers without a hand lens or a stereomicroscope.

Serial number

9. Counterfeit currency uses red and blue inks that are often blurred. This blurring may be detected with a hand lens.

10. Examine a bill looking for the following:

   a. *Security thread.* Hold the bill up to the light, and a thin line appears with the denomination of the bill written in it. The position of the thread varies from denomination to denomination but always runs from top to bottom.

Security thread

   b. *Color-shifting ink.* When the bill is tilted, the color of the left-corner 10 shifts from copper to green.

Color-shifting ink

Teaching Tip

Students should view projected images of these bill. If it is not feasible to project an actual redesigned $10 bill, project the image of the $10 bill shown at www.newmoney.gov.

Watermark

c. *Watermark*. Appears on the right side of the face of the bill if it is held up to a light. The image also appears on the left side of the bill if viewed from the back of the bill.

d. *Color*. The background color on both sides of the bill is enhanced.

e. *Symbols of freedom*. A large, red image of the Statue of Liberty's flame is printed to the left of Hamilton, and a smaller, red metallic image is found to the right ($10). Other seals are affixed to other denominations in the same position.

f. *Enhanced portrait*. The oval border around the portrait has been removed, and the shoulder extends to the border of the bill. The portrait appears to be in front of the bill.

g. *Multiple 10s, 20s, 50s, etc.* Small yellow numeral 10s, 20s, and 50s are printed on the front and back, of the bill marking its denomination.

11. Using a counterfeit-detecting pen, mark the edge of the bill and examine the color. A genuine bill will be pale yellow to tan, whereas a counterfeit bill will turn brown.

Enhanced portrait

The old $10 note, front

The series 2001 $10 note, front

Part E: Internet Tutorial (Optional)
Go to the following Website and click on the link to view the safety precautions taken in the design of the new $100 bill.
http://www.newmoney.gov/newmoney/flash/interactive100/index.html

Questions:

1. Counterfeiters sometimes collect dollar bills and bleach them to remove the ink. Using an old-style printer, they will print images of a higher-denomination bill on the bleached paper. What is the advantage of bleaching the dollar bill over just printing the higher-denomination bill onto clean paper?

2. Why has it been necessary to make so many changes to our paper currency in the past 30 years as compared to the last 100 years?

3. Of all the safeguards added to our higher-denomination currency, which do you consider the most important and why?

4. Counterfeiters try to pass off their counterfeit money at public events where many people gather. Many people are working retail for the first time and are not trained in checking larger bills to see if they are genuine or counterfeit. Provide a list of four items to check that will quickly and easily tell you whether a new $10 bill is authentic.

© Rob Marmion/Shutterstock.com

Answer
Check students' data tables.

Questions

1. Sample answer: Bleached paper is exactly the right paper to print money on, and it will pass the counterfeit-pen test. Bleached paper also has all the security safeguards built in.

2. Advances in technology, such as high-quality color printers, have made it easier to counterfeit currency.

3. Answers will vary.

4. Sample answer: Hold the bill up to a light to check if a thin line appears with the denomination of the bill written on it. See if the color of the left corner 10 shifts from copper to green when the bill is tilted. Hold the bill up to a light to check if a watermark showing the face of Alexander Hamilton appears on the right side of the face of the bill. Check if the bill stock has red and blue fibers woven throughout.

Further Research and Extensions

Invite local business owners to come and talk to the class about what devices they have, if any, to detect and prevent counterfeit bills used in business transactions. Also ask what type of training, if any, they provide to their employees to help them detect counterfeit currency.

Chapter Overview

Forensic entomology plays an important role in solving crimes. Often overlooked, insect evidence can be used to establish postmortem intervals, identify the location of a crime scene, or link a suspect to a victim or crime scene. Using insect clues, it's possible to determine injury sites on the victim, if the body was moved, and whether or not the victim was under the influence of drugs or toxins. As the body decomposes, a predictable sequence of insects inhabits the body in a process known as insect succession. Common forensic insects include flies, beetles, wasps, and ants. A forensic entomologist identifies the insects at a crime scene and uses accumulated degree hours to estimate a postmortem interval. Proper evidence collection is required for insect evidence to be accepted in court. Forensic entomologists use scanning electron microscopes, gas chromatography, and mass spectrometry.

The Big Ideas

Forensic entomology is an exciting field that uses insect evidence at a crime scene to help solve a crime. This chapter focuses primarily on flies and beetles and their roles in forensic entomology. Crime-scene investigators must proper procedures of locating, documenting, and collecting insect evidence. Specimens are analyzed by forensic entomologists who identify species

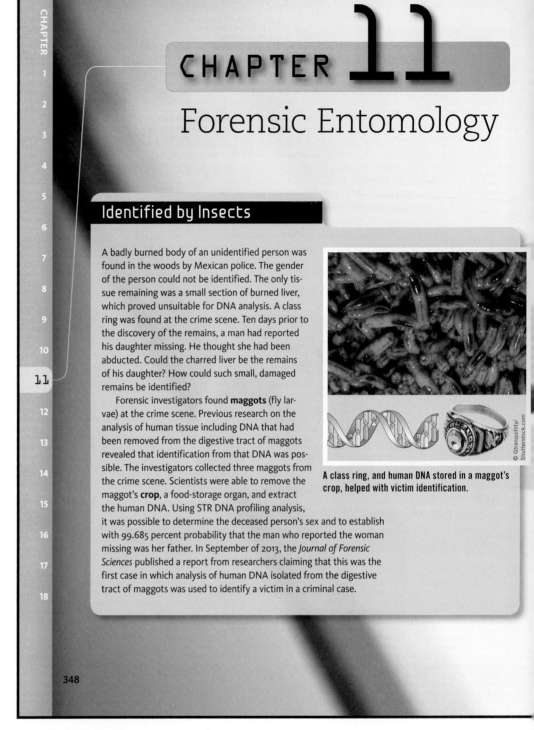

CHAPTER 11
Forensic Entomology

Identified by Insects

A badly burned body of an unidentified person was found in the woods by Mexican police. The gender of the person could not be identified. The only tissue remaining was a small section of burned liver, which proved unsuitable for DNA analysis. A class ring was found at the crime scene. Ten days prior to the discovery of the remains, a man had reported his daughter missing. He thought she had been abducted. Could the charred liver be the remains of his daughter? How could such small, damaged remains be identified?

Forensic investigators found **maggots** (fly larvae) at the crime scene. Previous research on the analysis of human tissue including DNA that had been removed from the digestive tract of maggots revealed that identification from that DNA was possible. The investigators collected three maggots from the crime scene. Scientists were able to remove the maggot's **crop**, a food-storage organ, and extract the human DNA. Using STR DNA profiling analysis, it was possible to determine the deceased person's sex and to establish with 99.685 percent probability that the man who reported the woman missing was her father. In September of 2013, the *Journal of Forensic Sciences* published a report from researchers claiming that this was the first case in which analysis of human DNA isolated from the digestive tract of maggots was used to identify a victim in a criminal case.

A class ring, and human DNA stored in a maggot's crop, helped with victim identification.

© Gtranquillity/Shutterstock.com

SCENARIO

After students read the scenario, brainstorm answers to the following questions as a class:

1. The identity of a badly burned victim was established in this case by using maggots. Think of other types of situations where maggots could be used to identify a victim.
2. If the human tissue was ingested by the maggot, why wouldn't the human tissue have been digested?
3. If the human DNA sample was obtained from only three maggots, how could there be enough DNA to run a DNA profile?

and stages of development and consider the local meteorological data to estimate a postmortem interval. Using accumulated degree hour studies, an entomologist can estimates how long it took for the insects collected at the crime scene to develop to their current stage under local conditions. The pattern of insect succession that occurs on a body undergoing decomposition is predictable and provides evidence of first colonization of a body.

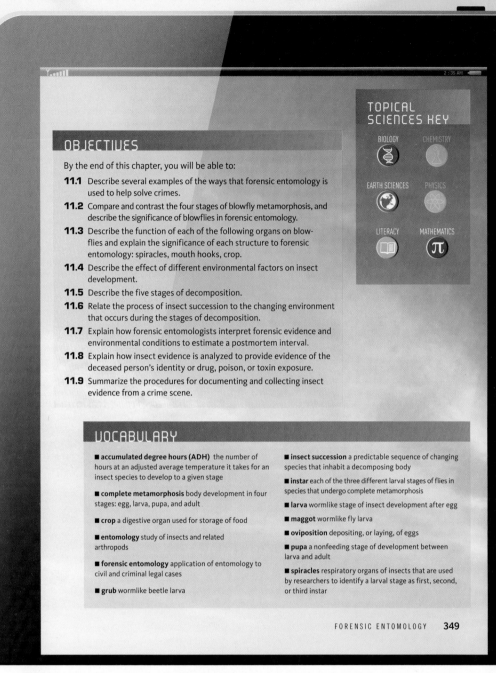

OBJECTIVES

By the end of this chapter, you will be able to:

11.1 Describe several examples of the ways that forensic entomology is used to help solve crimes.

11.2 Compare and contrast the four stages of blowfly metamorphosis, and describe the significance of blowflies in forensic entomology.

11.3 Describe the function of each of the following organs on blowflies and explain the significance of each structure to forensic entomology: spiracles, mouth hooks, crop.

11.4 Describe the effect of different environmental factors on insect development.

11.5 Describe the five stages of decomposition.

11.6 Relate the process of insect succession to the changing environment that occurs during the stages of decomposition.

11.7 Explain how forensic entomologists interpret forensic evidence and environmental conditions to estimate a postmortem interval.

11.8 Explain how insect evidence is analyzed to provide evidence of the deceased person's identity or drug, poison, or toxin exposure.

11.9 Summarize the procedures for documenting and collecting insect evidence from a crime scene.

TOPICAL SCIENCES KEY

BIOLOGY

CHEMISTRY

EARTH SCIENCES

PHYSICS

LITERACY

MATHEMATICS

VOCABULARY

■ **accumulated degree hours (ADH)** the number of hours at an adjusted average temperature it takes for an insect species to develop to a given stage

■ **complete metamorphosis** body development in four stages: egg, larva, pupa, and adult

■ **crop** a digestive organ used for storage of food

■ **entomology** study of insects and related arthropods

■ **forensic entomology** application of entomology to civil and criminal legal cases

■ **grub** wormlike beetle larva

■ **insect succession** a predictable sequence of changing species that inhabit a decomposing body

■ **instar** each of the three different larval stages of flies in species that undergo complete metamorphosis

■ **larva** wormlike stage of insect development after egg

■ **maggot** wormlike fly larva

■ **oviposition** depositing, or laying, of eggs

■ **pupa** a nonfeeding stage of development between larva and adult

■ **spiracles** respiratory organs of insects that are used by researchers to identify a larval stage as first, second, or third instar

FORENSIC ENTOMOLOGY **349**

KEY SCIENCE CONCEPTS

Biology: life cycles of flies and beetles

Earth Science: monitoring temperature variation

Mathematics: calculating accumulated degree hours

TEACHING RESOURCES

 Instructor's Resource CD-ROM includes:

- Activities and Student Handouts
- Alternative Assessments
- Consolidated Bibliography
- Correlations to NGSS and CCSS
- Figure Files
- Lesson Plans
- Nonfiction Readings
- PowerPoint Presentations
- Student Learning Objectives (SLOs)

CL Testing powered by Cognero

Website: ngl.cengage.com/forensicscience2e

Teaching Tip

Before starting the unit on forensic entomology, conduct a carousel brainstorming activity (Ch 11 TN Pre-Assessment Carousel, on the IRCD, Chapter 11). This method serves as a good introduction to the topic of forensic entomology. Students should work in small collaborative groups and respond to eight different questions. This is a brainstorming activity, so responses are added to the sheet whether they are right or wrong. At the conclusion of the activity, a discussion will follow where each response is reviewed. This method makes it easier for reserved students to participate. It also is a good indication of what students know. Misconceptions can also be clarified using this method.

Engage

Allow students to observe live maggots (fly larvae). Do not tell students what the organisms are. Ask:

- Are these alive? How can you tell?
- What structures do you observe? What functions do you expect these structures have?
- What is the role of these organisms in the ecosystem?
- How do these organisms relate to forensics?
- What are they?

(Consider placing maggots in closed petri dishes or jars during the observation period.)

Did you know

Insect stings to the driver are among the top 20 causes of automobile collisions.

INTRODUCTION

Did you know that there are approximately a million species of insects? An insect has three body segments: a head, thorax, and abdomen (Figure 11-1). They have three pairs of jointed legs joined at the thorax, and their bodies are supported by an *exoskeleton* (an exterior skeletal structure). Most have wings. Most insects begin life as eggs, from which they hatch into *larvae* (singular *larva*). A **larva** is basically a wormlike eating machine. Most insects you will read about in this chapter undergo **complete metamorphosis,** which means the larva then turns into a **pupa,** or non-eating subadult, before it becomes an adult. Insects are the most abundant, diverse, strange, and beautiful group of animals on Earth, and new species are identified each day. You may think of insects as annoying creatures that bite, spoil your food, or destroy gardens and crops, but they serve many important roles in the environment. Without pollinating insects, there would be fewer flowers and fruits. Without the action of decomposing insects, dead bodies and animal remains would take longer to decompose. The air would be filled with foul odors, and the environment would be littered with slowly decomposing bodies, leading to disease. This chapter will reveal how insects can be a homicide detective's friends.

The study of insects and other arthropods (spiders, crustaceans) is called **entomology.** It has been estimated that insects have existed for more than 250 million years, whereas humans have been on Earth about 200,000 years. **Forensic entomology** is the interpretation of insect evidence used in civil or criminal investigations. Evidence may be in the form of adults, nymphs (subadults in insect species that undergo incomplete metamorphosis), pupae, larvae, eggs, or insect body parts collected from a body or crime scene (Figure 11-2). Insects removed from a car's windshield or radiator can contribute vital information for solving crimes. The job of the *forensic entomologist* is to collect and identify insect evidence and interpret it in relation to the environmental conditions and other variables that exist at a crime scene. Forensic entomology provides an estimate of the minimum and maximum amounts of time that could have passed since *colonization*, the arrival

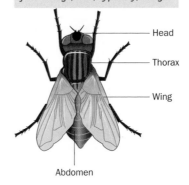

Figure 11-1 *Insects have a head, thorax, abdomen, three pairs of jointed legs, and, typically, wings.*

Head

Thorax

Wing

Abdomen

Figure 11-2 *Blowflies lay eggs in clusters on decomposing flesh. The eggs look like small rice grains.*

© Cengage Learning®

of the first insects on a dead body. The forensic entomology report along with all the other evidence reports from toxicology, botany, and the autopsy are then evaluated by the medical examiner or pathologist who estimates the *postmortem interval (PMI)*, the time between death and discovery of the body. The primary focus of this chapter is *medico-legal forensic entomology*—the study of how insects or their remains are used in the investigations of death, abuse, and neglect cases.

HOW IS FORENSIC ENTOMOLOGY USED? *Obj. 11.1*

Forensic entomology can be applied to estimate a *postmortem interval (PMI)*. Recall that a postmortem interval is the time interval between a person's death and the time the body was discovered. If a body is badly burned or if a body is found more than two to three days after death, it is difficult to estimate time of death using temperature, rigor mortis, or other common techniques. However, by using insect evidence and factoring in *ambient*, or environmental, variables such as location, temperature, humidity, and amount of rainfall and sunlight, it may be possible to provide a postmortem interval. This information may help to exclude or include a suspect. Forensic entomology can also accomplish the following:

- Help reveal a body or remains by the presence of flies, their eggs or larvae, or other insects (Figure 11-3).

Figure 11-3 *A larva mass can indicate the presence of remains.*

© Cengage Learning®

- Determine if the body was moved. Were the insects found on the body normally found in that environment, or are they inhabitants of a different area?
- Identify a geographic range of the crime scene based on the types of insects found on a body that has been moved. Geographic ranges where specific insects can survive are limited.
- Link a suspect to a crime scene or to a victim by the presence of insect evidence or similar bites on both the suspect and victim.
- Indicate where the suspect had been traveling, based on insect evidence on the suspect's vehicle and/or belongings.
- Trace the origin of drugs in drug trafficking based on insect evidence found in the drug packaging.

Limitations of Forensic Entomology

Insect data are less helpful in estimating a postmortem interval if the body was moved after death. A person might be murdered at home and then be hidden hours later in the woods. Insects found on a body in the woods

Explore
Divide the class into six groups, each corresponding to one of the bulleted items on this page. Have each group investigate an example or case study pertaining to the bulleted item assigned to them.

Explore

Have students research the work of early forensic entomologists. Have them investigate how they conducted their studies and what type of experimentation was done. Have students discuss how the field of forensic entomology was advanced by their work.

Pioneers in forensic entomology include the following:

- Jerry Payne, who created a piglet Body Farm in 1962 to study insect succession on corpses
- Lamar Meek, who in 1981 replicated conditions of a crime scene using pig studies
- William Rodriquez, who studied how insects could be used to estimate postmortem interval
- Bernard Greenberg, who used the concept of accumulated degree hours, a computation of developmental time, to calibrate the time it takes for insects to reach different stages of development

LITERACY

Read Jessica Snyder Sachs's book *Corpse* to learn more about the work of an early forensic entomologist.

can be used to estimate how long the body was in the woods, but not how long it was since the person died. However, the insect data could be helpful in constructing leads or a case against a suspect.

Forensic Entomologists

A forensic entomologist interprets insect evidence, applying environmental variables to help answer questions about a dead body. Entomologists' expertise about the particular *species* of insects attracted to bodies that have been exposed to certain conditions helps them answer many questions about a crime. (This is especially important when the body is severely decomposed or burned.)

- Where on the body are the injuries? **Maggots** (fly larvae) are attracted to open wounds; the presence of a maggot mass can indicate the site of an injury.
- Was the body moved after death? If the insects associated with the dead body differ from the insects found at the crime scene, it may indicate the body was moved.
- Was the victim restrained while alive? If so, urine and fecal matter would be (or would have been) present, attracting houseflies rather than blowflies.
- Was the body covered, buried, or submerged in water? This would affect the onset of insect colonization and the type of insects that would be attracted to the body.
- Was the deceased exposed to any toxic chemical or under the influence of recreational drugs? Even if the body is too decomposed to analyze, the feeding larvae may have human tissue stored in their crops that can be analyzed for drugs and other chemicals.

Forensic entomologists work with other scientists using electron and scanning microscopes, DNA analysis, toxicology, gas chromatography, and mass spectrometry to analyze insect evidence from crime scenes. Improvements in technology have led to more reliable identification of larvae, a challenge, even for experts.

HISTORY OF FORENSIC ENTOMOLOGY *Obj. 11.1*

One of the earliest cases to use insect evidence to solve a crime was described in the 1247 Chinese work by Sung Tz'u called *The Washing Away of Wrongs*. A bloody murder was discovered by a group of farmers returning home from their fields. All the workers were instructed to lay down their sickles. Soon flies identified the murderer by landing on the one sickle blade containing microscopic remnants of flesh and blood.

Bergeret d'Arbois was a French entomologist. In 1855, he collected insect evidence during an autopsy of a mummified body of a murdered infant hidden in the wall of a house. Four different tenants were considered suspects. Bergeret had observed that insects colonize dead bodies in a predictable sequence known as **insect succession**. As a body decomposes, the predictable physical and chemical changes it undergoes make it attractive to different species of organisms. Bergeret applied the concept of insect succession to the case and estimated the baby died in 1848. The police used this information to link the murder to the couple who lived in the house in 1848. Jean Pierre Megnin

DIGGING DEEPER

with Forensic Science eCollection

Visit the Gale Forensic Science eCollection at **ngl.cengage.com/ forensicscience2e** to learn how the government used radiation to eliminate the primary screwworm fly (*Cochliomyia hominivorax*) from the southwestern United States.

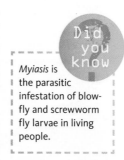

Scott Camazine/Alamy

published further insect succession studies in 1894.

In the early part of the 20th century, U.S. cattle and sheep herds in Texas were devastated by screwworm flies. These flies feed on the tissue of living cattle and sheep, weakening them. American entomologist Dr. David G. Hall of the National Museum of Natural History was funded by the government to study the problem. His research helped reduce the damage and number of livestock deaths due to flies. His book *Blowflies of North America* laid the groundwork for future forensic entomologists.

Insect evidence slowly gained acceptance with investigators and the court system through the research and casework of forensic entomologists Drs. Lee Goff, Paul Catts, Wayne Lord, and Gail Anderson. A concern was raised that much of the research was being done on pig carcasses. For evidence to meet the *Daubert* standard, it has to not only be generally accepted by the scientific community, but it also has to be tested under circumstances directly applicable to the case at trial. Dr. Neal Haskell's research comparing pig and human decomposition at the Body Farm at the University of Tennessee helped forensic entomology meet the *Daubert* standard. Dr. Haskell found no difference between the developmental time of blowflies on humans and pigs. Reliability of insect evidence analysis continues to be challenged in the courts, however, because every living thing is unique, and explaining biology to juries can be a challenge.

Did you know

Myiasis is the parasitic infestation of blow-fly and screwworm fly larvae in living people.

INSECTS AND DECOMPOSITION

Obj. 11.2, 11.3, 11.4, 11.5, 11.6, 11.8

All organisms have specific requirements for survival. A habitat must be favorable or the organisms will not survive. The most important factors any organism needs for survival are suitable temperatures, the correct amount of moisture, a suitable food source, and oxygen. Factors affecting survival are the presence of other organisms competing for food and living space, predation, reproduction limitations (Figure 11-4), and toxic effects of wastes due to crowding.

Figure 11-4 *Odors of decaying flesh attract multiple bottle flies to lay eggs.*

© Cengage Learning®

You can tell female and male bottle flies apart by the distance between their eyes. The male's eyes almost touch; the female's eyes are separated.

Decomposition *Obj. 11.5, 11.8*

In this chapter, you will study the primary insects of decomposition with an emphasis on flies and beetles. Decomposing bodies of animals provide a changing environment that serves as a source of nutrition for many different types of insects. The body undergoes a series of changes as organisms break it down and it decomposes. Different stages of decomposition make a body appropriate for different types of insects (and other organisms) as a food source. Insects that suck up liquids may get nourishment from moister parts of the body or during softer, earlier stages of decomposition. Insects with sharp mouthparts may get nourishment from a dry, decaying body in a later stage of decomposition.

Decomposition stages include the following:

- *Fresh:* a warm, newly dead body
- *Bloated:* a corpse emitting odors of decaying flesh
- *Decay:* a body emitting gases of decay with strong odors, and showing signs of darkened tissues
- *Active (or advanced) decay:* an organism starting to dry out; most flesh is gone
- *Dry, or skeletal, decay:* mostly bones remain

These changes in a decomposing body follow a regular pattern and provide changing habitats. These different habitats support the predictable sequence of insect succession on a dead body.

Figure 11-5 *Blowflies, also known as carrion flies or bottle flies, include blue bottles, green bottles (left), and bronze bottles (right). The shiny metallic green, blue, or bronze flies are among the first to arrive at a body.*

© Cengage Learning® (both)

Figure 11-6 *Head and proboscis (siphon-like mouthparts) of adult blowfly.*

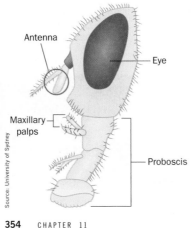

Antenna

Eye

Maxillary palps

Proboscis

Source: University of Sydney

Blowflies (Bottle Flies) *Obj. 11.2, 11.3,.11.8*

Within minutes of death, odors emitted from a dead body can be detected by blowflies from a mile away! The adult flies with their beautiful shiny metallic green, blue, or bronze bodies are among the first to arrive and can be very useful in determining the postmortem interval (Figure 11-5). As bacteria start to decompose tissue, two gases, putrescine and cadaverine, are released that alert the blowfly to a possible location to lay their eggs. The adult fly uses its siphon-like proboscis (mouthparts) (Figure 11-6) to suck up the protein-rich fluids from a decomposing body. Fortified with extra protein, the female flies deposit their eggs in clusters on the body, usually in natural openings such as the mouth, nose, ear, vagina, or anus. If there has been an injury to the skin, eggs will be laid there as well. The soft, moist tissue of the body will provide food for the larvae, or maggots.

DIFFERENTIATED LEARNING

At-Risk Students

Explore how various insects obtain food. Research the special adaptations of insects that enable some to feed on a fresh body, while others are able to digest drier tissues found in the later stages of decomposition. Find images of the mouthparts of a fly sucking up liquids, the piercing, biting mouthparts of lice or fleas, or the scraping mouthparts of hide beetles. Relate the structure of the mouthpart to the type of food ingested by the insect.

GROWTH AND DEVELOPMENT

Blowflies undergo **complete metamorphosis,** a change in body form, as they develop. As you see in Figures 11-7 and 11-8, the stages include *egg, larva* (plural *larvae*), *pupa* (plural *pupae*), and *adult*. If conditions are favorable, within an hour after arriving on a dead body, the female will lay approximately 50 eggs in a cluster. If you look back at Figure 11-2, you will see that the tiny eggs, about 1 millimeter long, look like miniature white rice grains.

Many environmental variables affect whether or not eggs are laid. If it's too hot or too cold, too windy, too sunny, or too shady, different species will not lay eggs. Forensic entomologist Dr. Neal Haskell conducted many experiments that documented the fact that blowflies do not lay eggs at night. After blowfly eggs are laid, the rate of development varies depending primarily on temperature; the warmer the temperature, the faster the development.

Given a suitable environment, a female deposits eggs and releases a chemical (pheromone) that attracts other blowflies to lay eggs in the same area. Eggs hatch usually in less than 24 hours. After hatching, the blowfly progresses through three stages of larvae, called **instars**. These stages are referred to as first, second, or third instar, with each stage larger than the one before. The pre-pupa stage follows with a decrease in size as the third instar stops feeding before it *pupates* (becomes a pupa).

Figure 11-7 *Blowfly life cycle: egg mass; first, second and third instar; pupa; and adult.*

© Cengage Learning®

Figure 11-8 *Blowfly life cycle (times are approximate).*

Stage	Size (mm)	Color	First Appearance	Duration of Phase	Characteristics
Egg	2	White	Soon after death	8 hours	Found in moist, warm areas of body (mouth, eyes, ears, anus)
Larva 1 (instar 1)	5	White	1.8 days	20 hours	Black mouth hooks visible (anterior) Thin body One spiracle slit near anus
Larva 2 (instar 2)	10	White	2.5 days	15–20 hours	Black mouth hooks (anterior) Dark crop seen on anterior dorsal side Feeds actively Two spiracle slits near anus
Larva 3 (instar 3)	17	White	4–5 days	36–56 hours	Black mouth hooks Crop not visible, covered by fat deposits Fat body Three spiracle slits near anus
Pre-pupa	9		8–12 days	86–180 hours	Larva migrates away from body to a dry area
Early and late pupa	9	Cream-colored; changes to dark brown	18–24 days	6–12 days	Immobile, does not feed Changes to dark brown with age "Balloon" inflates and deflates to help split open pupa case prior to adult emerging
Adult	Varies	Black or green	21–24 days	Several weeks	Incapable of flight for first few hours

Teaching Tip

View live larvae under a stereomicroscope. Have students observe and describe how the larvae use the mouth hooks. Another option is to project images of the live larvae for the class.

Teaching Tip

Spiracle slits are visible under a stereomicroscope. They are most easily viewed in the third stage. Place larvae into alcohol to kill and temporarily store them. Poke a larva-diameter hole in a piece of plastic foam with a pin or dissecting needle. Place the larva in the hole posterior-side-up. View under a stereomicroscope. (You could place the larva in the hole anterior-side-up to view the mouth hooks.) Ask students to identify the stage based on the spiracle slits. Stiff, preserved larvae are easier to view than living larvae.

Figure 11-9 *Note the hooks found at the thinner anterior (front) end of the blowfly larva (left). These are used to hold onto and scrape the food. The posterior end is more rounded. The darkened area is the crop where ingested food is stored (right).*

Image courtesy of CDC-DPDx

© Cengage Learning®

MORPHOLOGY (BODY SHAPE)

Note in Figure 11-9 that the front, or anterior, end of the white larva is slenderer and tapered. Two dark hooks at the anterior end can be seen when viewed under a hand lens. These hooks enable the larva to dig and scrape at decomposing flesh and move it toward the mouth.

The posterior (rear) end of the larva is more rounded in appearance. Note the two circular regions called **spiracles**. Inside each circular region are spiracle slits used for breathing. As you see in Figure 11-10, the first instar has one horseshoe-shaped spiracle slit. The second instar has two spiracle slits, and the third instar has three. Blowfly larvae "breathe through their butts," since their spiracles are at their posterior ends. It's really very convenient for them. Larvae feed on decomposing flesh in large groups with their mouths burrowed into flesh and have their posterior ends up in the air. This allows them to eat and breathe at the same time.

Figure 11-10 *Spiracles on the posterior end of blowfly larva are two circular regions that contain slits used for breathing. Spiracle slit configuration allows researchers to determine if a larva is first, second, or third instar. Illustrations, left to right: Spiracle slits in first instar, second instar, and third instar of blowfly. Photo, far right: This larva appears to be a third instar.*

First instar larva   Second instar larva   Third instar larva

Image courtesy of CDC-DPDx

As food is ingested, it passes into the maggot's crop. Because no digestion occurs in the crop, ingested body tissue containing DNA can be removed and analyzed. Also, if the person was exposed to toxins or drugs, their presence could be detected by analyzing the contents of the crops. "Maggot milkshakes," a blend of maggots recovered from a badly decomposed corpse, can be analyzed for the presence of drugs. In the second instar, it's possible to see a darkening crop on the dorsal (uppermost) anterior (front) end of the maggot. However, during the third instar, the crop is no longer visible. The addition of body fat acquired by the third instar stage obscures the crop.

The *cuticle* (outer covering) of the larvae does not grow with the maggot; the maggot sheds its cuticle (molts) in favor of a new, larger one. Toward the end of the third instar, the larva stops eating and empties its crop. It will move away from the decomposing flesh, sometimes crawling several feet in search of a dry, dark area to pupate. The thick skin of the third instar is not

Figure 11-11 *Blowfly pupae. Left: Head emerging from pupal case. Right: Empty pupal cases; pupae formed at the same time will emerge at approximately the same time.*

shed; instead, it hardens into a pupal case. The maggot becomes smaller and slowly darkens, changing from white to a light golden brown and then to a dark brown in its pupal case. As a pupa, the maggot develops into an adult fly (Figure 11-11). An empty pupal case can provide evidence that a body has been in an area long enough for the blowfly to complete its full life cycle.

Houseflies, Flesh Flies, and Coffin Flies *Obj. 11.4, 11.6*

Houseflies are smaller than blowflies. The housefly has a gray thorax with four dark longitudinal stripes (Figure 11-12). Food sources for the adults are sugar, sweat, blood, urine, and feces. Houseflies are common in normal houses but can also be indicators of abuse, due to their attraction to urine and feces. Flesh flies are medium-sized flies. They often arrive within minutes of death. Their distinctive markings include black and gray longitudinal stripes on the thorax and a checkerboard pattern on their abdomen (Figure 11-13). Instead of laying eggs, flesh flies deposit living larvae onto the flesh. If a victim is concealed or wrapped in blankets or plastic, tiny coffin flies may be the only ones able to reach the body. Coffin flies are about the size of fruit flies (Figure 11-14). In the Casey Anthony murder trial, Dr. Haskell observed evidence of coffin flies, indicating that a dead body was in the car for several days.

Figure 11-12 *You can identify a housefly by the four dark stripes on its thorax.*

DIGGING DEEPER

How does something the size of a blowfly emerge from a tiny pupal case? Watch a video or the actual process of a fly emerging from its pupal case. Inside the pupal case, the fly has a fluid-filled, inflatable, balloon-like structure called a *ptilium*. As it inflates and deflates, it causes one end of the pupal case to pop open. All six of the fly's legs, as well as its immature wings, are tightly wrapped around its body inside the cramped pupa case. Slowly, one pair of legs emerges, followed by the other two pair. The newly emerged fly looks very strange because its wings are not yet extended, and it can't fly for several hours. For more information, go to the Gale Forensic Science eCollection at **ngl.cengage.com/forensicscience2e** and enter the search term "pupa."

Teaching Tip

Using pinned collections of house-flies, blowflies, and flesh flies, ask students to observe the adults. Ask students to list distinguishing characteristics of the adults that could be used to help identify the species. Students should note: color, shiny or not shiny, stripes, number of stripes, checkerboard abdomen, eye color.

Figure 11-13 *Flesh fly. Notice the checkerboard pattern on the flesh fly's abdomen and the stripes on its thorax.*

© iStock.com/arlindo71

Figure 11-14 *The coffin fly is about the size of a fruit fly.*

Nigel Cattlin/Alamy

Beetles and Other Insects of Decomposition

Obj. 11.4, 11.6

Beetles are the most numerous of all insects. They have two sets of wings; the first is a hardened sheath or shell-like covering that protects the body and the other wings. The second set of wings is used for flying. Like flies, beetles undergo complete metamorphosis (Figure 11-15). **Grubs** (beetle larvae) are easy to distinguish from fly larvae because beetle larvae have three pairs of legs, whereas fly larvae have no legs (Figure 11-16). Beetles typically arrive after flies and will mate on the dead body. The female lays her eggs in the decomposing flesh. Like flies, beetles have diverse nutritional needs, and they follow the predictable path of insect succession on a decomposing body. The clown beetle, for example, feeds on fly eggs and on fly and beetle larvae, whereas the hide beetle prefers the dry remains of a corpse. Refer to Figure 11-17 for information on various species of beetles and the stage of decomposition at which they arrive.

Other insects also feed at decomposition sites. Ants, bees, and wasps feed on either the body or the eggs and larvae of flies and beetles. The presence of any of these insect predators may delay the development of blowfly larvae and affect the postmortem interval estimate.

Figure 11-15 *Beetle life cycle: (left to right) first instar, second instar, pupa, adult.*

© Dr. James L. Castner

Figure 11-16 *Larvae from four families of beetles: (left to right) scarab beetle, carrion beetle, rove beetle, and skin beetle.*

© Dr. James L. Castner

Figure 11-17 *Beetle Succession on a Decomposing Body.*

Beetle Species (In Order of Arrival on Body)	Preferred Food	Arrival on Corpse	Notes
Clown beetle	Fly eggs, maggots, beetle larvae	Early	Adults 1/8 to 3/8 inch; body oval, shiny metallic black or green; found under body
Surinam carrion beetle	Maggots	Early	Dominant beetle species on decomposing human bodies; adults 5/8 to 1 inch; orange marking on wings
American carrion beetle	Maggots	Early to advanced decomposition	Adults 5/8 to 3/4 inch; yellow patch behind head
Sexton beetle	Maggots	Fresh to advanced	Adults 5/8 to 1 inch; black with reddish-orange markings; common in forested areas
Hairy rove beetle	Maggots	Fresh to advanced	Adults 1/2 to 3/4 inch; black with pale yellow bristles
Hide beetle	Dried remains	Advanced	Adults 1/4 to 3/4 inch; ridges and bumps on body

Teaching Tip
Refer to the article "New Insects Revealed in Entomological Decomposition" by the Entomological Society of America in *The Forensic Magazine,* January 22, 2015.

Teaching Tip

Have students discuss the advantages of maggots feeding in concentrated masses. Ask them: Are there disadvantages to the maggots of feeding en masse?

Explore

Have students view maggots under a stereomicroscope and note the differences in the anterior and posterior ends. Find the hooks and crop. If they look very closely, they might be able to see hair-like structures called setae that help anchor the maggot as it moves.

ESTIMATING POSTMORTEM INTERVAL *Obj. 11.2, 11.4, 11.6, 11.7*

Figure 11-18 *This entomologist is rearing larvae in a lab.*

AP Images/Houston Chronicle/ Johnny Hanson

Insects and insect larvae found on or near a body can help forensic scientists estimate postmortem intervals. Different species will arrive in an area at different times of the year depending on environmental conditions. Because of insect succession, the presence of a particular species of insect can also provide important data for estimating postmortem interval. At crime scenes, live insects are collected and some are immediately preserved. The most developed larvae (oldest) should be collected to provide the most accurate estimate of postmortem intervals. The live specimens are sent to a forensic entomologist who will raise them to adulthood in the laboratory. It is easier to identify species from adults than from larvae (Figure 11-18).

Blowfly Importance *Obj. 11.2*

Because blowflies arrive usually within minutes after death, blowflies are timekeepers for postmortem intervals. Knowing that insects follow a predictable succession, and knowing how long it takes for each species to reach their different stages of development, the estimate of postmortem interval can be calculated by going backward. For example, if only blowfly eggs are present and no blowfly larvae are present, the estimated postmortem interval is usually less than 24 hours because the eggs have not developed into larvae. If most of the insects are in the third instar stage, calculations are made to determine how long it took for those insects to develop to the third instar stage. Finding empty pupal cases at a crime scene is important because it indicates a minimum postmortem interval long enough for insects to develop to adulthood.

Factors Affecting Development *Obj. 11.4, 11.6*

Forensic entomologists must take into consideration many factors that affect insect development, such as local temperatures and environmental conditions. **Oviposition** (egg laying) will not occur at night, in the rain, or if temperatures and other environmental conditions are not suitable. Feeding maggot masses can have temperatures of 5°F to 20°F (3°C to 12°C) higher than the *ambient* (surrounding) temperature, which can speed up development. This is why maggot mass temperatures are taken at the crime scene. Forensic entomologists must ask other questions when assessing insect development:

- Was the body clothed?
- Was the body wrapped, frozen, or inaccessible to insects, thus delaying insect colonization?
- Was the body buried? If so, how deep? Was the burial medium permeable to insects? Could the medium release decomposition gases?
- In what environment was the victim found: sandy beach, wooded area, desert, urban, rural?
- Was the body exposed to sun, shade, or wind—factors that affect when eggs are laid?
- Was the body found at night or during the daytime? (Insects don't lay eggs at night.)

- Was the victim exposed to toxins, chemicals, or drugs that would affect growth rates in the insects?
- Did the insects have an adequate food source?
- What body fluids were at the crime scene that would attract insects?
- Were any predators in the area that fed upon insects or the body?
- How many insects were found on the body?

Degree Hours *Obj. 11.2, 11.4, 11.6*

MATHEMATICS

How is it possible to determine how long it takes insects to develop to each of the different stages when temperatures differ throughout the day? To help answer this question, insects are raised at a constant temperature in a laboratory setting. The number of hours at an adjusted average temperature that it takes an insect species to reach a particular stage of development is expressed in **accumulated degree hours (ADH)** using degrees Celsius. When calculating degree hours for insects in an uncontrolled environment, such as the outdoors, it's necessary to factor in the insect's *lower limit threshold*. This is the temperature below which growth and development cease. For most insects, this is 10°C. To find the adjusted temperature, factoring in the lower-limit threshold, a forensic entomologist will do the following:

- Add the maximum and minimum temperature in degrees Celsius for a 24-hour period and divide by 2 to get the *average temperature* for each day.
- Subtract the lower-limit threshold, usually 10°C, from the *average* daily temperature to get the *adjusted temperature.*
- Multiply the adjusted average temperature by the number of hours in the day to obtain the ADH for that day. (For example, if a body was found at 3 P.M., then the number of hours for that day would be 15 hours. If the body was found at 6 A.M., then the number of hours for that day would be 6 hours. Full days are 24 hours.) This product represents the *thermal units,* or accumulated degree hours, for that day. Degree hours with a lower-limit threshold of 10 degrees Celsius are written as DH-B10 (degree hours –10°C).

A forensic entomologist who collected third instars from the crime scene would examine data from the controlled environment studies to determine the total number of ADH it would take to reach the third instar stage. Using reliable temperature records for that area (weather stations), the ADH for each day would be calculated starting with the day the body was found. The postmortem interval would be estimated by calculating how long it would take an insect to reach the third instar stage. That postmortem interval will only be an estimate; the forensic entomologist can only provide a range of times when insects could have colonized the body.

PROCESSING A CRIME SCENE FOR INSECT EVIDENCE *Obj. 11.9*

Proper procedures for processing a crime scene should be followed as outlined in Chapter 2. The crime scene and evidence must be photographed and documented. Trained crime-scene investigators collect insect evidence.

Did you know?

Crime-scene investigators may mistake brownish flyspecks for blood spatter. Flies ingest blood and mix it with enzymes. The mixture is regurgitated, and enzymes break down the food that will be later re-ingested. Wastes create more flyspecks. Unlike blood spatter, flyspecks are randomly distributed. Also, flyspecks have a depression in the center that is produced by the sucking action of the fly.

Teaching Tip

Only eggs and no larvae are found on a corpse. Have students discuss reasons for the absence of larvae *other than* that the body was not in the location long enough.

Explore

Have students research aquatic forensic insects. What is the pattern of insect succession on a body submerged in water? Ask volunteers to report their findings to the class.

Teaching Tip

Bring an insect collection net to class. Demonstrate how to collect flying insects by quickly moving the net back and forth over the corpse. The net should be twisted at the end of each sweep. The final sweep should include several twists so the adults can't climb or fly out of the net. Invert the twisted net over a collection jar containing cotton balls soaked in alcohol to kill the insects.

Many of the eggs and first instars are very small, and third instars move away from the body before they pupate, so great care must be taken when looking for insect evidence. Too often, insect evidence is overlooked, not collected, or not photographed. If the evidence collection, documentation, and handling are not done correctly, the evidence cannot be used. The Website of forensic entomologist Dr. Jason Byrd (Figure 11-20) is the source of the following summarized procedures.

1. **Death-Scene Observations**
   * Location of crime scene, description of general habitat, weather conditions, locations of any open windows or doors near the body, whether the body is inside or outside
   * Location of body in reference to vegetation, sun, shade
   * Body condition: locations of any wounds or visible injuries, state of decomposition
   * Insect observations: locations of insects on or around the body, types of insects, stages of development

EARTH SCIENCES

2. **Collection of Meteorological Data**
   * Ambient temperature at scene taken at chest level
   * Maggot mass temperature taken from the center of the mass
   * Ground surface temperature
   * Interface between the body and ground
   * Soil directly under the body
   * Maximum and minimum daily temperatures from an accurate source
   * Rainfall amounts for a period from 1–2 weeks before the victim's disappearance to 3–5 days after the body was discovered

3. **Two Collections: Collect live insects, and collect and preserve other insects from the body at the crime scene (Figure 11-19).**

Figure 11-19 *Entomologists collect insects on and around a body.*

© Kirsanov Valeriy Vladimirovich/Shutterstock.com

Collect Adults First

* Adults can be trapped with a net and placed in a killing jar containing cotton balls or plaster soaked with ethyl acetate and later transferred to vials with 75%–80% ethyl alcohol.
* Jars should be labeled using a graphite pencil and paper placed both inside the jar and outside the jar.
* Labels should include geographic location, date and hour of collection, case number, location on body where the insect was collected, and name of the collector.

Larvae and Eggs

* If there is more than one maggot mass, treat each mass separately.
* Collect about 50 maggots per mass, collecting the most-developed larvae.
* Place larvae in killing jars with 75%–80% alcohol.
* Living specimens should be placed in containers with tight-fitting lids; add air holes, moist paper towel, and a meat source. Insert that container into a slightly larger container with ½ inch of soil or vermiculite to absorb any liquids and ship it overnight to an entomologist.

362   CHAPTER 11

4. **After Body Removal: Collect insects from the surrounding soil.**
   - Collect insects from the area where the corpse was located and in the immediate vicinity. Keep some as live samples and preserve some of the insects. Label all specimen jars.
   - Collect and label soil and leaf litter samples from the area under the body and in the immediate location of the body (to a depth of 2 inches).

Evidence collectors and crime-scene investigators need training on how to recognize and collect forensic evidence. Forensic entomologists like Dr. Neal Haskell and Dr. Jason Byrd (Figure 11-20) are among many forensic entomologists who are involved in education as well as in their own casework. Future research involving advanced technologies and DNA profiling will help improve identification and refine estimates of postmortem intervals to enhance forensic entomology.

Figure 11-20 *Dr. Jason Byrd is the Associate Director of the William R. Maples Center for Forensic Medicine at the University of Florida's College of Medicine. Dr. Byrd is a Board-Certified forensic entomologist.*

Photo courtesy of Dr. Jason Byrd

Teaching Tip

Refer to Dr. Byrd's Website at http://www.forensic-entomology.com

Close

Remind students that insect evidence is only part of the evidence presented in any murder trial. It may not be presented at all. But as with all the other topics they have studied (fiber, hair, blood, DNA, etc.), it *may* only take one item of correctly collected and analyzed evidence of *any type,* properly presented in court, to bring a perpetrator to justice.

SUMMARY

- Insects, the most numerous of all animals, provide valuable evidence in solving crimes.

- Forensic entomology is used to estimate postmortem intervals, identify the geographic location of the crime scene, link a suspect to a victim or crime scene, determine if a body was moved, locate injury sites, determine exposure to drugs or toxins, and provide evidence of neglect or abuse.

- The five stages of decomposition include fresh, bloated, active decay, advanced decay, and dry decay; stages of decomposition cause predictable changes in the chemical and physical environment of a body and the area surrounding it.

- Forensic insects include flies, beetles, wasps, ants, and more. Insects follow a predictable sequence of inhabiting a dead body, known as insect succession.

- Blowflies, usually the first to inhabit a dead body, undergo four stages of complete metamorphosis: egg, larva (first instar, second instar, third instar), pupa, and adult.

- Larvae use mouth hooks to help ingest food and move, a crop to store food, and spiracle slits to breathe.

LITERACY

Read Dr. M. Lee Goff's *A Fly for the Prosecution: How Forensic Evidence Solves Crimes* and Dr. Neal Haskell's article "Using Timelines to Learn Forensics" in the Spring 2014 issue *of The Forensic Teacher Magazine.*

- Beetles usually arrive after flies and may consume the dead body or consume eggs and larvae found on the body.

- Variables affecting the rate of insect growth include temperature, sun, shade, wind, moisture, injuries to the deceased, and a body that is clothed or wrapped. All must be considered when a forensic entomologist interprets insect evidence.

- The postmortem interval is an estimate of the interval of time between when the body was found and death.

- Accumulated degree hours (ADH) are the number of hours at an adjusted average temperature it takes for an insect species to develop to a given developmental stage. ADH are used to estimate postmortem intervals.

- Evidence collection includes crime-scene observations, collection of live insects and eggs, preserving insects, and collection of meteorological data.

Explore

Ask students to investigate and summarize forensic entomology case studies that involve the different factors that affect postmortem estimates. Students can research true case studies or cases in forensic TV programs, novels, or movies.

CASE STUDIES

Where's the Body?

When authorities received a tip that a dead body was hidden in an old well somewhere in Illinois, they embarked on a mission of trying to find one well among many wells. After searching for hours, the investigators received a second tip, this time from flies. Apparently, the suspect covered the well with tires, hoping to disguise the fact that there was a body at the bottom. When investigators arrived, they found a dark cloud of flies buzzing over the top of the well.

Paul Catts's Case of the Massive Maggots: Effect of Cocaine on Maggots

"You are what you eat." When maggots feed on the body tissues of a drug user, the maggots also become drug users. In October 1988, in Spokane, Washington, forensic entomologist Paul Catt was confused. The body of a woman was found lying face down. Large maggots of 17–18 millimeters were feeding in the victim's nose. However, on other sites on her body, only small maggots measuring just 6–9 millimeters were found. To reach a size of 17–18 millimeters for the two species of flies found on the body, it would have taken three weeks in that environment. To grow 6–9 millimeters, it would have taken only seven days.

Other forensic evidence indicated that a three-week postmortem interval was not possible. The victim was last seen alive 10 days earlier. How could the larger maggots be accounted for? Forensic tests showed that maggots collected from her nose contained cocaine. To determine if cocaine could affect maggot growth rate, tissues containing cocaine were provided to maggots in the lab. The results showed that under the influence of cocaine (a stimulant), maggots could grow to 16–17 millimeters in only one week. Paul Catt's postmortem interval estimate of approximately one week was consistent with the other forensic evidence.

Casey Anthony Murder Trial

On July 15, 2008, a Florida woman's call to a 911 operator stated that her two-year-old granddaughter, Caylee, had been missing for 31 days. The woman also reported that Caylee's mother's car smelled like a dead body. On December 11, 2008, Caylee's skeletal remains were found wrapped in a blanket inside a plastic trash bag in a wooded area near her home. Duct tape still adhered to the decomposing skull. Casey Anthony, the mother of two-year-old Caylee, was suspected of suffocating her young daughter, leaving her in the trunk of the car, and later dumping the body in the wooded area. Crime-scene investigators found other evidence at Casey's home that seemed to link Casey to the murder.

In court, forensic entomologist Dr. Neal Haskell testified for the prosecution. Dr. Haskell's expert opinion was that the insect evidence found in the car was consistent with a dead body being in the car 3–5 days. Forensic expert Dr. Arpad Vass testified that he found gases consistent with a decomposing body present in the car where flies also were found. A blowfly's leg and hundreds of dried coffin fly larvae, pupae, and adults were recovered from the car. Coffin flies, which are small enough to get into tight spaces, are so named because they have been known to breed on human corpses sealed in coffins. They are not the first to arrive on a dead body, preferring later stages of decomposition. Given the high temperatures in Florida, the arrival of coffin flies in a 3–5 day interval was possible. Dr. Haskell testified that the low number of blowflies was due to the body being wrapped in blankets and plastic and locked in the car. Blowflies were too large to get to the wrapped body.

Casey Anthony's car.

For the defense, forensic entomologist Dr. Tim Huntington testified that the flies were in the car due to garbage, and that there was no evidence that a dead body was ever in the car. Dr. Haskell countered Dr. Huntington's claim by stating that coffin flies are not typically garbage feeders; they feed primarily on the products of human and animal decomposition. The highly publicized six-week trial resulted in the jury finding Casey Anthony not guilty of the murder of her daughter. The jury's verdict surprised many who had closely followed the court proceedings.

Chigger Bites Link Suspect to a Crime Scene

The body of a 24-year-old woman was discovered under a large eucalyptus tree in California. The sheriff's department investigated the scene from 10 P.M. until 2 A.M.. Twenty of the twenty-three members of the investigation team complained of itchy red bites on their ankles, waist, and buttocks, which were identified as chigger bites. (Chiggers are mite larvae.) The same types of bites in similar locations were found on one of the suspects. Dr. James Webb, an entomologist, was consulted and confirmed the presence of chiggers at the crime scene. The suspect claimed to have fleabites he received at his sister's home. However, when investigators went to his sister's home, they found no evidence of fleas or chiggers. Because of the pattern and type of bite marks and the limited distribution of chiggers in that area, the jury convicted him of murder.

DIFFERENTIATED LEARNERS

Teaching Gifted Students
Research the chemistry of decomposition. Investigate the work of decomposition expert Dr. Arpad Vass. How has new technology assisted in the identification of decomposition gases?

DIFFERENTIATED LEARNERS

Teaching Gifted Students
Have students read the transcripts of the expert testimony of Dr. Neal Haskell and Dr. Timothy Huntington at the Casey Anthony murder trial. The two experts disagreed on the implications of the insect evidence in Casey Anthony's car. Have students summarize who built the stronger case and who provided stronger rebuttal testimony.

Explore

Have students research the evidence that was found to link Casey Anthony to the death of her daughter. How did the defense dispute the evidence? Besides forensic entomology expert witnesses, what other types of expert witnesses were called by the prosecutor's office? Research how the hot Florida temperatures would affect the rate of decomposition of a body left locked in a car during the summer.

Careers *in Forensics*

Careers

To see some of Dr. Haskell's work on accumulated degree hours, see his article "Using Timelines to Learn Forensics," in the Spring 2014 issue of *Forensic Teacher Magazine*.

Dr. Neal Haskell is the "go-to guy" when it comes to maggots. Dr. Haskell is one of the pioneers in forensic entomology and one of the few certified forensic entomologists in the country. He was the first person in the United States to graduate with a Master's and Ph.D. in forensic entomology and the first full-time forensic entomologist consultant. His pig research projects from 1984 to 1993 helped answer questions such as, What types of flies arrive on dead bodies? What are the high and low temperature limits for insects? Is there a difference between urban and rural insects of decomposition? When do flies get up in the morning and when do they sleep? And does insect succession occur on pig carcasses the same way it does on dead human bodies? Dr. Haskell was one of the founders of the American Board of Forensic Entomology. He has given hundreds of scientific lectures, seminars, and training sessions to medical examiners, coroners, death-scene investigators, and teachers on how to use entomological evidence from death scenes. Dr. Haskell works with many police departments, the FBI, and coroner's offices, and has worked on more than 1,200 cases worldwide. He's provided expert testimony in more than 125 trials and hearings throughout the United States and Canada. He provides simple explanations to help jurors understand the fascinating world of maggots, flies, and dead bodies.

How does someone get involved in the world of insects, maggots, and decomposition? Dr. Haskell had a career path filled with twists and turns that ultimately provided him with a background in farming, entomology, and criminal investigation. At the age of 12, he attended a 4-H conservation camp where an instructor named Dave Matthews ignited a spark that resulted in a love of entomology. In 1969, Dr. Haskell completed his degree in entomology from Purdue University. After graduation, he

Photo by Jean Witherington

returned to the family farm. While farming, he worked as a special deputy for the Sheriff's Department and he assisted with death investigations. In 1984, he decided to go back to school. His former professors at Purdue suggested that he combine his background in crime fighting with his academic background in entomology to study forensic entomology.

At the 1984 Entomology Society of America Symposium, the first-ever forensic entomology symposium, Dr. Haskell met leading forensic entomologists Paul Catts, Bernard Greenbergh, M. Lee Goff, and Lamar Meek. After learning that most of the work on insects at that time was being done on the primary screwworm fly of Texas, Dr. Haskell decided to document forensic insects in other areas. On his Indiana farm, he spent nights camped out alongside decomposing pigs to determine if any fly activity took place at night. In 1988, Bill Bass (director of the Knoxville, Tennessee, Body Farm) invited Dr. Haskell to conduct research to compare the effects of flies on human and pig decomposition.

Currently, Dr. Haskell is a Professor of Forensic Science and Biology at Saint Joseph's College in Rensselaer, Indiana, and director of a Master's of Science program in Forensic Science and Forensic Entomology. At his Indiana farm, law-enforcement officers, coroners, lawyers, and teachers attend his forensics workshops. He frequently provides expert witness testimony in court cases such as the Casey Anthony murder trial in Florida, the Van Dam murder in California, and the West Memphis Three trial in Arkansas (the Damien Echols trial). Dr. Haskell has appeared on many real-crime television programs such as *Forensic Files*. When asked if he will retire soon, his answer is an emphatic *"No."* He claims he's having too much fun. He also hopes to continue educating future forensic entomologists for quite some time.

APPS

▶ **"SmartInsects" crime-scene insect identification**

True or False

1. Adult flies are attracted to dead bodies because of the odors.
   Obj. 11.5, 11.6

2. Wasps arrive after the blowflies because they feed on blowfly larvae and eggs. *Obj. 11.6*

3. Insect evidence is the most accurate method to estimate a postmortem interval if the victim has been dead less than 24 hours. *Obj. 11.7*

4. A well-trained forensic entomologist can always determine PMI using insect evidence only. *Obj. 11.1*

5. When estimating a postmortem interval, it's important to factor into the interval the fact that flies and beetles don't lay eggs at night. *Obj. 11.7*

Multiple Choice

6. Which is the correct sequence of developmental stages for blowflies?
   Obj. 11.2
   a) egg, larva, pupa, adult
   b) egg, second instar, third instar, pupa, adult
   c) egg, pupa, maggot, adult
   d) first instar, second instar, third instar, pupa, adult

7. What is one reason why insect evidence at crime scenes is often not collected? *Obj. 11.9*
   a) Most insects are only active at night.
   b) Insect evidence is only found during active decay.
   c) Investigators are often not properly trained to find and collect insects.
   d) Insects can't be found if the body is buried or covered.

8. Which represents the normal sequence of decomposition? *Obj. 11.5*
   a) fresh, active decay, dry decay, bloated, advanced decay
   b) bloated, advanced decay, active decay, dry decay, fresh
   c) fresh, dry decay, bloated, active decay, advanced decay
   d) fresh, bloated, active decay, advanced decay, dry decay

9. Which is true regarding spiracle slits of a blowfly larva? *Obj. 11.3*
   a) They are found only on the first instar.
   b) They are useful in estimating the age of a blowfly larva.
   c) They are used for release of undigested food.
   d) Both a and b are correct.

Compare and Contrast

10. Second instar and third instar of the blowfly *Obj. 11.2, 11.3*

11. The preferred food source for blowfly larvae and the preferred food source for carrion beetle larvae *Obj. 11.6*

12. The anterior end of a blowfly and the posterior end of a blowfly *Obj. 11.3*

Chapter 11 Review

True or False

1. True
2. True. Wasps are insect predators.
3. False. Other methods are more accurate if the body is dead for less than 2 days.
4. False. They can provide a range of time from when insects colonize the body until when the body was found. If the body was moved and insects could not get to the body, the person could have died earlier.
5. True

Multiple Choice

6. a
7. c
8. d; active decay precedes advanced decay (see the Summary)
9. b

Compare and Contrast

10. Second instar is smaller than third. The second has a visible crop seen on the back (dorsal) anterior region. The third instar no longer has a visible crop due to accumulation of fat, and at the end of that stage, the crop is emptied. The third instar will migrate away from the body to find a dry, shady area to pupate.

11. Blowfly larvae feed on fresh decomposing tissue, whereas carrion beetle larvae may feed on drier later-stage decomposing tissue or eggs and larvae of other organisms.

12. Anterior end: more pointed; two black moving hooks to anchor into food and scrape food. Posterior end: more rounded; last segment contains two circular regions that contain spiracle slits used for respiration.

Short Answer

13. a. The presence of flies may indicates a decomposing body.

b. Insects inhabit an area based on its environmental conditions. Insects collected from a crime scene can help determine the location of the crime.

c. If the body was buried shortly after death, there would be less blowfly evidence on the body.

d. Drug use of a deceased person may be determined by analyzing the human tissue ingested by larvae.

14. The environmental conditions determine the vegetation in an area. Environmental conditions are important to determine what species of insects would be found in an area and to factor into how conditions affected the growth of any insects found at the crime scene.

15. Maggots migrate to pupate; those off the body are older than the ones on the body. If you fail to look in the area around the body, you may think that no insects inhabited the body.

16. This shows that a full life cycle of insects has taken place and can provide a minimum amount of time since death.

17. These are the oldest and will best give you a better estimate of a postmortem interval.

18. Beetles eat each other.

19. Live larvae are sent to the lab so they can be raised to adulthood. Identification of larvae is much more difficult than identification of adults. A second reason for sending the live larvae is that the lab can raise adults that then can mate and lay eggs. At the lab, the technicians will try to duplicate the crime-scene environmental

Short Answer

13. For each of the following, describe how insects can be useful in solving a crime: *Obj. 11.1*
    a) indicating where a body is hidden *Obj. 11.2, 11.5, 11.6*
    b) determining the primary crime scene: rural road, vacant lot, desert, woods, open field, etc. *Obj. 11.4*
    c) determining that the body was buried shortly after death *Obj. 11.2, 11.4, 11.5, 11.6, 11.7*
    d) determining if the deceased was under the influence of drugs *Obj. 11.8*

14. At crime scenes, investigators need to record information about the habitat and the environmental conditions. Relate the importance of habitat and environmental conditions to the forensic entomologist's interpretation of the insect evidence. *Obj. 11.1, 11.6*

15. Why is it necessary to collect larvae from around a body, not just on the body? *Obj. 11.2, 11.4, 11.6*

16. What value is there in collecting empty pupal cases from a crime scene where no live insects are evident? *Obj. 11.2, 11.4*

17. If there are various stages of larvae on the corpse, why should you collect the largest samples? *Obj. 11.1, 11.4*

18. If live adult beetles are collected using a net, why is it important to place them in individual jars when shipping them to a forensic entomologist? *Obj. 11.6, 11.9*

19. What is the significance of sending live larvae to a forensic lab? Why not send just preserved specimens? *Obj. 11.1, 11.7, 11.9*

20. Refer to the case studies described above.
    a) In the Casey Anthony murder trial, what was the basis for Dr. Haskell's opinion that a dead body had been in the car for 3–5 days? *Obj. 11.1, 11.5, 11.6*
    b) In the chigger bite case study, what evidence did the forensic scientist cite that supported his claim that the bites on the ankles of both the investigators and suspect were chigger bites and not from some other insect? *Obj. 11.1, 11.9*
    c) Refer to Paul Catts's Case of the Massive Maggots. *Obj. 11.1, 11.4, 11.8*
        i. What is the significance of the phrase "massive maggots?"
        ii. Since maggots of the same fly species but of two very different sizes were collected from the corpse, how did Dr. Catts determine that both sizes of maggots were on the body for seven days?

Going Further

1. Investigate the different types of forensically useful insects that can be found in your region. Research the times of year different insects are found, and describe their food source.

2. Read Dr. Neal Haskell's article "Using Timelines to Learn Forensics," *The Forensic Teacher Magazine*, Spring 2014, Vol. 8 No. 23, pp. 25–32. Complete the activity on calculating postmortem intervals. Summarize how to calculate postmortem intervals using accumulated degree days.

conditions as closely as possible to determine how long it takes to reach the developmental stages found at the time of collection.

20. a. Coffin flies are not attracted to a fresh body; they arrive after the body has started to decompose. With the high temperatures of a closed car in Florida during the summer, a body would decompose rapidly and seep decomposition fluid. Finding coffin flies in the car would be consistent with the presence of decomposition fluids and a body that had been in the car for several days.

b. Chiggers have specific environmental restrictions. When chiggers bite, they tend to bite in areas where skin and clothing meet, such as the ankles, waist, and buttocks. Similar bite marks and bite patterns were found on the suspect and investigators. Also, no fleas or chiggers were present on the sister's property where the suspect stated he received the bite marks.

3. Design an experiment to collect data to answer one of the following questions:
    a) How does temperature affect the developmental rate of blowflies?
    b) How far will larvae migrate when looking for areas to pupate?
    c) What is the temperature difference between a maggot mass and the ambient temperature?
    d) Which of the factors below seems to have the greatest effect on when egg-laying occurs?
        i. direct sunlight versus shade
        ii. strong wind versus no breeze
        iii. clothed versus unclothed body

c. i. Some maggots of the same species were more than twice as large as others on the body.
   ii. Paul Catts conducted an experiment in the lab where he fed larvae cocaine to see if it was possible for insects to grow to lengths of 16–17 mm in just seven days. His experiment provided evidence that supported his claim that larvae of two different sizes could have been on the body for only seven days.

Bibliography

Bass, Bill, and Jon Jefferson. *Death's Acre: Inside the Legendary Forensic Lab, the Body Farm, Where the Dead Do Tell Tales.* New York: Putnam, 2003.

Byrd, J. H., and J. L. Castner, editors. *Entomological Evidence: The Utility of Arthropods in Legal Investigations, 2nd Edition.* Florida: CRC, 2000.

Castner, J. L., and J. H. Byrd. *Forensic Insect Identification Cards.* Gainesville, FL: Feline, 2001.

Catts, E. Paul, and Neal H. Haskell, editors. *Entomology and Death, a Procedural Guide.* Forensic Entomology Associates, 1990.

Erzinclioglu, Zakaria. *Maggots, Murder, and Men.* New York: St. Martin's, 2000.

Goff, M. Lee. *A Fly for the Prosecution: How Insect Evidence Helps Solve Crimes.* Cambridge, MA: Harvard University Press, 2000.

Haskell, Neal. "Using Timelines to Learn Forensics." *The Forensic Teacher Magazine*, Spring 2014, Vol. 8 No. 23, pp. 25–32.

Kamal, A. S. "Comparative study of thirteen species of *Sarcosaprophagous Calliphoridae* and *Sarcophagidae (Diptera)* I. Bionomics." *Ann. Entomology. Soc. Am.* 51 (1958): 261–271.

Sachs, Jessica Snyder. *Corpse.* New York: Basic Books, 2001.

Walker, Maryalice. *Entomology and Palynology.* Philadelphia: Mason Crest, 2006.

Internet Resources

ngl.cengage.com/forensicscience2e (Gale Forensic Science eCollection)
https://canvas.instructure.com/courses/825004
http://www.forensic-entomology.com/index.html
www.wired.co.uk/news/archive/2012-09/28/corpse-dna-identified-maggots
http://www.pbs.org/wnet/nature/episodes/crime-scene-creatures/
    interactive-determine-the-time-of-death/4390/
www.theforensicteacher.com/Home_files/Haskell_lab.pdf
http://thedragonflywoman.com/2011/02/21/hand-sanitizer-preservation
http://www.forensicmag.com/articles/2009/08/crime-scene-photography-capturing-scene
http://extension.entm.purdue.edu/401Book/default.php?page=know_insects
http://www.hexapod.ca/invertebrates/preparing1.htm
www.forensicentomology.org
http://www.arkive.org/house-fly/musca-domestica/photos.html

Tutorials

Search the Internet for "NCSSMDistanceEd" and "Postmortem Interval" Parts 1 through 5
https://canvas.instructure.com/courses/825004 Online interactive activity on postmortem intervals

Background

There are four additional activities on the IRCD:

11-5 Processing a Crime Scene for Forensic Insect Evidence (Act 11-5 Processing)

11-6 Jigsaw Activity (Act 11-6 Jigsaw)

11-7 Calculating Accumulated Degree Hours (Act 11-7 ADH)

11-8 Forensic Entomology Case Study (Act 11-8 CS)

Time Required to Complete the Activity

4–6 weeks; time will vary depending on the environmental conditions.

Safety Precautions

Instruct students to wear gloves and avoid directly handling the flies in order to reduce exposure to bacteria. After handling the flies or their growing chamber, remind students to wash their hands. Sometimes mold will develop on the liver. Make sure that students who are allergic to mold do not come in contact with it. Properly dispose of the trash. Remind students to wash their hands thoroughly with soap and water before leaving the lab.

Teaching Tip

If raising flies is not feasible at your school, suggest this as a student project that would be completed at home. Not every student (or parent) will be interested in raising flies, so this could be an extended project or quarterly project for a student or a group of students. Students should record video clips and take digital images that can be shared with the class.

Teaching Tip

- Do not use metal cans because these will conduct heat and may get too hot outside.
- Liver is only one of many raw meat sources that can be used for this experiment.

ACTIVITY 11-1

How to Raise Blowflies for Forensic Entomology

Obj. 11.2, 11.3, 11.4, 11.6

Objectives:

By the end of this activity, you will be able to:

1. Raise blowflies using beef liver.
2. Photograph the different stages of development of the blowfly.
3. Distinguish among stages of development.
4. Document each stage of development recording the time and temperature.
5. Determine the accumulated degree hours required for each stage of development at a constant temperature.
6. Determine the accumulated degree hours required for development from egg to adult when raised at a constant temperature.

Scenario:

On a hot summer day in Florida, a decomposing female body was found in a park. An elderly woman suffering from dementia is on the missing person's list. When the crime-scene investigators arrived, they found blowfly larvae around the head. Unopened pupal cases were under the leaf litter near the body. The forensic entomologist needs to determine how long the body has been colonized by blowfly larvae. Is the postmortem interval estimate consistent with the length of time that the woman was missing?

Introduction:

Raising, observing, and photographing the different blowfly stages of development is exciting and inexpensive. The body changes that occur during this complete metamorphosis are amazing. This activity simulates the growth of blowflies on decomposing bodies. You will be able to observe each stage and the amount of time the insect spends at each developmental stage.

Female flies are attracted to rotting meat or decomposing bodies by the odor, usually within minutes. However, if the environment is too hot, cold, sunny, shady, windy, or rainy, the flies may not lay eggs. By placing the food container inside an open cardboard box, it is possible to modify the environment to ensure more egg-laying. Before laying eggs, adult female flies suck up some of the fluids around the meat or decomposing body. Egg-laying usually occurs within an hour of the flies' arrival. Once one female begins laying eggs, pheromones (species-specific odors) are released and more flies will lay eggs. Preferred egg-laying sites on the meat will be inside cuts and inside folds.

Female blowfly; note that her eyes are widely separated.

© iStock.com/Gewoldi

Note that fly larvae move away from light. Be prepared to immediately photograph the larvae when you take the cover off of your collection container or remove the larvae from the meat.

Teaching Gifted Students
Rather than provide the procedure for raising flies, ask students to design a way to collect flies and raise them under controlled temperatures.

At-Risk Students
Review with students how to calculate the degree hours required for each stage of development.

Time Required to Complete the Activity: 4–6 weeks

Blowfly developmental rates depend on environmental conditions. Development occurs faster in warmer temperatures. Once the eggs are deposited, the remaining development can be accomplished inside under controlled temperatures.

SAFETY PRECAUTIONS:

Wear gloves and avoid directly handling the flies in order to reduce exposure to bacteria. After handling the flies or their growing chamber, wash your hands. Sometimes mold will develop on the liver if it is covered. Do not smell the mold. If you are allergic to mold, alert your teacher. Properly dispose of the trash as instructed by your teacher. Wash your hands thoroughly with soap and water before leaving the lab.

Materials:

Act 11-1 SH

Act 11-1 SH Daily Data (optional)

frozen beef liver (Do not use chicken liver due to the foul odor.)

large (27.8 oz or larger) empty *plastic* coffee container (Containers with a recessed handle work well, but any wide-mouthed plastic container that is at least 8" tall will do.)

Some materials for the activity.

© Cengage Learning®

sharp knife to cut the liver

tall kitchen-sized trash can with a top (If no top is available, use a cardboard box for a top; the top of a printer-paper box usually works well.)

open cardboard box at least 12" tall

torn-up pieces of cardboard

4 plastic kitchen trash can liners

thermometer

digital camera (optional)

Procedure:
Photographing the Process

1. Take close-up photos of each stage of development using a zoom lens. With a zoom lens, it is possible to see the ovipositor (egg depositor on the posterior end of the female) as the female lays eggs. When larvae are visible, take short videos that show the use of their hooks while they feed and move across the liver. Photograph the spiracles and the crop. For better close-up photos, remove larvae and pupae from the container.

2. Try to videotape adults emerging from their pupal cases. When the adults attempt to emerge from the pupal case, you will see the ptilium, a fluid-filled balloon-like structure, inflate and deflate from one end of the pupal case. The immature adult's head emerges from the "popped top," followed by the first pair of legs. Once the head comes out, emergence progresses quickly. Note that the immature adult's wings are not fully extended.

Teaching Tip

Ask students to devise a way to make sure that the rearing chamber of the eggs, larvae, and pupae is kept at a constant temperature throughout the experiment.

Teaching Tip

Not all students understand how to use the zoom lens when taking photos. It would be beneficial to review this with your students in advance. You might use student experts who work with different groups of students and show them the best way to photograph the developing flies.

Not all students know how to edit and crop photos. Working in small groups, assign one student in each group who can provide instruction for his or her group on how to edit photos.

Teaching Tip

Students who do not want to handle the flies and the larvae can view them from a distance by using a flex camera or a projecting device. Remember that larvae do not like light, so keep the meat with the larvae covered until just before you want to show them.

Teaching Tip

You can get very good looks at larvae by photographing them with a computer tablet at the highest possible resolution and then enlarging the images onscreen.

Teaching Tip

Review with students the concept of how to draw insects to scale. Review the average size of eggs, larvae, and pupae so that students understand how much larger the third instar will be than the egg.

Teaching Tip

Review with students how to distinguish first, second, and third instar before they begin to rear the larvae.

Teaching Tip

Place examples of the second instar larvae in closed glass dishes. Students can view the larvae under a stereomicroscope or hand lens. Ask students to observe and describe differences in the anterior and dorsal ends, and ventral and dorsal sides. See if any students can observe the crop, spiracles, or mouth hooks. If a larger lens is available, students may be able to see setae on the larvae.

Rearing Chambers and Collecting Fly Eggs

3. Defrost the liver. Using a knife, make several slices on the surface of the liver. Add the liver to the plastic empty coffee container. If possible, fold the liver to create a surface that is not totally flat.

4. Place the container with the liver inside an open cardboard box (at least 12 inches tall). For size reference in your photos, place a coin on top of the liver. Put the box with the liver outside or in an area that has flies. To avoid disturbance by other animals, elevate the box. Leave the can in that area for several hours until you can see white masses of fly eggs.

Flies depositing eggs.

5. Once egg masses are deposited, bring the container with the liver inside where temperatures can be regulated above 16 degrees Celsius (61 degrees Fahrenheit). A small, dark closet could be converted into a temporary fly nursery. If flies are raised outside, you run the risk of fly eggs and larvae being consumed by insect predators.

6. Line the inside of a tall kitchen-sized trash can with two plastic trash liners. Tear up and fold pieces of cardboard and place them in the bottom of the trash can. This provides a dry, dark place for the larvae to hide. Once eggs are laid on the liver, put the plastic container with the liver and eggs inside the trash can on top of the folded cardboard. *Do not cover* the plastic container holding the liver or the top of the trash can at this point. If you do, it may result in mold growing on the liver. There should not be any odor at this point and the larvae will not migrate for at least a few days.

7. After a couple of days, cover the trash can with the top of a cardboard box. This keeps the area dark and prevents insect predators from entering.

Developing Flies

8. The most rapid developmental changes occur in the first seven days. Therefore, you will want to make more observations during the first week. In Data Table 1, record the total time an individual stays in each stage of development. To calculate the degree hours spent at each stage, multiply the temperature (in degrees Celsius) times the number of hours spent at each stage.

Changing the Lining of the Trash Can

9. At the end of the third instar stage, the larvae will stop eating and migrate away from the liver. They crawl up the coffee container and drop down into the cut-up cardboard at the bottom of the trash can. Once all larvae have left the liver, remove and discard the plastic container with the residual liver.

DIFFERENTIATED LEARNERS

Gifted Students
Ask that your more-advanced students read Neal Haskell's article on accumulated degree hours. Students with math issues would find it challenging, but more-advanced students should have no problems with the article.

DIFFERENTIATED LEARNERS

English-Language Learners
Ask these students to use a camera and film short video clips of the developing flies. Narrations can be added after the video clip is filmed.

10. Wearing gloves, shake out, remove, and discard the torn-up cardboard. Because the larvae feed on the liver and crawl over it, they will leave some liver residue on the sides of the liner and on the cardboard. Remove the soiled plastic liner and larvae from the garbage container. Put the bag of larvae aside for a moment.

Maggots migrating.

© Cengage Learning®

11. Add a clean plastic liner to the trash can. (There should always be two inside the can.) Add freshly torn and folded cardboard to the bottom of the trash can. Empty the larvae from the soiled bag into the newly lined trash can. (There is no need to handle any of the larvae at this point unless you want to take a better close-up photo.)

12. Discard the soiled trash can liner and cardboard. Once the soiled cardboard and liner have been removed, there should no longer be any odor. To ensure that the larvae will not escape from the lined trash can, you can fold over or tie the top of the bag.

Act 11-1 Data Table

Stage	Date and Time First Noted	Date and Time Last Observed	Sketch	Temperature (Degrees Celsius)	Hours at the Stage	Degree Hours (Temp × Hours)
Egg						
First Instar						
Second Instar						
Third Instar						
Pupa						
Adult						

Reflecting on the Activity

1. Reflect on this activity and your observations of fly development.
   a. What part of this activity did you find the most interesting and why?
   b. Describe three important concepts that you learned about fly development.
   c. What obstacles did you encounter while trying to raise the flies?
   d. How would you modify this activity to improve your results?

2. Refer to the opening scenario describing the recovery of a body in Florida and the blowfly evidence. Summarize how the data from this experiment on blowfly development could be applied to estimating the postmortem interval for that case.

Going Further:

1. Prepare a presentation featuring your photos of each stage of development. The presentation can be done using PowerPoint, posters, scrapbooking, or another method approved by your teacher. Each stage should be identified and described.

2. Refer to the article by Dr. Neal Haskell entitled "Using Timelines to Learn Forensics," *The Forensic Teacher*, Vol. 8 Issue 23, Spring 2014, p. 25 to learn more about how accumulated degree hours are calculated to help solve crimes.

3. Design and conduct an experiment to test whether egg-laying blowflies have a food preference.

DIFFERENTIATED LEARNING

Teaching Gifted Students

Encourage motivated students to research carrion beetles and design an investigation to study their development. Students should include the food they require, and a table of the descriptions of different life stages and the time spent at each stage.

Mini-Projects for Forensic Entomology
Obj. 11.1, 11.2, 11.4, 11.7, 11.9

Your teacher may suggest that you do one or more of the following mini-projects in lieu of some of the longer activities in the chapter. When your project is completed, you will have the opportunity to present it to your class or a larger group.

For Activities 1 through 5, you should include the following information:

- Physical description of the insect at different stages of development
- Physical description of the insect's habitat and surroundings
- Description of the insect's food at different stages of development
- Description of how the insect ingests and digests its food at different stages of development
- Description of how the insect obtains oxygen
- Description of any movements or migrations made during development
- Any encounters with predators and a description of the predator
- Digital photos taken as the insect progresses from one stage to another

1. **Blowfly Autobiography**

   Write an autobiography from the viewpoint of the fly as it develops on decomposing tissue from an egg into adulthood.

2. **Baby Book, Scrapbook, or PowerPoint Presentation**

   Document the development of the blowfly in the format of a baby book, scrapbook, or PowerPoint presentation. This can be done on paper, on poster board, or electronically. Each photo should have a label with a brief description.

3. **Maggot Home Movies**

   Using footage of developing insects, document the development of blowflies. Add a voiceover narrating the development of the blowfly.

4. **Creative Writing**

   Select from a variety of genres such as poems, rap, songs, or short stories. Your writing should contain sound scientific information that describes in some manner the development of a blowfly egg on decomposing flesh through adulthood. Be creative in the nonscience portion of the writing, but make sure your science is accurate.

5. **Insect Stage Models**

   Construct a model depicting the stages in blowfly development from egg on decomposing flesh to adult. Make sure that the structures on your developing blowfly and the relative sizes of the stages are accurate and correct size proportions. Present your completed model to the class, describing each stage.

6. **Expert Witness Testimony**

   Partner with another student to present testimony from an actual or fictitious case study. One of you will be the expert forensic entomologist testifying, and the other will play the role of the lawyer cross-examining the entomologist. (Remember that the best cross-examiners have an excellent knowledge of the expert witness's field of expertise.) The forensic entomologist expert witness

Time Required to Complete the Activity
Time depends on the projects chosen.

Safety Precautions
There are no safety precautions for this activity.

Teaching Tip
You may prefer that students complete one or more of these projects as alternative assessments in lieu of a chapter test. The formats described could all be useful as alternative assessments. If you do not have enough class time for all students to present their topics, consider doing the presentations after school and invite parents, teachers, and other students. Consider having the students present to senior citizens, community groups, or other classes (keeping in mind that the topic of body decomposition is an unpalatable or upsetting one for some individuals).

Teaching Tip
Expert Witness Testimony: Working in pairs, one student supplies expert witness testimony regarding an actual or fictitious case study. The other student plays the role of the lawyer cross-examining the expert. Students should support any claims. The forensic entomologist expert witness should assume that the jurors have no science background and the educational level of middle school students. This presentation can be done live in front of the class (jurors), or if students prefer, they can videotape the presentation and then present it to the class.

Mini-poster: Each pair selects one species of insect to research. Mini-poster presentations are constructed and then presented to the class. Many colleges use this format. This is an excellent way to have students cover the variety of forensically useful flies, beetles, and wasps that are attracted to a decomposing body. Divide the class in half and then into groups of two: one group presents their mini-posters while the other group moves among the presenting groups in groups of two, listening and asking questions. Switch roles after all students have viewed and heard the presentations.

Teaching Tip

You may wish to provide students with presentation review sheets to fill out for each presentation they visit to keep both visitors and presenters on task.

should assume that the jurors have no science background and have only the educational level of middle-school students. Remember to support any claims with sufficient and reliable scientific evidence. Your presentation to the class (jurors) can be done live, or if your teacher allows, you may present it on video.

7. **Mini-Poster**

With a partner, select one species of insect useful to forensic research. Staple three manila folders together to create a foldable, free-standing mini-poster. Each team selects one type of insect to research. One half of the class will present while another group reviews the presentations. Then the presenters become the reviewers while the other half of the class presents. Include in your poster the following:

- Classification (fly, beetle, wasp, ant)
- Basic body form
- Diet for the adult and larva
- Habitat and niche
- Time of arrival at the decomposing body
- Photos or other images

8. **Engineering and Design**

Design one of the following projects, or design a different project that is related to insect development. All projects will be presented to the class.

A. Design a way to collect and raise blowflies in two different environments. Observe differences in their development. Prepare data tables that document the difference in growth.

B. Design a chamber to collect blowflies and other forensic insects outdoors in an open environment. Your design should include some type of structure that will allow odors to escape and blowflies to enter. Your design also needs a component that excludes predators that may disturb the experiment. Photograph your decomposition insect study, documenting the various types of insects that arrive and the different growth stages that they exhibit.

C. Design a rearing chamber for blowflies that will be kept at a constant temperature (above 16 degrees Celsius or 61 degrees Fahrenheit) throughout the experiment. Determine the accumulated degree hours required for each stage of development using the constant temperature of your rearing chamber and the number of hours you observed the insect to be at that stage.

ACTIVITY 11-3

Observation of Blowflies or Houseflies *Obj. 11.2, 11.3, 11.4*

Objectives:

By the end of this activity, you will be able to:

1. Distinguish between male and female adult blowflies based on eye position.
2. Define the terms *anterior, posterior, dorsal,* and *ventral* and locate those areas on both adults and larvae.
3. Locate and describe the function of mouth hooks, spiracles, crops, and setae in the larval forms.
4. Locate and state the function of antennae, proboscis, and maxillary palps.
5. Compare and contrast the feeding mechanisms of fly adults and larvae.
6. Relate the significance of larval structures to forensic entomology.

Introduction:

This activity provides an opportunity to view blowflies and/or houseflies and to view some of the important organs in larvae, pupae, and adults. Adult flies ingest food using a *proboscis,* a siphon-like mouthpart. Larvae feed on decomposing body tissues by using hooks to scrape it off in "bite-size" pieces. Larvae store food in a *crop,* which is a dark structure visible through the skin in the second instar larval stage.

Head
Thorax
Wing
Abdomen

Antenna
Eye
Maxillary palps
Proboscis

Source: University of Sydney

SAFETY PRECAUTIONS:

Wear gloves during this activity. Live specimens can be kept inside closed petri dishes to prevent any spread of bacteria. Wash hands thoroughly after working with flies.

Time Required to Complete the Activity: Two 45-minute periods

Materials:

Act 11-3 SH Data Table 1
Act 11-3 SH Data Table 2
preserved or living specimens of adult blowflies or houseflies
preserved or living specimens of second or third instar larvae of blowflies or houseflies
preserved, pinned, or living specimens of blowfly or housefly pupae

Time Required to Complete the Activity

Two 45-minute periods for observation and research

Safety Precautions

Students should wear gloves when working with flies. Live specimens can be kept inside closed petri dishes to prevent any spread of bacteria. Wash hands thoroughly after working with flies.

Teaching Tip

Depending on the level of your students and the time you have to complete this activity, you can either give this guided activity procedure to the students, or give the students the organisms and ask them to observe, discover, research, and identify different structures without any background information other than what was presented in the chapter. Students should discuss their observations in group or class discussions.

Teaching Tip

The instructor should prepare larvae in viewing chambers in advance of class. One method is to use a small piece of plastic foam and cut a small opening (with a dissecting needle or drill bit) into the surface large enough that just the larva's anterior region fits. The posterior end will remain upright and it will be much easier to focus on the spiracles using the stereomicroscope. This is much easier and cleaner than the students trying to hold the larva upright while focusing the microscope on the spiracles. Remind students that the stage of larval development can be determined by checking the shape of the spiracle openings.

Teaching Tip

To preserve larvae for a short time, place them in near-boiling water for 30 seconds and transfer them to 75–90% ethyl alcohol. The boiling water is not essential, but it will help maintain the size of the larvae. (If you want to preserve larvae for a longer time, a stronger chemical solution such as KAA solution is needed to fix them before they are placed in alcohol.) Insects can be preserved in hand sanitizer for several months. Refer to the Website Dragonflywoman. com and search on preserving insects.

Teaching Tip

Preserving insects for an extended time requires that you fix them in KAA solution before they are placed in ethyl alcohol or hand sanitizer. Leave them in the KAA no longer than overnight.(CAUTION: Students should not handle KAA solution or any insects preserved in KAA solution.)

preserved specimens of adult blowflies or houseflies *or* close-up images showing their anterior, posterior, ventral, and dorsal surfaces

gloves

reference books on entomology or forensic entomology

computer with Internet access for research

closed glass petri dishes for viewing specimens

plastic forceps

stereomicroscope or hand lens

ethyl alcohol or hand sanitizer solution

ruler calibrated in millimeters

Procedure Part 1: Larval Forms of Flies

Observe the fly larvae using a hand lens or a stereomicroscope. Complete Data Tables 1 and 2 as you view the insects.

a. Note the shape of the *anterior*, or front, end of the larva. This end is usually more pointed and is the location of the mouth and mouth hooks. Observe how the larva uses these hooks.

b. Observe the more rounded rear, or *posterior*, end of the larva. If you view it directly from the back, you will notice two circular regions that appear as eyes. These are not eyes but are spiracles used for obtaining oxygen.

c. The larva crawls on its *ventral*, or belly surface. If you look very closely with a hand lens, you may be able to see bristle-like structures called *setae*.

d. On the uppermost surface of the larva, or the *dorsal* side, you may see a darkened region under the skin toward the anterior surface. This is the *crop*.

e. Under a stereomicroscope or with a hand lens, you may be able to see inside the posterior area so that you can see the two circular regions that contain spiracle slits. Refer to your text for the difference in the spiracle slits in the second and third instar stages.

f. Measure the length and width of the larva. If the specimen is preserved, it may be somewhat shorter than its living length. You can measure the larva while it's inside the petri dish by aligning a ruler along its body on the outside of the dish.

Procedure Part 2: Pupae

Observe pupal cases using a stereomicroscope or a hand lens. Record all your observations and measurements in Data Table 1.

Procedure Part 3: Adults

Observe a fly under the stereomicroscope. Dead specimens can be viewed more easily than live flies.

1. Notice the three body parts of an adult fly: head, thorax, and abdomen.
   a. The eye position can help distinguish male and female. The female's eyes are broad and spread apart, whereas the male's eyes are so close together that they almost touch. View several flies under the stereomicroscope and see if you can detect any difference in the placement of their eyes.
   b. Notice any markings found on the thorax and abdomen. View other adults and see if they have the same markings. Research houseflies and blowfly adults, and describe the markings found on the thorax of the adults that can be used to identify them. Go to http://www.arkive.org/house-fly/musca-domestica/photos.html and view images of houseflies.
2. Focus on the head of the fly and view it head-on and from the side.
   a. Note the multiple lenses found in the compound eye.
   b. Distinguish the proboscis, antennae, and maxillary palps. Research and describe the function of each of those parts and record your observations in Data Table 2.
3. If you have live adult flies, observe them feeding from close range, noting how the adult sucks up its food using its proboscis. If you don't have a live specimen, go to Arkive.org and search on "housefly" to view images of the mouthparts. Also view the video House fly feeding there, or go to http://www.arkive.org/house-fly/musca-domestica/video-o8.html
4. View the ends of the feet. Notice the hook-like appearance.

Act 11-3 Data Table 1: Morphology of Fly Adults, Larvae, and Pupae

Stage	Sketch	Description	Length (mm)	Width (mm)
Larva anterior				
Larva posterior			Only one larva measurement needed	
Larva ventral				
Larva dorsal				
Pupa				
Adult head				
Adult thorax				
Adult abdomen				

Teaching Tip

Adult flies can be killed by placing them in the freezer for several minutes. Remove them from the freezer and wait 5 minutes before pinning them. An alternative method is to put them in a kill jar that contains cotton balls moistened with 1 or 2 drops of ethyl acetate. Larvae can be killed by putting them into ethyl alcohol.

Teaching Tip

Pin flies soon after they die. Pin the flies to plastic foam plates, cardboard, or wood. Small pins for insects can be purchased from biological supply houses. Flies are pinned through the thorax slightly to the right of center. Beetles are pinned through the wing cover. Make sure the beetle is level, and then push the pin through the insect.

Teaching Tip

Making a forensic fly and beetle collection is an excellent project for students, one that you could use and add to year after year. Obtain the insects from decomposition experiments. References can be found at the end of the activity.

Teaching Tip

Show students the slides and video from the Website http://www.arkive.org/house-fly/musca-domestica/ (Note: Houseflies and blowflies are very similar.)

Answers

1. A more tapered anterior end makes it easier for the flies to burrow into the decomposing flesh.

2. Spiracles on the posterior end make it easier for the larva to feed and breathe at the same time. The larva, once embedded in the decomposing flesh, does not have to come up for air to breathe and can spend more time feeding.

3. A first instar may not have enough food in the crop to be visible. In third instar stage, the larva often has emptied its crop in preparation for pupation.

4. The crop contains ingested tissues of the host and can be used to extract human DNA from the ingested tissues to identify the person; or its contents may be helpful in determining if the human had been using drugs or was poisoned.

5. Maggot masses have temperatures higher than ambient temperatures and can accelerate the rate of growth. A forensic entomologist must consider this when estimating the postmortem interval.

Act 11-3 Data Table 2

Structure	Location	Function	How does this part relate to forensics?
Setae			
Mouth hooks			
Spiracles			
Antennae			
Maxillary palps			
Proboscis			

Questions:

1. Why is it advantageous for the larval forms of flies that feed on decomposing flesh to have a more pointed anterior end?
2. What is the advantage of having spiracle openings on the posterior end of the larvae, and how does this help larvae develop on decomposing bodies?
3. Why is the crop not easily seen in first and third instars?
4. Of what significance is the crop of a larva in forensic entomology?
5. Maggots feeding in a maggot mass on the body can have elevated body temperatures inside the mass. How does this elevated temperature affect the postmortem interval estimate?

Reflections:

1. What did you learn about flies that surprised you?
2. Did you have any misconceptions about flies that were corrected by this activity? If so, what were they?
3. What else would you like to know about flies?

Further Study:

1. Design a way to observe the fly larva's posterior end using a stereomicroscope. The design should allow you to place the larva into an opening so that the posterior end is pointed upward in a fixed position. Once the larva is supported in a fixed position, it is much easier to move the coarse-adjustment knobs of the stereomicroscope to focus on the inside of the spiracle openings.
2. Research the major observable differences in a housefly, blowfly, and flesh fly. How is it possible to easily distinguish among these three flies?
3. Prepare a forensic fly and beetle collection. Research how to kill, pin, identify, and properly label your specimens.

380   **Forensic Entomology**

DIFFERENTIATED LEARNERS

Teaching English-Language Learners

Ask English-language learners to use a camera and film short video clips of the developing flies. Narrations can be added after the video clip is filmed.

Factors Affecting Postmortem Interval Estimates and Accumulated Degree Hours *Obj. 11.2, 11.4, 11.6, 11.7*

Objectives:

At the conclusion of this activity, you will be able to:

1. Analyze and use data regarding the presence of insects found at a crime scene to estimate postmortem intervals.
2. Describe how the presence or absence of insects found at a crime scene provides clues as to what occurred at the crime scene.
3. Apply lower-limit thresholds, adjusted average temperatures, and accumulated degree hours to estimate postmortem intervals.

Introduction:

This activity examines how different factors affect estimation of postmortem intervals. A forensic scientist identifies insects and insect evidence found at a crime scene and calculates when insects first colonized the body. This estimate is made using the accumulated degree hours and local weather conditions. However, since they are living things, insects and their arrival and survival are dependent on other variables, such as when the body arrived at the scene, the condition of the body at the crime scene, and the effects of other organisms at the scene. In this activity, you are asked to analyze and discuss how all those variables can affect the postmortem estimate. You will apply data from accumulated degree-hour studies to estimate a postmortem interval.

SAFETY PRECAUTIONS:

There are no safety precautions for this activity.

Materials:

Act 11-4 SH
paper, pencil, calculator

Procedure:

Read each of the five sections of questions. Analyze the data and discuss the answers while working in small collaborative groups.

Part 1:

The police received a report about a body in the woods behind a local shopping center. The forensic investigators collected five different types of living insects from the body. The insects, eggs, larvae, and pupae were sent to a forensic entomology lab where the eggs, larvae, and pupae were raised to adulthood. Under conditions similar to those found around the dead body. The table below indicates when technicians at the lab found evidence of life for each species.

Forensic Entomology   381

Time Required to Complete the Activity

Two 45-minute class periods

Safety Precautions

There are no safety precautions for this activity.

Teaching Tip

Because of different ability levels of students, you may wish to form small cooperative groups to discuss and analyze each of these questions. Select the cooperative groups to ensure that each group has one student with a strong math background. While students are in their cooperative groups, circulate among the teams to clarify information.

As an alternative to all students answering all questions, each group could be assigned a question and prepare to present and review the question with the entire class.

Part 1 Answers

1. Species A is most likely a blowfly because they arrive soon after the body dies. They are usually the first to arrive on a corpse. The table shows that they are present on day 1.

2. Species D, which did not appear until day 9. In this table, they are the last to arrive. As the corpse decomposes, it would become more dried out. Since these are the last to arrive, it would appear that they prefer a drier habitat to lay their eggs.

3. Possible reasons for no evidence of any living egg, larva, or pupa for species A on day 10: The insects reached adulthood and left the body; the habitat (body) was no longer suitable for producing generations; or predators of species A could have eaten or taken away all of species A.

4. Since species B is the second species to arrive on the corpse, it is possible that species B feeds on the eggs and larvae of Species A.

5. It appears that the person has been dead at least nine days because that is the only day when all five species were present and alive. When insects were reared in the lab under similar conditions, day 9 was the only day that all species were present and alive.

Part 2 Answers

1. If a body was wrapped in a carpet, colonization by blowflies would be delayed due to lack of access. The postmortem interval estimate may need to be adjusted because flies didn't have immediate access to the body.

2. The larger maggot mass would have an elevated temperature due to the activity of all the maggots. Their rate of growth would be accelerated compared to the rate of the growth of the isolated maggots. The postmortem interval estimate would take this into account.

Insect	1	2	3	4	5	6	7	8	9	10
Species A	1	1	1	1	1	1	1	1	1	0
Species B	0	0	0	0	1	1	1	1	1	1
Species C	0	0	0	0	0	0	1	1	1	0
Species D	0	0	0	0	0	0	0	0	1	1
Species E	0	0	0	0	0	1	1	1	1	1

o = No evidence of fly species 1 = Evidence of egg, larva (maggot), or pupa

For each of the following questions, support your answer with evidence from the preceding table.

1. Which species is most likely a blowfly?
2. Which species would prefer the driest habitat for laying its eggs?
3. Notice that on day 10, there was no evidence of any living form of species A. Provide possible explanations as to why no living examples of species A were found on day 10.
4. Based on the data in the chart, which species would most likely feed on blowfly eggs and larvae?
5. Based on the data, how many days have passed since insects first colonized the body?

Part 2:

The postmortem interval is not the same as the time of death. Forensic scientists use insect evidence to determine when insects first colonized the body, which *may* help determine the postmortem interval. But it may not. Death could have occurred days before insects deposited eggs. Consider the following situations and discuss how each could affect when insect eggs were deposited and thus the postmortem interval estimate.

1. The body was wrapped in a large carpet.
2. Maggots were collected from two areas on the body: a large mass was found in a large open wound on the abdomen and a few isolated maggots were found in a small cut on the foot. The maggots from the two sites were of the same species, but the maggots in the large mass were more developed. How can you account for the different rates of development?
3. The body was found next to an active anthill.
4. The meteorological data for the area included two days of heavy rain in the week prior to discovery of the body.
5. It was believed that the person died after sunset.

3. Bodies buried next to an anthill may have a slightly slower rate of development of larvae because the ants are predators of the eggs and could carry them away before they had time to develop into larvae.

4. Most flies will not lay eggs during periods of heavy rain. If the body died on those days, insects would most likely not deposit any eggs during the rain.

5. If the person died after sunset, it is very unlikely that any flies deposited eggs until the next day, since flies do not lay eggs at night. This would need to be considered in the estimation of the postmortem interval.

Part 3:

Discuss what clues about the deceased person could be learned from the following insect evidence:

1. A *buried* body in a field was found with blowfly larvae present on the body.
2. A body found in the *country* in an abandoned barn had blowfly pupal cases near it that were more typical of *urban* species of blowflies.
3. A body found in the bloated stage of decay had an unusually large number of housefly larvae in the genital and anal region of the body.
4. A person known to have died a week earlier was found with fly evidence more typically found in the first few days after death.
5. A body in active decomposition had three maggot masses found—one each on the head, abdomen, and upper back.

Part 4:

Refer to the table below and information in the chapter to answer each of the following questions:

Succession of Adult Insects on Human Cadavers in Tennessee

Key: (-) Small Number; (x) Moderate Number; (X) Large Number				
Insect	**Stages of Decomposition**			
	Fresh	**Bloated**	**Decay**	**Dry Decay**
Blowflies	—xxxxxx	XXXXXXXX	XXxxx——	——
Houseflies	——-xxxx	xXXXXXX	XXXXxxx-	—
Carrion Beetles	—xxx	xXXXXX	Xxxx——	-
Flesh Flies	———	xxxXXXXX	XXXxxxxxx	x—-
Dermestid Beetles		——-	———xxX	XXXXXx—

Sources: Rosina Kyerematen et. al. "Decomposition and insect succession pattern of exposed domestic pig carrion," *Journal of Agricultural and Biological Science*, vol 8 # 11, Nov 2013, p. 761–762; W.C. Rodriguez and W. Bass. 1982. Insect activity and its relationship to decay rates of human cadavers in East Tennessee. University of Tennessee, Knoxville, Tennessee, USA.

1. Notice that the carrion beetle arrives later in the succession than the blowflies and the houseflies. Discuss reasons the carrion beetle's arrival follows the arrival of the flies.
2. According to the table, what stage of decomposition is most likely to have the greatest number of adult insects on the body?
3. Refer to the text discussion of stages of decomposition. How does the bloated stage of decomposition present a different environment than the decay stage of decomposition?
4. Provide an explanation why a predictable insect succession occurs on a body. Include in your answer the chemical and physical effects of decomposition and the effects of different organisms colonizing the body.

Forensic Entomology   383

Explore

Ask students how this type of information (Part 4) can be collected. How could they design an experiment to collect this type of data, not from humans but from something like a store-bought chicken or roadkill?

Refer students to the experimentation that is done on the Body Farm in Tennessee. Ask them to read about how Dr. Neal Haskell researched insects and human decomposition. Ask students why this type of research is needed to help solve crimes.

Part 3 Answers

1. Blowflies do not burrow into the soil to lay their eggs. Therefore, it appears that the body was not immediately buried. During the time between death and when the body was buried, blowflies laid eggs on the body and the body and eggs were later buried together.

2. Insects that are more typical in urban areas but are found in a rural area indicate that the victim died in an urban region and was moved to the rural area.

3. Houseflies are known to be attracted to urine and feces. The high number of houseflies in the genital and anal area indicates the presence of urine and or feces. This may indicate neglect or the person could have been restricted from movement before death.

4. Several explanations are possible. The body could have been refrigerated after death or stored in a cool area without any flies and later taken into a warmer area where flies were present. If the body was immediately buried, flies would not easily get to the body and decomposition would be slowed. If the body was exhumed or if the body was exposed after burial, then it would be available for insects to lay their eggs on the body several days after death.

5. Most insects inhabit the head first due to the number of body openings. The presence of two other maggot masses found on the abdomen and upper back indicate that there was some type of injury or trauma to that area of the body. Areas of trauma or injury are ideal sites for egg deposition.

Part 4 Answers

1. Carrion beetles feed on the larvae of flies as well as on the decomposing body. A later arrival ensures that they would have a greater food supply.

2. The bloated stage would have a greater number of adult insects.

3. The bloated stage is earlier in the decomposition cycle than the decay stage. More fluids are present.

4. Insect succession occurs because the condition of the body changes in a predictable way as the body decomposes. Also, each organism modifies the environment and changes the environment to a point where it may no longer be suitable for that insect. Different organisms that prefer the changed environment follow. The cycle continues in a predicable sequence.

Teaching Tip

Advise students to read the questions in Part 5 carefully. Questions 1 and 2 refer to actual hours spent at a developmental stage, whereas Question 3 refers to accumulated degree hours.

Part 5 Answers

1. Pupa

2. The third instar stage is longer; 48 hours compared to only 20 hours for the second instar stage.

3. It would take 508 hours divided by 24 hours, or 508/24, or approximately 21 days to develop from egg to pupa.

4. Development is faster with increasing temperatures and fewer days are required.

Part 5:

Calliphora vicina was raised in a lab at a constant temperature of 26.7 degrees Celsius. In the lab, it was possible to determine the number of thermal units, or degree hours, required for the insect to reach each stage of development at controlled temperatures. This measurement of thermal units known as degree hours (DH) is obtained by multiplying the number of hours at a stage by the average temperature in degrees Celsius. The accumulated degree hours (ADH) is the sum of the degree hours required to reach that stage.

The temperature must be adjusted using a lower-limit threshold, a temperature below which growth and development cease. In this example, the lower-limit threshold is 10 degrees Celsius. The adjusted temperature reading is 26.7 degrees − 10 degrees or an adjusted temperature of 16.7 degrees. It is written as DH-B10.

To estimate the degree hours (adjusted for the lower-limit threshold) or DH-B10 for egg development, multiply the adjusted average temperature (26.7 − 10 = 16.7) by the number of hour at that stage (24 hours). (16.7 degrees Celsius × 24 hours = 400.8 degree hours. See examples in the following data table.)

Rearing of Calliphora vicina *at a Constant Temperature of 26.7 Degrees Celsius*

Stages	Time (hr)	Accumulated (hr)	Rearing Temperature (degrees Celsius)	Adjusted Temperature Minus Lower Threshold	DH-B10 (adjusted temp × 24 hours)	ADH-B10 (sum of all stages DH-B10)
Egg	24	24	26.7	16.7	400.8	400.8
1st Instar	24	48	26.7	16.7	400.8	801.6
2nd Instar	20	68	26.7	16.7	334.0	1,135.6
3rd Instar	48	116	26.7	16.7	801.6	1,937.2
Prepupa (Migrating Larva)	128	244	26.7	16.7	2,137.6	4,074.8
Pupa	264	508	26.7	16.7	4,408.8	8,483.6

Adapted from A. S. Kamal. "Comparative study of thirteen species of *sarcosaprophagous Calliphoridae* and *Sarcophagidae (Diptera)* I. Bionomics." *Ann. Entomology. Soc. Am. 51 (1958)*:261–271.

Refer to the table "Rearing of *Calliphora vicina* at a Constant Temperature of 26.7 degrees Celsius" to answer the following questions.

1. According to the data, what developmental stage is longest?
2. According to the data, which developmental stage is longer: second or third instar stage?
3. According to the data, if it takes 508 (accumulated) hours to develop from egg to pupa. Convert 508 hours to days.
4. If the temperature were raised to 35 degrees instead of 26.7 degrees Celsius, how would that affect the developmental times?

5. According to the data, at a constant temperature of 26.7 degrees Celsius and a lower limit threshold of 10 degrees, how many degree hours are spent in the second instar larval stage?

6. According to the data, how many accumulated degree hours are required to complete development through the second instar stage?

7. According to the data, how many accumulated degree hours at 26.7 degrees Celsius are required before you see any second instar larvae?

8. Development from egg through the second instar stage requires 1,135.6 ADH when raised at 26.7 degrees Celsius. If the temperature were a constant 20 degrees Celsius, would the ADH be greater, lesser, or the same as the ADH for development through second instar at 26.7 degrees Celsius? Explain your answer.

Going Further:

Refer to the article by Neal Haskell entitled "Using Timelines to Learn Forensics," *The Forensic Science Teacher*, Spring 2014, pp. 25–32. Complete the activity using adjusted average temperatures to estimate the accumulated degree hours and post-mortem intervals.

5. 334 degree hours are spent in the second instar stage.

6. 1,135.6 accumulated degree hours are required to get to the second instar stage.

7. a. Average temperature — lower threshold of 10 degrees C

   b. 20 degrees C — 10 degrees C ~ 10 degrees C.

8. The ADH stays the same.

Chapter Overview

Death is a process that occurs gradually. A precise and universal definition of death does not exist. Evidence collected from the body both at a crime scene and during an autopsy can only allow an estimate of a postmortem interval. Accurate descriptions of the ambient conditions of a crime scene are needed because they affect the rate of chemical and physical postmortem changes that occur during decomposition.

The Big Ideas

When a person dies under unknown or suspicious circumstances, a medical examiner determines the cause, manner, and mechanism of death, along with providing an estimated postmortem interval. These are determined by examining evidence from the body, its location, and the surrounding area. Evidence from decomposition, algor mortis, rigor mortis, livor mortis, and autopsy reports that include imaging and body fluid examination combine to provide this information. The forensic significance of establishing when a person died can be used to include or exclude a suspect. Understanding autolysis and putrefaction, along with marbling, is important. When examining a body, it is important to distinguish what findings are due to factors that occurred before death and what findings are caused by normal decomposition or damage after death.

CHAPTER 12

Death: Manner, Mechanism, Cause

Mysterious Deaths at The Fair

The Washington County Fairgrounds in upstate New York was the site of the 1999 annual county fair. After a rainstorm, well water, the source of drinking water for the event, became contaminated by manure runoff from a nearby cattle barn. The cattle manure carried a variant of *Escherichia coli* bacteria. *E. coli* is a natural, and necessary, inhabitant of our digestive systems, but one strain carried by cattle produces a powerful toxin. The cattle that carry this strain of *E. coli* are unharmed, but humans can become very sick and die from an infection. Two of the 127 confirmed cases of *E. coli* poisoning from the fair died from the infection. The two deaths that occurred included one of the oldest victims, a 79-year-old man, and one of the youngest, a 3-year-old girl. Manner of death—accidental; cause of death—food poisoning/water contamination; mechanism of death—kidney failure.

E. coli bacteria.

NIAID/CDC/Science Source

Escherichia coli is a leading cause of food-borne illness. Scientists estimate there are 265,000 cases of infection and 100 deaths in the United States each year. In addition to eating undercooked meat, people can become infected in many other ways. People have become ill from eating contaminated bean sprouts or fresh leafy vegetables, or through person-to-person contact in families and child-care centers. Infection also can result from drinking raw milk or swimming in or drinking sewage-contaminated water.

386

SCENARIO

Write this sentence from the scenario on the board: Manner of death—accidental; cause of death—food poisoning/water contamination; mechanism of death—kidney failure. Organize students into groups of two, have them read the scenario, and answer the following questions: How would you define manner of death, cause of death, and mechanism of death? What other descriptions or adjectives could be used for manner of death, cause of death, and mechanism of death? What environmental factors contributed to the *E. coli* infections? What precautions could have been taken to prevent the *E. coli* infections?

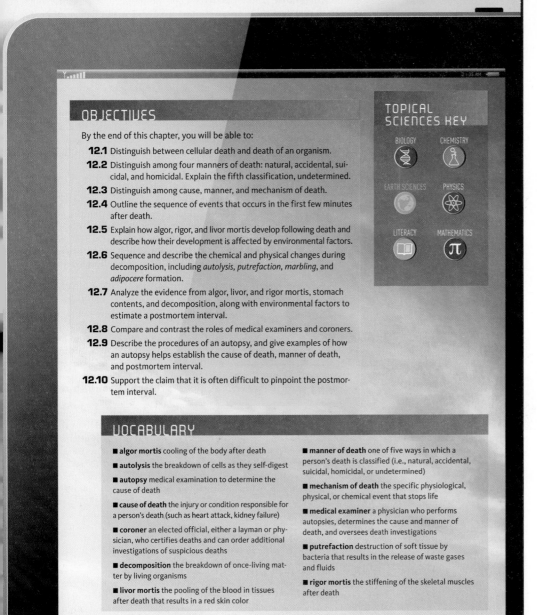

OBJECTIVES

By the end of this chapter, you will be able to:

12.1 Distinguish between cellular death and death of an organism.

12.2 Distinguish among four manners of death: natural, accidental, suicidal, and homicidal. Explain the fifth classification, undetermined.

12.3 Distinguish among cause, manner, and mechanism of death.

12.4 Outline the sequence of events that occurs in the first few minutes after death.

12.5 Explain how algor, rigor, and livor mortis develop following death and describe how their development is affected by environmental factors.

12.6 Sequence and describe the chemical and physical changes during decomposition, including *autolysis, putrefaction, marbling,* and *adipocere* formation.

12.7 Analyze the evidence from algor, livor, and rigor mortis, stomach contents, and decomposition, along with environmental factors to estimate a postmortem interval.

12.8 Compare and contrast the roles of medical examiners and coroners.

12.9 Describe the procedures of an autopsy, and give examples of how an autopsy helps establish the cause of death, manner of death, and postmortem interval.

12.10 Support the claim that it is often difficult to pinpoint the postmortem interval.

TOPICAL SCIENCES KEY

BIOLOGY

CHEMISTRY

EARTH SCIENCES

PHYSICS

LITERACY

MATHEMATICS

VOCABULARY

- **algor mortis** cooling of the body after death
- **autolysis** the breakdown of cells as they self-digest
- **autopsy** medical examination to determine the cause of death
- **cause of death** the injury or condition responsible for a person's death (such as heart attack, kidney failure)
- **coroner** an elected official, either a layman or physician, who certifies deaths and can order additional investigations of suspicious deaths
- **decomposition** the breakdown of once-living matter by living organisms
- **livor mortis** the pooling of the blood in tissues after death that results in a red skin color

- **manner of death** one of five ways in which a person's death is classified (i.e., natural, accidental, suicidal, homicidal, or undetermined)
- **mechanism of death** the specific physiological, physical, or chemical event that stops life
- **medical examiner** a physician who performs autopsies, determines the cause and manner of death, and oversees death investigations
- **putrefaction** destruction of soft tissue by bacteria that results in the release of waste gases and fluids
- **rigor mortis** the stiffening of the skeletal muscles after death

DEATH: MANNER, MECHANISM, CAUSE   **387**

KEY SCIENCE CONCEPTS

Biology: medical definition of death; processes of bodily death; autolysis; physiology of muscle contraction, rigor mortis, livor mortis; factors affecting decomposition, autopsy procedures

Chemistry: Anaerobic respiration; decomposition processes leading to marbling

Physics: heat loss by convection, conduction, and radiation (algor mortis)

Math: calculation of PMI from algor mortis

Teaching Tip

The descriptions of the conditions of a body after death are quite graphic in this chapter. Some students, particularly those who have suffered recent loss of a family member or pet, may find such content disturbing. You might consider sending a note home to parents to elicit information about any recent student challenges of this type. Also, in discussing decomposition of animals, use examples that are not typically pets: pigs, deer, etc.

TEACHING RESOURCES

Instructor's Resource CD-ROM includes:
- Activities and Student Handouts
- Alternative Assessments
- Consolidated Bibliography
- Correlations to NGSS and CCSS
- Figure Files
- Lesson Plans
- Nonfiction Readings
- PowerPoint Presentations
- (Student Learning Objectives (SLOs)

CL Testing powered by Cognero

Website: ngl.cengage.com/forensicscience2e

Engage

Before students read the Introduction, make a two-column chart on an overhead or chalkboard. Label one column "alive" and one column "dead." Ask students how they know someone is alive or dead. Write their answers in the appropriate column and discuss. After the discussion, ask students to read the Introduction.

Explore

Not only is the phrase "saved by the bell" associated with being buried with a bell, but the phrase "dead ringer" is also associated with this behavior.

Evaluate

You may want to share newspaper, magazine, and Internet articles that report the facts of the case of Terri Schiavo. Search the Gale Forensic Science eCollection at ngl.cengage.com/forensicscience2e for additional articles.

Did you know?

To avoid burying people before they were dead, "waiting mortuaries" were established in the 17th century. People thought to be dead were placed on cots and observed until the body began to decompose. Only then was the person declared dead.

INTRODUCTION *Obj. 12.1*

In the 17th century, before the stethoscope was invented, anyone in a coma or with a weak heartbeat was presumed dead and was in danger of being buried. The fear of being buried alive led to the practice of placing a bell above a grave with a string that ran inside the coffin. If someone was buried by mistake and awoke, he or she could ring the bell.

Today, people no longer fear being buried alive—as much. It is, however, sometimes unclear if a person is dead or alive. Some signs of death, such as being cold to the touch and unresponsive, can be present even though a person is still alive. Is a person with a heartbeat alive even if there is no brain activity? Is a person alive if he or she must remain on life-support systems? On television or in movies, you might hear a character say something like "time of death was 1:22 P.M." Perhaps the heart stopped beating at that time or there were no longer brain waves. However, death of individual body cells is a gradual process that does not occur at the exact moment the heart or brain stops. A single definition of death is something experts still debate.

When someone is found dead due to unknown causes, or in suspicious circumstances, a coroner is called. The coroner certifies that the person is dead and obtains preliminary observations about the death. A **coroner** may be elected or appointed and may or may not be a physician. The job of the coroner is to identify the body, notify the family, collect and return personal items of the deceased, and issue a death certificate. A **medical examiner** is a physician who oversees the death scene and performs autopsies. The testing done during an autopsy (discussed later in the chapter) helps the medical examiner to establish the cause, manner, and mechanism of death.

Establishing a *postmortem interval (PMI)*, the time between death and body discovery, has great forensic importance. If a suspect had an alibi for the time a person was killed, he or she may be excluded because he or she was not in the same place as the victim at the time of death. There are many other forensic questions knowing the PMI of a victim can assist with: Was a person dead before or after being trapped in a fire or in a lake? Is the deceased a murder or accident victim? Are changes on the body the result of trauma before or after death?

Medical examiners do not rely on a single method of establishing a postmortem interval. A combination of methods is required, due to the many environmental factors that influence the condition of a body after someone dies. The longer the postmortem interval, the less accurate the estimate. A broken watch on the victim; the timestamps of his or her social media posts, unread emails, texts, and voicemails; and statements from people who last saw the victim alive are also used to estimate a postmortem interval.

MANNER OF DEATH *Obj. 12.2*

There are four ways a person can die, referred to in official terms as the **manner of death:** natural death, accidental death, suicidal death, and homicidal death. A fifth manner of death, undetermined, is occasionally the official cause recorded on a death certificate. Natural death is caused

388   CHAPTER 12

Science

BIOLOGY

One definition of death refers to the cessation of the circulation of blood and brain activity. When the heart stops beating, the cells of the body begin to die, because they no longer receive a fresh supply of oxygen.

Science

BIOLOGY

In order for cells to make enough ATP (energy useful to the body) to support all bodily functions, oxygen must be present. Once a person stops breathing, there is insufficient oxygen, and thus insufficient energy, to support life.

by interruption and failure of body functions resulting from age or disease. This is the most common manner of death. Accidental death is caused by unplanned events, such as a car accident or falling from a roof. Suicide occurs when a person purposefully kills himself or herself. A homicide is the death of one person intentionally caused by another person. Examples of homicide include beating, shooting, burning, drowning, strangulation, hanging, and suffocation.

Sometimes it is difficult to determine if the manner of death was a suicide, an accidental death, or even a homicide. Did the person deliberately take an overdose of pills, or was it an accident? Did a person mean to shoot himself, or was it a mistake? In some cases, the medical examiner cannot make the determination and, if it is clear no crime was committed, marks the manner of death as *undetermined* on the death certificate.

Consider the following two examples. How would you categorize the manner of death?

- A man with a heart condition is assaulted and dies from a heart attack during the assault. Is the manner of death natural or homicide?
- An elderly woman dies due to neglect by her son, who lived with her. Is the manner of death natural or homicide?

In both cases, homicide would be the manner of death. Proving in court that the manner of death was a homicide, however, may be difficult.

CAUSE AND MECHANISM OF DEATH *Obj. 12.3*

The reason someone dies is called the **cause of death** (Figure 12-1). Disease, physical injuries, a stroke, poisoning, and a heart attack can all cause death. Have you ever heard the term "proximate cause of death"? It refers to an underlying cause of death, as opposed to the final cause. If a healthy person is repeatedly kicked in the kidneys during a beating, and soon after dies of kidney failure, the proximate cause of death is the beating.

Mechanism of death describes the specific change in the body that brought about the cessation of life. For example, if the cause of death is shooting, the mechanism of death might be loss of blood, or it might be the cessation of brain function. If the cause of death is a heart attack, the mechanism of death is the heart ceasing to beat, or cardiac arrest.

A forensic pathologist's report may indicate the cause and mechanisms of death in a single statement (as do some death certificates, Figure 12-2). For example, someone killed in a car accident may be said to have died from "massive trauma

Figure 12-1 *Cause of death describes the event that led to a person's death (e.g., hanging).*

Comstock/Jupiter Images

Did you know

Pathologists are physicians who specialize in analyzing body tissues and fluids. Forensic pathologists help determine the cause of death in suspicious or unexplained circumstances. They frequently work closely with toxicologists.

DEATH: MANNER, MECHANISM, CAUSE **389**

Teaching Tip

Information obtained by homicide detectives or investigators can also aid in the estimation of time since death. Because so many factors influence algor, rigor, and livor mortis, information such as who saw the person last is often most useful in estimating the time a person died.

Teaching Tip

Relate the process of autolysis to the peeling of skin. Ask students what happens to the skin when it's badly sunburned. Why does skin peel? Relate this to the process of peeling *(apoptosis)* to the autolysis of cells as they die.

Teaching Tip

Explain to students that the adjective "livid" means bruised-looking or dark, and it is used to describe how people look when angry. Point out that lividity will not be present where clothing or accessories, such as belts and watches, restrict the flow of blood.

Teaching Tip

Heat loss approximations are used to calculate algor mortis. Heat loss follows a sigmoid curve with its greatest linear accuracy in the midrange of the time interval. At death, heat loss is reduced by the natural insulating ability of the body. As the body temperature approaches the ambient temperature, the temperature gradient becomes less steep and heat loss slows down. The values given for calculation purposes are most accurate after the first five hours and before the body reaches ambient temperature.

Figure 12-2 *The official death certificate lists the cause and sometimes the mechanism of death.*

©Susan Van Etten

> **Did you know?**
>
> Rule of thumb: According to Casper's Law, the amount of decomposition that would take one week in air would take two weeks in water and approximately eight weeks if the body were buried.

to the body leading to respiratory arrest." Trauma to the body is the cause of death; respiratory arrest is the mechanism of death.

BODY CHANGES AFTER DEATH Obj. 12.4, 12.5, 12.10

Death can be defined as occurring when enough individual cells die that the heart or brain stops functioning. Death is a sequence of events that affect some cells sooner than others. To simplify the sequence, it is broken into two stages:

Stage 1: Stoppage

1. The heart stops, so blood is no longer pumped, and the delivery of oxygen and glucose to cells stops. This triggers a number of chemical and physical changes that ultimately lead to cell death.
2. The lack of oxygen and glucose means that there is less energy for cells. Cells with greater reserves of oxygen and glucose survive longer than cells lacking oxygen and glucose.
3. Cellular respiration converts to anaerobic respiration (without oxygen), resulting in less energy and a buildup of lactic acid.
4. Toxic wastes accumulate. The increased level of lactic acid lowers the pH of the cells. The cell membranes rupture, and the cytoplasm seeps out of the cells.

Stage 2: Autolysis, or Cell Self-Digestion

Damaged or injured cells trigger a cellular process known as **autolysis**—basically, cellular demolition. Cellular enzymes are released inside the cell that break down the cell contents and rupture the cell membrane, destroying the cell (Figure 12-3).

Figure 12-3 *During autolysis, cells self-digest, and fluids leak out, producing some of the leakage of decomposition.*

Algor Mortis Obj. 12.7

Algor mortis is the cooling of the body following death. In life, the body systems work together to maintain temperature within a normal range. In death, those systems no longer function and the body cools down.

DIFFERENTIATED LEARNING

Teaching English-Language Learners
There are many scientific terms in this chapter. When students are asked to work in groups, assign the groups instead of allowing students to choose their own groups. This way, you can place English learners with native speakers in the same group. The native speakers should assist the non-native speakers.

DIFFERENTIATED LEARNING

Teaching At-Risk Students
Students might have trouble calculating temperatures using the decimals. Give them several scenarios so they can practice the calculations.

To take a corpse's temperature, forensic investigators insert a thermometer into the liver or rectum. Having a standard location for taking body temperature ensures that investigators can compare their results. Algor mortis postmortem interval estimates can be accurate for deaths that occurred within the past 24 hours if the corpse has not been subject to unusual heat-loss conditions. Factors to consider when making an estimate include body temperature before death. A person who had a fever or heat stroke would have had a body temperature higher than normal at death. If the person was in shock, had congestive heart failure, or had lost a significant amount of blood, then his or her body temperature would have been lower than normal at death.

How fast a corpse loses heat has been studied, and as a result, investigators can calculate an estimate of the postmortem interval. (Note that the longer the postmortem interval has been, the less accurate the estimate.) Approximately 1 hour after death, the body cools at a rate of 0.78°C (1.4°F) per hour. After the first 12 hours, the body cools about 0.39°C (0.7°F) per hour until the body reaches the same temperature as the surroundings. This is an estimate and will vary depending on surrounding temperature and conditions.

Factors affecting heat loss:

- Body surface area relative to mass: Thin bodies lose heat faster than heavy bodies.
- Body position: An extended body presents greater surface area than a curled-up body, so it loses heat more readily.
- Clothing on body: Clothes help insulate the body, reducing heat loss.
- Retention of fluids: With congestive heart failure, the body retains fluids. Water has a high specific heat, so it tends to slow heat loss.
- Colder environment: Heat loss is faster in cooler environments.
- Windy areas: Heat loss is faster due to better heat conduction away from the body.
- Submerged bodies: Heat loss is faster if water is cooler than the body, because water is a good conductor of heat. Water warmer than body temperature, such as in hot baths or hot tubs, will slow heat loss.

Livor Mortis   Obj. 12.7

A deceased person lying flat on his stomach when he died would show a reddish coloration on the skin on the face, neck, chest, abdomen, and the front of his legs. Pressure areas such as the shoulder, elbows, hip bones, and the area under a wrist watch lack this coloration. Areas where items such as belts or elastic have constricted the body also lack this coloration. What causes this phenomenon? Why is it reddish in color?

This death color, or **livor mortis**, results when blood cells and blood vessels decompose. Red blood cells contain hemoglobin, the substance that carries oxygen and gives blood its red color. During autolysis, hemoglobin is released from red blood cells and spills into the blood vessels. As the blood vessels break down, this substance pools. The reddish-purple color that results is known as *lividity*. Areas of pressure on the body prohibit the blood from settling and lack this coloration.

PHYSICS

Did you know?

A body will cool in still water twice as fast as it will cool in air. A body will cool in running water about three times as fast as it will cool in air.

Did you know?

As capillaries rupture, blood collects between cells, and Tardieu spots form. These are small pools of blood that look like dots under the skin. Tardieu spots sometimes occur when a person dies with his or her head hanging over the edge of a bed. Tardieu spots can appear anywhere on the body.

DEATH: MANNER, MECHANISM, CAUSE   **391**

Teaching Tip

Ask students to flex an arm and notice the effect on the biceps. As the biceps contracts, the muscle becomes thicker. The triceps is now relaxed. When the arm is straightened, the triceps contracts and the biceps relaxes. What would happen if a person were to die while the biceps were flexed? The muscle would be locked in that position for a time and would become rigid (rigor).

Teaching Tip

In the living, calcium ions are actively transported to the outside of the muscle cells. After death (postmortem), there is no energy (ATP) to continue the process, and the calcium builds up inside the cells. The calcium promotes cross-bridge attachment of the muscle fibers actin and myosin, causing rigor. Rigor remains until the muscles begin to decompose. You might want to review muscle function with students. The How Stuff Works Website (http://health .howstuffworks.com/muscle2.htm) has an easy-to-understand model.

Science

BIOLOGY

Rigor mortis (death stiffness) occurs because the skeletal muscles are unable to relax. Instead, they remain contracted and rigid as a result of calcium buildup.

Teaching Tip

Review with students the difference between skeletal, smooth, and cardiac muscle. Discuss how skeletal muscle contractions enable the body to move bones by working in antagonistic pairs.

Figure 12-4 *The location of livor mortis can reveal the position of the body during the first 8 hours after death.*

Livor mortis

Lividity first becomes noticeable approximately 2 hours after death. The discoloration becomes permanent after 8 hours. If death occurred between 2 and 8 hours earlier, lividity will be present, but if the skin is pressed, the color disappears. After 8 hours, if the skin is pressed, the lividity remains.

Many variables affect the rate of lividity. If the corpse is left outside on a hot, summer day, livor mortis will progress faster. If the body is left in a cool room, livor mortis will progress more slowly. Livor mortis may not develop at all in persons who suffered from anemia or who experienced a loss of blood due to injuries.

Because lividity is the effect of gravity on blood, lividity reveals the position of a corpse during the first 8 hours after death. If the corpse lay on the back with extended legs, the back and the back of the arms and legs would exhibit lividity (Figure 12-4).

Suppose a person was found with lividity in two different areas, such as along his back *and* along his stomach. This *dual lividity* provides evidence that the body was kept in one position for at least 2 hours and then moved to a second position before lividity became permanent. This is not uncommon if a murder victim is killed in one place and then moved.

Rigor Mortis *Obj. 12.7*

BIOLOGY Have you ever seen a dead animal along a roadside with all four of its legs stiff and sticking in the air (Figure 12-5)? If the animal were still there a few days later, you would notice that the animal was no longer stiff. **Rigor mortis** means, roughly, death stiffness. It is temporary and can provide clues in estimating the postmortem interval.

Rigor mortis in humans usually becomes apparent within 2 hours after death. The stiffness progresses from smaller muscle groups to larger muscle groups. After 12 hours, the body is at its most rigid state. The stiffness gradually disappears after approximately 36 hours as cells start to break down during autolysis. Sometimes, depending on body weight and ambient temperature, rigor may remain as long as 48 hours. If a body shows no visible rigor, it has probably been dead less than 2 hours or more than 48 hours. If a body is very rigid, then the body has been dead for approximately 12 hours. If the body exhibits rigor only in the face, jaw, and neck, then rigor has just started, and the time of death is just over 2 hours. If there is some rigor throughout the body, but a lack of

Figure 12-5 *During the first 48 hours of death, the skeletal muscles are stiff—a condition known as rigor mortis.*

AP Images/Damian Dovarganes

rigor in the face, jaw, and neck, then the body is likely to be losing rigor, and the death occurred more than 15 hours ago.

The stiffness occurs because the skeletal muscles are unable to relax. In life, the contracting and relaxing of muscles occurs as the muscle fibers slide back and forth. When live muscles relax, they release calcium. This requires energy, and for cells to get energy, they need oxygen. Since there is no circulation after death, muscles cannot get oxygen, so calcium accumulates in the muscle tissue, and muscles remain rigid until autolysis of the muscle cells occurs. Because the muscles control the movement of bones, the joints are also rigid.

Many factors affect when rigor mortis sets in and how long it lasts. When trying to estimate the time of death, the following factors need to be taken into account. (See also Figures 12-6 and 12-7.)

- Ambient temperature
- A person's weight
- Presence, absence, and weight of clothing
- Illness
- Level of physical activity shortly before death
- Exposure to heat, cold, sun, and wind

Because so many variables can affect how fast rigor mortis progresses, a precise postmortem interval cannot be determined solely from rigor mortis; it can only be estimated. However, when rigor mortis is combined with other evidence, a more accurate postmortem interval can be estimated.

Did you know

If a death was violent or if it occurred under intense emotion, a phenomenon called *cadaveric spasm* may occur. Objects held in the hand of the body are firmly gripped and difficult to remove. This might be seen in suicide victims holding a gun or the assailant's hair held firmly in a victim's hand.

Figure 12-6 *Progression of rigor mortis (times vary with environmental factors).*

Time After Death	Event	Appearance	Circumstances
2 to 6 hours	Rigor begins	Body becomes stiff and stiffness moves through body.	Stiffness begins in small muscles, such as those of the face, and progresses to larger muscle groups.
12 hours	Rigor complete	Peak rigor is exhibited.	Entire body is rigid.
15 to 36 hours	Slow loss of rigor	Rigor is uneven.	Rigor is slowly lost first in smaller muscles and later in larger muscles.
36 to 48 hours	Rigor absent	Muscles relaxed.	Many variables may extend rigor beyond the normal 36 hours.

Figure 12-7 *Factors affecting rigor mortis.*

Factors Affecting Rigor	Event	Effect	Circumstances
Temperature	Cold temperature	Inhibits rigor	Slower onset and slower progression of rigor
	Warm temperature	Accelerates rigor	Faster onset and faster progression of rigor
Activity before death	Anaerobic exercise	Accelerates rigor	Lack of oxygen to muscle, buildup of lactic acid, and higher body temperature accelerates rigor.
	Sleep	Slows rigor	Fully oxygenated muscles exhibit rigor more slowly.
Body mass	Obese	Slows rigor	Fat stores oxygen.
	Thin	Accelerates rigor	Body loses oxygen quickly.

DEATH: MANNER, MECHANISM, CAUSE   **393**

Engage

Many crime-scene television programs discuss or show parts of autopsies. Brainstorm with students:

- What happens during an autopsy?
- What type of information is learned as a result?
- How can an autopsy show that a death was not by suicide?

Explore

Death by drowning is difficult to ascertain. Encourage interested students to research "wet" and "dry" drowning and the Oxford Lake Death Penalty Case (Rachel Timmerman).

Teaching Tip

Dr. Michael Baden, a brilliant forensic pathologist, hosted a television show called *Autopsy Files*. Because of its graphic nature, the show may not be suitable for class use, but some episodes may be useful as instruction support or in digest form for class discussion.

Autopsy *Obj. 12.8*

An autopsy is conducted when someone dies as a result of a crime or under certain other unusual conditions. State laws vary, but all states require autopsies for deaths due to injury, poisoning, unusual infections, and foul play. Suspicious deaths must be reported to the coroner or medical examiner, who determines if an autopsy is necessary.

An **autopsy** is a medical examination to determine the cause and manner of death. When looking for a cause of death, the medical examiner looks to the obvious possibilities first but must keep an open mind. The two types of autopsies are clinical and forensic. Clinical autopsies are done for medical research study purposes when foul play is not considered. When a person in apparent good health dies unexpectedly, the doctor or family may request an autopsy to determine the cause of death. This is a clinical autopsy.

The forensic autopsy (*medico-legal autopsy*) is performed when foul play is suspected. The autopsy itself has two parts: the external examination of the body, followed by the internal examination, both of which are outlined in this section. The forensic aspects of this sort of autopsy may include wound examination to determine the type of weapon; wound depth; path of the bullet; and the nature, number, and type of wounds (for example, defensive or offensive); bullet recovery to compare to bullets test-fired from the suspect's firearm; a determination of cause of death, for example, homicide versus suicide (to determine the plausibility of a "staged" suicide). The medical examiner may be called to testify at court proceedings about the results of the autopsy, so precise documentation is essential.

DIGGING DEEPER

With Forensic Science eCollection

The medical examiner's work can be hazardous. Search the Gale Forensic Science eCollection on **ngl.cengage .com/forensicscience2e** for the safety precautions and possible health consequences involved in working with the following: blood and tissues contaminated by pathogens; blood and tissues contaminated by drugs, poisons, or toxins; preservatives used on tissues.

AUTOPSY: EXTERNAL EXAMINATION

1. The medical examiner begins dictation of all pertinent information into a recorder.
2. The medical examiner receives the body in a new sealed body bag or sealed evidence sheet. The body is photographed and X-rayed before removal of the bag or sheet, which is then checked for trace evidence, including insect evidence.
3. After removal from the bag, the body temperature is taken and observations of liver mortis and rigor mortis are made.
4. The position and presence of clothing and other items collected are noted before removal. Clothes are examined for evidence of struggle.
5. The external surface of the body is examined for any evidence of injury, and trace evidence is removed.

394 CHAPTER 12

6. If hands have been bagged (in the case of a shooting or fight), they are swabbed for gunshot residue and/or tissue samples under the fingernails. The bags used to protect the hands are also preserved for evidence.

7. The body may be examined using an alternative light source to enhance visibility of any secretions on the body.

8. Any wounds are examined before the body is cleaned and prepared for internal examination. Wound measurements are taken to help identify the weapon.

9. The body is weighed, measured, and sex, ethnic background, hair length and color, eye color, and approximate age are recorded. Any tattoos, body piercings, or other identifying marks are noted, documented, and photographed.

10. Fingerprints are taken.

AUTOPSY: INTERNAL EXAMINATION

1. A Y-shaped incision is made from shoulder to shoulder meeting at the breastbone and extending to the pubic bone. The ribcage is cut.

2. The internal organs are removed. Various arteries and veins are cut, as are the larynx and esophagus. The internal organ mass is removed as a unit for further examination.

3. Stomach contents are removed for examination.

4. A cut from ear to ear across the forehead exposes the skull, which is opened. The brain is removed and examined.

5. Tissue samples are taken from various organs, including the liver (to check for poisoning).

6. All organs are examined for unusual appearance and trauma.

7. Body fluids such as urine, blood, saliva, and ocular fluid are extracted, and a vaginal swab may be taken.

8. Upon completion of the examination, the body is prepared for the funeral home, and reports are completed. A typical autopsy takes as much as 6 hours.

Did you know

Autopsy storage refrigerators are kept at temperatures of 38–40°F (3.3–4.4°C) to prevent further decomposition of stored bodies.

Stomach and Intestinal Contents *Obj. 12.7*

Medical examiners study a corpse's stomach contents for evidence of a crime or for help in estimating postmortem interval. In general, it takes 2 to 6 hours for the stomach to empty its contents into the small intestine and another 12 hours for the food to leave the small intestine (Figure 12-8 on the next page). It takes approximately 24 hours from when a meal was eaten until wastes are released through the rectum. From this, one can estimate that

1. If undigested stomach contents are present, then death likely occurred between 2 and 6 hours after the last meal.

2. If the stomach is empty, but food is found in the small intestine, then death occurred at least between 6 and 12 hours after a meal.

3. If the small intestine is empty and wastes are found in the large intestine, then death probably occurred 12 or more hours after a meal.

Teaching Tip

Read excerpts from *Cause of Death* by Stephen Cohle and Tobin T. Buhk. Dr. Cohle uses different case studies that show how manner of death was resolved only after conducting an autopsy. Another option is to assign different student groups to read different chapters and report back to the class how the autopsy resolved the manner of death. (Case studies in this book may be too graphic for younger students)

Teaching Tip

To illustrate examining stomach contents, you may want to show a clip from *Jaws* or *CSI Miami* in which the stomach contents of a shark are examined to see if that shark is the one that attacked a swimmer.

DIFFERENTIATED LEARNING

Teaching Gifted Students
If students are interested, try getting them to shadow a medical examiner in your area. You will also need written permission from the students' parents or guardians. Another option might be the cadaver lab of nearby colleges.

Explore

Tell students that digestion is both a mechanical and a chemical process. Biting, tearing, and chewing our food, breaking it down into smaller and smaller pieces, is the mechanical process of digestion. Food is broken down by chemicals in our mouth and stomach. For example, our bodies cannot use an apple in its original state. They must break down the apple, mechanically and chemically, into a usable form. Our digestive system begins with the mouth and moves on to the esophagus, stomach, small intestines, and then large intestines, ending with solid waste release from the anus.

Teaching Tip

Cellular recognition of different vegetables has been researched and published in Bock, J. H., M. A. Lane, and D. O. Norris. *Identifying Plant Food Cells in Gastric Contents for Use in Forensic Investigations: A Laboratory Manual.* U.S. Department of Justice, National Institute of Justice Research Report, January, 1988.

Figure 12-8 *The state of undigested food provides a clue to the postmortem interval.*

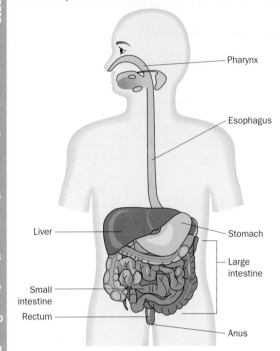

Pharynx

Esophagus

Liver

Stomach

Large intestine

Small intestine

Rectum

Anus

Variables affecting digestion include the amount, type, and temperature of the food, as well as illness and stress. If the person was under emotional stress, that can affect digestion. The forensic value of examination of food contents from a deceased person is greatest if the deceased was known to have consumed a specific meal at a particular time.

POSTMORTEM CHANGES IN THE EYE

In life, the surface of the eye is kept moist by blinking. Following death, the surface of the eye dries out. A cloudy film is observed within 2 to 3 hours if the eyes were open at death and within 24 hours if the eyes were closed or covered at death.

Following death, potassium accumulates inside the eye. Because decomposition progresses at a predictable rate, the buildup of potassium could hypothetically be used to estimate the time of death. But this method is not yet considered reliable as an estimate of time of death.

STAGES OF DECOMPOSITION *Obj. 12.6*

An animal's body undergoes a progressive series of physical and chemical changes after death. It provides a changing habitat for a succession of different bacteria, fungi, and insects. Understanding what happens during decomposition is of forensic importance because a decomposing body can provides clues to the identity of an unknown victim (or suspect), and to the approximate time, location, and manner of death. The following descriptions are generalizations about decomposition. The time durations cited will vary due to the environmental and physiological factors discussed earlier in the chapter.

1. Several hours after death
   - Cell autolysis begins
   - Muscles lose tone
   - Bladder and rectum empty due to loss of muscle control
   - Onset of algor, livor, and rigor mortis
   - Cloudy film forms over eye if eyes are left open
   - Flies arrive to deposit eggs on the body

DIFFERENTIATED LEARNING

Teaching English-Language Learners
Have nonnative speakers name the parts of the digestive system in their native language and then identify the English words for the parts.

2. After several days
   - Blistering of the skin and internal organs results in *skin slippage* (easy separation of outer skin from underlying tissues).
   - **Putrefaction** the destruction of soft tissues due to bacterial activity, begins. The process is evident from gases, seepage, and changes in body color.
   - Abdominal swelling occurs as anaerobic bacteria of the intestines consume tissues and release carbon dioxide.
   - Internal pressure from fluids and foul-smelling decomposition gases may force fluids from body openings.
   - Marbling (skin discoloration) occurs as a result of protein decomposition. Sulfur compounds combine with hemoglobin and lend a brown color to veins and the skin. This begins in the abdomen and ultimately spreads. Sulfurous odors (like rotten eggs) are evident.
   - Loss of rigor mortis
   - Increased insect activity

3. Days 7–23
   - Bloating continues as more gases such as hydrogen sulfide, methane, sulfur dioxide, putrescine, and cadaverine are released inside the body.
   - Discoloration of the skin may make identification of skin color impossible.
   - Ruptures in the skin occur, leading to seepage of more fluids into the surrounding areas. Ruptured areas increase bacterial and insect activity.
   - Soft tissues of the body start to liquefy.

4. After 3 weeks to 2 months
   - The greatest loss of mass occurs as a result of insect infestation, action of bacteria, and purging of fluids.
   - Fats of the body start to undergo decomposition, forming a greasy wax, or *adipocere*. In moist conditions, bacterial action breaks down fats into a greasy material that can coat the body. This process can go on for months. The forensic value of adipocere is that it prevents oxygen from getting to the underlying tissues and can preserve the tissue.

5. After 2 months
   - Soft tissues are usually gone.
   - Bones remain.
   - Odors are mostly gone.

Figure 12-9 provides more information about the stages of decomposition.

Did you know
Decomposition does not affect your body, hair, or fingernail length.

CHEMISTRY

Figure 12-9 *The stages of decomposition provide information about time of death.*

Stage	What Happens During Decomposition
1. Fresh (initial)	Corpse appears normal on the outside, but is starting to decompose from the actions of bacteria and autolysis. The body temperature drops. Insects lay eggs.
2. Bloating (putrefaction)	Odor of decaying flesh is present, and the corpse appears swollen. The skin becomes marbled in coloration and may split open from collected gases, resulting in fluid seepage. Insect activity increases.
3. Active decay (black putrefaction)	Very strong odor. Flesh is discolored. Skin is rupturing, allowing gases to escape and body to collapse while seepage of fluid continues. Most body mass is lost to insect activity at this stage.
4. Advanced decay	Corpse is drying out. Most flesh is gone. Adipocere is forming. Fewer insects remain.
5. Dry or skeletal	Mostly bones remain.

Explore

Adipocere, also known as corpse, grave, or mortuary wax, is a substance formed by the anaerobic bacterial breakdown of fat in tissue. It is the result of a process called *saponification*. Have students research how saponification is used to make soap (obviously not with human adipocere).

Explore

Tell students that dogs can be trained to find dead bodies. These dogs are called cadaver dogs. Their noses are sensitive enough to pick up the trace gases given off by bodies undergoing decay. These dogs have been used to find mass graves, missing persons, and victims of natural disasters, such as Hurricane Katrina. Have students research finds by cadaver dogs.

Science

CHEMISTRY

CHEMISTRY
Investigate the chemical reaction that results in the marbling seen on the skin.

Evaluate

At six to ten days, the corpse bloats with carbon dioxide from the waste gases of bacteria that feed on internal tissues. Ask students if these bacteria are aerobic or anaerobic. Where did these bacteria come from?

DIFFERENTIATED LEARNING

Teaching Gifted Students
Have students research the method a forensic dentist uses to help identify a dead body. Typically, a dentist will receive a radiograph of the teeth and jaw from the medical examiner's office. This postmortem radiograph is then compared to a database of antemortem radiographs to determine the identity of the deceased. Students might contact the city or county forensic dentist, CSI, or field investigators for information.

CHAPTER

1

2

3

4

5

6

7

8

9

10

11

12

13

14

15

16

17

18

Because of skin slip-page, it is possible to obtain a fingerprint from a decomposed body. The skin of the deceased is placed over someone else's gloved finger to obtain a fingerprint of the victim.

Decomposition fluids and gases are toxic to plants; most plant growth around a decomposing body is inhibited.

The rate of **decomposition** depends on the person's age, size of the body, and the nature of the death. Ill individuals may decompose faster than healthy people, depending on the nature of the illness. The young decompose faster than the elderly. Bodies with large deposits of fat and body fluids break down faster than bodies of average mass.

Environmental conditions also influence decomposition. Unclothed bodies decompose faster than clothed bodies. Bodies decompose fastest in the 21–37°C (70–99°F) temperature range. Higher temperatures with low humidity tend to dry out corpses, preserving them. Lower temperatures tend to prevent bacterial growth and slow down decomposition. Moist environments rich in oxygen speed up decomposition. Bodies decompose most quickly in air and more slowly in water or if buried.

"Rule of Thumb" PMI estimate

- Body feels warm and is limp (dead less than 3 hours)
- Body feels warm and is stiff (dead 3–8 hours)
- Body feels cold and is stiff (dead 8–36 hours)
- Body feels cold and is limp (dead more than 36 hours)

Petechial hemorrhages are a forensic clue that can provide data for postmortem interval as well as evidence about the cause of death. Search the Gale Forensic Science eCollection on **ngl .cengage.com/forensicscience2e** for the article "Factors and Circumstances Influencing the Development of Hemorrhages in Livor Mortis." Read the article and then research the topic online. In 500 words or fewer, describe and characterize petechial hemorrhages: what they are, what they look like, what causes them, how forensic scientists use them, and how reliable they are as a tool for determining postmortem interval.

Source: Britta Bockholdt, H. Maxeiner, and W. Hegenbarth. "Factors and circumstances influencing the development of hemorrhages in livor mortis." *Forensic Science International* 149.2–3 (May 10, 2005): pp. 133(5). From *Forensic Science Journals.*

SUMMARY

- Death is a process that involves both individual cell death and organism death. The medical and legal communities have been unable to agree upon a precise definition of death.

- When a person dies, it is important to establish the manner, cause, and mechanism of death. An exact time since death, or postmortem interval (PMI), is sometimes difficult to estimate.

- Shortly after death, the body undergoes algor, rigor, and livor mortis. The rate at which they occur is affected by environmental and physiological factors such as ambient temperature, clothing, body mass, age, state of disease, and burial site (if any) of the body.

- Physical and chemical changes that occur after death, such as bloating, skin marbling, and adipocere formation, are caused by decomposition. The process begins with autolysis of cells, is followed by putrefaction, and proceeds to the total degradation of soft tissues.

- Autopsies are typically performed by medical examiners. During an autopsy, the medical examiner performs external and internal examinations, images various pertinent body regions, removes and weighs organs, and takes tissue and fluid samples from organs, often including the eye, stomach, liver, and brain.

- To estimate a postmortem interval, evidence is compiled from the body, the environment, the autopsy findings, and the person's social contacts, if necessary. A PMI is never precise because of the many environmental variables and other factors that influence what happens to a body after death.

LITERACY

Jessica Snyder Sachs, *Corpse: Nature, Forensics and the Struggle to Pinpoint Time of Death.*
Stephen, Cohle, M.D., and Tobin T. Buhk, *Cause of Death.*

MAURO FERMARIELLO/Science Photo Library/Corbis

Close

Organize students into four groups and assign each group one of the following topics: manner of death, mechanism of death, cause of death, and postmortem interval. Have each group prepare a summary of the chapter information about their topic and present it to the class.

Evaluate

Ask students what additional evidence related to postmortem interval might have been relevant to the first Hendricks case. Have interested students research and summarize the retrial and acquittal.

CASE STUDIES

David Hendricks (1983)

One Friday evening, prior to a business trip, David Hendricks took his wife and three children out at 7:30 for a pizza dinner. Hendricks left on a business trip at midnight. Upon his arrival home the following Tuesday, he was greeted by police, who had a grim story for him.

His wife Susan and their children had been murdered. Their home showed some overturned furniture but no evidence of theft, and the police were unable to find a motive for the crime. In separate statements, David Hendricks talked about stolen items, and the police began to question his motives. Hendricks maintained his family was fine when he left at midnight.

Stomach contents from the children helped establish a timeline for events. The pizza toppings were intact, indicating that the food was still in a very early stage of digestion when death occurred, which was probably before the midnight trip departure time indicated by Hendricks. Hendricks was convicted of the deaths of his family in 1984 and given four consecutive life sentences based on this circumstantial evidence. He served seven years in an Illinois prison and was later acquitted and released after a retrial.

Nicole Brown Simpson and Ronald Goldman (1994)

The lengthy trial of former football player O. J. Simpson for the murder of his ex-wife, Nicole, and Ronald Goldman was televised and called the "Trial of the Century." The defense attorneys alleged misconduct by the Los Angeles Police Department in violating the crime scene and in the collecting and handling of evidence. The role of the medical examiner is crucial in helping to determine what evidence should be collected, photographed, secured, and examined. Timely examination of the body is vital. In the Simpson-Goldman case, the medical examiner was not called to the scene until approximately 10 hours after the crime was discovered. This delay interfered greatly in the determination of algor, rigor, and livor mortis. In addition, evidence that might have been critical to the case was overlooked, contaminated, and mishandled. For example, a bag of groceries, ice cream, and pills found at the crime scene was not documented into evidence. Poor forensic procedures and questionable police testimony contributed to a "not guilty" verdict. In 1997, O. J. Simpson was found responsible in civil court for financial damages related to the case. The victims' families were awarded $33.5 million in compensatory and punitive damages.

Think Critically ➔ Research the O. J. Simpson criminal trial. List the evidence-handling procedures that led many to believe that crime-scene evidence was overlooked, contaminated, and/or mishandled.

Careers *in Forensics*

Michael Baden

Dr. Michael M. Baden is an internationally known and respected board-certified forensic pathologist. In his long, fascinating career, he has performed more than 20,000 autopsies. After earning a Bachelor of Science degree from the City College of New York, he attended New York University School of Medicine and was awarded a medical degree in 1959. He worked in the Office of the Chief Medical Examiner in New York City from 1961 to 1986, either as Medical Examiner or Chief Medical Examiner. Dr. Baden has held professorships at several medical, law, and criminal justice schools.

He was the chairperson of the Forensic Pathology Panel of the U.S. Congress Select Committee on Assassinations that investigated the deaths of President John F. Kennedy and Dr. Martin Luther King, Jr.

During his career, Dr. Baden has published articles on aspects of forensic medicine in several national and international medical journals. He has also written two nonfiction books, *Unnatural Death: Confessions of a Medical Examiner* and *Dead Reckoning: the New Science of Catching Killers*. Dr. Baden is also a forensics science contributor to an international news network and has hosted an autopsy documentary series on television.

Dr. Baden has appeared as an expert in forensic pathology in many high-profile cases of national and international interest. He served as an expert witness in the O. J. Simpson murder trial. Dr. Baden was the forensic pathologist on a team of U.S. forensic scientists invited by the Russian government to examine the remains of Tsar Nicholas II of Russia and other

Dr. Michael Baden, forensic pathologist.

AP Images/Robyn Beck, Pool

members of the Romanov family found in the Ural region of Russia in the 1990s. In 2014, he performed an autopsy on Michael Brown, who was shot and killed by a police officer while unarmed. Dr. Baden's services were requested by the family of the young man.

In addition to practicing forensic pathology, Dr. Baden has served on the boards of several substance abuse treatment programs. Dr. Baden calls himself "a witness for the dead." Of the autopsy table, he says, "It's a sacred place, and I always treat a body with the utmost care. I'm not religious, but when I'm looking inside a person's body, which is the first time a human being has done that, it's a wondrous thing. And it never fails to convince me that each one of us is a miracle."

Learn More About It

▷ To learn more about a career in forensic pathology, go to **ngl.cengage.com/forensicscience2e**.

APPS

▶ **Time of Death app considers ambient temperature, body weight, amount and type of clothing, and body location when calculating postmortem interval.**

Chapter 12 Review

True or False

1. False
2. True
3. True
4. False
5. False
6. True
7. False

Multiple Choice

8. d
9. c
10. a
11. b
12. c

Short Answer

13. a. Cellular death is localized and individual to a cell. The death of an organism occurs when enough individual cells have died that the life of the organism cannot be supported.

    b. During autolysis, the cell is demolished through the release of the body's own enzymes. During putrefaction, cell breakdown progresses to the point of liquefaction of tissues.

14. a. natural, emphysema, respiratory and heart failure

    b. accidental, drug overdose, respiratory failure

    c. homicide, blunt-force trauma, cerebral hemorrhage

15. The belly is distended not due to pregnancy but due to bloating that occurs during decomposition. Bacteria within the digestive tract consume any residual food left in the digestive tract. When that food is depleted, bacteria start to digest the body of the dead animal. As the bacteria break down the food or tissues, decomposition gases are released within the intestines, resulting in bloating of the intestine.

True or False

1. Adipocere is a waxy material formed from the breakdown of fat during decomposition under very dry conditions. *Obj. 12.6*

2. A person who was running away from someone before he or she died will go into rigor mortis *sooner* than a person who was sitting quietly. *Obj. 12.5*

3. An autopsy is performed after an unexplained death to help explain the cause and manner of death. *Obj. 12.5*

4. Usually, children will lose body heat *more slowly* than adults. *Obj. 12.5*

5. Body heat loss speeds up after 12 hours following death. *Obj. 12.5*

6. Cloudiness of the eyes occurs usually after 2 hours if the eyelids are open. *Obj. 12.6*

7. Once skin slippage begins, it is impossible to obtain fingerprints. *Obj. 12.6*

Multiple Choice

8. The body of a person known to have eaten Mexican food at 12 noon was found dead at 11 P.M. During autopsy, the medical examiner found no food in the stomach but did find evidence of Mexican food in the first half of the small intestine. Based on the postmortem interval estimate from the stomach contents only, which of the following times would be the best estimate of a postmortem interval? *Obj. 12.7, 12.9*
    a) between noon and 1 P.M.
    b) between 1 P.M. and 2 P.M.
    c) between 2 P.M. and 5 P.M.
    d) between 4 P.M. and 11 P.M.

9. Which method of estimating postmortem interval is least reliable if a person has been dead less than 12 hours? *Obj. 12.10*
    a) rigor mortis
    b) livor mortis
    c) potassium levels in the eye
    d) algor mortis

10. Which can issue death certificates but cannot perform autopsies? *Obj. 12.8*
    a) coroner
    b) pathologist
    c) medical examiner
    d) both the coroner and the pathologist

11. Marbling occurs as a result of *Obj. 12.6*
    a) fats being broken down by bacteria
    b) chemical reactions of sulfur and hemoglobin
    c) lactic acid formation as a result of reduced oxygen levels in the blood
    d) muscles contracting after death

12. Which statement about the rate of decomposition is generally true? *Obj. 12.6*
    a) The body of an overweight person will decompose faster than the body of a person who was not overweight.
    b) Decomposition will occur faster if the body is submerged in water than if it is on land.
    c) A buried body decomposes more slowly than a body that is not buried.
    d) Ambient temperature does not affect the rate of decomposition.

Short Answer

13. Compare and contrast:
    a) cellular death and death of the organism *Obj. 12.1*
    b) autolysis and putrefaction *Obj. 12.6*

14. For each of the following situations, state the cause, manner, and mechanism of death: *Obj. 12.2*
    a) A chronic smoker develops emphysema (lung damage) and dies.
    b) A teenager was found dead after consuming alcohol and heroin together.
    c) While being mugged on the street, a person is struck on the head with a pipe and dies after losing a large volume of blood.

15. As you drive along a roadside, you and your friend notice a dead deer. Your friend comments that the deer must have been pregnant. "Did you see the size of its belly? It was huge!" What other explanation could you give your friend as to why the abdominal region of the dead deer was so large? *Obj. 12.6*

16. List the following events in the sequence they occur when a person dies: *Obj. 12.4*

    Heart stops
    Fluid escapes
    Anaerobic respiration occurs with reduced oxygen, producing lactic acid
    Organism death
    Circulation stops
    Lack of oxygen
    Widespread cell death
    Buildup of CO_2 creates a lower-pH environment
    Cell membranes rupture

17. a) A body was found with rigor mortis in only the large muscles of the body. The doctor who found the body told the investigator that rigor was just starting so the body had been dead for less than 2 hours. Based on your knowledge of forensics, do agree or disagree with this evaluation? Support your claim with evidence from the chapter. *Obj. 12.5, 12.10*
    b) What other evidence could support the conclusion that the body was just beginning rigor or just losing rigor?

16. 1. Heart stops
    2. Circulation stops
    3. Lack of oxygen
    4. Buildup of CO_2 creates a lower pH environment
    5. Anaerobic respiration occurs with reduced oxygen, producing lactic acid
    6. Cell membranes rupture
    7. Fluid escapes from cells
    8. Widespread cell death
    9. Organism death

17. a. Rigor typically starts in small muscle groups and progresses to larger muscle groups. It is unusual for rigor to just be in the lower half of the body and not in the top half. The evidence is consistent with the body *losing* rigor because rigor is typically lost in the small muscles of the head and neck first, and the loss of rigor occurs in the legs last. Instead of just beginning rigor with a postmortem interval less than 2 hours, it is more likely that the person is losing rigor, which would put the postmortem interval more than 12 hours and less than 24.

    b. Body temperature, state of lividity, state of decomposition, cloudiness of eyes, insect evidence

18. This body demonstrates dual
lividity. Dual lividity indicates
that a body was moved after
lividity started. Lividity along
the right side of the body
indicates that the person was
lying on his or her right side.
Lividity on the back of the
buttocks, lower legs, and soles
of the feet is consistent with a
body sitting in a chair. In most
cases, it takes at least 2 hours
after death for lividity to occur.
Because the skin lost the color
when pressed, it would be
consistent with the body being
dead less than 8 hours. The
postmortem interval appears
to be between 2 and 8 hours.
However, other variables must
be considered to determine
their effect on the lividity of
the body.

19. An explanation for this bloody
mixture is that as bodies
decompose and bacteria
release gases, the body
becomes bloated. Added pressure inside the intestine and
body cavity forces fluids out of
the body openings.

20. Student summaries will
vary, but they should list the
pertinent points of the internal
and external examinations
of an autopsy as described
in the text. Data from all
examinations and trace
evidence can be useful in
establishing cause and manner
of death and in estimating
postmortem interval if that
has not yet been done.

18. A body was found with lividity appearing all along the right side from head
to toe and on the bottoms of the feet, the buttocks, and the lower legs.
When the skin was pressed in the areas of lividity, the redness disappeared. What information can be derived from this body based on the
lividity evidence? *Obj. 12.5*

19. A body that seemed dead for several days was found with a bloody mixture coming out of the nose and mouth. The inexperienced first responder
thought that the person must have suffered an injury that caused blood to
seep out of the mouth and nose. Is there another interpretation?
Obj. 12.6, 12.10

20. Briefly summarize the procedures of an autopsy. Explain which of those
procedures help in establishing cause of death, manner of death, and postmortem interval and how.

Going Further

1. Describe the relationships between algor mortis and the processes of
conduction, convection, and radiation.

2. Research Newton's Law of Cooling. Summarized, it states that "the rate
of heat loss of a body is proportional to the difference in temperatures
between the body and its surroundings." Can this law be applied to heat
loss during human decomposition?

3. Research the chemical reaction that occurs between sulfur and hemoglobin, resulting in the marbling effect of the body during putrefaction.
Describe the reaction.

4. When Billy Martin, former New York Yankees manager, died in a car
accident, he was found in the driver's seat. His injured friend was found
in the passenger's seat. Both men had been drinking. There were rumors
that Martin was not driving, and his friend moved Martin's body into the
driver's side to prevent himself from being arrested for driving under the
influence. Research evidence from the autopsy that might provide clues as
to where each person was sitting at the time of the accident.

Bibliography

Books and Journals

Baden, Michael M., M.D. *Unnatural Death: Confessions of a Medical Examiner*. New York: Ivy, 1989.

Blass, Bill. *Death's Acre: Inside the Body Farm*. New York: Ballantine Books, 1989.

Cohle, Stephen, M.D., and Tobin T. Buhk, *Cause of Death*. Amherst, New York: Prometheus, 2007.

Dix, Jay. *Death Investigator's Manual*. Public Agency Training Council.

Geberth, Vernon J. *Practical Homicide Investigation, 3rd Edition*. Boca Raton, FL: CRC Press, 1996.

Haskell, Neal, and Robert D. Hall. "Forensic (Medicocriminal) Entomology—Applications in Medicolegal Investigations." *Forensic Sciences*. Cyril H. Wecht, General Editor. Matthew Bender & Company, Inc., 2005.

Larkin, Glenn M. "Time of Death." *Forensic Sciences*, Cyril H. Wecht, General Editor. Matthew Bender & Company, Inc., 2005.

Nickell, Joe, and John Fischer. *Crime Science: Methods of Forensic Detection*. Lexington, KY: The University Press of Kentucky, 1999.

Roach, Mary. *Stiff: The Curious Lives of Human Cadavers*. New York: W. W. Norton and Company, 2002.

Sachs, Jessica. *Time of Death*. New York: New Arrow Books Ltd., 2003.

_____. *Corpse: Nature, Forensics, and the Struggle to Pinpoint the Time of Death*. New York: Perseus Publishing, 2002.

Internet Resources

ngl.cengage.com/forensicscience2e (Gale Forensic Science eCollection)

http://video.pbs.org/video/1774485437 (Video *Frontline: Post Mortem*; may be disturbing)

http://health.howstuffworks.com/human-body/systems/musculoskeletal/muscle2.htm

http://youtu.be/R1CD6gNmhr0 ("Decomposition of a Baby Pig")

http://health.howstuffworks.com/diseases-conditions/death-dying/dying3.htm

http://science.howstuffworks.com/life/inside-the-mind/human-brain/brain-death.htm

http://www.necrosearch.org

http://www.forensicmag.com/articles/2013/10/reviewing-and-comprehending-autopsy-reports

http://science.howstuffworks.com/forensic-science-channel.htm research ("How Autopsies Work")

http://www.abc.net.au/science/articles/2006/05/18/2809176.htm

Teaching Tip

Additional sources: Steve Down "Dentin Used in Forensic Drug Detection, *The Forensic Magazine*, Dec. 22, 2014. Wecht, Cyril. *Tales from the Morgue*. Amherst (NY): Prometheus, 2005.

Background

In this activity, students work in pairs to analyze and discuss scenarios in which they must estimate the postmortem interval based on rigor mortis evidence.

Time Required to Complete Activity

30 minutes

Safety Precautions

There are no safety precautions for this activity.

Procedures

1. Print, copy, and distribute Act 12-1 SH from the IRCD, Chapter 12.

2. Make sure students read all directions *before* beginning the activity.

3. Review the Rigor Mortis reference tables with students before beginning this activity.

4. Remind students to include as much detail as possible in their answers.

5. Emphasize that no single estimate such as rigor mortis provides reliable evidence due to the number of factors influencing its rate.

Answers

Remind students that establishing postmortem interval solely on rigor evidence is very approximate. Students should be reminded that other variables have not been taken into consideration as they would be in a real investigation. The ambient temperature and environmental conditions, clothing, body mass, body position, and activity level of the deceased prior to death need to be factored into the postmortem estimate. Other types of evidence would also be examined.

Part A

1. There is not enough information to determine postmortem

Calculating Postmortem Interval Using Rigor Mortis   Obj. 12.7

Background:

In old detective movies, a dead body was often referred to as a "stiff." The term refers to the onset of rigor mortis that follows soon after death. In this activity, you will estimate the postmortem interval by analyzing the degree of rigor of the deceased body. Postmortem interval is greatly affected by many variables. In this activity, you will make estimates based only on the state of rigor mortis. Actual postmortem interval estimates require examination of other types of evidence in combination with rigor mortis.

Objective:

By the end of this activity, you will be able to:
Estimate the postmortem interval using rigor mortis evidence.

Time Required to Complete Activity: 30 minutes

Materials (for each group of two students):

Act 12-1 SH
paper
pen or pencil
calculator (optional)
Rigor Mortis section of the chapter

SAFETY PRECAUTIONS:

None

Procedure:

Working in pairs, discuss and answer the following questions dealing with approximating postmortem interval. Refer to the Rigor Mortis section in your textbook, including the reference tables. Discuss variables that could affect PMI. List questions that should be asked and answered about the crime scene and victim before you could refine an estimated PMI.

Questions:

PART A

Estimate the postmortem interval for the following situations. Explain each of your answers:

1. A body was found with no evidence of rigor.
2. A body was found exhibiting rigor throughout the entire body.

---

interval (PMI) solely from knowledge of rigor mortis. The person could have just died and rigor had not yet begun, or the person may have died 36 hours ago and lost all signs of rigor. Other factors such as decomposition evidence might help.

2. Peak rigor is usually noted 12 hours after someone dies, but that varies. See the text section "Rigor Mortis."

3. It appears that rigor is in its early stages. Because rigor is also found in the chest, arms, and neck, as well as the small muscles of the face, the PMI is more than 2 hours. The legs have not yet started to undergo rigor, however, so the PMI is between 4 and 9 hours.

4. Because no rigor is evident in the upper body, peak rigor likely has already occurred, and is slowly releasing. The larger muscles of the legs tend to be the last place on the body with rigor. Peak rigor occurs at 12 hours, and rigor is usually gone by 36 hours. Postmortem interval is estimated to be 12–30 hours.

3. A body was found exhibiting rigor in the chest, arms, face, and neck.
4. A body was discovered with rigor present in the legs, but no rigor in the upper torso.
5. A body was discovered with most muscles relaxed, except for the face.
6. A body was discovered in the weight room of a gym. A man had been doing "biceps curls" with heavy weights. The only place rigor was present was in his arms.

PART B

Estimate the postmortem interval based on the following information:

7. A frail elderly woman's body was found in her apartment on a hot summer evening. Her body exhibited advanced rigor in all places except her face and neck.
8. A body was discovered in the woods. The man had been missing for two days. The average temperature the previous 48 hours was 10°C. When the body was discovered, it was at peak rigor.
9. An obese man's body was discovered in his air-conditioned hotel room sitting in a chair in front of the television. The air conditioner was set for 18.3°C. When the coroner arrived, the man's body exhibited rigor in his upper body only.
10. While jogging, a young woman was attacked and killed. The perpetrator hid the body in the trunk of a car and fled. When the woman's body was discovered, rigor was noticed in her thighs only.
11. The body is completely stiff. How long has the deceased been dead? Explain your answer.
12. The victim was found in a snowbank alongside a road. His body is rigid. How long has he been dead? Explain your answer, remembering the cold temperature.
13. The body of a runner was found in the park one early, hot summer morning. Her body shows rigor in her face, neck, arms, and torso. How long has she been dead? Explain your answer.

Death: Manner, Mechanism, Cause   407

5. Because rigor begins in the smaller muscles and works its way to the larger muscles, it is possible that rigor is just commencing. This would put the postmortem interval around 2 hours.
6. This form of exercise would result in lactic acid buildup in his biceps and not in other parts of his body, resulting in rigor occurring there first. Rigor usually begins in smaller muscles and works its way down to the arms. It appears rigor has not begun in small muscles, which would put the estimated postmortem interval to be less than 2 hours.

Part B

7. This woman seems to be past the peak 12 hours of rigor and is just starting to lose rigor. Based on this information, her estimated PMI would be approximately 15 hours. However, it is also noted that the woman is frail. This usually accelerates rigor. This might bring her PMI closer to 12 hours. Finally, another variable must be considered: The apartment was hot. High ambient temperature accelerates rigor mortis. This would make her PMI between 9 and 12 hours.
8. Because the body was outside in 10 degrees C (50 degrees F) temperature, both rigor and decomposition may be delayed. Peak rigor is usually around 12 hours. Due to the cold temperature, his PMI may be closer to 24 hours.
9. Rigor is not complete. Rigor has not yet progressed to the man's thighs. This would put the PMI at approximately 6 hours. The obesity of the man and the air conditioning in the room would have slowed down the onset of rigor, making the PMI closer to 9 hours. Post-mortem interval could be approximated sometime between 8 to 12 hours.

10. Possible questions: What was the temperature inside the car? Other types of evidence (body temperature, lividity, cloudiness of the cornea, etc.) should be considered to determine if the body had not yet begun rigor or if rigor had released.
11. More information is needed. Sample questions: What were the environmental conditions? Was the deceased clothed? Had she been exercising?
12. Full rigor occurs approximately 12 hours after death. Cold temperatures will delay full rigor.

However, more information is needed: Is there any evidence that the body was killed in one location and moved to this location? Are there any signs of decomposition, lividity, eye changes?

13. Rigor has started but not yet progressed to the larger muscles of the legs. PMI estimate is more than 4 hours but less than 12. However, warm temperature and exercise prior to death could have accelerated the rigor.

DEATH: MANNER, MECHANISM, CAUSE   **407**

Background

In this activity, students work in pairs to estimate the postmortem interval using algor mortis evidence.

Safety Precautions

There are no safety precautions for this activity.

Time Required to Complete Activity

45 minutes

Procedures

1. Make sure students read all directions *before* beginning the activity.

2. Read through the activity examples as a class to make sure students understand what is expected of them.

Teaching Tip

An online converter between Fahrenheit and Celsius can be found at http://www.onlineconversion.com/temperature.htm

Teaching Tip

PMI calculations are approximate because so many variables affect it. Determination of PMI in minutes is not realistic.

Calculating Postmortem Interval Using Algor Mortis Obj. 12.7

Objective:

By the end of this activity, you will be able to:
Estimate the postmortem interval using algor mortis evidence.

Time Required to Complete Activity: 45 minutes

Materials:

paper
pen or pencil
calculator
Algor Mortis section of the chapter

Background:

Estimating a postmortem interval (PMI) using algor mortis evidence only is inexact and unreliable because many variables affect the change of body temperature. However, when algor mortis evidence is considered in combination with other types of evidence, a more reliable PMI estimate is possible. In this activity, you will use the following formulas to estimate PMI based solely on algor mortis evidence. Recall that normal body temperature is approximately 37°C.

SAFETY PRECAUTIONS:

None

Procedure:

Working in pairs, review each of the following examples before discussing and answering the questions. Use the formulas below to estimate the amount of heat loss:

- For the first 12 hours, the body loses 0.78°C per hour.
- After the first 12 hours, the body loses about 0.39°C per hour.

Example 1: What is the temperature decrease for someone who has been dead for 12 hours?

Answer: Temperature decrease ~ (0.78°C/hour) × 12 hours ~ 9.36°C

Example 2: If a person has been dead for less than 12 hours, or the body has lost less than 9.36°C, calculate the estimated PMI. (Use a heat-loss rate of 0.78°C per hour.)

Answer: Temperature of dead body is 32.2°C.
Normal body temperature is 37°C.
37°C − 32.2°C = 4.8°C decrease since death.
How long did it take to decrease 4.8°C?
0.78 (°C/hour) × (unknown number of hours) = degrees lost
0.78 (°C/hour) × (unknown number of hours) = 4.8°C lost by body
Solve for the unknown number of hours since death occurred:
number of hours ~ 4.8°C ÷ 0.78 (°C/hour)
number of hours ~ 6.1 hours ~ 6 hours

Example 3: Is the PMI more than 12 hours or less than 12 hours?

Answer: Recall that if a person has been dead 12 hours or less, the average body loses heat at a rate of 0.78°C per hour. If the person has been dead 12 hours, then 0.78°C/hour × 12 hours ~ 9.36°C.
If a body's temperature decreases by 9.36°C, then the person has been dead for ~12 hours.
If a body's temperature decreases by more than 9.36°C, then the person has been dead for more than 12 hours.
If a body's temperature decreases by less than 9.36°C, then the person has been dead for less than 12 hours.
For each of the following, state if the person had been dead for more than or less than 12 hours based on the number of degrees decrease in temperature:
1. total decrease of 7.9°C
2. total decrease of 4.4°C
3. total decrease of 11.7°C
4. total decrease of 17.2°C
5. total decrease of 10.6°C

(**Answers:** 1: less than; 2: less than; 3: more than; 4: more than; 5: more than)

Example 4: Calculate the PMI if a person was dead for more than 12 hours. The temperature of the body when discovered was 22.2°C.

Answer: If the body has cooled more than 9.36°C, then you know that the victim has likely been dead for more than 12 hours. After 12 hours, the body loses heat at a slower rate of approximately 0.39°C per hour. Calculate how many hours beyond the first 12 hours the victim died and add it to the 12-hours heat-loss estimate.
A. What was the total decrease in temperature from the time of death until the body was found?
37°C − 22.2°C = 14.8°C

Teaching Tip

PMI estimates are always approximate, as they are based on multiple conditions.

Part A

1. 37°C − 33.1°C = 3.9°C

   0.78°C/hour × unknown hours = 3.9°C

   unknown hours = 3.9°C/0.78°C = 5 hours

2. PMI is less than 5 hours since the body would have lost heat at a faster rate being outside in the winter. The rate of body heat lost would be much greater than the calculated 0.78°C per hour.

3. 37°C − 25.9°C = 11.1°C lost since death

   9.36°C would be lost in the first 12 hours

   11.1°C − 9.36°C = approximately 1.7°C lost after 12 hours

   (0.39°C/hour) × (unknown hours) = 1.7°C

   unknown hours = 1.7°C/0.39°C

   unknown hours = 4.36 hours or 4 hours and 22 min.

   (0.36 hours × 60 min/1 hr = 22 min)

   total time dead = initial 12 hours plus 4 hours and 22 minutes = 16 hours 22 minutes (approximately)

4. 37°C − 15.6°C = 21.4°C lost during PMI

   9.36°C, or approximately 9.4°C, lost in the first 12 hours

   21.4°C − 9.4°C = 12°C lost after 12 hours

   (0.39°C/hour) × unknown number of hours = 12°C

   unknown number of hours = 12°C / (0.39°C/hour) = 30.8 hours or approximately 31 hours

   (0.39 hours 3 60 min/hour) = 48 minutes

   12 hours + approximately 31 hours approximately 43 hours PMI

5. $37°C - 10°C = 27°C$ lost since time of death

$27°C - 9.36°C =$ approximately $17.6°C$ lost in first 12 hours

$(0.39°C/hour) \times$ unknown # of hours $= 17.6°C$

unknown # of hours $= 17.6°C \times (0.39°C/hour)$

$= 45.1$ hours or 45 hours approximately

Approximate PMI 12 hours + 45 hours ~ 57 hours PMI

6. $37°C - 29.4°C = 7.6°C$ lost. (Note: less than 12 hours PMI)

$(0.78°C/hour) \times$ unknown hours $= 7.6°C$

unknown hours $= 7.6°C ((0.78°C/hour)$

~9.7 hours

Approximate PMI 10 hours

7. $37°C - 24°C = 13°C$ lost

$13°C - 9.4°C = 3.6°C$ lost after first 12 hours

$0.39°C/hr \times$ unknown # hours ~3.6°C

unknown hours $= 3.6°C$ divided by $(0.39°C/hour) = 9.23$ hours or ~ 9 hours

Approximate PMI 12 hours + 9 hours ~ 21 hours

Part B

1. Reduce PMI estimate.

2. Reduce PMI estimate.

3. Increase PMI estimate if they had a fever.

4. Probably reduce the PMI estimate because most bodies of water are cooler than body temperature.

B. Since 14.8°C is more than 9.36°C, you know that the person was dead longer than 12 hours. How many degrees did the temperature decrease after the first 12 hours?

14.8°C decrease since death — 9.36°C decrease the first 12 hours ~ 5.44°C
5.44°C decrease after the first 12 hours

C. Recall that the rate of temperature decrease after 12 hours is ~0.39°C per hour.
Determine how many hours it took to decrease 5.44°C at the reduced rate.

$(0.39°C/hour) \times$ (unknown number of hours) ~ decrease after 12 hours

Solve for number of hours:

number of hours ~ 5.44°C ÷ (0.39°C/hour) = 13.9 or approximately 14 hours since death

D. In the first 12 hours, there was a decrease of 9.36°C.
In the next 13.9 hours, there was an additional decrease of 5.44°C.
This results in a PMI of about 25.9 hours (approximately 26 hours).

Questions:

PART A

1. Determine the approximate PMI using evidence from algor mortis. Show your work. Estimate the PMI if the victim's body temperature at the crime scene was 33.1°C.

2. If you discovered that the body in question 1 was found in an air-conditioned room, would that variable increase or decrease your estimated PMI? Explain. What would the new PMI be?

3. Approximately how long has the victim been dead if his body temperature was 25.9°C?

4. What is the approximate PMI if the body temperature was 15.6°C?

5. What is the approximate PMI if the body temperature was 10°C?

6. What is the approximate PMI if the body temperature was 29.4°C?

7. What is the approximate PMI if the body temperature was 24°C?

PART B

If you based your PMI estimate of 10 hours solely on temperature decrease, would you reduce or increase your 10-hour estimate if the body had been:

1. Naked

2. Exposed to windy conditions

3. Suffering from an illness prior to death

4. Submerged in a lake

Further Study:

Investigate the procedures used by crime-scene investigators to take accurate body temperature readings.

Tommy the Tub *Obj. 12.7*

Background:

Whether you are playing volleyball on a hot beach in August or snowboarding down a mountain on a cold, windy day in January, your body is constantly working to maintain a normal body temperature. Living organisms are equipped with mechanisms that maintain this balance (homeostasis). However, if a person becomes ill or dies, the mechanisms fail.

Human bodies are mostly water. A tub filled with approximately the same volume of water as a human body ("Tommy the Tub") is used to simulate a corpse. This allows us to compare the rate of heat loss of Tommy the Tub to the projected rate of heat loss of a human corpse: 0.78°C for the first 12 hours and 0.39°C for the next 12 hours.

Objectives:

By the end of this activity, you will be able to:

1. Observe and record the heat loss each hour of a simulated human body, "Tommy the Tub," over a 24-hour period.
2. Compare the rate of heat loss to the projected rate of heat loss of a human corpse.
3. Discuss ways to improve upon the experimental design to obtain a more accurate way to simulate heat loss from a human body.

Materials:

Act 12-3 SH
66-L plastic tub
probeware interface and two temperature probes or two thermometers
computer or calculator
cart for transporting the tub
graph paper

SAFETY PRECAUTIONS:
None

Time Required to Complete Activity:

Two consecutive days (30 minutes per day)

Procedure:

1. Fill a tub with approximately 66 liters of warm water, adjusting the temperature to about 37°C.

Background

In this activity, students observe and record the heat loss of a simulated human body, "Tommy the Tub," over a 24-hour period. Students compare Tommy the Tub's heat loss to the projected heat loss of a human corpse.

Time Required to Complete Activity

2 consecutive days, 30 minutes each day

Safety Precautions

There are no safety precautions for this activity; however, avoid getting water on electronic equipment.

Procedures

1. Print, copy, and distribute Act 12-3 SH from the IRCD, Chapter 12.
2. Make sure students read all directions before beginning the activity.
3. Make sure the tub is set on a cart when empty so it can be moved at the end of the activity. Once filled, the tub is very heavy.

Teaching Tip

Probes are optional. Regular thermometers used at several intervals during the investigation will work fine.

Teaching Tip

Directions are intentionally vague regarding where and how to measure the ambient temperature and the temperature of the water in the tub. Ask students to plan a procedure that will standardize where these temperatures should be taken. Discuss with students the need for standardized techniques so that someone else can replicate the experiment and get reliable results. If this is not discussed in advance, ask students to evaluate their experiment when they have completed collecting the data. If collection sites were inconsistent, then this should be noted as an experimental error.

2. Connect the two temperature probes to record temperature readings over an extended period. One probe or thermometer should record the ambient air temperature. The second should be submerged in the tub to record the "body temperature."

3. Set the probe to measure temperature or assign someone to take the temperature at 1-hour intervals for a 24-hour period. If you are using thermometers, have someone record the temperature readings every hour during the school day.

4. Record air and tub temperatures in the data table.

5. From the probeware data or your data table, determine the average air temperature over the 24-hour period.
   Average air temperature = _____ °C

6. From the probeware data or your data table, determine the average decrease in tub water temperature for the first 12 hours _____ °C, average decrease in tub water temperature for hours 13 to 24 _____ °C, and average decrease in tub water temperature for hours 1 to 24 _____ °C.

7. Generate a best-fit graph of Tommy's temperature decrease over a 24-hour period. Include in your graph:
   a. Title of graph
   b. Labeled x- and y-axes (with units)
   c. Draw the best-fit line. (This line is approximated. It will be a straight line that will pass through some of the points but not necessarily all of them. There will be some points on either side of the line and not on the line.)

Tommy the Tub

Time (Hours)	Tub Actual Temp. °C	Tub Temp. Decrease Since Last Hour °C	Ambient Temp. °C	Time (Hours)	Tub Actual Temp. °C	Tub Temp. Decrease Since Last Hour °C	Ambient Temp. °C
0				13			
1				14			
2				15			
3				16			
4				17			
5				18			
6				19			
7				20			
8				21			
9				22			
10				23			
11				24			
12							
	Avg. Temp Decrease per Hour From 0–12 Hours _____ °C	Avg. Temp. 0–12 Hours _____ °C			Avg. Temp. Decrease per Hour From 13–24 Hours _____ °C	Avg. Temp. 13–24 Hours _____ °C	

Further Research and Extensions

You may want to modify other variables and investigate them after the main trial. Other variables could include: different body size (smaller/larger tubs), wearing clothes (wrap a tub with a blanket, or changing ambient temperature by setting tub under a lamp to mildly increase temperature.

Questions:

1. Compare and contrast Tommy the Tub's temperature decrease over the first 12 hours with that of a real human corpse. Support your claims citing data from your experiment.
   a. decrease over the first 12 hours
   b. decrease from 12 hours to 24 hours
2. Explain some of the limitations of using Tommy the Tub as an appropriate model for a human body.
3. In small groups, discuss how to redesign a more realistic and reliable model of a human corpse to be used in a heat-loss experiment like this.
4. What is the significance of taking the ambient temperature over 24 hours?
5. Using a similar experimental setup, design an experiment that includes one of the many variables that affect algor mortis.

Answers

1. Check students' data tables and graphs. Over a 24-hour period, the results should be somewhat similar. Student answers should include specific data regarding the average loss of temperature over the first 12 hours and continue for the next 12 hours.

2. Some of the limitations include: (1) the tub is not made of cells, (2) the tub does not have variable thicknesses as those found in a human body, and (3) the tub does not have any insulating materials such as skin or fat.

3. Students' answers will vary. Sample answer: A pig would present a more realistic model for this experiment.

4. Answers will vary. If the temperature in the room changed, this would affect the loss of temperature of Tommy the Tub. Students should compare temperature loss when the ambient temperature changes, compared to the temperature loss when the ambient temperature is more stable.

5. Variables affecting heat loss include whether the body (tub) was clothed or naked, ambient temperatures during the 24-hour period, presence of wind, the amount of fat insulating the body, if the "body" was buried or submerged in water. Students need to devise ways to vary Tommy the Tub and record the heat losses.

Background

In this activity, students work in pairs to estimate the postmortem interval using algor, rigor, and livor mortis evidence. Students need to be reminded to first estimate postmortem interval (PMI) based solely on temperature change and then factor in the variables. PMI can be estimated by examining all the evidence from insects, algor, rigor, and livor mortis but will never be exact.

Time Required to Complete Activity

45 minutes

Safety Precautions

There are no safety precautions for this activity.

Procedure

Print, copy, and distribute Act 12-4 SH from the IRCD, Chapter 12.

Teaching Tip

Prior to students completing this activity, review the many different types of evidence used to establish PMI. Discuss what type of observations and documentation should be made of both the victim and the crime scene. What meteorological data should be documented? What types of items found at the crime scene could provide clues?

Answers

1. a. PMI is probably around 2–3 hours. This is based on evidence from algor, rigor, and livor (if any) mortis. Variables include a naked body.

   b. Based on algor mortis evidence:

      3.3 hours

      Based on livor mortis: PMI less than 2 hours, no evidence of lividity

      Based on rigor mortis: limited rigor suggesting PMI more than 2 and probably fewer than 6 hours.

Analysis of Evidence From Death Scenes

Obj. 12.5, 12.8, 12.9, 12.10

Objective:

By the end of this activity, you will be able to:

1. Identify and analyze evidence from various death scenes.
2. Calculate an estimated PMI based on different types of evidence.

Time Required to Complete Activity: 45 minutes

Materials:

Act 12-4 SH (or refer to text Figures 12-6 and 12-7 concerning rigor mortis)
Act 12-4 SH Reference
paper
pen or pencil
calculator

SAFETY PRECAUTIONS:
None

Procedure:

Working in pairs, identify, analyze, and discuss the evidence, and answer the following questions. First, analyze each type of evidence individually. Then, using all the evidence, estimate a PMI.

Questions:

1. A naked male corpse was found at 8 A.M. on Tuesday, July 9. The air temperature was 26.7°C. The body exhibited some stiffness in the face and eyelids and had a temperature of 34.4°C. Livor mortis was not evident.
   a. Identify all evidence that would factor into estimating a postmortem interval (PMI). Using that information, what would you consider to be a reasonable PMI estimate?
   b. Use the evidence collected to justify your claim. Show your work for all calculations.
   c. Discuss and list what other factors at the crime scene should be observed by the crime-scene investigator to help in establishing a more accurate PMI.
2. At noon, a female corpse was found partially submerged on the shore of a lake. The air temperature was 26.7°C, and the water temperature was about 15.6°C. Rigor mortis was not evident, and the body's temperature was 15.6°C. Livor mortis showed as a noticeable reddening on the victim's back that did not disappear when pressed. Bacterial activity was not significant, and the lungs were filled with water.
   a. What is the estimated PMI?
   b. Justify your claim using evidence from the preceding paragraph. Show all work and calculations.

Variables: cooler temperatures and naked body would cause the body to cool at a faster rate.

   c. A lack of clothing would cause the body to lose body heat faster. Other variables include the man's weight and size, body position, and whether he was on the surface, buried, or in water. Was he in the sun or shade? Is there any evidence of insects? Was the area windy or still?

2. a. PMI approximately 36 to 43 hours

   b. Based on algor mortis evidence:

   ~ 43 hours

Based on livor mortis evidence:

Permanent livor mortis indicates that death occurred at least 8 hours earlier. With lividity on the back, it appears the woman died on her back. Since water was in her lungs, it seems that she drowned.

Permanent lividity on her back indicates that she laid on her back for at least 8 hours. She may have drowned, been removed from the water and then been put back into the water.

3. The body felt cold to the touch. The thermometer gave a reading of 21.1°C for the body temperature. No rigor mortis was evident, but livor mortis had set in with blood pooling along the back. There was no bloating or bacterial activity in the digestive system and no putrefaction. The man had been dead for more than 48 hours. How is that possible? Justify your answer using knowledge of rigor mortis, livor mortis, algor mortis, and extenuating circumstances.

4. The body of a 20-year-old female college student was found in her dorm at 5 P.M. Her roommate said she had been distraught about learning of an unplanned pregnancy. She was last seen alive eating pizza, salad, and ice cream with her boyfriend at 1 P.M. on the day she died. The crime-scene investigators noted the following:

   Her body was found in a stairwell in the dorm suspended by the neck from a 2-inch-wide belt. The belt created a V-shape in the front of her neck just under her chin. No bruising was evident around this mark. When the belt was removed, a dark red bruise varying in width from ½ inch to ¾ inch was evident below it. The bruise was circular in appearance. Skin above and below this bruised area showed extensive petechial hemorrhaging. The body temperature was 34.5°C, and rigor was present in the face, eyelids, and jaw. Light lividity was present in her feet, lower legs, hands, and lower portion of her arms. Her eyes were open and cloudy.

   The autopsy report indicated the following:

   Dark red bruising, ½-inch to ¾-inch wide, was evident in the skin and tissues at the base of the throat. There was no sign of bruising under the belt. There was evidence of a broken hyoid bone (throat) and damage to other cartilage in her neck. Stomach contents showed a partially digested meal of pizza, salad, and ice cream.

   Was this a suicide or a homicide? If a homicide, was the boyfriend a suspect? From 3 P.M. to 6 P.M., he was playing basketball with friends.

   Analyze all the evidence and discuss the case. What is the PMI? What other information about the crime scene is needed to establish a more accurate PMI? Does the evidence support a manner of death of suicide or homicide? Does the boyfriend's alibi exclude him as a suspect?

Going Further:

Working in small groups, write a short story or create a short video of a staged crime scene. Include descriptions of all the evidence found at the crime scene. Exchange your short story or video with another team and ask them to analyze the crime scene and estimate the PMI.

   An alternative is to record a crime scene depicted on TV or in a movie. Analyze the evidence at the crime scene and establish a PMI.

No rigor is evident, which is consistent with the time of death being more than 36 hours.

Bacterial evidence:

There is not much evidence of bacterial decomposition.

Variables to consider:

When bodies are submerged or partially submerged in water, it is difficult to accurately determine PMI.

The water temperature was cool at 15.6°C (60°F), which could slow down decomposition while accelerating heat loss.

3. It appears that the body might have been refrigerated sometime after death, slowing down heat loss as well as reducing bacterial decomposition.

Algor mortis evidence:

~29 hours since death.

Livor mortis evidence:

Pooling of blood indicates that death occurred at least 8 hours before the discovery of the body.

Rigor mortis evidence:

It appears that rigor has gone and that the body has been dead at least 36 hours.

Bacterial evidence:

Lack of significant bacterial evidence seems to indicate that the body was kept refrigerated. This would also explain how the body temperature had cooled to less than 21.1°C (70°F) over 2 days'.

4. Algor mortis: Body temperature of 34.5 indicates a PMI of about 3 hours. $37 - 34.5 = 2.5$ degrees lost. $2.5/0.78 \sim 3$ hours
Rigor mortis: In the beginning stages with rigidity only in the face, neck, and jaw, indicating a PMI of 2–3 hours.
Livor mortis: Just beginning to appear, consistent with a PMI of more than 2 hours. Since the victim was hanging, lividity is expected in hands, feet, and lower appendages.

(continues at left)

No bruising under the belt and lack of 2-inch-wide bruising under the belt is inconsistent with belt causing death and more consistent with the belt placed there after death. Around it is consistent with the belt being applied after she died. This could have been set up to appear as a suicide.

The circular, irregular width, dark bruising is consistent with a soft material wrapped around the neck. This was applied prior to death.

The broken hyoid bone and damaged cartilage are consistent with pressure being exerted on the neck.

Stomach contents of only partially digested food would indicate that time of death was less than 2 hours after the ingestion of the meal.

Summary: PMI is somewhere between 2 and 3 hours. Evidence is consistent with a homicide rather than a suicide. The boyfriend's alibi would therefore not exclude him as a suspect.

CHAPTER 13
Soil Examination

Chapter Overview

Soil is more than just dirt or rock. It is the medium that supports plant growth. Soil is primarily made up of weathered rock, but it is also composed of air, water, and organic matter. Soil has three different textures that differ in size: from coarsest to finest, they are sand, clay, and silt. Soil samples also differ in shape, color, and mineral composition. Each sample of soil has unique characteristics. Forensic scientists use soil's unique characteristics to help solve crimes. Soil can be examined for its general texture and then further analyzed for its mineral and chemical composition.

The Big Ideas

Soil scientists agree that no two places on Earth have precisely the same soil. Soil recovered from a crime scene, a victim, or a suspect can be analyzed for consistency that can link the suspect to the crime scene or victim. Soil is part of the top layer of Earth's crust and contains minerals, decaying organisms, water, and air in uniquely varying amounts in each location. Soil is classified by its texture, or grain size. Soils form in horizons, or layers, and each horizon has characteristic properties that differ. The horizons unique to an area make up its soil profile. Being able to recognize alterations to soil in an area can help forensic scientists locate a burial site. Proper collection and documentation of soil evidence are required. While soil evidence has been used in many cases, its reliability has been questioned in the courts.

When Soil Is Not Just Dirt

Police in California found a dead body on the platform of an oil well. Investigators noticed the rocks and soil on the platform were not from the area. Tests showed that the rocks and soil were an unusual type that came from a site 300 miles away. Investigators knew finding matching samples of the soil on a suspect would be key to solving the case.

Police arrested an acquaintance of the victim. The suspect kept repeating, "I wasn't anywhere near the crime scene!" The police suspected otherwise. Physical evidence linking the suspect to the crime scene was needed. After they obtained a search warrant, the police took possession of work boots that had been worn by the suspect. They took the boots to a laboratory. In the lab, forensic scientists attempted to find soil samples from the suspect's boots that were consistent with soil from the area where the body was found. The suspect was not worried. He was unaware of the testing that could be done to compare the soil from his boots to the soil found on the body.

Examining soil evidence.

Forensic geologists performed chemical and microscopic tests on the soil on the suspect's boots, as well as on samples taken from his car. These tests demonstrated that the samples from the suspect had a composition consistent with the unusual rocks and soil at the site where the body was found. Faced with this compelling evidence, the suspect admitted his guilt. He was tried, convicted, and sentenced for the crime.

416

SCENARIO

Organize students into small groups to read the scenario. Then have the class brainstorm the following questions:
What are the different kinds of soils?
What kinds of soil would you expect to find on a beach? In a desert? In a rainforest?
How are these types of soils similar and how are they different?
What do you think makes each of these soils different?
What type of tests could be performed on soil samples to determine if they were from the same area?

OBJECTIVES

By the end of this chapter, you will be able to:

13.1 Describe the distinguishing characteristics and compositions of different soils.

13.2 Compare and contrast the different soil layers found in a soil profile.

13.3 Compare and contrast the four different sources of sand.

13.4 Analyze soils using macroscopic and microscopic examination, as well as chemical and physical testing.

13.5 Describe the effects of different physical and chemical compositions of soils on the decomposition of a corpse.

13.6 Explain how soil analysis can link a suspect, victim, tool, or other evidence item to a crime scene.

13.7 Explain how soil profiles and differences in the soil surface can be used to locate a gravesite.

13.8 Summarize how to collect and document soil evidence.

TOPICAL SCIENCES KEY

BIOLOGY   CHEMISTRY

EARTH SCIENCES   PHYSICS

LITERACY   MATHEMATICS

VOCABULARY

- **clay** the finest soil particles that can absorb and hold water

- **geology** the study of soil and rocks

- **humus** material in the uppermost layer of soil made up of the decaying remains of plants and animals

- **mineral** a naturally occurring, crystalline solid formed over time

- **sand** granules of fine rock particles

- **sediment** soil that has settled after having been transported to a new location by water, wind, or glaciers

- **silt** a type of soil whose particles are coarser than clay and finer than sand

- **soil** a mixture of minerals, water, gases, and the remains of dead organisms, that covers Earth's surface

- **soil profile** a cross section of horizontal layers, or horizons, in the soil that have distinct compositions and properties

- **weathering** formation of soil through the actions of wind and water on rock

SOIL EXAMINATION   **417**

Teaching Tip

For a pre-assessment, consider arranging students in small groups and having them prepare lists responding to the following. Then lead a class discussion to address misconceptions.

1. What do they know about soil?

2. How could soil be used to help solve a crime?

Engage

Ask students to describe the soil around their houses. Continue the discussion with the following questions:

- What kinds of plants are growing around your house?
- What do you think forensic scientists would find unique about the soil around your house?
- How do you think they could determine that soil came from your house and not a house in the next town?

Explore

Allow students to make their own observations of soil. In separate, clear containers, place samples of sand, silt, and clay. Ask students to study the samples and write down their observations of each soil. Pour water into the containers and ask students to make further observations. Provide the students with the terms *sand*, *silt*, and *clay*, and ask them to research which container has each soil type.

DIGGING DEEPER

Sir Arthur Conan Doyle is best known as a writer, introducing Sherlock Holmes for the first time in *A Study in Scarlet* (1887). Doyle's inspiration for Sherlock Holmes was Dr. Joseph Bell, a professor of Doyle's when he attended medical school at the University of Edinburgh. Sherlock Holmes's stories have been translated into more than 50 languages and made into plays, films, television series, a musical comedy, a ballet, cartoons, and comic books. Go to the Gale Forensic Science eCollection at ngl.cengage .com/forensicscience2e for more information about Doyle.

Did you know

What is the difference between soil and dirt? Soil is a naturally occurring product that has mineral and organic (both living and non-living) components. Dirt is soil without any organic material.

Did you know

In the 1880s, a railroad company laying tracks in northwest Colorado named a town Silt because of the composition of the soil in the area.

CHEMISTRY

INTRODUCTION

Soil is produced by a complicated process that is influenced by factors such as temperature, rainfall, and the chemicals and minerals present in the material from which it forms. Because of all the factors that affect soil formation, soil from different locations has different physical and chemical characteristics that are useful to forensic scientists. The uniqueness of soil composition, along with its ability to be easily transferred, located, collected, and described, makes soil a valuable type of trace evidence.

In one case, rustlers stole a herd of cattle from Missouri and took it to Montana. The rustlers changed the brands on the cattle, thinking they would not get caught. Forensic scientists analyzed a sample of cow manure taken from the back of a truck thought to be used in the theft. They found small fragments of a silica-containing rock in the manure. This type of rock could only have come from Missouri. Police used this soil evidence to convict the rustlers.

During World War II, Japanese scientists devised a plan for delivering explosives to the United States. The explosives would be carried in the air from Japan to the United States using hydrogen-filled balloons. The balloons also carried bags of sand as counterweights. More than 9,000 of these balloons were launched. Physical evidence indicated that about 300 balloons reached America. The explosives carried by the balloons did little property damage. However, six people lost their lives when one of the explosive-laden balloons detonated. By analyzing the sand used in the counterweights, geologists were able to determine that the sand came from one particular beach in Japan. With this information, the American forces bombed the area, destroying the site where the balloons were constructed.

HISTORY OF FORENSIC SOIL EXAMINATION

Real and fictional investigators have been using soil samples to identify criminals since the late 1800s. Between 1887 and 1893, Sir Arthur Conan Doyle wrote about the use of **geology** (the study of soil and rocks) in the investigation of crime in his novels. His character, Sherlock Holmes, used soil and mud samples to help link an individual to a specific location where a crime had been committed.

An Austrian, Dr. Hans Gross, is believed to be one of the first investigators to apply science to crime investigation. His book *Criminal Investigation*, written in 1893, contained groundbreaking material in this new science. Dr. Gross, a university professor, founded the Institute of Criminology in Graz, Austria. He firmly believed in the value of trace evidence, including soils found at crime scenes.

A German investigator, Georg Popp, is credited with being one of the first forensic scientists to use soil evidence to solve a crime. During a murder investigation in 1904, he examined a handkerchief left at the crime scene and found it contained bits of coal and particles of hornblende, a mineral. Popp linked this evidence to a suspect who worked in a gravel pit that contained hornblende. Popp found soil samples taken from the suspect's trousers were consistent with samples collected at the crime scene. When confronted with all of the evidence, the suspect admitted his crime.

SOIL COMPOSITION Obj. 13.1

Soil is part of the top layer of Earth's crust, where most plants grow. Soil contains **minerals** from weathered rocks, decaying organisms, water, and air in varying amounts. Soil texture describes the size of the mineral particles that make up soil. There are three main soil textures: **sand, silt,** and **clay.** Sand is the coarsest texture, and clay is the finest texture. Most soil samples are mixtures that contain a combination of sand, silt, and clay. *Loam* is a fertile type of soil composed of approximately equal amounts of sand and silt, and about half as much clay. Figure 13-1 contains more information about soil textures.

Figure 13-1 *Soil Textures.*

Soil Texture	Particle Size	Feels Like	Location	Characteristics
Sand	Coarse	Coarse granular	Deserts, beaches, riverbeds	Loses water, air circulates easily
Silt	Medium	Gritty	Sediment in riverbeds	Retains water
Clay	Fine	Sticky when wet, smooth when dry	Varies	Retains water

Soil also contains organic material, or **humus**, such as decaying plants and animals, and mineral particles. Soil with more than 20 percent decaying organic material is called peaty soil, which is acidic. Chalky soil is alkaline and contains various-sized pieces of a soft rock called chalk. The unique texture, amount and type of organic material, and chemistry of a soil are what makes soils so useful in forensics.

Soil Profiles Obj. 13.2

Sand, silt, or clay that is deposited by wind or water is called **sediment**. Sediment on dry land will settle into soil horizons, or layers, that are more or less parallel to Earth's surface. The soil in each horizon has characteristic properties, as described in Figure 13-2 on the next page. Soil in a given area will have a unique **soil profile,** or sequence of layers. Each soil horizon within the profile is labeled with an uppercase letter—commonly O, A, E, B, C, and R, from top to bottom.

What is the forensic value of studying the layers of a soil profile? Humans disturb these layers when they dig into the soil—when they are burying a body, for example. When crime-scene investigators search for a buried body in an area, they look for disturbed soil. Topsoil and humus may be lower

Did you know

Soil color may reflect its composition. White or gray soil contains limestone or chalk. Red, yellow, or brown soil contains iron. Black or gray soil contains organic materials and moisture.

EARTH SCIENCES

Did you know

Stratigraphy is the study of how soil and rock layers have formed and are arranged. A soil profile can be described as a soil layer cake. The United States Department of Agriculture has identified more than a thousand soil profiles in the United States. Go to the USDA's Web site at usda.gov and follow the link to their Web soil survey to learn more about soil profiles in your area.

Explore

Tell students that *hornblende* is a name given to collections of minerals. The chemical makeup of hornblende is quite variable. It often makes up the dark part of igneous rocks, which are composed of light and dark crystals.

Explore

Provide students with samples of dried peat moss to examine with a hand lens or stereomicroscope. Have students place the peat moss in water and describe what happens. Have students determine if peat soils are acidic or basic using pH paper.

Science

EARTH SCIENCES

EARTH SCIENCE

When the remains of plants partially decompose, they form a brownish-black material called *peat*. Peat deposits are still forming today. In some parts of the world, people burn peat to heat their houses and cook their meals.

Science

EARTH SCIENCES

EARTH SCIENCE

Peat deposits are covered by layers of sediment. Over time, the weight of the sediment forces water and gases out of the peat and forms brown coal. As sediments accumulate on top of the coal, more water is forced out, forming a type of coal called anthracite.

Figure 13-2 *Soil profile key.*

Humus O
Topsoil A
Sand and silt E
Subsoil B
Broken rock C
Solid rock R

Layer	Common Name	Description
O	Humus	Decaying organic matter
A	Topsoil	Dark; mixture of humus and minerals; plants sprout here.
E	Sand and silt	Light; water leaches away most minerals.
B	Subsoil	Clay and mineral deposits
C	Broken rock	No plant growth, little humus
R	Solid rock	Solid rock

in the profile and the subsoil and rocks may be on the surface. When a gravesite is filled after a burial, the soil profile is changed. Also, the layers of an area's soil profile may still be detectable on equipment or clothes used to dig a grave, leaving clues to a specific location. Databases of soil profiles are readily available to forensic investigators who need to compare the soil profile of the evidence to find locations in which to search.

EARTH SCIENCES

SAND Obj. 13.3

Sand is formed by the action of wind and water on rocks, called **weathering.** As wind and water move rocks, they collide with other rocks. These collisions break the rock into smaller and smaller pieces until small grains, called sand, remain.

Sand grains can be anywhere from 0.05 mm to 2 mm in diameter. Grains can be rounded or angular, depending on the amount of weathering and the mineral composition of the rocks that formed the sand. Note the varying textures, colors, and shapes of the grains in the stereomicroscope photos in Figure 13-3.

Figure 13-3 *Examples of different sands.*

a. Bermuda   *b. Myrtle Beach, SC*   *c. Vero Beach, FL*

d. Hawaii   *e. Bahamas*   *f. Rhode Island*

All photos © Cengage Learning®

Aging and Rounding of Sand

Compare images of river sand, desert sand, and beach sand. Go to the Gale Forensic Science eCollection at **ngl.cengage.com/forensicscience2e** and enter the search term "sand types" for more information.

During weathering, if rocks in wind or water strike one another along their edges, the edges may break off. As the edges break off, the rock pieces become more rounded. The rounding process may take place over millions of years. Sand grains carried by water become rounded more slowly than wind-blown sand grains because water acts as a buffer.

Sand grains are classified as immature, young, old, or mature. Immature sand contains a large portion of clay, and the grains have a high percentage of fragments. Immature sand is found near the rocks from which it was formed, usually in areas not exposed to waves or currents, such as the bottom of bays and lagoons, or in swamps or river floodplains. Mature sand does not contain clay and has fewer jagged edges. Mature sand is found in areas, such as beaches and desert dunes, where much weathering has taken place.

Mineral Composition of Sand *Obj. 13.3*

Sand has four primary sources: continental, volcanic, skeletal (biogenic), and precipitate. Sand from different sources contains different combinations of minerals. The most common mineral found in sand is quartz. Many other minerals, such as feldspar, mica, and iron compounds, may be present in smaller quantities (Figure 13-4).

Did you know?

The color of a sand grain reflects its mineral composition.
▶ Clear or frosty is quartz.
▶ Shiny black is magnetite.
▶ Green is olivine.
▶ Pink or red glassy is garnet.
▶ Pink or white opaque is shells or coral.
▶ Silver or gold is mica.
▶ Beige, red-brown, or peach is feldspar.

Figure 13-4 *Mineral components of sand.*

a. Feldspar is light in color and opaque. It makes up about 60 percent of Earth's surface.

b. Magnetite is opaque black or gray. It is a form of iron oxide.

c. Quartz can be many colors, but is often white, clear, or rose. It is very abundant.

d. Granite is usually found in massive deposits. It may contain visible grains of quartz, feldspar and mica.

e. Mica appears in flakes and flat sheets.

All photos © Cengage Learning®

SOIL EXAMINATION **421**

Explore

Sand grains are generally measured by sieving. A sand sample of standard mass is passed through a set of sieves of standard mesh sizes. The sieves are arranged in decreasing mesh diameters. The sieves are mechanically vibrated for a fixed period of time. The mass of sediment retained on each sieve is measured and converted into a percentage of the total sediment sample for later comparison to other samples. This method is quick and accurate enough for most purposes.

Engage

Students do not realize how beautiful sand is or how different the grains are until they have viewed it under a stereomicroscope. Provide different samples for students to view or project sand images that are magnified. Ask students to explain why there are different colors and shapes. (Note: Do not provide black sand or oolithic sand for this activity.)

Teaching Tip

Tell students that feldspar is pink because it contains high levels of oxidized potassium compounds. Feldspar and quartz are also two of the main components of granite. Feldspar and quartz sand grains are commonly the result of erosion of granite.

Explore

There are also green sand beaches. Ask interested students to find out how green sand is formed and where these beaches exist.

Teaching Tip

Explain to students that another type of skeletal sand is diatomaceous earth. This fine sand is made up of tiny silica shells of diatoms, a microscopic alga, and is common in both fresh and saltwater. Diatomaceous earth has many uses, such as an abrasive, a component of swimming pool filters, and an insect control for plants.

Evaluate

Ask students what gas is given off in the bubbles when acid is placed on skeletal sand (carbon dioxide, CO_2). If they do not know, write the chemical formula for calcium carbonate ($CaCO3$) on the board. Ask if they can deduce the gas formed from this formula.

Teaching Tip

Point out that in the word *oolite*, the first part *oo-* refers to "egg" and the second part *-lite* refers to "stone." Combined, the parts means an "egg stone," referring to the sand grain's resemblance to a tiny bird egg.

Teaching Tip

Remind students to write pH with a lowercase p and an uppercase H.

Science

CHEMISTRY

CHEMISTRY

According to one definition of acids and bases, an acid releases hydrogen ions when it combines with water, and a base releases hydroxide ions in combination with water. The concentration of hydrogen ions in a solution is commonly expressed in terms of pH.

Figure 13-5 *Continental sand from Big Sur, California.*

Figure 13-6 *Volcanic sand from Hawaii.*

Figure 13-7 *Skeletal sand from Bermuda and the Bahamas.*

CONTINENTAL SAND

Continental sand is composed mostly of quartz, mica, feldspar, and dark-colored minerals like hornblende and magnetite (Figure 13-5). If feldspar is present, the sand probably came from a temperate or polar climate or from a high elevation. In warm, tropical climates, feldspar weathers quickly. A high percentage of quartz means the sand is very old, because quartz weathers very slowly and often remains after other minerals have weathered away.

VOLCANIC SAND

Volcanic sand is usually dark as a result of the presence of black basalt or green olivine (Figure 13-6). The source of this sand is mid-ocean volcanoes or hot-spot volcanoes like those found in Hawaii. It sometimes contains volcanic cinders or other volcanic debris. Volcanic sand is very young and contains little or no quartz, except for black obsidian particles.

SKELETAL (BIOGENIC) SAND

Skeletal sand is made of the remains of marine organisms, such as microorganisms, shells, and coral (Figure 13-7). It takes less time to form than other types of sand. Skeletal sand occurs all over the world. Skeletal sand derived from shells or from coral remains occurs only in tropical regions. Because of the high amounts of calcium carbonate, skeletal sand gives off bubbles when mixed with a few drops of acid.

Figure 13-8 *Precipitate sand containing oolites from the Great Salt Lake, Utah.*

PRECIPITATE SAND

Water contains dissolved minerals. When water evaporates, these minerals precipitate, or come out of, the water solution. Calcium carbonate will sometimes precipitate out of seawater, forming layers of hard particles that resemble layers of an onion. These layers eventually form small, round structures called *oolites*. Oolite formation is an example of *deposition*, the depositing of layers of material. Sand containing oolites is called *oolitic sand* and can be found in various places, including the Great Salt Lake in Utah (Figure 13-8).

Soil Chemistry *Obj. 13.5, 13.7*

Soil chemistry influences and is influenced by the plant and animal life living and decomposing in the area. The amounts of nitrogen, phosphorus, potassium, and calcium in the soil influence plant growth. (See Figure 13-9.) These nutrients also affect the pH of the soil—its level of acidity or alkalinity (basicity). The pH scale ranges from 0 to 14. A pH higher than 7 is acidic and a pH lower than 7 is alkaline (basic). The pH of soil plays a part in determining which organisms can survive. Most, bacteria, for example, require a neutral pH, so soil pH can affect the rate and manner of decomposition.

CHEMISTRY

DIFFERENTIATED LEARNING

Teaching Gifted Students
Have interested students use a flex cam and a microscope to examine various sand samples. Ask students to describe and compare them.

DIFFERENTIATED LEARNING

Teaching At-Risk Students
To have students learn about the different types of sand, encourage them to draw a picture of each. Have volunteers explain their drawings. Display them in the classroom.

Figure 13-9 *Effects of nutrient deficiencies in plants.*

Nutrient Deficiency	Appearance of Plants
Nitrogen	Leaves of plants are yellow.
Phosphorus	Small, frail plants with reddish leaves
Potassium	Leaves at bottom of plant dying from lack of chlorophyll (leaves no longer green)
Calcium	Stems and leaves drooping

When a body is buried directly in soil, it affects the soil chemistry in a complex series of ways. Toxic chemical products of decomposition, along with nutrient-rich decomposition fluids, seep out of the body and enter the soil. A *cadaver decomposition island* (CDI) is formed by these concentrated decomposition products. The CDI undergoes a rapid change in pH and chemistry that initially kills vegetation. An isolated area barren of plant growth reveals that plant growth has been disturbed and has not resumed. It could mark a recent burial (Figure 13-10).

As decomposition continues, insects, predators, and scavengers are drawn to the site. Their waste products improve soil fertility. In an area where a body is buried, the soil is disturbed. The soil becomes aerated and has improved water circulation. Following the initial period of reduced fertility, the area then undergoes rapid growth and succession due to increased fertility and increased insect activity. A small area containing different plants from the rest of the vicinity arises, potentially helping to identify an older burial.

SOIL EVIDENCE *Obj. 13.8*

Proper procedures must be followed when collecting, labeling, and packaging soil evidence (including sand). (Refer to Chapter 2.)

1. Photograph and document the crime scene.
2. The artist should sketch the evidence as the evidence collector notes the locations and types of evidence.
3. Collect at least four tablespoons of material from several locations at the crime scene (Figure 13-10):
   a. surface soil to be used as a baseline
   b. any soil that looks different from surrounding soils
   c. soil from different levels
   d. soil from shoes, clothing, tools, vehicles, or other objects at the crime scene

Figure 13-10 *Investigators examine a gravesite for evidence.*

© Cengage Learning®

Teaching Tip

Review procedures for mapping an outdoor crime scene in Chapter 2.

DIGGING DEEPER

Instruct students to write out an actual or fictitious crime-scene scenario that involves soil evidence. Then, have students exchange scenarios with a classmate and describe what soil evidence is present and how investigators should properly collect each soil sample. Go to the Gale Forensic Science eCollection at ngl.cengage .com/school/forensicscience2e for additional information on soil collection and analysis.

Explore

X-ray powder diffraction (XRD) is used to identify minerals in soil. In the past, XRD was not used extensively because of the expense of the equipment involved and the need for a trained individual to read the results. The same principle used to analyze minerals in soils is also used to analyze building materials, paints, and cosmetics.

Teaching Tip

Refer to the discussion of the excavation of the remains that became the African Burial Ground National Monument in New York City in *Breaking Ground, Breaking Silence* by Joyce Hansen and Gary McGowan. Share with students how the gravesites were located by the outlines of the biodegraded wooden coffin lids in the clay soil.

4. Collect soil samples beyond the crime scene:
   a. from a few feet north, south, east, and west of the crime scene
   b. in a perimeter 20 to 25 feet from the crime scene
5. Document, package, and label all samples according to guidelines in Chapter 2.

DIGGING DEEPER With Forensic Science eCollection

Why is it important for crime-scene investigators to properly collect and handle soil evidence? Go to the Gale Forensic Science eCollection at **ngl.cengage.com/school/ forensicscience2e** and enter the search term "soil analysis." Click on "Magazines" and read about the investigation into the burial of five murder victims. Use information from the article and what you have learned about soil evidence collection procedures to write a brief essay describing the methods the investigators used to make sure their evidence was collected properly and not contaminated. Be sure to cite your resources.

Soil Evidence Analysis *Obj. 13.6*

Soil evidence collected at a crime scene, on an object, or on a victim or suspect is analyzed both macroscopically and microscopically. Forensic analysts conduct many tests on the chemical and physical properties of soil. Chemical testing is done on each sample to determine its pH, its chemical and mineral compositions, and its reactions to different reagents. Soil samples are heated, and the wet and dry masses are compared. The moisture content is calculated. Reactions of the soil components to magnets and UV light are noted.

X-ray diffraction is a method of determining the mineral composition of soil. The soil is crushed and exposed to X-rays, and the diffraction pattern image is produced and examined. Each mineral and chemical produces a unique pattern. The pattern allows scientists to determine the unique mineral composition of the soil. Scientists compare and contrast the patterns produced by evidence samples to patterns from samples from a known location. Although it is not possible to say conclusively that an evidence sample came from a specific location, it is possible to determine if a soil sample is or is not consistent with another sample. The more evidence that can be linked to a suspect, the greater the probability that the suspect is associated with the crime.

Although many cases have used soil samples as evidence, its reliability continues to be questioned by the courts. The Organization for Scientific Area Committees (OSAC) has a special subcommittee to establish protocols and standards for working with geological materials.

Finding Gravesites *Obj. 13.5, 13.6, 13.7*

It's difficult to convict a murderer if you can't find the body. How and where does one look for a body or a gravesite? Hilltops and rocky, dry areas are usually avoided for hasty burials due to the difficulty of transporting the body. Locating a burial site depends on being able to distinguish natural from disturbed areas, as described earlier. When someone digs a grave, subsoil and surface soil are mixed, causing discolorations. The backfill soil

DIFFERENTIATED LEARNERS

Teaching At-Risk Students
Invite a law-enforcement officer to be a guest speaker and describe how dogs are used in searches for missing persons. If a guest speaker cannot visit in person, ask if he or she is willing to be interviewed via a computer videochat.

DIFFERENTIATED LEARNERS

Teaching Gifted Students
Suggest that interested students research how the new technologies used to find gravesites discussed in the section are used. Suggest students prepare a presentation for the class on one technique.

has a different color from undisturbed soil away from the grave. Excess soil may be mounded above a new grave because, with a body in the grave, it's difficult to return all of the original soil (Figure 13-11). Older gravesites tend to sink, in contrast, as the loose soil becomes compacted and the body decomposes. Sighting possible gravesites is best done when the sun is low and shadows are easier to see. Gravesites are more easily detected from the air or from a treetop or nearby hilltop because they may cast a shadow unusual for the terrain.

Soil properties such as burial depth, rock content, water content, soil texture, pH, and oxygen level all affect what happens to the buried decomposing body.

CHEMISTRY

EARTH SCIENCES

BIOLOGY

- **Burial depth and rock content**—Heavy concentrations of rock in soil may discourage someone from digging a deep grave and cause them to leave a body more exposed to surface animal activity and the elements. The deeper the body is buried, the more limited the invertebrate and other predator activity. A burial of three feet or more will protect the body from temperature fluctuations. The closer to the surface, the greater the availability of oxygen and the higher the bacterial, insect, and predator activity.

- **Soil moisture and underground water**—Soils with higher moisture content increase the likelihood of adipocere formation, which, as you recall from Chapter 12, is a waxy substance sometimes produced in the later stages of decomposition.

- **Soil texture**—Clay soil moistens bones. Bones expand when they absorb moisture. Bones contract when the soil around them is drier. Cycles of expanding and contracting can weaken bones. Fine soil packs more closely around a body, reducing the surface area in contact with oxygen and therefore slowing decomposition. Bodies in coarse soils or sandy soils dry more quickly due to better drainage. Bodies mummify into a leathery state and can be preserved for hundreds of years. Desert regions can produce this type of mummified corpse.

- **Soil pH**—Acidic areas such as peat bogs lead to tanning of the skin and can preserve bodies for centuries. Both highly alkaline and highly acidic areas reduce decomposition due to reduced microorganism activity. Microorganisms are most active at a neutral pH.

- **Oxygen level**—In *anaerobic* (low-oxygen) environments, the gases cadaverine and putrescine are produced by the decomposition of body proteins. Their stench can attract trained *cadaver dogs* to bodies in shallow graves. Cadaver dogs, with their keen sense of smell, have been trained to locate buried bodies.

Figure 13-11 *A shallow grave may be elevated and have disturbed vegetation.*

© Cengage Learning®

Evaluate

Ask students where they would look for soil on a vehicle. Also, ask what factors might make using soil stuck to vehicles challenging.

Evaluate

Organize students into groups of two to four and have them read the case studies together. Then, ask them to compare and contrast where soil was found, how the pieces of each case were put together, and how the soil evidence was used to support the case against the suspect.

Geophysicists are improving search techniques. Ground-penetrating radar, thermal imaging, air reconnaissance, satellite photography, multi-spectral imaging, electrical resistivity testing, magnetometry, and geophysical prospecting are some advanced techniques for locating bodies. However, due to cost limitations, forensic investigators often rely on observations of altered soil and/or plant life and the assistance of cadaver dogs in locating gravesites.

SUMMARY

LITERACY

Joyce Hansen and Gary McGowan. *Breaking Ground, Breaking Silence.* Zakaria Erzinclioglu, M.D. *Forensics: True Crime-Scene Investigations.*

Elena Rooraid/ PhotoEdit, Inc

- Soil evidence from crime scenes, victims, and suspects has helped to solve crimes since the late 1800s.

- There are three textures of soil, based on particle size: clay, silt, and sand. Most soils are a mixture of minerals, decaying organic matter, water, and air.

- Soil forms layers called horizons and makes up a profile unique to an area. An altered soil profile can indicate the soil was disturbed and can be of forensic value.

- The pH of soil influences the type of microorganisms and plants living in it. Soil pH of also affects how a body decomposes.

- Sand is formed when weathering breaks up rock into small grains ranging from 0.05 millimeters to 2 millimeters in diameter.

- There are four main sources of sand: continental sand, volcanic sand, skeletal sand, and precipitate sand.

- There are special procedures crime-scene investigators must follow when photographing, documenting, and collecting soil evidence.

- Understanding soil and sand helps forensic investigators link a person or object to a crime scene, locate a potential gravesite, and better understand the speed and manner in which a body decomposes.

- Soil analysis can involve macroscopic and microscopic examination, chemical testing, exposure to ultraviolet radiation, and X-ray diffraction analysis.

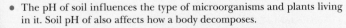

CASE STUDIES

Enrique "Kiki" Camarena (1985)

Enrique Camarena, an undercover agent for the U.S. Drug Enforcement Agency, infiltrated drug dealings in Mexico and helped destroy millions of dollars of illegal drugs. One of the drug trafficking groups under his investigation identified him as an agent. On February 7, 1985, Enrique and his pilot, Alfredo Zavala, were kidnapped in Guadalajara, Mexico. They were reported to have been killed by drug dealers during a shootout between Mexican police and the drug dealers. Soil samples taken from the two bodies were found to contain an unusual

DIFFERENTIATED LEARNING

Teaching Gifted Students
Interested students may want to research the uses of XRD. For example, using XRD analysis, it is possible to identify the mineral components in a lipstick smear and potentially identify the manufacturer of the lipstick or to otherwise connect a victim and suspect.

combination of minerals and volcanic particles. Investigators claimed this evidence proved that the men's bodies were originally buried in the mountains, far away from the shootout. The soil evidence, along with other evidence, suggested that the Mexican federal police had been involved in the murders.

Matthew Holding (2000), South Australia

A woman, her mother, and her son were reported missing in September of 2000 in South Australia. On the following day, the woman's car and her son were found miles from her home. A muddy, bloodstained shovel was found in the trunk of the car. The woman's son, Matthew Holding, was arrested for the murder of his mother and grandmother but remained silent during questioning.

Where were the missing women? South Australia is vast and sparsely inhabited. Dr. Rob Fitzpatrick, a soil scientist, was called to assist the investigation. Dr. Fitzpatrick is the director of the Centre for Australian Forensic Soil Science (CAFSS). Australia has been using soil analysis in forensic examination for many years and has developed a countrywide map of soil profiles. Dr. Fitzpatrick had soil samples on the front and back of the shovel examined. The position of the soil samples suggested that the shovel was used to both dig up and tamp down soil in a wet location. Analysis of the soil showed it to be acidic and to contain talc (a powdery mineral) found only in local mountains and foothills. When the soil was viewed microscopically, particles with an angular cut typical of mining were revealed.

The absence of plant matter in the soil indicated that the soil had been dug from below the surface. This narrowed the search area to a region about 100 miles from where Matthew Holding was arrested. Dr. Fitzpatrick believed that the soil was consistent with samples from the Oakbank Quarry of the Adelaide Hills. Samples from the quarry and the shovel were compared using X-ray diffraction techniques and found to be consistent. Soil samples were compared for composition and found to be almost identical. Detectives searched the quarry on several days, and finally found that foxes had uncovered the hand of one of the corpses. The other corpse was found buried about 50 meters from the first. Matthew Holding confessed and was sentenced to prison for the murders.

Janice Dodson (1995)

John B. Dodson died while on a hunting trip with his new wife, Janice. John appeared to be the victim of a hunting accident. Janice stated that she was standing in a nearby muddy field when John was shot. She returned to their campsite and removed her muddy overalls before seeking help for her wounded husband from some hunters nearby.

Police determined that John was shot with a .308 caliber firearm, but no weapon was ever recovered. Police found two shell casings by a nearby fence. At the time of the shooting, Janice's ex-husband was staying at a campsite nearby. He reported that his .308 rifle and some cartridges were stolen from his tent. The ex-husband had an alibi for the time of the shooting, and the case went unsolved for three years.

In 1998, investigators returned to the area where John had been shot. They noted that the campsite where Janice's ex-husband had camped was next to a cattle-watering pond. The investigators found bentonite, a mineral used to filter particles from the water, had been added to the pond water. This means that

Close

Create a list of the types of soil textures. Organize students into groups and assign each group one of the soils. Have the group describe the soil as a forensic expert would.

Evaluate

Refer students to the article "How Pedology and Mineralogy Helped Solve a Double Murder Case: Using Forensics to Inspire Future Generations of Soil Scientists." *Soil Horizons* 2012. 53. doi:10.2136/sh12-05-0016. In a class discussion, elicit student opinions regarding the soil evidence. If Matthew Holding had not confessed to the crime, was the soil evidence sufficient, objective, and reliable enough for a jury to convict Holding?

Teaching Tip

Refer students to Sally M. Walker's book *Written in Bone: Buried Lives of Jamestown and Colonial Maryland* (or read excerpts for students). Read how scientists were able to locate James Fort, a part of Jamestown, Virginia in 1607. Soil stains produced by decomposed building logs and shroud pins revealed the location of the fort and gravesites. Soil from backfill of graves looked different from that of nearby undisturbed areas.

Teaching Tip

Have students view the PBS *Nova* episode "Perfect Corpse" to view slide shows, interactives and/or program about the bog people. http://www.pbs.org/wgbh/nova/bog Buried in peat bogs, these people of the Bronze and Iron Age were astonishingly well preserved. Believed to have been victims of ritual sacrifices, these bodies have been found in Scotland, Ireland, Germany, and Denmark. Tannic acid produced by decomposition of the sphagnum moss in the bogs preserved the bodies.

the mud next to the pond would also contain bentonite, and would be very different from mud taken anywhere else in the area. They reexamined the mud from Janice Dodson's overalls and found that it was consistent with the sample containing bentonite taken from near the pond. This exposed Janice's lie about her location at the time of the shooting and placed her at the site of the stolen rifle. Janice Dodson was tried and found guilty of her husband's murder. She is now serving a life sentence for her crime.

Think Critically

How could soil on a suspect's shoes show a sequence of where the suspect had traveled?

DIFFERENTIATED LEARNING

Teaching Gifted Students
Have motivated students research Tollund Man, the bog man who lived in the 4th century B.C.

Careers *in Forensics*

Forensic Geologists

Forensic geologists use Earth science and geologic materials, such as soil and rocks, to help solve criminal and civil cases. To become a forensic geologist, you need to take college-level courses in geology, mathematics, chemistry, law, and forensic science. Some laboratories that employ forensic geologists include the FBI Laboratory in the United States, La Polizia Scientifica in Italy, the Centre of Forensic Sciences in Toronto, and the National Institute of Police Science in Japan.

Dr. Rob Fitzpatrick, an Australian soil biochemist, is one of the leading forensic soil science experts. Dr. Fitzpatrick has been the director of the Centre for Australian Forensic Soil Science (CAFSS) for more than ten years and recently developed a manual to assist other forensic soil examiners. The double murder case involving Matthew Holding in the case studies was solved with the help of Dr. Fitzpatrick's soil analyses, which linked the soil on the shovel in the suspect's car to a quarry in Australia.

Forensic geologists like Dr. Fitzpatrick often work primarily in areas other than law enforcement. They may help authenticate paintings by identifying the amount of mineral or organic material used to make the paints. This information is used to determine when the painting was painted and possibly by whom.

Forensic geologists may be hired to test soil and rocks in an area being sold as a mine. The results of their tests provide information on whether that area will yield enough of the resources to be profitable. A forensic geologist may also examine precious stones to determine their worth before purchase.

Forensic geologist working in the field.

Catherine Ursillo/Science Source

Criminal investigations can depend on a forensic geologist's analysis of soil evidence. They determine if the soil on a body, suspect, tool, or other evidence item is consistent with the soil at the location at which the body was found. If it is not consistent, it may help identify the area from which the body was moved.

A developing area of forensic geology is in intelligence work. A person may claim to have never been to a particular location, but if soil and rock evidence from that area is found at the person's home, that evidence may link the person to that location. After the terrorist bombings of September 11, 2001, a video of Osama bin Laden was occasionally broadcast on U.S. television. The video showed bin Laden standing in front of a rocky background. John Shroder, a geologist with experience in Afghanistan, was able to identify the region. His expertise helped narrow the search area for bin Laden.

Careers

Another potential use of forensic geology is in the investigation of wildlife crimes. Illegal specimens of endangered or imported animals and plants might have traces of soil on them that could be linked to a specific locale. The National Fish and Wildlife Forensic Laboratory, the only forensic lab dedicated solely to wildlife crimes, is located in Ashland, Oregon. Suggest that students go to www.lab.fws.gov/index.html for more information. The University of Florida has a degree program in wildlife forensic science. See http://wildlife.forensics.med.ufl.edu for more information.

Chapter 13 Review

True or False

1. False
2. True
3. True
4. True
5. True

Multiple Choice

6. C
7. D
8. A
9. C

Short Answer

10. Answers may vary; sample answers: Immature—large amount of clay; grains have a high percentage of fragments with jagged edges; found close to where it formed, not exposed to waves or currents. Mature—at beaches and desert dunes where much weathering due to water and wind has taken place; grains more rounded. Answers will vary as to the forensic significance but should be consistent with content in the text.

11. From different depths of the gravesite; from areas beyond the immediate gravesite; from objects at the crime scene; from suspects' clothing, shoes, cars; any soil that appears to be out of place from the crime scene or nearby.

CHAPTER 13 REVIEW

True or False

1. If the soil evidence on a suspect is consistent with soil evidence at a crime scene, this always provides sufficient evidence for conviction. *Obj. 13.6*

2. Soils are mixtures of materials formed from weathered rocks, water, air, and decomposing organisms. *Obj. 13.1*

3. Cadaver dogs find bodies due to the odor of gases emitted during decomposition under anaerobic conditions. *Obj. 13.5*

4. X-ray diffraction of soil is used to determine its mineral and chemical composition. *Obj. 13.4*

5. High moisture levels in soil stimulate the formation of adipocere. *Obj. 13.5*

Multiple Choice

6. Which of the following is the finest of all soil textures? *Obj. 13.1*
   a) silt
   b) loam
   c) clay
   d) sand

7. Which descriptions below would most likely indicate the presence of a recent gravesite? *Obj. 13.7*
   a) soil level raised, increased plant life
   b) soil level lowered, increased plant life
   c) soil level lowered, no plant life on surface
   d) soil level raised, no plant life on surface

8. Which of the following represents an undisturbed soil profile, starting at the surface? *Obj. 13.2*
   a) humus, topsoil, sand and silt, subsoil, broken rock, solid rock
   b) topsoil, humus, subsoil, sand and silt, broken rock, solid rock
   c) topsoil, subsoil, humus, sand and silt, solid rock, broken rock
   d) none of the above

9. Which of the following locations is the most likely source of young sand with little quartz, that is dark in color, and that does not bubble when acid is added to it? *Obj. 13.3*
   a) Great Salt Lake in Utah
   b) a North American beach with pounding waves
   c) a volcanic island
   d) a beach near a coral reef

Short Answer

10. Compare and contrast immature (young) sand and mature sand. What is the forensic significance of determining the age of sand? *Obj. 13.3*

11. Refer to the section on evidence collection in this chapter. A crime-scene investigator collected soil from the surface of a suspected gravesite. Describe other surfaces and/or locations where soil should be collected. *Obj. 13.8*

12. Reread the Matthew Holding case study. *Obj. 13.6*
    a) Given the evidence presented in the case study, briefly support each of the following claims:
        i. The bodies were buried in the mountains or foothills of the mountains.
        ii. Soil was taken from a mining area.
        iii. Soil was moved from an area below the surface.
        iv. The shovel had been used both to dig up and to tamp down the soil.
        v. The soil at the gravesite and on the shovel were consistent with each other.
        vi. Animals helped solve the crime.
    b) List the different types of analysis used to compare the soil found on the shovel and the soil found at the crime scene.

13. Discuss the role of soil pH in terms of how it affects decomposition of a body. *Obj. 13.5*

14. "Bodies buried in sand tend to dry out and mummify." Do you agree or disagree with this claim? Cite evidence from the chapter to support your statement. Include in your answer how soil texture affects the decomposition of a body. *Obj. 13.5*

15. Summarize the different soil and vegetation clues that can indicate a gravesite. *Obj. 13.5, 13.7*

16. What is the significance of collecting soil and sand samples from within a few feet of the crime scene and from within 20–25 feet of the crime scene? *Obj. 13.8*

Going Further

1. Design an experiment to compare how quickly a body would decompose in different soil textures (sand, silt, or clay) or in soils with different pH values. (*Hint*: Use similar body parts, such as chicken tenders of the same weight.)

2. In the Matthew Holding case study, if the suspect had not confessed when confronted with the evidence, do think the evidence was sufficient to lead to a conviction? If you claim it wasn't, write a closing argument as if you were the defense attorney in the case. If you claim it was, write a closing argument as if you were the prosecuting attorney in the case.

© iStock.com/CEFutcher

12. a. i. The soil was acidic and contained talc found only in the local mountains and foothills.

    ii. Microscopic analysis showed particles to be angular, typical of a mining area.

    iii. No plant evidence was found on the shovel, indicating the material was from below the surface.

    iv. The location and pattern of the soil on the shovel indicated it was used for digging and tamping.

    v. X-ray diffraction analyses of the soil from the gravesite and the soil on the shovel were almost identical.

    vi. Foxes had uncovered one of the victims.

    b. Macroscopic examination of soil and the shovel; microscopic examination to view shape of particles; X-ray diffraction of soil

13. Both alkaline and acidic soils inhibit the growth of bacteria and therefore reduce the rate of decomposition. Bacteria function best at a neutral pH, so a neutral pH results in faster decomposition.

14. I agree with the statement because bodies buried in sand are known to mummify. Sand has larger grains and a coarse texture, which allow for better drainage and air circulation, enhancing the drying-out (mummification) process.

15. Soil would be mounded up over a recent grave; soil would be sunken over an older grave due to settling of the soil and decomposition of the body; plants over a recent grave are dead or missing; plant succession occurs months after a body decomposes—different plants grow and do not resemble the typical plants found in the area; multiple soil colors are evident due to the mixing of different soil horizons while digging.

16. It is important to establish a baseline of what is found both in the immediate vicinity and within 20–25 feet of the crime scene. The types of soil can differ. If looking for evidence on a suspect, it is important to know what type of soil is within 20–25 feet of the crime scene.

Teaching Tip

Additional resource: http://www
.pbs.org/wgbh/nova/bog PBS *Nova*
"The Perfect Corpse"

Bibliography

Books and Journals

Carne, Nick. "Digging Deep to Find the Culprit." *Forensic Magazine.* May 28, 2014.

Erzinclioglu, Zakaria, M.D. *Forensics: True Crime Scene Investigations.* Barnes and Noble, 2004.

Fitzpatrick, Dr. Robert W., and Mark D. Raven. "How Pedology and Mineralogy Helped Solve a Double Murder Case: Using Forensics to Inspire Future Generations of Soil Scientists." *Soil Horizons,* September 2012: 14–29.

Galloway, A., W. H. Birkby, A. M. Jones, T. E. Henry, and B. O. Parks. "Decay rates of human remains in an arid environment." *J. Forensic Sci.,* 34, 1989.

Gordon, C. C., and J. E. Buikstra. "Soil, pH, Bone Preservation, and Sampling Bias at Mortuary Sites." *American Antiquity,* 46, 1981.

Hansen, Joyce, and Gary McGowan. *Breaking Ground, Breaking Silence.* New York: Henry Holt, 1998.

Murray, R. C., Tedwow, J. C. F. *Forensic Geology: Earth Science and Criminal Investigation.* New Brunswick (NJ): Rutgers University Press, 1975.

Murray, R. C., Tedwow, J. C. F. *Forensic Geology.* Englewood Cliffs (NJ): Prentice Hall, 1992.

_____. "The Geologist as Private Eye." *Natural History Magazine,* February 1975.

_____.*Soil in Trace Evidence Analysis.* Proceedings of the International Symposium on the Forensic Aspects of Trace Evidence 1991: 75–78.

_____. "Devil in the Details, The Science of Forensic Geology." *Geotimes,* February 2000: 14–17.

Murray, Raymond. *Evidence from the Earth.* Missoula (MT): Mountain Press Publishing, 2004.

Ritz, Karl, Lorna Dawson, and David Filler. *Criminal and Environmental Soil Forensics.* Springer Science, 2009.

Rodriguez, W. C. "Decomposition of buried and submerged bodies," in Haglund, W. D., and M. H. Sorg (eds.) *Forensic Taphonomy: The Postmortem Fate of Human Remains.* Florida: CRC Press, 1997.

Stewart, Melissa. *Soil.* Portsmouth (NH): Heinemann Library, 2002.

Surabian, Deborah A. "Soil Characteristics That Impact Clandestine Gravesites." *Forensic Magazine,* February 2, 2012.

Tarbuck, Edward J., Frederick K. Lutgens, and Dennis Tasa. *Earth: An Introduction to Physical Geology, 8th Edition.* Upper Saddle River (NJ): Prentice Hall, 2005.

Tibbet, M., and D. O. Carter. "Soil Analysis," in *Forensic Taphonomy: Chemical and Biological Effects of Buried Human Remains.* Florida: CRC Press, 2008.

Walker, Sally M. *Written in Bone.* Minneapolis: Carolrhoda, 2009.

Internet Resources

ngl.cengage.com/forensicscience2e (Gale Forensic Science eCollection)

http://www.scienceofsand.info/

http://www.forensicmag.com/articles/2012/02/soil-characteristics-impact-clandestine-graves

http://soil.gsfc.nasa.gov/fss/4thblock.htm

http://soil.gsfc.nasa.gov/basics.htm

http://www.pssac.org/SoilTeachingUnit/SoilUnitIntro.htm

http://www.juliantrubin.com/encyclopedia/environment/degradation.html

https://www.soils.org/publications/sh/articles/53/5/14(Matthew Holding murder case)

www.ct.nrcs.usda.gov/soils.html

http://soils.usda.gov

FBI Handbook of Forensic Services, Revised 2003, www.fbi.gov/hq/lab/handbook/intro.htm

http://query.nytimes.com/gst/fullpage.html?res=9402E5DC123BF930A25751C0A962948260&sec=health&spon=&pagewanted=1 (geophagy, or dirt-eating)

www.lab.fws.gov/index.html (National Fish and Wildlife forensic lab)

Examination of Sand *Obj. 13.1, 13.4*

Objectives:

By the end of this activity, you will be able to:

1. Compare and contrast various samples of sand.
2. Perform an acid test on sand samples.
3. Analyze the sand recovered from five suspects, and determine if any of the suspect sand is consistent with the crime-scene sand.

Time Required to Complete Activity: 45 minutes

Materials (per each pair of students):

Act 13-1 SH
stereomicroscope or hand lens
sand samples from five suspects and the crime scene
microscope slides
sieve set (to share with other groups)
dropper bottle of dilute hydrochloric acid (0.1 M)
small paintbrush
microscope slides or petri dish
1/4-teaspoon measuring spoon or other small measuring device
UV light (optional)

SAFETY PRECAUTIONS:

Goggles should be worn when working with hydrochloric acid. Materials should be discarded as directed by your instructor.

Background:

Five suspects were identified in a theft of property from a beach house. The suspects' shoes were examined, and the sand found was compared to that at the beachfront property. Microscopic examination, acid tests, analyses of mineral compositions, and determinations of size and texture are used to compare sand samples.

Sand from Vero Beach, Florida.

© Cengage Learning®

Procedure:

Record all information in the Act 13-1 SH Data Table.

1. Place approximately 50 grains of sand from Sample 1 onto a slide or petri dish. Using a stereomicroscope, projecting device, or hand lens, examine the sand. Record the presence of any plant or animal evidence in the data table.

Soil Examination 433

Background

In this activity, students work in pairs to examine, analyze, and compare various sand samples to determine if the sand sample found on any of the suspects is consistent with the sand at the crime scene.

Time Required to Complete Activity

45 minutes

Safety Precautions

1. Print, copy, and distribute Act 13-1 SH from the IRCD, Chapter 13. For instructional support, refer to Act 13-1 TN on the IRCD, Chapter 13.

2. Emphasize that safety goggles should be worn when working with dilute hydrochloric acid. An eyewash should be available in case of an accident, and students should know how to use it.

3. Remind students to use both hands to carry a microscope.

4. Instruct students on how to discard all materials.

Teaching Tip

Five different types of sand are needed if you are going to have five suspects. One of the five samples will also be used for the crime-scene sand. Ask students to bring in different sand samples in plastic bags, each labeled with its source location. If it is beach sand, ask them to state if the sand came from near the water or far away from the water. Playground sand and building sand can be purchased from large discount houses.

Procedures

1. Make sure students read all directions before beginning the activity.

2. If you have one, a stereomicroscope will allow students to view the sand samples in three dimensions.

3. Make sure the sand samples are labeled, and remind students not to mix up the samples.

4. Instead of using 50 grains of sand, it might be easier to have students use a 1/4-teaspoon measuring spoon. If so, be sure to have students count out 50 grains for the calculation used in the data table.

5. Provide a small bucket for students to wash the sand from the slides, instead of dumping the sand into the sink.

6. Sand samples must all be dried before comparisons are made.

Teaching Tip

Before students analyze their sand, provide control sands that demonstrate very rounded, rounded, or angular edges.

Teaching Tip

If you do not have a sieve set, use kitchen sieves of varying sizes. Measure the diameter of each opening of the sieve and record the size of the sieve in the data table.

Explore

If you are located in an area near an ocean, ask students if it is possible to determine from what part of a local beach sand is collected. Is there a difference in sand collected at the low-water mark, 5 feet up the beach from the high-water mark, and 20 feet up from the high-water mark? Ask students to design an experiment testing this idea.

2. Determine if the soil sample consists of just one type of mineral (crystal) or a combination of crystals known as fragments.

3. Count how many of the 50 magnified grains are composed of quartz, feldspar, dark-colored minerals, or other. Recall that quartz is usually translucent and light-colored, while feldspar is peach, beige, or red-brown. Multiply each number by 2 to calculate the percentage.

4. Examine the sand for degree of rounding. Degree of rounding can be described as *very round*, *rounded*, or *angular edged*.

5. Use the sieve stack to separate the 50 grains of Sample 1, and determine which size sieve has separated them. Record the amount of each particle size as *most*, *some*, *least*, or *none*. This will give you a rough estimate of the percentage of each particle size in the sample.

6. On a clean slide, add approximately 25 grains of Sample 1. Add a drop of hydrochloric acid to this slide. Bubbling indicates the presence of carbonates, a main component of the shells and skeletons of marine organisms. Record if bubbling occurs and to what degree.

7. Wipe off the slide as instructed by your teacher. Do not wash the sand down the drain.

8. Repeat the process with Samples 2 through 5.

9. Repeat the process for the crime-scene sample (beachfront area). Decide whether the soil from the crime scene is consistent with any of the samples taken from the suspects.

Data Table 1: Comparison of Sand Analysis

Characteristics	Sample 1	Sample 2	Sample 3	Sample 4	Sample 5	Crime Scene
Plant or animal evidence						
Crystals or fragments or both						
Minerals found per 50 grains: Quartz_____ Feldspar_____ Black minerals_____ Other_____	% of total _____% _____% _____% _____%	% of total _____% _____% _____% _____%	% of total _____% _____% _____% _____%	% of total _____% _____% _____% _____%	% of total _____% _____% _____% _____%	% of total _____% _____% _____% _____%
Rounding: Very rounded, rounded, or angular edged						
Particle size: Record as most, some, least, or none. Top sieve (4 mm) 4th sieve (2–3.99 mm) 3rd sieve (0.25–1.99 mm) 2nd sieve (0.062–0.249 mm) Bottom sieve (≤0.062 mm)	_____ _____ _____ _____ _____	_____ _____ _____ _____ _____	_____ _____ _____ _____ _____	_____ _____ _____ _____ _____	_____ _____ _____ _____ _____	_____ _____ _____ _____ _____
Reaction with hydrochloric acid: 1. Bubbles, and sand totally dissolves 2. Bubbles slightly 3. Does not bubble at all						

DIFFERENTIATED LEARNING

Teaching Gifted Students

Ask motivated students to investigate if it is possible to determine from what part of a local beach sand is collected. Is there a difference in sand collected at the low-water mark, 5 feet up the beach from the high-water mark, and 20 feet up from the high-water mark? Ask students to design an experiment testing their hypotheses.

Questions:

1. Do any of Samples 1–5 seem to be consistent with the crime-scene sample? Justify your answer with the data collected from your soil examination.

2. If you found that one of the samples had characteristics consistent with the crime-scene sand, do you think that would be sufficient grounds for a conviction? Explain your answer.

Going Further:

Examine each sand sample in a darkened room using an ultraviolet light. Determine if the ultraviolet light helps you to distinguish among sand samples. Do not look directly into the ultraviolet light.

Answers

Check students' data tables.

Questions

1. Answers will vary.

2. Answers will vary. Students should mention that soil evidence is just one type of trace evidence found at a crime scene. If this evidence links a suspect to the crime, it is only one piece of the puzzle. Investigators will need more information to develop a clear picture as to what happened. Although the sand seems to be consistent, there is no proof that the sand came from the site on the beach where the crime was committed. Another factor to consider is that the sand could have been obtained the day before the crime was committed.

Teaching Tip

Use plastic petri dishes and clear nail polish to create a permanent reusable sand sample collection. You might purchase divided petri dishes with four separate chambers. Pour a small amount of clear nail polish over the 50 grains of sand, spread out so that students can see each individual grain. To complete this activity, students will need loose sand.

Further Research and Extensions

An alternate way to examine samples in this lab is to put the sand samples into glass or plastic petri dishes and use a stereomicroscope capable of viewing up to 40×. Use both the top and bottom lights of the stereomicroscope. Sand can be set in place with clear nail polish to make a permanent collection.

Background

In this activity, students observe, analyze, and compare soil samples using magnification, UV light, pH analysis, and sedimentation jars. Soil samples taken from suspects are compared to soil samples from a crime scene to determine if any of the suspects' soil samples are consistent with soil samples from the crime scene.

Time Required to Complete Activity

60 minutes over two consecutive days

Safety Precautions

1. Students must wear proper eye protection when using the UV light.

2. Remind students to use both hands to carry a microscope.

Teaching Tip

A total of four soil samples are required for this activity. One suspect soil sample will also be used as the crime-scene sample. Soil samples should be dried prior to beginning the activity.

Procedures

1. Print, copy, and distribute Act 13-2 SH from the IRCD, Chapter 13. Instructional support is available on the Act 13-2 TN on the IRCD.

2. Make sure students read all directions *before* beginning the activity.

3. Some students may need help with adjectives and other descriptors for color, texture, and odor. Discuss this in advance of completing the activity to avoid getting ambiguous data recorded, such as "smells like dirt."

Soil Evidence Examination *Obj. 13.1, 13.2, 13.4, 13.6, 13.8*

Objective:

By the end of this activity, you will be able to:

1. Compare and contrast soil samples using magnification, UV light, pH, and sedimentation.

2. Analyze your data to determine if any of the soil samples are consistent with the crime-scene soil.

3. Discuss whether the evidence is sufficient to convict someone of a crime.

Time Required to Complete Activity:

60 minutes over two consecutive days

Materials (each team of four):

Act 13-2 SH
4 hand lenses or stereomicroscope with 40× magnification
projecting unit (optional)
4 graduated cylinders, 250 mL
4 soil samples, four from suspects and a crime-scene sample
4 rubber bands
4 beakers, 250 mL
4 pieces of cheesecloth approximately 8" × 8"
4 teaspoons
4 pieces universal range pH paper
4 watch glasses
distilled water
4 ultraviolet lights
4 flat toothpicks
paper towels

SAFETY PRECAUTIONS:

Proper eye protection is needed for use with the UV light.

Background:

Police recovered a kidnapped child who was taken from his home and hidden in an abandoned barn. Witnesses reported the license plates of four different vehicles seen at the abandoned barn over the past week. The four vehicles were found, and the suspects were questioned. Soil samples were recovered from the wheel wells of each of the suspects' vehicles. Determine if any of the soil samples taken from the suspects' cars' wheel wells are consistent with soil found at the crime scene.

---

4. Make sure that all students use the same spoonful measurement, because standardization of sample size is important to obtaining data that can be compared among lab groups.

5. Before beginning the activity, discuss why it would be an improper lab technique to not use standardized samples, volume of water, and soaking time.

Procedure:

Perform each of the tests on all five soil samples.

PART A: MICROSCOPIC EXAMINATION

Obtain four dry soil samples (1 to 4) and a crime-scene sample.

1. Examine and analyze each of the soil samples using a hand lens, stereomicroscope, or projecting unit.
2. Complete and record all information in Act 13-2 SH Data Table 1.
3. Describe or sketch any organisms, fragments of organisms, or foreign objects found in the soil.
4. Describe the color, texture, odor, and overall appearance of the soil.

Data Table 1: Soil Analysis

Soil Sample	Description or Sketch of Any Organisms or Foreign Objects	Color of Dry Sample (black, brown, gray, etc.)	Sample Texture (crumbly, gritty, loose, sticky)	Odor of Sample ("smells like" or no odor)	Overall Appearance (sandlike, organic, rocks, minerals)	Appearance Under UV Light (glow, no glow)
1						
2						
3						
4						
Crime Scene						

©2016 Cengage Learning

PART B: UV EXAMINATION

5. View each of the soil samples in a darkened room using a UV light, and describe what you see. Enter your observations in Act 13-2 Data Table 1.

PART C: DETERMINATION OF pH OF EACH OF THE SOIL SAMPLES

The pH value indicates whether something is acidic, neutral, or basic (alkaline).

6. Place a piece of cheesecloth on a paper towel. Place two spoonfuls of soil from Sample 1 in the center of the cheesecloth. Gather the sides of the cheesecloth together, and place a rubber band around the cheesecloth, capturing the soil sample in a ball.
7. Place 50 mL of distilled water in a 250-mL beaker and label it Suspect 1.
8. Place the ball of soil in the water and leave it undisturbed for 10 minutes.
9. Repeat Steps 6–8 for Samples 2, 3, 4, and the crime-scene sample. Let each sample sit for 10 minutes.
10. Using pH paper, determine the pH of the water for each of the soil samples. If the pH is less than 7, the soil is acidic. If the pH equals 7, the soil is neutral. If the pH is greater than 7, the soil is basic (alkaline).
11. Record your results in Act 13-2 SH Data Table 2.

Teaching Tip

Either hand lenses or stereo-microscopes can be used for magnification. If a projecting unit is available, you could project the image of each soil sample. Another option would be to take close-up views of each soil sample and have students view the images.

Teaching Tip

If time is an issue, divide lab procedures between partners in a group.

Teaching Tip

Review with students the pH scale. Seven is neutral. The lower the number, the stronger the acid. The higher the number, the stronger the base. Discuss what might be present in the soil to make it either more acidic or more basic. How would pH values be used to identify soils? If your school has a pH meter, compare your results using a pH meter to those using pH paper.

Evaluate

Encourage students to photograph each sample of the soil as they perform the testing. Students could incorporate their photos in a PowerPoint presentation, poster, or oral presentation that is prepared for evidence presentation during expert-witness testimony. Students can role-play expert witness, defense lawyer, prosecuting lawyer, or jury. "Jury members" should prepare questions for each of the lawyers. Students are encouraged to challenge the evidence reliability of the various tests and the claims made regarding the evidence.

Answers

Check students' data tables.

- -

Questions

1. Answers will vary.

2. Answers will vary. Additional chemical analysis could be done. More sophisticated testing using X-ray diffraction and gas chromatography would provide more information regarding the composition of the soils.

3. To improve evidence reliability:
   a. Use larger samples of the soil for testing.
   b. Have more than one team do the testing to see if results can be replicated.
   c. Have more precise measurements than a "rounded teaspoon."
   d. Use a narrow container for the sedimentation test to more easily observe the soil profile.
   e. Perform more chemical testing of each soil sample. Testing could include salt content, nitrogen content, etc.
   f. Include more sophisticated testing using X-ray diffraction to test for mineral composition of the soil.

Data Table 2: pH Determination

Soil Sample	pH	Acidic or Basic?
1		
2		
3		
4		
Crime Scene		

© 2016 Cengage Learning®

PART D: SEDIMENTATION OF SOIL SAMPLES

Soil samples that seem identical can be further examined by creating a *sedimentation column*. As soil mixtures settle, they form layers, or *sediments*, of varying densities, with the densest on the bottom.

12. Fill a graduated cylinder to the 250-mL mark with tap water. Add 50 mL of soil from Sample 1.
13. Cover the top of the cylinder; shake the contents for 30 seconds.
14. Repeat Steps 12 and 13 for each of the other samples in identical graduated cylinders.
15. Allow all samples to settle overnight, and compare the overall appearance of each sample. Note any floating material in your description.
16. Record your results in Act 13-2 SH Data Table 3.

Data Table 3: Soil Sedimentation Results

Sample	1	2	3	4	Crime Scene
Using Colored Pencils, Draw a Sketch to Scale of the Variously Colored Layers in the Column					
Number of Distinct Layers					
Description of Floating Material					

© 2016 Cengage Learning®

Questions:

1. Based on your analysis of the five soil samples, can you claim that any of the suspect's soil samples is consistent with the crime-scene soil samples? Support your claim with data from your soil evidence examination.
2. If one of the suspect's soil samples was consistent with the crime-scene sample, what other information or testing should be performed to either include or exclude this suspect?
3. Suggest ways to improve upon this lab to ensure more reliable results.

Further Research and Extensions

Sometimes soil evidence has maggots in it. Interested students may want to combine what they have learned about insect evidence and soil evidence and research cases that used both kinds of evidence.

Chemical and Physical Analysis of Sand

Obj. 13.3, 13.4, 13.6

Objectives:

By the end of this activity, you will be able to:

1. Analyze sand using chemical testing and pH testing.
2. Describe how to test the fluorescent and magnetic properties of sand grains.
3. Analyze data from your testing to determine if any of the sand samples are consistent with the crime-scene samples.
4. Suggest revisions to the procedures and redesign them to obtain more reliable results.

Time Required to Complete Activity:

two periods, 45 minutes each

Materials (per each pair of students):

Act 13-3 SH
1 dropper bottle of acetic acid (0.1 M CH$_3$COOH)
1 dropper bottle of barium chloride (0.1 M BaCl$_2$)
1 dropper bottle of dilute hydrochloric acid (0.1 M HCl)
1 polyethylene dropper bottle of silver nitrate (0.1 M AgNO$_3$)
5 sand samples numbered locations 1 to 4 and crime scene
5 microscope depression slides (if available), or 5 watch glasses, or a well plate tray with 15 wells
2 hand lenses or stereomicroscope
magnet
5 flat toothpicks
UV light (to share with other groups)
5 squares of black paper, 3" × 3"

SAFETY PRECAUTIONS:

Wear goggles to protect your eyes from harmful solutions. All materials are to be handled as described by your instructor and discarded as directed. Silver nitrate solution will stain clothing and skin temporarily. Avoid looking directly into a UV light source. Proper eye protection is needed for the UV light source.

Background:

Customs officials from New York City noted the presence of sand in a crate containing narcotics. The sand was analyzed and found to be composed of quartz, feldspar, and shell fragments from a high-energy beach (a beach with powerful wave action). Sand samples from each of the four possible ports were compared to the sample found with the narcotics in an attempt to trace the drugs back to their origin.

Background

In this activity, students conduct tests on sand, examining its chemical, magnetic, and fluorescent properties. Students compare samples, analyzing the test results to determine if any of the sand samples are consistent with the sand at the crime scene. The tests may establish the port of origin of drugs.

Time Required to Complete Activity

Two periods, 45 minutes each

Safety Precautions

1. Emphasize that students must wear safety goggles to protect their eyes from harmful solutions and from UV light.

2. Remind students to use both hands to carry a stereomicroscope.

3. Instruct students in the proper ways to handle and discard all materials.

4. Caution students that silver nitrate solution will stain clothing and skin.

5. Tell students never to look directly into a UV light source.

Teaching Tip

If possible, select sand samples from different areas:

- Beach sand near the shoreline to show sand that is weathered
- Beach sand from the same area but higher up on the beach where there is less wave action
- Sand from a bay with less wave action and therefore more jagged grains
- Sand from a coral beach or a beach with more shells so there is more skeletal (biogenic) sand that will react with the carbonate testing.
- Sand with oolites that react to carbonate testing

Teaching Tip

Before the activity, explain to students the difference between ultraviolet and visible light.

Procedures

1. Print, copy, and distribute Act 13-3 SH from the IRCD, Chapter 13. Refer to Act 13-3 TN for instructional support.

2. Make sure students read all directions *before* beginning the activity.

3. Silver nitrate is an expensive and caustic reagent, which can stain clothing and skin even in low concentrations. Handle it with care, dispensing it from polyethylene dropper bottles. Make sure there is money in the budget to buy this solution.

4. Suggest to students that they slide the magnet underneath the plastic well plate or watch glass. If they place the magnet directly in the dirt, it will work, but the soil particles will be difficult to remove from the magnet. This test works best when the soil is dry.

REACTIONS TO BE EXAMINED:

1. Test for sulfates:
   sample $+ BaCl_2 + CH_3COOH \rightarrow BaSO_4 \downarrow$ (white precipitate) + dissolved materials

2. Test for chlorides:
   sample $+ AgNO_3 + CH_3COOH \rightarrow AgCl_2 \downarrow$ (white precipitate) + dissolved materials

3. Test for carbonates (skeletons of once-living material):
   sample $+ HCl \rightarrow CO_2 \uparrow$ (gas bubbles) $+ H_2O +$ dissolved materials

Procedure:

SULFATE TEST:

1. Place about 50 grains of the Location 1 sample in a depression slide, and add two drops of the 0.1 M barium chloride solution and two drops of the 0.1 M acetic acid solution.

2. Stir gently with a toothpick and observe under a hand lens or stereomicroscope at low power. If a white precipitate forms, sulfates are present in the sand sample.

3. Record your results in Data Table 1.

4. Repeat Steps 1 to 3 for each of the other sample locations and record the results in Table 1.

5. Wash off all of the slides.

CHLORIDE TEST:

6. Place about 50 grains of the Location 1 sample in a depression slide and add two drops of the 0.1 M silver nitrate solution and two drops of the 0.1 M acetic acid solution.

7. Gently stir with a toothpick and observe under a hand lens or microscope on low power. If a white precipitate forms, chlorides are present in the sand sample.

8. Record your results in Data Table 1.

9. Repeat Steps 6 to 8 for sand Samples 2, 3, and 4, and record the results in Data Table 1.

10. Wash off all of the slides.

CARBONATE TEST:

11. Place about 50 grains of the Location 1 sample in a depression slide and add two drops of the 0.1 hydrochloric acid solution.

12. Observe under a hand lens or microscope. If bubbles form, carbonates are present in the sample.

13. Record your results in Data Table 1.
14. Repeat Steps 11 to 13 for sand Samples 2, 3, and 4, and record the results in Data Table 1.

MAGNET TEST:

15. Using a magnet, determine if any of the samples contain any magnetic components.
16. Record your observations in Data Table 1.

FLUORESCENCE TEST:

17. In a darkened area, determine the fluorescence of each sample of sand. The UV light will cause fluorescent material to glow.
18. Remove 50 grains of sand from Location 1 and place them on a piece of black paper to observe under UV light.
19. Using a hand lens, observe and record the size, shape, and approximate percentage of fluorescent particles in Data Table 1. To determine the percentage, count the number of granules that fluoresce and multiply by 2.
20. Repeat Steps 18 and 19 for sand Samples 2, 3, and 4 and the crime-scene sample. Record your observations in Data Table 1.

Data Table 1: Sand Testing Results

Beach Sand Sample	Sulfate Test (white precipitate? yes or no)	Chloride Test (white precipitate? yes or no)	Carbonate Test (bubbles? yes or no)	Magnetic Particles (yes or no)	UV Reaction: Fluorescence		
					Size	Shape (angular or rounded)	%
1							
2							
3							
4							
Crime Scene							

© 2016 Cengage Learning®

Questions:

1. Based on your data, are any sand samples consistent with the sand sample from the crime scene? Support your claim using your data.
2. Reflect on your lab procedures. Suggest modifications to the protocol of this activity that would improve the reliability of the results.
3. Research and briefly summarize the process of X-ray diffraction and its use to analyze sand and soil.

Teaching Tip

Review the concept of fluorescence with students. When UV light (which has shorter wavelength) is absorbed by a substance, the light energy is re-emitted in a form of light with a longer wavelength. How a substance reacts to UV light varies and can be used as a means of identification. Demonstrate examples of fluorescence in sand particles.

Answers

Check students' data tables.

Questions

1. Check student data tables. Answers will vary depending on the sand samples used.
2. To improve results, larger quantities of sand should be tested with more precise measurements. Students should repeat each test.
3. Soil is crushed and exposed to X-rays. Each mineral and chemical contained in the soil has its own unique diffraction pattern. Scientists compare and contrast the diffraction patterns found in the evidence sample to known diffraction patterns and can identify the chemical composition of the components of the soil.

Further Research and Extensions

A challenging extension to this lab would be to prepare an unknown mixture of two of the sand types and have students not only determine which two were mixed, but also in what proportions.

Chapter Overview

Bones seem not to have any obvious function besides making our bodies rigid, but they are living tissue that stores minerals and provides attachments for muscles. Forensic anthropologists know that by analyzing data from bones, such as measurements, texture, shape, and DNA, clues to one's age, sex, ethnic background, height, and health can be revealed. Forensic anthropologists study skeletal remains and create what is called a biological profile of a person as told by his or her bones. In cases where decomposition is advanced or a body is burned, skeletal and dental remains may be all that are left to establish the identity of an unknown decedent.

The Big Ideas

Ossification is the deposition of minerals in cartilage that hardens it to form bone. Bones complete development gradually at predictable times, making age estimates possible. Throughout our lives, bone is broken down and replaced. Visible differences exist among the skeletons of males and females, people of different ancestries, and the young and the old. A history of one's health, nutrition, injuries, and certain activities can be discovered in the bones.

Techniques including radiology, photographic and video superimposition, and craniofacial reconstruction are used to help identify skeletal remains.

CHAPTER 14

Forensic Anthropology

Clay Model of Face Leads to Murder Charge

A surveyor finds a skull in a remote wooded area in Missouri used as a Boy Scout camp. The county coroner, a pathologist, and a member of the sheriff's department return to search and excavate the gravesite further. They recover a lower jaw, 40 other bones, a few strands of hair, tattered jeans, and a plastic shopping bag. Crime-scene investigators later recover a button with the name *Texwood* on it. What could this evidence tell them?

The skeletal remains were sent to Dr. Michael Charney, a forensic anthropologist. From the pelvis, he determined the remains belonged to a woman who had given birth. Her short, broad facial structure was typical of someone of Asian ancestry. Based on the long bones of her body, he estimated she was a slim woman about five feet tall. This was substantiated by measuring the length of a deteriorated pair of jeans found with the remains. After a long inquiry, the detectives discovered that the Texwood logo was used by a company in Hong Kong that made jeans for Asian women.

Dr. Charney decided to create a three-dimensional clay facial reconstruction based on the skull. When a photograph of the clay model was published in the newspaper, a reader identified the clay model as her missing neighbor Bun Chee Nyhuis, a native of Thailand who had three children. A photograph of her was sent to Dr. Charney, who then superimposed a photograph of the skull onto the supplied photograph. The nasal bone, chin, forehead, and cheeks were consistent, and Dr. Charney told the police the remains were likely Bun Chee Nyhuis.

When presented with the evidence, former Assistant Scoutmaster Richard Nyhuis confessed, admitting he killed his wife and buried her at the Boy Scout camp. In court, Dr. Charney testified that the skeletal remains were consistent with Bun Chee Nyhuis's photograph based on the photographic superimposition. The jury deliberated only two hours before returning a "guilty" verdict on the charge of first-degree murder.

Images courtesy of Missouri State Highway Patrol; image files supplied by St. Louis Post-Dispatch

Photos of Bun Chee Nyhuis in life (left) and the clay model created by Dr. Charney (right).

After reading the scenario, have students analyze the case and discuss the following:

1. What evidence linked Richard Nyhuis to the crime scene?
2. Discuss how the pelvis of a female differs from the pelvis of a male.
3. What evidence found in the gravesite supported the findings of the forensic anthropologist?
4. How was technology used to help in the identification of this Bun Chee Nyhuis?

OBJECTIVES

By the end of this chapter, you will be able to:

14.1 Summarize the information a forensic anthropologist derives from skeletal remains to construct a biological profile.

14.2 Distinguish among growth plates, bone caps, bone shafts, and sutures, and explain their significance for forensic anthropology.

14.3 Compare and contrast an adult's skeleton and a child's skeleton in terms of composition, number of bones, suture marks, and growth plates.

14.4 Apply knowledge of bone growth (ossification) to estimate the age of the deceased at the time of death based on skeletal remains.

14.5 Apply appropriate formulas to estimate the height of a person based on individual bone length.

14.6 Distinguish between male and female skeletal remains based on the structure, the size and shape of the skull, the pelvis, and the long bones.

14.7 Provide examples of different types of skeletal trauma due to disease, injuries, occupation, or environmental factors that can provide clues to the identification of skeletal remains.

14.8 Discuss the significance of isotopes in determining where someone lived.

14.9 Describe methods used to analyze skeletal remains, including radiology, computer imaging, DNA technology, video or photographic superimposition, and craniofacial reconstruction.

TOPICAL SCIENCES KEY

BIOLOGY

CHEMISTRY

EARTH SCIENCES

PHYSICS

LITERACY

MATHEMATICS

VOCABULARY

- **biological profile** estimation of the deceased's sex, age, stature, and ancestry, along with diseases and injuries, as derived from analysis of skeletal remains

- **diaphysis** the shaft of a bone

- **epiphysis** the unattached end of a bone that eventually becomes fused with the bone shaft

- **forensic anthropology** the use of skeletal anatomy to identify remains for legal purposes

- **growth plate (epiphyseal plate)** area of cartilage between the shaft and cap of an

immature bone responsible for the lengthening of bone

- **joints** locations where bones meet

- **ossification** the process that replaces cartilage with bone by the deposition of minerals

- **osteoporosis** loss of bone density that can result in an increased risk of fractures

- **skeletal trauma analysis** the investigation of bones and the marks on them to uncover a potential cause of death

FORENSIC ANTHROPOLOGY **443**

KEY SCIENCE CONCEPTS

Biology: bone biology and anatomy; mitochondrial DNA; DNA technology

Mathematics: determining height from long bones; bone proportions

Chemistry: analysis of isotopes in bones

Teaching Tip

Before beginning this unit, post X-rays on windows or post photos of X-rays in the classroom to provoke discussion. Especially useful bones would be skulls, pelvises, and femurs.

TEACHING RESOURCES

 Instructor's Resource CD-ROM includes:

- Activities and Student Handouts
- Alternative Assessments
- Consolidated Bibliography
- Correlations to NGSS and CCSS
- Figure Files
- Lesson Plans
- Nonfiction Readings
- PowerPoint Presentations
- Student Learning Objectives (SLOs)

CL Testing powered by Cognero

Website: ngl.cengage.com/forensicscience2e

Engage

After reading the Introduction, ask students to brainstorm about what they think a medical examiner would be looking for to help identify bones. Other options include showing an X-ray of a pelvis and asking students to predict whether it is male or female, reading selected passages from William Maples's *Dead Men Do Tell Tales*, or showing clips from the TV series *Bones*.

Explore

As students browse this chapter, they may begin to get concerned as they see all of the scientific terminology. Help students suppress an initial concern when they see multiple terms with which they are unfamiliar, and assure them they will be able to read and understand the text.

Explore

Ask students if they have heard of biometric facial scanning, and how it is used in facial recognition (at airports, for example). Suggest interested students research the applications of the process and the facial features used.

INTRODUCTION

How is it possible to identify skeletal remains, victims of mass disasters, severely burned victims, or those in the advanced stages of decomposition? That work often involves **forensic anthropology**, the use of skeletal anatomy to identify remains. It is the job of a *forensic anthropologist*. Identifying skeletal remains can be a critical step in linking a suspect to a crime. Forensic anthropologists may work with many other professionals, including detectives, forensic pathologists, toxicologists, DNA analysts, odontologists (dental specialists), and entomologists when investigating a crime.

When skeletal remains are found, they are first examined to determine if they are human. If so, then each bone and tooth is identified and cataloged. Observations of the shape, structure, condition, and measurements of the remains are recorded. The estimated age, sex, stature, and ancestry (Figure 14-1) of the deceased, along with any evidence of trauma or disease, might be derived from skeletal analysis and make up a **biological profile**. A biological profile may be helpful in identification of the remains. When decomposition has progressed to a point that the only remains are skeletal and dental, investigators may still be able to extract DNA from the remains or gain clues from serial numbers of implanted medical devices. Identification is important in both criminal cases and cases involving inheritance and insurance payments (as well as for emotional reasons in accidental deaths).

Figure 14-1 *People of different ancestries have differently shaped facial bones.*

HISTORICAL DEVELOPMENT *Obj. 14.9*

Forensic anthropology has been used to solve crimes and other mysteries for more than 200 years.

- In 1878, Thomas Dwight published *The Identification of the Human Skeleton: A Medicolegal Study*.
- In 1895, the first known use of craniofacial superimposition identified the remains of composer Johann Sebastian Bach.

DIFFERENTIATED LEARNING

Teaching Gifted Students

Suggest that students research and report on the FBI's first crime lab, the Luetgert murder, or the Krogman book.

- In 1897, in what is known as the Luetgert murder case, a sausage maker was convicted of killing his wife and boiling down her corpse in one of his sausage vats. Remains found in the factory were shown to be fragments of his wife's skull, finger, and arm. This is one of the first times that a forensic expert testified as an expert witness.
- In 1932, the FBI announced the opening of its first crime lab. The Smithsonian Institution became a working partner, aiding in the identification of human remains.
- In 1939, William Krogman published the *Guide to the Identification of Human Skeletal Material*.
- In 1947, the United States military established the Central Identification Laboratory in Hawaii (CILHI) to recover and identify United States war dead using anthropological techniques.
- In 1970, the C. A. Pound Human Identification Laboratory (CAPHIL) opened at the University of Florida to assist medical examiners and coroners with analysis of skeletal remains.
- In 1977, the American Board of Forensic Anthropology (ABFA) was established to certify forensic anthropologists.
- In 1986, The Physical Anthropology Section of the American Academy for Forensic Science (AAFS) created a database of modern human skeletons from documented cases.
- In 2003, CILHI joined forces with the Joint Task Force—Full Accounting in an effort to identify POW/MIA and other unaccounted-for Americans from the Vietnam War.
- In 2014, an anthropology subcommittee of OSAC (Organization of Scientific Area Committees) was established to standardize recovery and analysis of human remains.

DNA analysis of bones and other skeletal tissue has identified historical figures; victims of the September 11 attacks; victims of war and genocide; and victims of crimes, accidents, and disasters. Continued improvements in radiographic techniques, including magnetic resonance imaging (MRI) and computerized tomography (CT), provide images of skeletal patterns that further increase identification reliability.

CHARACTERISTICS OF BONE *Obj. 14.2, 14.3*

Bones provide the framework for our bodies and anchor our muscles to allow movement, while they protect our vital organs (Figure 14-2). There are sufficient differences among bones that they can sometimes

Did you know

Bones can reveal if a person had tuberculosis, arthritis, or leprosy, as well as an iron or vitamin D deficiency. Bones always show evidence of having been broken, no matter how long they have been healed.

Figure 14-2 *Our skeletons support our bodies, anchor our muscles, and protect our internal organs.*

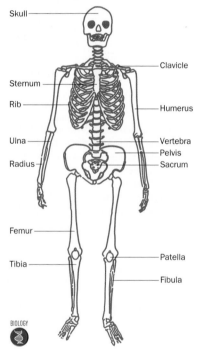

Skull
Clavicle
Sternum
Rib
Humerus
Ulna
Radius
Vertebra
Pelvis
Sacrum
Femur
Tibia
Patella
Fibula

BIOLOGY

FORENSIC ANTHROPOLOGY   **445**

Teaching Tip

The internal support structure of an animal is called an *endoskeleton*. The prefix *endo-* means "within" or "inside," indicating the skeleton is inside the organism. You might tell students that organisms such as the lobster have an exoskeleton, which means their support structure is on the outside of the organism. Students may be surprised to hear that even some invertebrates, such as sea stars, have endoskeletons (though they are not bone).

Teaching Tip

It is important for students to be able to label and locate some of the bones in Figure 14-2 (skull, sternum, vertebra, humerus, pelvis, sacrum, femur), but it is not essential that they memorize the names and locations of all the bones. To help students feel comfortable with the names, post an enlarged copy of Figure 14-2. Another suggestion is to project an image of the diagram onto an old flat bedsheet and ask an adept student to trace it (or trace it yourself. This could be used year after year and it could be easily stored.

DIFFERENTIATED LEARNING

Teaching English-Language Learners
Provide all students with a copy of Figure 14-2. Have all students pronounce the names out loud. Then play a game of Simon Sez. Ask students to stand. When you call out the name of the bone, students point to its location on their body. Although this sounds juvenile, high school students have fun with it, and it helps them learn the names of the bones. It only takes a few minutes, and it gets them out of their seat and laughing.

Teaching Tip

Some students may be interested in reading the forensic science case studies in the nonfiction book *Dead Men Do Tell Tales*, by the late William Maples, former forensic anthropologist for University of Florida.

Evaluate

Ask students why bones are considered living tissue.

Explore

Show students an image of an infant and an adult. Ask who has more bones. Facilitate a discussion of how many bones each has, and what happens to an infant's extra bones.

Teaching Tip

To help students better understand the differences between a ligament and tendon, demonstrate dissection of a chicken wing for students. Show students how the tendons are attached to both the muscle and bone whereas the ligaments connect bone to bone.

Teaching Tip

Students may have difficulty remembering the difference between tendons and ligaments. Help them to remember by asking them to feel their Achilles tendon in their ankle. Ask them where and to what this tendon is attached. One end of the tendon is attached to bone in the heel and the other is attached to the calf (gastrocnemius) muscle.

Teaching Tip

Long bones are so called because they are longer than they are wide. The bones of the legs, arms, fingers, and toes are all long bones. They grow mostly by elongation.

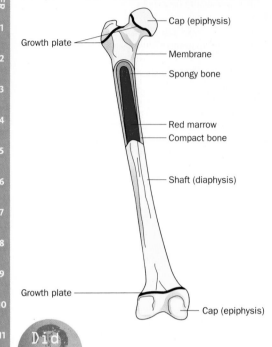

Figure 14-3 *A cross section of bone, showing its different components. Note that the shaft and caps of the bone are separated by growth (epiphyseal) plates of cartilage.*

Growth plate — Cap (epiphysis)

— Membrane

— Spongy bone

— Red marrow

— Compact bone

— Shaft (diaphysis)

Growth plate —

Cap (epiphysis)

Did you know?

Nonhuman animal bones can be confused with human bones by an untrained observer. Bear forepaws and bear foot bones lacking claws are similar to human hand and foot bones. Understanding bone shape as well as understanding how bones grow and mature helps to understand the differences.

be used to distinguish between male and female, young and old, and among different ancestries.

Bones contain calcium and phosphate along with living bone cells. Bone maintenance is performed by hormones that regulate growth and mineral levels within the bone. The red marrow inside bones produces our body's blood cells (Figure 14-3).

How Bones Connect

A **joint** is the location where bones meet. Joints contain three major types of connective tissue:

- *Cartilage.* Wraps the ends of the bones for protection and keeps them from scraping against one another.
- *Ligaments.* Bands of tissue connecting two or more bones.
- *Tendons.* Connect muscle to bone.

Number and Development of Bones *Obj. 14.1*

How many bones are in the human body? Most sources will tell you 206. But that answer is correct only for adults. A baby has 270 bones. During the development of the fetus, bones begin as cartilage, the flexible material that makes up our outer ears. The process of bone replacing cartilage is called **ossification**. It begins before birth, though for some bones, ossification takes more than 50 years. By the eighth week of pregnancy, the bony parts of a fetal skeleton are visible in an X-ray.

During childhood, bones thicken, ossify, and grow longer. The 270 baby bones gradually fuse to form the 206 adult bones. For example, the ends of the long bones, the caps (**epiphyses**, singular **epiphysis**), start to fuse to the shafts of the bones (**diaphyses**, singular **diaphysis**). The cartilaginous area between the caps and the shaft is an area of active bone formation known as the **growth plate**, or **epiphyseal plate**. You can see these features in Figures 14-3 and 14-4. As bones ossify, they are reshaped (Figure 14-5). When bones are fully grown, ossification is complete, the bones are fused, and only a thin line is left of the cartilaginous growth plate, the *cartilaginous,* or *epiphyseal, line.* Most bones attain full growth at the end of puberty—for most males, around age 19 or 20 and for most females, around age 16 or 17. There is much individual variation, however.

446 CHAPTER 14

Figure 14-4 *X-ray of femur of a girl showing growth plates, cartilage, and bone.*

Figure 14-5 *Growth changes in tibias (lower leg bones). Note the cap is eventually fused with the shaft.*

Living Art Enterprises, LLC/Science Source

Image © by Pieter A. Folkens

Explore

Articulation is the joining of structures, such as bones, at a joint. How bones connect to one another, and the degree of movement between the articulating bones, are the two ways in which joints are classified. Suggest that interested students further research the different types of joints.

Did you know

The smallest bone in your body is 2.5 to 3.3 millimeters long. It is the stirrup bone, located within your ear.

Aging of Bone

Throughout our lifetime, bones are always being produced, repaired, and broken down. Children build more bones at a faster rate than the rate of bones being broken down. As a result, bones increase in length until the growth plate is ossified. After age 30, the process begins to reverse; bones lose minerals and break down faster than they are built.

People with **osteoporosis** are at risk of bone fractures because their bones have especially low density. As the vertebrae lose calcium and other minerals, they begin to collapse and can give a person a hunched appearance. Some elderly people lose height, a condition caused by vertebrae collapsing.

BONES AND BIOLOGICAL PROFILES *Obj. 14.1, 14.7*

In addition to information on age, sex, and ancestry of the deceased, bones contain a "diary" of injuries, disease, and nutritional deficiencies. This "diary" of the bone can be used to construct a biological profile. Broken bones heal, but they retain evidence of the break. When bones break while someone is alive, the breaks are usually uneven. Bones broken in advanced decomposition stages tend to snap off evenly. Conditions such as osteoarthritis (Figure 14-6) and osteoporosis (loss of bone density) are easily observed in skeletal remains. Rickets is caused by a lack of Vitamin D and results in bowed legs, a thinner

Figure 14-6 *This spine shows advanced arthritis. Many vertebrae are fused due to large bony outgrowths associated not only with heavy labor, but also with the disorder.*

Brittney Tatchell, Smithsonian Institution

DIFFERENTIATED LEARNING

Teaching At-Risk Students
Organize students into heterogeneous groups. To help them understand cartilage, ligaments, and tendons, have students take turns explaining the illustrations above to the group.

Evaluate

Ask students why a right-handed person's bones might be thicker in his or her right arm.

Teaching Tip

Read students the passage about carbon-12 and carbon-13 ratios in food and the geographic origins of skeletal remains from Sally Walker's book *Written in Bone*.

Explore

One of the most famous archaeological frauds is the Piltdown Man, which was originally thought to be the fossilized remains of an early human. Skull fragments and a jawbone were discovered in 1912 in a gravel pit in Piltdown, England. It took more than 40 years for researchers to discover that the Piltdown Man was a fake and that the bones were actually a jawbone of an orangutan and the skull of a modern man. Have students view the PBS *NOVA* program "The Boldest Hoax."

skull in a baby, and a deformed spine. Severe anemia, which is usually due to a lack of iron in the diet, can result in holes in the eye sockets and skull. In the mid-1920s, the radioactive element radium was painted on watch dials to make them glow in the dark. Women who painted the watches developed many illnesses, including cancer, after their bones absorbed the radioactive radium.

Bones and Geography
Obj. 14.1, 14.8

 CHEMISTRY

You are what you eat, and where you ate it is documented in your bones. Forensic anthropologists test bones for the presence of different isotopes of carbon and strontium to provide clues as to where a person lived and how long they lived in that area. Strontium is an element found dissolved in groundwater. Different areas have varying levels of strontium in their water. When strontium is ingested, it is deposited in your teeth. By comparing the amounts of strontium in different geographical regions to the levels of strontium found in teeth, it's possible to determine where a person lived.

Foods contain different amounts of the stable isotopes carbon-13 and carbon-12. Upon ingestion of food, these isotopes get absorbed into the bone. By comparing the carbon-13 and carbon-12 ratios in the skeletal remains of the Jamestown colonist in Figure 14-7, forensic anthropologists could estimate how long the colonist lived in England versus how long he lived in America.

Figure 14-7 *Skull of a teenage male from Chesapeake Bay Colony shows a front jaw that has degenerated due to infection. The infection began in a broken left central incisor tooth, which allowed bacteria to enter the tooth pulp chamber and then enter the jaw.*

Chip Clark, Smithsonian Institution

How to Distinguish Males from Females *Obj. 14.6*

A detective's first question to a forensic anthropologist is whether the skeleton belongs to a male or female. How can one determine sex from bone fragments? The overall appearance of the adult female's skeleton tends to be more slender (gracile) than that of an adult male's skeleton, which is thicker and more robust. Because of male hormones, muscles tend to be more developed in a male. Larger muscles require a stronger attachment site on the bones. To accommodate the larger muscles and their tendons, male bones where muscles and tendons attach are thicker, resulting in a skeleton generally more robust than that of a female. (Note that determination of sex by skeletal remains can only be done if the deceased is past puberty.)

SKULL

The male skull is typically more robust than the female skull. There are many specific differences to discuss, but the first step is to review Figures 14-8 and 14-9, which depict the major bones of the skull.

Figure 14-8 *Front view of skull with major bones and sutures labeled.*

1. Mandible
2. Maxilla
3. Zygomatic process (cheekbone)
4. Orbits of the eyes (eye sockets)
5. Coronal suture
6. Frontal bone
7. Parietal bone
8. Temporal bone
9. Nasal bone
10. Nasal cavity

Figure 14-9 *Side view of skull with major bones and sutures labeled.*

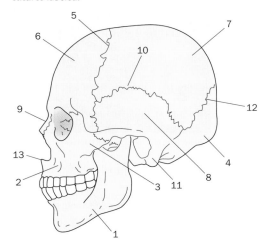

1. Mandible
2. Maxilla
3. Zygomatic process (cheekbone)
4. Occipital protuberance
5. Coronal suture
6. Frontal bone
7. Parietal bone
8. Temporal bone
9. Nasal bone
10. Squamous suture
11. Mastoid bone
12. Lambdoidal suture
13. Nasal spine

In Figures 14-10 and 14-11 on the next page, note the differences between the male and female skulls. The male's frontal bone is low and sloping, whereas the female's frontal bone is higher and more rounded. Male eye orbits are often more square than those of females, and many male lower jaws have an angle closer to 90 degrees than many female lower jaws. These features are not reliable for sex identification, however.

The occipital protuberance, a bony knob on the male skull, serves as an attachment site for the many muscles and tendons of the neck. Because the muscles in a man's neck are larger than the muscles in a woman's neck, the area of attachment needs to be thicker, making for a larger protuberance on the male skull.

FORENSIC ANTHROPOLOGY **449**

DIFFERENTIATED LEARNING

Teaching At-Risk Students

Students might be interested in learning about bones as they relate to sports. Ask students how they think the bones of someone who regularly works out with weights would look compared to someone who does not. Ask them what differences they would expect to find in the bones of athletes of different sports, such as soccer, football, and basketball. Ask students why using steroids to build muscle may cause bones to break.

Teaching Tip

Students may have the misconception that the frontal bone is the same as the forehead. It is not. The frontal bone extends beyond the forehead to the coronal suture. When students compare male and female skulls and look for a low, sloping frontal bone on the male, be sure they refer to the entire frontal bone, not just the area immediately above the eyebrows.

Teaching Tip

If using plastic bones, it will be important to emphasize that there are differences in surface features of the skull (smooth or rough).

Figure 14-10 *A side view of male and female skulls, noting the differences.*

Male; note the low sloping frontal bone.

Female; note the rounded frontal bone.

Images © by Pieter A. Folkens

Figure 14-11 *Summary of male and female skull differences.*

Male Front View	Male Characteristics	Trait	Female Characteristics	Female Front View
	More square	Shape of eye	More rounded	
	More square	Mandible shape from underside	More V-shaped	
	Thick and larger (robust)	Upper brow ridge	Thin and slender (gracile)	

Male Side View	Male Characteristics	Trait	Female Characteristics	Female Side View
	Prominent	Occipital protuberance	Less prominent	
	Low and sloping	Frontal bone	Higher and more rounded	
	Rough, robust	Surface of skull	Smooth, gracile	
	Extends to ear opening or past the ear opening	Zygomatic process	Stops short of ear opening	
	Larger, more robust	Mastoid process	Smaller	

Images © by Pieter A. Folkens

PELVIS

Figure 14-12 shows the bones and major features of the human pelvis. One of the most reliable methods of determining the sex of an adult skeleton is to examine the pelvis. Because of the anatomical characteristics needed for child-bearing, this region of the body exhibits many differences. The surface of a woman's pelvis is engraved with scars if she has borne children. During the fourth month of pregnancy, the cartilage of the pubic symphysis (see Figure 14-12) in the pelvic area softens, allowing some separation of the bones during childbirth. The cartilage re-hardens after the delivery. Scars of separation (parturition) may form on the back of the pubic bones. Analysis of this area may indicate if the woman had given birth. (Note that these scars do not always appear, and they may appear in women who have not given birth.)

In general, the pelvis of the female is wider, the sacrum is curved more away from the body, the tailbone is shorter, the subpubic angle is larger (Figure 14-13), and the pelvic cavity opening is bigger (Figure 14-14) than that of the male.

To distinguish between the male and female pelvis, compare the following:

- Subpubic angle (Figure 14-13)
- Length, width, shape, and angle of the sacrum (Figure 14-14)

Figure 14-12 *Major features of the pelvis.*

1.	Pubic bone
2.	Ilium
3.	Sacrum
4.	Coccyx
5.	Ilium
6.	Pubic bone
7.	Ischium
8.	Pubic symphysis (cartilage)
9.	Ischium
10.	Greater sciatic notch

Figure 14-13 *The subpubic angle tends to be greater than 90 degrees on the adult female and less than 90 degrees on the adult male.*

Adult male   **Adult female**

VideoSurgery/Science Source

Figure 14-14 *The female's pelvic cavity is broader than the male's.*

Male pelvic cavity (heart-shaped)

Female pelvic cavity (oval)

Images © by Pieter A. Folkens

Teaching Tip

To best view the inside pelvic cavity, place the pelvis on the table so that the pubic symphysis is in contact with the table. Move your head so that you are looking into the pelvis at eye level.

Teaching Tip

Point out to students that the female pelvis also weighs less than the male pelvis.

Teaching Tip

Tell students that the *coccyx* (*kok-siks*) is commonly called the tailbone. It is the lowest of the vertebrae in our spinal column. The largest muscle in our body, the *gluteus maximus*, is attached to the coccyx.

Evaluate

Ask students with which bone the pelvis connects.

Explore

The sciatic notch is the large indentation on the pelvic posterior where the ileum and the ischium connect. The angle formed by the greater sciatic notch can be measured using a protractor. Place the pelvis on a piece of paper so that the sciatic notch is level against the surface. Trace the sciatic notch on the paper and trace it. Then use a protractor to measure the angle. Ask students to research the differences in the angle for males and females.

Evaluate

Ask students why the angle of the femur in relationship to the pelvis is greater in a female. Suggest that students review the section in the text on the pelvis if they do not know the answer.

Explore

Explain that the pubic symphysis is the cartilaginous joint at the midline of the pelvis. In forensic anthropology, analysis of the pubic symphysis is the primary tool for determining a victim's age. The surfaces of the pubic symphysis are worn at an expected rate throughout life. Anthropologists can examine the wear on these surfaces and estimate age.

Teaching Tip

Explain that *foramen* means "hole," or "opening." Write some anatomical terms from the chapter and their definitions in large letters, and display them in the room to help students become familiar with the terms. Include terms such as *sacrum*, *femur*, *humerus*, *suture*, and *cartilage*.

Evaluate

Point out that the femur is the longest and strongest bone in the body. Ask students to speculate why it is the strongest bone.

Explore

Tell students that computer programs exist that can "age" a person's picture. Have interested students research how these programs work and how they are used.

Explore

Ask students what clues might be visible on a small older adult skeleton that would distinguish it from the skeleton of a child?

- Width of the ilieum (Figure 14-14)
- Angle of the sciatic notch

Figure 14-15 has a summary of these differences.

Figure 14-15 *Summary of Male and Female Pelvis Differences.*

Region	Bone	Male	Female
Pelvic	Subpubic angle	Usually less than 90 degrees	Greater than 90 degrees
	Hips (ilium)	Narrow	Rectangular pubis, wide
	Shape of pelvic cavity	Heart-shaped	Flattened oval
Sacral	Sacrum and tailbone	Longer tailbone, sacrum curved inward	Shorter tailbone, sacrum curved outward

Did you know?

Because of the lesser width of the male pelvis, the male femur typically joins the pelvis at a straighter angle than the female femur does.

Estimating Age *Obj. 14.2, 14.4*

Bones become fully ossified at different and predictable rates, although much variation exists among individuals, sexes, and different populations. A forensic anthropologist examines skeletal remains to note the number of bones, the degree of ossification, presence or absence of growth plates (epiphyseal plates), and the degree of wear on bones. By comparing their observations with data obtained from studies done on skeletons of known ages (Figure 14-16), the forensic anthropologist estimates the age at death of the skeletal remains. The more bones analyzed, the more accurate the age estimate.

Figure 14-16 *Estimation of age based on ossification of bones.*

Region of the Body	Bone	Approximate Age
Arm	Humerus cap bones fused	4–6
	Humerus cap fused to shaft	18–20
Leg	Femur: Greater trochanter (muscle attachment site) first appears	4
	Lesser trochanter (muscle attachment site) first appears	13–14
	Femur head fused to shaft	16–18
	Condyles (rounded projections at the end of bone) join shaft	20
Shoulder	Clavicle and sternum (breastbone) close	22–30
Pelvis	Pubic bone and ischium almost completely united	7–8
	Ilium, ischium, and pubic bones fully ossified	20–25
	All segments of sacrum united	25–30
Skull	Lambdoidal suture close	Begins 21 ends 30
	Sagittal suture close	32
	Coronal suture close	50

Teeth and bones are sometimes the only evidence remaining after decomposition. Specific bones and teeth are particularly useful in estimating age. Fusion of the collarbone to the breastbone (sternum) begins in the early twenties and is usually completed by age 30. The skull has several bones that fuse between the ages of 30 and 60. If the deceased was older than 60, all bones should be fully ossified and may show wear due to aging.

TEETH *Obj. 14.4*

Tooth development is used to estimate age in children because tooth eruption reliably follows chronological age (Figure 14-17). Age estimates can be made by noting which teeth are present, even if teeth are *unerupted,* or still in the gums. Baby teeth begin to fall out around age 5 or 6, first molars come in around age 7, second molars come in around age 12. Third molars (wisdom teeth) come in after age 17 (if at all). Forensic anthropologists also examine teeth for wear.

Figure 14-17 *Pathologists or odontologists can estimate the age of a person from an impression of his or her teeth.*

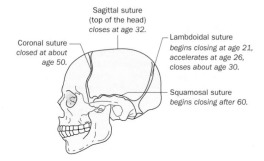

	When teeth "come in" (months)	When teeth "fall out" (years)
Top	7–12	6–8
	9–13	7–8
	16–22	10–12
	13–19	9–11
	25–33	10–12
	20–31	10–12
	12–18	9–11
	16–23	9–12
	7–16	7–8
	6–10	6–8

This chart is a guideline only. Children grow at their own pace.

Bottom   Baby teeth

	Age tooth comes in (years)
Top	
Central Incisor	7.35
Lateral Incisor	8.45
Canine (Cuspid)	11.35
First Premolar (Bicuspid)	10.20
Second Premolar (Bicuspid)	11.05
First Molar	6.30
Second Molar	12.25
Third Molar	
Third Molar	Variable 17 to 21
Second Molar	11.90
First Molar	6.05
Second Premolar (Bicuspid)	11.20
First Premolar (Bicuspid)	10.50
Canine (Cuspid)	10.35
Lateral Incisor	7.50
Central Incisor	6.40

Bottom   Adult teeth

SKULL SUTURE MARKS

Suture marks are found on the adult's skull (Figure 14-18a). They form as cartilage has almost replaced the soft cartilaginous areas on the skull (Figure 14-18b). As bones mature, usually after age 60, the suture marks disappear, being fully ossified. Today, forensic age estimates based on suture marks have been replaced by more reliable methods.

Figure 14-18a *The main suture marks on a skull, marking where the bones eventually join.*

Sagittal suture (top of the head) closes at age 32.

Coronal suture closed at about age 50.

Lambdoidal suture begins closing at age 21, accelerates at age 26, closes about age 30.

Squamosal suture begins closing after 60.

Figure 14-18b *Infant skull showing areas of the skull that have not yet ossified.*

Coronal suture

Lambdoidal suture

Squamosal suture

FORENSIC ANTHROPOLOGY   453

Teaching Tip

Aging remains by examining the pubic bones and sternal rib surfaces typically requires a great deal of practice and expertise.

Explore

Anthropologists can study the curvature of a femur and determine the ancestry of an individual. The femur of a European curves enough to allow you to place your hand underneath the bone when it lies flat, but an African femur does not.

Teaching Tip

Point out that because so many people are of mixed ancestries, the word race is more of a cultural term than a biological one. In fact, there are more differences within a group of people of the same ancestry than there are differences between people of different ancestries. For this reason, anthropologists often have a difficult time establishing the dominant ancestry of an individual.

Teaching Tip

Try to obtain images of skulls of different ancestries to show students. There are many images available on the Internet.

Teaching Tip

Tell students that *auxology* is the study of human height.

Science

MATHEMATICS

Measuring long bones can help determine the approximate height of an individual. However, the mathematical formula using bone length to estimate height varies with ancestry and the bone used. Databases of averages have been compiled for people of different ancestries.

PUBIC BONE AND STERNAL RIB SURFACES

More reliable methods of estimating age involve examining the changes that regularly occur on the surfaces of two different bones. The edges of the two pubic bones surrounding the pubic symphysis can be used to estimate age. As a person ages, the surface progresses from a heavily contoured face to an increasingly porous and pitted surface.

Another method for estimating age is viewing the ends of the ribs that attach to the breastbone (sternum). Changes similar to those that occur in the pubic symphysis occur in this bone as a person ages.

How to Distinguish Ancestry

Determination of ancestry from skeletal remains is difficult. Ancestry is probably best indicated by the bones of the skull. (See Figure 14-19)

- Shape of the eye sockets.
- Shape of the nasal cavity; absence or presence of a nasal spine, a sharp, bony projection found under the nasal cavity at the top of the *maxilla*.
- The *nasal index* (the ratio of the width of the nasal opening to the height of the opening, multiplied by 100). The height is measured from the *nasion*, the indented area between the eyes, to the base of the nasal cavity.
- *Prognathism:* the projection of the upper jaw (maxilla) and/or the lower jaw (mandible) beyond the face.

Figure 14-19 *Comparing ancestral characteristics of bones. (Much variation exists within people of the same ancestral background.)*

	European	African	Asian
Shape of Eye Orbits	Rounded, somewhat square	Rectangular	Rounded, somewhat circular
Nasal Spine	Prominent spine	Very small spine	Somewhat prominent spine
Nasal Index (width/length)	Less than 0.48	Less than 0.53	0.48 to 0.53
Prognathism	Flat	Prognathic	Variable
Nasal Opening	Teardrop	Round	Oval

How to Estimate Height Obj. 14.5

MATHEMATICS

Measuring bones like the humerus or femur can help in estimating the height of an individual. Many databases have been established that use mathematical relationships to calculate the height of an individual from one of the long bones. There are separate formulas for males, females, and different ancestries, and for different bones (Figure 14-20.) If the ancestry and sex of the individual are known, the calculation of height will be more accurate.

454   CHAPTER 14

DIFFERENTIATED LEARNING

Teaching Gifted Students

Ask students to research the average heights of males and females in different countries. Then present their research to the class in a poster. (Remind students that nationality does not equate to ancestry.)

Figure 14-20 *Height estimation formulas (continued on following page).*

American males of European ancestry.

Factor × bone length	plus	Accuracy
Height (cm) = 2.89 × humerus	+ 78.10 cm	± 4.57
Height (cm) = 3.79 × radius	+ 79.42 cm	± 4.66
Height (cm) = 3.76 × ulna	+ 75.55 cm	± 4.72
Height (cm) = 2.32 × femur	+ 65.53 cm	± 3.94
Height (cm) = 2.60 × fibula	+ 75.50 cm	± 3.86
Height (cm) = 1.82 × (humerus + radius)	+ 67.97 cm	± 4.31
Height (cm) = 1.78 × (humerus + ulna)	+ 66.98 cm	± 4.37
Height (cm) = 1.31 × (femur + fibula)	+ 63.05 cm	± 3.62

American females of European ancestry.

Factor × bone length	plus	Accuracy
Height (cm) = 3.36 × humerus	+ 57.97 cm	± 4.45
Height (cm) = 4.74 × radius	+ 54.93 cm	± 4.24
Height (cm) = 4.27 × ulna	+ 57.76 cm	± 4.30
Height (cm) = 2.47 × femur	+ 54.10 cm	± 3.72
Height (cm) = 2.93 × fibula	+ 59.61 cm	± 3.57

Both sexes of European ancestry.

Factor × bone length	plus	Accuracy
Height = 4.74 × humerus	+ 15.26 cm	± 4.94
Height = 4.03 × radius	+ 69.96 cm	± 4.98
Height = 4.65 × ulna	+ 47.96 cm	± 4.96
Height = 3.10 × femur	+ 28.82 cm	± 3.85
Height = 3.02 × tibia	+ 58.94 cm	± 4.11
Height = 3.78 × fibula	+ 30.15 cm	± 4.06

American males of African ancestry.

Factor × bone length	plus	Accuracy
Height (cm) = 2.88 × humerus	+ 75.48 cm	± 4.23
Height (cm) = 3.32 × radius	+ 85.43 cm	± 4.57
Height (cm) = 3.20 × ulna	+ 82.77 cm	± 4.74
Height (cm) = 2.10 × femur	+ 72.22 cm	± 3.91
Height (cm) = 2.34 × fibula	+ 80.07 cm	± 4.02
Height (cm) = 1.66 × (humerus + radius)	+ 73.08 cm	± 4.18
Height (cm) = 1.65 × (humerus + ulna)	+ 70.67 cm	± 4.23
Height (cm) = 1.20 × (femur + fibula)	+ 67.77 cm	± 3.63

American females of African ancestry.

Factor × bone length	plus	Accuracy
Height = 3.08 × humerus	+ 64.67 cm	± 4.25
Height = 3.67 × radius	+ 71.79 cm	± 4.59
Height = 3.31 × ulna	+ 75.38 cm	± 4.83
Height = 2.28 × femur	+ 59.76 cm	± 3.41
Height = 2.49 × fibula	+ 70.90 cm	± 3.80

Both sexes, ethnicity unknown.

Factor × bone length	plus	Accuracy
Height = 4.62 × humerus	+ 19.00 cm	± 4.89
Height = 3.78 × radius	+ 74.70 cm	± 5.01
Height = 4.61 × ulna	+ 46.83 cm	± 4.97
Height = 2.71 × femur	+ 45.86 cm	± 4.49
Height = 3.29 × tibia	+ 47.34 cm	± 4.15
Height = 3.59 × fibula	+ 36.31 cm	± 4.10

Science

MATHEMATICS

Students can measure the length of their femur in centimeters, multiply by 2.6, and add 65 to estimate their approximate height. Suggest students use a measuring tape to measure their actual height, in centimeters, and see how accurate the estimate is. Point out that estimating a teenager's height is less accurate than estimating an adult's height. (For this reason, the formula also carries with it a margin of error.) Ask why the estimate for a teenager might be less accurate.

Teaching Tip

Tell students that alternative formulas have been given to relate height and femur length.

Explore

Ask students if they have ever seen a bone-in ham. Tell them that the bone they see is a femur.

For example, a femur measuring 49 cm belonging to an African American male is found. Use the formula in Figure 14-20 to estimate his height.

$$\text{height (cm)} = 2.10 \text{ femur} + 72.22 \text{ cm } (\pm 3.91 \text{ cm})$$
$$= 2.10(49 \text{ cm}) + 72.22 \text{ cm } (\pm 3.91 \text{ cm})$$
$$= 102.9 \text{ cm} + 72.22 \text{ cm } (\pm 3.91 \text{ cm})$$
$$= 175.12 \text{ cm } (\pm 3.91 \text{ cm})$$

height estimate
$$175.12 \text{ cm} + 3.91 \text{ cm to } 175.12 \text{ cm} - 3.91 \text{ cm}$$
$$\sim 171.21 \text{ cm to } 179.03 \text{ cm}$$

SKELETAL TRAUMA ANALYSIS

Obj. 14.7

Skeletal trauma analysis is the process by which a forensic anthropologist attempts to distinguish between damage to bones made during life (for example, by weapons) and damage to bones caused by the environment and organisms after death. Note that living bone is stronger and much more flexible than dried-out, dead bone.

By examining the characteristics of bone damage, a forensic anthropologist may also attempt to determine what weapon or object caused the damage. Punctures resulting from sharp-force trauma, blunt-force trauma, and gunshot wounds all have distinctive patterns. Gunshot wounds typically have a smaller entrance wound and a larger, beveled exit wound (Figure 14-21). In blunt-force trauma and sharp-force trauma, there is a difference in the shatter pattern and the amount of damage to the bone. Blunt objects generally create more cracks radiating from the site of impact, and they typically cause more damage to the surface of the bone. (See Figure 14-22.)

Figure 14-21 *Views of a skull with a gunshot entrance wound (left) and a larger beveled exit wound (right).*

Brittney Tatchell, Smithsonian Institution

Figure 14-22 *Blunt-force trauma from multiple hammer blows.*

Brittney Tatchell, Smithsonian Institution

SKELETAL EVIDENCE COLLECTION AND EXAMINATION

Bone evidence collection and documentation must follow the evidence procedures discussed in Chapter 2. Bones, especially those that have been buried for a while, are fragile and must be removed with great care. Soft brushes and dental picks may be used to slowly remove them from soil around them. Bones are dried and are sometimes coated with acrylic mixtures similar to glue if they are especially fragile. Once freed from soil, bones are kept in climate-controlled environments. Remember that skeletal remains don't always include a complete skeleton, or even a complete bone.

Examining Remains Obj. 14.1, 14.7

A forensic anthropologist must answer many questions, including the following:

- Is a fragment a bone?
  — Bone texture: compact with some degree of graininess
  — Bone color and luster varies from creamy white to brown with a dull luster.
  — Bone interior: porous, and the ends and middle may contain marrow.
- Is it a human or animal bone?
- Which bone is it?
- Does the gravesite contain remains from one person or more?
- How long have the remains been buried?
- Were the markings on the bones made before death (antemortem) or after death (postmortem)?

DIGGING DEEPER
With Forensic Science eCollection

What happens to mass burial sites after the bones have been analyzed? Until the last half of the twentieth century, museums and collectors desecrated and looted graves of Native Americans in search of artifacts. In 1990, the Native American Graves Protection and Repatriation Act (NAGPRA) became federal law. Laws protecting known gravesites and procedures for returning Native American remains and cultural items to descendants or tribes were established. The American Anthropological Association also established a code of ethics regarding these issues. Go to the Gale Forensic Science eCollection at **ngl.cengage.com/forensicscience2e** for more information.

Teaching Tip

Since the advent of DNA extraction and analysis from bones and teeth, students may wonder if the assessment of skeletal remains is even necessary. Explain that despite the technological advances in molecular biology, the examination of a skeleton remains a vital part of the identification process. Examining the skeletal record can result in relatively fast and accurate inferences about the victim's identity. Also, studying bones can quickly establish characteristics that allow investigators to narrow their search, and may be used to support DNA evidence.

DIFFERENTIATED LEARNING

Teaching Gifted Students

Allow interested students to conduct a survey of local and state law enforcement agencies to determine the methods they use for facial reconstruction.

Explore

After the World Trade Center attacks in 2001, victims were primarily identified using DNA profiling, which requires a reference sample of some type. A DNA analysis was performed either by taking a sample directly from a toothbrush or hairbrush of a victim or gathering DNA from a close relative and comparing the sample with DNA found at the scene. Nuclear DNA was used when available to make an exact identification. Mitochondrial DNA was used if nuclear DNA was not available. Mitochondrial DNA identifies a relationship between a victim and a close maternal relative.

Teaching Tip

There is DNA in a bone cell's nucleus and in the mitochondria in its cytoplasm. Scientists may still be able to extract nuclear DNA from marrow in bones or pulp cavities in teeth, even if the victim has been dead for years. But nuclear DNA has also been successfully extracted from Egyptian and Incan mummies that are thousands of years old, and from a frozen plant in Siberia that was 400,000 years old. Mitochondrial DNA is even more long-lasting.

Explore

Have interested students research and report on craniofacial reconstructions for identification and crimes.

Teaching Tip

Facial reconstruction modeling kits are available for Julius Caesar and *Homo neanderthalensis* from PegSculpture (The Natural History Museum).

Teaching Tip

Have students view an episode of the television series *Bones* showing facial reconstruction.

Image © by Charlie Fellenbaum, Page One Photography, LLC

Image courtesy of Missouri State Highway Patrol; Image file supplied by St. Louis Post-Dispatch

Figure 14-23 *Craniofacial reconstruction uses the "tissue-depth" method to create a model. Using reference tables of the average amounts of flesh at different points on a skull, rubber pegs of varying lengths are attached to a model of the person's skull. Clay is layered over the pegs. Ears, lips, and eyes are then added. This reconstruction allowed a neighbor to identify Bun Chee Nyhuis for the police, helping to solve her murder case after nine years.*

Skeletal Analysis and Identification   Obj. 14.9

Comparative Radiography Comparative radiography is nondestructive imaging of bones with electromagnetic energy. It is particularly useful when identification is impossible due to burns or decomposition. Radiography includes X-rays, computerized tomography (CT scans), and magnetic resonance imaging (MRI). The challenge of comparative radiography is that bones are always being remodeled, so antemortem and postmortem images taken many years apart can be hard to compare.

Nonimaged Records Comparison Medical notes or records regarding skeletal or dental conditions, procedures, and implants can be valuable in deciding if remains belong to a specific person. Many medical implants have serial numbers that can be traced.

DNA Analysis DNA analysis supports forensic anthropological investigations by confirming identities and by enabling the separation of commingled (mixed) remains in mass burial grounds. When other body parts have decomposed, DNA can still be recovered from skeletal and dental remains. Nuclear DNA can be extracted from bones and teeth and analyzed using STR profiling, yielding personal identification. If the nuclear DNA is degraded or damaged, mitochondrial DNA (mtDNA), which is more plentiful and durable, may be analyzed. The results of mtDNA analysis cannot establish individual identity, but it can find individuals with common maternal relatives. Y-chromosome tracing can indicate individuals in the same paternal line.

Photographic or Video Superimposition An image of the skull is superimposed over a photograph or video and compared. These techniques are used when a set of remains is suspected to belong to a particular person.

Craniofacial Reconstruction These models "reconstruct" the facial features of an individual so that an approximation of his or her face is produced. They often utilize the "tissue-depth" method that involves building up clay on a model of the skull in order to represent soft tissues. Publicized images of facial reconstructions have helped identify people (Figure 14-23).

SUMMARY

- Bone cells are alive and carry on the same functions as other body cells.
- Ossification is the formation of bone as calcium phosphate replaces cartilage.
- The condition and chemical analysis of bones provide clues to a person's origin, health, nutrition, occupation, and activity level during his or her life.
- Adult male and adult female skeletons differ in many ways, including the roughness and thickness of bones, size and shape of the skull and pelvic bones, and the shape of the pelvic cavity.
- The age of a person at death can be estimated from the number of bones and teeth, skull suture marks, the presence or absence of growth plates, wear on bones and teeth, along with the observation of the surface of pubic and sternal rib bones.
- The height of a person can be estimated from the length of the long bones in the arms and legs using standardized formulas. (Estimates are most accurate when the sex and ancestry of the deceased are known.)
- Current methods to identify skeletal remains include nuclear DNA STR profiling; radiology: X-rays, CT, and MRI scanning; photographic facial superimposition; and facial reconstruction.
- DNA extracted from bones is used to help establish individual identity using nuclear STR testing or to establish maternal ancestry using mitochondrial DNA. Familial ancestry through the paternal line can be traced through the Y chromosome.
- Skeletal trauma analysis examines the bones for evidence of damage, which may provide clues to the person's identity and to the manner and cause of death.
- X-rays are used to reveal skeletal features, number of bones, conditions of bones, previous fractures, implants, disease, and disorders of the bone.

LITERACY

Written in Bone, by Sally Walker. *Breaking Ground, Breaking Silence*, by Joyce Hansen and Gary McGowan. *Dead Men Do Tell Tales*, by William R. Maples. *Bone Detectives*, by Donna Jackson.

Teaching Tip

Explain to students that mitochondrial DNA can never be inherited from the father, because human sperm do not contribute mitochondria to an embryo.

Teaching Tip

Find images of bones with weapon trauma and show them to the class. Encourage interested students to read *Human Skeletal Remains, Excavation, Analysis and Interpretation* by Douglas Ubelaker, or search the Internet for information.

Explore

Dead Men's Tales is a series presented on PBS. In the episode "A Texan Tall Tale," forensic scientists examine the tale of Wild Bill Longley. Go to www.pbs.org to get a copy of this episode and show it to your class.

CASE STUDIES

Captain Bartholomew Gosnold (2003)

In her book *Written in Bone*, Sally Walker describes how in 2003, Dr. Douglas Owsley, a forensic anthropologist from the Smithsonian Institution, "reached into the graves" of the earliest colonists of Jamestown, Virginia. Their life stories are "written in their bones." One of those graves is believed to belong to Bartholomew Gosnold, a lawyer, explorer, and one of the captains of the three ships that landed at the Jamestown Settlement in 1607. Bartholomew Gosnold died in 1607 and was buried with the iron tip of a staff used by the seventeenth-century British military. This staff, along with other evidence and artifacts found in the grave, helped establish the age of the gravesite and his military connection.

Teaching Tip

Discuss with students the importance of X-rays in revealing evidence in bone remains.

Explore

Encourage interested students to research and report on the African Burial Ground National Monument, the site in New York where the remains of many slaves were buried. They can go to the Website www.nps.gov/afbg/index.htm

CAPSTONE ACTIVITY

In Capstone Activity 10, "Gravesite Excavation," Students locate and excavate a gravesite, as well as document and collect skeletal remains and other evidence from the site.

The well-preserved skeletal remains were found in sandy soil. The shape of the gravesite indicated the captain was buried in a coffin, which meant he was a person with high status. Only discolored soil remained from the rotted wood of the coffin. Green stains in the soil remained from the oxidation of the copper shroud pins that wrapped the body.

Dr. Owsley and his team were able to "read the bones" of Captain Gosnold and inferred the following details.

- *Sex:* male, based on pelvis shape
- *Age:* between 33 and 39 years, based on the caps fused (epiphyses) with the shafts (diaphyses) of his long bones and other bone fusion sites, combined with evidence of arthritis in his spine and right arm
- *Height:* approximately 5 feet, 3 inches, based on the length of his leg bones
- *Right-handed:* based on the greater development of bones in the right arm than in the left arm
- *Slender build:* based on bone size
- *Type of work:* based on bone size, indicative of an active man but not one who did heavy labor
- *Facial features:* based on bone structure, a large broad nose and a small square chin
- *Dental health:* loss of one tooth during his life as evidenced by a healed jaw
- *Bone health:* mostly good other than healed ankle fractures
- *Physical health:* chronic nasal infection evidenced by the extra bone formation inside the nasal cavity. Otherwise, he was apparently in good health.

African Burial Ground in New York City (1991)

In 1991, all construction for a new federal office building in New York City came to an abrupt halt. While excavating the wet clay soil 16 feet below the surface, workers found a rectangular, dark outline in the clay along with rows of rusted coffin nails. The workers had found a burial ground. Using dental picks and fine tools, soil was carefully removed. Eventually, 400 skeletal remains were recovered from this eighteenth-century burial site. Forensic anthropologists and historians concluded that the burial grounds were the final resting place for more than 15,000 people of African ancestry, most of whom had been part of the enslaved population in New York when they were buried. Their skeletal remains give voice to the story of an oppressed population who once accounted for one fourth of the city. Enslaved Africans and Caribbeans built much of the earliest New York City infrastructure.

Colonial life was difficult, but life for enslaved workers was even more challenging, as evidenced by information their skeletons revealed:

- Half of the skeletal remains were those of children under the age of two, indicating high infant mortality.
- A high rate of birth defects and delayed brain development.
- Poor nutrition indicated by delayed bone development and deformed bones.
- High incidence of diseases such as tuberculosis left scars on rib cages and deformed spines. Anemia left evidence in the orbits of the eyes.
- Teeth showed high incidence of tooth decay. Enamel failed to develop in some children, probably because of poor nutrition.

- Young men and women had arthritis; fractures at the base of skulls and in spines could have been caused by carrying cargo and heavy loads on their heads.
- Children's bones showed evidence of tearing of muscles from the bones and lesions on the bone surface that could have been due to heavy labor.
- Robust muscle-attachment sites on bones reveal work that was hard and heavy.
- Vertical cracking on chalk-like bones with white and black blotching (referred to as calcination) suggests some individuals were burned to death.
- DNA evidence revealed ancestry of west Africa or the Caribbean Islands.

Excavation of the African Burial Ground in New York City, which revealed skeletal remains.

John A Giordano/Corbis News/Corbis

Archaeologists, forensic anthropologists, politicians, and activists worked together to ensure the excavation was conducted with respect and sensitivity. Today, the site is a National Monument dedicated to Africans in early New York.

The Romanovs
(2006)

In Chapter 7, you learned how DNA analysis led to the identification of the executed bodies of the Romanov family. Because the bodies were in a mass grave, the first tasks were to determine how many people were buried in the grave and to distinguish the bones of the royal family from others in the grave.

Individual identification of family members using evidence from teeth and bones was provided by forensic odontologist Dr. Lowell Levine and forensic

The Romanovs, the royal family of Russia.

AP Images

FORENSIC ANTHROPOLOGY   461

Teaching Tip

Work cross-cutting concepts into your classroom by working with a history and biology teacher to develop lessons that involve history, politics, and biology by studying the African Burial Grounds National Monument. Ask them to touch respond to questions such as: What information was learned about the life of enslaved workers in New York in the seventeen century? What information was revealed through analysis of their skeletal remains? What information was learned through artifact recovery? How did political issues complicate the recovery?

Teaching Tip

Review the information about the Romanovs from Chapter 7. Additional information about the history of the Romanovs can be viewed on www.DNAi.org at Recovering the Romanovs.

Close

Organize students into three groups and assign each group one of the following: skull, pelvis, and long bones. Have the group describe what information about a person can be detected from the bones and how it is done.

Teaching Tip

For more information about the Romanovs, refer to Robert K. Massie's book *The Romanovs: The Final Chapter*.

Did you know

Wormian bones are small bones formed between additional cranial suture marks that are found in some populations. Their presence was used to establish familial connections among remains in the Romanov gravesites.

Think Critically

anthropologist Dr. William Maples. They noted that one female had poor dental work, and calcification of knee joints that suggested she had spent time doing manual labor. One male skeleton was older and likely belonged to the royal family physician, Dr. Botkin. A recovered dental plate and skull similarities to a photograph confirmed the doctor's identity. Expensive dental repairs and dental records identified the rest of the royal party. Because some of the leg bones were crushed, height estimations were made using arm length. The remains of Anastasia and Alexei, who were 17 and 14, respectively, were located in a second gravesite in 2006.

Select one of the case studies and describe the forensic anthropology techniques that were used for identification.

DIFFERENTIATED LEARNING

Teaching Gifted Students

Fragments of bones can be aged from microscopic examination. Research this topic in *Bones*, by Dr. Douglas Ubelaker and Henry Scammell.

Careers *in Forensics*

Dr. Clyde Snow: The Bone Digger

"The bones don't lie and they don't forget. And they're hard to cross-examine." So said the late Dr. Clyde Snow, one of the world's leading forensic anthropologists, as he explained why it is so important to present the evidence of skeletal remains in court.

Dr. Snow studied thousands of skeletons all over the world, revealing their secrets. Dr. Snow's driving force was international human rights. He served on the United Nations Human Rights Commission, working in Argentina, Guatemala, the Philippines, Ethiopia, Bosnia, and Iraq. Closer to home, he worked on many important criminal cases, including those of mass murderers John Wayne Gacy and Jeffrey Dahmer, as well as the victims of the 1995 Oklahoma City bombing. He also participated in historic investigations, such as the assassination of President John F. Kennedy, searching for the remains of Butch Cassidy and the Sundance Kid in Bolivia, excavating bones at the site of Custer's Last Stand, and examining King Tut's mummy.

Dr. Snow's accomplishments are great—much greater than his early school experiences might have suggested. Born in 1928 in Texas, Dr. Snow was expelled from high school and transferred to a military school, where his grades dropped. When he finally made his way to college, he failed at first, but then remarkably achieved a Ph.D. in anthropology. Dr. Snow began his career working for the Civil Aeromedical Institute, examining the bodies of victims of air crashes. In 1979, he decided to focus solely on forensics.

Only a few years later, Dr. Snow traveled to Argentina to see if it was possible to investigate—and

AP Images/Victor Ruiz C

"As those who study them have come to learn, bones make good witnesses—although they speak softly, they never lie and they never forget." —Dr. Clyde Snow

ultimately hold accountable—those responsible for the genocide committed by the previous Argentine government. It is believed the Junta militia killed tens of thousands of civilians. Mass killings on a similar scale have been investigated by Dr. Snow in Guatemala and Iraq. In 2006, he testified against Saddam Hussein in the war crimes trial involving the mass murder of Kurdish people. Dr. Snow has exhumed the remains of victims all over the world, many of whom were killed by their own governments.

Why did he do it? He was forthright about his reasons. One was to return the remains of victims to their families. Another was to try to bring about justice. A third was to let governing people worldwide know that they cannot kill their citizens without someone trying to do something about it. His final reason was to provide a historical record. Examining bones of murder victims is emotional work. Dr. Snow told his students to "do the work in the daytime and cry at night."

Dr. Clyde Snow passed away on May 16, 2014.

FORENSIC ANTHROPOLOGY   **463**

DIFFERENTIATED LEARNING

Teaching Gifted Students

Ask students to create a PowerPoint presentation on one of the following notable forensic anthropologists: Mildred Trotter, T. Dale Stewart, William Maples, Sue Black, Jane Buikstra, Emily Craig, Michael Finnegan, Lee and/or Richard Jantz, Jerry Melbye, or Douglas Ubelaker.

Explore

Encourage interested students to research Dr. Snow's testimony against Saddam Hussein in his trial for his genocide of the Kurdish people.

Chapter 14 Review

True or False

1. F
2. T
3. F
4. F

Multiple Choice

5. D
6. C
7. B
8. D
9. B

CHAPTER 14 REVIEW

True or False

1. The number of bones in the body increases from the time of birth to adulthood. *Obj. 14.3*

2. Bones that break when someone is still alive tend to break unevenly, whereas bones broken long after death show clean breaks. *Obj. 14.1*

3. Because bones can heal, a bone fracture is no longer evident after 10 years. *Obj. 14.7*

4. Mitochondrial DNA analysis of skeletal remains can be used to establish individual identity. *Obj. 14.9*

Multiple Choice

5. Refer to Figure 14-16 in the text for estimating age using bones. Based on the following characteristics of a set of skeletal remains, which estimate best represents the age of the deceased? *Obj. 14.4*
   - femur head fused to shaft
   - clavicle and sternum closed
   - lambdoidal suture closed
   - coronal suture closed
   a) between the ages of 30 and 40
   b) between the ages of 16 and 18
   c) between the ages 10 and 24
   d) at least 50 years old

6. Which is the most reliable bone to determine the sex of a skeleton? *Obj. 14.6*
   a) femur
   b) skull
   c) pelvic bone
   d) collarbone

7. Which ethnic background tends to have a round nasal cavity, rectangular eye orbits, and some degree of prognathism (extension of the maxilla beyond the face)?
   a) European
   b) African
   c) Asian
   d) none of the above

8. A forensic anthropologist noted that a set of skeletal remains exhibited the following traits: wide subpubic angle, a sacrum curved outward, no visible growth plates, and porous bones. Which description is consistent with these characteristics? *Obj. 14.1, 14.6*
   a) female under 30 with arthritis
   b) male over 50 with scoliosis
   c) female under 20 with Asian ancestry
   d) female over 30 with osteoporosis

9. What connects a muscle to a bone? *Obj. 14.3*
   a) cartilage
   b) tendon
   c) growth plate
   d) ligament

Short Answer

10. Compare and contrast the following:
    a) growth plate (epiphyseal plate) and cartilaginous line (epiphyseal line) *Obj. 14.2*
    b) photographic superimposition and craniofacial reconstruction *Obj. 14.9*
    c) The teeth found in the skeletal remains of a 4-year-old child and the teeth found in the skeletal remains of an 8-year-old child

11. Summarize the process of ossification. Include the terms *cartilage, bone,* and *growth plate* in your answer. *Obj. 14.2, 14.3*

12. Describe how levels of different isotopes in skeletal remains have been used to help determine where someone lived. *Obj. 14.8*

13. A male's bones are more robust than a female's. Relate the structure of a bone to its function. Provide an explanation for male bones being more robust than female bones. *Obj. 14.6*

14. Small skeletal remains were found. At first, the remains were thought to belong to a girl in her early teens. Could the skeletal remains be those of a small adult woman? List features that would help determine if the skeletal remains were from a girl in her early teens or from a mature, small-framed woman. *Obj. 14.1, 14.3, 14.4*

15. Estimate body height based on a 38-centimeter fibula thought to belong to a female of European ancestry. Refer to Figure 14-20 for the appropriate formula. *Obj. 14.5*

16. Refer to the case study regarding Captain Bartholomew Gosnold. *Obj. 14.1, 14.2, 14.4, 14.5, 14.7, 14.9*
    a) What characteristics of the pelvis could be used to determine the skeletal remains belonged to a male?
    b) Since his age at death was estimated between 33 and 39, which skull sutures were most likely closed?
    c) Bone size was used to determine that he was right-handed, his type of build, and the type of work he performed. Describe the relationship between increased use of muscle and bone size.
    d) Outline how craniofacial reconstruction could be used to produce a three-dimensional image of the captain's face using the skull.
    e) Some people could argue that the lost tooth could have occurred after death. What evidence would you cite that refutes that claim?
    f) The skeletal remains were believed to belong to a man of the military, and part of the upper class. What evidence supports these claims?

Short Answer

10. a. A growth plate is a region of cartilage between the shaft of a long bone and the bone caps (epiphyses). As ossification continues, the growth plate gets smaller. The growth plate eventually is replaced by bone, leaving just a line where the cartilage was.

    b. Photographic superimposition is the projection of a photograph or video over skeletal remains to compare the video or photograph with the skull. It is used to confirm the identity of a person. Craniofacial reconstruction uses the tissue-depth method, which involves the layering of clay over a model of the person's skull to produce a three-dimensional image of the missing person's head and face. It is intended to provide leads.

    c. A 4-year-old will have all of his or her baby teeth; an 8-year-old will have lost the front top and bottom baby incisors as well as the lateral top and bottom baby incisors and first molars. Some adult teeth may be present, including the top and bottom front incisors, lateral incisors, and first molars.

11. Many of a baby's "bones" are composed of cartilage that is replaced by bone during ossification. A growth plate (epiphyseal plate) is an area of cartilage found at the cap (epiphysis) of a bone and is the site of growth. As the bone becomes ossified, the growth plate becomes smaller. Eventually, bones fuse at the site of growth plates.

12. Strontium is found in water. When ingested, strontium becomes embedded in teeth. By comparing the strontium level

(continues at left)

in teeth with the strontium levels in groundwater, it is possible to obtain information as to where a person lived. Carbon-13 and carbon-12 are both stable isotopes in wheat and corn that do not break down. When these grains are ingested, the isotopes become part of the bones. By comparing the ratio of carbon-13 to carbon-12, it is possible to determine if the person's diet included more wheat or more corn.

13. Male bones tend to be thicker than female bones because male muscles tend to be larger, so they need stronger attachment sites.

14. Features include the following:
    • progress of fusion at growth plates (epiphyseal plates)
    • suture marks on the skull
    • teeth: presence or absence of wisdom teeth; wear on the teeth; coloration; signs of lost enamel
    • arthritis or wear in spine and other joints
    • pelvis: progress of fusion in the pubic symphysis and signs of pregnancy in the pubic bone

15. Female European 38-cm fibula
    2.93 × 38 cm + 59.61 cm =
    170.95 cm (± 3.35 cm)
    ~ 174.3 cm to 167.6 cm

16. a. Measure the subpubic width and sacrum. Were the bones robust or gracile? Check muscle attachment sites.

    b. The sagittal suture and the lambdoidal sutures were probably closed.

    c. Because he was right-handed, the muscles in his right arm would have been used more than the muscles in his left arm. The muscle would be slightly larger and require larger bone-attachment sites and therefore larger bones.

    d. Use reference charts showing the average amount of flesh on different points of the skull. Insert rubber pegs of varying lengths into a cast model of the skull based on the reference chart. Apply clay over the rubber pins. Add eyes, ears, and lips.

    e. If bone healed over the tooth socket, tooth loss occurred was while he was alive.

    f. A military staff was buried with the captain, a common practice for military burials.

Additional Resources

Walker, Sally M. and Owsley, Douglas W. *Their Skeletons Speak*. Minneapolis: Carolrhoda Books, 2012.
http://www.kuleuven.be/english/news/2012/strontium-in-bones-reveals-geographical-origin-of-human-remains202c "Strontium in Bones Reveals Geographical Origin of Human Remains," KU Leuven News, 2012.
https://www.med-ed.virginia.edu/courses/rad/ext/index.html (Skeletal Trauma Radiology tutorial)

Going Further

1. Research how the age at death is estimated using the changes that occur to the pubic symphyseal surface (edge of the pubic bone closest to the pubic symphysis) or the sternal rib end (end that fuses to the breastbone (sternum).

2. Research and describe the effects of the following environmental influences on skeletal remains:
   a) clay soil
   b) dry soil
   c) periods of wet and dry
   d) fire

Bibliography

Books and Journals

Evans, C. *A Question of Evidence*. New York: Wiley, 2002.
Ferlini, R. *Silent Witness: How Forensic Anthropology Is Used to Solve the World's Toughest Crimes*. Ontario, Canada: Firefly Books, 2002.
Hansen, Joyce, and Gary McGowan. *Breaking Ground, Breaking Silence*. New York: Henry Holt, 1998.
Jackson, Donna. *The Bone Detectives*. Boston: Little, Brown & Company, 1996.
Maples, W., and M. Browning. *Dead Men Do Tell Tales*. Main Street Books, 1995.
Massie, R. *The Romanovs: The Final Chapter*. New York: Ballantine Books, 1996.
Snyder Sachs, J. *Corpse: Nature, Forensics, and the Struggle to Pinpoint Time of Death*. New York: Perseus Books Group, 2002.
Turek, S. L. *Orthopaedics: Principles and Their Application, Volume 2, 4th edition*. Philadelphia: J.B. Lippincott, 1984.
Ubelaker, D., and Henry Scammell. *Bones: A Forensic Detective's Casebook*. New York: M. Evans and Company, 1992.
Ubelaker, D., *Human Skeletal Remains, Excavation, Analysis and Interpretation, 2nd edition*. Washington, DC: Taraxacum, 1989.
Walker, Sally M. *Written in Bone: Buried Lives of Jamestown and Colonial Maryland*. Minneapolis: Carolrhoda, 2009.
White, Tim D., and Pieter A. Folkens. *The Human Bone Manual*. Burlington, MA: Elsevier, 2005.
Wolff, K., et al. "Skeletal age estimation in Hungarian populations of known age and sex." *Forensic Science International*, Volume 223, Issue 1, 374.e1–374.e8,

Internet Resources

ngl.cengage.com/forensicscience2e (Gale Forensic Science eCollection)
The Golden Ratio:
    http://www.youtube.com/watch?v=kKWV-uU_SoI
    http://www.youtube.com/watch?v=46f6ozRTVsU
"Skeletal age estimation in Hungarian populations of known age and sex."
    http://dx.doi.org/10.1016/j.forsciint.2012.08.033
American Society of Bone and Mineral Reconstruction
    http://depts.washington.edu/bonebio/ASBMRed/ASBMRed.html
"Pubic Symphysis and Age Determination"
    https://www3.nd.edu/~stephens/pubsymphysis.html
Gupta, Pankaj, et al. "Age Determination for Sternal Ends of the Ribs—an Autopsy Study."
    http://www.ncbi.nlm.nih.gov/pubmed/6507605
http://www.dnai.org/d/index.html
African Burial Ground National Monument
    http://www.nps.gov/afbg/index.htm
American Dental Association
    http://www.mouthhealthy.org/en/az-topics/e/eruption-charts

Determining the Age of a Skull *Obj. 14.2, 14.4*

Objectives:

By the end of this activity, you will be able to:
1. Estimate the age of an adult skull by studying the cranial suture marks.
2. Compare and contrast a newborn or young child's skull to the skull of an adult.

SAFETY PRECAUTIONS:
None

Time Required to Complete Activity:
----
30 minutes (groups of two students)

Materials:

Text Figures 14-18a and 14-18b
access to the Internet or reference books

Procedure:

PART A:
Using Figures 14-18a and Figure 14-18b in your textbook showing the relationship between age and skull sutures, determine the approximate age of a skull with the following features:

1. Lambdoidal and sagittal sutures fused. Age _____
   Coronal sutures not fused.
2. Lambdoidal sutures almost fused. Age _____
   Sagittal and coronal sutures not fused.
3. All sutures fused. Age _____
4. Lambdoidal suture open. Age _____
   Sagittal and coronal sutures open.

PART B:
Using the Internet, your text, and other references, compare and contrast an infant's or child's skull to an adult skull.

Include in your answer differences in the following:
a. composition of the skull
b. structure of the skull
c. ratio of skull to body size
d. ratio of skull to face size

Mature skull

Newborn skull

Images © by Pieter A. Folkens

Forensic Anthropology **467**

---

b. Infant: eye orbits larger in comparison to face than in adult. Eye orbits, nasal opening, and mouth lower on face than in adult. Infant has soft spots (cartilage), and bones are not fused in the skull. Infant skull is more elongated than adults.
c. Skull to body ratio: infants approximately 1 : 4; adults approximately 1 : 7.
d. Skull to face ratio: infants approximately 1 : 2; adults approximately 2 : 3.

Teaching Tip
Remind students that the sagittal suture runs along the top of the skull from the coronal suture to the lambdoidal suture. The sagittal suture closes by age 32. The lambdoidal suture starts to close by age 21, accelerates by age 26, and closes by about age 30. The coronal suture closes around age 50. The squamosal suture closes around age 60. Refer to Figures 14-17a and 14-17b.

Background

In this activity, students work in groups of two to study the cranial suture marks to estimate the age of a skull. Students compare and contrast infant and adult skulls using photos in the activity, along with reference books or Internet resources.

Teaching Tip
Models of infant skulls can be purchased from Wards or other scientific supply companies. If models are unavailable, use photos from the Internet.

Safety Precautions

There are no safety precautions for this activity.

Time Required to Complete Activity
30 minutes

Procedure

A week or two before you plan to assign this activity, ask your school librarian to set aside some reference books for you to have available in your classroom on the day of the activity.

Answers
Part A
1. Approximately 32 to 49 years.
2. Approximately 26 to 30 years.
3. Approximately 60 or more years.
4. Less than 21 years.

Part B
a. Infant: mostly cartilage, adult less cartilage, more bone.

(continues at left)

Background

In this activity, students work in groups of two to determine if remains belong to a male or female.

Safety Precautions

There are no safety precautions for this activity.

Time Required to Complete Activity

25 minutes

Procedures

1. If possible, try joining with other teachers (e.g., anatomy/ physiology, sports medicine) in your school to purchase bones.

2. Good sources for purchasing bones include Bone Clones, Skulls Unlimited, and Ward's Science.

3. Make sure students read all directions *before* beginning the activity.

Answers

Case 1: Female
Case 2: Male
Case 3: Larger
Case 4: Female
Case 5: male

Bones: Male or Female? *Obj. 14.6*

Objective:

By the end of this activity, you will be able to:
Determine if skeletal remains belong to a male or female by comparing data to reference tables.

SAFETY PRECAUTIONS:
None

Time Required to Complete Activity:

25 minutes (groups of two students)

Materials:

figures throughout the text
pencil or pen

Procedure:

Refer to the figures in Chapter 14 of your text to help you decide if the remains listed are from a male or female.

Case 1
Remains exhibit round eye orbits, a subpubic angle of 103 degrees, an oval pelvic cavity, and a smooth and slender skull.

Case 2
The pelvis is narrow, there is a prominent protuberance on occipital bone, and a sloping frontal bone.

Case 3
Would you expect to find a subpubic angle larger or smaller than 90 degrees if the skull had a rounded frontal bone with small brow ridges and a small mastoid bone (bone located behind the ear)?

Case 4
The remains have a short sacrum that curves outward, no protuberance on the occipital bone is evident, the underside of lower jaw (mandible) is triangular, and the brow ridges are narrow.

Case 5
The occipital protuberance is very prominent, the sacrum is curved inward, and the pelvic cavity is heart-shaped with a subpubic angle of 78 degrees.

Case 6 _____

The skeletal remains are from a small person. The usual indicators of sex are not present. How might you explain the lack of sexual indicators?

Case 7 _____

Two skeletons were analyzed. Based on the pelvic and facial features, Skeleton A was identified as female and Skeleton B was identified as male. The female skeleton had more robust bones with larger muscle attachments than the male skeleton. Provide possible explanations to account for a female having greater bone mass and attachment sites than a male.

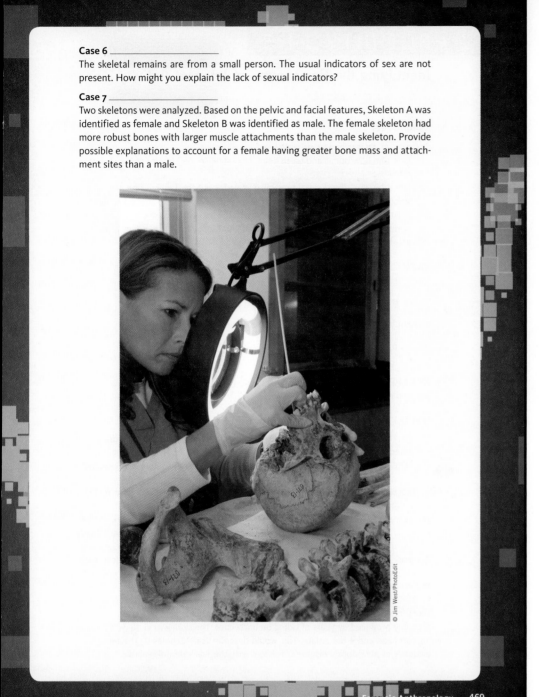

© Jim West/PhotoEdit

Case 6: The skeletal remains are from a child who has not yet entered puberty.

Case 7a: The female could be involved in heavy lifting or exercise that resulted in greater muscle mass. The greater the muscle mass, the stronger the bone and the thicker the attachment sites on the bone.

b: The male's muscles might be less developed due to disease, illness, inactivity, or poor nutrition, resulting in smaller attachment sites on the bones.

Teaching Tip

Resource for bone images: Tim D. White and Pieter A. Folkens, _The Human Bone Manual._

Further Research and Extensions

Ask students to create their own scenarios describing remains that were found. Then have them switch scenarios with other students and identify the skull as male or female.

Background

In this activity, students use the Internet to examine how the Romanovs were identified using their remains, what the remains revealed about how the family was killed, and how DNA technology can be used in these types of cases.

Safety Precautions

There are no safety precautions for this activity.

Time Required to Complete Activity

60 minutes plus additional time to answer questions

Procedures

1. Print, copy, and distribute Act 14-3 SH from the IRCD, Chapter 14. Before planning this activity, go to the Website www.dnai.org/

2. Remind students that identity determination after death is called *taphonomy*.

3. Make sure students read all directions before beginning the activity.

4. Explain to students that the number of the question pertains to the number of that slide. For example, Question 4 pertains to slide 4.

5. Make sure students understand that they are to only visit the Websites listed in this activity.

Answers

1. Yekaterinburg, Russia
2. a. The Russian scientists were undecided.
   b. i. determination of male or female
      ii. determination of male or female
      iii. determination of male or female
      iv. age estimation and pregnancy information
      v. age estimation
3. a. 9 skeletons,
   b. 11

Identifying the Romanovs—an Internet Activity

Obj. 14.1, 14.4, 14.5, 14.6, 14.7, 14.9

Objectives:

By the end of this activity, you will be able to:

1. Describe how bones and teeth helped to establish the identity of the skeletal remains.
2. Describe what the skeletal remains revealed about the family's fate.
3. Apply your knowledge about bones and teeth to distinguish age, ethnic background, and sex of the skeletal remains in the mass grave.
4. Summarize how mitochondrial DNA (mtDNA) recovered from bones is used to establish family relationships and personal identity.

SAFETY PRECAUTIONS:

None

Time Required to Complete Activity:

60 minutes plus additional time to complete questions

Materials:

Act 14-3 SH
access to the Internet
pen and paper (per student)

Background:

BIOLOGY

In 1991, the skeletal remains of Tsar Nicolas II and his wife, Tsarina Alexandra, were identified among the remains discovered in a mass grave in Russia. Evidence from the bone fragments indicated the sex, age, and family relationships, but the dental work and DNA evidence provided the definitive identification.

The skeletons were labeled numerically. Skeletal remains 7 were of a middle-aged woman whose ribs showed possible signs of damage from bayonet thrusts. Dr. Lowell Levine, forensic odontologist, noted elaborate dental work in her remains. Two crowns were made of platinum and other crowns were made from porcelain with gold fillings. This type of dental work was practiced in Germany, Alexandra's homeland. None of the servants would have been able to afford such expensive dental work. Therefore, skeletal remains 7 were believed to belong to Tsarina Alexandra.

Skeletal remains 4 were identified as Tsar Nicholas II. The skeleton was of a fairly short, middle-aged man who had signs of wear and deformation in the hipbones, probably produced by years of riding on horseback. The skull was wide with a sloping forehead and a flat palate. This would describe Tsar Nicholas II. The teeth had evidence of periodontal disease consistent with the Tsar's dental record.

Teaching Tip

Flip your classroom? The dnai.org website provides easy-to-understand information regarding the evidence used to identify the Romanovs. Students can independently view the Website and answer questions before coming to class to gain a better background in identification of skeletal remains. Class time can then be used for discussion of what students learned.

Teaching Tip

This activity is a good opportunity for students to apply cross-cutting concepts to solving a problem. Prior to the activity, invite a history teacher to your class to discuss world events of 1918 to help set the stage.

What were the identities of the other seven skeletal remains in that mass grave? How did the evidence obtained from the bones and teeth help establish their identity?

Procedure:

1. Go to the www.dnai.org
   Click on *Applications*.
   Click on *Recovering the Romanovs*. Notice that there are three modules:
   - *The Romanov Family*
   - *Mystery of Anna Anderson*
   - *Science Solves a Mystery*
2. Click on *The Romanov Family* to learn about the family background.
3. Click on *Science Solves a Mystery*. Note there are 22 frames in this section. As you view the presentation, answer the questions on a sheet of paper. Note that the number of each question corresponds to the number of the frame in the presentation (22 frames and 22 questions).
4. While viewing the Website and answering the questions, complete the Act 14-3 SH Data Table using the information from the Website and from your textbook.

Data Table

How to Estimate Age, Height, Sex, and Ancestry From Skeletal and Dental Remains		
Age	Which bone or tooth?	How does this help to estimate the age?
Height	Which bone(s)?	Refer to the textbook. What formula would you use?
Sex	Which bones?	Explain the differences in male and female traits of these bones.
Ancestry	Which bones?	Describe the European characteristics.

Forensic Anthropology   471

Skeleton	Dental Analysis	Vertebral Analysis	Pelvic Area Analysis
1	22 or over	18 or older	Female
2	22 or over	18 or older	Male
3	21 or younger	18 or older	Female
4	22 or over	18 or older	Male
5	22 or over	18 or older	Female
6	21 or younger	18 or older	Female
7	22 or over	18 or older	Female
8	22 or over	18 or older	Male
9	22 or over	18 or older	Female

4. a. age (over 18 or under 18)
   b. age (21 or younger or 22 or older)
   c. sex

5. 3 males, 6 females; 2 under 21 years of age, 7 age 22 or older, all over 18 (see table below of the nine skeletal remains)

6. Anastasia and Alexei; the skeletal remains indicated both were under 18 when they died and no remains of children under 18 years of age were found at the gravesite.

7. DNA

8. (Tutorial only; no questions)

9. a. They are both inherited forms of DNA.
   b. Mitochondrial DNA comes only from the mother. Nuclear DNA is inherited from both mother and father and is found in the nuclei of the sperm and egg.

10. our mothers

11. a. their mother, Tsarina Alexandra
    b. from her mother
    c. No. He and his children had different mothers.
    d. Compare the mitochondrial DNA from the skeletal remains to the mtDNA of existing maternal relatives.

12. a. Queen Victoria of England
    b. Prince Philip of England, Duke of Edinburgh (Queen Elizabeth II's husband)

13. Skeletal remains 3, 5, 6, and 7 all had mtDNA consistent with that of Prince Philip

14. not a relative; she was assumed to be an adult nurse

15. James, Duke of Fife was a maternal relative of Tsar Nicholas II.

16. the skeleton of Nicholas II, 4

17. No, the three adult males were two servants and a doctor

Materials

The table at the left refers to slide 5: Analyzing the Skeletons

FORENSIC ANTHROPOLOGY   471

18. To determine if she was Anastasia, descendant of Tsarina Alexandra; if she was, she would have the same mtDNA as Prince Philip.

19. Carl Maucher was a maternal relative of Franziska Schanzkowska (a missing factory worker thought to be Anna Anderson) and would have the same mtDNA as Schanzkowska.

20. (Video only; no question)

21. a. from a previous surgical tissue sample and from hair samples

    b. no

    c. Their bodies were burned after the execution. (However, in 2006, after this Website was created, both bodies were recovered from a second gravesite not far from the gravesite discussed in this feature.)

22. Completed Act 14-3 answer may vary among students. Answers should be from both the text and the Website feature.

Questions:

1. In 1991, what was the location of the burial site for the tsar, tsarina, and family members?
2. Listen to the two video clips narrated by Dr. Michael Baden.
   a. Why was an American team called in to help identify the bodies?
   b. View the video *Remains in Yekaterinburg*. Answer the questions below based on the information in the video. What information can be gained by a study of the following?
      i. ridges and thick muscular insertions
      ii. orbits of the eye and mandible and maxilla of the jaw
      iii. pelvic girdle measurements
      iv. ridges in the pubic bone
      v. leg and arm bones
3. Click the box *Count the Skeletons*.
   a. How many skeletons were recovered?
   b. How many people died in Yekaterinberg?
4. What can be determined by examination of the following?
   a. wisdom teeth
   b. vertebrae
   c. pelvic regions
5. Click on the box *Analyzing the Skeletons*.
   Follow the directions to estimate the age and sex of each of the skeletal remains.
6. Which two family members were thought to be missing from the gravesite? Explain how this was determined.
7. The skeletal remains were buried for nearly 75 years. What type of evidence was preserved that enabled scientists to determine who was buried in the grave?
8. a. Click on the *Nuclear DNA* box and read the information. Click on the *Next* button in the upper-right corner.
   b. Click on *Mitochondrial DNA (mtDNA)* and read the information. Click on the *Next* button in the upper-right corner.
9. Compare and contrast mitochondrial DNA (mtDNA) with nuclear DNA.
   a. How are they alike?
   b. How are they different?
10. From whom do we inherit all of our mitochondrial mtDNA? Click on *Maternal Inheritance*.
11. Refer to *Test Yourself on Mitochondrial DNA*.
    a. From whom did the Romanov children inherit their mitochondrial DNA (mtDNA)?
    b. Where did the person from whom they got their mtDNA get his or her mtDNA?
    c. Did Nicholas II have the same mtDNA as his children? Explain your answer.
    d. How could the identity of the skeletal remains be determined?

12. Double-click on *Tsarina's Pedigrees* located in the lower-right corner. Find Nicholas II and Alexandra in the pedigree chart.

    a. All mtDNA of the tsar's children can be traced back to whom?

    b. According to this pedigree, who is the relative still alive today that has the same mtDNA as the Romanov children?

13. Go to Bioserver Sequence Server.

    Recall that differences in the mtDNA sequence are highlighted in yellow. Which of the skeletons had the same mtDNA sequence as Prince Philip, Duke of Edinburgh?

14. Whose skeleton was 9?

15. Click on the tsar's pedigree. Why was James, Duke of Fife, selected to have his mtDNA examined?

16. Go to Bioserver's Sequence Server.

    Which of the male skeletons had all mtDNA sequences consistent with the mtDNA of James, Duke of Fife?

17. Did the other male skeletal remains belong to members of the royal family? If not, to whom did they belong?

18. Why was Anna Anderson's mtDNA compared to the mtDNA of Prince Philip?

19. Why was Carl Maucher's mtDNA examined?

20. Double-click on the *Hair Sample* video.

21. Watch the two videos by Dr. Michael Baden and scientist Syd Mandelbaum.

    a. If Anna Anderson was cremated, then how was a sample of her DNA obtained?

    b. Based on Dr. Michael Baden's and Syd Mandelbaum's findings, were Anna Anderson and Anastasia, the princess, the same person? Explain your answer.

    c. What is believed to have happened to the bodies of the two youngest children, Anastasia and Alexei?

22. Using the information from the Website and your text, complete Act 14-3 SH Data Table.

Going Further:

1. Dr. William Maples determined that Skeletal Remains 5 was Maria, age 19 at the time of her death. He determined that the remains in the 1991 gravesite were not the remains of Anastasia, who was 17 at the time of her death. He supported his evidence using two main identifying features, vertebral rings and root tips of molars. Research and explain how the presence or absence of vertebral rings and the location of the root tips of molars might aid in distinguishing Maria, aged 19, from Anastasia, aged 17.

2. Dr. William Maples used evidence from a pelvis, sacrum, and collarbone (clavicle) to conclude that skeletal remains 6 (Tatiana) and skeletal remains 3 (Olga) were both over the age of 18. Refer to your text or research how the growth of these bones could be used to determine whether the deceased was younger or older than 18 at the time of death.

3. In Robert K. Massie's book *The Romanovs: The Final Chapter,* the author describes how Wormian bones were found in skeletons 3, 5, and 6 (believed to be Olga, Maria, and Tatiana) and that Wormian bones were similar to the Wormian bones also found in Skeleton 7, Tsarina Alexandra.

   Research and explain the following:

   a. What are Wormian bones?

   b. Where are Wormian bones located?

   c. How common are Wormian bones?

   d. Explain why the presence of Wormian bones provides evidence for a connection between the daughters and the mother.

4. Read Robert K. Massie's book *The Romanovs: The Final Chapter,* pages 61–68. Prepare a chart or poster showing how dental and bone evidence were used to estimate the ages of the skeletal remains.

Estimation of Body Size From Individual Bones Obj. 14.5

Objective:

By the end of this activity, you will be able to:
Estimate the approximate height of a person from one of the long bones of the body.

SAFETY PRECAUTIONS:
None

Time Required to Complete Activity: 40 minutes

Materials:

text Figure 14-20
pencil or pen
calculator (optional)

Procedure:

1. Refer to the bone length table in your textbook (Figure 14-20).
2. For each example, locate the appropriate formula to calculate an estimate of a person's height based on the length of the recovered bone.
3. Estimate the height range of each person based the length of the bone noted. For each estimate, indicate the formula you used.
   a. European male, femur of 50.6 cm
   b. African female, femur of 49.5 cm
   c. European person, sex unknown, tibia of 34.2 cm
   d. European female, humerus of 33.4 cm
   e. African male, humerus of 41.1 cm
   f. Person of unknown sex or ethnic group, humerus of 31.6 cm

Questions:

1. Why would height estimates from using these formulas with the skeletal remains of teenagers be unreliable?
2. These calculations are only estimates because of the variables other than bone length that can affect an individual's height. List some variables that can affect someone's height.

Forensic Anthropology   475

e. Height ~ (2.88 × 41.1 cm) + 75.48 cm 193.85 cm ± 4.23 cm range 198.1 cm to 189.6 cm

f. Height ~ (4.62 × 31.6 cm) + 19.00 cm 164.99 cm ± 4.89 cm range 169.88 cm to 160.10 cm

Further Research and Extensions

To extend the length of this activity, ask students to measure the lengths of their own humerus and femur and see if those measurements accurately estimate their own height. Have students measure their heights in centimeters and then work these formulas backward to estimate their bone lengths. You can hold a 30-cm ruler or a meter stick next to your arm or leg and see how close the calculation is to the estimated height based on bone length.

Background

In this activity, students determine the approximate height of a person from a femur.

Safety Precautions

There are no safety precautions for this activity.

Time Required to Complete Activity

40 minutes

Procedures

1. This activity should not take the entire 40 minutes if your plan is to just have students calculate the results. If possible, try to obtain different samples of humerus and femur bones and have students make calculations on bones that have slightly different lengths.

2. Make sure students read all directions before beginning the activity.

Answers

1. Teenagers are still growing. Growth occurs at different rates in different teens, so standardization isn't possible.

2. Nutrition, disease, exercise, genetics

3. a. Height ~ (2.32 × 50.6 cm) + 65.53 cm 182.92 cm ± 3.94 cm range 186.9 cm to 179 cm

   b. Height ~ (2.28 × 49.5 cm) + 59.76 cm 172.62 cm ± 3.41 cm range from 176.0 cm to 169.2 cm

   c. Height ~ (3.02 × 34.2 cm) + 58.94 cm 162.22 cm ± 4.11 cm range from 166.3 cm to 158.1 cm

   d. Height ~ (3.36 × 33.4 cm) + 57.97 cm 170.19 cm ± 4.45 cm range 174.6 cm to 165.7 cm

(continues at left)

Background

In this activity, students apply their knowledge of bone and teeth analysis to case studies to help provide characteristics that would help lead to the identity of a person.

Safety Precautions

There are no safety precautions for this activity.

Time Required to Complete Activity

40 minutes

Procedure

Make sure students read all directions *before* beginning the activity.

Answers

1. a. age close to 30
   b. male
   c. male
   d. African ancestry
   e. male
   f. lost front teeth while alive, evidenced by healing
   g. African ancestry
2. a. either juvenile or female
   b. estimated age older than 17
   c. either young person or a person with good dental hygiene and health
3. a. female of small body size or a male who is sedentary or ill
   b. probably over 30 due to the presence of osteoporosis
   c. 2.71×47 cm $+$ 45.86 cm $= 173.23$ cm $\pm$ 4.49 cm

      Approximate range of height is 177.7 cm to 168.74 cm

   d. The plate may have a serial number to help trace the owner, or bone growth at the site may provide information as to when the break took place.

What Bones Tell Us *Obj. 14.1, 14.2, 14.4, 14.5, 14.6*

Objective:

By the end of this activity, you will be able to:
Apply your knowledge of bone and teeth analysis to several case studies in an effort to construct biological profiles.

SAFETY PRECAUTIONS:
None

Time Required to Complete Activity: 40 minutes

Materials:

text
pen and paper
calculators (optional)

Procedure:

Use the information in your text and the following evidence to prepare a biological profile of the person based on his or her skeletal and dental remains. Cite facts from the chapter to support your conclusions.

Case Studies:

1. What can you tell about a skull that has the following features?
   a. lambdoidal suture nearly closed
   b. large brow ridge
   c. robust skull
   d. nasal opening round in shape, mandible projecting beyond face (prognathism), no nasal spine
   e. large mastoid bone
   f. front upper teeth missing with bone healed over tooth socket
   g. nasal index 0.58
2. A lower jaw (mandible) has been recovered from a crime scene. What can you conclude from the following characteristics?
   a. small, slender (gracile), tapering into a V-shape
   b. wisdom teeth erupted
   c. no fillings or bridgework

3. What can you tell about a femur from the following characteristics?

   a. thin with very small muscle-attachment sites

   b. osteoporosis present

   c. length 47 cm

   d. A plate has been screwed into the femur—evidence of an earlier fracture.

4. A mass grave is found. What can you tell about the remains from the following characteristics?

   a. skull occipital protuberance, large mastoid bone, and sloping frontal bone

   b. subpubic angle 80 degrees

   c. left femur 49 cm

   d. right femur 49.1 cm

   e. left femur 45.5 cm

   f. right humerus 20 cm

   g. pelvis intact with pubic bone and ischium fused and all sacrum segments fused

   h. one partial skull with teardrop-shaped nasal cavity, small mastoid bone, and small brow ridges

   i. humerus bones with the caps fused to the shafts; clavicle not fused to the sternum (breastbone)

5. A student of forensic anthropology examined the skeletal remains of a body found in a shallow grave. He noted the following information about the skeletal remains:

   a. Skull: none of the sutures were closed; nasal cavity teardrop-shaped, nasal spine prominent, large muscle attachments, large brow ridges, occipital protuberance, large mastoid bone; wisdom teeth not erupted.

   b. Arm: shaft and cap (end) of the humerus bone were not fused.

   c. Pelvis: the pubic bone and ischium were fused, the sacrum was not fused, and the subpubic angle was less than 90 degrees.

   His report stated that the skeletal remains appear to be male of European ancestry with an age estimate between 7 and 32.

   Do you agree or disagree with his biological profile based on his observations? Cite evidence to support your claim.

6. Refer to Question 5. What additional remains would you need to estimate the following?

   a. age

   b. ancestry

   c. sex (which part(s) of the pelvic area)

4. a. male

   b. male

   c. height 2.71 × 49 cm + 45.86 cm = 178.65 ± 4.49 cm ~ 183.1 cm to 174.2 cm

   d. height 2.71 × 49.1 cm + 45.86 cm = 178.92 cm ± 4.49 cm ~ 174.4 cm to 183.4 cm

   e. height 2.71 × 45.5 cm + 45.86 cm = 169.2 cm ± 0.49 cm ~ 173.7 cm to 164.7 cm

   f. height 4.62 × 20 cm + 19 cm = 111.4 cm ± 4.89 cm ~ 116.3 cm to 106.5 cm

   g. Age of fusion of pubis and ischium is 7–8; approximate age of sacrum fusion between 25 and 30. Age estimate is at least 25.

   h. European descent, either a female or juvenile:

   i. humerus head is fused to shaft around age 18 to 20. Clavicle is fused by age 24. Age estimate is between 18 and 24.

5. Agreed that the sex is male based on narrow subpubic angle, large mastoid bone, large muscle attachments; agreed that ethnic background is European, based on teardrop-shaped nasal cavity and the prominent nasal spine. However, the age range could be smaller. Cranial sutures not closed—under 32; humerus cap and shaft not fused—under 18; unerupted wisdom teeth—likely under 22; sacrum not fused, under 30; pubis and ischium fused—around 7 or 8. The age range estimate is between 7 and 18, not 7 and 32.

6. a. Examine clavicle and sternum ends, check if bones of the humerus head are fused, check other references that provide bone fusion estimates for children.

   b. nasal index

   c. lengths of the sacrum and coccyx, width of hips, pelvic cavity shape

Background

In this activity, students determine which body proportions most accurately allow them to estimate height.

Safety Precautions

There are no safety precautions for this activity.

Time Required to Complete Activity

40 minutes

Teaching Tip

Students will be measuring body parts. It is suggested that student pairs be of the same sex. Give students advance notice before doing this lab to allow any students who might be uncomfortable to discuss that with you in advance. Also inform students they will be removing their shoes to obtain a foot measurement.

Height and Body Proportions   *Obj. 14.4, 14.5*

Background:

Leonardo da Vinci drew the "Canons of Proportions" around 1490 and described what he considered the ideal proportions of a man were. The drawing was based on the writings of Vitruvius, a Roman architect. Some of the relationships described:

Leonardo da Vinci's "Canons of Proportions."

Photo by Susan Van Etten

- A man's height is 24 times the width of his palm.
- The length of the hand is one tenth of a man's height.
- The distance from the elbow to the armpit is one eighth of a man's height.
- The maximum width at the shoulders is one quarter of a man's height.
- The distance from the top of the head to the bottom of the chin is one eighth of a man's height.
- The length of a man's outstretched arms is equal to his height.

Objectives:

By the end of this activity, you will be able to:

1. Determine which of these relationships most accurately parallels your body proportions in estimating height.
2. Apply the Canons of Proportions to estimate someone's height from a limited number of different body parts.

SAFETY PRECAUTIONS:

None

Time Required to Complete Activity: 40 minutes

Materials:

Act 14-6 SH
(students working in pairs)
metric ruler
pen and paper
calculator (optional)
graph paper

Part A:

PROCEDURE:

1. Standing in your stocking feet with your back to a wall, have your partner carefully measure your height to the nearest tenth of a centimeter. Keep the top of your head level (parallel to the floor).

2. Record your results in Data Table 1.

3. Have your partner measure to the nearest 0.1 cm and record each of the following measurements of your body:

   a. width of your palm at the widest point

   b. length of the hand from first wrist crease nearest your hand to the tip of the longest finger

   c. distance from elbow to highest point in the armpit

   d. maximum width of shoulders

   e. the distance from the top of the head to the bottom of the chin

   f. the length of outstretched arms

4. Repeat Steps 1 to 3, taking the body measurements of your partner, and recording them in Data Table 2.

5. Your partner records your data in his or her Data Table 2.

6. Calculate and record your own and your partner's estimated height using the proportions given on the data tables.

7. Determine and record the difference between your actual height and your calculated height in Data Tables 1 and 2. Use + and – symbols to indicate if your height is over or under the height based on these ratios.

Data Table 1: Your Body Relationships
All measurements in centimeters
Gender of person measured _____

A	B	C	D	E
Trait	Measurement (cm)	Multiply by	Calculated Height (cm)	Difference Between Actual and Calculated Heights (cm)
Height		1		
Palm width		24		
Hand length		10		
Distance from armpit to elbow		8		
Width of shoulders		4		
Head to chin length		8		
Outstretched arms		1		

Procedures

1. Print, copy, and distribute Act 14-6 SH from the IRCD, Chapter 14.

2. Make sure students read all directions *before* beginning the activity.

Answers

Part A

Check students' data tables.

Questions

1. Answers will vary.

2. Answers will vary.

3. Answers will vary.

4. Answers will vary.

5. Teenagers are still growing and have not yet reached adult size. When teenagers grow, different parts of the body develop before others. For example, the feet tend to grow early during the growth spurt. Teenagers will be at different stages of their growth spurts.

Teaching Tip

Remind students how to prepare a graph a draw a best-fit line. Some students may prefer to draw the graph electronically.

Data Table 2: Your Partner's Body Relationships
All measurements in centimeters
Gender of person measured _____

A Trait	B Measurement (cm)	C Multiply by	D Calculated Height (cm)	E Difference Between Actual and Calculated Heights (cm)
Height		1		
Palm width		24		
Hand length		10		
Distance from armpit to elbow		8		
Width of shoulders		4		
Head to chin length		8		
Outstretched arms		1		

Questions:

1. Which measurement and relationship most accurately reflected your height?

2. Was this the same measurement that most people of your gender found to most accurately estimate their actual height? Explain.

3. Which measurement and relationship most accurately reflected your partner's height?

4. Which measurement was the least accurate in estimating your height?

5. Explain why using the Canons of Proportions on teenagers to estimate height would provide less accurate height estimates than using the Canons of Proportions on adults.

Part B:

PROCEDURE:

1. The distance from your elbow to armpit is roughly the length of your humerus. Record both your humerus length and your *actual measured height* in Data Table 3. Record your classmate's humerus length and his or her actual measured height in Data Table 3.

2. Graph the length of the humerus (*x*-axis) vs. height (*y*-axis). Be sure to include on your graph the following:
   - appropriate title for graph
   - appropriate scale on each axis
   - labels for units (cm) on each of the *x*- and *y*-axes
   - a circle around each data point
   - a line of best fit

Data Table 3: Comparison of Humerus to Measured Height

Name	Length of Humerus (cm)	Measured Height (cm)
1		
2		
3		
4		
5		
6		
7		
8		
9		
10		
11		
12		
13		
14		

Questions:

1. Analyze the graph of your data. Is there a relationship between humerus length and height? State evidence for your claim.
2. Suppose a humerus bone was discovered at a construction site. From the graph, explain how you could estimate the person's height in life from the length of the humerus.
3. Consider possible sources of error in your measurements. How would you modify the instructions so that the measurements taken would be more accurate?

Going Further:

1. Research how Leonardo da Vinci arrived at the numbers used in his body relationships for the Canons of Proportions.
2. Research Fibonacci numbers or the golden ratio in nature. How is the golden ratio important in our sense of proportion?

Part B
Check students' data tables and graphs.

- -

Questions

1. Check students' graphs.
2. Sample answer: Find the size of the humerus on the bestfit line and follow it across to where it intersects with the y-axis. That value should be the approximate height.
3. Standardization of measurement should be addressed.
   - Do you measure your height with or without shoes?
   - Discuss what is meant by *palm*: the distance across the hand, or the distance from little finger to thumb?
   - Use a more precise measuring tool.
   - Demonstrate how each measurement should be taken.

Further Research and Extensions

Give students this additional scenario: Part of a skeleton containing a humerus, pelvis, and mandible is found in the woods. What might be determined about the individual from these bones?

Chapter Overview

People have been producing and improving upon glass for hundreds of years. Most common forms of glass are considered to be class evidence because they are mass-produced. Specific properties of glass, such as density, refractive index, and fracture patterns, give investigators clues to help link a suspect to a crime scene.

The Big Ideas

Combining silica, lime, and sodium oxide at very high temperatures forms most types of glass. Heat-resistant glass is made for cooking and laboratory use. Glass used in different locations of vehicles has different properties intended to protect the inhabitants of the vehicle. Glass can be identified by the compounds used to make it, its density, and its refractive index. By analyzing the fracture patterns that form when glass is hit, investigators can determine what type of object hit the glass, roughly how fast it was moving, and from which direction it came. If multiple objects hit the same piece of glass, investigators may be able to tell the order of the impacts by analyzing the fracture patterns.

CHAPTER 15

Glass Evidence

If You Break It . . .

Glass evidence.

The woman quickly slipped the crystal vase under her coat. She thought she could easily hide it and leave the store without getting caught. However, the vase slipped and fell to the floor, shattering into many small pieces. The woman quickly ran from the store. A store clerk remembered seeing a young woman near the vase before the incident occurred. The clerk gave a detailed description to the police, who found the woman in a nearby jewelry store.

When questioned by the police, the woman claimed she was not in the store where the incident occurred. Upon further investigation, the police found broken glass in her boot tread. Was the glass in her boot tread consistent with the glass from the broken vase? What type of testing could be performed to determine if the glass in the boot was consistent with the broken vase in the store? If the glass was consistent, would that be enough evidence to charge the woman?

In this chapter, we will explore the formation, characteristics, and types of glass and various methods of glass analysis used in forensic investigations.

482

SCENARIO

Ask students what they know about glass. What are the components of glass? How is it made? How are crystal, window glass, picture frame glass, and the glass in a vehicle windshield different? Have students describe the fracture patterns in a broken window. Does all glass break in the same manner? If a bullet strikes glass, ask if they think it would be possible to determine the entrance hole versus the exit hole. What types of tests could compare one glass fragment with other glass fragments?

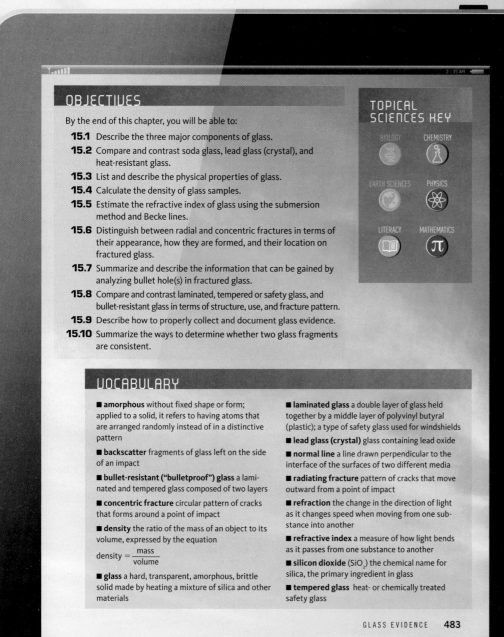

OBJECTIVES

By the end of this chapter, you will be able to:

15.1 Describe the three major components of glass.

15.2 Compare and contrast soda glass, lead glass (crystal), and heat-resistant glass.

15.3 List and describe the physical properties of glass.

15.4 Calculate the density of glass samples.

15.5 Estimate the refractive index of glass using the submersion method and Becke lines.

15.6 Distinguish between radial and concentric fractures in terms of their appearance, how they are formed, and their location on fractured glass.

15.7 Summarize and describe the information that can be gained by analyzing bullet hole(s) in fractured glass.

15.8 Compare and contrast laminated, tempered or safety glass, and bullet-resistant glass in terms of structure, use, and fracture pattern.

15.9 Describe how to properly collect and document glass evidence.

15.10 Summarize the ways to determine whether two glass fragments are consistent.

TOPICAL SCIENCES KEY

BIOLOGY

CHEMISTRY

EARTH SCIENCES

PHYSICS

LITERACY

MATHEMATICS

VOCABULARY

■ **amorphous** without fixed shape or form; applied to a solid, it refers to having atoms that are arranged randomly instead of in a distinctive pattern

■ **backscatter** fragments of glass left on the side of an impact

■ **bullet-resistant ("bulletproof") glass** a laminated and tempered glass composed of two layers

■ **concentric fracture** circular pattern of cracks that forms around a point of impact

■ **density** the ratio of the mass of an object to its volume, expressed by the equation

$$\text{density} = \frac{\text{mass}}{\text{volume}}$$

■ **glass** a hard, transparent, amorphous, brittle solid made by heating a mixture of silica and other materials

■ **laminated glass** a double layer of glass held together by a middle layer of polyvinyl butyral (plastic); a type of safety glass used for windshields

■ **lead glass (crystal)** glass containing lead oxide

■ **normal line** a line drawn perpendicular to the interface of the surfaces of two different media

■ **radiating fracture** pattern of cracks that move outward from a point of impact

■ **refraction** the change in the direction of light as it changes speed when moving from one substance into another

■ **refractive index** a measure of how light bends as it passes from one substance to another

■ **silicon dioxide** (SiO_2) the chemical name for silica, the primary ingredient in glass

■ **tempered glass** heat- or chemically treated safety glass

GLASS EVIDENCE **483**

TEACHING RESOURCES

Instructor's Resource CD-ROM includes:

- Activities and Student Handouts
- Alternative Assessments
- Consolidated Bibliography
- Correlations to NGSS and CCSS
- Figure Files
- Lesson Plans
- Nonfiction Readings
- PowerPoint Presentations
- Student Learning Objectives (SLOs)

CL Testing powered by Cognero

Website: ngl.cengage.com/forensicscience2e

Engage

Show students samples (or photos) of different types of broken glass including window glass, windshield glass, or headlight glass, and ask: What was the source? Why did the glass fracture as it did?

Explore

Explain to students that glass is considered class evidence, because a piece of glass cannot be unique to a particular suspect, no matter how unusual it is, since it can break into pieces. However, if pieces of glass from a suspect reconstruct perfectly into a whole object from the crime scene, that could be very persuasive evidence. For example, a broken headlight may be pieced together to form the original. Suggest that students explore databases that specify the characteristics of windshield glass produced by a particular manufacturer for different years. For example, due to safety regulations, the amount of tinting in windshields varies year to year, so windshield tint could help identify the year a particular windshield was produced.

Engage

Show students glass of varying thicknesses, colors, and reflective capabilities. Begin a class brainstorming session on how glass is produced and what is added or done to glass to produce the different types.

Teaching Tip

Contact Corning Glass for a video on the making of glass, or check the Internet for online videos on how glass is made.

Did you know

The earliest manufactured glass objects were beads found in Egypt that date back to 2500 B.C.

CHAPTER 1 2 3 4 5 6 7 8 9 10 11 12 13 14 **15** 16 17 18

INTRODUCTION

Glass evidence can be found at many crime scenes. Automobile collision sites may be littered with broken headlight or windshield glass. The site of a store break-in may contain shards of window glass with fibers or blood on them. A broken bottle used as an assault weapon may leave glass fragments with hair or blood on them. If shots are fired into a window, the sequence and direction of the bullets can often be determined by examining the glass fracture patterns. Minute particles of glass may be transferred to a suspect's shoes or clothing (recall Locard's Principle of Exchange) and can provide trace evidence linking a suspect to a crime scene.

Most glass today is mass-produced, so glass is typically considered class evidence, not individual evidence. Glass analysts determine the type, thickness, density, and other physical and chemical properties of glass. Sometimes it's possible to determine the manufacturer of the glass. Technology that analyzes trace elements in glass provides a better estimation of whether or not two glass pieces are consistent. The only method that can produce individualized glass evidence is called a fracture match. If glass pieces are large enough to handle, they are fitted together as in a jigsaw puzzle. If the unique stress fractures along the edges of both glass fragments align, then the fragments are from the same piece of glass.

WHAT IS GLASS? *Obj. 15.1, 15.2*

CHEMISTRY

Glass is a hard, **amorphous,** brittle material made by melting **silicon dioxide,** or **silica** (SiO_2), lime—also called calcium oxide (CaO), and sodium oxide (Na_2O) at very high temperatures. Sodium oxide reduces the melting point of silica. This type of glass is known as soda-lime glass because it contains sodium oxide and lime. Once it cools, the glass can be polished, ground or cut for useful or decorative purposes.

Humans have made glass for thousands of years, but glass also forms naturally. When certain types of sand are exposed to extremely high temperatures, such as lightning strikes or volcanic eruptions, *obsidian* glass can form.

Glass is considered an amorphous solid because its atoms are arranged in a random fashion (Figure 15-1). Because of its irregular atomic structure, when glass is broken, it produces a variety of fracture patterns.

Figure 15-1 *Random locations of atoms in an amorphous solid.*

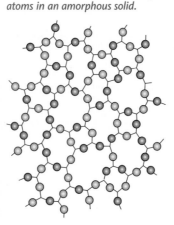

484 CHAPTER 15

TYPES OF GLASS *Obj. 15.2, 15.8*

Because glass is a stable material that does not deteriorate over time, it has a variety of uses. The most common type of glass, soda-lime glass, is inexpensive, easy to melt and shape, and

Teaching Tip

Obsidian is a naturally occurring glass formed as volcanic lava cools quickly. During the Stone Age, obsidian was shaped and used as arrowheads and blades for knives. Obsidian is being investigated as a material for human surgical scalpels. Obsidian scalpels are sharper and smoother than steel and can be made extremely thin to reduce trauma to the area being cut. At this point, obsidian scalpels have only been approved for surgical use on research animals.

DIFFERENTIATED LEARNING

Teaching At-Risk Students
Engage students by asking them to describe a two-car accident in which glass evidence is present. What kind of glass would be present as evidence? How would they determine which car the glass came from? How would they, step by step, collect and document it? (See Chapter 2.)

reasonably strong. Manufacturers of most glass containers use the same basic soda-lime composition, making recycling easier.

Fine glassware and decorative art glasses, called *crystal,* or **lead glass,** may substitute lead oxide (PbO) for calcium oxide. The addition of lead oxide makes the glass denser and less brittle. The lead oxide also makes the light waves bend more, making the glass more sparkly than ordinary glass.

Heat-resistant kitchen and laboratory glassware is often sold as Pyrex® or Kimax® glass. These types of glass contain compounds that improve the ability of the glass to withstand a wide range of temperatures without breaking, which is needed for the high heat in a kitchen or laboratory.

Adding certain metal oxides to the glass mixture produces different colors of glass. For example, nickel oxide produces colors ranging from yellow to purple, depending on the composition of the glass to which it is added. Cobalt oxide makes a purple-blue glass, whereas oxides of selenium make red glass.

Laminated Glass

Two or more panes of glass bonded by a plastic middle layer are called **laminated glass**. Laminated glass resists breakage and penetration. Thin layers of laminated glass are used in motor vehicle windshields. If a vehicle is in a collision and the windshield breaks, the broken glass tends to remain in the frame, as in Figure 15-2a, preventing broken glass from injuring the passengers. Fractured laminated glass tends to produce a pattern with fewer concentric fractures than other types of glass. Laminated glass is also found in entrance doors, glass floors, aquariums, and display cases.

Tempered Glass

Glass that has been subjected to extreme temperatures or chemical treatments to improve its strength is called **tempered glass,** or *safety glass.* Tempering puts the outer surface under compression while the inner layers are under tension. As a result, when the glass breaks, the glass crumbles into small, granular chunks, or pebbles, instead of forming long, jagged shards that can cause injury. Tempered glass is used in side and rear car windows, shower doors, glass tables, and some cookware (Figure 15-2b).

Figure 15-2a *Broken laminated glass of a car windshield stays in its frame, protecting the car's passengers.*

Figure 15-2b *Broken tempered glass of a car's side window shatters into very small granules, or "pebbles." (A dime is shown for scale.)*

GLASS EVIDENCE **485**

Teaching Tip

Bulletproof glass can be as thick as 100 millimeters and is usually made of several layers of tempered or toughened glass with a Perspex, or tough plastic panel, between each layer. Mention to students that bulletproof glass is not totally bulletproof; it is more "bullet-resistant."

Science

MATHEMATICS

MATHEMATICS

Density is a physical property. Density is calculated by determining the mass (*m*) per unit volume (*v*) of an object. Mass is typically measured in grams (g) when using the SI system. Volume is the amount of space an object takes up. The typical unit for volume is milliliters (mL). Volume can also be measured in cubic centimeters (cc), since 1 milliliter is equal to 1 cubic centimeter. Pure water has a density of 1.0 g/mL, and therefore, anything with a density less than 1.0 g/mL will float in water, and anything with a density greater than 1.0 g/mL will sink in water.

Explore

Explain to students that Archimedes' principle states that a body immersed in a fluid is subject to an upward force equal to the weight of the fluid it displaces. This principle explains why it is possible to measure the density of glass by measuring the volume of water it displaces.

Figure 15-2c *A bullet hole in bullet-resistant glass.*

AFP/Getty Images

Bullet-resistant Glass

Bullet-resistant ("bulletproof") glass is a laminated and tempered glass composed of two layers, one hard and one soft. The softer layer makes the glass more flexible, so it is less prone to shattering. Bullet-resistant glass varies in thickness from 3/4 of an inch to 3 inches. The thicker glass flattens the bullet, while the plastic absorbs some of the impact energy (Figure 15-2c).

PROPERTIES OF GLASS *Obj. 15.3*

Because glass is made of a variety of compounds, it is possible to compare and contrast one type of glass with another by examining the different physical and chemical properties. These properties of glass, such as thickness, density, refractive index, and fracture patterns, are used in forensic analysis. Keep in mind that these traits cannot be used to identify a specific glass fragment.

Thickness

The thickness of glass is related to its function. Thickness provides additional class evidence. Picture frame glass is ⅛ inch thick, while window glass must be 3⁄32 inch to ⅛ inch thick to resist wind gusts without breaking. Door glass varies from 3⁄16 inch to ¼ inch thick and may be reinforced with wires running through it.

Density *Obj. 15.4*

MATHEMATICS

Each type of glass has a **density** that is specific to that glass. One method of comparing glass evidence is by a density comparison.

Density (*D*) is calculated by dividing the mass (*m*) of a substance by its volume (*V*). The formula for calculating density can be written as $D = \frac{m}{V}$. Comparing the densities of two glass fragments is one way to determine if the fragments are consistent with each other. Some of the more common glass densities are shown in Figure 15-3.

1. The density of small glass fragments can be determined by using the concept of water displacement.
2. Determine the mass (g) of the glass fragments using a balance.
3. To determine the volume of the glass fragments, add 6 mL of water to a 10-mL graduated cylinder (or a plastic, graduated syringe).
4. Using forceps, add the fragment(s) of glass to the water (without splashing any water) and record the new level of the water.
5. Calculate the difference in the water levels. The difference is the amount of water displaced by the glass fragment

Figure 15-3 *Common glass densities.*

Type of Glass	Density (g/mL)
Bottle glass	2.50
Window glass	2.53
Lead glass (crystal)	2.98–3.01
Heat-resistant glass	2.27
Tempered glass (auto)	2.98

486   CHAPTER 15

(Figure 15-4). The volume of the glass fragment is equal to the amount of water displaced by the glass (mL).

6. Calculate the average density of the glass fragments by dividing their total mass by the volume of the water displaced by them.

Refractive Index

Figure 15-5 shows a straw in a glass of water. Why does the straw appear to be broken? This illusion occurs because light changes direction as it passes from one medium (plural *media*), such as air, into another medium, such as water. The change in direction is called **refraction.**

In Figures 15-6 and 15-7, you can see a perpendicular line at the interface of the two media. That line is called the **normal line.** In Figure 15-6, as the beam of light moves from the air into the glass, the light slows down and bends, or refracts, toward the normal line. In Figure 15-7, light speeds up as it moves from the oil into the air. The beam of light refracts, or bends, away from the normal line.

Figure 15-4 *The volume of a glass fragment can be determined by calculating the volume of water displaced by it.*

Graduated cylinder with 6 mL of water

Graduated cylinder showing 8 mL of volume (water and glass fragment in bottom of cylinder)

Figure 15-5 *The illusion of the broken straw occurs because light travels at different speeds through air and water, a phenomenon called* refraction.

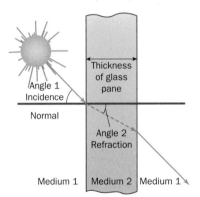

Figure 15-6 *Light travels through air (medium 1) and then passes through the glass of a windowpane (medium 2). The light slows down as it moves through the more-refractive glass and bends toward the normal (red line).*

Thickness of glass pane

Angle 1 Incidence

Normal

Angle 2 Refraction

Medium 1 | Medium 2 | Medium 1

GLASS EVIDENCE   **487**

Evaluate
Ask students to identify one or more drawbacks of the submersion method. *(Fragment must be large enough to make measurable volume change in water; might be hard to drop glass into water without splashing water out)*

Teaching Tip
If you wish to determine density using smaller pieces of glass, here is a method: Obtain some free calibrated baby medicine droppers (oral syringes) from your pharmacy or purchase graduated 10-mL pipettes. Remove the plungers and seal the spout with glue or by heating and melting the tip shut. The procedure for calculating density remains the same, but your dropper, syringe, or pipette is now a miniature graduated cylinder you can use for more accurate measurement.

Engage
A fun way to introduce refractive index is to perform the disappearing beaker trick (or show the YouTube video). Use beakers that have no writing on them. Before class, fill a 500-mL beaker that has a 50-mL beaker in it 3/4-full with cooking oil. Add broken pieces of 50-mL beaker. In class, say some "magic" words and remove the intact 50-mL beaker. Ask students how this was possible. *(The oil and heat-resistant beakers have the same refractive indexes, so the 50 mL beaker was hidden.)*

Teaching Tip

Based on the refractive index alone, experts would not be able to prove a piece of glass matches glass found on a suspect's shoes. Experts would say the glass was consistent with what was found on the suspect's shoes. If the edges of two pieces of glass match and fit together, the evidence is even more compelling.

Explore

To demonstrate the submersion method, use two heat-resistant beakers, one 250-mL and one 500-mL, and place the smaller into the larger. Confirm that students can still see the smaller beaker. Add vegetable oil, which has approximately the same refractive index as heat-resistant glass, to the smaller beaker. Again confirm that students can still see both beakers. Then, fill the larger beaker with the same oil until the smaller is fully submerged. When submerged, the smaller beaker completely disappears.

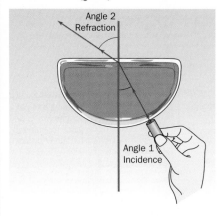

Figure 15-7 *Light travels through oil (medium 1) and then passes through air (medium 2). The light beam bends away from the normal line (green).*

Figure 15-8 *Refractive indexes of liquids and types of glass.*

Liquid	Refractive Index
Methanol	1.33
Water	1.33
Isopropyl alcohol	1.37
Olive oil	1.47
Glycerin	1.47
Castor oil	1.48
Clove oil	1.54
Cinnamon oil	1.62

Type of Glass	Refractive Index
Heat-resistant glass	1.47
Automotive headlight glass	1.47–1.49
Television glass	1.49–1.51
Window glass	1.49–1.51
Bottle glass	1.51–1.52
Eyeglass lenses	1.52–1.53
Quartz glass	1.54–1.55
Lead glass (crystal)	1.56–1.61

REFRACTION

Any substance through which light can pass has its own characteristic refractive index (Figure 15-8). The **refractive index** is determined by dividing the speed of light in a vacuum by the speed of light through that particular substance. Light travels fastest in a vacuum, so a vacuum has a refractive index of 1. Light travels more slowly through other substances, so they have higher indexes of refraction. Pure water has a refractive index of 1.33, and most window glass has a refractive index of 1.49. Light travels nearly as fast through air as it does through a vacuum, so we will use 1 as the refractive index of air.

FORENSIC USE OF REFRACTIVE INDEX *Obj. 15.5*

Glass evidence from a suspect is often too small to easily compare with glass evidence from a crime scene. To determine the refractive index of the small glass fragments recovered from the suspect, the submersion method may be used (Figure 15-9). This method involves placing the glass fragment into a series of different liquids of known refractive indexes. If the glass and a liquid have the same refractive index, the glass fragment will seem to disappear when placed in the liquid.

In the opening scenario, a crystal vase was broken. The suspect was found to have broken glass in the tread of her boot. The suspect claimed that the glass was from a broken heat-resistant beaker recently dropped in the science lab. Refer to Figure 15-8 that lists the refractive indexes of liquids and different types of glass. Note that the refractive index for heat-resistant glass is 1.47, and the refractive index for crystal is 1.56–1.61. If the refractive index of the evidence glass in the boot tread is inconsistent with the glass found at the crime

Figure 15-9 *In this example of the submersion method, the glass must have a refraction index closest to 1.54, that of the liquid in test tube 5.*

1	2	3	4	5
1.33	1.37	1.47	1.48	1.54

Index of refraction increases ⟶

scene, the suspect may be excluded. However, if the glass in the boot and the glass from the crime scene are consistent, will this prove she broke the vase? Consistent refractive indexes cannot prove that the crystal in her boot tread was from the crystal vase broken at the crime scene. You must consider where and when she picked up the glass evidence in her boot. Refractive index comparisons result in circumstantial class evidence and can't confirm guilt.

BECKE LINES *Obj. 15.5*
You have learned that a piece of glass will seem to disappear when submerged in a transparent liquid that has the same refractive index. If the glass fragment is very small, then submerge it in a series of liquids of varying refractive indexes and view it under a compound microscope using 100× magnification. If the refractive index (*n*) of the liquid medium is different from the refractive index of the piece of glass, a halo-like ring appears around the edge of the glass. This halo-like effect is called a **Becke line.** It appears because the refracted light becomes concentrated around the edges of the glass fragment. The Becke line appears in the medium that has the higher refractive index.

If the Becke line is located inside the perimeter of the glass fragment, then the refractive index of the glass is higher than the refractive index of the surrounding liquid. If the Becke line is located outside the perimeter of the glass fragment, then the refractive index of the surrounding medium is higher than the refractive index of the glass. If the refractive index of the liquid and the glass are the same, then no Becke line appears. Refer to Figure 15-10. Submersion tests and Becke lines are inexpensive methods used to estimate the refractive index of glass. Forensic analysts often use equipment such as the GRIM 2 (Glass Refractive Index Measurement), which measures the refractive index of glass. However, these instruments are too expensive for most high school laboratories to own.

Figure 15-10 *Estimating the refractive index of a glass sample using a compound microscope and Becke lines.*

Refractive index same	**Glass has higher refractive index**	**Liquid has higher refractive index**
No Becke line. Glass and liquid have the same refractive index. Glass seems to disappear.	Becke line appears inside the perimeter of the glass.	Becke line appears in the liquid.

Fracture Patterns *Obj. 15.6*

Glass has some flexibility. When glass is hit, it can stretch slightly. However, when the glass is forced to stretch too far, fracture lines appear and the glass will break. Recall that glass is an amorphous solid. Its atoms are arranged randomly. Therefore, glass breaks into irregular fragments, not into regular pieces.

GLASS EVIDENCE   **489**

Teaching Tip
Tell students that *Becke* is pronounced like the name Becky.

Teaching Tip
Point out to students that when equipment is too expensive (or used too infrequently to justify the cost) for a small forensic lab, the lab can often have the evidence processed by a larger regional or state lab, for a fee.

Teaching Tip
If your classroom is equipped to project images from a microscope, show students Becke lines by projecting images of heat-resistant glass in water and then in cooking oil. Ask students to identify the halo and to determine which substance has the higher refractive index in each case.

DIFFERENTIATED LEARNING

Teaching English-Language Learners
Students may not know what a halo is, and therefore will not be able to envision the halo effect of the Becke lines. Use pictures or illustrations to describe halos to the class before students read this section.

Teaching Tip

Relate radial fractures to the radius of a circle, a line from the center extending outward.

Explore

Allow students to watch one of the several videos online at YouTube that show a bullet going through glass at ultra-slow speed. Point out that if they look carefully, for a split second they should be able to see the glass stretching.

Teaching Tip

Because glass fractures, early humans were able to chip obsidian into shapes that fit their needs, such as knives and arrow points. Show students a close-up image of an obsidian spear point and show them the conchoidal fracture patterns (fracture patterns that occur when materials break without following any natural planes of separation).

Evaluate

Ask students how fracture patterns might be different if the glass were struck on the edge.

Figure 15-11 *Note that the radial fracture lines originate in the center and extend outward. The concentric fractures are circles around the point of impact.*

Mike Theiler/Getty Images

RADIAL AND CONCENTRIC FRACTURES

When an object such as a bullet or rock hits glass, the glass stretches. On the side where the impact takes place, the glass surface is compressed, or squeezed together. The opposite side of the glass (the side away from the impact) stretches and is under tension. Glass is weaker under tension than under compression. It will break first on the weaker side, the side opposite the strike, producing **radial fractures**. The radial fracture lines, also called primary fractures, start at the point of impact and move outward (Figure 15-11).

After the primary radial fractures form, the secondary, or **concentric fractures,** form. These are in the shape of concentric circles, circles that share the same center. They are formed on the same side as the impact on the glass. Knowing how and where glass fractures form, it is possible to determine where the force came from that broke the glass. Figures 15-12 and 15-13 compare radial and concentric glass fractures.

Figure 15-12 *When glass is hit, radial fractures form on the tension side, and then concentric fractures form on the side of impact.*

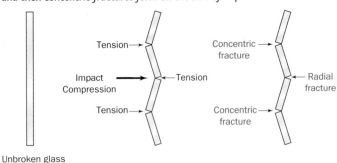

Figure 15-13 *Comparison of radial and concentric fractures in glass.*

	Radial Fracture	Concentric Fracture
When formed?	First (primary)	Second (secondary)
On which side of the glass?	Opposite the side of impact	Same side as impact
Description	Lines originating from point of impact and extending to edge of glass (like spokes in a bicycle wheel)	Series of partial circles, one inside the other, sharing the same center

DIFFERENTIATED LEARNING

Teaching Gifted Students

Allow responsible students to perform the following activity in class (or perform it as a demonstration yourself). Using an inexpensive picture frame, cover the glass in the frame entirely with clear adhesive tape. (Don't remove the glass from the frame.) As you slowly apply each layer of tape, use the edge of a plastic card or small ruler to press the tape to remove any air bubbles. Put on safety goggles and gloves. Then use a nail and hammer to strike a hole in the upper left of the glass, through the tape. Put a second hole near the lower-right edge. Identify radial and concentric fractures. From the fracture evidence, describe how it is possible to determine the sequence of the fractures.

The speed of an object when it hits a piece of glass influences the number and location of concentric circles in the fracture pattern. An object moving at high speed upon impact, such as a bullet, produces tighter concentric circles. An object moving at a slower speed upon impact, such as a rock thrown at a window, produces widely spaced concentric circles.

BULLET FRACTURES *Obj. 15.7*

Bullet holes in glass can be distinguished from other impacts by the greater number of concentric fractures that result from high-velocity impact. The direction of a single bullet fired through glass can be easily determined. As the bullet passes through the glass, it pushes some glass ahead of it, causing a cone-shaped piece of glass to exit along with the bullet. This removal of glass makes the exit hole larger than the entrance hole of the bullet.

When several bullets are fired through the glass, the order in which the bullets were fired can be determined if enough of the glass remains or if the glass can be reconstructed. The first bullet produces the first set of fracture lines. Any fracture lines produced by later bullets will be stopped by fracture lines from earlier impacts. Notice in Figure 15-14 that the fracture pattern on the lower left was produced before the other fracture pattern on the right. The first shot made fracture lines that blocked the fracture lines made by the other two bullets.

Figure 15-14 *Three bullet holes and the fracture patterns they produced in glass.*

© Cengage Learning®

EVIDENCE FROM BULLET FRACTURES

The distance from the shooter to the window can be estimated based on the type of ammunition and its effect on the window. Bullets fired at close range have greater velocity than those fired from a distance. Concentric fractures resulting from higher velocity are smaller, and radial fractures resulting from higher velocity are shorter. However, a higher-velocity bullet fired from a great distance will often exhibit velocity characteristics of a lower-velocity bullet fired from closer range.

When a window breaks, most of the fragments are propelled away from the impact. However, some of the fragments, known as **backscatter,** fall back toward the direction of impact because as glass shatters, fragments collide and tumble in various directions. Backscatter is trace evidence that may link a suspect to the crime scene.

The angle at which a bullet enters window glass can help determine the position of the shooter. If the bullet was fired perpendicular to the windowpane, the entry hole of the bullet will be round and glass fragments evenly distributed. If the bullet enters from the right, there will be short, radial fractures on the right and longer fractures on the left. If the bullet enters from the left, there will be short, radial fractures on the left and longer fractures on the right. The longer radial fractures run in the direction of travel.

GLASS EVIDENCE   **491**

GLASS EVIDENCE   **491**

Explore

Show students the *MythBusters* episode from the Discovery Channel titled "What Is Bulletproof?" This is episode 16, which premiered on September 29, 2004, and is available online at http://www .shopping.discovery.com. It answers the question: "Will a bulletproof shield really stop a direct hit from a bullet?" Afterward, discuss the findings as a class.

Explore

Ask students to think of the places you would find bulletproof glass. Create a class list (e.g., windows of banks, jewelry stores, and similar businesses; the limousine used by the president, pope, and other leaders).

Teaching Tip

Contact your local fire department and ask if they have any glass that has been in a fire that they could donate to you for students to view.

Explore

Fire-resistant glass has a special glaze applied to achieve specific levels of protection from a fire. Fire-resistant glass receives a rating that depends on the amount of time it can withstand a certain heat and temperature, as well as if the glass allows the heat to transfer from one side of the glass to another. Many products, such as ovens and woodburning stoves, require fire-resistant glass.

Did you know

Glass fragments may adhere to clothing or tools used in a break-in.

Figure 15-15 *The glass pattern left by a projectile can help determine the position of the shooter. Note the entrance hole (tan) is smaller than the exit hole (dotted), and in this diagram, all the glass fragments appear on the* exit *side.*

Projectile strikes perpendicular to glass.

Projectile strikes from the left.

Projectile strikes from the right.

If the shooter fires at an angle from the left, glass pieces will be forced out of the hole toward the right. Glass fragments may be found to the right of the exit hole. The bullet's exit hole will form an irregular oval angled toward the right. If the shot originated at an angle from the right, glass pieces will be forced out of the hole to the left, with glass fragments found to the left of the bullet hole. An irregular oval hole angled toward the left may be noted (Figure 15-15).

HEAT FRACTURES

During a fire, glass may break as a result of heat fracturing. Heat fracturing produces breakage patterns on glass that are different from breakage patterns caused by an impact. Wavy fracture lines develop in glass that has been exposed to high heat. Also, glass will tend to crack on the surface exposed to the higher temperature. If the wavy glass was not broken before the fire, and there are no radial or concentric fracture patterns in the glass, then it's likely that the glass was broken by a fire. Heat-fractured glass evidence is important in arson investigation.

DIGGING DEEPER

With Forensic Science eCollection

Not all bulletproof glass will stop bullets. Go to the Gale Forensic Science eCollection at **ngl.cengage .com/forensicscience2e** and research safety glass. Prepare a short presentation on what you find. Include these topics in your presentation: What is the rating system for the level of protection given by each material? What other materials besides glass are used to protect people and property?

SCRATCHES

Patterns or scratches may also be found on glass evidence. For example, windshield wipers may leave unique scratches on a windshield (Figure 15-16a).

Any dirt or hard particles embedded in the rubber insulation of a car window may leave scratch marks when the window is opened and closed (Figure 15-16b). Two pieces of glass thought to have come from the same larger piece of glass can checked under a microscope to see if any of the surface scratches can be aligned. This is not a definitive test to confirm the two pieces were once joined, but it does provide circumstantial evidence.

Figure 15-16a *Wiper marks on a windshield.*

Figure 15-16b *Scratch marks on a car window.*

COLLECTION AND DOCUMENTING GLASS EVIDENCE *Obj. 15.9*

When collecting glass evidence, it is important to follow the correct evidence-collection procedures to avoid the loss or contamination of any evidence. (Refer to Chapter 2.) Here are some general rules to follow when collecting glass evidence:

- Identify, photograph, and label glass samples before moving them.
- Collect the largest fragments that can be reasonably collected. Wear gloves to protect hands and wrap glass securely.
- Identify the outside and inside surfaces of broken pieces of any glass objects.
- If multiple window panes are involved, indicate their relative position in a diagram.
- Note any other trace evidence found on or embedded in the glass, such as skin, hair, blood, or fibers.
- Properly package all materials collected to maintain the proper chain of custody.

Glass collected by crime-scene investigators should be initially separated by physical properties, such as size, color, and texture. Samples should be carefully catalogued and kept separate to avoid contamination.

Once in the lab, other trace evidence (e.g., hair, fibers, blood) can be separated from glass fragments. Any clothing related to the crime scene should be examined for glass fragments and other trace evidence. Any

Did you know

Some people erroneously say that glass is a liquid because it "flows" over time. They note that glass in very old windows is thicker at the bottom of the pane than at the top, claiming that the glass has flowed to the bottom. Actually, the panes were installed with the thicker part at the bottom, for stability.

Teaching Tip

Tell students that glass evidence is always packaged in a paper container, never plastic. If the glass evidence is small, it should be collected in an envelope or paper bindle. Make sure to stipulate it cannot be a regular mailing envelope, because they often have gaps in the corners. If the glass evidence is large, it should be collected in a cardboard box, sealed, and labeled.

Teaching Tip

The 4R rule for determining direction of force: "**R**idge fractures are on **R**adial lines are at **R**ight angles to the **R**ear." First, locate radial fractures within the first concentric circle. Then, view the edge of the glass, and locate the fractures. The shell-shaped fractures on the edge of the glass are known as conchoidal fractures. Find the side of the glass where the radial lines form right angles to the glass. That side of the glass is the side *away* from the compression or force.

Teaching Tip

Explain to students that the collection of the filaments from headlights or taillights of vehicles is important. The filaments can be analyzed to determine if these lights were on or off at the time of the accident or crime. (The filaments of lights that were on are reduced to white ash, while filaments of lights not turned on during an accident are intact, or broken with no ash.)

Explore

Point out to students there are specialty products that help preserve broken glass at a crime scene. One such product is spray foam. This product is portable and can be sprayed on any piece of glass evidence. The foam is sticky and hardens quickly, allowing investigators to "freeze" the evidence in the state in which it was found.

Teaching Tip

Invite a law-enforcement officer to your class to discuss how glass evidence is collected, documented, and analyzed. Consider inviting a lawyer to class to discuss the typical admissibility of glass evidence in court.

objects that might have been used to break the glass should also be collected and examined for glass fragments.

Cleaning and Preparing Glass Fragments

After glass fragments have been documented, photographed, and examined, and any trace evidence has been removed, they should be cleaned. Any surface debris (e.g., grease or soil particles) that might serve as additional evidence should be noted and collected before cleaning. Cleaning solvents or ultrasound cleaners may be used to clean the glass.

During analysis, avoid destroying any glass samples collected as evidence, if possible. Since glass fragments may be needed for further analysis, nondestructive methods, such as examination under a compound microscope, should be considered first. However, sometimes techniques must be used that destroy evidence during analysis. If this is the case, it is important to avoid using all of the evidence. Additional material may be needed for duplicate lab tests.

Forensic Glass Analysis Technology

The latest techniques in the forensic analysis of glass involve sophisticated technology. A great advantage of these techniques is that they are largely nondestructive.

Scanning electron microscopy (SEM) examines the filaments in motor vehicle headlights. If a headlight was on at the time of a collision, the heat of the filament causes the glass to fuse with the filament. This information is used to help determine the cause of a collision.

X-ray fluorescence (XRF) is the emission of characteristic "secondary" (or fluorescent) X-rays from glass that has been irradiated. It is used to analyze the elements in a glass sample.

Inductively coupled plasma-mass spectrometry (ICP-MS) analyzes the composition of glass and can distinguish between glass fragments that cannot be distinguished by refractive index or density.

The analysis of glass evidence involves physics, chemistry, and mathematics in technologies such as SEM, ICP-MS, and XRF. Go to the Gale Forensic Science eCollection at **ngl.cengage.com/ forensicscience2e** to learn more about technologies used in analyzing trace evidence such as glass.

LITERACY

Hard Evidence, by David Fisher, describes cases handled by investigators at the FBI.

SUMMARY

- Glass is an amorphous solid usually made from silica, calcium oxide, and sodium oxide. Because most glass is mass-produced, it is difficult to prove that two different glass pieces came from the same source. Glass is almost always class evidence.

- Laminated glass is used in windshields. Tempered glass is used in side and back windows. These types of glass protect passengers from the dangers of flying shards. Bulletproof glass is laminated and tempered.

- Characteristics that provide class evidence of glass include the type of glass, its density, its thickness, and its refractive index.

- The density of an object is calculated by dividing its mass (usually in grams) by its volume (usually in milliliters).

- The refractive index of a material is a measure of how much light bends, or refracts, as it travels through that material.

- Light will bend, or refract, when it moves between media with different refractive indexes.

- The submersion method can be used to estimate the refractive index of a glass sample.

- The position of a Becke line is another method used to estimate the refractive index of a piece of glass.

- When glass is hit, it first stretches, and then breaks, forming radial fracture and concentric fracture patterns. Radial fracture patterns occur on the side of the glass opposite the point of impact. Concentric fracture patterns occur on the same side as the point of impact.

- Fire fractures in glass appear wavy and tend to appear on the surface exposed to higher temperatures.

- When a bullet is shot through glass, the exit hole is larger than the entry hole.

- The angle of entrance of a bullet into glass can be estimated from the pattern of glass fragments left near the bullet's exit hole.

- Forensic glass-analysis methods include fracture matching, scanning electron microscopy of headlight filaments after collisions, and the use of X-ray fluorescence (XRF) and inductively coupled plasma-mass spectrometry (ICP-MS), which help determine properties of glass evidence samples.

Close

Write the key vocabulary terms on the board: *density, refraction, concentric fracture, radiating fracture.* Organize the class into groups and assign each group one of the terms. Have each group explain its term and how it relates to the forensic analysis of glass.

Explore

Have students investigate the guidelines and standards for reliability of glass evidence from the OSAC (Organization of Scientific Area Committees) for Materials (Trace).

CASE STUDY

Susan Nutt
(1987)

At 9:30 P.M. on a cloudy, dark night in February, 19-year-old Craig Elliott Kalani went for a walk in his neighborhood in northwest Oregon but never returned home. A hit-and-run driver killed him. Crime-scene investigators collected pieces of glass embedded in Craig's jacket and other glass fragments found on the ground near his body.

Police searched for a vehicle that had damage consistent with a hit-and-run accident. They found a car with that type of damage. It belonged to a woman named Susan Nutt. In order to connect Ms. Nutt and her car with the crime, the police had to show that the glass from the crime scene was consistent with the glass from her car. Researchers at Oregon State University's

Radiation Center compared the glass from both sources. The scientists found that windshield glass from the crime scene contained the same 22 chemical elements as those used to make the glass in Ms. Nutt's car. The scientists considered the samples of glass consistent with each other.

© Cengage Learning®

The glass evidence helped convict Susan Nutt of failure to perform the duties of a driver for an injured person. She was sentenced to up to five years in prison and five years' probation.

Wrong Place, Right Time (2006)

Early one morning, police responded to an emergency call at a grocery store. A store employee reported that he heard glass breaking and found a person entering through a window. The employee shouted at the perpetrator, who exited and drove away with another person in a van. At the same time, a break-in took place at a business in a neighboring city. The glass front door was broken, and the responding officer collected glass fragments from the scene. As the officer was getting ready to leave the crime scene, he noticed a van driving with its lights off. He chased the van, which crashed, and he arrested the suspects. Their clothing was sent to the local crime laboratory.

The examiner at the crime lab collected numerous glass fragments from the shoes and pants of one of the suspects and measured the refractive index. Surprisingly, it did not match the refractive index of the glass door fragments collected by the police officer. The police officer was puzzled because he had caught the suspects in the area of the break-in. Several scientific studies have concluded that most people do not walk around with glass fragments on their clothing.

The examiner then recalled hearing about the other break-in, through the grocery store window. He obtained glass from that crime scene and compared the refractive index of the glass collected from the suspect's clothing to the glass from the store window and determined those samples to be consistent. It was poor planning on the part of the perpetrators to leave one crime scene only to drive by another! However, it did allow the examiner to obtain the suspects' clothing promptly. Glass fragments usually do not stay on clothing very long. Glass was the only evidence collected, but it was all the crime-lab examiner needed to connect the suspects to the break-in at the grocery store.

Think Critically

Describe a scenario in which glass evidence would be important in solving a crime.

Careers *in Forensics*

Criminalist

David Green is a criminalist—an expert on trace evidence, including paint, hair, fibers, glass, shoe prints, tire tracks, explosives, and fire debris. He works every day with stereomicroscopes, comparison microscopes, X-ray fluorescence spectrometers, mass spectrometers, and infrared spectrometers. He occasionally carries out drug analysis, as well. Green considers himself lucky to have such an interesting job. "Ninety-nine percent of crime labs in the country don't do crime scenes. We come in and work with police. We complement good police work. We're working together to try and make a case."

David A. Green

Making a case means combining technical training with common sense. Green recalls a case of a woman who had been assaulted. He found camel hair on her clothing, but he was "confident that a camel had not been the perpetrator." He told investigators they should look for someone with camel-hair clothing, and when a suspect arrived for an interview, he was wearing a camel-hair coat. "Case closed," Green says.

A criminalist's involvement in a case does not end with laboratory work. David Green estimates that he has testified at more than 100 trials. He is happy to speak about his work outside court as well, and frequently addresses schools, police academies, and other groups. "You can really choose to make a difference for your community," he has said. Green's father was a court bailiff, and David has been interested in law enforcement all his life. In 1987, he received his Bachelor's Degree in forensic chemistry from Ohio University. He took an internship at the Painesville laboratory, and two years later

he joined the staff. He's worked there ever since. One of his own daughters might follow in his footsteps as a criminalist. While his job doesn't involve making arrests, it has its own stress. A call to a crime scene can come at any time, and he has "had to miss people's weddings." Green has learned to live with stress, though. As a colleague describes him, "He's got a great sense of life—an upbeat attitude. He's always positive."

Professional concerns also keep David Green busy outside the lab. He has inspected city, state, and federal laboratories, and even some in Canada as part of the accreditation process. As part of the Scientific Working Group for Materials (SWGMAT), an association of scientists from the United States, Canada, Australia, and Europe, Green helped establish guidelines for examining trace evidence. He served as president of the Midwestern Association of Forensic Scientists. The group has 1,000 members and supports continuing education in forensics by conducting workshops. Green has presented more than 50 professional seminars and workshops. He is a member of ten professional organizations, a Fellow of the American Board of Chemists, and is certified by the Accreditation Board of the American Society of Crime Laboratory Directors.

It really does seem, as the director of David Green's lab says, that he "pretty much does about everything you can think of regarding trace evidence!"

Learn More About It
▷ To learn more about a career as a criminalist, go to **ngl.cengage.com/forensicscience2e**.

Careers

Ask students what they think about the career of criminalist for themselves. The varied responsibilities may appeal to some. Criminalists are typically, like David Green, "jack-of-all-trades" forensics science technicians. (He does more field work than many criminalists.) Getting the job usually requires a bachelor's degree in forensic science or criminal justice (with a natural science concentration), along with a great deal of field training and/or apprenticeship.

Chapter 15 Review

True or False

1. T
2. T
3. F
4. F
5. T
6. T
7. F

Multiple Choice

8. a
9. c
10. c
11. a
12. b

CHAPTER 15 REVIEW

True or False

1. Glass fractures in a variety of patterns due to its amorphous atomic structure. *Obj. 15.6*

2. The components of most glass are silica, lime, and sodium oxide. *Obj. 15.1*

3. To determine if fractures in glass occurred due to heat fractures or due to the glass being struck by an object, one examines the pattern of radial and concentric fractures. *Obj. 15.6*

4. High-velocity projectiles such as bullets tend to produce longer radial fractures than a low-velocity strike, such as from a hammer. *Obj. 15.6*

5. Metal oxides added to glass produce glass of different colors. *Obj. 15.2*

6. When glass is hit, it bends and stretches before breaking. *Obj. 15.3, 15.6*

7. Two pieces of glass are considered to be from the same original piece of glass if they have the same density, thickness, and refractive index. *Obj. 15.3, 15.10*

Multiple Choice

8. The refractive index of glass refers to its ability to *Obj. 15.5*
   a) bend light
   b) reflect light
   c) absorb light
   d) convert light to heat

9. Most glass evidence is considered to be *Obj. 15.9*
   a) circumstantial evidence
   b) class evidence
   c) both (a) and (b)
   d) individual evidence

10. Refer to the tables in Figure 15-8 that list the refractive indexes of some liquids and types of glass. Suppose you performed a submersion test to determine if a glass fragment had a refractive index consistent with that of a broken automobile headlight. In which liquid would the glass fragment seem to disappear? *Obj. 15.5*
    a) clove oil
    b) methanol
    c) olive oil
    d) cinnamon oil

11. Becke lines used in glass analysis are used to detect *Obj. 15.5*
    a) the substance of greater refractive index
    b) the direction of impact
    c) the relative velocity of a projectile
    d) the angle of impact of a projectile

12. A normal line is a line that is *Obj. 15.5*
    a) parallel to the surface where two media meet
    b) perpendicular to the surface where two media meet
    c) the line of incidence
    d) the line of refraction

498   CHAPTER 15

Short Response

13. Compare and contrast
    a) angle of incidence and angle of refraction *Obj. 15.5*
    b) laminated glass and tempered glass (Include the structure and uses of each type of glass.) *Obj. 15.8*
    c) radial fractures and concentric fractures *Obj. 15.6*

14. At a crime scene, a glass analyst viewed two holes in the large living room window. Based on glass fracture patterns, the analyst stated that two bullets traveled from outside the window into the house. The projectiles were most likely high-velocity bullets rather than rocks. The first bullet was fired directly in front of the window. The second bullet was fired from the right side of the house. *Obj. 15.6, 15.7*
    a) Describe glass evidence from the crime scene that could support the statement of the glass analyst. Include in your answer evidence that supports her claims regarding direction of the projectiles; the order in which they were fired; the likelihood that projectiles were bullets rather than rocks.
    b) Tell whether you agree or disagree with the following statement: "There must have been two people shooting because two bullets entered the house from different angles." Explain your answer.

15. Refer to the scenario at the beginning of this chapter concerning the broken vase. The suspect claimed that the broken glass pieces found in her boot came from a heat-resistant beaker that broke during her chemistry class that morning. Knowing that you are a student of forensics, the suspect asked you to help her show that the glass in her boot was heat-resistant glass and not crystal (lead glass). Describe two different forms of testing noted in this chapter you could perform that would demonstrate that the glass in her boot was not consistent with crystal. *Obj. 15.4, 15.5, 15.10*

Short Answer

13. a. Angle of incidence is the angle formed with the normal line as light passes through Medium 1. Angle of refraction is the angle formed with the normal line as light passes through Medium 2.

    b. Laminated glass is a layer of plastic between two glass layers. It is found in car front windshields. It is designed this way to keep any glass fragments in the frame if the glass breaks and reduce the chance of injury from large shards of glass. Tempered glass is treated with extreme temperature or chemicals. It is found in car rear wind-shields and side windows or shower doors. The treatment of the glass makes the glass break into many small cubes to reduce injuries.

    c. Radial fractures form first on the side opposite the compression (tension side); fracture lines originate from the central area where glass was struck. Concentric fractures form second, on the compression side or side of impact. They appear as concentric circles.

14. a. • The exit hole is larger than the entry hole, revealing direction.
    • Concentric fractures were found on the outside of the glass, the place of impact.
    • High-velocity impact shows more concentric fractures around the impact site, whereas a low-velocity impact of a rock would show more radial fractures.
    • Sequence of the bullets is detected by examining which radial fractures were stopped by the

(continues at left)

14. a. *(continued)*
    other radial fractures and which radial fractures were not stopped.
    • A round entry hole indicated a bullet was fired perpendicular to the window.
    • A bullet fired from the right side of the house would produce an elongated exit hole angled to the left with more glass fragments found on the left side.

    b. There is insufficient evidence to claim that there were two different shooters. Based on this limited evidence, it could be two

different shooters or the same person firing a shot in front of the window and then firing a second shot from the right side of the window.

15. Perform a density test: Lead crystal glass has a density of 2.98–3.01 g/mL, and heat-resistant glass has a density of 2.27 g/mL; perform a submersion refractive index test. Lead crystal glass has a refractive index of 1.56–1.61, and heat-resistant glass has a refractive index of 1.47.

Bibliography

Books and Journals

Fisher, David. *Hard Evidence*. New York: Dell, 1995.

Giancoli, Douglas C. *Physics, Principles and Applications, 5th Edition*. Englewood Cliffs, NJ: Prentice Hall, 1998.

Stratton, David R. "Reading the Clues in Fractured Glass." *Security Management* 38(1): 56, January 2004.

Internet Resources

ngl.cengage.com/forensicscience2e (Gale Forensic Science eCollection)

https://www.ncjrs.gov/pdffiles1/nij/grants/241445.pdf

http://chicagowindowexpert.com/windowtags/glass-impact/

http://hypertextbook.com/facts/2004/ShayeStorm.shtml

http://scienceworld.wolfram.com/physics/SnellsLaw.html

http://www.newton.dep.anl.gov/askasci/chem00/chem00135.htm

http://www.matter.org.uk/schools/SchoolsGlossary/refractive_index.html

http://www.fbi.gov/about-us/lab/forensic-science-communications/fsc/april2009/review/2009_04_review01.htm/

© Cengage Learning®

Glass Fracture Pattern Analysis *Obj. 15.6, 15.7, 15.8*

Objectives:

By the end of this activity, you will be able to:

1. Summarize how to determine the sequence of impacts on glass based on the fracture patterns.
2. Compare and contrast fracture patterns in tempered glass (safety glass), and window glass.
3. Analyze glass fracture patterns and determine the sequence of impacts on the glass.

Time Required to Complete Activity: 45 minutes

Materials (per group of two students):

Act 15-1 SH
pencil
ruler
demonstration table
piece of broken window glass
piece of broken tempered glass (safety glass)

SAFETY PRECAUTIONS:

This activity involves paper exercises only. If your teacher chooses to include hands-on work with fractured glass, wear gloves and goggles while handling glass. Spread newspaper or kraft paper in your work area. Dispose of all materials as directed by your teacher.

Background:

Forensic examiners need to look at evidence left at a crime scene and determine what happened. If witnesses or suspects are at the crime scene, they should describe their version of the incident. Evidence can either corroborate their stories or present a new version of an incident. In this activity, you will examine glass fracture patterns to determine the sequence of events that led to the breaking of the glass. The fracture patterns may also indicate where force was applied to break the glass, and, if there were multiple impacts, help determine which impact occurred first.

Procedure:

1. Examine the diagrams at the right, which show a side view of a window before and after impact. Determine the point of impact and direction of force.

Side view of window before impact.

Side view of window after impact.

Teaching Tip

You might also prepare a demo display showing different types of glass:

- heat-resistant glass such as Pyrex
- lead glass (crystal)
- automotive headlight glass
- bottle glass
- eyeglass lenses (Make sure they are glass; most are not.)
- television or computer monitor glass (cathode-ray tube screen)
- windshield glass

ACTIVITY 15-1

Background

In this activity, students examine glass fracture patterns to determine the sequence of breaks in the glass.

Time Required to Complete Activity

45 minutes

Safety Precautions

1. The text activity involves paper exercises only. If you include hands-on work with glass pieces, students must wear gloves and goggles while handling glass, and you should carefully follow safety precautions 2 through 5 while preparing the glass.
2. Spread newspaper or kraft paper in your work area.
3. Window glass to be broken should be taped with overlapping strips of clean, clear shipping tape to contain all fragments.
4. Glass should be broken using a hammer and nail to represent each strike point.
5. All loose, broken glass should be wrapped in paper, which should then be taped for disposal.

Procedures

Print, copy, and distribute Act 15-1 SH from the IRCD, Chapter 15. Make sure students read all directions *before* beginning the activity.

Teaching Tips

1. If you use actual glass, you may want to contact a windshield-replacement shop and ask them for some windshield glass.
2. Glass can also be obtained from auto salvage yards, secondhand stores, garage sales, and construction sites, or you may purchase inexpensive picture frames from a dollar store. If possible, document (manufacturer and type of glass) these samples to create a teaching collection.

Answers

Collect all activity pages, and grade students on accuracy and completeness.

1. Check students' diagrams.

2. Radial fractures are always on the stress side, opposite impact (exit side), and concentric rings are on the side of impact (entry side); the exit side of the glass will have a larger opening due to the bullet forcing broken glass out as it moves through the glass.

3. a. Safety glass has no radial or concentric fractures; the pieces are small and square. Window glass breaks in a combination of large and small, sharp pieces and has both radial and concentric fractures.

   b. Tempered glass is safer for car windows because it will shatter into small pieces that are less likely to cut car passengers, whereas window glass might produce large shards of glass that could cause serious injury.

4. a. A occurred first. Radial fracture lines from B are stopped when they reach fracture lines from A.

   b. Look for glass fragments on the ground. More fragments would be found on the exit side of the projectile. Concentric fractures will form on the entry side of the glass, and radiating fractures will form on the exit side.

   c. By examining the shape of the bullet hole, direction could be estimated:

      i. If the shot is fired perpendicular to the window surface, the entrance side of the bullet hole is round.

2. List two ways to determine the direction of the bullet.

3. Examine the photos of safety and window glass. (If you have actual pieces of broken safety glass and window glass, examine them.)

   a. Compare and contrast the fracture patterns of tempered glass and window glass and record your notes on Act 15-1 SH.

   b. How does the fracture pattern of tempered glass reduce serious injuries?

4. Two bullets penetrated the window of an old shed. Study the fracture patterns in the following diagram, and answer the following questions.

   a. Which bullet struck first? Support your claim citing the fracture patterns in the diagram.

   b. If you were able to see the fractured window in the window frame of the shed, describe at least two ways to determine whether the bullets were moving into the shed or out of the shed.

   c. It was reported that at least one of the bullets was fired from the right side of the shed. If you could view the fractured window, describe how the location of the shooter could be determined by viewing the bullet hole in the fractured glass.

(a) Broken tempered glass.

(b) Broken window glass.

   ii. If the shot is fired at an angle from the right, then the exit side of the hole is more of an elongated oval angled to the left. It is the opposite if the shot is fired from the left; the exit side of the hole is more of an oval elongated to the right.

5. Refer to the following diagram of the glass fracture patterns produced by three different impacts. Which occurred first, second, and third? Justify your answer by referring to the diagram and using terms such as *boundary* and *radial fracture*.

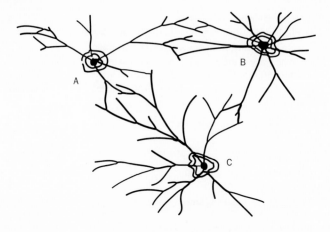

6. Review the following diagram showing four different impacts.
   a. What is the sequence of impacts?
   b. Prepare expert witness testimony citing your claims and your evidence for making those claims.

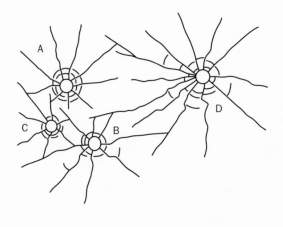

5. C, A, B; Radial fracture lines from C stop the radial fractures of A and B, so C must have been first. The radial fractures of B are stopped by A, meaning A formed before B. The radial fractures of A are stopped by C, meaning that C came before A.

6. a. D, B, C, A

   b. Examine two fractures at a time to determine which was first. D stops B therefore D was before B: DB. C is stopped by B therefore B was before C: BC.
   A is stopped by C therefore C was before A: CA.
   DB
    BC
     CA
Sequence: DBCA

The expert witness testimony should include explanations of how radial and concentric fractures form and how the sequence of fracture lines can be determined.

Further Research and Extensions

Allow students to actually perform the two tests they think they will need to gather more information about the glass. Provide materials and equipment for them to perform their experiments.

Background

In this activity, students determine the density of glass fragments found at the crime scene and the densities of glass fragments found on the suspects. They then compare the densities to discover whether any of the suspect densities are consistent with the crime-scene density.

Time Required to Complete Activity

45 minutes

Safety Precautions

1. Students should always wear gloves and goggles while handling glass.
2. Spread newspaper or kraft paper in the work area.
3. Tell students how to dispose of all materials.
4. Emphasize that students should report any accidents immediately.

Teaching Tip

Review Evidence Inventory Label completion, chain of custody control, and evidence collection in Chapter 2 with students. Prepare evidence bags labeled Suspect 1, Suspect 2, Suspect 3, Suspect 4, and CS (Crime Scene). In preparing the bags, place the glass fragments inside the bags. Be sure that glass from at least one of the suspects is consistent with that from the crime scene. Each bag should have an Evidence Inventory Label on the front of the bag (which you may choose to fill out in advance). The bag should be sealed and should also have a signature of the person who collected the evidence written across the tape and the package.

Glass Density Obj. 15.4, 15.9, 15.10

Objectives:

By the end of this activity, you will be able to:

1. Describe how density is determined using a water displacement method.
2. Calculate the density of various samples of glass fragments.
3. Determine if any of the glass evidence obtained from the four suspects has the same density as the glass found at the crime scene.
4. Maintain the proper chain of evidence when collecting and examining glass evidence.

Time Required to Complete Activity: 45 minutes

Materials (per group of two students):

Act 15-2 SH Evidence Inventory Label
Act 15-2 SH Data Table
4 evidence bags each containing broken tempered (safety) glass and labeled Suspect 1, 2, 3, or 4
1 evidence bag containing crime-scene evidence labeled CS
5-mL or 10-mL plastic syringes with plungers removed and tips sealed or 10-mL graduated cylinders
paper towels
dropper bottle containing 50 mL of water
balance (accurate to at least 0.01 gram)
forceps
2 pairs of gloves
safety goggles for each student
scissors
labeling tape
permanent marker pen

SAFETY PRECAUTIONS:

Wear gloves and goggles while handling glass. Spread newspaper or kraft paper in your work area. Dispose of all materials as directed by your teacher. Immediately report any accidents with glass to the teacher.

Background:

The density of glass fragments found at a crime scene can be compared to the glass fragments found on suspects. If the glass densities are inconsistent, then the suspects may be excluded (eliminated). Keep in mind that if the densities are consistent, this does not prove that the suspect is guilty, because glass is class evidence.

Procedure:

1. Obtain the following evidence bags:
   Suspect 1
   Suspect 2
   Suspect 3
   Suspect 4
   CS
2. Record your name, date, and time on the Evidence Inventory Label on the evidence bag.
3. Put on safety goggles and gloves. Without disturbing the signatures already on evidence bag 1, use scissors to cut open the evidence envelope.
4. Using forceps, remove several glass fragments from the evidence bag labeled Suspect 1. Using a balance, determine the combined mass of the pieces. Record the mass in the Data Table. Leave the pieces of glass on the balance for further testing.
5. Properly reseal the evidence bag with a piece of tape over the opened edge. Write your signature or initials across the seam of the tape and the bag to maintain chain of custody. Refer to chain of custody information described in Chapter 2.
6. Using clean forceps, remove the glass fragments from the balance and place them on the paper towel labeled Suspect 1.
7. Add 5 mL of water to a 10-mL graduated cylinder or to a 10-mL syringe. If you are using a 5-mL syringe, add 2.5 mL of water. Record the volume of water in the syringe or graduated cylinder in the Data Table. If using a syringe, place the upright syringe in the 250-mL beaker.
8. Using forceps, gently add the glass fragments of glass Sample 1 to the plastic syringe or graduated cylinder that is half-filled with water.
9. After adding the glass pieces to the syringe or graduated cylinder, record the volume of the glass fragments plus the water in the Data Table.
10. Determine the volume of the glass fragments by subtracting the volume of the water alone from the volume of the water with the glass fragments. Record the volume of the glass fragments in the Data Table.
11. Calculate the density (mass/volume) of the glass fragments from the Suspect 1 evidence bag, and record your answer in the Data Table.
12. Remove the glass fragments from the syringe or graduated cylinder using the forceps, and dispose of the glass as directed by your teacher.
13. Repeat Steps 2–12 for Suspects 2, 3, 4, and CS.
14. Analyze the data in the Data Table. Can you exclude any suspects? Did you find any of the suspects' glass consistent with the crime-scene glass?
15. Complete all the information in the Data Table, and record your answers to the activity questions located at the end of this activity.

Procedures

1. Print, copy, and distribute five copies of Act 15-2 SH Evidence Inv Label and one Act 15-2 SH Data Table per team from the IRCD, Chapter 15.
2. Make sure students read all directions *before* beginning the activity.

Teaching Tips

1. Make sure students know that the glass must be totally submerged when doing the submersion test.
2. Cross-contamination of glass pieces is an important issue. It can be difficult to identify the glass types by visual comparison if the lab materials get mixed up. One way to prevent this is to take four different colors of permanent markers and lightly mark the edges of the glass. This should not be done, however, if the same glass pieces will also be used for either refractive index or Becke line analysis.
3. Use a balance with accuracy to the nearest 0.01 gram.

Teaching Tips

1. Use pieces of glass at least 0.5 cm in length.
2. Use a variety of glass types— heat-resistant, window, safety, etc.
3. Use the smallest graduated cylinder or syringe in which the glass will fit. If using a syringe, remove the plunger and seal the tip with a burner flame, soldering iron, or glue.
4. Ensure that balance batteries are working.
5. Have beakers of water easily accessible to lab benches to cut down on traffic in the room.
6. Check the density of your glass fragments in advance.

7. Tables will reflect your choices of glass samples. Choose samples similar in appearance but different in composition.
8. Be sure to remind students to get the mass of the glass *before* submerging it.
9. Remind students to submerge the glass slowly, and not to drop it in the water. This avoids the formation of bubbles and the loss of water by splashing.
10. Remind students how to use weighing paper and how to read the balance; they must either deduct the mass of the weighing paper from the glass, or zero out the balance with the weighing paper on it.

(continues at left)

Answers

Check students' data tables.

1. Answers will vary.

2. Answers will vary.

3. Answers will vary, but might include: double-check calculations for math errors replicate the activity and take the average of your readings; have someone else take the reading with your glass and compare it with yours.

4. Answers will vary; sample answer: You could perform a Becke line test or submersion test to check the refractive index.

5. Answers will vary.

Glass Density:

Directions: Refer to the figures in your textbook for common glass densities and the method of calculating density. Complete the activity in your textbook, and record your results in the following table.

Data Table: Density of Glass Samples

Sample	Mass of Glass Fragments (grams)	Volume of Water (mL)	Combined Volume of Glass and Water (mL)	Volume of Glass Only (mL)	Density (grams/mL)
Suspect 1					
Suspect 2					
Suspect 3					
Suspect 4					
Crime Scene					

Questions:

1. Was the density of the glass found on any of the four suspects consistent with the density of the glass found at the crime scene? Which suspects can you exclude (eliminate) from the suspect list, and which suspects are still included?

2. Compare your results to other groups in the class. Discuss reasons for any differences between the results of your group and other groups.

3. How could you modify the procedure or materials to ensure more reliable results?

4. If you found that one or more suspects had glass densities that were consistent with the glass density of the evidence glass, what other testing or investigating would you do to further link the suspect to the crime?

5. A student claimed that using more glass fragments would have provided more reliable results in calculating the density. Do you agree or disagree with that statement? Provide evidence to support your claim.

© iStock.com/Kali Nine LLC

Approximating the Refractive Index of Glass Using a Submersion Test *Obj. 15.5 15.9, 15.10*

Objectives:

By the end of this activity, you will be able to:

1. Perform a submersion test on a glass fragment to find an approximate refractive index.
2. Compare the refractive indexes of the evidence glass pieces to the refractive index of the crime-scene glass fragments.
3. Based on the results of the submersion test, determine if either or both of two suspects can be excluded from this crime scene.
4. Maintain a proper chain of custody.

Time Required to Complete Activity: 45 minutes

Materials (per group of two or three students):

Act 15-3 SH Evidence Inventory Labels

Act 15-3 SH Data Table

3 samples of tempered (safety) glass fragments each contained in a separate evidence bag labeled Crime Scene, Suspect 1, or Suspect 2

4 pairs of forceps

adhesive tape (to reseal evidence bags)

3 small dishes (petri dishes or small plastic drinking cups)

permanent marker

1 test tube rack

labeling tape

paper toweling

gloves

safety goggles

test tubes half-filled with

    water

    isopropyl alcohol

    olive oil

    cinnamon oil*

    castor oil

    clove oil*

*Because of expense and odor, these two tubes may be set up by your teacher as a demonstration for the entire class to use in a well-ventilated area.

Background

In this activity, students compare glass found in the sneakers on the two suspects to the glass found in the broken display case by estimating the refractive indexes of the glass samples. They use the refractive indexes to compare glass from the suspects to the crime-scene glass.

Time Required to Complete Activity

45 minutes

Safety Precautions

1. Spread newspaper or kraft paper in the work area to capture small fragments of glass.
2. Remind students to always handle glass with forceps.
3. Stress that isopropyl alcohol is highly flammable, and the fumes are volatile and irritating to the respiratory tract.
4. Have a designated area to dispose of any broken glass.
5. Use a vent or hood when using cinnamon oil due to the strong odor.

Teaching Tip

Three evidence bags containing glass need to be prepared for each team before the activity. At least one of the glass fragments of Suspect 1 or 2 should be the same as the crime-scene glass fragments.

The evidence bags should be sealed to maintain proper chain of custody. (See Chapter 2.) The Evidence Inventory Label should have at least one name, date, and time entered before the student receives the evidence bag.

Procedures

1. Print, copy, and distribute Act 15-3 SH Evidence Inv Label and Act 15-3 SH Data Table from the IRCD, Chapter 15.

2. Make sure students read all directions *before* beginning the activity.

3. Because there will inevitably be some accidental dropping of glass pieces into the test tubes, plan ahead of time how you will have students retrieve them from the tube.

Teaching Tips

Pea-sized glass fragments work well.

Set up a demonstration rack for clove and cinnamon oil. They are difficult to clean, so after use, turn over test tubes and let them drain thoroughly.

Inexpensive plastic dishes can be purchased from supply houses.

Teaching Tip

Cinnamon oil and clove oil are relatively expensive. You may also consider using different types of motor oils or engine-oil sealer.

SAFETY PRECAUTIONS:

Spread newspaper or kraft paper in the work area to capture small fragments of glass. Handle glass with forceps. Wear safety goggles and gloves. Tests involving cinnamon or clove oil should be conducted inside a vented hood.

Scenario:

Students at a local high school decided to steal the basketball trophy in the locked display case near the gym. They planned to steal the trophy after 7 P.M., when few workers would be in the building. Once they had the trophy, they planned to escape by running out the back door by the gym. They didn't anticipate the coach returning to his office. The coach heard the glass breaking and saw two boys running.

The coach thought he recognized one of the boys by numerous old snowboard lift tickets on his coat. The coach reported the incident and gave a description to the police, who quickly located both boys at a pizza parlor.

Did those boys break into the display case and steal the trophy? The police brought the boys to the police station, where investigators examined the bottom of the boys' sneakers. Small particles of glass were embedded in the soles. What type of testing could be used to determine if the glass in their sneakers is consistent with the broken display case glass?

Background:

The refractive indexes of different pieces of glass can be estimated by performing a submersion test.

Liquids of known refractive indexes are used to visually estimate the refractive index of glass samples. When submerged, if the glass seems to disappear, then the glass has a refractive index similar to the liquid in which it is submerged. If the refractive index of the glass differs from the refractive index of the solution in which it is immersed, you will be able to see an outline of the glass. This is known as a submersion test for refractive index.

Procedure:

1. Put on gloves and safety goggles. Obtain a test tube rack with four test tubes. Use labeling tape and label the tops of the test tubes 1 through 4.

2. Using tape, label four forceps 1 through 4. Place the numbered forceps on a paper towel in front of the test tube with the same number. Use only the forceps designated for that particular liquid when doing the submersion testing.

3. Half-fill each of the four test tubes with one of the four different liquids. The liquids are numbered in increasing order of refractive index.
   a. Water
   b. Isopropyl alcohol
   c. Olive oil
   d. Castor oil

   (Your instructor may have two other test tubes set up as a demonstration: 5 Clove oil and 6 Cinnamon oil.)

Refractive Indexes of Liquids

Liquid	Refractive Index
1. Water	1.33
2. Isopropyl alcohol	1.37
3. Olive oil	1.47
4. Castor oil	1.48
5. Clove oil (optional; teacher display)	1.54
6. Cinnamon oil (optional; teacher display)	1.62

4. Using tape, label three different dishes Crime Scene, Suspect 1, and Suspect 2.

5. Obtain evidence bags containing glass fragments from your instructor labeled Crime Scene, Suspect 1, and Suspect 2.

6. Maintain a proper chain of custody when opening and resealing each of the evidence bags. Remember to
   a. Cut open the bag in an area that does not disturb the previous signature.
   b. Sign and date the Evidence Inventory Label on the evidence bag.
   c. When resealing the bag, tape it and sign your name or initials across the seam between the tape and the package.

7. Open the crime-scene glass evidence bag first. Remove at least four pieces of glass that will fit inside the test tube. Put the glass fragments in the dish or cup labeled Crime Scene. Reseal the bag, tape it, and sign your name across the tape.

8. Using forceps 1, submerge a fragment of the crime-scene glass in test tube 1. Hold the glass fragment with the forceps. Do not let go of the glass fragment.

9. View the submerged glass at eye level. Is the glass easily visible, slightly visible, or invisible? Remove the glass from the liquid and dispose of it as instructed by your teacher. Record your observations in the Data Table.

10. Repeat Steps 8 and 9 using the crime-scene glass with forceps and test tubes 2, 3, and 4. Use a new piece of glass for each test tube. Record your observations.

11. Repeat the submersion test (Steps 8 through 10) on glass fragments from Suspect 1. Record your observations in the Data Table.

12. Repeat Steps 8 through 10 for glass fragments from Suspect 2. Record your data in the Data Table.

13. Observe your teacher's demonstration of the submersion tests on the Crime-Scene, Suspect 1, and Suspect 2 samples using clove oil and cinnamon oil. Record your observations in the Data Table.

14. Analyze your data, and then discuss with your partners if the glass from either suspect is consistent with the crime-scene glass.

Teaching Tip

Remind students to hold the piece of glass securely during the submersion tests. The same piece should be used for each liquid. It should be washed, blotted, and then submerged in each consecutive liquid.

Teaching Tips

The lowest refractive index in which the glass disappears will be the closest to the refractive index for that sample of glass. Heat-resistant glass such as Pyrex in olive or vegetable oil works well.

DIFFERENTIATED LEARNING

Teaching Gifted Students

Ask students to estimate the refractive liquids of different motor oils by following the procedure in Activity 15-3. Ask them to devise a submersion test that uses motor oils in place of the more expensive clove oil and cinnamon oil. Suggest they ask jewelers or visit thrift shops for (broken) pieces of lead or crystal glass.

Answers

Check students' data tables and calculations.

Questions

1. Answers will vary.

2. Answers will vary. Some answers might include not having a large enough piece of glass or not thoroughly cleaning and drying glass prior to new submersion.

3. Repeat the test using another glass sample, have your partner repeat the sampling, and compare results.

4. If the refractive indexes were inconsistent, the suspect may be excluded. If the refractive indexes were consistent, the suspect would be included.

5. Similarity of glass from a suspect and crime scene is class evidence, because most glass has little variation.

Data Table: Submersion Test Results

Test Tube	Refractive Index of Liquid	Visibility (Easily Visible, Slightly Visible, Invisible)		
		Crime Scene	Suspect 1	Suspect 2
1. Water	1.33			
2. Isopropyl alcohol	1.37			
3. Olive oil	1.47			
4. Castor oil	1.48			
5. Clove oil (optional; teacher display only)	1.54			
6. Cinnamon oil (optional; teacher display only)	1.62			

Questions:

1. Based on the results of your submersion test, record the estimated refractive indexes for each of the glass fragments.

   The estimated refractive index of the Crime-Scene glass is _____

   The estimated refractive index of the glass from Suspect 1 is _____

   The estimated refractive index of the glass from Suspect 2 is _____

2. What would you consider to be possible sources of error in using this technique?

3. Suggest changes to the lab procedure that could improve the reliability of this experiment.

4. Is it possible to exclude or include either of the two suspects? Cite evidence from this activity to support your claim.

5. Why would similar refractive indexes of glass from a crime scene and suspect be considered class evidence?

Further Research and Extensions

Have several additional liquids of known refractive indexes available for students who complete the activity early, or who are interested in further investigation.

Determining the Refractive Index of Liquids Using Snell's Law *Obj. 15.5*

Objectives:

By the end of this activity, you will be able to:

1. Draw and measure the angle of refraction as light passes from one medium to another.
2. Apply Snell's Law to calculate the refractive indexes of two different liquids.
3. Describe the effect on the angle of refraction as light passes from a medium with a higher refractive index to a medium with a lower refractive index.
4. Relate refractive index to forensic glass analysis.

Time Required to Complete Activity: 45 minutes

Materials (per group of two students):

Act 15-4 SH Data Table (two sheets per team of students)
Act 15-4 SH Polar Graph Paper
laser pointer
protractor
calculator with sine function, or sine table
two different liquids, cooking oil and water (Samples 1 and 2)
ruler or straightedge
two semicircular plastic dishes
sharp pencil

SAFETY PRECAUTIONS:

Do not look directly at the laser light.

Background:

Light passes more slowly through substances (media) with higher refractive indexes and more quickly through media with lower refractive indexes. Recall that the bending of light as it changes speed passing through different media is known as *refraction*. A *normal line* is a line drawn perpendicular to the interface of two different media.

Teaching Tip

See an additional activity, Act 15-5 SH, and instructional support, Act 15-5 TN, for Snell's Law in the IRCD, Chapter 15.

Background

In this activity, students use Snell's Law to determine the refractive index of three liquids.

Time Required to Complete Activity

45 minutes

Safety Precautions

Before attempting this activity, ensure that your school allows students to handle laser pointers. Laser pointers are dangerous if aimed directly into the eye. Strict supervision is required while students have the laser pointers.

Teaching Tip

Inexpensive semicircular plastic dishes can be purchased from supply houses (usually in the physics section). Have detergent on hand to wash oil from dishes if they are reused for new sample tests.

Procedures

1. Print, copy, and distribute Act 15-3 SH Polar Graph Paper and Act 15-3 SH Data Table from the IRCD.

2. Make sure students read all directions *before* beginning the activity.

Teaching Tips

1. Start with water as Medium 1. That way, if there is a shortage of dishes, the water can be emptied and the dish dried and used for Medium 2 (oil).

2. Provide oil and water containers that can be used at the students' desk or lab bench, or that can be shared. Students should not walk around with full dishes.

3. The laser pointer should touch the plastic dish when students measure angle of incidence.

4. Darken the room and demonstrate how the laser must be positioned to focus at the interface, as shown. The laser pointer must be positioned against the edge of the dish.

5. With the laser pointer in place, draw a line on the paper indicating the angle of refraction.

6. Make sure that students measure the angle of incidence and angle of refraction from the normal line.

7. Be sure that your protractor is aligned correctly. Some protractors use the bottom edge of the protractor to align the protractor. Other protractors have the center slightly above the edge of the protractor (see diagram at right).

8. Fill the plastic dishes with oil. If you do not have enough oil in the plastic dish, it is more difficult to obtain accurate readings.

9. This activity could be done as a demonstration if your school or district has a policy against student use of laser pointers.

Procedure:

SNELL'S LAW:

Mathematically, the relationship between the refractive indexes and the angle of incidence and angle of refraction is expressed as Snell's Law:

$$n_1(\text{sine of angle of incidence}) = n_2(\text{sine angle of refraction})$$

$$n_1 = \text{refractive index of Medium 1}$$
$$n_2 = \text{refractive index of Medium 2}$$

Comparison of the angle of incidence and the angle of refraction as light passes through two different media.

In the diagram, note that light moves through Medium 1 (air) and passes through Medium 2 (glass). The green line is the normal line, the line perpendicular to the interface of the two media. Light is directed through Medium 1 at a 45 degree angle (angle of incidence). When light moves into Medium 2 (glass), the light is refracted toward the normal line. By applying Snell's Law, it is possible to estimate the refractive index of Medium 2 (n_2).

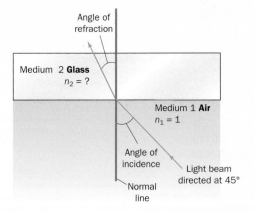

Background:

This activity demonstrates how a beam of light is refracted as it moves from water to air. The beam of light will enter the water from a 30-degree angle measured from the normal line (the line perpendicular to the interface of the two media). By applying Snell's Law, you will be able to determine the refractive index of the liquid:

$n_1 = ?$ refractive index of Medium 1 (water)
angle of incidence = 30 degrees (preselected)
$n_2 = 1$ refractive index of Medium 2 (air)
Angle of refraction will be measured during the activity.

512   Glass Evidence

Center is slightly above the edge.

Procedure:

1. Refer to Act 15-4 SH Polar Graph Paper or use a sheet of polar graph paper. On your paper, in the lower-right corner, label Medium 1 "Water." Record that the angle of incidence is 30 degrees. Put a question mark for the refractive index (n_1) of water. This is the unknown during this activity. In the upper-left corner, label Medium 2 "Air" and record the refractive index for air $n_2 = 1$. The angle of refraction will be determined later in the experiment.

2. On the polar graph paper in Act 15-4 SH Polar Graph Paper, find the red vertical normal line that is perpendicular to the interface of the two media.

3. Place the semicircular dish on the polar graph paper. Align the flat side of the dish along the horizontal, as indicated in the image above. Be sure to center the dish on the graph paper. The center of the flat side of the dish should be positioned at the origin on the graph paper. The dish should be evenly aligned along the center line.

4. Fill the dish at least ¾ full of tap water.

5. Position the laser beam on the outside of the curved plastic dish so that the light enters the dish at 30 degrees *measured from the normal line*. The light should almost touch the dish. Move the laser light slightly up and down. Be sure the light is on top of the 30-degree line and the light passes directly through the origin.

6. Notice how the beam of light is bent as it passes from the container of water and into the second medium of air. Using a pencil, mark a series of dots along this refracted light beam on the other side of the dish. Use a pencil and a straightedge to draw a line through these dots to show the refracted light as it moves from Medium 1 (water) into Medium 2 (air).

Polar graph paper.

Medium 2 **Air**

$n_2 = 1$

30°

$n_1 = ?$

Medium 1

Snell's Law

n_1 (sine of angle = n_2 (sine of angle
 of incidence)   of refraction)

Direct laser pointer as indicated along 30-degree angle of incidence line.

Problem: Calculate the refractive index of the liquid using Snell's Law using _____ (oil or water)

Medium 2 = Air

© Cengage Learning®

Teaching Tip

In an equation such as the one representing Snell's Law, students can use algebra to solve for one variable when they know the values of the other three.

Teaching Tip

Troubleshooting Tips:

- The dish should be placed squarely along the center line. Students should look down at the dish from different angles to check.
- Fill dishes at least 3/4 full with fluids.
- The laser pointer must touch the dish.
- Wiggle the light up and down to see the refracted light.
- Ensure the refracted light travels through the origin of the graph paper before marking it.
- Make sure to measure the refracted angle from the *normal* line.

Teaching Tip

Trigonometric ratios, such as sine, are usually expressed as decimals. It may be helpful to students to demonstrate how to find a sine value before teaching this section. To find the sine using a scientific calculator, first enter the angle measure, and then press the key labeled SIN. To find the sine using a sine table, find the angle measure in the first column, and then look across the table to find the sine value given in decimal format.

Teaching Tip

The sine of an angle is one of the trigonometric ratios used to describe the relationship between two parts of a right triangle. For example, the sine of angle x is the length of the leg b, divided by the length of the hypotenuse c.

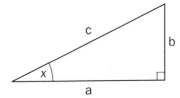

Answers

Check students' diagrams, calculations, and data tables.

Questions

1. The refractive index of oil was greater than the refractive index of water.

2. The light bends away from the normal line.

3. The angle of refraction was greater than the angle of incidence.

7. Using the line you have drawn, the normal line, and a protractor, measure the angle of refraction. *Be sure you are measuring the angle from the normal line.* Record the angle of refraction in Act 15-4 SH Data Table.

8. Using a calculator or a sine table (Appendix A), determine the sine value of your angle of incidence and the angle of refraction. Record this information in the Data Table.

9. Calculate the refractive index n_1 for Medium 1 (water) by applying Snell's Law.

n_1(sine of angle of incidence) = n_2(sine of angle of refraction)

10. Repeat Steps 1–9 using a new sheet of polar graph paper. This time, replace the water with oil. If you are reusing a dish, be sure to dry the dish with soft paper towels to avoid scratching the dish before you fill it with oil. Label Act 15-4 SH Polar Graph Paper with the following information:

    Medium 1 is oil.
    n_1 is your unknown.
    Angle of incidence is 30 degrees.

    Medium 2 is air.
    $n_2 = 1$
    Angle of refraction will be measured.

11. Record all information in the Data Table.

12. Dispose of oil and liquids and clean all your dishes according to your instructor's directions.

Data Table: Refractive Index of Two Liquid Samples

Medium	Angle of Incidence (degrees)	Sine of Angle of Incidence	Angle of Refraction (degrees)	Sine of Angle of Refraction	Refractive Index
1 Water	30				
2 Oil	30				

Questions:

1. Refer to your Data Table. Which liquid had the higher refractive index: oil or water?

2. As light moved from water and into air, did the light bend toward or away from the normal line? Support your answer, citing data from this activity.

3. As the light moved from oil and into the air, was the angle of refraction greater than or less than the angle of incidence? Support your answer, citing data from this activity.

Further Research and Extensions

If all of the liquids you are testing are similar in color, after completing this activity, give students an unknown liquid and have them identify which of the three liquids it is based on its refractive index.

Sample	Angle of Incidence (I)	Sine Angle I	Angle of Refraction	Sine Angle R	Refractive Index (sine R/sine I)
Water	30°	0.5000	~41°	0.6561	1.29
Vegetable oil	30°	0.5000	~45°	0.7071	1.42–1.48
Motor oil	30°	0.5000	~50°	0.7660	1.53

4. Suppose you set your angle of incidence at 45 degrees instead of 30 degrees. Would you have obtained a different refractive index using the 45-degree angle of incidence instead of the 30-degree angle of incidence? Explain your answer, citing data from this activity.

5. Reflect on your experimental technique and procedure. Where were the possible sources of error? How could you modify the procedure to obtain more accurate results?

6. In your own words, describe light refraction: What is it, when does it occur, and why does it happen?

7. Describe the application of refractive index to forensic glass analysis. How can it be used to exclude or include a suspect? What are the limitations of using refractive indexes in solving crimes?

4. The refractive index would still be the same. The angle of incidence is arbitrary. If you used 45 degrees instead of 30 degrees, then the angle of refraction would also change. The refractive index would remain constant.

5. Possible sources of error:
- Not filling the dish at least 3/4 full of liquid
- Holding the light source too far from the dish
- Not aligning the dish evenly along the graph paper
- Measuring the angle of refraction from a line other than the normal

6. Light refraction is the bending of light that occurs when light passes from one medium into another. It occurs because of the change in the speed of the light when it encounters a medium with a different index of refraction. Refractive index is a measure of the speed of light in a vacuum divided by the speed of light in the medium.

7. Refractive index is a physical property of glass that can be used to compare one piece of glass with another piece of glass. If the refractive index of the evidence glass is found to be inconsistent with the refractive index of glass found on a suspect, then that suspect may be excluded. If the refractive indexes are found to be consistent, the evidence is considered to be class circumstantial evidence and it cannot by itself be considered sufficient evidence for a conviction.

Chapter Overview

Forensic specialists use impressions left by shoes, feet, tires, and teeth during crime-scene investigations. Forensic investigators have developed procedures for observing and capturing information from each kind of impression. In some criminal investigations, impressions and the casts made of impressions found at a crime scene are the only evidence that can help an investigator reconstruct a crime. Shoe, footprint, tire tread, and bite-mark evidence is usually class evidence.

The Big Ideas

Evidence in the form of impressions is often found at the scene of a crime. There are three kinds of impressions: latent, patent, and plastic. Each kind of impression tells an important part of what happened at the scene of a crime. Foot, shoe, and tire impressions can be collected. From tire tracks, investigators can obtain width and wheelbase information that will help identify a vehicle. Bite marks also can be used but are not as reliable. One of the most important aspects of working with impressions in forensic investigations is the need for investigators to observe and record observations carefully at the crime scene because of the transitory nature of impressions. Shoe, footprint, tire tread, and bite mark impression evidence is considered class evidence unless something unique personalized the item making the mark.

CHAPTER 16

Casts and Impressions

The Man in the Bruno Magli Shoes

One morning, the residents of Los Angeles's South Bundy Drive woke to sirens. Two bodies had been found, having suffered a horrific knife attack. Bloody footprints, eventually determined to have been made by size 12 Bruno Magli shoes, tracked the victims' blood along the path. The date was June 13, 1994, and the bodies were those of Nicole Brown Simpson and Ronald Goldman. Who was the man in the Bruno Magli shoes?

The ensuing criminal case culminated in one of the most-watched television events in U.S. history. Many people were surprised by the "not guilty" verdict in favor of defendant Orenthal James (O. J.) Simpson, Nicole's ex-husband and Hall of Fame football player, because of the significant evidence linking Simpson to the crime scene.

The size 12 Bruno Magli shoe prints were created when the individual wearing the shoes walked through a pool of congealing blood. Specialists determined that the prints were made about 20 minutes after the attack. Simpson, whose shoe size is 12, denied owning a pair of Bruno Maglis. The shoe print evidence was of little value in the criminal case, because there was no evidence of Simpson owning these shoes. However, after the criminal trial, a photograph was found showing Simpson wearing similar shoes. So in a later civil case, jurors believed that Simpson made the shoe prints, and he was found responsible for the deaths of his ex-wife Nicole Brown Simpson and Ronald Goldman.

Bloody footprints at the Nicole Brown Simpson and Ronald Goldman murder scene.

516

SCENARIO

After reading the scenario, lead the class in discussing these questions:

What role did footprints play in the O. J. Simpson murder trial?

Was this evidence important in the criminal case? The civil case?

What other information, in addition to the kind of shoes that made the print, do you think investigators can determine from shoe prints?

Do you think that evidence from shoe prints should be enough to convict a suspect? Explain your answer.

OBJECTIVES

By the end of this chapter, you will be able to:

16.1 Provide examples of how impression evidence gives clues about the crime scene, person(s) at the scene, and events that occurred at the scene.

16.2 Provide well-supported arguments that evidence such as foot, shoe, and dental impressions is usually considered class evidence.

16.3 Distinguish among latent, patent, and plastic impressions.

16.4 Summarize the significance of foot and shoe impression evidence, and outline procedures for collecting impression evidence from different types of surfaces.

16.5 Describe the features of tire impressions and skid marks used to help identify tire(s) or a vehicle's wheelbase, track width, and/or turning diameter.

16.6 Compare and contrast skid marks, including how they are produced, when they are produced, what they look like, and how they can be used to reconstruct events leading to a collision.

16.7 Summarize the methods used to produce an impression or cast.

16.8 Analyze impression evidence to determine if it is consistent with evidence from a crime scene.

TOPICAL SCIENCES KEY

BIOLOGY

CHEMISTRY

EARTH SCIENCES

PHYSICS

LITERACY

MATHEMATICS

VOCABULARY

- **groove (of a tire)** a depression in the tread

- **latent impression** impression requiring special techniques to be visible to the unaided eye

- **patent impression** impression visible to the unaided eye

- **plastic impression** impression in soft materials such as soil, snow, or congealing blood

- **rib (of a tire)** an individual ridge of tread running around the circumference

- **sole** the bottom of a piece of footwear

- **track width** the distance from the center of the tread of a left tire to the center of the tread of the corresponding right tire

- **tread** the part of a tire that meets the road; the pattern on the sole of footwear

- **turning diameter** the diameter of the smallest circle that can be driven by a vehicle

- **wheelbase** the distance from the center of the front wheel of a vehicle to the center of the rear wheel on the same side

CASTS AND IMPRESSIONS **517**

TEACHING RESOURCES

Instructor's Resource CD-ROM includes:
- Activities and Student Handouts
- Alternative Assessments
- Consolidated Bibliography
- Correlations to NGSS and CCSS
- Figure Files

- Lesson Plans
- Nonfiction Readings
- PowerPoint Presentations
- Student Learning Objectives (SLOs)

CL Testing powered by Cognero

Website: ngl.cengage.com/forensicscience2e

Engage

Discuss the following as a class:

- At the location of a hit-and-run accident, tire tracks are found in a muddy part of the road. What kinds of information might be contained in the tire tracks?

- What should investigators do first if they find tire impression evidence?

- Why must special care be used when working with teeth, tire, and foot or shoe impressions?

Teaching Tip

Explain to students that latent impressions can be made when small quantities of oil, soil, or other substances are left on an otherwise clean surface. Oily impressions, in particular, can be easily lifted with special techniques that cause a thin film of powder to adhere to the sticky surface of the oil.

Explore

Use plaster of Paris or a similar material to create several shoe prints. See Activity 16-1. Be sure to use different kinds, sizes, and models of shoes. Ask students to interpret the prints. What can they tell about the person who left these prints? Challenge students to base their conclusions on their observations.

Teaching Tip

Paris, France, is built on one of the largest gypsum deposits in the world. Gypsum is calcium sulfate, which makes plaster when it gets wet. It became known as plaster of Paris.

INTRODUCTION

Responding to an anonymous 911 call, the police arrive at a burglarized home. Who had been there? How many people had been there? Did they walk or drive away from the crime scene? Without security cameras or eyewitnesses, crime-scene investigators must rely on other evidence, including marks and prints, some of which may be invisible at first. The investigators find, photograph, and document those "silent witnesses" in the form of fingerprints (Chapter 6); and foot, shoe, teeth, and tire impressions.

Types of Impressions *Obj. 16.3*

Impressions fall into three basic categories: *patent, latent,* and *plastic* (Figure 16-1). **Patent impressions** are visible when an object picks up soil, dust, paint, blood, or other material and transfers it elsewhere. By contrast, **latent impressions** are hidden from the unaided eye but can be made visible, or *lifted,* through the use of special dusting and electrostatic techniques or with chemical developers. Oils, fine soil, and other minute debris can be transferred onto clean surfaces and leave latent impressions. Clean shoes or feet can transfer materials onto newly waxed or polished floors and make latent impressions.

Figure 16-1 *Examples of latent (left), patent (center), and plastic (right) impressions. The latent shoe impression (left) was made visible by dusting with orange powder and viewing with an orange filter and an alternate light source.*

Plastic impressions can be left in soft materials, such as snow, mud, soil, or congealing blood. One difficulty in dealing with plastic impressions is that they are easily lost. A strong wind or a sudden change in the weather can mean the loss of important evidence. It is critical that photographs be taken immediately before trying to make a permanent cast from a plastic impression.

DIFFERENTIATED LEARNING

Teaching At-Risk Students

The many hands-on activities should help at-risk students more easily understand this chapter's content. Allow at-risk students to practice making casts of impressions by directing the class in making casts of small impressions left in sand.

Individual or Class Evidence? *Obj. 16.2*

Depending on how it is made, impression evidence may be either class evidence or individual evidence. A particular **tread** in shoe soles or in tires may identify the brand and size, but it does not identify a specific individual or tire. Distinguishing characteristics, such as a split shoe sole tread, or unusual wear or damage on a car tire, can be used as individual evidence. Dental *work*, such as fillings, crowns, root canals, and the associated X-ray imagery, is typically considered individual evidence and has a long history of use to identify the remains of individuals, especially during wartime. However, dental *impression* evidence ("bite" evidence) has been challenged in court. Unless a dental impression is extremely unusual, it is not considered individual evidence.

SHOE AND FOOT IMPRESSIONS

Obj. 16.1, 16.2, 16.4

Shoe and foot impressions may provide clues about the crime scene by answering questions such as the following:

- What were the entrance and exit routes?
- How many people were at the crime scene?
- Is there evidence of any confrontation or disturbance within the crime scene?
- Is there evidence of anyone sustaining injuries?

Information about an individual may be revealed by impressions. The size of a foot or shoe print suggests an estimate of the person's height. A deep impression may suggest the impression was made by a heavy person. Foot or shoe impressions also may reveal whether a person typically walks with toes pointed outward or inward.

If the impression was made by a bare foot, additional identifying features may be noted. Are the toes curled or straight? Is the second toe longer than the big toe? Is the person missing any toes? Is the arch high, or is the person flat-footed? Measurements of the distance from heel to big toe, big toe to second toe, and so on can be made. These features are class evidence. However, together, the features can help investigators build a description of the person(s) at the crime scene.

Databases contain the names of specific manufacturers and tread patterns used to identify different types of shoes. When a shoe impression is found at a crime scene, the crime-scene investigator will search databases to find the manufacturer that produced the **sole** pattern as well as to search for the company that purchased that sole for the shoes. When a large number of manufacturers use the same generic sole patterns, it complicates sole identification. Once the footwear has been identified, the impression can be used as class evidence to link a suspect to the crime scene by comparing their footwear to an impression. Finding footwear consistent with the evidence footwear is not sufficient to prosecute a suspect.

Teaching Tip

Help students understand that making assumptions is not a characteristic of a skilled forensic investigator. Evidence based on assumptions is unlikely to stand up in court. For example, if the foot or shoe impressions left at a crime scene were made by worn tennis shoes, it is still possible that a wealthy woman or man could have worn those shoes. Additional information is necessary to make an informed judgement. Basing decisions on evidence is an important trait of the successful forensic scientist.

Teaching Tip

Reinforce the importance of collecting many different kinds of evidence in a criminal investigation. There are only a few cases in which one piece of evidence has been used to convict a person. Most of the time, the total of all the class and individual evidence is used to construct the case against an individual.

Explore

Challenge students to prepare a presentation of prints that show someone
- walking normally
- running
- limping

Have the students present their prints to the class, covering up the labels. Have the class act as CSIs, documenting and analyzing the prints as if they were from crime scenes.

Figure 16-2 *A stride pattern may provide clues about a person's identity.*

Brand X Pictures/Jupiter Images

Figure 16-3 *This impression in snow reveals two things about the gait of the person who left it: he or she was walking, not running, and he or she walked with toes pointed outward.*

© 2016 Cengage Learning®

Shoe Wear Patterns

Although two different people can purchase the same type of shoes, the wear pattern on the shoes may become quite different (Figure 16-2). People personalize shoes with their own characteristic ways of walking. A shoe tread showing strong individual character provides additional clues in trying to link a suspect to a crime. Some factors that personalize footwear include:

- Whether a person walks on his or her toes or heels
- Body weight
- If the person tends to walk with toes pointed inward or outward
- The shape of the foot and the wearer's activities
- The surface on which the person usually walks
- Unique holes, cuts, or debris that become part of the shoe

Gait and Tracks

If you examine a series of consecutive foot or shoe prints, it is possible to observe a person's *gait*, or pattern of moving. Tracks indicate if the person was running or walking by the length of the stride and the pressure or shape of the impression (Figures 16-2 and 16-3). If someone is limping due to an injury, the impressions may reveal an asymmetrical gait: one foot leaving only a partial impression or one at a different angle or depth than the other. Older or disabled persons may take smaller steps and scuff their feet instead of completely lifting their feet.

Collection of Shoe Impression Evidence

The steps in collecting shoe impression evidence are (1) photographing and documenting impressions, (2) lifting latent impressions, and (3) casting plastic impressions.

PHOTOGRAPHING IMPRESSIONS

Use the following guidelines when photographing impressions:

Figure 16-4 *Impression evidence is documented before any attempt is made at casting.*

© Cengage Learning®

- Take photographs before anyone touches or alters an impression!
- Fill the camera's view-finder with the impression.
- Take photographs with the lens perpendicular to the impression to reduce distortion.
- Take multiple photographs of the impression from at least two different orientations (angles), with and without measuring devices for scale (Figure 16-4).

- If using a digital camera, check your photographs for clarity and retake them when necessary. A single-lens reflex digital camera is now widely used in photographing crime scenes because many photos can be taken quickly and inexpensively.
- Place an identifying label and a ruler in position with the impression and rephotograph, making sure to focus on the impression, not the ruler.
- Use indirect lighting when possible. Direct sunlight can produce a glare.
- If an additional flash is needed, position the flash at least three to four feet away to avoid reflection in the photograph.
- If the impression is faint, spray it with a *light* coat of color-contrasting paint.

In court, the defense will try to discredit the prosecution's evidence in every way. Photographs of impression evidence found at a crime scene document that the evidence was indeed *at the crime scene*. Because impression evidence is easily destroyed or altered by rain, wind, or other factors, it's important that the crime-scene investigator take photos as soon as possible after arriving at the crime scene.

LIFTING LATENT IMPRESSIONS

When a shoe or bare foot walks on a smooth surface, it leaves a print that is not usually visible to the unaided eye. A bare foot leaves a thin layer of body oil, while a shoe leaves a thin film of substances from the sole or dirt. It takes a trained crime-scene investigator to know where to look for latent prints. If the entry and exit areas have been identified, the task of latent print identification is made easier. Several different methods are used to make latent prints visible, including the following:

- Luminol makes latent bloody footprints visible so they can be photographed.
- Dusting of a latent footprint, similar to dusting for fingerprints, reveals an impression and makes it visible so it can be lifted and photographed.
- Electrostatic lifting and gel-lifting techniques capture invisible impressions.

Electrostatic Dusting and Lifting
Electrostatic dusting can reveal the fine dust left by a dry shoe. An impression is produced by applying an electrostatic charge to a piece of lifting film, which is then placed over the latent print. The film retains the dust, creating a latent print. When the film is viewed with a special light source, the impression becomes visible and can be photographed (Figure 16-5).
Electrostatic charges can lift impressions from paper, flooring, and pavements. This method helps clean surface debris and reveals a more complete impression.

Figure 16-5 *Electrostatic lifting uses a charge to hold the dust particles of a latent print in place.*

© Cengage Learning®

Multiple lifts of the same print are possible using gel lifters. The second lift is fainter, but generally sharper in detail. Electrostatic lifting can also be done before gel lifting.

Explore
Do a class demonstration showing how Luminol can reveal latent bloody prints by using a solution of Tide laundry detergent. (Luminol reacts with Tide in a similar way to the way it reacts with blood.) Have a student walk through the solution and let it dry. Then spray the tracks with Luminol to reveal them.

DIFFERENTIATED LEARNING

Teaching Gifted Students
Encourage students to research the process and equipment used in gel lifting. Have them present their findings to the class.

Teaching Tip

If students create plaster of Paris shoe impression casts, have them photograph both the casts and the soles of their shoes.

Ask a small group of students to create a database of the casts and corresponding sole photos. Ask students what other information should be included in the database.

Figure 16-6 *Plaster cast of a plastic impression of a shoe.*

© 2016 Cengage Learning®

Figure 16-7 *Prints in snow must be photographed before casting.*

© 2016 Cengage Learning®

Gel Lifting Gel lifting is also used to lift latent prints. A gel lifter is a layer of gel sandwiched between paper backing and a plastic cover sheet. It is thick and flexible to conform to uneven surfaces, and it is best used on oily or moist prints. The print is first dusted with powder, which sticks to the moist parts. The protective plastic cover is peeled off the gel lifter, which is pressed firmly over the print. Because the gel is not very sticky, it can be used on surfaces, such as paper, from which it would be impossible to lift a print using fingerprint tape. The gel lifter is lifted off and the protective cover replaced. The gel lifter is photographed to reveal the print. Latent prints can be dusted using white, black, gold, or silver powders before gel lifting. Black, white, or clear gel lifters are available to provide the greatest contrast with the colored powders.

CASTING PLASTIC IMPRESSIONS *Obj. 16.7*

When evidence is in the form of a plastic impression, such as a shoe print in mud or snow, a *cast* may be made (Figure 16-6). Casting materials and techniques vary with the conditions at the crime scene. If the impression is in sand or soil, a plaster of Paris impression is made. Before pouring in the mixed plaster of Paris, a light film of hair spray may be applied to prevent the impression from collapsing under the weight of the plaster.

Impressions in snow (Figure 16-7) present a problem because they melt. Casting material needs to be used that will set at low temperatures and will not generate heat. An impression in snow can be cast by first spraying snow print wax in thin layers over the snow. Hardening instantly, the wax provides contrast and protection to the delicate impression before the casting material is poured into it. The casting material used for snow is called *dental stone*. Mixed with very cold water, it hardens faster than plaster of Paris, generating little heat.

Foot Length, Shoe Size, and Height

The length and width of a shoe vary by the shoe type. For example, a dress shoe will leave a smaller impression than a workboot of the same shoe size. The shoe model is first identified in order to gauge the correct shoe size to estimate the size of the foot. An adult's height is generally related to his or her foot size, but it is impossible to determine someone's exact height from foot size. Figure 16-8 compares men's (M) and women's (W) foot lengths and shoe sizes. Figure 16-9 compares shoe sizes and heights.

Figure 16-8 *Comparison of foot length and U.S. shoe sizing.*

Foot Length (Inches)		9	9 ⅛	9 ¼	9 ⅜	9 ½	9 ⅝	9 ¾	9 ⅞	10	10 ⅛	10 ¼	10 ½	10 ¾	11	11 ¼	11 ½
Shoe Size	M	3 ½	4	4 ½	5	5 ½	6	6 ½	7	7 ½	8	8 ½	9	10	11	12 ½	14
	W	5	5 ½	6	6 ½	7	7 ½	8	8 ½	9	9 ½	10	11	12	13	14	15 ½

TIRE TREADS AND IMPRESSIONS *Obj. 16.6, 16.7, 16.8*

Tire evidence may be used to link a suspect or victim to a crime scene and can also reveal the sequence of events. Tire marks may indicate the speed a car traveled when it left a road or the direction it traveled when fleeing a crime scene. Skid marks at the scene of a fatal collision may be used to determine who was at fault. A forensic scientist examines tire tread and tire impressions for two characteristics:

1. Tire tread patterns and their measurements to identify the type of tire and the possible make and model of car

2. Nature of the impression to determine how the vehicle was driven: tire condition, level of inflation

Motor vehicles can leave patent, latent, or plastic tire patterns. Patent impressions appear after the vehicle has driven through a fluid like oil, tar, or blood. Latent tracks may be left on asphalt or concrete roads by manufacturers' oils used to keep tires soft and pliable. Plastic or three-dimensional impressions may be left in off-road surfaces, such as mud, grass, sand, or snow.

The Anatomy of a Tire

A tire's tread surface is divided into **ribs** (ridges running around the circumference of the tire) and **grooves** (indentations). The purpose of these ribs and grooves is to channel water away and provide traction as the surface makes contact with the road or ground. Generally, every model of tire is unique, as manufacturers continually try to improve handling qualities. The width and angle of the grooves in the tread are engineered to perform best on a specific surface. Touring tires have many smaller grooves to channel air and water at high speeds on smooth pavement, and knobby off-road tires have very wide grooves for traction in slippery mud. A tire tread usually indicates the general type of vehicle that left the mark.

Figure 16-9 *Comparison of shoe size and height.*

Explore

Use Figure 16-10 for this activity. Ask students to draw what they think will be the impression made by the tire shown in the diagram. Remind them to label their drawings to reflect the names of the different parts of the tire that left the impression.

Teaching Tip

Tell students to be aware that the front and rear wheelbase of a vehicle may be different.

Evaluate

Ask students to make a table with two columns labeled *foot/shoe impressions* and *tire impressions*. Instruct them to list the ways foot impressions and tire impressions are used as evidence. Then encourage them to discuss the advantages and disadvantages of each kind of evidence.

Recording Tread Impressions

Tread patterns are usually symmetrical; the left and right sides of the tread are mirror images of each other. Ribs and grooves are counted across the entire tread width from shoulder to shoulder. If the tire has a central rib, then it will have an odd number of ribs. Any unique characteristics in the tread pattern are noted, including imperfections in the tread pattern of the tire, such as wear patterns or a pebble embedded in the grooves. Figure 16-10 shows different elements of a tire tread.

Figure 16-10 *A tire tread.*

Tread area   Rib

Groove

The impression from a crime scene is compared to the tires on a suspect's vehicle. A tire impression of the suspect's vehicle is taken. As with lifting a fingerprint, ink is painted onto a tire, and the vehicle is driven over smooth pavement covered with paper or cardboard. A print at least three meters long is produced to ensure that the tire made one revolution. All possible individual characteristics are noted, such as cuts, bulges, loss of tread, or evidence of objects embedded in the tire. The individual characteristics may link a specific vehicle with a tread impression from a crime scene.

Identifying a Vehicle *Obj. 16.5*

Tire impressions alone cannot identify the make and model of a vehicle that was driven at a crime scene. Because the same type of tire may be used on many vehicles, identifying the tread pattern is not enough. The track width and the wheelbase of the treads narrow the search. **Track width** is measured from the center of the tread of a tire to the center of the tread of the *opposite* tire. Note that the front and rear track width measurements may differ. The **wheelbase** of a vehicle is the distance between the center of the front wheel and the center of the rear wheel (Figure 16-11). Measurements should be taken to the nearest millimeter.

Figure 16-11 *Every make and model of vehicle has its own track width and wheelbase measurements.*

◄— 2731 mm —►
Wheelbase

◄1508 mm►
Front track width

◄1525 mm►
Rear track width

The **turning diameter** is the diameter of the smallest circle that can be driven by a vehicle or, put another way, the minimal space required for a car to make a 360-degree turn (Figure 16-12). When a vehicle turns a sharp corner, the wheels are turned as far as possible. Even at moderate speeds, a mark is created by the additional stress put on the front outer tire. A longer wheelbase increases the turning diameter. This information helps the investigator determine the size of the vehicle. Sometimes investigators work with the turning radius, which is half the turning diameter. For either quantity, the distance is given in millimeters, inches, or the nearest one-tenth foot.

A large database contains the track width, wheelbase, and turning diameter measurements for all makes and models of cars and can be easily checked to identify the vehicle that left the impressions (Figure 16-13).

524   CHAPTER 16

DIFFERENTIATED LEARNING

Teaching At-Risk Students
To engage at-risk students, ask them to determine the turning radius and other tire-related characteristics of vehicles owned by their family members or friends. (Turning radius may be found on the Internet, along with other automobile statistics.) Alternately, provide a demonstration for them so they can make the determinations on a car themselves. Be sure to stress the importance of safety when measuring or observing any moving vehicle.

Figure 16-12 *Tread marks revealing turning diameter can help identify a vehicle. Which of these vehicles has the smallest turning diameter?*

Dodge Ram (52.3 ft)
GMC Sierra Denali w/o 4WD (46.2 ft)
Ford F-150 (50.4 ft)
Toyota Tundra (44.3 ft)
Ford Excursion (43.7 ft)
Saturn 3-Door Coupe (37.1 ft)

Turning Diameter
GMC Sierra Denali w/4WD (37.4 ft)

Figure 16-13 *Examples from a database of automobile statistics by make and model.*

Make	Model	Wheelbase (mm)	Turning Diameter (mm)	Tire Size (mm)	Tire Make
ALFA ROMEO	Alfa 156	2,595	11,600	185	Michelin Energy XH-1
AUDI	A4	2,617	11,100	195	Michelin Energy MXT
AUDI	A8	2,882	12,300	225	Michelin Pilot CX
BMW	3 series	2,725	10,500	225	Michelin Pilot HX
CADILLAC	Seville	2,850	12,340	235	Goodyear Eagle Touring
CHEVROLET	Blazer	3,122	12,600	205	Uniroyal Tiger Paws
CHEVROLET	Corvette	2,444	12,200	285	Goodyear
CHRYSLER	Grand Voyager	3,030	12,500	215	Goodyear NCT2 Touring
CHRYSLER	Neon	2,642	10,800	175	Goodyear Eagle NCT2
DODGE	Viper	2,444	12,300	335	Michelin Pilot SX MXX3
FERRARI	550	2,500	11,600	295	Pirelli P Zero
FORD	Escort	2,525	10,000	185	Michelin MXV2
FORD	Focus	2,615	10,900	185	Pirelli P6000
FORD	Galaxy	2,835	11,700	215	Conti Sport Contact
HONDA	Accord	2,720	11,000	185	Pirelli P4000
HONDA	Civic	2,620	10,200	175	Dunlop SP9
HONDA	Prelude	2,585	9,400	205	Yokohama A085
HYUNDAI	Excel	2,400	9,700	175	Hankook Radial 884
INFINITI	J 30 t	2,761	11,000	215	Dunlop SP Sport D31
JEEP	Grand Cherokee	2,691	11,100	245	Goodyear Wrangler HP
LEXUS	GS 300	2,780	11,800	275	Yokohama
MERCEDES	A	2,423	10,300	175	Goodyear GT

CASTS AND IMPRESSIONS   **525**

Teaching Tip

Point out to students that cars are complex machines full of a variety of chemicals. When a car is involved in an accident or crime, a great deal of physical evidence like paint, oil, and glass will be left behind by the car. Comparing these substances with those found on or in a suspect's car (or on a suspect) is an important part of any investigation.

Teaching Tip

Invite a police accident-reconstruction specialist to class in person or via a Webcast for a presentation on how he or she determines the sequence of events related to an accident.

Establishing Car Movements

A vehicle's direction of travel can be determined by studying the following:

- Vegetation disturbed as a vehicle entered or left a road
- Patterns of debris cast off by a moving vehicle
- Splash patterns created as a vehicle moved through a puddle of water (or some other substance) or from a wet to dry pavement
- Substance transfer, such as oil leakage from vehicle to pavement or soil (The drips are farther apart as the vehicle accelerates.)
- Tire marks on the pavement or ground (Figure 16-14)

Figure 16-14 *In a multiple-car collision, skid marks can help to determine the path and speed of each vehicle.*

David Frazier/PhotoEdit

Accident Reconstruction

The goal of accident reconstruction is to determine what happened, when it happened, where it happened, why it happened, who was involved, and ultimately, who was at fault. In a hit-and-run situation, one vehicle is gone, but the tire marks found at the scene provide information about the collision and the vehicles involved.

Those involved in the accident may not recall what happened, may lie about what happened, or may have conflicting views of the chain of events leading up to the accident. (Recall that eyewitness accounts of an incident are often unreliable.) However, physical evidence in the form of tire marks at the scene of the accident provide unbiased evidence (aside from human error in the analysis).

When a car accelerates quickly, the tires spin. If brakes are applied hard, the brakes lock. Cars speeding around a turn will produce different types of tire marks. Crime-scene investigators are trained to measure, photograph, identify, and interpret different tire marks.

DIGGING DEEPER
With Forensic Science eCollection

Collision investigators define nine major types of skid marks. Go to the Gale Forensic Science eCollection at **ngl.cengage.com/forensicscience2e** and research the different types. Explain the significance of each type to the reconstruction of an accident.

DIFFERENTIATED LEARNING

Teaching English-Language Learners

Encourage English-language learners to participate in class discussions by first asking them to write down their thoughts in the language with which they are most comfortable. After the class discussion, talk briefly to each student about what he or she thought. Encourage students to keep participating in this way until they feel more comfortable sharing their thoughts with the class as a whole.

Three basic types of tire marks are made during braking when one or more wheels stops turning:

1. Skid marks
   - form when someone brakes suddenly and the wheels lock.
   - provide evidence of the distance brakes were applied.
   - enable calculation of velocity.
   Note the skid marks in Figure 16-15.

2. Yaw marks
   - are produced when a vehicle travels in a curved path faster than the vehicle can handle and skids sideways.
   - occur when tire and road surfaces melt from extreme temperatures.
   - often occur with squealing and smoke.
   - are always curved.
   - are striations (stripes) that form as a tire is dragged sideways in the direction of the spin.

3. Tire scrubs
   - are produced by a damaged or overloaded tire or tires during or immediately after impact.
   - are usually curved and irregular in width.
   - may have striations (stripes).
   - determine the area of impact.

Through experience and experimentation, investigators can also estimate speeds of vehicles using the "skid-to-stop" formula. Measuring the weight of the car, the texture of the road surface, and the total length of the skid marks, and factoring in braking efficiency, investigators can calculate the approximate speed of the vehicle when the brakes were pressed. This information is used to determine if any of the cars involved in the accident were exceeding the speed limit.

Figure 16-15 *Skid marks.*

© Cengage Learning®

DENTAL IMPRESSIONS *Obj. 16.2*

BIOLOGY Locard's Principle of Exchange refers to an exchange of materials between a suspect and a victim or a suspect and a crime scene. Occasionally, a perpetrator will leave behind a bite mark. If a suspect provides a dental impression consistent with the bite mark on a victim, that evidence would once have been considered individual evidence. Today, consistent bite mark evidence alone is not sufficient for a conviction, but it does provide circumstantial evidence that may be helpful in building a case.

Dental Evidence and Forensics

Teeth may be used in forensic investigations in two ways. First, dental records or DNA extracted from teeth can be used to identify remains, such as those of Adolf Hitler, Joseph Mengele, and the victims of the Texas Branch Davidian Church disaster (1993). DNA from teeth can also be used as individual evidence in investigations.

Did you know

Different surfaces have a different capacity for tires to slide, known as a *drag factor*. In estimating a vehicle's speed when the driver applied the brakes, the drag factor of the road surface needs to be factored into the equation. For asphalt, the drag factor is 0.5–0.9, for gravel 0.4–0.8, for ice 0.10–0.25, and for snow 0.10 –0.55.

Teaching Gifted Learners

In accident reconstruction, crime-scene investigators apply the following formula to estimate the speed S (in miles per hour) that a vehicle was traveling at the time its brakes were applied:

$S = \sqrt{30\ Dfn}$

D is the distance (in feet) traveled during the skid,
f is the drag factor of the road, and n is the braking efficiency.

Teaching Tip

Tell students that *skid marks* on pavement are in the direction of travel. *Yaw marks* from rear tires usually track outside the skid marks made by front tires. These yaw marks are curved and caused by steering changes while the brakes are applied. *Tire scrubs* are a type of yaw mark that show zebra-like striping.

Teaching Tip

Human beings have just one set of adult teeth. This means that as teeth are worn down or damaged, artificial substances may be used to replace missing or damaged material. Individuals have unique dental patterns that become more pronounced as they age.

Evaluate

Ask students to explain how braces could change dental impressions. Have them discuss how this might affect dental impression evidence.

Teaching Tip

Ask your state or regional law enforcement agency if a forensic odontologist could make a personal or Web presentation to your class about his or her responsibilities.

Evaluate

Have a class brainstorming session about the pros and cons of the reliability of bite-mark evidence. Keep two lists on the board for the chapter, updating the lists as students raise new ideas.

Evaluate

Have a class brainstorming discussion about the circumstances in which bite marks or teeth could be used as class evidence, and instances in which either could be used as individual evidence. Ask students to describe a circumstance in which bite marks could yield DNA for analysis.

Figure 16-16 *The difference in tooth placement is used to individualize an impression.*

© Cengage Learning®

Second, dental evidence such as bite patterns can help profile suspects in an investigation. The dental pattern of a suspect can be compared to the bite marks associated with a crime scene. As many as 76 points of comparison may be used when comparing dental impressions and bite marks, including number of teeth, position of teeth, chipped teeth, surface indentations, distances between teeth, individual tooth dimensions, alignment of teeth, and the angle of the mouth arch (Figure 16-16). The presence or absence of certain teeth may provide clues about age, diet, economic status, and country of origin. Dental procedures and materials also vary from country to country. All of these factors can provide clues to a person's identity.

Collecting and Analyzing Dental Evidence

If an assailant bites a victim, it is important that the bite marks be photographed as soon as possible. The photographs should include a ruler to establish a reference for size to better compare bite marks to a suspect's dental pattern. When an attacker bites a victim, saliva may be left on the victim's skin. If the bite mark is swabbed with a sterile cotton swab, DNA from the saliva of the bite may be collected and analyzed. The DNA profile is then compared to the DNA of suspects.

Comparing dental patterns is very difficult, and the process is subject to error. The ABFO (American Board of Forensic Odontology) has estimated the error rate of identification to be as high as 63 percent. The Innocence Project has estimated the rate of incorrect identification to be as high as 91 percent. To be admissible in court, at least two forensic odontologists (dental experts) must agree on the identification.

DIGGING DEEPER

With Forensic Science eCollection

Research Canadian serial killer and rapist Wayne Boden's conviction based on bite-mark evidence. Had Canadian authorities ever convicted anyone based on bite mark evidence before? To which country or countries did they turn for help? For information, go to the Gale Forensic Science eCollection at **ngl.cengage.com/forensicscience2e**.

LITERACY

In *Coroner*, Dr. Thomas Noguchi tells the story of his career as "coroner to the stars." He was one of the first to use bite marks as evidence.

528 CHAPTER 16

SUMMARY

- There are three types of impressions: patent impressions, latent impressions, and plastic impressions.

- Generally, any impression evidence made by an object will be considered class evidence unless it has individualizing features.

- Tire impressions at a crime scene may provide information to help identify of a vehicle and provide evidence pertaining to events that occurred before an accident.

DIFFERENTIATED LEARNING

Teaching At-Risk Students

Diet, which varies throughout the world, plays a major role in the health of a person's teeth. Ask students to predict what kind of diet would best promote dental health and what kind might be harmful to teeth. Encourage students to research the case of Ray Krone, a man falsely convicted of a crime on the basis of bite-mark evidence. Ask students to summarize the crime, the evidence, the court case, and his exoneration and the effect it has had on the reputation of bite marks as evidence.

- Tire impressions such as skid marks, yaw marks, or scrubs provide evidence of the car's turning diameter, track width, wheelbase, speed, direction, and when the brakes were applied.

- Dental impressions are considered class evidence, and reliability depends on the number of points of comparison and the clarity of the impression.

- Impression evidence must be carefully documented before it is moved. Photographs of the original impression always accompany the cast or impression or record, such as a gel or electrostatic lift, used in court.

- Impressions may be used several ways: (1) to help identify a person or object, (2) to determine actions that occurred in committing the crime, and (3) to verify accounts given by eyewitnesses.

Did you know

Courts have ruled dental impressions are a manifestation of a physical condition, and suspects cannot refuse to give them.

Close

Organize students into three groups—one each responsible for shoe, tire, and bite mark evidence. Ask each group to summarize how the impression is made and documented (including casting and photography) and whether (and why) the impression is typically class or individual evidence.

CASE STUDIES

Gordon Hay (1967)

In Scotland, the dead body of 15-year-old Linda Peacock was found with a distinct bite mark on her body. Dental impressions were taken from the residents of a nearby boy's detention facility, and a consistent bike mark was found. Gordon Hay became the first person convicted of murder based on a bite mark.

Theodore Bundy (1978)

An escaped death-row inmate wearing a stocking cap entered a Florida State University sorority house and attacked several women inside. Two women were killed and two more seriously injured. One of the women had a bite mark that was photographed as evidence. Subsequent attacks followed in other states. Ted Bundy was charged with the Florida State University attacks after his dental impressions were compared to those left on a victim. The FBI's Behavioral Science Unit had profiled Bundy as a very neat, organized, serial killer. Bundy was so meticulous that he never left fingerprints, even in his own apartment. Bundy was found guilty of murder and was executed in 1989. Before his execution, he implied having committed approximately 50 murders.

AP Images/ASSOCIATED PRESS

Lemuel Smith (1983)

Lemuel Smith had a history of violence, which started while he was a teenager. After spending 17 years in prison for multiple violent crimes, Smith was released. Six weeks later, the bodies of two people were found murdered in the neighborhood where Smith was living. Another rape and murder occurred later the same year. Seven months later, the mutilated body of another female victim was found.

Smith was finally arrested during the kidnapping of another woman. A bite mark on the nose of one of his victims was consistent with an imprint of his teeth. In March 1978, Smith confessed to five murders. Based partly on the bite-mark evidence, Smith was ultimately found guilty of multiple murders, kidnappings, and rapes and sentenced to more than 100 years of prison time.

In 1981, in New York's Green Haven Correctional Facility, a female corrections officer named Donna Payant disappeared. Her mutilated body was found in a landfill. This was the first time in the United States that a female corrections officer was killed on duty. On examination, Payant's body showed a bite mark. Dr. Lowell Levine, a forensic odontologist who worked on one of Smith's earlier convictions, recognized the very distinctive bite mark. Smith was charged, convicted, and sentenced to death. On a legal technicality, his sentence was changed to life imprisonment.

Tire Evidence Solves a Murder (1976)

In Largo, Florida, tire tracks were found next to a dead woman's body. Police sent photographs of the tracks to the late Pete McDonald, Firestone Tire & Rubber Co. tire design engineer. McDonald helped police across the United States solve crimes by analyzing photographs of tire impressions. McDonald could determine the type, size, and brand of the tire that made an impression, as well as the vehicle that was likely to be fitted with the tire. Author of *Tire Imprint Evidence*, he appeared on "true-crime" TV shows as a tire-tread expert and taught tire forensics to the FBI.

In the Florida case, McDonald identified the brand and size of the tire and the likely vehicle. Police checked purchase records for local tire dealerships and found a tire that was consistent with the evidence. A woman who purchased the tire lived with a man who had recently served time in prison for violent crime. Using the tire impression information, police found a suspect.

Pete McDonald

The police asked the tire dealer who sold the tire for help in gathering evidence against the suspected murderer. The dealer agreed and called the suspect and told him his tires had been recalled. The dealer offered new tires to replace the old ones. The suspect came to the shop and traded for the new set of tires. The old tires were sent to McDonald for further analysis. The tire impression, combined with other evidence, convinced a jury to convict the man and send him back to prison for murder.

Randal Gene Mars, a 48-year-old homeless man, was found dead outside an abandoned building in Las Vegas, Nevada. He had died from strangulation with blunt-force trauma as a contributing factor, and his death was ruled a homicide.

Investigators noted severe bruising on Mars's face and a shoe print on his forehead. After a search of the building, two men were arrested for trespassing. One of the men had a bloodstain on his jacket and had been previously convicted of burglary. The other suspect had a bloody shoe. The pattern of the shoe's sole was consistent with the shoe print pattern on Mars's forehead. After being confronted with the shoe-print evidence, the men admitted to beating Mars and were charged with murder.

Think Critically

Evidence is considered more reliable—and more likely admissible by the court and acceptable by juries—if the side presenting it can assign a statistical probability that it came from a specific individual. In the Mars case, what type of data would have been needed to demonstrate that the shoe print was more likely to have come from someone other than the person who was convicted? Is this evidence considered class or individual evidence? What other evidence was found that linked the suspect to the victim?

CASTS AND IMPRESSIONS   531

Careers

Dr. Lowell Levine, a forensic odontologist from New York, has helped connect Lemuel Smith to his victims using bite marks. Check out http://www.crimelibrary.com/notorious_ murders/not_guilty/ lemuel_smith/7.html. For more information about Dr. Levine and the Lemuel Smith case, as well as standards set up for bite mark evidence by the American Board of Forensic Odontologists (ABFO), go to the Gale Forensic Science eCollection at ngl.cengage.com/forensicscience2e

Careers *in Forensics*

Before CSI, There Was Quincy; Before Quincy, There Was Thomas Noguchi

Thomas Noguchi

In 1961, Thomas Noguchi emigrated from Japan and was hired as a coroner with Los Angeles County. Just a year into the job, he performed the autopsy on Marilyn Monroe. Fame and fortune have followed him ever since. He did the autopsies on Senator Robert F. Kennedy, Sharon Tate, Natalie Wood, and John Belushi. If a case seemed particularly important or perplexing, Dr. Noguchi was called. Before the age of big forensic labs, Dr. Noguchi was a pioneer forensic investigator, going over every crime scene with a fine-toothed comb. With a career as a coroner spanning decades, Dr. Noguchi has numerous stories to tell about how his forensic investigations have helped the dead tell their tales.

In an interview with *Omni* magazine, Dr. Noguchi told of "one homicide I investigated, the homeowner returned early, surprising the burglar, so the burglary ended in murder. But the burglar was hungry, so he had a bite to eat before leaving. We found distinct teeth marks in the cheese!" In another case, Dr. Noguchi examined the body right at the crime scene, to determine if a truck had dumped her, as it appeared. The corpse told Dr. Noguchi otherwise. She had been brought to the site alive, and later shot. Because the murderer had to get out of his van to shoot the victim,

the area was searched for footprints. When the footprints were found, an arrest was made.

One of Dr. Noguchi's claims to fame was that he invented a unique technique to cast a stab wound. Through trial and error, Dr. Noguchi found just what he needed: a metal alloy that was liquid at the boiling temperature of water, but quickly hardened into a solid. He injects the alloy into the stab wound, and five minutes later can pull out a detailed three-dimensional replica of the weapon. You can read more about Dr. Noguchi's cases in his book, *Coroner*, published in 1983, in which he demonstrates one of his favorite sayings, "Let the dead speak for himself."

The career of Thomas Noguchi has its own tales to tell. He was fired from his job as coroner for L.A. County twice because of his willingness to openly talk to the media about a case. In each instance, he was reinstated. In fact, Dr. Noguchi has been very outspoken about the consequences of recreational drug use and speaks of drug designers as mass murderers. Dr. Noguchi is now in his eighties, but he continues to write and to educate. He feels death and its study are very important. He has said, "There are lessons to be learned from death. And because these death events are repeated over and over again, we must strive to understand them."

Learn More About It
▶ To learn more about careers casting impressions at crime scenes, go to
ngl.cengage.com/forensicscience2e.

True or False

1. From tire marks left on pavement, it is possible to estimate the speed of a vehicle at the time it began braking. *Obj. 16.6*

2. Knowing the sole pattern on a shoe may enable investigators to identify the shoe's manufacturer. *Obj. 16.1*

3. If you can measure the length of the foot or shoe impression, then you can accurately estimate the person's height. *Obj. 16.1, 16.2*

4. It is possible to cast an impression in the snow if you use a casting material that does not generate heat. *Obj. 16.7*

Multiple Choice

5. When processing a crime scene for impression evidence, which of the following steps should be taken first? *Obj. 16.4*
   a) Document the location of the impression.
   b) Photograph the impression.
   c) Measure the impression.
   d) Note any unique characteristics of the impression.

6. Which of the following is true? *Obj. 16.5, 16.6*
   a) A vehicle's direction of travel can be detected by careful observation of disturbed vegetation and splash patterns cast off from the vehicle.
   b) Ribs are the indentations found in a tire.
   c) Since tires have the same pattern over the entire tire, it's only necessary to ink half of the tire when getting its ink impression.
   d) Wheelbase can be measured from a single tire.

7. What information can be learned from skid-mark analysis of an accident? *Obj. 16.6*
   a) manufacturer of the car
   b) direction of travel
   c) when brakes were applied
   d) Both b and c are correct.

Short Answer

8. Compare and contrast patent, latent, and plastic impressions. *Obj. 16.3*

9. Design a demonstration to compare and contrast the foot or shoe impressions of *Obj. 16.1, 16.2, 16.4*
   a) a person running versus walking.
   b) a person limping versus walking normally.
   c) the prints of a tall person versus a shorter person.
   d) the prints of a heavy person versus a light person.

10. Elaborate on the tire characteristics that can be used to compare a tire impression with a suspect's tire. *Obj. 16.5*

Chapter 16 Review

True or False

1. True
2. True
3. False
4. True

Multiple Choice

5. B
6. A
7. D

Short Answer

8. Latent prints are not visible to the unaided eye, but patent and plastic impressions are. Plastic impressions have more depth than latent and patent impressions.

9. Using inked sneakers on newsprint, compare and contrast marks made by the following:
   a. running across paper and then walking across paper
   b. limping across paper and then walking normally across paper
   c. a tall person walking next to a short person
   d. a heavy person walking next to a light person

10. Size, width, tread pattern, wear pattern, presence or absence of foreign objects embedded in tire, damage to tire

11. If the impression had unique characteristics, it could be considered individual evidence—for example, if the person had distinctive tooth alignment or broken teeth. If the tire or shoe impression had unique wear patterns or objects embedded in it, it could be considered individual evidence.

12. a. Luminol is sprayed onto latent bloodstains. Luminol makes the stain visible so it can be photographed and preserved.

    b. Dry powders are good for dry surfaces.

    c. Electrostatic lifting can reveal the fine dust left by a shoe. An impression is made by applying an electrostatic charge to a piece of lifting paper. The dust adheres to the lifting film and a photograph can be taken of the image.

    d. Plaster casting is most useful for foot and tire impressions.

13. See Figures 16-11 and 16-12.

14. a. The shoes had blood on them from the crime scene, and O. J. Simpson was a suspect.

    b. O. J. Simpson wears size 12 shoes.

    c. A photograph was found showing O. J. Simpson wearing Bruno Magli shoes. This photo was not available during the criminal trial. At the civil trial with this new evidence, Simpson was found responsible for the death of his former wife and Ron Goldman.

15. Blood evidence could identify a victim. Tire tracks could reveal type of tread pattern and brand of tire. Track width and wheelbase may provide clues to the type of car. The turn could provide evidence of the turning

11. A defense lawyer argues that any type of impression evidence—foot, shoe, tire, or dental—must be considered class evidence and not individual evidence. With what type of impression evidence could you counter that argument? *Obj. 16.1, 16.2*

12. Compare and contrast the different methods of revealing latent impressions. Include in your answer the type of surface that is most suited to each of the methods. *Obj. 16.6*
    a) Luminol for dried blood
    b) dusting with dry powders
    c) electrostatic lifting
    d) plaster of Paris casting

13. Draw a simple sketch of a car and indicate how the following measurements are taken:
    a) wheelbase
    b) front track width
    c) rear track width
    d) turning diameter

14. Summarize the significance of the bloody size 12 Bruno Magli shoe prints in the O. J. Simpson civil trial. Include answers to the following in your brief summary: *Obj. 16.1, 16.2, 16.4*
    a) How did this evidence link the wearer of the shoes to the crime scene?
    b) Why were the shoes believed to belong to O. J. Simpson?
    c) What new evidence was presented at the civil trial that was not known during the criminal trial?

15. A house was burglarized. A vehicle left tracks in the muddy driveway. It appeared that the car parked in front of the home and made a U-turn when it departed. Although no body was found, crime-scene investigators found blood in the kitchen and hallway. What type of evidence could help the investigators learn more about the suspect(s), vehicle, and events at the crime scene? *Obj. 16.1, 16.2, 16.5*

16. Describe the role of each of the following when trying to document a foot or tire impression: *Obj. 16.7*
    a) plaster of Paris
    b) snow wax
    c) hair spray
    d) ruler

Going Further

1. Prepare a table, poster, or PowerPoint presentation that distinguishes different tire marks: skids, yaws, and scrubs. Include the following in your answer:
   a) whether they are curved or straight
   b) how they are formed
   c) what information can be obtained through their examination

diameter, which could also help identify the type of car that left the crime scene. If the ground was muddy, footprint impressions might be found in the mud that could be used to help include or exclude suspects. Footprints could also indicate the number of people at the crime scene. If the car had an oil leak, evidence would be on the ground. This damage would narrow the pool of suspect cars.

16. a. Dental stone or plaster of Paris is used to make the cast.

    b. Snow wax is used to fix impressions in the snow. It does not generate heat and will not melt the snow.

    c. Hair spray is used to solidify the surface so the impression will not collapse.

    d. A ruler should be in all photos of impressions as a size reference.

2. Research how the speed of a vehicle involved in an accident can be calculated using skid marks. One formula used is

$$speed = \sqrt{30Dfn}$$

Speed is in miles per hour.

D is the skid distance in feet.

f is the drag factor of the road surface.

n is the braking efficiency of the vehicle.

Bibliography

Books and Journals

Bodziak, W. J. *Footwear Impression Evidence: Detection, Recovery, and Examination, 2nd Edition.* Boca Raton, FL: CRC Press, 2000.

Evans, Colin. *The Casebook of Forensic Detection.* New York: John Wiley & Sons, 1998.

Hilderbrand, Dwayne S., and Tia Kalla (illustrator). *Footwear: The Missed Evidence—A Field Guide to the Collection and Preservation of Forensic Footwear Impression Evidence.* Wildomar, CA: Staggs Publishing, 1999.

Johansen, Raymond J., and C. M. Bowers. *Digital Analysis of Bite Mark Evidence.* Indianapolis, IN: Forensic Imaging Institute, 2000.

DiMaggio, John A., and Wesley Vernon. *Forensic Podiatry.* New York: Humana Press, 2011.

McDonald, Peter. *Tire Imprint Evidence (Practical Aspects of Criminal and Forensic Investigations).* Boca Raton, FL: CRC Press, 1992.

Nause, Lawren. *Forensic Tire Impression Identification.* Ottawa (ON), Canada: Canadian Police Research Center, 2001.

Noguchi, Thomas. *Coroner.* New York: Pocket Books, 1985.

Internet Resources

ngl.cengage.com/forensicscience2e (Gale Forensic Science eCollection)

http://www.evidencemagazine.com/index.php?option=com_content&task=view&id=41 (John A. DiMaggio, D.P.M. "Forensic Podiatry, Part One of Two")

http://www.evidencemagazine.com/index.php?option=com_content&task=view&id=27 (John A. DiMaggio, D.P.M. "Forensic Podiatry, Part Two of Two")

http://science.howstuffworks.com/impression-evidence1.htm

http://www.forensicsciencesimplified.org/fwtt/how.html

https://dps.mn.gov/divisions/bca/bca-divisions/forensic-science/Pages/trace-shoeprints-tiretracks.aspx

http://science.howstuffworks.com/forensic-dentistry3.htm

www.crimelibrary.com/criminal_minds/forensics/bite marks/4.htm

www.crimelibrary.com/notorious_murders/famous/simpson/brentwood_2.html

Teaching Tip

Ask a dentist to give you dental impressions that are no longer in use. These provide good teaching tools to show students the variety of teeth found in individuals. From the casts, students could make dental impressions (refer to Activity 16-5). Ask students to observe the top and bottom casts. Ask students to make measurements from the casts that could be used to help identify a bite impression made from the cast. Provide students with rulers, calipers, and a protractor.

Teaching Tip

Ask students to measure and record information about their family car or obtain the information from the Internet.

Car: wheelbase and track width (front and rear)

Tires: tread pattern (either a photo or an inked impression)

Create a database that could be used when investigating crime scenes.

Teaching Tip

Additional Resource: Warrington, Dick. "Impression Evidence." *Forensic Magazine.* April 1, 2007.

Background

In this activity, students make a plaster cast of a shoe print and a tire impression both inside and outside the classroom.

Time Required to Complete Activity

two 45-minute periods

Safety Precautions

1. Students must wear safety goggles when mixing plaster and when using hair spray.

2. Remind students to dispose of unused plaster correctly and not to dump it down a drain.

3. If doing the lab inside, then use pump-style hair spray and not aerosol. Using aerosol sprays may pose a problem for students with respiratory problems, such as asthma.

4. Plaster of Paris dust may be irritating for students with respiratory problems, such as asthma.

Material Costs

1 bag of sandbox sand, *not* white sand (50 lb ~$6.00); sand can be reused.
1 bag plaster of Paris (40 lb ~$9.00); this will make about 20 footprint impressions.
1 can hair spray (~$2.50)

Teaching Tip

Cardboard boxes with handles are useful because students can carry the box by the handles. Large distribution stores usually have free boxes. To make the impression, line the bottom of the cardboard box with the kitchen-sized garbage bag. Pour all of the sand from the 39-ounce coffee can onto the garbage bag.

Making a Plaster of Paris Cast *Obj. 16.7, 16.8*

Objective:

By the end of this activity, you will be able to:

1. Make a plaster of Paris cast of shoe or tire impressions.
2. Analyze the cast and describe features that may help lead to the identity of the person or tire.

Background:

Shoeprints and other impressions made by suspects can often provide clues that help solve a crime. In addition to photographing the shoe or tire print, investigators produce a cast of the print. In this activity, you will make a plaster of Paris cast of an impression.

Materials:

(per group of two students making one shoe impression)

© Cengage Learning®

1 cardboard box (shoe box-size or larger)
1 large plastic garbage bag (at least kitchen-sized)
1 empty plastic 39-oz. coffee can filled with sandbox sand
1 quart-sized resealable plastic bag filled with plaster of Paris (premeasured)
1 sneaker or boot that shows a tread pattern on the sole
1 empty, small coffee can (any 13-oz. metal or plastic coffee can)
1 can inexpensive aerosol hair spray (to share with other groups)
1 paintbrush
1 pencil, awl, or sharpened skewer
1 stiff toothbrush (A used one is fine.)
1 wooden paint stir stick or paddle
12-inch ruler
safety goggles
1 spray bottle of water (to share)
newspapers
(optional) 1 gallon freezer plastic bag
(optional) several tree twigs or wooden cooking skewers
(optional) digital camera
(optional) shoe box for storage of cast

Teaching Tip

Gallon-sized plastic bags can be used for mixing the plaster of Paris.

Teaching Tip

Recycle/reuse:
Plastic bags
Coffee cans
Paint stirrers
Paint brushes
Store the sand inside the large coffee cans to reuse the following year. The other materials can all be stored either in a box or plastic containers. Each year, refill the plaster of Paris, restock hair spray, and get new cardboard boxes.

Time Required to Complete Activity:

Two 45-minute periods: one to make the cast and one the following day to clean and analyze the cast

SAFETY PRECAUTIONS:

1. Handle all materials as directed by your instructor.
2. Wear safety goggles when mixing plaster of Paris and when using the hair-spray. Don't spray toward any of your classmates. The hair spray may irritate respiratory passages.
3. Dispose of unused plaster of Paris in a garbage container; do not dump it down the sink drain!
4. Thoroughly wash all equipment as soon as possible after use. After dumping out any excess plaster of Paris, allow the remaining plaster to dry. The old plaster can be removed after it dries by pounding on the sides of the plastic coffee can.
5. Work outside if conditions permit. If you are working inside, use newspaper to cover any desktops. The sand may scratch the surface of some countertops.
6. Students with respiratory problems should avoid working in confined areas near plaster of Paris dust and hair spray.

Procedure:

PART A: PREPARING A SHOE IMPRESSION

This procedure allows you to prepare the impression inside the classroom, or produce an impression of a footprint left in the sand or soil outside the classroom.

1. Remove all materials from the cardboard box.
2. Place the cardboard box on top of newspapers. Line the cardboard box with the plastic garbage bag.
3. Empty the sand from the large coffee container onto the garbage bag liner in the bottom of the cardboard box.
4. Using the water spray bottle, moisten the sand thoroughly and mix with your hands. Moist soil will produce a better impression. Using your hand or the paint stir stick, smooth out the surface of the sand in the cardboard box.
5. Step firmly into the sand. Do not rock your foot back and forth. Gently remove your foot from the sand by lifting your foot straight up. View your impression. If it does not seem to be a good impression, smooth out the sand and repeat the process.
6. Hold the hair spray can 12 inches above the impression and spray. If you hold the can too close, the spray will destroy your impression. Spray the entire area of the impression, along with one inch of the sand surrounding the impression. The sand will be wet.
7. Place a ruler next to the impression. Photograph the impression and the ruler. Take several photos from directly above the impression and perpendicular to it.
8. Fill the small coffee container halfway with cool tap water and then pour the water into the large coffee can. (Note: The water is added *before* the plaster.)

Teaching TIp

In advance of the lab, ask students to bring in shoe boxes for their finished casts. Wrap the cast in newspaper and put it in the shoe box to avoid leaving a trail of sand in the hallway.

Teaching Tip

If students create a bare foot print instead of a shoe print, provide an area where they can wash sand off their feet without washing the sand down the drain.

Procedures

1. Print, copy, and distribute Act 16-1 SH from the IRCD, Chapter 16. Make sure students read all directions before beginning the activity.
2. Casting plaster of Paris impressions can be done easily both inside or outside the classroom.
3. This lab activity requires just a few materials and costs very little. The students can supply many of these items, such as the empty coffee cans, old paintbrushes, and toothbrushes. Hardware stores are usually willing to provide you with free paint stirrers.
4. A key to making this quick and easy is setting up the lab kits for each team in advance. This reduces the time needed to cast the impression, and provides an easy way to reassemble materials after the labs are completed.
5. If you choose to set up lab boxes in advance, the impressions can be made in one class period. The cardboard box can later be used to contain the sand when preparing the impression.
6. The impressions need to dry before the students move them. If doing this activity inside, be sure to have the students set them up in an area where the impression will be able to harden for at least one hour, preferably overnight, after pouring the plaster of Paris.

   Use an empty 39-ounce coffee can to mix the plaster of Paris. Be sure to *first* add water to the can, and *then* slowly stir in the plaster. Use cool water to lengthen the hardening time. Stir until the mixture has the consistency of pancake batter. This will take a few minutes. If it appears to be too thin, either stir longer or add a small amount of plaster. If students stir too long, the plaster will set before use.
7. Substitute as you see fit any materials for the frame you have on hand. (Shoeboxes work well.)

Teaching Tips

1. Do not use white playground sand. It does not provide enough contrast when cleaning and visualizing the print.

2. Store premeasured sand in large 39-oz. plastic coffee containers. Completely fill the container with sand. Do not substitute regular soil because the impression will not be as distinct as an impression made from sand.

3. The ratio of plaster to water is approximately two parts plaster to one part water.

4. Premeasure the plaster (one full small canister for coffee, 13 oz.) and dump the plaster for one impression into your mixing container. Have the students save the resealable bag and the kitchen garbage bag so that you can reuse them for the next class.

5. An alternative to mixing in the large coffee can is to use a gallon-sized plastic bag. This creates less mess as they just squeeze to mix and then pour directly from the bags.

6. Using warm (or hot) water makes plaster harden quicker, so it is best to use cool or room-temperature water.

7. Be sure that students do not overstir the plaster. If students continue to stir, the plaster will begin to harden. Students should only stir till the plaster has the consistency of pancake batter.

8. Adding twigs (or skewers) to the casting as it hardens gives the casting additional strength.

9. Sand can be reused. Before storing, allow the sand to dry and remove any pieces of leftover plaster.

10. When photographing the prints before casting the impression, you may want to have one student assume the role of forensic photographer and photograph all of the impressions. Be sure students include a ruler in the photograph. Photograph using natural sunlight or indirect lighting if possible.

11. Dental stone may be preferable to plaster of Paris because it is two to three times stronger, but it is about 10 times more expensive.

12. Premeasuring and prepackaging the plaster of Paris in resealable bags can save time. It also prevents excess plaster dust from being spread around.

13. Do not dump plaster of Paris down the sink drain. Have large trash containers available.

9. Slowly add the plaster of Paris to the water. Do not dump the plaster into the water all at once. Stir continuously as the plaster is being added to the water.

10. Stir just until you have a smooth consistency (similar to pancake batter) and until the plaster is dissolved. Do not overstir, because this will cause your plaster to become too thick.

11. Hold the paint stirrer about an inch or two above the footprint. Pour the plaster of Paris onto the paint stirrer, not directly onto the impression. (This keeps the plaster from splashing into the impression and collapsing it.)

12. If the impression of the shoe is small, you will not need to use all of the plaster of Paris. Add enough plaster of Paris to cover the impression, but do not overload the impression.

13. Discard the unused plaster of Paris in the garbage. *Do not dump plaster of Paris down the sink drain.*

14. Gently smooth out the top of the plaster of Paris with the paint stirrer, distributing the plaster evenly over the footprint. Twigs or wooden skewers can be added to the plaster at this point to provide additional strength while hardening. They should be gently placed lengthwise in the impression. Do not move the cast for at least 45 minutes.

15. Allow the cast to harden for at least five minutes. Use an awl, stick, or pencil to label the shoe print with your initials, date, and case number.

16. Do not attempt to lift the cast until the plaster has set, at least 45 minutes. Lifting the cast too early results in the plaster cracking.

17. After the plaster has set, gently pry up the plaster cast with your fingers along its edge. Turn it over. It will probably still be damp on the side next to the sand.

18. Gently brush away the sand with the paintbrush.

19. Use the toothbrush or awl to remove any additional loose sand.

Cleanup:

20. Wipe clean and dry the pencil, awl, stirring stick, and small coffee can.

21. Save the resealable plastic bag so that it can be refilled for later use.

22. Tap on the side of the coffee can with your hand to loosen any dried plaster, and discard the loose plaster in the garbage. Wipe the inside of the can with a paper towel.

23. Mix sand by hand to break up the hair spray coating.

24. Remove and discard any residual plaster from the sand.

25. Pick up the opposite sides of the plastic bag liner (filled with sand) and funnel the sand back into the now-clean, dry, 39-oz. coffee can.

26. Shake out and save the plastic liner.

27. Shake out the paintbrush and toothbrush to remove any residual sand.

28. Place all lab materials in the cardboard box and return them to your instructor.

29. Sweep and clean the area surrounding your setup to remove all sand.

Analysis

30. Measure the length and width of the cast. Record any characteristics of the cast that may provide clues to the identity of the person who made it.

31. Consider how you could improve upon this method of producing a cast of an impression.

Storage of Castings:

32. After the casts are dry, wrap them in newspapers or paper towels, tape them closed with masking tape, and store them in shoe boxes.

PART B: CASTING AN IMPRESSION FROM A TIRE TRACK

Prepare a cast of an impression found in soil outside the building. Follow the same directions as in Part A, except if the tire impression is long, you will need to mix more than one can of plaster of Paris.

Cleaning a sneaker impression.

© Cengage Learning®

Questions:

1. Based on your measurements and observations of the cast of the impression, are there any clues to the identity of the individual? Cite evidence from your observations to support your claims.

2. What was the purpose of spraying with the hair spray?

3. Why is it important to brush the excess sand from the plaster cast?

4. Shoe prints can be cast in the winter from snow, but plaster of Paris cannot be used. What would happen if you tried to produce a cast of an impression in snow using plaster of Paris?

5. Do you agree or disagree with the following? If the sole pattern, shoe shape, and shoe size are consistent with the shoe of the suspect, then there is sufficient evidence for a conviction.

6. Suppose two people both wear size 10 sneakers of the same brand and model. Describe characteristics that could be found in the impressions of these two sneakers that could determine which of the people left the print.

7. Describe the shoe impression patterns that might distinguish between the following:
   a. an obese person and a thin person
   b. a person shuffling and a person walking normally
   c. a person who is running and a person who is walking
   d. a person walking with an injured right foot and a person walking with two uninjured feet
   e. a person walking who is in a hurry and a person walking at normal speed

8. Prepare a list of characteristics of tires that could be used to distinguish one tire from another.

Answers

Check students' castings and cleanup techniques.

- -

Questions

1. Usually, impression evidence is considered class evidence, unless the impression has particularly unusual characteristics.

2. The hair spray forms a barrier between the plaster and the print and helps protect the shape of the print.

3. Removing excess sand speeds up drying and allows you to see more detail.

4. Plaster of Paris generates heat, which would melt the snow print.

5. These characteristics are class evidence, not individual evidence.

6. Sample answers: degree of wear on the soles; depth of impression because of weight; where the wear patterns are most pronounced would depend on the person's foot (e.g., some people wear down the heel before the ball of the foot, and some people wear the inside of the sole before the outside).

7. a. A heavier person makes a deeper impression.
   b. In between footprints, a scuff mark would be visible.
   c. The stride is longer if someone is running.
   d. The injured foot may not have as deep an impression as the healthy foot. The footprint may only show the toe or heel of the shoe.
   e. A person in a hurry will make longer strides with uneven footprints.

8. Size, tread pattern, wear pattern, depth of tread, uneven tread, damaged tread, or items embedded in the tire.

ACTIVITY 16-2

Background
In this activity, students explore the relationship between foot length, shoe size, shoe length, and height.

Safety Precautions
There are no safety precautions for this lab.

Time Required to Complete Activity
40 minutes

Procedures

1. Print, copy, and distribute Activity Sheet 16-2 SH and Act 16-2 SH Table and Graph from the IRCD, Chapter 16.

2. Make sure students read all directions *before* beginning the activity.

3. Before measuring their shoes and feet, be sure that all students measure using the same technique. Make sure they:
   - Use the right foot.
   - Stand up when taking all measurements.
   - Measure foot length while wearing socks.
   - Measure their foot length from their heel to the end of their *longest* toe, even if it is not their big toe.
   - Be sure that the top of the head is level when measuring height.

4. Be careful when using plastic rulers. Some students may stand on the ruler to measure their foot and can easily break the ruler. Ask a local shoe store to donate a shoe sizer; this will eliminate any differences resulting from brand and type of shoes. If this is used, wipe the surface with an alcohol prep pad between students.

5. If personal measurements are listed on the board, suggest that students use a code name. Some students may be sensitive about the size of their feet.

ACTIVITY 16-2

Shoe Size, Foot Size, and Height *Obj. 16.1, 16.2, 16.4*

Objectives:
By the end of this activity, you will be able to:
1. Measure your foot and shoe lengths.
2. Collect data from your classmates comparing shoe length to height.
3. Analyze the data to determine if there is any relationship between shoe length and height.
4. Compare the class data of shoe length and height to the Figure 16-9 graph.
5. Discuss why the relationship of shoe length to height is more reliable for adults than for teenagers.

Background:
Shoe prints left at a crime scene have been photographed, and casts have been made of the impressions. Is it possible to estimate the suspect's height based on shoe size? In this activity, you will compare and contrast shoe size and height data from your class and explore the relationships between shoe size, foot size, and height.

Materials:
Act 16-2 SH
Act 16-2 SH Table and Graph or Figures 16-8 and 16-9 from the text
1 pen or pencil
1 calculator
1 yardstick
12-inch ruler
4 large sheets of poster paper (or projector with Excel spreadsheet) and markers

Time Required to Complete Activity:
40 minutes (students in pairs)

SAFETY PRECAUTIONS:
none

Procedure:

PART A: SHOE AND FOOT LENGTH COMPARISON
1. Measure the length of your right shoe (or footprint cast) at its greatest length to the nearest one quarter of an inch. To measure your shoe size, stand next to a 12-inch ruler. Place the end of the ruler next to the end of your heel and measure to the end of your big toe.

540   Casts and Impressions

Teaching Tip
Warn students a day ahead that they will be measuring their foot size in their stocking feet. This gives students time to discuss any concerns with you before the class and gives them a chance to wear socks without holes.

540   CHAPTER 16

2. Record the length of your shoe in Act 16-2 Data Table 1. This should be approximately 1 to 1¼ inches longer than your foot.

3. Remove your right shoe. Stand alongside the ruler. Place the ruler at the end of your heel and measure the length of your right foot at its longest point. (Some people's second toe is longer than their big toe.) Measure to the nearest ⅛ inch.

4. Record the length of your foot in Data Table 1.

5. Refer to Figure 16-8 (or Act 16-2 SH Table and Graph). What shoe size is given *in the table* for your foot length? Record your answer in Data Table 1.

6. When you purchase shoes, what shoe size do you buy? Record your answer in Data Table 1.

7. Are your shoe size and the estimated shoe size in Figure 16-8 the same? Record your answer.

8. Record your gender in Data Table 1. Record the difference (if any) between your shoe size and your estimated shoe size. If your shoe size is larger than the estimated shoe size in the table, indicate that with a + sign. If it is smaller, then use a − sign.

9. Repeat Steps 1 to 8 and take your partner's measurements. Record all answers in Data Table 1.

Data Table 1: Foot Length and Shoe Size

Question	Your Measurements (inches)	Your Partner's Measurements (inches)
Length of shoe		
Length of foot		
Shoe size according to Figure 16-8		
Shoe size		
Is your shoe size the same as the size in Figure 16-8 in your text? (Yes or No)		
Difference between size and estimated size (+ or −)		
Gender (Male or Female)		

PART B: ESTIMATING HEIGHT BASED ON SHOE SIZE

10. Measure your height. To do this, remove your shoes. Stand against a wall looking straight ahead. Have your partner measure your height to the nearest half-inch. Record your answer in Data Table 2.

11. Using your shoe size and the information found in Figure 16-9, what is your height estimate in inches? Record your answer in Data Table 2.

12. Are your height and the height estimate according to Figure 16-9 the same? Record your answer in Data Table 2 as "Yes" or "No."

13. What is the difference between your height and your height estimate according to the table? Record your answer in Data Table 2.

14. Repeat Steps 10 to 13 for your lab partner. Record the information in Data Table 2. Record your answers and gender in Data Table 2.

Teaching Tip

Some students may be sensitive about the size of their feet. To avoid any issues, announce in advance when you will do this activity and ask students to see you in advance if there are any concerns. Each of those students can be placed in a group of three instead of two.

Science

MATHEMATICS

MATHEMATICS

A scatter plot is a graph that shows the relationship between two sets of data. In this case, the scatter plot in Figure 16-9 shows a person's shoe size and height. Scatter plots can be used to show trends. Three different types of trends can be illustrated in a scatter plot: positive correlation, negative correlation, and no correlation.

Questions

1. There is some variation; one foot is usually slightly bigger than the other. Also, if the feet are especially wide, then the person may require a larger size.

2. Answers may vary, but estimated height is usually within 2 inches of the data listed on the graph.

3. Females typically find that their data more closely relate to the graph. Because females typically complete their growth earlier than males, they do not find as much variation between shoe size and height. Because high school boys have not completed their growth, it's not unusual for them to have larger feet in proportion to their height.

4. Twelfth-grade data would most likely better correspond to the graph because those students are closer to completing their growth.

5. Variables affecting height, shoe size, and growth rate are many: weight, individual differences in the growth process, nutrition, disease, and injuries.

6. Time of day should be factored into these data; later in the day, the foot may be slightly larger than earlier in the day. To improve consistency, the same person should take measurements to ensure the same method is employed. A smaller unit of measure could be used to improve accuracy in measurement. To take more accurate measurements, use calipers instead of a ruler. Collect data from the males, examine it, and compare it for accuracy, and then repeat the process for the females.

15. Using the board or two large sheets of poster paper, have each student record the difference between his or her shoe size and estimated shoe size according to Figure 16-9. Separate the data for males and females.

16. Using the board or two large sheets sheet of poster paper, have each student record the difference between his or her height and estimated height from Data Table 2. Separate the data for males and females.

Data Table 2: Shoe Size and Height Comparison

Question	Your Data (inches)	Your Partner's Data (inches)
Height		
Estimated height according to Figure 16-9 in your text		
Are your height and the estimated height the same? (Yes or No)		
What is the difference between your height and the estimated height according to the graph?		
Gender (Male or Female)		

Questions:

1. Do the class data show a relationship between shoe size and foot length? Cite data from the activity that support your claim.
2. Do the class data show a relationship between shoe size and height?
3. Do males or females have data that more closely correspond to Figure 16-9? Explain.
4. If you did this activity with ninth-graders rather than twelfth-graders, whose data would better correspond to the graph? Explain why.
5. What variables can influence someone's height, shoe size, and growth rate?
6. How could you modify this procedure to ensure more reliable results?
7. Should crime-scene investigators use shoe size to estimate a suspect's height? Cite evidence to support your claim.
8. Consider another formula to estimate someone's height based on foot length:
   foot length (in inches) $\times$ 6.54 = height (in inches)
   Use this formula to calculate your own height:
   Your height based on this formula = _____ inches.
   Your actual height = _____ inches.
   Is this a more accurate mathematical relationship between foot size and height? Explain why or why not.

Going Further:

1. Graph the data for your class, comparing shoe size and height in females. Draw a best-fit line.
2. Graph the data for your class, comparing shoe size and height in males. Draw a best-fit line.

Combine the results and re-examine the accuracy for the total population. Measure the foot and shoe twice and take the average. Students wearing sneakers, work boots, or dress shoes would alter the data. The graph comparing shoe size and height did not indicate if the height measurement should be taken with or without shoes.

7. Crime-scene investigators should measure the impression size to get an estimate of the height. The height is not exact, but an estimate could provide a height range to help exclude or include suspects.

8. Answers will vary. This formula was derived by combining values for this activity over a few years.

Tire Impressions and Analysis *Obj. 16.5, 16.8*

Objectives:

By the end of this activity, you will be able to:

1. Prepare tire tread impressions from a tire.
2. Describe how to create tire tread impressions using four different methods.
3. Analyze and photograph tire treads.
4. Compare a partial tire tread impression with two complete tire tread patterns.
5. Evaluate the partial tire tread impression to determine if it is consistent with one of the suspect's tires.

Background:

Mailboxes were being knocked down and vandalized on Oak Hill Drive. Bicycle tire tracks were identified near all the damaged mailboxes. Two neighborhood teenagers were on the list of suspects. Tread impressions were made from their bike tires and compared with tread impressions found at the sites of vandalism. Determine if the tread impressions made at the crime scene are consistent with the treads of the bicycles.

Time Required to Complete Activity: 40 minutes

Materials:

Act 16-3 SH Data Tables
(for each team of two students)
petroleum jelly and fingerprint powder *or*
ink pad and small paint roller *or*
    inkless pad and sensitive paper
newsprint or a cardboard box
marker
gloves
scissors
large chalk
rulers and a meter stick
at least two bicycle tires on rims or two small tractor
    tires or lawn mower tires
unknown tire tread sample approximately 0.6 meter
    in length
camera to photograph evidence

Chalked tire impression.

© Cengage Learning®

Background

In this activity, students create two tire impressions, examine them, and record their findings. They also examine a partial tire tread pattern and attempt to match this pattern to one of the other two.

Time Required to Complete Activity

40 minutes

Safety Precautions

1. Ensure that students do not take tire impressions in an area with moving vehicles.
2. Students need to wear gloves when working with tires.
3. It is best to complete this activity outside. It can be very messy.

Procedures

1. Print, copy, and distribute Act 16-3 SH from the IRCD, Chapter 16.

2. Make sure students read all directions *before* beginning the activity.

3. Use the same materials for Suspects 1 and 2.

Teaching Tips

- Use one of the two suspect's tires to produce a tire tread sample that will be used for the crime scene.

- Use any of the three different methods mentioned to produce a tire tread mark. The least messy method is using an inkless ink pad and a small roller. However, this tends to be more expensive than simply using a fingerprint ink pad. The petroleum jelly and fingerprint powder give you a good impression, but the method is quite messy.

- To conserve materials, use a small tire such as a mountain bike tire that shows a tread pattern or a small lawn mower tire. Some toy trucks could be used if they have a tread pattern.

- Provide gloves to students who will be handling tires.

SAFETY PRECAUTIONS:

Make sure the surface of the tire to be examined is free from hazardous materials (e.g., glass, nails). Wear gloves when working. This activity can be very messy and is best done outside. If working inside, be sure to cover the floor with newspaper or cardboard.

Procedure:

1. Place either a piece of newsprint about 2.5 meters long or cardboard pieces at least 2.5 meters long on the floor (cardboard boxes cut into 1-meter lengths and a width of at least 20 cm).

2. Wear gloves.

3. Select one of the following four methods to produce your tread impression:
   a. Method 1: Using your gloved hand, smear a thin layer of petroleum jelly over the surface of the tread and brush the tread with fingerprint powder.
   b. Method 2: Roll the small paint roller over the fingerprint ink pad. Roll the inked roller over the tire to ink the entire tread of the tire.
   c. Method 3: If the tire is small, use an inkless ink pad and roll the tire over the inkless ink pad and the sensitive paper.
   d. Method 4: Chalk the tread surface of the tire.

4. Label the tire impression paper or cardboard (where you plan to roll the tire) with the following information:
   a. Date and tire number: Suspect 1 or Suspect 2
   b. Names of investigating team members
   c. Case number
   d. Tire size
   e. Tire manufacturer
   f. Serial number from tire
   g. Tire placement on vehicle (i.e., front or rear, left or right side)

5. Obtain the Suspect 1 tire. Mark the tire and paper (or cardboard) with a marker as a starting point. Be sure the tire completes at least one entire revolution as it marks the paper or cardboard. Mark the end point of the revolution on the paper. One revolution is approximately 7 feet for a 26-inch bicycle tire.

6. Put the paper or cardboard aside to dry.

7. Examine the tread impression. Label all unique identifiers you find on the impression with a pen. Measure the distance of any unique identifiers from the starting point. Record the distance to the nearest millimeter.

8. Record your information in Data Table 1 (Suspect 1).

9. Repeat Steps 1 to 8 using the Suspect 2 tire. Record your information in Data Table 2 (Suspect 2).

10. Obtain a copy of a partial crime-scene tire tread impression from your instructor; examine it as you did tire samples 1 and 2.

11. Record your answers in Data Table 3 (Crime Scene).

12. Compare the crime-scene tire impressions to Suspect 1 and 2 tire impressions. Does either of the suspects' tire impressions seem to be consistent with the crime-scene tire impression? Do you have at least six to eight identifiers?

Data Table 1: Tire 1 Data (Suspect 1)

Identifier	Distance From Starting Mark (cm)	Description

Data Table 2: Tire 2 Data (Suspect 2)

Identifier	Distance From Starting Mark (cm)	Description

Data Table 3: Crime-Scene Data

Identifier	Distance from Starting Mark (cm)	Description

Questions:

1. Was the tread impression from Suspect 1 or Suspect 2 consistent with the partial tread impression found at the crime scene? Cite evidence from your analysis to support your claim.
2. Why is a complete rotation of the tire necessary when doing a tire analysis?
3. When doing an analysis of tread impressions, what type of tire characteristics can be measured, or quantified?
4. When viewing a tread pattern analysis, what type of information could be obtained from the tread pattern that would help identify a specific car? Explain.

Answers

Check students' data tables. Identifiers for tables include the following:

Blemishes
Nicks
Wear bars
Depth of tread
Direction of tread
Sipes
Overall pattern
Number of grooves
Bald spots on the tire
Tread on side of the tire
Number of ribs
Angle of sipes
Damage to the tire
Anything embedded in the tire

Questions

1. Answers will vary. Students should have detailed information, including measurements of the tire and tire tread along with any unique or identifying information. If the students found one of the tires to be consistent with one of the suspect's tires, they should indicate the exact location on the tire that is consistent with the tread impression.

2. To ensure the entire circumference of the tire's tread pattern is examined.

3. The following measurements can be made:
   a. tire width
   b. rib width
   c. the length of one full rotation
   d. distance between two identifying markers
   e. unusual wear pattern

4. Any embedded or damaged parts of the tire may help identify a specific tire. Unique wear patterns due to low air pressure or damaged or nicked tires help identify a specific tire.

5. Variables affecting tires:
   a. amount of air in the tire
   b. temperature of the surrounding air
   c. weight of the rider
   d. type of bike riding: road or mountain biking, racing or touring
   e. whether or not the bike was stationary for a long period of time
6. Search the Internet for bicycle brands such as Schwinn, Shimano, Trek, Specialized, BMC, and LeMond and determine the tread patterns available.

5. What variables may influence a tread impression that could result in a bicycle's tread impression looking different from the impression left at the crime scene?

6. Conduct an Internet search and find a tire identification database that could be used to help identify a tire.

Further Study:

1. Obtain old tires from a garage or auto salvage yard. Prepare tread impressions that would demonstrate the following:
   a. Car that did not have its wheels balanced properly
   b. Car that did not have its wheels aligned properly
   c. Car that was driven with underinflated tires
   d. Car that has a damaged tire
   e. Car that was driven without sufficient tire tread
   f. Car that was driven with snow tires

2. Research OSAC (Organization of Scientific Area Committees), and review the guidelines for collecting and documenting impression evidence. Footwear and tire tread is a subcommittee under Physics and Pattern.

Vehicle Identification *Obj. 16.5, 16.8*

Objectives:

By the end of this activity, you will be able to:

1. Measure the tire width, track width, and wheelbase of a car.
2. Describe identifying features of tires on a vehicle, including tread pattern and wear patterns.
3. Analyze data from the suspects' cars and tires. Compare and contrast those data to data obtained from tire marks at the scene of an accident.
4. Determine if a suspect's car can be included or excluded based on tire width, track width, wheelbase, and tire information.

Time Required to Complete Activity:

90 minutes for each part of activity

Materials:

Act 16-4 SH
(per team of 3–4 students for each car)
3 tape measures or 3 meter sticks (or yardsticks) or 3 laser measuring tools and one 4" × 4" piece of cardboard or wood
1 vehicle for each team

SAFETY PRECAUTIONS:

Be aware of traffic patterns in the area where vehicles are being measured. Vehicle measurements can be done at home or in a garage to ensure greater safety. Traffic should be blocked off before students begin their measurements.

Scenario:

An eyewitness said that a young, male driver in a blue car ran a stop sign, striking an oncoming car in the middle of the intersection. It appeared that the young man was talking on his cell phone at the time of the incident. Brakes were applied too late and the vehicles crashed. In a panic, the young driver of the blue car quickly backed up, made a U-turn, and left the scene of the accident. When the police arrived, the blue car was gone. All that was left at the crime scene were tire marks and the other damaged car. The crime-scene investigators took photographs and began diagramming and photographing the crime scene. All tire marks were carefully measured and documented. From the tire and tread marks, the investigators obtained information about the accident and information that could be used to identify the car that drove away.

The police located three cars that fit the description provided by eyewitnesses. Based on the tire marks left at the accident and information obtained from the three cars, can any of the suspects' cars be excluded or included?

Casts and Impressions   547

Background

In this activity, students measure the tire size, track width, and wheelbase of three different cars and record their findings. They then compare crime-scene data to their measurements and try to link one of the three cars to the crime scene.

Time Required to Complete Activity

40 minutes for each part of the activity

Safety Precautions

1. All traffic should be blocked before students begin their measurements.
2. Students should be aware at all times of any vehicles or people in the area when they are taking measurements of the cars. Do not take tire impressions in an area with moving vehicles.
3. If time is a factor, ask students to take measurements of the family car and bring their results to school.

Teaching Tip

A. Prior to doing this lab, review with students the information that can be obtained from tire marks.

B. Ask students how tire marks can indicate the following:
   - Someone running a stop sign
   - The location of a collision
   - Someone quickly accelerating and driving away
   - Someone taking a turn too quickly

Teaching Tip

If going outside to measure cars is considered too time-consuming or is unsafe, students can do the same calculations using toy or model cars or other model vehicles. Ask students to bring in models from home that exhibit some tread pattern. Do all of the calculations in the classroom using the toy cars. If any of the models have wheels that steer, ask students to devise a method to calculate the turning diameter. (The class will not be able to perform Part B with a toy car.)

Procedures

1. Print, copy, and distribute Act 16-4 SH from the IRCD, Chapter 16.

2. Make sure students read all directions *before* beginning the activity.

3. Determine which cars in your school parking lot can be used for students to record their data on car measurements. If possible, have the chosen cars be in an area of the parking lot that will be easily accessible and away from traffic. In choosing cars, try to find three different types of cars to accentuate the differences in data.

4. Select one of the cars as the car used at a crime scene. You will supply data on the crime-scene evidence that should match one of these cars. Do not give students the crime-scene data until after they have recorded their own data.

5. Depending on time constraints, allow students to work in teams. Each team can either measure one car and then share their data with the other groups, or teams may rotate and take measurements of all three cars and then compare their data.

6. Students can share one or two laser measuring devices. These devices are more accurate than stretching a tape measure.

7. Use the metric system when taking measurements. This will avoid the confusion of converting measurements to the nearest $\frac{1}{16}$ of an inch to decimal form before converting to the metric system.

Procedure:

PART A: MEASURING A CAR'S TIRE WIDTH, TRACK WIDTH, AND WHEELBASE

1. Review definitions for track width and wheelbase in the chapter. Refer to Figures 16-11 and 16-13.

2. Each team is assigned a different vehicle and is responsible for obtaining all measurements on that vehicle. Each team also is responsible for sharing its information with other teams.

3. In the data table, record the manufacturer, model, and year of the car that you are measuring.

4. To measure the front track width, place a board or piece of cardboard in front of the tire. The right edge of the board or cardboard should be aligned with the center of the front tire.

5. Using the cardboard (or board) and the laser pointer or measuring tape, measure the track width of the front tires of the assigned vehicle to the nearest millimeter.

6. This measurement is taken from tire center to tire center using a tape measure or laser measuring tool.

7. Record your information in the data table.

8. Repeat the process for the rear tires, and record the rear track width in the data table. (See the figure.)

Measuring track width.

Piece of wood or cardboard

Track width is measured in millimeters from center of tire to center of opposite tire.

Tape measure or laser measuring tool

The board's edge should be aligned with the middle of the tire.

Front edge of ruler (or laser) aligned with the middle of the tire.

9. Measure the wheelbase of the vehicle. Recall that your measurements are taken from the center of the front tire (wheel) to the center of the rear tire (wheel). Record your answer in the data table.

10. Note the tire width of a front tire and back tire on the driver's side. (Tire width is stamped on the side of a tire after the letter P (for "passenger"). For example, "P215" means the width is 215 millimeters.) Record your answer in the data table.

11. Record information about the number and patterns of the tire ridges in the data table.

12. Record other observations or unusual characteristics of the tire in the data table.

13. Obtain other vehicle information from other teams and record it in the data table.

14. Obtain the crime-scene vehicle information from your teacher and record it in the data table.

15. Analyze the data and determine if any of the vehicles can be excluded or included. Support your claims using your data.

PART B: LINKING A CAR TO A CRIME SCENE

If a car left the scene of an accident, the accident investigators might be able to measure front and rear track widths, wheelbase, and track width from tire marks left on the pavement. Photographs of the tire marks may show ridge patterns of the tires. Using up-to-date tire and vehicle databases, investigators might be able to exclude or include suspects based on such data.

For each of the examples listed, identify the car model using information obtained from tire-mark evidence at an accident site and the vehicle database in Figure 16-13.

1. Wheelbase ~2,689 mm
   Turning diameter ~11,100 mm
   Tire size = 245
   Vehicle was probably a _____
   Justify your answer.

2. Wheelbase ~2,620 mm
   Turning diameter = 11,102 mm
   Tire size = 195
   Vehicle was probably a _____
   Justify your answer.

3. Wheelbase = 2,446 mm
   Turning diameter = 12,200 mm
   Tire size = 285
   Vehicle was probably a _____
   Justify your answer.

Teaching Tip

Review the difference between track width and wheelbase with students. Refer to Figure 16-11.

Answers

Check students' data tables and vehicle identifications.

1. Jeep Cherokee
2. Audi A4
3. Chevrolet Corvette
4. Ford Galaxy
5. Lexus GS 300

Data Table: Car and Tire Measurements

Vehicle Number	Manufacturer	Model	Year	Front Track Width (mm)	Rear Track Width (mm)	Wheelbase (mm)
Car 1						
Car 2						
Car 3						
Evidence From Crime Scene						

Vehicle Number	Tire Width Front (mm)	Tire Width Rear (mm)	Number of Tire Ridges	Number of Tire Grooves	Ridge Pattern (Angular, Straight, Direction)	Other Observations
Car 1						
Car 2						
Car 3						
Evidence From Crime Scene						

4. Wheelbase ~2,835 mm

   Turning diameter ~11,700 mm

   Tire size = 215

   Vehicle was probably a _____

   Justify your answer.

5. Wheelbase ~2,780 mm

   Turning diameter ~11,800 mm

   Tire size = 275

   Vehicle was probably a _____

   Justify your answer.

© iStock.com/fcafotodigital

Questions:

1. In Part A, did any of the skid marks found at the crime scene appear consistent with any of the suspects' cars? Support your claim with data from your investigation.

2. If any of the cars' data appear consistent with the crime scene, would this be sufficient evidence to convict? Support your claim with evidence from the text or scientifically reliable reference materials.

3. From the skid marks formed as the hit-and-run car made a U-turn, what other measurable characteristic of a vehicle could be obtained?

4. Suppose a car was identified that had data consistent with the vehicle data from the crime scene. Describe additional testing that would help determine if that car was involved in this particular accident.

Further Study:

1. Design an experiment to determine the turning diameter of three different cars. Measure the turning diameter of each car. Research automobile databases and compare your measurements with the information published by the cars' manufacturers.

2. Contact your local police department and ask to speak with the person who performs accident reconstruction. Obtain photos of a collision's tire marks and ask the accident reconstruction investigator to explain his or her analysis of the event. Prepare an expert witness presentation that describes the accident reconstruction. Include photos of the tire marks and the information that was revealed by the tire marks.

Questions

1. Answers will vary.

2. No. This would still be considered class evidence and would need to be supported by other evidence.

3. Turning diameter

4. Investigators would look for specific tire wear patterns; evidence of involvement in a recent collision, such as dents, scratches, broken lights, or paint from the other car on the area of impact; and other types of trace evidence from the environment or passengers.

Background

In this activity, students create dental impressions and transparencies of their own bite patterns. They compare five different dental impressions with bite marks to determine if any of the dental impressions are consistent with the bite mark.

Time Required to Complete Activity

45 minutes

Safety Precautions

1. Large amounts of saliva tend to be produced during this activity. Provide paper towels or tissues. Make sure all paper is discarded properly to avoid the spread of bacteria from saliva.

2. Make sure students wash their hands with soap and water after wiping the saliva from their dental impressions.

Teaching Tip

The dental impression part of this activity produces a lot of saliva, which can transmit illness. Students who are ill should not make their own dental impressions.

Teaching Tip

Students with a very sensitive gag reflex may choose not to make their own dental impressions.

Dental Impressions *Obj. 16.8*

Objectives:

By the end of this activity, you will be able to:

1. Create your own plastic foam dental impression.

2. Produce a transparency film impression of the bite marks from your own dental impression or from the bite marks from the professional dental castings.

3. Analyze images of bite marks on a victim and a suspect's dental impressions to determine if the suspect can be either included or excluded.

Plaster casts and plastic overlays are often made of a suspect's teeth to compare a photograph of a bite mark on a victim to the suspect's dental impression.

Materials (per each team of two):

Act 16-5 SH
Act 16-5 SH Dental Comparison Key
4 plastic foam bite plates, approximately 6 × 7.5 cm
2 hand lenses
tissues
4 transparency sheets (8 × 8 cm)
2 permanent markers
scissors
1 resealable plastic bag (for the trash)
two sets of professional dental impressions (optional)
2 metric rulers
digital camera (optional)

PART B

1 blank transparency sheet (10 × 14 cm)
permanent marker
rulers
protractor (optional)

Time Required to Complete Activity: 60 minutes

SAFETY PRECAUTIONS:

Use tissues to wipe any residual saliva from the dental impressions. When the activity is completed, all tissues should be discarded in the trash (in a resealable plastic bag) to avoid spreading bacteria. Wash your hands with soap and water after wiping your dental impressions. Note that putting something in the back of the mouth can trigger a gagging reflex.

Procedure:

PART A: MAKING DENTAL IMPRESSIONS

1. Obtain two equally sized plastic foam plates from your instructor. The plates must be large enough to be in contact with all of your teeth but small enough to fit into your mouth. If the pieces are too large, cut the foam plate with the scissors. You need to put in the largest size possible to get a good impression of your back teeth. It will be a tight fit and a little bit uncomfortable!

2. Label one plate *upper* and the other plate *lower* in the top corner.

3. With the upper and lower plates aligned, place both plates in your mouth at once. Make sure they are placed back far enough to sit between your back molars.

4. Bite down firmly on the plates. Do not chew on the plastic foam or bite completely through the plates. Remember that all you are trying to do is to get an impression of your teeth.

5. Remove the plates and wipe off any residual saliva with a tissue. Immediately place the used tissue in a resealable bag and discard the bag.

6. Wash your hands with soap and water to avoid spreading bacteria.

7. Obtain two transparency sheets. Label both with your initials in the lower-right corner. In the top center of the sheet, label one *top* and the other *bottom*.

8. Place a transparency sheet labeled *top* over the upper impression.

9. With a permanent marker, *outline* the pattern made by each of your upper teeth. Be careful to trace each tooth individually.

10. Repeat the process for your lower teeth.

11. Compare your dental transparencies with those of your partner.

12. Place your transparencies over your partner's dental impression in the plastic foam.

Can you see that your impressions are not consistent with your partner's dental impressions? Once the dental impression is produced, a transparent overlay is used to see if the bite impression of the suspect is consistent with the bite impression on the victim.

Casts and Impressions   553

Procedures

1. Print, copy, and distribute Act 16-5 SH and Act 16-5 SH Dental Comparison Key from the IRCD, Chapter 16.

2. Obtain plastic foam trays from a supermarket and cut them for use. Cut several different widths to accommodate different-sized dental patterns.

3. Cut overhead transparencies in fourths.

4. Obtain dental castings from your local dentist. These are often disposed of, and a local dentist should give them to you for free.

5. Always photograph a ruler with your dental impressions. That way you can adjust the photograph size later if necessary.

6. Be aware that some students may be very sensitive about their teeth, especially if they are crooked. If you have dental castings available, you might make these available for any students who do not want to make impressions of their own mouths or for students who have a sore throat or cold.

Teaching Tip

Demonstrate the process of making an impression. If the plastic foam plate is too wide, they should cut it to fit into their mouth. Include in the demonstration how students should blot the impression with a paper towel to remove saliva. That paper towel should be placed inside the ziptop bag to prevent the spread of germs. Remind students not to bite too hard, as that may break the foam plate.

Teaching Tip

Students using the pre-made dental casts should place the top dental cast onto the foam plate. After making that impression, they should use the other half to make the bottom impression.

Plastic foam dental impressions.

PART B: IDENTIFYING DENTAL PATTERNS

Compare the photographs of five dental impressions made from the upper and lower jaws of five different people.

1. Using a permanent marker and half of a transparency sheet, carefully trace the dental pattern of each of the five upper jaws (1 through 5). The front incisors can be drawn as dashes, while the side and rear teeth can be drawn as ovals. Label your transparency with your initials, and label each dental pattern 1 through 5.

2. Using your tracings of the upper jaws (1 through 5), attempt to match the upper jaw with the lower jaws labeled A through E. Because the tracing was made of the top teeth, turn your transparency sheet over before trying to align it with the photos of the lower teeth. Record your results in Data Table 1.

Data Table 1: Matching Upper and Lower (1–5) Dental Plates

Upper Teeth (Number)	Matches Lower Teeth (Letter)
1	
2	
3	
4	
5	

Data Table 2: Bite Marks

Bite Mark (Letter)	Upper Teeth (Number)
X	
Y	
Z	

Answers

Student data tables should be consistent with the following data:

1 B

2 C

3 D

4 A

5 E

X 5

Y 2

Z 4

Five sample sets of teeth, upper teeth (top photo) and lower teeth (bottom photo).

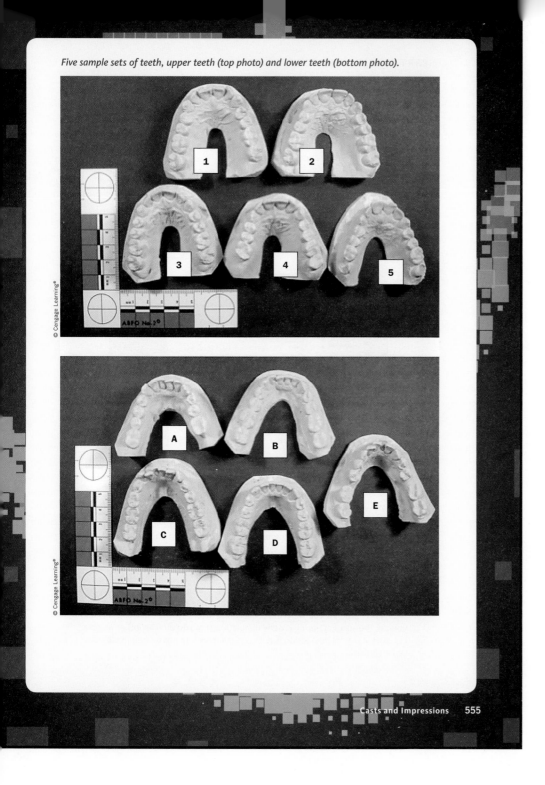

© Cengage Learning®

Questions

1. Sample answer: tooth position, the arch of the plate, the width of the plate, unique spacing, the number of teeth, missing or broken teeth, measurement between last molars and front incisors, presence or absence of baby or wisdom teeth.

2. Measure the following:
   a. size of teeth
   b. distance between teeth

3. The suspect should be questioned about his dental history during those two years: Did he get braces, crowns, implants, veneers, or any other cosmetic work that would change his bite? His answers should then be confirmed with local dentists.

PART C: BITE MARK IDENTIFICATION

Compare your five tracings of *upper* dental impressions from Part B (1 through 5) with photographs labeled X, Y, and Z of the lower teeth bite marks found in cheese. Remember to turn over the transparency of the upper bite marks when trying to align the transparency with the bite marks in the cheese. Usually, the top front teeth will be outside the lower teeth.

Lower teeth bite marks in cheese.

© Cengage Learning®

Questions:

1. Make a list of traits that can be used to determine if someone's dental impression is consistent with a photograph of a bite mark left on a victim.

2. Given a ruler and a protractor, what type of measurements of a dental impression could be used to compare a suspect's dental impression with the bite-mark evidence from a crime scene?

3. A lawyer stated that his client was innocent because his client's dental impression was not consistent with a photograph of a bite mark on a victim taken two years earlier. If you were the prosecuting attorney, what questions would you ask the suspect during cross-examination that could reveal other reasons his current dental impression is not consistent with the bite mark made two years earlier?

Further Study:

1. Using the transparencies of your dental impressions and those of several other classmates, design a demonstration that requires the use of dental impressions to help solve the crime. Do *not* bite anyone! Someone in your team could bite into a slice of cheese to provide the evidence. Others in your team could be suspects. Using the bite marks in cheese and the dental transparencies of your teammates, demonstrate how the suspect's bite mark could link the suspect to the crime.

2. Ray Krone was convicted of and served time for a crime he did not commit based on dental impression (bite mark) analysis. Research this case and provide answers to the following questions:
   - Why is dental evidence being challenged in the courts?
   - What role did The Innocence Project play in getting Ray Krone exonerated?
   - How is dental evidence viewed today?
   - Research the OSAC (Organization of Scientific Area Committees) for Odontology (the study of teeth). (It is a subcommittee of crime-scene investigation). What are the guidelines and standards for bite-mark and dental impression evidence?

Chapter Overview

We use tools to make our lives easier. Criminals also use tools— or make tools out of everyday items—to help them commit crimes. Even when a tool is no longer at the scene of a crime, it may leave behind unique clues that are useful to a forensic investigator during his or her investigation of the crime scene. Crime-scene investigators must follow proper procedures when identifying, photographing, and documenting tool-mark evidence to ensure no evidence is lost, displaced, or contaminated. Although advances in technology have improved the ability to distinguish one tool from another, tool-mark evidence is still considered circumstantial class evidence.

The Big Ideas

One of the most common kinds of physical evidence left at a crime scene is a tool mark. Tools, even those manufactured in bulk, develop unique characteristics that can be used to identify them. There are three major categories of tool marks: indentation marks, abrasion marks, and cutting marks. The first thing an investigator does, when finding a tool or tool marks at a crime scene, is to photograph the evidence using oblique lighting. Careful observation of the crime scene, including examining tools or tool marks for foreign materials and fingerprints, is essential. A cast may be made of the tool mark, which is also taken back to a lab for analysis. Tools are bagged according to proper evidence collection procedure. Technology such as a tool-mark image database and profilometry can help investigators link tools and tool marks to suspects and crime scenes. Tool-mark evidence, although circumstantial, has helped link suspects to crimes.

CHAPTER 17

Tool Marks

Tool Marks Link a Chain of Robberies

A young man watches as a family drives away. Assured that no one is home, he circles to the back of the house, where a fence and several trees shield him from onlookers. He removes a crowbar from his duffel bag. After wedging a crowbar between the doorjamb and the door, he gains entry to the home. Ten minutes later, he flees the home, taking with him money, electronics, and jewelry. The burglar uses gloves to avoid leaving fingerprints.

When investigators arrive, they photograph the pry marks on the jamb and door. After photographing and measuring the pry marks, they take a silicone cast of the tool mark. It is an impression made by the end of the tool. The doorjamb around the pry marks is cut away, preserved, and labeled as evidence. The investigators take it back to the lab.

Tools can leave marks that provide physical evidence at a crime scene.

Several other burglaries occur over the next month. The same crowbar impression is found at each crime scene. Each time the burglar is able to escape. A break finally occurs when a vigilant neighbor reports an unknown person repeatedly driving slowly around his neighborhood. The police pull the suspicious stranger over. While questioning him, they notice his open duffel bag in the back seat. They see a crowbar in it. The man agrees to permit police to examine his crowbar.

A forensic expert compares the crowbar with the crime-scene tool-mark evidence on the doorjamb. The crowbar is consistent with the pry marks at several of the recent crime scenes. When faced with the evidence, the man confesses to the series of burglaries.

558

SCENARIO

Police were able to capture the thief involved in these robberies because of a vigilant neighbor and because the arresting officers were aware of what to look for. Lead a class discussion of the following questions:

1. Describe the physical evidence recovered at the crime scene that was used to identify the tool used in the burglary.

2. Provide arguments to support the view that tool-mark impression evidence is circumstantial evidence.

3. Neighborhood watch groups have been helpful in preventing crime. What part did a watchful neighbor play in this case?

4. Why do you think photographing tool marks is an important first step in their investigation?

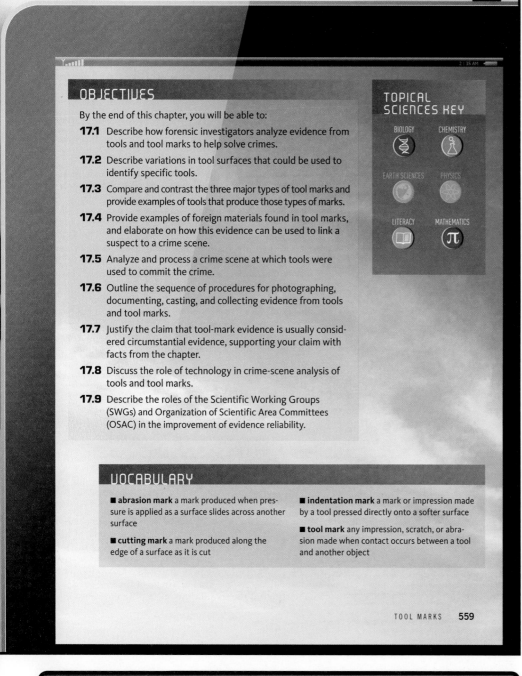

OBJECTIVES

By the end of this chapter, you will be able to:

17.1 Describe how forensic investigators analyze evidence from tools and tool marks to help solve crimes.

17.2 Describe variations in tool surfaces that could be used to identify specific tools.

17.3 Compare and contrast the three major types of tool marks and provide examples of tools that produce those types of marks.

17.4 Provide examples of foreign materials found in tool marks, and elaborate on how this evidence can be used to link a suspect to a crime scene.

17.5 Analyze and process a crime scene at which tools were used to commit the crime.

17.6 Outline the sequence of procedures for photographing, documenting, casting, and collecting evidence from tools and tool marks.

17.7 Justify the claim that tool-mark evidence is usually considered circumstantial evidence, supporting your claim with facts from the chapter.

17.8 Discuss the role of technology in crime-scene analysis of tools and tool marks.

17.9 Describe the roles of the Scientific Working Groups (SWGs) and Organization of Scientific Area Committees (OSAC) in the improvement of evidence reliability.

TOPICAL SCIENCES KEY

BIOLOGY

CHEMISTRY

EARTH SCIENCES

PHYSICS

LITERACY

MATHEMATICS

VOCABULARY

■ **abrasion mark** a mark produced when pressure is applied as a surface slides across another surface

■ **cutting mark** a mark produced along the edge of a surface as it is cut

■ **indentation mark** a mark or impression made by a tool pressed directly onto a softer surface

■ **tool mark** any impression, scratch, or abrasion made when contact occurs between a tool and another object

TOOL MARKS **559**

TEACHING RESOURCES

Instructor's Resource CD-ROM includes:
- Activities and Student Handouts
- Alternative Assessments
- Consolidated Bibliography
- Correlations to NGSS and CCSS
- Figure Files
- Lesson Plans

- Nonfiction Readings
- PowerPoint Presentations
- Student Learning Objectives (SLOs)

CL Testing powered by Cognero

Website: ngl.cengage.com/forensicscience2e

Engage

Lead the class in a discussion of the following questions:

- How do you think an investigator could determine whether a tool has been used at a crime scene?

- Do you think it is possible that tools produced at the same factory, with the same materials, could still be distinguished from one another? If so, how? Show students two tools that were produced by the same company and seem identical, and ask if they can distinguish between them.

Teaching Tip

Use Figure 17-1 to engage students about this topic. Ask students to identify the areas in the photo where a tool was most likely used. Next, ask students to describe the kinds of marks they see in the figure and what type of tool could have made them.

Evaluate

The text states that ownership of a tool used in the commission of a crime is not enough for a conviction. Ask students to support this claim with facts from earlier chapters of the text.

INTRODUCTION

A "tool" in the context of this chapter may be something manufactured as a tool, such as a crowbar or a hammer, or it may be an object hastily put to use, such as a length of pipe or a wine bottle. Whatever it is, its surface leaves distinctive marks when it is forced against another surface. A **tool mark** is any indentation, scratch, or cut mark made when contact occurs between a tool and an object. The impressions made by any tool could link the tool to a crime scene and ultimately to the tool's owner. Tool marks, however, are circumstantial evidence. More evidence is usually needed to arrest a suspect.

Figure 17-1 *Tool marks are often found at points of forced entry (entrances of burglarized houses, for example).*

Gary Roebuck/Alamy

TOOLS AND CRIME SCENES
Obj. 17.1

Tools simplify everyday living. They serve as extensions to our hands, multiplying our ability to do work. Simple tools such as crowbars, knives, screwdrivers, and hammers increase our ability to handle manual tasks. But the same tools that help us with everyday tasks can also be used in crimes. Criminals use tools to force their way into locked buildings and cars (Figure 17-1).

The tool used in a crime may link a suspect to the crime. Possession of the tool consistent with one used in the commission of a crime, however, is only circumstantial evidence. Possession of a tool does not establish the suspect's presence at the time of the crime. The suspect's fingerprints on the tool make for a stronger case, but still do not eliminate the possibility that someone else used the tool at the crime scene. Although tool-mark evidence is circumstantial evidence, when combined with other evidence, it may persuade a perpetrator to admit his or her guilt.

TOOL MARKS *Obj. 17.3*

Tools usually leave distinctive marks where they are used. The hardness of a tool influences the marks left in softer material. There are three major categories of tool marks: indentation marks (Figure 17-2), abrasion marks (Figure 17-3), and cutting marks (Figure 17-4).

Indentation Marks

Indentation mark are impressions made by a tool when it is pressed against a softer surface (Figure 17-2), such as the wood of a door or window frame. Such a mark is the negative impression of the tool, such as a nick or depression. These tool marks are typically made as a perpetrator attempts to pry open an item such as a cash box, window, or door. It is possible to determine the size and shape of the tool used, as well as other characteristics of the tool, by measuring the impression.

Figure 17-2 *Indentation: Screwdrivers and crowbars often make a nick or impression in a surface.*

Figure 17-3 *Abrasion: This door strike plate shows scratch marks made by a screwdriver.*

Figure 17-4 *Cutting: Hacksaws leave striations (stripes) on a surface they cut.*

Abrasion Marks

Abrasion mark are made when surfaces slide across one another (Figure 17-3). Objects such as pliers, knives, axes, or gun barrels make this type of mark. The harder surface leaves scratches or striations on the softer surface. Sometimes abrasion and indentation marks are made at the same time, as when a pry bar scratches one side of a doorjamb while leaving an impression on the wood on the other side.

Cutting Marks

Cutting marks are produced along the edge of a surface as it is cut (Figure 17-4). Knives, saws, wire cutters, and other devices that cut through materials such as wire, bolts, hinges, locks, and bone leave cutting marks.

The type of saw blade used to dismember a body can be determined by examining the cut surface of the bone. In his book entitled *Dead Men Do Tell Tales,* Dr. William Maples describes a collection of cow bones belonging to the C. A. Pound Human Identification Lab in Florida. Cuts made by various saws were used to prepare a reference catalog of cut marks identifying simi-

BIOLOGY

lar cut marks on dismembered human bodies. Each type of saw leaves a specific type of mark on bone, as described in Figure 17-5 on the next page. Microscopic examination of the saw marks on bone provides clues to what type of blade was used. Identification of the type and brand of saw blade can help link a suspect to a murder.

DIGGING DEEPER With Forensic Science eCollection

Research the work of the late forensic anthropologist Dr. William Maples using the Gale Forensic Science eCollection at **ngl.cengage.com/ forensicscience2e**. How are tool marks found on bones similar to rifling marks found on bullets? Bones left outside for a period of time may be chewed by animals. Discuss how scientists try to distinguish between marks made by animals postmortem and those made by weapons or tools.

Evaluate

Tools leave impressions just as teeth, tires, and shoes do. Ask students to think about what they learned about impressions. Have them brainstorm ways to make casts of a tool mark.

Explore

Help students understand the differences among types of tool marks. Divide students into small groups, and give each group some small tools such as a plastic dinner knife and a metal file, as well as a piece of modeling clay and a soft piece of wood, such as balsa. Ask students to use these things to create an example of an indentation mark, an abrasion mark, and a cutting mark. Go over the examples in class and correct any misconceptions that may arise.

DIGGING DEEPER

Have students research the late forensic anthropologist William Maples, if they have not already done so. Students may want to research Maples's analysis of the remains of Tsar Nicholas II; President Zachary Taylor; Spanish conquistador Francisco Pizarro; and Joseph Merrick, the "Elephant Man." For more information, go to the Gale Forensic Science eCollection at ngl.cengage .com/forensicscience2e

Science

BIOLOGY

BIOLOGY

Bones are unique organs in the human body because of their rigidity. Despite how hard a bone appears when compared to other human organs, it can be easily damaged by materials such as those used in many tools. Refer students to Figure 14-3 to review the structure of a bone.

Teaching Tip

The idea of cutting marks on bones will be disturbing for some students. Clarify for the class the pertinence of this topic, and make it clear that cutting is usually done postmortem (for ease of disposal). As an option, read the section from Chapter 5 of William Maples's book *Dead Men Do Tell Tales* that describes tool marks on bone.

Teaching Tip

Refer to the Matthew Holding Case Study in Chapter 13, in which foxes began to uncover a body. Start a class brainstorming session regarding the forensic importance of distinguishing between animal damage to a body and tool damage to a body.

Teaching Tip

Discuss why crime-scene evidence needs to be evaluated by a variety of forensic specialists.

Figure 17-5 *Saw marks on bones.*

Type of Saw	Cut Characteristics	Teeth-Mark Pattern	Example
Stryker	Circular areas of short radii; some overlapping marks	Few teeth marks	Steve Turner/Alamy
Band saw	Very smooth; seldom overlapping marks	Few teeth marks; straight fine cut	© Luciano Queiroz/Shutterstock.com
Hacksaw	Overlapping marks	Like a tiny tic-tac-toe board with thousands of squares	Image Farm Inc./Alamy
Chain saw	Messy cut	Rough-edged	Burke/Triolo/Brand X Pictures/Getty Images
Table saw	Parallel, curved striations	Ridged grooves	Steve Skjold/Alamy
Handsaw	Rough cut with overlapping marks	Irregular cut	Burke/Triolo/Brand X/Getty Images
Circular saw	Parallel, curved striations	Ridged grooves	Burke/Triolo/Brand X Pictures/Getty Images

562   CHAPTER 17

DIFFERENTIATED LEARNING

Teaching Gifted Students
Have students research the following question: If skeletal remains are discovered in a wooded area, how can police distinguish animal bite marks from cut marks made by a weapon?

TOOL SURFACE CHARACTERISTICS *Obj. 17.2*

Tools have unique characteristics resulting from manufacturing processes and from use over time. These characteristics help investigators differentiate one tool's mark from another's. Tools change over time as they are used repeatedly, as shown by the three hammers in Figure 17-6. Nicks, ridge marks, and blemishes may develop on the striking surface of the tool. These characteristics from natural wear and tear affect impressions made by the tools, and these distinctive markings help to distinguish one tool from another.

Other characteristics that help to distinguish tool marks are oxidation or rusting of tools and uneven sharpening. Foreign material attached to a tool when it makes a mark can also make a tool mark unique.

Figure 17-6 *Unique markings such as nicks and ridge marks can be seen on the striking surface of these hammers.*

© Cengage Learning®

TOOL MARK EVIDENCE *Obj. 17.6, 17.7*

Tool evidence includes both the mark left at the scene and the tool. The tool may be recovered from the suspect or the crime scene, or may have been discarded elsewhere. A crime-scene investigator may not have the benefit of finding a tool used during the crime. In that case, the investigator will search for indirect evidence of any tools used during the crime, such as tool marks (Figure 17-7). Any tool-mark evidence is photographed, documented, and preserved to create a permanent record of the evidence in its original state of discovery. This record of evidence is often introduced and described during a trial.

Documenting The Evidence

The best way to document tool and tool-mark evidence is to use photography. All evidence is photographed with a measuring device to show the appropriate scale for reference. A comparison is then made between the tool mark and the tool.

Figure 17-7 *A crime-scene investigator looking for tool-mark evidence.*

Bob Daemmrich/PhotoEdit

TOOL MARKS **563**

Teaching Tip

Invite a crime-scene investigator to your class to discuss any crimes that were solved using tool-mark evidence. Ask him or her to discuss how the evidence was documented, photographed, and packaged.

Evaluate

Determine if students have connected their prior knowledge of casts to the new material on casting tool marks by asking students to outline the basic procedure for taking impressions left by each of the following objects: shoes, tires, teeth, tools.

Science

CHEMISTRY

CHEMISTRY

Magnesium is one of the alkaline-Earth metals. It is a grayish-white metal that can be rolled out into thin ribbons. Magnesium oxidizes, or tarnishes, when exposed to air. Magnesium burns hot, brightly, and vigorously when ignited. When magnesium oxidizes, either slowly by tarnishing, or quickly by burning, it combines with oxygen to form the compound magnesium oxide.

Science

CHEMISTRY

CHEMISTRY

Silicone compounds are polymers. In general, they are made of a backbone of silicon and oxygen atoms with side groups attached that are made mostly of carbon and hydrogen atoms. Silicones can be made with a wide variety of properties. Silicones can be liquids, gels, synthetic rubbers, or hard plastics. Silicone compounds have many uses. They are used as caulking to seal out water or air. They are also used as lubricants in plumbing and automobile brakes. Electronic components are sometimes enclosed in silicone for protection.

CHEMISTRY

PHOTOGRAPHING TOOLS

When photographing an evidence tool, experts focus on any scratches or gouges as well as any trace evidence on its surface, such as blood, fibers, hairs, or tissue. Oblique (indirect) lighting is preferred to direct lighting because it casts shadows and highlights details that are not easily visible under direct lighting. Magnesium oxide smoking was formerly used on dark-colored tools. In this method, magnesium ribbon is burned, which produces a white, powdery film of magnesium oxide that coats the surface of the tool. Coating the tool highlights the detail for photography. Today, images obtained using a comparison microscope show sufficient contrast. The comparison microscope has replaced the use of magnesium oxide.

PHOTOGRAPHING TOOL MARKS

While photographing and recording tool-mark evidence, the investigator uses oblique lighting to search the surface of the tool mark for bits of foreign material. If the surface is painted, the expert records if any paint was chipped away and provides a description. Photographing the tool mark and making an impression of it are common ways to further analyze the evidence.

Casting Impressions

If it is possible, tool-mark evidence should be collected and preserved for analysis. The crime-scene investigator may actually cut a part from a door or doorjamb that contains tool-mark evidence.

When the physical removal of a tool mark from the crime scene is not possible, investigators often prepare a cast of it. Casting preserves the unique indentations made by a specific tool. Prior to casting an impression, all impression evidence must be photographed with a ruler for scale. Measurements of the impression are documented. The surfaces of the impression must be examined for the presence of any valuable evidence such as blood, hair, fibers, body tissues, or paint. Once the impression is cast, this evidence will be lost or altered by the impression and cannot be submitted as evidence.

Silicone or rubber-based casting materials are usually used to record tool marks, as shown in Figure 17-8. The casting material used depends upon the climate and the surface on which the tool mark was made. The liquid casting material generally takes about 10 to 30 minutes to solidify. Once the cast is ready, it is examined with a comparison microscope. You can see a cast of various hammer and crowbar strikes in Figure 17-9.

Figure 17-8 *Types of casting material.*

Material	Description
AccuTrans auto-mix casting system	Silicone base material applied by extruder gun
Mikrosil (Forensic Sil) casting material	Putty that requires a separate catalyst to harden; applied by spatula
Powdered sulfur	Melted sulfur is quickly poured into impressions left in snow and allowed to harden.
Liquid silicone	Applied by extruder gun or from tube
Room-temperature silicone vulcanizing rubber	Silicone mold rubber; requires a separate catalyst to harden at room temperature
Dental store or plaster of Paris	Compound hardens when water is added

Figure 17-9 *Hammer and crowbar impressions cast in plaster of Paris.*

© 2016 Cengage Learning®

Collecting and Preserving a Sample

CHEMISTRY

All tool evidence is collected and packaged separately in containers or boxes and submitted to a laboratory for analysis. If possible, the object containing the impression, such as an entire door or window frame, is removed and sent directly to the lab. If removal of the entire impression is not feasible, then a cast of the impression is made and is packaged and submitted to the laboratory for examination. Small objects are wrapped with clean paper and placed in small containers or plastic bags, while larger objects are packed in cartons or boxes.

All evidence must also be correctly labeled to ensure the proper chain of custody. (See Chapter 2.) Important information to be recorded includes the case number, date, name, and signature of the evidence collector, description of where and when the evidence was located, and why the evidence was collected.

DIGGING DEEPER
with Forensic Science eCollection

Tool marks are documented in a manner similar to that used to document and preserve fingerprints. Silicone-based materials are used to cast impressions of fingerprints and tool marks on objects. Photography is an important way to document both fingerprints and tool marks. Go to the Gale Forensic Science eCollection at **ngl.cengage.com/forensicscience2e** and research the methods used to document fingerprints and tool marks. Write a summary of the techniques used and how they are similar to or different from the methods used to collect and preserve tool marks.

Explore

Have students bring tools with serial numbers to class. Place them where students can observe them and give them time to look at the numbers. Ask: What is the purpose of serial numbers? (For quality control by manufacturers.) Then ask: How do they serve as evidence in crimes? (They may help investigators identify where tools were purchased. They can even help to link a specific tool to a crime scene.)

Science

MATHEMATICS

An algorithm is a step-by-step procedure for solving a problem. Algorithms are commonly used in mathematics and computer science. An algorithm generally takes some input (in this case, a tool-mark image), carries out a number of steps, and produces some output.

CHAPTER

1 2 3 4 5 6 7 8 9 10 11 12 13 14 15 16 **17** 18

Serial numbers that have been removed from firearms and other devices may leave indentation marks that can be detected using magneto-optical sensor technology, which is nondestructive.

Test results using a profilometer to identify tool marks show that the reproducibility of this instrument is an average of 95 percent accurate on known samples.

MATHEMATICS

ANALYZING TOOL-MARK EVIDENCE *Obj. 17.1, 17.2*

The goal of laboratory tool-mark analysis is to identify major characteristics of the type of tool used in the crime. The analysis aims to identify unique characteristics, such as nicks and blemishes, that can distinguish among different tools of the same type. If a tool mark's characteristics are consistent with a suspect's tool, the mark may be examined further using a comparison microscope. If the tool mark is not consistent with the crime-scene evidence, then that suspect may be excluded.

If tools are found in a suspect's possession, they may be used to create a new set of tool marks to be compared to those found at the crime scene. Crime-scene tool marks and suspect tools are never fitted together. This might compromise the integrity of the evidence. Instead, impressions from the crime scene and impressions made from the suspected tool are compared.

Another important feature of tools used in identification is serial numbers. Many tools are stamped or printed with these numbers. For quality control, the manufacturer commonly assigns them, making it easier to identify a batch of tools if a defect is found. Investigators use serial numbers to trace a tool to the manufacturer and possibly to the store where it was purchased. Criminals often try to remove serial numbers. Recovering these numbers has become an important forensic technique for investigators.

Tool-Mark Identification Technology

Forensics experts have traditionally used visual pattern recognition to compare marks found at crime scenes with those made with suspect tools. This method was challenged in a famous 2000 Florida court case that established knife blade tool-mark evidence to be inconclusive because of inadequate scientific testing. In response, the Department of Energy's Ames Laboratory at Iowa State University began developing new technology to scientifically determine the uniqueness of tool marks.

Research projects at the Ames Laboratory include building a tool-mark image database and developing an algorithm to statistically analyze the images. A forensic comparison microscope is used to compare tool marks found at a crime scene with the images of tool marks found in the database. The image database includes many tools, such as screwdrivers, pliers, wire cutters, bolt cutters, tin snips, wood chisels, and crowbars.

Another research project at the Ames Laboratory involves the use of three-dimensional characterization methods and statistical methods to distinguish tool marks. The researchers use a *profilometer,* a scanning tool that measures the depth or height of tool marks. The profilometer uses the information to create a contour map of the marks from the scan to precisely identify a tool mark. This technology reduces the subjective nature of tool-mark comparison and replaces it with more objective and statistical means of comparison. This technology also allows forensic specialists to compare marks on a tool to the marks made by a tool at the crime scene. Further research on using profilometers to reproduce a tool using its marks is underway.

DIFFERENTIATED LEARNING

Teaching English-Language Learners

English-language learners will understand, better than native speakers, how easy it is to be misunderstood. Point out to all students that forensic scientists are careful to be very clear in the way they communicate or represent their findings because of the serious consequences if they are misunderstood.

Tool-Mark Evidence in the Courtroom

After tool-mark comparisons are scientifically analyzed, the expert witness prepares a written report that is sent to the prosecuting attorney. Original evidence, such as a tool or an actual tool mark, is presented in court whenever possible. In any case, casts and magnified images of tool-mark comparisons are presented at a trial. Such evidence may be used to link a series of crimes. As tool-mark analysis technology continues to advance, forensic experts will be even better able to link a tool and its impression.

SUMMARY

- Tools have major and minor surface differences that can help differentiate one tool's impression from another's.

- Tool marks are categorized into one of three categories: indentation marks, abrasion marks, and cutting marks.

- The marks made by tools can link a tool to a crime scene and ultimately link the owner of the tool to a crime.

- Tool-mark evidence should be photographed, documented, collected, or cast.

- Advancing technology for distinguishing tool marks is helping forensic experts link tools to tool marks and convict criminals.

- Organizations such as the Scientific Working Groups and Organization of Scientific Area Committees are establishing guidelines and protocols that will improve evidence reliability.

LITERACY

David Baldwin, John Birkett, Owen Facey, and Gilleon Rabey. *The Forensic Examination and Interpretation of Tool Marks.*
William R. Maples and Michael Browning. *Dead Men Do Tell Tales.* (Chapter 5)

DIGGING DEEPER
with Forensic Science eCollection

The National Institute of Standards and Technology (NIST), the Scientific Working Groups (SWGs), and the Organization of Scientific Area Committees (OSAC) have been working on new standards for tool-mark identification and the reliability of the analysis of other trace evidence to improve their admissibility as evidence in criminal cases. Search the Gale Forensic Science eCollection at **ngl.cengage.com/forensicscience2e** for more information.

TOOL MARKS **567**

Teaching Tip

Discuss the value of quantifying the comparisons of crime-scene evidence and suspect tool marks. What effect might such statistics have on the prosecution's case in court?

Teaching Tip

Emphasize to students that crime-scene investigators, law-enforcement officers, and expert witnesses all may need to prepare reports to present to a jury at a trial. They may need to answer questions from lawyers regarding their methodology and procedures. Many students do not understand the importance of being able to write reports and to practice public speaking. Any student contemplating a career in forensics should develop these skills in addition to those of collecting and evaluating evidence.

Close

Project on a screen, or make copies of, a variety of tools and tool marks from the chapter. Ask students to identify distinguishing characteristics and other evidence.

Teaching Tip

Another term for a tooth cap is a "crown" or "dental crown." A dental crown is used on a chipped or broken tooth to restore the tooth to its original shape. A crown can also be used to strengthen a weak tooth or to improve the appearance of a tooth. Caps, or crowns, are typically made of porcelain today. Porcelain crowns are actually stronger than teeth.

Refer students to the late Dr. William Maples's work on telltale saw marks on bone in his book *Dead Men Do Tell Tales*.

CASE STUDIES

Richard Crafts
(1986)

Pan American flight attendant Helle Crafts disappeared after she returned home from a trip to Germany. Her body could not be located, and her husband Richard Crafts, a potential suspect, passed a lie detector test. The police investigated and found that her husband had purchased a new freezer the week before Helle's disappearance and rented a wood chipper a few days before Helle's return from Germany. An eyewitness remembered seeing a man using a wood chipper along the banks of the Housatonic River early one morning. The date was November 19, two days after Helle's return from Europe.

The police systematically examined the area along the river and the river itself. They found more than 50 pieces of human bone, including parts of a finger, several thousand strands of hair similar to Helle's, two tooth caps, and several ounces of human tissue. A chain saw with its serial numbers filed off was found in the river. Identification of the body was based primarily on one of the recovered tooth caps. It was consistent with the dental records of Helle Crafts. Police theorized that Richard was facing a financially disastrous divorce and decided to kill Helle upon her return from Germany. After killing her with a blunt object, Richard placed her body in the freezer. He cut her body into small pieces and fed her remains through the wood chipper and into the river. Richard Crafts was convicted of murder and sentenced to a term of 50 years in prison.

William Maples's
***Dead Men Do Tell
Tales*** (1995)

The late Dr. William Maples was one of America's best-known forensic anthropologists. One of his famous cases involved using tool marks to collect evidence in a mysterious, grisly murder. In Dr. Maples's book, *Dead Men Do Tell Tales*, he describes a case involving the discovery of a headless body. Eventually he determined that bite marks on the remains of the body had been made by sharks after death. Maples also determined from fine saw marks on the victim's neck vertebra that the head had been sawed off before the sharks had attacked the body. From the saw-mark pattern on the bone, Maples was able to identify a hacksaw as the tool used to separate the head from the body. Unfortunately, the case has never been solved.

© iStock.com/cdascher

CHAPTER: 1 2 3 4 5 6 7 8 9 10 11 12 13 14 15 16 **17** 18

Credit Union Break-in (New York State, 2011)

A break-in at a credit union damaged the outer doorjamb (see photos), and the marks were photographed and documented. But when investigation revealed no damage to the ATM just inside, investigators were puzzled. A photo taken by the ATM security camera provided a time stamp and an impatient customer having trouble opening the door. Upon closer examination, it was determined that what had appeared to be pry marks made by a tool used to pry open the door were actually marks made by screw heads in the doorjamb coming loose as the customer forced the door open. The customer stuck his foot on the doorjamb and yanked on the door handle. When the door flew open, the screws tore out of the doorjamb, leaving what appeared to be tool marks. The man was quickly identified from the security camera images and was questioned by the police. He apologized and agreed to pay for the damage.

The "presumed pry marks" were actually marks made by the screw heads as the strike plate was torn off.

Think Critically

Explain how shoe prints and tool marks are similar types of evidence. Explain how they might be considered either as class or individual evidence.

Careers

Students may be very interested in learning about the newest technology used in forensic investigations. Also, they may be interested to know that many of the techniques used come from other fields, such as medicine and analytical chemistry. Organize the class into teams to construct a brochure of the newest techniques in the field of forensic investigation.

Careers *in Forensics*

Dr. David P. Baldwin and Colleagues, Forensic Scientists and Tool-Mark Experts

Dr. David Baldwin demonstrating shadowgraphy. Shadowgraphs can show individualizing tool marks on transparent materials, such as plastic wrap.

Dr. David Baldwin has been the director of Ames Laboratory's Environmental and Protection Sciences Program since 1999. Dr. Baldwin also served as chair of the Scientific Working Group on Bloodstain Pattern Analysis (SWGSTAIN) in 2002. In addition, he has been the director of the Midwest Forensics Resource Center (MFRC) since 2002. This center assists midwestern state crime labs, universities, the Federal Bureau of Investigation, the Department of Justice, the Department of Energy, and the Bureau of Alcohol, Tobacco, Firearms, and Explosives. The MFRC focuses on forensic science training, education, and research. One of the MFRC's major goals is to develop new techniques and to expand technology for conducting forensic science work. By providing scientific equipment for analyzing crime-scene evidence, the MFRC hopes to help forensic investigators in crime laboratories and law enforcement agencies solve crimes. Baldwin believes that "Through our casework-assistance program, we make available to our partners experts and instrumentation that they don't have in their own crime labs." In 2014, Dr. Baldwin was appointed to serve on the Organization of Scientific Area Committees (OSAC) for Physics and Patterns to help establish standardized procedures, protocols, and guidelines in the nation's crime labs.

Baldwin has extensive training in analytical chemistry and instrumentation, and he has worked in several different areas of environmental chemistry research. His work, and that of his collaborators in forensic research, includes developing ways to analyze tool-mark uniqueness and statistical tests to analyze tool-mark individuality. One of the methods developed by Baldwin and Ames Lab senior chemist Sam Houk is a type of mass spectroscopy to identify metals, ceramics, and other materials commonly found in tools.

Another Iowa State University professor of materials science and engineering, Scott Chumbley has been researching the forensic applications of scanning devices called profilometers. He has found that they accurately measure the height or depth of tool marks. Profilometers can also develop a three-dimensional contour map and profile of each tool, but feasibility for forensics work is still being researched.

Todd Zdorkowski is the associate director of the MFRC. Work in forensics is not as glamorous as it appears on TV, says Zdorkowski. He says, "The backlogs are huge and always growing. Most analytical procedures must be done with a high degree of precision and careful attention to every detail associated with handling the evidence *and* performed on deadline." He goes on to say, "Every examiner's work must be inspected and corroborated by another examiner before it can be released, and some examiners also find their work challenged in public."

A specialized degree in tool-mark examination does not currently exist. Many investigators begin with a degree in the sciences, specifically chemistry and chemical engineering, for proper training in scientific analysis and using chemistry instrumentation. Skills and expertise in forensics and tool-mark analysis are often acquired through graduate degrees, job experience, and certified training programs.

Learn More About It
▶ To learn more about the work of a tool-mark expert, go to **ngl.cengage.com/forensicscience2e**.

DIFFERENTIATED LEARNING

Teaching Gifted Students
Encourage interested students to research and prepare a report on profilometers—how they work and what they can do. Have them include pictures of a profilometer and a profile.

True or False

1. Forensic investigators use databases of tool marks to determine the type of tool used in a crime. *Obj. 17.1, 17.8*

2. In court, a lawyer must be able to fit the tool into the tool marks to convince a jury that they are consistent. *Obj. 17.1, 17.2, 17.3*

3. When forensic investigators identify a tool that is consistent with tool marks, they know that the owner of the tool was at the crime scene. *Obj. 17.7*

4. Chips and dents on a hammerhead can produce unique tool marks. *Obj. 17.2*

5. Tool marks are considered to be a form of circumstantial evidence. *Obj. 17.7*

6. As a screwdriver slides against a doorjamb, the softer material leaves an abrasion on the other surface. *Obj. 17.3*

7. Tool-mark casts from a variety of materials, including silicone-based materials, may be used to compare a specific tool with the crime-scene tool mark. *Obj. 17.6*

8. There is little forensic value in examining cut marks in wood because all cut wood looks similar. *Obj. 17.2, 17.3*

9. Pry-bar and crowbar marks cannot be distinguished from each other because they produce the same tool marks. *Obj. 17.2, 17.3*

Short Answer

10. Two different hammers were used to strike a wooden board. Assuming the same person made the impressions, describe what characteristics of the impressions could be used to distinguish the hammers. *Obj. 17.2*

11. Prepare a table that distinguishes among abrasions, cuts, and indentations, including examples of tools that could make these marks. *Obj. 17.3*

12. Fingerprints left on tools found at a crime scene provide individual evidence that may link a person to the tool and crime scene. Discuss the role of each of the following when trying to lift and photograph fingerprints from a tool. *Obj. 17.6*
    a) magnesium smoking
    b) oblique lighting

13. Put the following steps in the correct sequence to show the appropriate order when processing a crime scene for tool-mark evidence. Explain why you arranged the steps in the order you did. *Obj. 17.6*
    a) Cast the impression.
    b) Dust for fingerprints.
    c) Observe the surface for foreign materials left at the crime scene.
    d) Photograph the impression.

Chapter 17 Review

True or False

1. True
2. False
3. False
4. True
5. True
6. False
7. True
8. False
9. False

Short Answer

10. Sample answer: size and shape of indentations, imperfections on the tools' surfaces shown in the impressions; scrapes, chips, uneven surfaces; presence of any material transferred from tools, such as paint, rust, debris

11. Tables will vary. Sample entries:
    Abrasions: Surface scratch
    Sources: Pliers, knife, axe, gun barrel, pry bar
    Cuts: Cut surface, edge marks
    Sources: Saw, wire cutters, knife
    Indentations: Impression made by tool
    Sources: Impression of tool that pried open window, doors, cash box

12. a. Magnesium ribbon is burned to produce a white powder that coats the tool mark. The powder enhances contrast and acts like fingerprint powder on a latent fingerprint.
    b. Oblique lighting is lighting that is directed at the side of the impression. This is better than direct lighting because it produces shadows that can highlight imperfections in the tool mark.

13. d, c, b, a

14. a. i. Purchased a new freezer the week before her disappearance

   ii. Rented a wood chipper a few days before her disappearance

   iii. Faced a financially disastrous divorce and had a motive to kill his wife.

   b. Eyewitness saw a man using a wood chipper on the river but could not identify the man as Richard Crafts.

   c. Investigators linked one of the recovered tooth caps to her dental records.

   d. The serial number had been filed off.

15. Sample answer: Many tool marks have microscopic clues that newer instruments, such as the profilometer, can detect. The profilometer can measure the depth of an indentation and give a three-dimensional image. Some laboratories have a tool-mark database that can statistically analyze an image to find similar marks. Microscopic analysis using a comparison microscope or a scanning electron microscope provides detailed images of the surfaces of tools or tool marks.

Connections

Sample answer: Forensic scientists use mathematical measurements to compare tool marks and suspect tools. A screwdriver with a 7-mm tip probably did not make a tool mark measuring only 4 mm across.

---

14. Refer to the case study concerning Richard Crafts. *Obj. 17.8*
   a) What evidence linked Richard Crafts to the crime?
   b) If there was an eyewitness to the body dumping, why wasn't that testimony sufficient to convict Richard Crafts?
   c) Describe how the police were able to make a positive identification of the remains of Helle Crafts.
   d) Why wasn't the serial number on the chain saw used to help prosecute Richard Crafts?

15. Give an example of how technology has advanced tool-mark evidence analysis. *Obj. 17.8*

Going Further

Research how the National Institute for Standards and Technology (NIST) is strengthening the reputation of forensic science through the establishment of the Scientific Working Groups (SWGs) and the Organization of Scientific Area Committees (OSAC) on Physics and Patterns. What guidelines have been established to improve trace evidence reliability and the power of trace evidence in the courtroom?

Connections

Mathematics Tool-mark databases are currently being developed. How can tool marks be quantified and analyzed mathematically?

Further Study

Research and report on the significance of tool marks in solving the Lindbergh kidnapping case.

Bibliography

Books and Journals

Baldwin, David, John Birkett, Owen Facey, and Gilleon Rabey. *The Forensic Examination and Interpretation of Tool Marks*. London: John Wiley and Sons, 2013.

Cannon, Roger J. "Justice for All," *Security Management*, 34(3): 63, March 1990. From *Forensic Science Journals*.

Du Pasquier, E., J. Hebrad, P. Margot, and M. Ineichen. "Evaluation and comparison of casting materials in forensic sciences applications to tool marks and foot/shoe impressions." *Forensic Science International*, 82(1): 33–43, September 15, 1996. From *Forensic Science Journals*.

Evans, Colin. *The Casebook of Forensic Detection*. New York: Berkley Trade, 2007.

Fisher, B. *Techniques of Crime Scene Investigation*. Boca Raton, FL: CRC Press, 2000.

Maples, William R., and Michael Browning. *Dead Men Do Tell Tales: The Strange and Fascinating Cases of a Forensic Anthropologist*. Jackson, TN: Main Street Books, 1995.

Sehgal, V. N., S. R. Singh, M. R. Kumar, C. K. Jain, K. K. Grover, and D. K. Dua. "Tool marks comparison of a wire cut ends by scanning electron microscopy—A forensic study." *Forensic Science International* 36(1–2): 21–29, January 1988. From *Forensic Science Journals*.

Internet Resources

ngl.cengage.com/forensicscience2e (Gale Forensic Science eCollection)

http://www.firearmsid.com/Case%20Profiles/ToolmarkID/toolmark.htm

http://www.crime-scene-investigator.net/otherimpressionevidence.html

http://www.abc.net.au/science/news/stories/s1089160.htm

http://www.external.ameslab.gov/forensics/Baldwin.htm

https://www.theiai.org/disciplines/firearms_toolmark/

http://www.fbi.gov/about-us/lab/scientific-analysis/fire_tool

http://www.indy.gov/eGov/County/FSA/Documents/Toolmark.pdf

http://www.afte.org/

http://science.howstuffworks.com/impression-evidence1.htm

https://www.ncjrs.gov/pdffiles1/nij/grants/230162.pdf (profilometers)

http://www.crime-scene-investigator.net/manipulative-virtual-tools-for-tool-mark-characterization.pdf (profilometers that create three-dimensional images of tool parts)

https://www.ncjrs.gov/pdffiles1/nij/grants/230162.pdf

www.wiley.com/go/baldwin/forensictoolmarks

TOOL MARKS   573

Background

In this activity, students analyze photos of tools and tool markings. Then they try to determine if tool marks found at the scene of a burglary are consistent with a suspect's tools.

Time Required to Complete Activity

30 minutes

Safety Precautions

There are no safety precautions for this lab.

Procedures

1. Print, copy, and distribute Act 17-1 SH from the IRCD, Chapter 17.

2. See Act 17-1 TN for how to make a demo board using clay and screwdrivers.

3. Make sure students read all directions *before* beginning the activity.

Explore

Encourage interested students to design an activity similar to this one using tools from home. Students should provide photos of tools and create a set of impressions. Students should share their designs with the class.

Teaching Tip

Depending on your student population, use either the photos of the tools and tool marks, or bring in samples of screwdrivers and chisels. Have students prepare tool marks by pressing the tip of the tool into a soft material such as modeling clay or silicone. Students should prepare a database of information for each tool, in which they include the type of tool, width of tip, width at widest point, and any unique characteristics.

Tool Marks: Screwdrivers and Chisels Obj. 17.1, 17.2

Scenario:

A break-in has occurred. Bud and Arthur are both suspects. A screwdriver or chisel was used in the course of a burglary, and pry marks were left behind. Can you identify which tool was used in the crime?

Objectives:

By the end of this activity, you will be able to:

1. Analyze the photographs of the tools to detect any individualizing features.
2. Measure the tool marks using the photographs.
3. Determine if any of the tools in the photograph are consistent with the tool mark left at the crime scene.

Time Required to Complete Activity: 30 minutes

Materials (per group):

Act 17-1 SH
6" metric ruler or calipers
hand lenses

SAFETY PRECAUTIONS:
None

Procedure:

1. Examine the photos of each of the tool marks pictured on the following page, including the crime-scene tool mark and the other 16 tool marks.
2. Note any characteristics that would make a screwdriver or chisel unique and easy to identify, such as damage or unique markings.
3. Measure the blade of the screwdriver or chisel along its tip and at its widest point using a metric ruler or calipers. Record your measurements in the table provided.
4. Analyze the data in your data table. Determine if any of the tool marks made from Arthur's and Bud's tools are consistent with the tool mark from the crime scene.

Questions:

1. Describe characteristics that helped you distinguish the different types of tools.
2. The tool-mark that was consistent with the crime scene was number _____ owned by _____.
3. Would there be sufficient evidence for an arrest? Why or why not?

Answers

Check students' databases.

Questions

1. Some have parallel striations; some do not. Measurements of the tool and defects on the tool are the best distinguishing characteristics. Size, shape, depth of impression, cuts, abrasions, and the presence of trace evidence also distinguish tools.

2. 9, Bud

3. No. Although Bud's screwdriver was used, it does not prove Bud used it; or if he did use it, when. The evidence is circumstantial.

4. Viewing only photographs of the tools and tool impressions limits the analysis. If you had the actual tool and the tool impression or were able to view a three-dimensional cast of the impression, what other measurements and observations might you be able to make?

5. Give an example of how technology has improved tool-mark analysis.

Crime-scene tool marks

1

2

3 chisel

4 chisel

5

6

7

8

9

10

11

12

13

14

15

16

Art's tools

1 2 3 4 5

Tools are not to scale with their impressions.

Bud's tools

6

7 8 9

10 11

12

13

14

15

16

All photos: © Cengage Learning®

4. It is easier to see abrasions and easier to measure dimensions, including depth of impression. The silicone mold could show more detail as well.

5. Answers will vary. Sample answer: the profilometer

Teaching Tip

To enlarge the images, take a digital photo of the page and enlarge it onscreen. If a digital camera is not available, a high-quality computer tablet camera or cell phone camera will work well.

Answers

Data Table: Screwdriver and Chisel Comparison (Descriptions may vary, but measurements should be accurate.)

Tool	Description of Tool Mark	Width at Tip (mm)	Width at Widest Point (mm)
1	Scratches on tip	8	10
2		9	10
3	Beveled	10	10
4	Beveled	11	11
5		5	9
6	Ribbed	7	9
7		6	10
8	Ribbed	5	7
9	Ribbed	8	11
10	Ribbed	8	9
11		8	9
12		7	9
13		9	10
14		6	8
15		8	8
16		7	8
Crime Scene	Ribbed	8	11

Data Table: Screwdriver and Chisel Comparison

Tool	Description of Tool Mark	Width at Tip (mm)	Width at Widest Point (mm)
1			
2			
3			
4			
5			
6			
7			
8			
8			
9			
10			
11			
12			
13			
14			
15			
16			
Crime Scene			

Further Research:

Instead of working with photographs, use four different screwdrivers to prepare tool impressions. Select one screwdriver to be the crime-scene tool and prepare an impression on a piece of soft wood (like pine) or modeling clay to serve as crime-scene evidence. Take photographs and measurements, and prepare a cast of the tool impressions. Prepare your testimony as an expert witness on tool marks. Include measurement tables of four screwdrivers and the crime-scene photographs along with casts to support your testimony. State your claim, citing evidence from your investigation.

Hammers and Hammer Impressions *Ch. Obj. 17.1, 17.2, 17.4*

Scenario:

Hammers collected from five different suspects are compared to a cast of an indentation tool mark found at a crime scene. Is it possible to exclude any of the suspects based on the cast of the indentation mark and the hammers in their possession?

Objectives:

By the end of this activity, you will be able to:

1. Analyze the photographs of the tools to detect any distinguishing features.
2. Record the measurements of the hammerheads' diameters using the photographs provided.
3. Compare and contrast the cast to the five suspects' hammers to determine if any suspects can be excluded.

Time Required to Complete Activity: 15 minutes

Materials (per group of two):

Act 17-2 SH
diagrams provided in text
hand lenses
calipers

SAFETY PRECAUTIONS:
None

Procedure:

PART A: MEASUREMENT OF HAMMER

1. Use the example and hammerhead photos A through E on the next page. Read the calipers and record the diameter of each hammerhead in the data table.
   a. Refer to the top scale (or outside scale) of the calipers.
   b. Locate the zero mark on the outside scale to obtain the number of whole millimeters (top line).
   c. To determine the measurement to the nearest 0.1 mm, look at the top scale that is marked 0 to 1.0 mm. (You may need a hand lens to view this.) Find where one of the markings on that 0 to 1.0 mm lines up directly over one of the lines beneath it. (Refer to the example on the top of the next page.)
   d. Record the reading (0 to 1.0 mm) on the top line where the two marks are aligned directly over each other to obtain the measurement to the nearest 0.1 mm.

Background

In this activity, students take measurements of hammers from photographs. They also analyze casting impressions of hammers and use this evidence to try to match one of the hammers to a hammer used in a crime.

Time Required to Complete Activity

15 minutes

Safety Precautions

There are no safety precautions for this lab.

Procedures

1. Print, copy, and distribute Act 17-2 SH from the IRCD, Chapter 17.

2. Make sure students read all directions *before* beginning the activity.

3. Review with students how to measure using calipers. Refer to Capstone 9, "How to Read Calipers," for detailed instructions.

Explore

The following activities are extensions of this activity. Students my complete only Part 1 or may extend the activity to Parts 2 and 3.

Part 1

Ask students working in small, collaborative groups to create a database of different tools. Each group investigates a different type of tool. (screwdrivers, chisels, pliers, hammers, etc.). Borrow tools from the school custodian or technology shops. The database should consist of at least five different tools. Students should include
- photographs of the tool
- measurement of the tool
- distinguishing characteristics

These databases would be used for reference when setting up crime scenes.

Part 2

An extension of the database project in Part 1 is to have students write a short crime-scene scenario that involves tool-mark evidence. One of the tools in the database is used to create evidence. Other students read the scenario and try to include or exclude suspects based on a comparison of the evidence and the tools described in databases. If time is short, have two groups exchange scenarios and databases so that all groups are solving at least one crime.

Part 3

Expert Witness Testimony
After the groups have investigated other groups' evidence, each group prepares expert witness testimony and a rebuttal. Each group states a claim; provides data supporting the claim; and analyzes the evidence for its relevance and reliability. Each group has an opportunity to present a rebuttal to other teams' testimony and to defend rebuttals against their own.

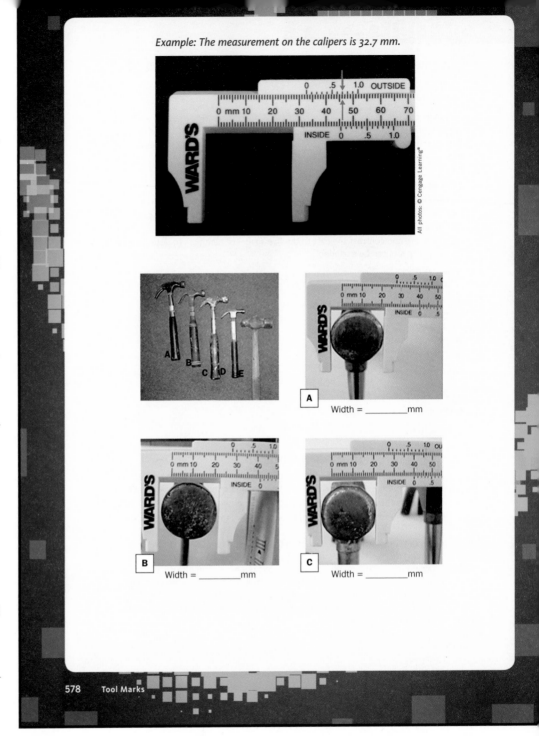

Example: The measurement on the calipers is 32.7 mm.

All photos: © Cengage Learning®

A   Width = _____ mm

B   Width = _____ mm

C   Width = _____ mm

D Width = _____mm

All photos: © Cengage Learning®

E Width = _____mm

Data Table: Hammerhead Diameter

Hammer	Head Diameter (mm)
A (Orange Ring Neck)	
B (Two Bands)	
C (Silver Neck)	
D (Small Red Handle)	
E (Large Uncle Waldo)	
Cast from crime-scene impression = 41 mm	

2. Record your answers in the Data Table: Hammerhead Diameter
3. It was determined that the crime was committed with a hammer whose head measured approximately 41 mm. Do any of the evidence hammers seem to have a head diameter consistent with the crime weapon?

Student answers will likely be approximate.

Data Table: Hammer Width

Hammer	Width (mm)
A. (Orange Ring Neck)	27.5
B. (Two Bands)	28.1
C. (Silver Neck)	27.6
D. (Baby Red Handle)	22.6
E. (Large Uncle Waldo)	41.1
Casting from crime-scene impression = 41 mm	

Answers

Check students' data tables and worksheets.

Questions

1. The size (41 mm) of hammer E is consistent with the crime-scene impression.

2. Sample answer. If the student recorded readings between 27 mm and 42 mm, then the student was reading the inside scale and not the outside scale of the calipers.

3. Unique markings on the cast are consistent with hammer 2. Hammer 2 can be rotated 180 degrees clockwise to align it with the photo of the cast of the crime-scene impression.

   Note on the crime-scene cast photo:

   At "11:00," a series of many vertical lines

   At "7:00," a distinctive scratch mark that is also found on Hammer 2

   At "1:00," there are a series of unique scratches that are also noted on Hammer 2.

4. Sample answer: Include a photograph of the entire cast. Take several photographs, and use oblique (indirect) lighting to highlight superficial differences; use a lens that allows higher magnification; use a polarizing filter on the lens to prevent glare; if possible, take the photo using a stereomicroscope.

5. Sample answer: The hammer could have been used by anyone to commit the crime at any time; it may have been stolen to commit the crime. It does not link the suspect to the crime directly, making it *circumstantial evidence*. The hammer is only one of many made just like it, making it *class evidence*.

PART B: HAMMER PHOTOGRAPHS

1. Examine the photographs of hammerheads 1 through 5, which belong to five different suspects.
2. Compare each photograph to the cast of the crime-scene impression.
3. Determine if any of the photographs of the five suspects' hammers are consistent with the cast from the impression at the crime scene.

Evidence cast made from an indentation at the crime scene.

All photos: © Cengage Learning®

Questions:

1. In Part A, which hammer's diameter is consistent with the hammer used at the crime scene? Justify your claim using your measurements.
2. One student in the class got completely different measurements from the rest of the class. The class recorded measurements between 23 mm and 41 mm, but hers were between 35 mm and 54 mm. Look at the photos in Part A. Can you determine the source of her error in reading the calipers?
3. In Part B, which hammer photograph is consistent with the crime-scene impression? Cite evidence from the photos and the cast.
4. The director of the crime lab was not satisfied with the quality of the photographs of the hammerheads. Provide suggestions for the photographer that would improve his or her technique.
5. The prosecutor argued that the defendant was guilty because he owned a hammer that made an impression consistent with the crime-scene impression. As the defense attorney, how would you argue that ownership of a tool that makes impressions consistent with a crime-scene impression is insufficient evidence for conviction? Explain the term *circumstantial evidence* in your argument.

Casting Impressions of Hammer Strikes on Wood in Silicone *Obj. 17.1, 17.2, 17.4, 17.5, 17.6*

Scenario:

Police received a report of a construction site break-in. The specifics of the case suggested that it was an "inside job," involving one of the site's employees. The break-in involved a locked wooden toolbox that had clearly been broken with a hammer. The toolbox contained cash. No hammer was found at the site of the break-in, and it was assumed the thief used a personal hammer. Police collected all of the workers' hammers for testing. Your task is to produce casts of the hammer strikes for comparison to the tool-mark evidence found at the crime scene.

Objectives:

By the end of this activity, you will be able to:

1. Produce hammer impressions in wood from eight different suspects' hammers.
2. Compare the hammer impressions to the crime-scene impression.
3. Determine which hammer (if any) produced the tool mark that was consistent with the crime-scene tool mark.

Time Required to Complete Activity: 45 minutes

Materials (groups of three or four):

Act 17-3 SH
Act 17-3 SH Evidence Inv Label
8 hammers of varying size (for all groups to share) labeled 1 through 8
1 strike board (per group)
labeling pen
calipers or metric ruler (calibrated in millimeters)
crime-scene board with hammer impression
silicone casting material
digital camera (optional)
9 three-by-five-inch cards
1 roll of adhesive tape
9–18 evidence bags
9–18 evidence labels
small flashlight
forceps

Tool Marks   581

DIFFERENTIATED LEARNING

Teaching At-Risk Students
Before beginning this activity, encourage students to research the best wood to prepare a reference strike board for hammers. (Offer hints as to the best qualities of that wood, if necessary.) Suggest that volunteers present their results to the class.

Background

In this activity, students make hammer impressions from eight different suspects' hammers and compare those impressions to one found at a crime scene. Then, they try to determine which of the suspects' hammers was used at the crime scene.

Time Required to Complete Activity

45 minutes

Safety Precautions

1. Make sure students wear safety goggles when using the hammers.
2. Emphasize to students that they should be very careful when using the hammers.
3. Teachers in nearby classrooms should be alerted that this activity will be quite noisy.

Teaching Tip

You may not want to have hammers in class, depending on your student population.

Refer to Act 17-3 TN for information on creating strike patterns in advance for display and measurement. Soft pine boards work best for deep impressions.

Teaching Tips

- Obtain eight different hammers. Number the hammers 1 through 8. Select one of the hammers to be the "crime-scene" hammer.
- It would be helpful to have a single crime-scene impression board for all groups so that all the crime-scene impression evidence is the same. The other hammers can be shared during the lab. Record the number of the hammer used to make the crime-scene impression.
- To make the activity more interesting, include some trace evidence in the crime-scene impression such as hair, fibers, or soil.

Procedures

1. Print, copy, and distribute Act 17-3 SH and Act 17-3 SH Evidence Inv Label from the IRCD, Chapter 17.

2. You need to prepare, in advance, a board with the crime-scene impression. See Act 17-3 TN in the IRCD, Chapter 17 for information on how to create this board.

3. Select one of the hammers to be the crime-scene hammer, and create impressions that can be used for making a cast. Use one of the silicone-based products mentioned in the chapter (or even aquarium cement) to make your cast.

4. Make sure students read all directions *before* beginning the activity.

5. Groups should check for trace evidence in the impressions using adhesive tape. If using one crime-scene impression per class, inform students that the first group using the impression will most likely lift off the trace evidence. However, each team should still complete the procedure.

6. If using one set of hammers per class, establish a method for having hammers passed onto the next team before the students begin the activity.

7. Each group should photograph the crime-scene impression and the hammer impressions. Remind students to have an object for scale in view while photographing, and encourage them to try the oblique-light photography technique.

SAFETY PRECAUTIONS:
Wear safety goggles during this activity. Care must be taken when pounding with hammers to avoid contact with other students. Students should be warned that any unsafe acts will lead to their removal from the activity.

Procedure:

PART A: CAST THE CRIME-SCENE IMPRESSION

1. Examine the crime-scene board with the hammer impression. Photograph the crime-scene impression at an oblique angle alongside calipers or a ruler to show scale. Record any observations of the impression in the Data Table.

2. Using forceps, remove any trace evidence from the impression, and properly bag and document the evidence on the Evidence Inventory Label.

3. Obtain a 3" × 5" card and label it *Crime Scene*. Using adhesive tape, lift any small pieces of trace evidence from the impression and secure them to the 3" × 5" card. Bag and document the evidence on the evidence label. Record your findings in the Data Table.

4. Using the silicone casting material, prepare a cast of the crime-scene impression. Fill the indentation completely with the casting material.

5. Allow the silicone to solidify thoroughly before removing it (about 15 minutes).

6. While you are waiting for the impression to solidify, proceed to Part B, and prepare the strike impressions for hammers 1 through 8.

7. Once the silicone has solidified, examine the impression cast from the crime scene. Analyze the cast, noting any distinctive markings. Measure the diameter of the cast in millimeters. Record your observations in the Data Table.

PART B: MAKE THE HAMMER IMPRESSIONS

8. Obtain your strike board.

9. Divide the board into eight areas. Number the areas 1 through 8, one for each of the eight suspects' hammers.

10. For each of the eight hammers, make a single hammer impression on the strike board in the appropriate place on the board. The same person should make all eight strike marks using the same amount of force.

11. Photograph each impression next to calipers or a metric ruler. Hold a flashlight at an oblique angle to enhance the shadows, thereby improving the clarity of the photograph.

12. Examine each of the impressions with a flashlight held at an oblique angle. Record any observations in the Data Table.

13. Obtain eight 3" × 5" index cards, and label them 1 through 8, one for each of the eight hammers.

14. For each hammer impression, do the following:

    a. Use forceps to remove any larger trace evidence from the impression and properly bag and document the evidence on the evidence label. Be sure to record the number of each hammer on the evidence label.

    b. Use adhesive tape to lift any smaller pieces of trace evidence from the impressions. Secure the tape to the labeled 3" × 5" card. (Be sure evidence for hammer 1 is placed on trace evidence card 1, etc.) Record your observations for each hammer impression in the Data Table. Properly bag and document the evidence with an Evidence Inventory Label attached.

15. Using your calipers, measure the diameter of each impression to the nearest 0.1 millimeter, and record your measurements in the Data Table.

PART C: COMPARE THE CRIME-SCENE EVIDENCE CAST TO THE HAMMER IMPRESSIONS

16. Compare the measurements from your cast of the crime-scene impression to the measurements of your hammer impressions. Are the diameters of any of the suspects' hammer impressions consistent with the diameter of the cast of the crime-scene impression? Support your claim with your data.

17. Are any of the hammer-strike impressions with markings and/or trace evidence consistent with the crime-scene impression cast? Support your claim with your data and your photos.

Going Further:

Teams may prepare and present an expert witness report to the class. Support your claims using data and photographs of the hammer consistent with the cast from the crime scene.

Data Table: Hammer Impressions

Hammer Impression	Diameter (mm)	Description of Any Trace Evidence	Other Observations
1			
2			
3			
4			
5			
6			
7			
8			
Crime Scene			

Questions:

1. Based on your data, were you able to exclude any suspects? Support your claim with data and other evidence from your Data Table.

2. Tool-mark evidence alone is not sufficient evidence to convict someone of a crime. Prepare a list of questions that might provide additional evidence linking the suspect to this crime.

Answers

Check students' data tables, casts, and strike boards.

Questions

1. Answers will vary. Based on diameter, many of the hammer impressions could be excluded.

2. Additional questions should include the following:
   - Where was the suspect during the time the crime was committed?
   - Did the suspect have a motive in committing this crime?
   - Was any evidence linking the suspect to the crime, such as blood from the victim, found on the suspect?

Further Research and Extensions

Before they analyze the hammer impressions, have students write down their hypotheses about how varying strengths or sizes of the person swinging the hammer will affect the impressions created.

Chapter Overview

Ballistics is the study of fired projectiles, such as bullets, in flight. A firearm is any mechanism capable of firing a projectile by using an explosive in a confined space as a propellant. The barrel of a rifle or pistol leaves unique ridges (lands) and indentations (grooves), or rifling marks, on a bullet as it is fired. Both individual and class evidence can be obtained from the analysis of spent cartridges and fired projectiles. This evidence includes rifling marks, firing-pin marks, ejector marks, and headstamps. If a firearm used in a shooting is recovered, ballistics experts can test-fire it and compare the fired projectiles with the crime-scene evidence. Entrance and exit wounds, along with the discovery of any gunshot residue, are also evaluated. Investigators use two reference points to estimate the trajectory of the projectile and help locate its origin. Ideally, the location will yield evidence linked to the shooter. Technology, including ballistics databases and improved comparison microscopes, has helped ballistics experts solve crimes.

The Big Ideas

Modern firearms can be either long guns, such as rifles or shotguns, or handguns, such as revolvers and semi-automatics. Firearms fire projectiles, which, along with primer powder, gunpowder, and casing material, make up the cartridge. Shotguns fire shot or slugs. Bullets are classified by caliber, which is the measure of the inside of a rifled firearm and the diameter of the bullet. Each firearm leaves unique markings, or rifling marks, on bullets as they are fired. These markings allow investigators to compare a spent bullet to the gun that fired it. Further, by calculating a bullet's trajectory, or path, an investigator may be able to trace the path of a bullet back to the location of the shooter.

CHAPTER 18

Firearms and Ballistics

Suicide or Homicide?

Sandra Duyst's body was found lying on blood-spattered sheets next to a 9-millimeter pistol in March 2000. Gunshot residue and star-shaped skin tears around the wound indicated close-range firing consistent with a suicide. During the autopsy, however, one entrance wound but *two* exit wounds were discovered. When a second entrance wound was discovered upon further examination, the manner of death was changed from suicide to homicide.

Medical examiner Stephen D. Cohle, M.D., reported that the first wound would have completely incapacitated Duyst. Ballistics expert Greg Boer agreed that she could not have fired the weapon twice because the recoil would have prevented a second shot from hitting her. Boer also explained that the gun did not misfire, so someone else had to fire the second bullet.

More than a year before her death, Sandra Duyst had told her sister about a note to be read in the event of her untimely death. In the note, Duyst stated that she would not commit suicide, and "If anything has happened to me, look first to David Duyst, Sr." Her note revealed that head injuries she incurred a few years earlier were not accidental; they were inflicted by her husband, Duyst. A handwriting expert stated that the handwriting was consistent with that of Sandra Duyst.

Blood-spatter expert Rod Englert stated that the blood evidence at the crime scene included a void consistent with someone standing over the victim. Tiny blood spots consistent with a mist of blood produced by a high-velocity, close-range impact were found on a shirt belonging to David Duyst. DNA testing confirmed the blood was Sandra Duyst's. Further suspicion fell on David Duyst when it was discovered that he had recently taken out a large life insurance policy on his wife, he was having an affair, and he had financial difficulties. David Duyst, Sr., was arrested, tried, and convicted of first-degree murder of his wife, Sandra.

CHRIS CLARK/MLIVE.COM/Landov

Dr. Stephen D. Cohle

SCENARIO

1. What role did the autopsy play in solving this crime?
2. Describe the firearms and ballistics evidence presented in this case, and describe how that evidence helped solve this crime.
3. Besides an expert witness in ballistics, what other expert witnesses were called to testify in this hearing?
4. What evidence showed that Sandra Duyst's husband had a motive for killing her?

OBJECTIVES

By the end of this chapter, you will be able to:

18.1 Compare and contrast the different types of firearms, including handguns, rifles, and shotguns.

18.2 Put in order the sequence of events that result in a firearm discharging.

18.3 Estimate the trajectory of a projectile.

18.4 Discuss the composition and formation of gunshot residue and its reliability as a source of evidence.

18.5 Compare and contrast entrance and exit wounds, including size, shape, gunshot residue, and the presence of burns.

18.6 Distinguish among the various forms of firearms evidence, including rifling, markings on cartridges, marks on projectiles, and gunshot residue.

18.7 Discuss how technology has improved the ability to obtain, compare, analyze, store, and retrieve firearm and ballistics evidence.

18.8 Process and/or analyze a crime scene for firearm and ballistics evidence.

TOPICAL SCIENCES KEY

BIOLOGY   CHEMISTRY

EARTH SCIENCES   PHYSICS

LITERACY   MATHEMATICS

VOCABULARY

- **ballistics** the study of a projectile in flight; includes the launch and behavior of the projectile

- **breech** the end of the barrel attached to the firing mechanism of a firearm where the cartridge is loaded and unloaded

- **bullet** the projectile that is fired when a firearm is discharged

- **caliber** the inside diameter of a firearm barrel

- **cartridge** a case that holds a bullet, primer powder, and gunpowder

- **firearm** a portable gun that uses a confined propellant to expel a projectile out of a barrel

- **gunshot residue (GSR)** soot and particles of unburned gunpowder deposited on a

person who discharges a firearm; may also be found on close-range victims and adjacent surfaces

- **lands** and **grooves** the ridges (lands) and depressions (grooves) found on the inside of a firearm's barrel that are created when the firearm is manufactured

- **pistol** a handgun with a barrel and chamber that are connected

- **revolver** a handgun with a revolving cylinder

- **rifle** a long gun that has a barrel with spiral grooves and that is fired from shoulder level

- **rifling** the spiral pattern on a fired projectile made by the lands and grooves in the barrel of a firearm

- **trajectory** the flight path of a projectile

TEACHING RESOURCES

Instructor's Resource CD-ROM includes:

- Activities and Student Handouts
- Alternative Assessments
- Consolidated Bibliography
- Correlations to NGSS and CCSS
- Figure Files
- Nonfiction Readings

- PowerPoint Presentations
- Student Learning Objective (SLOs)

CL Testing powered by Cognero

Website: ngl.cengage.com/forensicscience2e

Engage

As a warm-up, ask students some of the following questions. Alternatively, use some in a carousel brainstorming session. Post questions around the classroom on poster board. Divide the class into small groups. Groups rotate from poster to poster and record brainstormed answers on the posters. At the end of a complete rotation, one person within each group summarizes the answers. Follow with class discussion.

1. What is the difference between a long gun and a handgun?

2. Which type of firearm is more accurate, a pistol or a rifle?

3. What is the difference between a rifle and a shotgun?

4. What is the difference between a bullet and a cartridge?

5. What is rifling of a firearm barrel?

6. What is inside a cartridge that enables a bullet to be projected?

7. What is the function of the hammer on a firearm?

8. What is the difference between gunpowder and primer powder?

9. What is inside a shotgun shell?

10. Which projectile has more energy, a bullet from a pistol, or shot from a shotgun?

11. When someone says he makes his own bullets, what does he mean?

12. What is the difference between a 12-gauge shotgun and a 20-gauge shotgun?

13. What is a .38 Winchester? (What does ".38" refer to?)

Teaching Tip

It is preferable to use the term *firearm*, not *gun* or *weapon*.

Did you know

The Minié ball (1849) was a lead bullet with a hollowed-out base that expanded to fit a rifle barrel when it was fired. It was used during the Civil War and was a precursor of modern ammunition.

INTRODUCTION

Did you ever wonder why police comb an area in search of the gun used in a crime? Why do crime-scene investigators use metal detectors to find spent cartridges? Why is it so important for a medical examiner to recover bullets embedded in murder victim? These are all ways of collecting ballistics evidence that can help link a suspect to a crime scene or to a particular gun—and ultimately, to solve a crime.

A **firearm** is a portable gun, capable of firing a projectile using a confined explosive. **Ballistics** is the study of a firearm projectile in flight. Ballistics evidence provides the clues to help police answer many questions pertaining to a crime scene. These questions include the following:

• What type of firearm was used?

• What was the caliber of the bullet?

• How many bullets were fired?

• Where was the shooter standing?

• What was the angle of impact?

• Has this firearm been used in a previous crime?

HISTORY OF GUNPOWDER AND FIREARMS

CHEMISTRY

More than one thousand years ago, the Chinese invented gunpowder. Gunpowder (now known as *black powder*) is potassium nitrate (saltpeter), charcoal, and sulfur. The Chinese used gunpowder to make fireworks and to shoot balls of flaming material at their enemies. When ignited, it produces a violent explosion.

Years later, in 14th-century Europe, inventors learned they could direct the explosive force of gunpowder down a cylinder to move a deadly projectile. The projectiles expelled from these early firearms were very effective in piercing suits of armor and wounding the enemy at a great distance—as much as 30 yards!

For a firearm to work reliably, it must ignite the gunpowder. The earliest firearms, matchlock firearms which date back to 1475, had wicks to carry a flame to the gunpowder. In the beginning of the 1600s, matchlock firearms were replaced by flintlock firearms, which used sparks from a chip of flint instead of wicks to ignite the powder, allowing them to work even in damp weather. Flintlocks were muzzle-loaders, which meant that the user put the gunpowder and the projectile down the firearm's barrel through the *muzzle*, the end from which the projectile exits. Flintlocks fired round projectiles made of lead.

Percussion-cap firearms replaced flintlock firearms around 1820 with the introduction of the **cartridge,** a case that holds a **bullet** (a pointed projectile), gunpowder, and a small amount of primer powder that detonates the gunpowder. A hammer strikes the back of the cartridge and ignites the primer powder, which ignites the gunpowder. (See Figure 18-1.) The force from the explosion expels the bullet. Firearms that used this method were more accurate than flintlocks. Cartridges were loaded into the gun from the opposite end of the

---

DIFFERENTIATED LEARNING

Teaching Gifted Students

The right to bear arms is protected by the United States Constitution. However, there is much debate about whether everyone should be able to purchase automatic firearms. Have students write an essay stating and justifying their position on these questions: Should all Americans who pass the screening test be able to purchase firearms? Should all firearms sold be registered with state or local authorities?

barrel—the **breech.** These breech-loading firearms could be loaded more quickly than the older, muzzle-loading firearms.

Figure 18-1 *A percussion-cap firearm ignites the gunpowder using a primer that explodes when struck by a small hammer.*

Pier Photography/Alamy

LONG GUNS AND HANDGUNS *Obj. 18.1*

Modern firearms are divided into two basic types—long guns and handguns. Long guns, such as rifles and shotguns (Figure 18-2), require the use of two hands. The long barrel of a rifle improves the accuracy. **Rifles** fire bullets, whereas shotguns can fire either small round pellets (shot) or a single projectile called a slug. The longer the barrel on a firearm, the greater the accuracy. Rifles fired at a distance are more accurate than handguns fired at a distance.

Handguns intended to be fired with one hand are called **pistols.** American inventor Samuel Colt developed and patented a model in 1835 that had a cylinder that could be loaded with several cartridges and fired in rapid succession. It was called a **revolver,** because the cylinder that held the cartridges turned as it fired. The empty shell casings must be manually removed from the cylinder.

Figure 18-2 *Shotguns, which are often used for hunting game birds, can fire many small pellets at once. Below right, you can see different types of shotgun projectiles, or "shells" (not to scale with the shotgun). Shells differ in size and shape depending on their use.*

Radlund & Associates/Brand X Pictures/Jupiterimages

©Epitavi/Shutterstock.com

Did you know ?

Shotgun shells are measured in gauge. The number of the gauge depends on the inside diameter of the barrel, and larger gauge numbers have smaller barrels. The most common shotgun, the 12-gauge, has a barrel with an inside diameter of 0.73 inch.

Evaluate

Modern firearms have individualized barrels that help in identification. Ask students if they expect this will change as technology advances.

Teaching Tip

The Website www.firearmsid.com has many activities, articles, and animations pertaining to firearms and projectiles. One activity contains a virtual comparison of lands and grooves on bullet samples, which you might like to share with your class.

Teaching Tip

Originally, rifling was placed in the barrel of a firearm to help provide a channel for black powder residue buildup. It did not work successfully for this purpose, but it did provide a way of spinning the bullet for a more accurate shot.

Teaching Tip

Figure 18-11 on p. 592 compares rimfired and centerfired cartridges.

Figure 18-3 *Bullets fired from a firearm show patterns of lands and grooves that are consistent with the rifling of the firearm.*

Base of bullet   Left twist   Right twist

Land

Groove

Front view of barrel

Today, handguns can be classified as revolvers or semiautomatic firearms. Revolvers hold cartridges in the cylinder. Semiautomatics carry cartridges in a magazine, which is locked into the grip of the firearm. *Semiautomatic* weapons, which fire only one bullet per pull of the trigger, differ from *fully automatic* weapons, which fire repeatedly as long as the trigger is pressed. In both, the empty cartridge is ejected, and the next cartridge is loaded automatically.

FIREARMS AND RIFLING
Obj. 18.6

An archer will hit a target with greater accuracy if there is a twist on the end of the arrow feathers. This same principle of spinning the projectile is part of the design of "rifled guns," or rifles. The word rifle refers to the **grooves,** or indentations, in the rifle's barrel. The ridges that surround the grooves are called **lands.** Within the gun's barrel, lands and grooves cause a bullet to spin when exiting the barrel of the gun, much in the same way a football spirals when thrown. The **rifling** pattern left on the bullet by the lands and grooves is unique to the firearm. Today, it is possible to compare the patterns of lands and grooves in pistols and rifles using a comparison microscope (Figure 18-3). These patterns can provide valuable evidence when the same firearm is used in multiple crimes.

Figure 18-4 *Cartridges of various types.*

50 BMG   338 LM   30 -06   308 Win   7.62 x39   223 Rem   22 LR

Image courtesy of Richard C. Wysong II

BULLETS AND CARTRIDGES
Obj. 18.2, 18.6

A bullet is a projectile propelled from a firearm. Bullets are normally made of metal. The term *bullet* is often incorrectly applied to the cartridge (Figure 18-4), which includes primer powder, gunpowder, the bullet, and the casing material that holds them all together. Cartridges are usually classified as rimfire or centerfire. *Rimfire* and *centerfire* refer to the area on the rear of the cartridge where the firing pin strikes the cartridge casing—either along the *rim* or in the *center.*

588 CHAPTER 18

Anatomy of a Cartridge

The typical cartridge is composed of the following parts (Figure 18-5):

1. The *bullet* (the projectile) can be composed of lead or combinations of various metals. It can be metal-jacketed, hollow-pointed, or even plastic-coated.

2. The *primer powder* mixture initiates the contained explosion that pushes the bullet down the barrel. The primer is struck by the firing pin of the firearm. The pressure causes the shock-sensitive primer powder to ignite, leading to the ignition of the larger gunpowder charge. The firearm's firing pin strikes the bottom of the cartridge *casing* in the centerfire cartridge, or it might strike anywhere on the rim of the rimfire cartridge. Modern smokeless gunpowder is a nitrocellulose mixture.

3. The *headstamp* on the bottom of the cartridge casing identifies the caliber (size) and manufacturer (Figure 18-6).

Figure 18-5 *A typical centerfire cartridge.*

- Bullet
- Cartridge casing
- Gunpowder
- Rim
- Primer

Figure 18-6 *Ammunition has a headstamp that identifies the caliber and manufacturer. The headstamp is on the bottom of the cartridge casing.*

© Cengage Learning®

Did you know?

Firearms and Ballistics Examination Advances

1923 FBI Bureau of Forensic Ballistics established

1929 Weapons used in the St. Valentine's Day massacre identified by matching bullets

1930s Earliest gunshot residue (GSR) test performed

1968 Scanning electron microscope first used to examine GSR for comparison

1992 FBI established the Drugfire database, which compiles details on bullet and cartridge markings

1996 U.S. Bureau of Alcohol, Tobacco, and Firearms (ATF) establishes a database for spent ammunition

2000 FBI and ATF begin merging their databases to establish the National Integrated Ballistic Information Network (NIBIN)

Teaching Tip

Go to www.remington.com/safety/10_commandments/ and print out "The 10 Commandments of Firearm Safety." Give a copy to each student. Ask one volunteer to read each commandment out loud, and then discuss each one as a class.

Teaching Tip

The first self-contained cartridges were produced by Samuel Colt (1873). Prior to this time, the projectile and the explosive gunpowder were separate from each other.

Teaching Tip

Contact a gun club or the local police and ask for some spent cartridge casings. Prepare an activity in which students examine spent casings and note caliber and manufacturer. Have students measure caliber using a ruler or calipers.

DIFFERENTIATED LEARNING

Teaching English-Language Learners

Let students work in pairs or small groups. If possible, give each group a different-sized empty bullet cartridge without the headstamp identifying the caliber. Ask them to explain how to determine the caliber.

Teaching Tip

Tracer ammunition containing magnesium and phosphate provides increased accuracy for the shooter. A visual path (tail) is produced as the projectile travels to the target.

Teaching Tip

3-D printed (plastic) firearms are very dangerous. They can shatter or explode upon firing.

The National Ballistics Intelligence Service (NABIS) in the United Kingdom has printed and fired 3-D printed guns. NABIS has also developed a scanner based on radio waves that can identify the shape of a firearm, plastic or metal, concealed under clothing.

Science

MATHEMATICS

MATHEMATICS

Bullet mass is expressed in grains. A grain is a unit of mass originally based on the mass of a single barley grain. Starting in the Bronze Age, the average mass of barley grains were part of the legal definition of "grain" in the English measurement system.

Science

MATHEMATICS

MATHEMATICS

Caliber measurements are often expressed in hundredths or thousandths of an inch, such as .22 or .357 or .38. Caliber can also be expressed in metric units, with millimeter being the unit of measurement, as in 9-millimeter cartridges.

How a Firearm Works

The sequence of events in the firing of a bullet follows (Figure 18-7):

1. When you pull the trigger, the firing pin of the firearm hits the base of the cartridge, igniting the primer powder mixture.
2. The tiny explosion—not much more than a spark—of the primer powder mixture delivers a spark through the flash hole to the main gunpowder supply.
3. The main gunpowder supply then ignites, and the pressure of the expanding gases propels the bullet from the casing and into the barrel of the firearm. The amount of gunpowder and the mass of the projectile determine the speed of the bullet.
4. The bullet spirals out of the barrel, marked by the unique lands and grooves as it exits.

Figure 18-7 *The sequence of events in the firing of a bullet.*

1. Trigger
2. Hammer
3. Cylinder
4. Barrel
5. Firing pin

Did you know?

The mass of a projectile is expressed in grains:

1 gram ~ 15.43 grains
1 pound ~ 7,000 grains

Caliber of a Cartridge

MATHEMATICS Bullets (and their cartridges) are classified by caliber and length. The **caliber** is a measure of the diameter of the bullet. Common calibers include .223, .25, .357, .38, .44, and .45. (See Figure 18-8.) These bullets are measured in hundredths or thousandths of an inch. Thus, a .45-caliber bullet measures 45/100 of an inch in diameter (almost ½ an inch). The .357 cartridge is 357/1,000 of an inch. The European method of naming firearm caliber uses the metric system for measurement of bullet diameter. Nine-millimeter firearms fire 9 mm bullets. Caliber also refers to the diameter of the inside of a firearm's barrel. Because the bullet moves through the barrel, the caliber of ammunition should match the firearm. If a bullet is removed from a wound or crime scene, its caliber and the lands and grooves on it may link it to the weapon used to fire it.

DIFFERENTIATED LEARNING

Teaching At-Risk Students

Organize the class into groups. To help them understand the steps in firing a gun, have them make a flow chart identifying the steps. Encourage visually oriented students to sketch what happens in each step.

Figure 18-8 *The caliber of a bullet is its diameter.*

EVIDENCE FROM BULLETS AND CARTRIDGES *Obj. 18.6*

The job of the firearms examiner involves examining used bullets and their spent cartridges for telltale markings made by a specific firearm. Recall that as a firearm is fired, the bullet exits the barrel with a pattern of lands and grooves made by the rifling of the barrel. A firearms examiner can compare the markings on the evidence bullet to the markings on the suspected firearm barrel by test-firing similar bullets from the suspected firearm (Figure 18-9). Investigators test-fire the firearm into a water tank or gel block. The bullet is not damaged and it can be easily recovered inside the tank. Ballistics soap can be used to determine the yaw (rotating) damage caused by a bullet. Ballistics gel retains the path of a fired bullet.

A comparison microscope is used to compare two different bullets. The bullets are mounted on two microscope stages with the ability for side-by-side comparison. Each bullet can be independently examined, rotated, and then compared.

Did you know

Virtual comparison microscopes (VCM) can be used to compare the rifling marks on multiple bullets at the same time.

Figure 18-9 *The barrel of a firearm has a unique pattern of rifling, which leaves a corresponding pattern of lands and grooves on the bullets it fires.*

Consistent lands (elevations)

Consistent grooves (indentations)

© Cengage Learning®

Teaching Tip

Engage students in a brainstorming discussion as to why it is so important that bullets are recovered during autopsies. What evidence can be recovered from a spent bullet?

Teaching Tip

Go to Firearmsid.com and register for the Resource Area. There, you and students can try the Virtual Comparison Microscope™ (VCM™). The VCM simulates what it is like to microscopically compare both bullets and cartridge cases. Several progressively difficult exercises for each are provided. A printable certificate is provided when you successfully complete an exercise.

Science

MATHEMATICS

MATHEMATICS

To calculate the number of lands and grooves (N) in a bullet:

$$N = \frac{\text{Estimated caliber (in.)} \times (3.1416)}{\text{Land width (in.)} + \text{groove width (in.)}}$$

The answer is approximate, so round to the nearest whole number.

Evaluate

Lead is a major component of most ammunition. Challenge students to think of how a suspect's hands or clothing could test positive for lead even though he or she had never fired a gun.

Explore

Encourage interested students to research the chemical composition of GSR and the procedures that detect it. (Most primers in ammunition sold in the U. S. contain lead, barium, antimony, and sometimes tin.)

Figure 18-10 *Breechblock markings come in various forms: parallel lines, circular lines, or stippling at the bottom of the cartridge casings.*

Circular breechblock mark.

Stippled breechblock mark.

Did you know

GSR testing is not perfectly reliable. A negative GSR result can mean that the GSR has worn off or been washed off. Secondary transfer can occur as well. Medical personnel can test positive for GSR from treating a gunshot victim.

Marks on Spent Cartridges

PHYSICS Breechblock markings are one kind of mark left on spent cartridges. When the firearm is fired, the explosive force pushes the bullet forward. At the same time, an equal and opposite force pushes the cartridge backward against the breechblock. This force is known as *recoil*. The markings are unique to the firearm and can be compared for similarity if the spent cartridges are recovered (Figure 18-10).

Firing pin marks left on spent cartridges can also be used to help identify a firearm (Figure 18-11). Firing pin marks are impressions made on the bottom of the cartridge casing when a bullet is discharged.

Other marks left on spent cartridges can include extractor and ejector marks. These minute scratches are produced by mechanisms that remove a spent cartridge from the firing chamber and eject it from the firearm. Not all firearms have extractors or ejectors. (Cartridges from firearms without them must be removed by hand.)

Figure 18-11 *Depending on the firearm and cartridge used, the firing pin mark appears on the center (left) or the rim (right) of the spent cartridge.*

Centerfire impression on a .40-caliber cartridge.

Rimfire impression on a .22-caliber cartridge.

Gunshot Residue *Obj. 18.5, 18.6*

CHEMISTRY Today's gunpowder is called "smokeless," but it still produces **gunshot residue (GSR)** when a firearm is fired (Figure 18-12). These residues consist of soot and unburned powder that are expelled from the firearm by the expansion of gases during the gunpowder explosion. Gunshot residue contains nitrates, lead, barium, and antimony and can adhere to the person holding the firearm, leaving evidence on him or her. In close-range shootings, some GSR may be deposited on the victim.

If someone fired a gun, GSR may be found on his or her hands or clothing. GSR testing can often detect residue despite attempted removal. In close-range shootings, the distance between the weapon and the victim may be estimated by examining the GSR pattern on the victim. The preferred method of GSR testing today involves particle analysis with scanning electron microscopy and X-ray spectrometry.

592   CHAPTER 18

18

Figure 18-12 *When the trigger is pulled, the firing pin strikes the primer, which explodes, igniting the gunpowder. As gases from the explosion expand, the bullet and GSR are propelled forward.*

colin Anderson/Jupiter Images

EVIDENCE FROM SPENT BULLETS AND WOUNDS

Obj. 18.5, 18.6

As you recall from Chapter 1, eyewitness accounts are not always accurate. It is helpful to examine bullet wounds to confirm or refute a witness's story. For example, if someone claims that a victim was running away from a shooter at the time of a shooting, an examination of the wounds can confirm or refute this claim.

Identifying and examining entrance and exit wound(s) is an important step in determining what happened at a crime scene. Generally, entrance wounds are smaller than exit wounds, because a bullet tends to flatten and expand as it passes through tissue. Therefore, the entry wound may appear smaller than the bullet.

If a bullet penetrates clothing first, fibers may be embedded in the wound, indicating the direction of penetration. Gunshot residue is usually found only around entrance wounds. Furthermore, if the bullet is fired when the muzzle is in contact with the skin, the hot gases released from the muzzle flash may burn the skin. Radial (star-shaped) tears in the skin occur if the gunshot is directly over bone. If contact is within 6 inches, GSR can be driven into the skin, which is known as *tattooing*. Beyond 4 feet, only a bullet hole is visible (Figure 18-13).

Figure 18-13 *Bullet holes from different distances. The GSR pattern (left) was produced by a close-range shot. The bullet hole on the right was produced by a shot from several feet away.*

Mikael Karlsson/Alamy

FIREARMS AND BALLISTICS **593**

Explore

Ask students to predict exactly where on the floor a ball bearing will land when it is pushed off a desktop. Allow volunteers to mark their predicted spots with pieces of tape. Then push a ball bearing off a desktop onto the floor and see how close their predictions were. Explain that when pushed, the ball bearing does not fall straight down because more than one force is acting on the ball—gravity and the force that was exerted on the ball due to someone pushing it. The interaction of the forces makes the ball's path curve outward as the ball falls.

Science

PHYSICS

PHYSICS

A bullet fired from a gun does not move forward in a straight line. It moves in a path that slopes downward as it moves forward. This type of motion is called projectile motion.

Science

PHYSICS

PHYSICS

If there were no gravity, a bullet fired from a gun would continue to move horizontally through the air, in a straight line, at a constant speed. However, gravity exerts a force on the bullet. The force of gravity causes the bullet to fall downward as it moves forward. Projectiles that move through the air actually do two things at once: (1) they move horizontally at a constant speed, and (2) they move downward because of gravity.

Bullets usually do not travel smoothly through a victim's body. Bones, organs, and other tissues bend their paths, causing a tumbling effect. The tumbling bullet may also tear a larger, more irregular exit wound than expected. A bullet may ricochet off bone and do considerable internal damage before exiting. A bullet may not exit the body at all.

Several factors influence whether a bullet will pass through a victim or remain lodged in the body. Larger caliber, higher-velocity bullets are more likely to pass through a body than are lower-velocity bullets. Small-caliber bullets, such as .22 caliber bullets, tend to lodge within the body.

TRAJECTORY *Obj. 18.3*

MATHEMATICS

To determine the path of a bullet and estimate the location of the shooter, ballistics experts look for evidence of the **trajectory,** or path, of a bullet. If you ignore the effects of gravity and assume that bullets travel in straight lines, two reference points are needed to determine the trajectory of a bullet. An investigator assumes that the shooter discharging the firearm would be located somewhere along that line. Reference points can be bullet holes in an object, such as a wall or window, or wound(s) on a victim. Even a victim's body can have the two reference points used to determine the location of the shooter—an entry wound and an exit wound. In such cases, the investigator would need to position the body as it was at the time of impact and use rods or lasers to indicate the path of the bullet. Less specific reference tools indicating the shooter's location include GSR found on objects, or spent cartridges. Sometimes trajectory can be difficult to determine because bullets ricochet and do not provide a direct path for measurement.

Gravity and Trajectory

PHYSICS

Understanding the physics of trajectory helps an investigator determine where a shooter was located during a crime. The downward force of gravity (Figure 18-14) causes a bullet to begin to drop as soon as it leaves the barrel of the firearm. If the shot is taken at a very distant object, the line of sight to the target must be adjusted to compensate for the effect of gravity on the bullet. If the target is closer, there is less adjustment. The trajectory also varies with the weight and shape of the projectile, with its initial velocity, and with the angle at which it is fired. Wind speed and direction are factors affecting the path of a projectile.

Figure 18-14 *A bullet's trajectory is slightly curved, because as it moves toward the target, gravity pulls it downward. The following diagram is highly exaggerated to demonstrate this effect. The greater the distance between the shooter and target, the greater the effects of gravity, wind, and humidity.*

(Horizontal scale reduced)

594 CHAPTER 18

DIFFERENTIATED LEARNING

Teaching At-Risk Students

Students might have a difficult time understanding why a slower-moving bullet might actually do significantly more harm than a high-speed one. Draw an outline of a body on the board and show them the difference between a bullet that passes directly through it and one that tumbles through it.

Using Trajectory to Estimate the Location of a Shooter

A bullet was found in a car's driver's seat (Figure 18-15). The bullet penetrated the car's windshield before becoming embedded in the seat. Using the bullet hole in the windshield and the hole in the seat as reference points, the investigators hypothesized that the bullet originated from an apartment building across the street. The investigators needed to search for more evidence such as cartridge casings and fingerprints, but they didn't want to search every room of the building.

Using a laser and the two reference points of the bullet hole in the car seat and the bullet hole in the windshield, the investigators estimated the trajectory of the bullet, following it to a window on the second floor of the building.

The investigators could also have estimated the origin of the bullet by taking some additional measurements. Refer to Figure 18-15. The distance from the bullet hole in the car seat to the building (*a*) was 60 feet, or 720 inches. Using the two bullet holes (car windshield and car seat), the investigators could then have calculated the angle of the trajectory using the bullet's trajectory and the horizon.

Note the right triangle in the diagram drawn from the trajectory of the bullet (*c*) and the horizontal line indicating the distance of the bullet hole in the car seat to the building (*a*). If the investigators determined the length of *b*, the distance from the hole in the car's cushion to the hole in the hotel window, then they could estimate where the shooter was located.

To determine the height of *b*, the unknown, the investigators applied the law of tangents. The tangent of an angle in a right triangle is equal to opposite side (*b*) divided by the adjacent side (*a*).

> tangent of angle = opposite side/adjacent side
> tangent of 11 degrees = *b*/*a*
>
> tangent of 11 degrees = *b*/720 inches
>   (0.1847) = *b*/720 inches
> (0.1847) × 720 inches = *b*
>
> 133 inches ~ *b*

To determine the distance from the ground to the hotel window, the investigators added 133 inches (height from bullet hole in car seat to the hotel window) to the height from the ground to the bullet hole in the car seat. The police measured that height to be approximately 48 inches.

> (133 inches) + (48 inches) ~ 181 inches

Converting 181 inches to feet (181/12 ~ 15) results in an approximate height of 15 feet above ground. This placed the shooter at a window on the second floor.

Figure 18-15 *The trajectory of the bullet is determined by using two points along its path: the hole in the windshield and the hole in the driver's seat. Notice the right triangle formed (in red).*

Explore

In the movies, when someone is shot, the body sometimes springs backward. This does not really happen. Have interested students research what really happens. (The person shot slumps over). Does a larger-caliber bullet cause a more violent reaction?

Science

MATHEMATICS

MATHEMATICS

The solution to this type of problem is similar to finding the height of a blood droplet using the tangent function.

DIGGING DEEPER

After they research the Warren Report, ask students to express their opinions on the findings. Do they agree with the findings of the Warren Report? What areas do they think needed more investigation? For more information about the Warren Report, visit the Gale Forensic Science eCollection at ngl.cengage.com/forensicscience2e

Explore

Invite your local police or a state trooper to the class or to visit via a Webcam. Ask them how they use firearms and ballistics evidence to help solve crimes. As part of the interview, inquire if their police department has used NIBIN to compare a projectile or cartridge to those that were previously used in the commission of a crime.

Teaching Tip

Engage students in a class brainstorming discussion as to how firearms evidence was compared before the advent of computers and databases such as NIBIN.

DIGGING DEEPER
with Forensic Science eCollection

According to the Warren Report, which investigated the assassination of President John F. Kennedy, the path of one of the bullets took some turns. Go to the Gale Forensic Science eCollection at **ngl.cengage.com/forensicscience2e** and research the Kennedy assassination. Examine the trajectory of the second bullet described by the Warren Report. How did the trajectory help determine the location(s) of the shooter(s)? What controversies are associated with this finding? Make a poster that explains how the investigators used ballistics to determine how many shooters were involved and the location(s).

DATABASES Obj. 18.7

Firearms databases can be searched by local, state, and federal law enforcement; forensic science; and attorney agencies in the United States. Databases can compare crime-scene projectile evidence to registered images of the markings made on fired ammunition recovered from previous crime scenes or from a test-fired firearm. Ballistics information from new crime scenes is constantly and quickly being added. In 2000, the FBI and the Bureau of Alcohol, Tobacco, Firearms, and Explosives merged their firearms and projectiles databases to form the National Integrated Ballistic Information Network (NIBIN). By using NIBIN, investigators can quickly link a single firearm to crimes in different neighborhoods, cities, and even states. The rifling patterns on cartridges and the markings on cartridge casings are converted to three-dimensional images and entered into the system. The breechblock marking (BF), the ejector mark (EM), and the firing pin impression (FP), which together make up the "fingerprint" of the firearm (Figure 18-16), are compared to thousands already in the system. Sometimes within minutes, the database shows whether the firearm was used in any other crime.

Some people believe that the development of a firearm "fingerprint" database that catalogs the rifling patterns of all registered guns could help solve future criminal investigations. Others worry that this is an unnecessary infringement on the privacy of gun owners. Go to the Gale Forensic Science eCollection on **ngl.cengage.com/forensicscience2e** and research the topic of ballistics databases. Then write a report on your findings. How are these databases useful for investigators? What kind of information do they store? What controversies surround their implementation?

BALLISTICS EVIDENCE STANDARDS *Obj. 18.6, 18.7*

The Organization of Scientific Area Committees (OSAC) coordinates the development of standards and guidelines that improve the quality and reliability of evidence produced by forensic science. These standards guide all forensics work including that on firearms and ballistics evidence. The process for analyzing casings found associated with a crime includes the following:

- Recovery of firearm and ballistics evidence from a crime scene

- Production of digital images of the cartridge casing using a specialized microscope to identify the breech face impression (BF), firing pin impression (FP), and ejector mark (EM). These three impressions constitute the "fingerprint" of the firearm. See Figure 18-16.

- Entering images of firearm evidence (projectile and cartridge casing information) into the NIBIN database. The firearm evidence images are then compared with images in NIBIN from previous crimes.

Figure 18-16 *This cartridge shows three distinct impressions—the firing pin (FP), the breechblock face (BF), and the ejector mark (EM).*

Image courtesy of NIST

Close

Organize students into groups. Assign each group one of the following topics: types of firearms and differences among them; bullets, cartridges, and caliber; evidence from casings; and trajectory. (You may want to add other chapter topics as well.) Have groups summarize what they have learned about the topic and why it would be important to a forensic investigator.

Teaching Tip

In Dr. Stephen Cohle's book *Cause of Death*, he describes how firearms evidence collected during autopsy can help resolve cause and manner of death.

LITERACY

See *Cause of Death: Forensic Files of a Medical Examiner*, by Stephen D. Cohle, M.D., and Tobin T. Buhk.

SUMMARY

- Ballistics is the study of the mechanics of the launching, flight, and behavior of fired projectiles.

- Modern firearms are divided into two basic types—long guns and handguns—that require two hands or one, respectively, for accurate firing.

- Handguns can be classified as revolvers or semiautomatic firearms, depending on the loading mechanism.

- Bullets fired from a firearm show patterns of lands and grooves that can be compared with the rifling pattern in the barrel of the firearm.

- A cartridge consists of primer powder, gunpowder, a bullet, and the casing material that holds them all together.

- The caliber of a cartridge is the diameter of its bullet and is included with the name of the manufacturer on the headstamp.

- In addition to examining lands and grooves on a bullet, investigators can examine firing pin marks, breechblock marks, and extractor and ejector marks on a spent cartridge to compare evidence at a crime scene with a specific firearm.

- Gunshot residue on shooters can help investigators identify a suspect.

- Investigators can use databases, such as the national database NIBIN, to compare crime-scene evidence to evidence collected from previous crimes.

- Using at least two reference points, an investigator can recreate a bullet's trajectory and estimate the location of the shooter.

- Advances in technology, including comparison microscopes and mass spectrometry, have improved the ability of firearms and ballistics experts to compare crime-scene evidence with test-fired projectiles and GSR analysis.

CASE STUDIES

Sacco and Vanzetti (1920)

Three different types of cartridges were found at the scene of a payroll holdup. Two security guards were killed. When suspects Nicola Sacco and Bartolomeo Vanzetti were arrested, they were both in possession of loaded guns of the same caliber and ammunition from the same three manufacturers as the casings found at the crime scene. Both were anarchists who openly advocated the violent overthrow of the government.

Their trial began in 1921. More than 140 witnesses were called to testify. The one fact that was incontrovertible was that the bullet that killed one of the

---

DIFFERENTIATED LEARNING

Teaching Gifted Students

Ask interested students to review the Firearms and Ballistics. Advances in the Did You Know? feature on p. 589. For each event, have them write a short explanation about why the advance was important to forensics.

security guards was so ancient in its manufacture that no similar ammunition could be found to test-fire Sacco's weapon except those equally ancient, similar cartridges found in his pocket upon arrest.

The defendant's lawyer, Fred Moore, aggressively turned the trial from murder to politics. He accused the prosecution of trying the men as part of the Red Scare of 1919–1920. It soon turned into a worldwide spectacle of "patriots" versus "foreigners." Despite Moore's argument, the defendants were found guilty and sentenced to death. In 1927, a committee was appointed to review the case. The comparison microscope had been recently invented and was used to conclusively link the murder bullet with Sacco's gun. Both men were executed by electric chair in 1927.

Lee Harvey Oswald (1963)

The Warren Commission concluded that Lee Harvey Oswald worked alone in his assassination of President John F. Kennedy on November 22, 1963. The bullets that were fired at President Kennedy were analyzed for chemical composition and left conflicting conclusions as to the number of bullets fired and their origin. However, many believe that the evidence contradicts the Warren Commission report on this point.

Lee Harvey Oswald speaking at a press conference after the assassination.

Of the three shots that Oswald is said to have fired, one missed the car completely. A second bullet struck Kennedy in the back and then proceeded through his body into the back of Texas Governor John Connally, who was also in the car. The bullet exited Connally's chest, striking his right wrist, and then proceeding through his left thigh. The last bullet struck Kennedy in the back of the head and was fatal. Modern recreations of the bullets' paths and damage patterns have been verified.

Explore
Students might be unfamiliar with the assassination of President Kennedy. Outline the basics of the case or have interested students research it and report to the class. You may suggest interested students view the PBS *Nova* series episode "Cold Case JFK," which can be found online at http://www.pbs.org/wgbh/nova/tech/cold-case-jfk.html

DIFFERENTIATED LEARNING

Teaching Gifted Students
Shock and sound waves can be analyzed as they leave the barrel of the firearm. Encourage interested students to research and report on the most recent advancements in detection of firearm shock and sound waves to the class.

John Muhammad and Lee Malvo
(2002)

Beginning in October 2002, a series of sniper murders terrorized residents of the Washington, D.C., area. Ten people were killed and three others wounded. At several crime scenes, the police were able to recover cartridges. At autopsy, bullet fragments were recovered from some victims. Investigators determined that most of the shootings were related to the same .223-caliber firearm. Police apprehended two suspects—John Allen Muhammad, 41, and John Lee Malvo, 17—and discovered a rifle in the suspects' car. The recovered crime-scene evidence was consistent with this rifle.

The firearms evidence could be linked to a specific gun, but further evidence was needed to identify the shooter. The police were eventually able to find fingerprints at two different crime scenes. In addition to fingerprint and firearms evidence, small traces of DNA found in saliva left at the scenes helped identify the suspects. Finally, document analysis of a letter and writing found in their car pointed to Muhammad and Malvo as the snipers. Both men were found guilty—Muhammad was sentenced to death in 2009, and Malvo was sentenced to life without parole.

Lee Malvo   *John Muhammad*

AP Images/Martin Smith-Rodden

AP Images/Dylan Moore

Think Critically

Although there are specific mathematical formulas and the opportunity to make precise measurements, the accuracy of trajectory calculations is still hard to "guarantee." What factors could influence trajectory calculations?

Careers *in Forensics*

Firearms Examiner

Gregory Klees is the firearms and tool-mark technical leader for the Federal Bureau of Alcohol, Tobacco, Firearms, and Explosives (ATF) laboratories. He is a recognized expert for court testimony in the forensic areas of firearms and tool-mark identification, restoration of firearm serial numbers, analysis of gunshot residue patterns on clothing, and analysis of projectile trajectories.

Greg Klees examines a shirt with bullet holes and suspected gunshot residue.

Klees has spent his career studying firearms for the U.S. government, first with the Federal Bureau of Investigation (FBI) and then with the ATF. He began working as a clerk at the FBI after attending Lawrence University, in Wisconsin. As Klees relates, "Back in 1976 ... I just started working as a 22-year-old clerk at the FBI. I tried for months to get a job in the FBI Lab, to no avail." An older FBI agent helped him obtain an interview, and Klees was hired by the Firearms Unit of the FBI laboratory where he worked for more than 17 years.

Leaving the FBI, Klees moved to the ATF, where he has been a firearms and tool-mark examiner for more than 21 years. He has been involved in more than 3,850 cases and has examined about 27,000 items of evidence. Some of his more notorious cases were the Ruby Ridge standoff in Idaho (1992), the Branch Davidian siege in Texas (1993), and the Washington, D.C., sniper murders (2002).

A major concern of Klees's career has been to set standards for firearms and tool-mark analysis. He has served for more than ten years on the Scientific Working Group for Firearms and Toolmarks (S W G G U N), which he chaired from 2007 to 2011. From 2008 to 2012, he co-chaired a working group of the National Institute of Science and Technology Council Subcommittee on Forensic Science. Klees has testified at admissibility hearings on evidence in Canada as well as in American courts. He was on the developmental committee for the ATF National Firearms Examiner Training Academy and was an instructor there as well. He has lectured widely on his areas of expertise, written numerous articles for forensic science journals, and contributed to the National Institute of Justice's guide to crime-scene investigation.

Klees's memberships include the American Academy of Forensic Sciences, the Association of Firearms and Tool Mark Examiners, the International Association of Automobile Theft Investigators, and the Midwestern Association of Forensic Scientists (firearms section coordinator 2008–2011). He writes that he has had "a very happy and fulfilling career in this specialized field."

Photo courtesy of Greg Klees

Careers

Capstone Project 7, "Forensic Science Career Exploration," helps students investigate the educational backgrounds and job descriptions of professionals working in forensics.

Learn More About It
▶ To learn more about the work of a forensic firearms examiner, go to **ngl.cengage.com/forensicscience2e**.

APPS

▶ **CSI: FirearmsID**
▶ **Arrow Forensics**
▶ **Winchester Ballistics Calculator**

FIREARMS AND BALLISTICS   **601**

Chapter 18 Review

True or False

1. True
2. False
3. True
4. False
5. False
6. True
7. False

Multiple Choice

8. d
9. b
10. d
11. a

Short response

12.
1. Trigger is pulled.
2. Firing pin strikes the back of the cartridge casing.
3. Primer powder makes a small explosion.
4. Primer powder explosion ignites the gunpowder, and an explosion of hot gases and soot occurs.
5. Bullet is propelled forward as the casing is forced back against the breech.
6. The ejector ejects the spent casing.

CHAPTER 18 REVIEW

True or False

1. When a firearm is discharged, the projectile is propelled forward, and the cartridge casing is forced backward toward the breech. *Obj. 18.2*

2. A higher-velocity bullet is more likely to remain inside the body than a lower-velocity bullet. *Obj. 18.5*

3. Test-firing of a firearm is used to compare the rifling of the firearm barrel with the lands and grooves on the bullet. *Obj. 18.6*

4. All firearms are rifled. *Obj. 18.1, 18.6*

5. Tattooing refers to the marks made as shotgun pellets are embedded in the skin. *Obj. 18.5*

6. A 12-gauge shotgun can fire larger shot than a 20-gauge shotgun. *Obj. 18.1*

7. NIBIN is a database that contains names of perpetrators convicted in firearms cases. *Obj. 18.7*

Multiple Choice

8. Which of the following statements is true? *Obj. 18.6*
   a) Gunshot residue is always present on an entrance wound.
   b) Gunshot residue can be washed off.
   c) Gunshot residue may be found on both the victim and the shooter.
   d) Both (b) and (c) are correct.

9. The trajectory of a projectile is best described as *Obj. 18.3*
   a) the target
   b) the flight path
   c) the housing for its gunpowder
   d) the pattern of lands and grooves on the projectile

10. What factor has the greatest effect on the distance a projectile will travel? *Obj. 18.3*
    a) the arrangement of the lands and grooves in the firearm barrel
    b) the size of the person squeezing the trigger
    c) the projectile's caliber
    d) the amount of gunpowder in the cartridge

11. The caliber of a bullet is its *Obj. 18.6*
    a) diameter
    b) length
    c) speed
    d) weight

Short Response

12. Outline the sequence of events that occur when a firearm is discharged and a projectile is expelled. Include the following terms: *gunpowder, primer powder, hammer, trigger, firing pin*, and *bullet*. *Obj. 18.2*

13. Refer to the opening scenario involving the murder of Sandra Duyst.
    Obj. 18.8
    a) Describe the firearm evidence that supports the claim that the gunshot wounds were close-range gunshot wounds.
    b) Describe the evidence that supports the claim that the manner of death could not be suicide.

14. List the types of individual and class evidence found on spent cartridge casings and spent projectiles. *Obj. 18.6*

15. Compare and contrast evidence recovered from a crime involving a handgun with the evidence recovered from a crime involving a shotgun. *Obj. 18.1, 18.6, 18.8*

Going Further

Today, firearms can be made entirely out of plastic using 3-D printers. These firearms are not recognized by metal detectors. Research legislation being proposed to regulate the production of this type of firearm.

Bibliography

Books and Journals

Cohle, Stephen D., M.D., and Tobin T. Buhk. *Cause of Death: Forensic Files of a Medical Examiner.* Amherst, NY: Prometheus, 2007.

Di Maio, Vincent J. *Gunshot Wounds: Practical Aspects of Firearms, Ballistics, and Forensic Techniques.* Boca Raton, FL: CRC Press, 1999.

Heard, Brian J. *Handbook on Firearms and Ballistics: Examining and Interpreting Forensic Evidence.* Boca Raton, FL: CRC Press, 1997.

Jany, Libor, "Minneapolis: the Forefront of New Gun ID Technology," *StarTribune*, October 16, 2014.

Pejsa, Arthur J. *Modern Practical Ballistics.* Minneapolis, MN: Kenwood Publishers, 2001.

Platt, Richard. *Crime Scene.* Englewood Cliffs, NJ: Prentice Hall, 2006.

Schwoeble, A. J., and David L. Exline. *Current Methods in Forensic Gunshot Residue Analysis.* Boca Raton, FL: CRC Press, 2000.

Internet Resources

ngl.cengage.com/forensicscience2e (Gale Forensic Science eCollection)
http://youtu.be/7qb0N9Mn7Vc (Firearms identification)
http://youtu.be/TWiw64gigUs (How guns are made)
http://www.pbs.org/wgbh/nova/tech/cold-case-jfk.html (President Kennedy assassination revisited)
http://library.med.utah.edu/WebPath/TUTORIAL/GUNS/GUNBLST.html (Free hunter education course)
http://www.firearmsID.com
http://cal.vet.upenn.edu/projects/saortho/chapter_36/36mast.htm
http://www.accurateshooter.com/cartridge-guides/competition-cartridges/
http://science.howstuffworks.com/liquid-body-armor.htm
http://www.nist.gov/pml/div683/casing-080812.cfm

13. a. Gunshot residue and burns found around the entry wounds were consistent with the gun being fired at close range. Star-shaped skin tears were consistent with the gun being fired in contact with the skin.
    b. i. Damage done by the first bullet would have incapacitated the victim, preventing her from firing a second bullet.
       ii. Recoil from a 9-millimeter handgun would prevent a second shot from striking her.
       iii. The firearm did not misfire during many test-firings, so someone had to fire the second bullet.

14. Spent cartridge casings—class evidence
    Name of Manufacturer
    Caliber
    Centerfire or rimfire

    Spent cartridge casings—individual evidence
    Ejector and extractor markings
    Breech marks

    Bullet—class evidence
    Caliber
    Lands and grooves

    Bullet—individual evidence
    Rifling

Short Answer

15. If a shotgun is used, you may or may not find spent casings because the casing is not ejected after firing. This may also be true if a revolver is used. The projectile from a shotgun would be either round shot of a uniform, definite size or a large, bullet-shaped lead slug. The bullet from a handgun would be caliber-specific and could be identified. Gunshot residue may be found on a suspect's hands if that person were found and tested within a short period of time after the crime. The wound pattern on the victim might show the "spray" pattern of a shotgun or be individual, well-defined wounds from a handgun.

Background

Additional activities for this chapter can be found in the IRCD, Chapter 18.

ACTIVITY 18-1

Background

In this activity, students are given three different crime-scene scenarios. They use measurements and calculations to determine the height and location of the shooter based on crime-scene evidence.

Time Required to Complete Activity

40 minutes (teams of two students)

Safety Precautions

There are no safety precautions for this activity.

ACTIVITY 18-1

Bullet Trajectory *Obj. 18.3*

Objectives:

By the end of this activity, you will be able to:

1. Determine a bullet trajectory given two reference points.
2. Calculate the angle of elevation given two reference points.
3. Estimate the location of a shooter using the law of tangents after analyzing sketches and measurements from a crime scene.

Time Required to Complete the Activity:

40 minutes (teams of two students)

Introduction:

Someone shouts, "Shots fired!" But who fired? And from where? To answer these questions, the investigators begin by identifying the trajectory or path of the bullet.

To track the bullet's trajectory, a line is drawn connecting two points along the bullet's known path. These two points could be an entry wound (A) and exit wound (B) on a victim (Figure 1) or a bullet hole in a car window and an entry wound on someone inside the car (Figure 2).

The *angle of elevation* is the angle created by the bullet's trajectory and the horizon. To determine the angle of elevation, draw a horizontal line (parallel to the horizon) that intersects the trajectory, and measure the angle formed by these two lines.

Figure 1 *The trajectory (red) is determined by the entry wound A and exit wound B. The angle of elevation (yellow) is formed by the trajectory and the horizon.*

Figure 2 *The trajectory (black dashed line) has been determined by drawing a line between the bullet hole in the side window and the entry wound in the victim's head. The angle of elevation (blue) is formed by the trajectory and horizon (green dotted) lines.*

Background:

Refer to the following right triangle. The angle of elevation is calculated using the trajectory c and horizon line a. If the adjacent side a (horizon) can be measured, then it is possible to calculate b, the opposite side, using the law of tangents.

$$\text{tangent of the angle of elevation} = \frac{\text{opposite side } (b)}{\text{adjacent side } (a)}$$

Materials:

Act 18-1 SH
two full-length sharpened pencils
protractor
metric ruler
calculator with tangent function, or tangent table
laser pointer (optional) or small flashlight
small cardboard box (cereal or juice box)

SAFETY PRECAUTIONS:

None

Procedure:

Trajectory Model: The model was made using two pieces of Plexiglas and three wooden dowels. Note the three different trajectories and three different angles of elevation that will be discussed in the three scenarios that follow.

SCENARIO 1: SIMULATED BULLET TRAJECTORY AND ANGLE OF ELEVATION MODEL

1. Push a sharpened pencil downward through one side of the box (entrance wound) and continue forcing the pencil through the other side of the cardboard box so that the tip of the pencil emerges (exit wound).

Safety Precautions

There are no safety precautions for this activity.

Procedures

1. Print, copy, and distribute Act 18-1 SH from the IRCD, Chapter 18.

2. You may wish to correlate this activity with a math lesson because of the level of trigonometry necessary to understand and complete the activity.

Scenario 1

Answer

The trajectory of the projectile will vary depending on where the student placed the entry and exit "wounds" in their cereal boxes. Students should follow the trajectory to the source of the projectile to locate the origin of the projectile.

Teaching Tip

The model pictured above was created with pieces of 2×4 lumber, drilled Plexiglas, and dowels.

Teaching Tip

For creating the model in Scenario 2, ask students to bring in empty, clean cereal boxes or cracker boxes.

Teaching Tip

Use a laser pointer in a darkened room to illustrate the path of the bullet and the possible position of the shooter.

Answers

Check students' calculations and crime-scene diagrams.

Scenario 2

Students can show their work on Act 18-1 SH.

tangent of angle of elevation = opposite side/adjacent side

Let b = height from point where shot was fired to entry wound in biker's head

$\tan 24° = b/152$ ft

$(0.4452) \sim b/152$ ft

$(0.4452) \times 152$ ft $\sim b$

67.7 ft $\sim b$

add distance from biker's head to the ground (6 ft)

67.7 ft + 6 ft $\sim$ 73.6 ft above ground

---

2. Using a second pencil, create a horizon line (parallel to the floor) by inserting the second pencil approximately two and a half inches below the exit hole.

3. Using a protractor, estimate the angle of elevation by measuring the angle formed where the trajectory and horizon pencils intersect.

4. Assume your desk surface was the crime scene. Place the cardboard box with the pencils (simulating entrance and exit wounds on a body) on top of your desk. Use a laser pointer or small flashlight aimed along the trajectory. Follow the trajectory to locate the origin of the bullet.

SCENARIO 2

A witness saw a victim fall while riding his bike. The cyclist had been struck in the head by a bullet. When the crime-scene investigators arrived, they estimated the angle of elevation of the shooter to be about 24 degrees based on the hole in his helmet and on the entry wound on his head. The distance from his head to the building where the bullet was fired was 152 feet. The height from the ground to the entry wound on the victim while on his bike measured 6 feet above the ground.

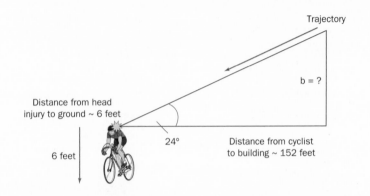

Based on this information, what is the distance from ground level to the window where the bullet was fired? Use the law of tangents to calculate your answer.
Show your work on Act 18-1 SH for Scenario 2.

SCENARIO 3

A bullet fired from a hotel window struck a victim. The bullet created both an entrance and an exit wound. On Act 18-1 SH, illustrate how you can estimate from which window the bullet was fired.

Head of victim

Entry wound

Exit wound

Floor level in hotel

8
7
6
5
4
3
2
1

Final Analysis:

1. Compare determining trajectories from two fixed objects such as a hole in a wall and a hole in a window to determining the trajectory of a bullet from entrance and exit wounds. Why would the evidence of bullet trajectory be less reliable based on entrance and exit wounds sustained by a victim as opposed to entrance and exit holes in walls or windows?

2. Describe the significance of determining the trajectory of a projectile when trying to solve a crime.

3. During autopsies, bullets need to be recovered and submitted to the police as evidence. Investigators have been known to drag rivers to recover a firearm. Describe the type of evidence that could be recovered from firearms, bullets, and cartridge casings that could help link evidence to a particular firearm or person.

Further Research and Extensions

Besides finding trajectories of fired bullets, have students brainstorm how the skills used in this activity would be useful in other real-life situations.

Scenario 3

Students draw a line through the exit and entrance wounds of the victim. The trajectory indicates the projectile came from a window on the sixth floor.

Final Analysis

1. Sample answers: Estimating the trajectory based on a hole in the wall and a hole in the window is more reliable than estimating the trajectory made from entrance and exit wounds on a person because the hole in the wall/window are fixed and can't move. Once the person is struck, the person will change position and it is necessary to estimate where the person was when struck; Also, between entrance and exit, there may be tumbling of the bullet within the head, which can affect the calculations and give an incorrect trajectory.

2. Knowing the trajectory of a bullet can help identify the location of the shooter and thus recover more evidence such as cartridge casings and fingerprints that can be used to help identify the shooter.

3. Recovery of a firearm, bullet, or cartridge casing provides evidence that could link a firearm, bullet, or cartridge casing to the one used in the crime. Bullets have rifling unique to individual guns. If the gun is recovered, then bullets can be test-fired from it and then compared to the evidence bullets recovered from the crime scene or victim. Information about the type of bullet and its size would be compared to the type and size of bullets found on suspects or found in the firearm. Used cartridge casings vary in type, size, and manufacturer and could be linked to the firearm used in the crime. Cartridge casings might also have fingerprints belonging to the shooter.

Background

In this activity, students examine various cartridge casings for caliber, headstamp, location of firing pin strike, and firing pin markings. Students compare cartridge casing photos from previous crimes to cartridge casing photos obtained by test-firing three suspects' firearms. Based on their analysis, students will be able to exclude suspects.

Time Required to Complete Activity

20 minutes

Safety Precautions

There are no safety precautions for this activity.

Procedures

1. Print, copy, and distribute Act 18-2 SH from the IRCD, Chapter 18.
2. Refer students to the text and photos on the following page.

Teaching Tip

Ask members of a local gun club for some spent cartridge shell casings to use with the class and to make your own set of crime-scene and suspect casings for students to compare. Collect at least 10 shell casings that were fired from the same firearm so that you have a variety to work with. Keep all casings that were fired from the same gun in separate containers. Prepare plastic bags of 5 different types of shell casings. Label these shell casings as being from test firing of suspects' guns. Ask students to try to show consistency between a "crime-scene" shell casing with one of five shell casings in the bag.

Teaching Tip

Photograph the headstamp of each of the different types of cartridge casings. The photograph should

Firing Pin Analysis *Obj. 18.6, 18.8*

Objectives:

By the end of this activity, you will be able to:

1. Compare and contrast firing pin impressions from various sources.
2. Determine the caliber, firing pin strike location, and manufacturer, based on the information on a cartridge headstamp.
3. Analyze data to determine if you can exclude any of the suspects based on firing pin impression evidence.

Time Required to Complete Activity: 20 minutes

Introduction:

When cartridge casings are recovered from a crime scene, they are photographed and compared to NIBIN database records to determine if they are consistent with any found at previous crime scenes. The NIBIN database allows investigators to link a series of crimes to the same perpetrator. Cartridge casings bear identifying marks, such as ejector marks, breechblock marks, and firing pin impressions. In this activity, you will compare marks on the suspect's cartridge casings to the marks on cartridge casings found at a crime scene. Include the following:

1. Caliber of the cartridge
2. Headstamp marking of the manufacturer
3. Location of the firing pin strike
4. Description of the unique firing pin characteristics

Materials (per pairs of students):

Act 18-2 SH
pencil
hand lens

SAFETY PRECAUTIONS:
None

Scenario:

Cartridge casings were found at two different recent crime scenes. Refer to photos labeled A through L on the next page. Three suspects were apprehended. Police test-fired firearms belonging to the suspects and compared firing pin marks and other marks on the cartridge casings to those marks on the crime-scene casings.

Procedure:

1. View the photos of the suspects' cartridge casings with a hand lens to determine the following: the caliber, headstamp, location of firing pin strike

show the caliber, headstamp markings, location of the firing pin strike, and any other distinctive markings. This provides a photographic database of examples of spent cartridges. Use indirect lighting if necessary.

Teaching Tip

Prepare class sets of at least three different types of spent cartridges for students to examine. Select one of the spent cartridges to represent

both one of the suspect's cartridges fired during a test fire and also the crime-scene evidence cartridge. Place only one cartridge in each evidence envelope. Label them as follows:

• Suspect 1
• Suspect 2
• Suspect 3
• Evidence (should be the same as one of the suspects)

(centerfire or rimfire), and description of firing pin marks. Record your data in the Data Table.

2. Review the photos of the cartridge casings from previous crimes. Determine if any of evidence photos A–L are consistent with the photo of the cartridge casing test-fired from Suspect 1's firearm.

3. Record the letters of any evidence photos that are consistent with the cartridge casing of Suspect 1 in the Data Table. If there are none, write *none*.

4. Repeat the process for Suspect 2 and Suspect 3 and record your answer in the Data Table.

5. Be prepared to defend your claims with data from your investigation.

Casings from test-firing of firearms from the three suspects.

Suspect 1   *Suspect 2*   *Suspect 3*

© Cengage Learning®

Data Table: Comparison of cartridge casings

	Suspect 1	Suspect 2	Suspect 3
Caliber			
Headstamp markings			
Firing pin strike (centerfire or rimfire)			
Description of unique markings			
Evidence casing consistent with suspect (Write the letters. If none, write *none*.)			

Evidence cartridge casings recovered from previous robberies.

© Cengage Learning®

DIFFERENTIATED LEARNING

Teaching Gifted Students

Encourage motivated students to perform the following activity.

a. Design an activity to compare and contrast cartridge casings. One of the cartridge casings should be both the cartridge casing recovered from a suspect's test-fired firearm and a cartridge casing recovered from the crime scene.

b. Photograph each of the cartridge casings under a stereomicroscope using oblique lighting.

c. Prepare a presentation using a format of their choice that describes how you analyzed the evidence.

d. Evaluate the evidence: was it relevant, reliable, sufficient, and scientific?

Answers

Check students' data tables.

A. 3

B. 3

C. 2

D. 2

E. 2

F. 3

G. 3

H. 2

I. 3

J. 2

K. 3

L. 3

Table answers

All cartridges are 40 caliber, centerfire. Students should describe distinguishing markings for each.

Suspect 1: no cartridge casings were consistent

Suspect 2: C, D ,E, H, J

Suspect 3: A, B, F, G, I, K, L

Final Analysis

Note: Answers are based on the comparisons of Suspect 1, 2, and 3 and the evidence cartridges in the text. If you use spent cartridge casings that you have collected, your answers will vary.

1. Suspect 1 can be excluded.

2. Evidence cartridge casings appeared to have come from two different firearms. The shapes of the area where the firing pins struck have different shapes and patterns.

3. Sample answer: Some shooters pick up any casings from their firearms so they do not leave this evidence behind to place them at the scene.

4. Sample answer: computerized firearms database and instruments such as gas chromatographs and mass spectrometers are used in powder and GSR analysis.

Teaching Tips

- Use a flex camera, projecting device, or stereomicroscope to project images of different cartridge casings. Ask students to compare and contrast the spent cartridges and to describe how to distinguish among them. Or, project photographs of empty cartridge casings. Be sure students can distinguish between centerfire and rimfire cartridges.
- Demonstrate how to measure the caliber of a spent cartridge with calipers. Before doing the activity, be sure students know how to read the calipers by practicing measuring nickels and dimes.

Final Analysis:

1. Were you able to exclude any of the suspects? Cite evidence from your data to support your claim.
2. Describe unusual characteristics that linked any of the suspect's casings to the crime-scene cartridge casings.
3. If you were a prosecuting attorney, what argument could you provide to counter the defense's argument that "if a suspect's cartridge shell casings were *not* found at a crime scene, he must be innocent"?
4. Crime labs today are better able to compare and analyze ballistics evidence. Describe two advances in technology that have allowed improved reliability of ballistics evidence.

Further Study:

Research the Washington, D.C. sniper case study. Explain how firearms evidence was used to link the two suspects to the series of killings.

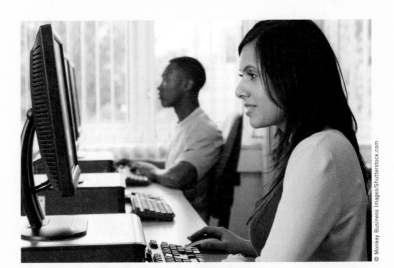

© Monkey Business Images/Shutterstock.com

ACTIVITY 18-3

Describing Spent Projectiles *Obj. 18.6*

Objectives:

By the end of this activity, you will be able to:

1. Measure the mass, length, and diameter (caliber) of both perfect (undamaged) spent projectiles and deformed spent projectiles.

2. Count the number of lands and grooves, and determine if the projectile has a right or left twist.

Five different types of .22 ammunition.

3. Describe the characteristics of both deformed and perfect spent projectiles, including size, mass, composition, and any unique markings.

4. Compare and contrast spent projectiles to determine if any could have been fired from the same firearm.

Time Required to Complete Activity: 40 minutes

Background:

Rules regarding ammunition and the firearm that fires the ammunition:

1. Ammunition must be compatible with the firearm. Both must have the same caliber.

2. Ammunition is usually composed of lead, possibly clad (covered) with metal (copper, brass), and has a solid or hollow point.

3. The number of lands and grooves can help identify the manufacturer of a firearm. The number of lands equals the number of grooves. However, the widths of lands and grooves may differ.

4. The pattern and number of lands and grooves produced by a firearm are unique. Test firings of the suspect firearm are performed. Then the lands and grooves made by the rifling of the suspect firearm on a projectile during test-firing are compared to the lands and grooves on the crime-scene projectile(s). If the marks are consistent, the projectiles were fired from the same firearm.

Introduction:

Ammunition is identified by its brand name, composition, caliber, and mass. The unit of mass for projectiles is a grain (15.43 grains ∼ 1 gram). Spent projectiles can be distinguished by the number and spacing of lands and grooves and the direction of the twist.

Perfect .22 projectiles.

Background

In this activity, students analyze spent projectiles and describe caliber, mass, and composition and attempt to identify the manufacturer.

Time Required to Complete Activity

40 minutes

Safety Precautions

Use only *spent* ammunition.

Procedures

1. Print, copy, and distribute Act 18-3 SH from the IRCD, Chapter 18.

2. Collect spent projectiles for this activity.

3. Label small envelopes 1 through 5 to represent each of the projectiles (bullets).

4. Place a deformed or perfect bullet into each envelope. In each set of five, Projectile 2 should be perfect.

5. Distribute sets of five envelopes to each group.

Teaching Tip

Perfect projectiles can usually be obtained at shooting ranges. Try to obtain different ammunition types. A pistol or rifle range backstop can provide plenty of spent ammunition. If possible, pick two different calibers for display.

Teaching Tip

If you are not a shooter, find someone who will help you.

A good method of capturing your own projectiles uses polyester fiberfill (which can be purchased from a building supply store) packed very tightly into three small boxes, each approximately 18" in length and taped shut. At the firing range, the three boxes are lined up *end* to *end* so that the shooter aims at the end of the first box. The projectiles should pass through the first box and be captured in the second or third box in perfect condition.

Answers Part 1

Answers to the data table will vary depending on the projectiles.

Teaching Tip

Show students photographs of live ammunition to demonstrate the difference in appearance between live ammunition and spent ammunition. (Do not bring live ammunition to class.)

Teaching Tip

Stress safety with firearms. Suggest that students who are interested in firearms take courses on the proper handling of firearms.

Materials:

Act 18-3 SH
2 or more intact (perfect) spent projectiles of the same or different calibers
2 or more deformed spent projectiles of the same or different calibers
balance capable of measuring grams or ounces
digital calipers
calculator

SAFETY PRECAUTIONS:

Only previously discharged projectiles and collected projectiles are needed. *No intact (live) ammunition is used.*

Procedure:

PART 1

Record all responses in Data Table 1.

1. Examine Projectile 1.
2. Describe its condition (perfect or deformed).
3. What is its composition? Is it lead or copper? Is it solid or hollow-pointed?
4. Using a balance, determine the mass (in grams) of perfect Projectile 1. Measure to the nearest 0.01 gram. Record your measurement in Data Table 1.
5. Convert grams to grains: 1 gram $\sim$ 15.43 grains. Record the result in Data Table 1.
6. Using digital calipers, measure and record the diameter (caliber) of Projectile 1 in inches and millimeters.
7. Determine the number of lands and grooves and the direction of the twist. Record these data in Data Table 1.
8. Repeat Steps 1–7 for perfect Projectile 2 and the remaining perfect projectiles.
9. Repeat Steps 1–7 for each of the deformed projectiles.

Data Table 1

Projectile	Condition (perfect or deformed)	Composition (lead, brass, copper) Solid or Hollow Point	Mass (grams)	Mass (grains)	Diameter or Caliber of Projectile (mm)	(in.)	Number of Lands and Grooves	Twist Direction (right or left)
1								
2								
3								
4								
5								

Procedure:

PART 2

Refer to the Projectile Characteristics table, which compares eight different projectiles. Use the data to answer the following questions.

Projectile Characteristics

Projectile	Mass (grains)	Diameter	Composition	Lands and Grooves	Twist (left or right)
1	39	.22 in.	lead	6	right
2	40	.215 in.	copper clad	6	right
3	20	.22 in.	lead	8	left
4	115	9 mm	copper clad	6	right
5	138	9 mm	copper clad	8	right
6	140	9 mm	copper clad	6	right
7	132	.38 in.	brass clad	8	right
8	130	.38 in.	brass clad	6	right

Questions:

1. Could Projectiles 1 and 3 have been fired from the same firearm? Defend your claim using the information in the Projectile Characteristics table above.
2. A measurement of 9 mm is about 0.353 inches. Could Projectiles 5 and 7 have been fired from the same firearm? Explain.
3. Refer to Projectiles 4, 5, and 6. Is there any evidence to support or refute the claim that they were all fired from the same firearm? What information should you consider when comparing projectiles?

Going Further:

Sometimes a projectile is badly deformed, and identification is difficult. You can estimate the number of lands and grooves by carefully measuring a single land and groove and applying this formula:

total number of projectile lands and grooves =
$2 \times$ (projectile diameter) $\times$ 3.1416 $\div$ (single land width + single groove width)
Round up or down to the nearest whole number.

Answers Part 2

1. No; although the caliber is the same, the number of lands and grooves differs, indicating that it was fired from a different firearm. Also, projectile 1 has a right twist, whereas projectile 3 has a left twist. The difference in mass of the projectiles is not a factor in determining if they could have been fired by the same firearm.

2. No. Ammunition is specific to firearms of the same caliber.

3. Although 4, 5, and 6 are all 9-mm projectiles with a right twist, they were not all fired from the same firearm. Projectile 5 has eight lands and grooves whereas the other two, 4 and 6, have six lands and grooves.

Background

By calculating the horizontal drop of a fired projectile, students will determine the amount of compensation needed to hit a target.

Time Required to Complete Activity

30 minutes

Safety Precautions

No specific safety precautions

Procedure

1. Print, copy, and distribute Act 18-4 SH from the IRCD, Chapter 18.

2. The best way to understand the activity is to work through it yourself before the students do.

3. Distance affects the time of flight of a projectile. The longer the flight, the more correction is necessary for the proper trajectory.

4. Three different types of projectiles are fired. The BB and pellet rifle can be spring-powered or CO_2-powered. The .22 projectile is powered by an explosive charge of smokeless powder. These projectiles were chosen based on their velocities. The BB and the pellet may not even cover the theoretical 300-foot range.

Teaching Tip

This activity demonstrates what happens to the trajectory of a projectile as it travels downrange. All the variables that would affect the projectile, such as wind speed and direction, humidity, temperature, etc., have been omitted for simplicity in calculation, but they can be included in your discussion with students.

ACTIVITY 18-4

How Good Is Your Aim? *Obj. 18.3*

Objectives:

By the end of this activity, you will be able to:

1. Calculate the time it takes for a bullet to reach a target, given the velocity of the projectile and the distance to the target.

2. Calculate the distance that a projectile drops over time due to gravity.

3. Determine the adjustment required for the projectile to hit a target's bull's-eye to compensate for the force of gravity.

Time Required to Complete Activity: 30 minutes

Materials (for each team of two):

Act 18-4 SH
calculator

SAFETY PRECAUTIONS:
None

Background:

A projectile fired horizontally will hit the ground *at exactly the same time* a bullet dropped from your hand will hit the ground. By calculating the amount of horizontal drop of a fired projectile, you can determine the amount of compensation needed to hit the target's bull's-eye.

To calculate the amount of time required for a bullet fired downrange to hit the target, use the following relationship:

travel time to the target $= T = d/v$
T = time (seconds)
d = distance to target (feet)
v = velocity, which is specific to each firearm (feet/second)

BBs, pellets, and a .22 cartridge.

© Cengage Learning®

A bullet would hit the ground at exactly the same time whether it was dropped or fired from a firearm.

Vertical drop 5 feet

300 feet

To calculate the horizontal drop of a fired projectile over time, use the following relationship:

distance traveled $= D = 1/2\ gt^2$
D = distance traveled (feet)
g, or gravitational acceleration $= 32$ ft/s^2
t = time to reach the ground (seconds)

Procedure:

PART 1: BB

1. Calculate the time required for a projectile to reach a target located 300 feet from the shooter if the projectile is fired from a BB rifle at a velocity (speed) of 500 ft/s. (Travel time to the target $= T = d/v$.)
Time = _____ seconds.
2. Calculate the distance D the projectile drops each tenth of a second ($D = 1/2\ gt^2$). Record your answer first in feet, and then convert feet to inches. Record the information in Data Table 1. (Recall $g = 32$ ft/s^2)

Data Table 1: BB

Time (t) (s)	t^2 (s^2)	Distance Traveled D (ft)	Distance Dropped (in.)
0.1			
0.2			
0.3			
0.4			
0.5			
0.6			

Group Discussion Questions:

1. By the time the projectile reaches the target at the end of 0.6 seconds, how many inches has the projectile dropped? Record your answer in Data Table 1.
2. How does a person discharging a firearm compensate for the gravitational drop of the projectile if he or she wants to hit the bull's-eye on a target 300 feet away?
3. Prepare a graph using the data in Data Table 1 that show the relationship between distance traveled and time. Title your graph, and include units and labels on both axes.
4. Refer to your graph. What claim can you make about the effect of time on the distance the projectile drops due to gravity? Support your claim with data from your graph.

Answers Part 1 BB

1. Time = 0.6 second
2. See data table below.

Procedure Part 1

Data Table 1: BB—Answers

Time (t) (s)	t^2 (s^2)	Distance Traveled D (ft)	Distance Dropped (in.)
0.1	0.01	0.16	1.92
0.2	0.04	0.64	7.68
0.3	0.09	1.44	17.28
0.4	0.16	2.56	30.72
0.5	0.25	4	48
0.6	0.36	5.76	69.12

Procedure:

PART 2: PELLET

In this example, the projectile was fired using a pellet rifle with a velocity of 1,000 ft/s.

1. Calculate the travel time to the target T if the target is located 300 ft away ($T = d/v$).
   Time = _____ seconds.
2. Calculate the distance D the projectile dropped over time ($D = 1/2\ gt^2$). Record your answers in Data Table 2.

Data Table 2: Pellet

Time (t) (s)	t^2 (s²)	Distance Traveled D (ft)	Distance Dropped (in.)
0.1			
0.2			
0.3			

Procedure:

PART 3: .22 BULLET

1. In this example, a firearm was fired using a .22 rifle bullet with a velocity of 1,200 ft/s. Calculate the travel time to the target T if the target is located 300 feet away ($T = d/v$).
   Time = _____ seconds.
2. Calculate the distance D the projectile dropped over time ($D = 1/2\ gt^2$). Record your answers in Data Table 3.

Data Table 3: .22 Bullet

Time (t) (s)	t^2 (s²)	Distance Traveled D (ft)	Distance Dropped (in.)
0.1			
0.2			
0.25			

3. In Data Table 4, organize your data from Part 1, Part 2, and Part 3. Compare the time required to reach the target and the distance the projectiles traveled over time. Record the information in Data Table 4.

Data Table 4: Summary

Firearm	Velocity (ft/s)	Time Projectile Was Airborne (s)	Distance Dropped (in.)
BB rifle	500		
Pellet rifle	1,000		
.22 rifle	1,200		

Answers Part 2 Pellet

1. Time = 0.3 second
2. See data table below.

Answers Part 3 .22 Bullet

1. Time = 0.25 second
2. See data table below.
3. See next page for Data Table 4 answers.

Procedure Part 2

Data Table 2: Pellet—Answers

Time (t) (sec)	t^2 (sec²)	Distance Traveled D (ft)	Distance Dropped (in.)
0.1	0.01	0.16	1.92
0.2	0.04	0.64	7.68
0.3	0.09	1.44	17.28

Procedure Part 3

Data Table 3: .22 Bullet—Answers

Time (t) (s)	t^2 (s²)	Distance Traveled D (ft)	Distance Dropped (in.)
0.1	0.01	0.16	1.92
0.2	0.04	0.64	7.68
0.25	0.06	1.0	11.52

Questions:

1. Which firearm's projectile took a longer time to strike the target: the 500 ft/s BB rifle or the 1,000 ft/s pellet gun?
2. Which projectile traveled farthest: the BB, the pellet, or the .22 bullet? Use your data to support your claim.
3. Which projectile dropped a greater distance over time? Support your claim with your data.
4. Based on your data, is there any relationship between the velocity of the projectile and the distance dropped (all traveled 300 feet)? Support your claim with your data.
5. What is the relationship between accuracy and the projectile's velocity? Use evidence to support your claim.

Going Further:

1. Many factors affect the accuracy of a fired projectile. Research the effect of each the following:
   a. wind and ambient temperature
   b. the caliber of the firearm
   c. the length of the barrel
   d. moisture
2. A sharpshooter practices firing her firearm at a target from a distance of 20 yards. If she plans to use the firearm at a distance of 100 yards, she will need to sight her gun for that distance. Based on the results of this activity, explain why guns need to be re-sighted for different distances.

Questions

1. The BB rifle took 0.6 seconds whereas the pellet rifle took 0.3 seconds.

2. All the same; all traveled 330 feet.

3. BB

4. The greater the velocity, the less the projectile dropped. The .22 rifle with a velocity of 1,200 ft/s dropped only ~12 inches, whereas the slower BB rifle projectile traveling at 500 ft/s dropped ~ 69 inches.

5. The higher the velocity, the more accurate the projectile.

Procedure Part 4

Data Table 4: Summary—Answers

Firearm	Velocity (ft/s)	Time Projectile Was Airborne (s)	Distance Dropped (inches)
BB Rifle	500	0.6	~69
Pellet Rifle	1,000	0.3	~17
.22 Rifle	1,200	0.25	~12

CAPSTONE PROJECTS

PROJECT 1

Physical Evidence Case Studies

OBJECTIVES

By the end of this project, you will be able to:

✔ Discuss four cases in which a selected type of physical evidence was used to solve the crime.

✔ Describe how the physical evidence was used to solve the crime.

INTRODUCTION

Working with a partner or a team of three students, select a type of physical evidence that will be used to help solve crimes. Research case studies in which this type of physical evidence eventually led to solving the crime. Your team will be presenting your favorite or most interesting case study using the type of physical evidence you were assigned. Your presentation should demonstrate how the evidence helped solve the case. Your team will instruct the class on proper protocols for photographing, documenting, collecting, and storing this type of evidence. Refer to the *Physical Evidence Due Dates Form* as you complete each step of this project.

MATERIALS

- CP-1 SH *Physical Evidence Due Dates Form*
- CP-1 SH *Individual Case Study Summary* (four copies)
- CP-1 SH *In-Depth Case Study Notes Form*
- CP-1 SH *Evidence Collection Notes Form*
- CP-1 SH *Death Notes Form*
- CP-1 SH *Peer Review Notes Form*

Background

Students work with a partner or on a team of three students to research cases in which a type of physical evidence eventually led to solving the crime.

Teaching Tips

Refer to the *Capstone Project 1 Instructor Notes* found on the IRCD, Capstone 1.

Before starting this project, review with students the different types of evidence discussed in Chapter 2. Direct evidence includes firsthand observations such as eyewitness accounts or videos from police dashboard cameras. Circumstantial evidence is indirect evidence that can be used to imply a fact but that does not directly prove it.

Teaching Tip

This is a good project for the first 10 weeks of the course. Each team selects one type of physical evidence to research. Each team then selects one case study that they will present to the class. Throughout the year, when you introduce a new type of evidence, students will start the discussion of the new topic by presenting its relevance to their in-depth case study. Each team is the class "resident experts" on how to collect, document, and process their chosen evidence. Have students submit their case studies electronically so that you can build up your own collection of case studies for each topic.

Procedures

1. Student teams should select one type of evidence from the list in the text. This same list is on the CP-1 *Physical Evidence Signup Sheet* on the IRCD, Capstone 1. Print the sheet so student teams can sign up for the type of physical evidence they want to research. Only one team should be assigned to a type of evidence.

2. Print, copy, and distribute to each team the following documents found on the IRCD, Capstone 1:
   - CP-1 SH *Physical Evidence Due Dates Form*
   - CP-1 SH *Individual Case Study Summary* (Figure 1; each team will need four copies.)
   - CP-1 SH *In-Depth Case Study Notes Form*
   - CP-1 SH *Evidence Collection Notes Form* (Figure 2)
   - CP-1 SH *Death Notes Form* (shown in Figure 3)
   - CP-1 SH *Peer Review Notes Form*

3. Encourage students to use the CP-1 SH *Physical Evidence Due Dates Form* to keep track of the various components they are required to complete for this project. Students may enter the due date for each component and the date it was completed to help them monitor their progress.

4. After student teams have selected their type of evidence, they are to research four cases in which the evidence was used to help solve the crime. Each team completes an CP-1 SH *Individual Case Study Summary Form* for *each* case.

PROCEDURE

1. Select one type of evidence from the list below. (Your instructor may ask you to sign up for a specific type of evidence on the *Physical Evidence Signup Sheet*.)

Anthropology (bones)	Glass
Ballistics (firearms)	Hair
Blood or blood spatter	Handwriting
Botanical (plants)	Saliva or semen
Dental impressions	Shoe or foot impressions
DNA	Soil or sand
Drugs	PMI (rigor mortis, algor mortis, livor mortis)
Entomology (insects)	
Fibers or textiles	Tire impressions
Forgery	Tool marks
Fingerprints	Other

2. Research four case studies not cited in the textbook that describe how your selected type of physical evidence was used to help solve the crime. Complete an *Individual Case Study Summary Form* (see Figure 1) for **each** case study. Or, you may research three actual case studies and write one hypothetical case study that demonstrates how your evidence was used to help solve the case.

3. Select one of the authentic case studies on which to conduct an in-depth study. Complete the *In-Depth Case Study Notes Form* (provided by your instructor) on the case you selected. See Figure 2. This form requires you to indicate basic information you've collected on the case as well as additional information such as the motive for the crime, how the evidence was used to solve the crime, and a crime-scene photo or sketch.

4. Research how to properly photograph, document, collect, label, and store the physical evidence that you are highlighting in your in-depth study. Prepare a training manual for crime-scene investigators that explains the proper procedures for evidence collection, handling, and labeling. You and your team should determine the best format for the training information. Suggestions include, but are not limited to the following: written report, slide show, narrated video, brochure, poster, original animation, or booklet.

Refer to your evidence training manual and notes on proper evidence collection to determine if the evidence collection, handling, and labeling in your selected case study were done properly. Complete the *Evidence Collection Notes Form* (Figure 3) provided by your instructor.

5. If any deaths occurred in the crime on which you are doing your in-depth study, complete the *Death Notes Form* provided by your instructor (see Figure 4) for *each* death. The form includes information on the manner, cause, and mechanism of death, and postmortem interval (PMI), if applicable.

6. Develop a presentation on your in-depth study. This can be in the form of a written report, slide show, narrated video, poster, brochure, three-dimensional model, recreated crime scene, etc. Any visuals should be colorful, relevant, and easily visible to all students.

7. Present your materials before a peer group. The peer group should complete the *Peer Review Notes Form* provided by your instructor to evaluate your presentation and provide suggestions for improvement.

8. Refer to the *Physical Evidence Due Dates* table provided by your instructor to ensure you submit all the required materials by the dates they are due.

9. Deliver the final presentation of your in-depth study to the class after it has been peer-reviewed and modified.

Figure 1 *Individual Case Study Summary Form.*

Case Study Number	
Name of Case	
Actual or hypothetical case?	
Who was involved?	
Plaintiff(s)	
Defendant(s)	
Where was crime committed?	
Date and approximate time crime was committed	
Synopsis of case	
How was your selected physical evidence used to solve the crime?	

5. From these four case studies, each team should select one case they want to investigate further and complete the CP-1 SH *In-Depth Case Study Notes Form* for that case.

As part of their in-depth study, each team prepares a training manual that explains the proper procedures for the collection, handling, and labeling of the evidence they have selected to research. Each team should use this training information to complete the CP-1 SH *Evidence Collection Notes Form.*

If any deaths occurred in the crime on which they are doing their in-depth study, they should complete the CP-1 SH *Death Notes Form* for *each* death.

6. Student teams will prepare a presentation on their in-depth case study to share with the class. Before giving their final presentation, have each team give its presentation to a peer group. Each peer group should complete the CP-1 SH *Peer Review Notes Form* to evaluate the presentation and provide suggestions on how it can be improved.

Teaching Tips

Use the CP-1 TN *Checklist* to help you evaluate each team's presentation. This form is on the IRCD. It lists each component the team is to complete in this project. You may want to determine a point system for each of the project's components as well as a rubric on how each item will be graded. The rubric should be discussed with your students.

This project may have multiple components with varying due dates. You need to stress the importance of completing the various components on schedule, perhaps offering bonus points for students who submit on time.

Peer review enables students to practice and verbalize their presentation to a small group prior to their class presentation. This can help reduce anxiety.

Suggest alternative ways for students to prepare their training manual.

Figure 2 *In-Depth Case Study Notes Form.*

Case Study Number	
Name of Case	
Name of Plaintiff(s)	
Name of Defendant(s)	
Date and Approximate Time Crime Was Committed	
Location of Crime Scene	
Case Summary	
Motive for Crime	
How was evidence used to solve the crime?	
Bibliography	

Include crime-scene photo or sketch as a separate attachment.

Figure 3 *Evidence Collection Notes Form.*

Type of physical evidence
Proper method of evidence collection
Proper method of evidence labeling, documenting, and photographing
Proper method of evidence storage (plastic bag, brown bag, or glass jar)
Name of in-depth case study
Describe how the evidence in this in-depth case study was collected, labeled, and recorded.
Describe any errors you identified in the evidence collection, labeling, and recording.

Figure 4 *Death Notes Form.**

Name of Case	
Name of Victim	
Manner of Death	
Cause of Death	
Mechanism of Death	
Estimated Time of Death or PMI	
Describe how time of death was calculated.	

*Complete a form for each death.

PROJECT 2

Personal Evidence Portfolio

By the end of this project, you will have:

✔ Assembled a personal evidence portfolio that contains samples of various types of physical evidence.

INTRODUCTION

Throughout this course, you learn how to identify, collect, label, and safely store different types of physical evidence. In many of the end-of-chapter activities, you practice the correct methods for evidence collection, handling, and storage. In this project, you will assemble your evidence in a personal evidence portfolio. You may use your personal evidence portfolio to create a mock crime scene in Capstone Project 8.

SAFETY PRECAUTIONS

Safety guidelines for evidence handling discussed in Chapter 2 should be followed for each type of evidence.

MATERIALS

General

- Cardboard box to store all personal evidence, labeled with your name
- Black permanent labeling pen
- Evidence bags or envelopes
- Masking tape
- CP-2 SH *Vehicle Identification Form*

CAPSTONE PROJECTS **623**

Background

Students collect the evidence samples listed under the *Specific* materials in the text. You may choose to have students store evidence samples as they prepare them in the various activities throughout this course; or, you may direct them to prepare the required samples all at once. The end-of-chapter activities and corresponding page numbers that explain the methods for collecting the various evidence samples are provided. The goal of this project is to have students assemble various types of evidence that they can then use in Capstone Project 8, in which they create their own mock crime scene.

Teaching Tips

Refer to the *Capstone Project 2 Instructor Notes* found on the IRCD, Capstone 2.

Make sure students understand that all evidence they collect must come from them, their home, or the school.

Teaching Tip

This activity provides students with practice collecting, documenting, and storing evidence. If students later construct their own crime scenes, it also provides evidence that can be used in their crime scenes.

Procedures

1. Print, copy, and distribute the following documents found on the IRCD, Capstone 2.
   - CP-2 SH *Vehicle Identification Form* (shown in Figure 1)
   - CP-2 SH *Tire Identification Form* (shown in Figure 2)
   Students use these tables to record the personal vehicle identification information and the tire impressions from their family vehicle.
   - CP-2 SH *Evidence Inventory Labels* (Each student should have at least nine copies.)
   - CP-2 SH *Evidence Portfolio* (one per student), to be stored in their evidence portfolio storage box.
   - CP-2 SH *Evidence Markers* (as needed by students)

2. Encourage students to review the procedures for securing and collecting evidence discussed in Chapter 2.

- CP-2 SH *Tire Identification Form*
- CP-2 SH *Evidence Inventory Labels*
- CP-2 SH *Evidence Markers*
- CP-2 SH *Evidence Portfolio*

Specific

- **Fingerprinting:** Two ten cards (Activity 6-4)
- **Hair:** Four permanent slides of hair (Activity 3-1) and an envelope of hair from your head
- **Fibers and textiles:** Four permanent slides (Activity 4-1); an envelope of fibers and 1-square-inch textile sample from same source (Activity 4-2)
- **Footprint impressions or casts:** Two inkless pad impressions or footprint cast (Activity 16-1)
- **Handwriting:** Two samples (Activity 10-1)
- **Dental impression:** Two sample sets of transparencies of bite patterns (Activity 16-5)
- **Blood typing results:** Documentation of your own blood type test results
- **Pollen:** Four permanent slides made from pollen near your home (or school grounds) (Activity 5-1)
- **Sand or soil sample:** Four samples from your property or school grounds (Activities 13-2 and 13-3)
- **Personal vehicle identification:** Completed *Vehicle Identification Form* on a family or school vehicle (Activity 16-4). *Vehicle Identification Form* provided by your instructor. (A bicycle could be substituted for a motor vehicle.)
- **Tire impression:** Inkless pad impressions or casts of all tires from a family or school vehicle (Activity 16-3); and completed *Tire Identification Form* provided by your instructor for all tires of the vehicle. (Bicycle tire impressions could be substituted for motor-vehicle tire impressions.)

PROCEDURE

1. As you complete each of the chapters, prepare and correctly label and package examples of your own personal evidence. When new evidence is added, add to the CP-2 SH *Evidence Portfolio* table of contents. Since this is a personal evidence file, whenever possible, *all evidence should come from you, your home, or your property*.

2. The evidence should be collected and labeled following the correct protocol for that type of evidence. You should prepare the number of samples of each type of evidence as specified in the preceding *Specific* list

of materials. Microscopic evidence should be stored on permanent slides in separate labeled envelopes.

3. For the personal vehicle identification evidence, complete the *Vehicle Identification Form* provided by your instructor. See Figure 1. Use a family vehicle or a school vehicle to complete the table.

4. For the tire impression, complete the *Tire Identification Form* provided by your instructor. See Figure 2. Use data from your family vehicle or a school vehicle to complete the form.

5. All evidence should be stored in your personal evidence portfolio box, labeled with your name and the date the evidence was collected.

Figure 1 *Vehicle Identification Form.*

Vehicle Identification	
Name of Owner	
Manufacturer	
Model	
Year	
Color	
Front track width (mm)	
Rear track width (mm)	
Wheelbase (mm)*	
Turning Diameter*	
Tire Width (front)	
Tire Width (rear)	
Number of Tire Grooves (indentations)	
Number of Tire Ribs (elevations)	
Ridge Pattern (angular or straight)	
Other Distinguishing Features	

*Check owner's manual.

Figure 2 *Tire Identification Form.*

Tire Position	Make	Model	Size	Rib Position: Centered or Off-Center	Number of Grooves	Number of Ribs	Ridge Pattern (angular or straight)	Distinguishing Features
Front Driver								
Front Passenger								
Rear Driver								
Rear Passenger								

Safety Precautions

It is important that evidence is handled and labeled properly to avoid any contamination. Safety guidelines for evidence handling should be followed for each type of evidence. Guidelines are discussed in Chapter 2.

Teaching Tip

Students should complete CP-2 *Evidence Portfolio* whenever they add information to their portfolios.

Background

The evidence indicates that a suspect is guilty. But how *reliable* is that evidence? This is the question being asked more and more in court. In the early days of DNA fingerprinting, inaccurate results were reported because of human error in performing the collection and testing of samples. After laboratory protocols were standardized, DNA evidence was considered more reliable.

In this project, students form debate teams to consider the reliability of different types of physical evidence.

Teaching Tips

Refer to the *Capstone Project 3 Instructor Notes* found on the IRCD, Capstone 3.

Refer students to Joseph Wambaugh's *The Blooding*, which describes the first time DNA was used to solve a crime.

Prior to a debate, it might be beneficial for students to view the format used in school debates. Ask your school debate team for a copy of their debate format model.

How Reliable Is the Evidence?

OBJECTIVES

By the end of this project, you will be able to:

✔ Discuss the reliability of different types of physical evidence.

✔ Debate the reliability of different types of physical evidence used in courts today.

INTRODUCTION

The validity of many different forms of physical evidence has been questioned. How reliable is the evidence? Have innocent people been convicted because of improperly handled or improperly interpreted evidence?

In this project, you will debate the reliability of different types of evidence used in criminal cases today.

BACKGROUND

Science is composed of claims supported by experimental data, or evidence. The evidence must be collected using protocols and procedures that ensure that the same results will be obtained by every investigator performing the same procedures. The quality of the claim depends on the relevance and reliability of the evidence. Claims based exclusively on repeatable protocols and reliable evidence will be unbiased.

In 2009, the National Academy of Sciences issued a report on the forensic sciences called "Strengthening Forensic Science in the United States: A Path Forward." The report questioned the reliability of evidence, the lack of statistical data to support claims, and a lack of certification and training. Specifically, it questioned whether there was adequate basis for individualization of evidence when linking crime-scene evidence to a particular defendant.

The Innocence Project reported that more than 50 percent of the DNA exonerations were a result of unvalidated or improper forensic work. Spencer Hsu (see Going Further) of *The Washington Post* published many articles that demonstrated how procedural errors in analyzing hair evidence resulted in wrongful convictions.

According to an article published by the American Bar Association (Nancy Gertner), errors were made by both forensic technicians and the legal system. Invalid forensic evidence has been admitted for years. The courts have often failed to hold admissibility hearings or failed to give reasons for admitting evidence when it would have been appropriate to do so.

As a result of these critiques, the National Institute of Standards and Technology (NIST) and the Department of Justice (DOJ) formed Scientific Working Groups, and later, the Organization of Science Area Committees (OSAC). The purpose of these groups is to develop standards to improve quality and consistency of work in the forensic science community and to ensure that evidence presented in criminal cases is valid and reliable.

MATERIALS

- CP-3 SH *Debate Strategy Form*
- CP-3 SH *Performance Evaluation Form*
- Computer with Internet access (optional)

PROCEDURE

1. Your instructor has placed posters around the room identifying four types of physical evidence:
   - Fingerprinting
   - DNA analysis
   - Dental impressions and bite marks
   - Hair

   When your instructor directs you, go to one of the four stations.

2. With the other students at your station, discuss your opinions and ideas regarding the reliability of this type of physical evidence. Then, divide the group into two teams: those who feel the evidence *is* reliable and those who feel it is *not* reliable.

   Each team should appoint a member to record ideas.

3. Each of the four groups will debate the reliability of their type of physical evidence, with half the team arguing that the evidence is reliable, and the other half arguing that it is not reliable. There will be a total of four debates.

Procedures

1. Prior to class, write the name of the four different types of physical evidence listed below on four separate pieces of poster board. Hang the four poster boards around the classroom.
   - Fingerprinting
   - DNA analysis
   - Dental impressions (bite marks)
   - Hair

2. Engage students by asking them if they have seen a television program or read a book, newspaper, or magazine article in which evidence was challenged. Lead a discussion on evidence reliability.

3. After the discussion, instruct students to go to one of the four posters. The groups at each station discuss their opinions and ideas regarding the reliability of this type of physical evidence.

4. Print, copy, and distribute the following documents found on the IRCD, Capstone 3.
   - CP-3 *Debate Strategy Form*
   - CP-3 *Performance Evaluation Form* (two copies per team)

5. After the initial discussion, each group divides into two teams that debate reliability versus nonreliability of the evidence to which they are assigned.

Following are some tips on debating:

- Focus on attacking the idea and *not* the other debaters.
- Gather accurate information to use in defending your position.
- Use words like *generally, often,* and *many.*
- Stress the positive in your argument.
- Quote reliable sources.
- Maintain a positive attitude.
- Don't lose a friend over a debate. Remember everyone is entitled to an opinion.

Some of the things you should avoid doing during a debate:

- Using words such as *never, always, all,* and *most.* They are inaccurate.
- Attacking the debater.
- Attempting to deceive your opponents by representing opinion as fact.
- Becoming hostile or raising your voice.
- Disagreeing with obvious facts.

4. Research your debate topic online (using the Gale Forensic Science eCollection and other resources); using educational materials, journals, magazines; and reference materials; and if possible, by conducting interviews with judges, lawyers, or law enforcement officials.

Include in your research the following:

- Proper evidence collection, handling, and storage
- Evidence analysis
- Statistical value of results within a population
- The latest research on acceptability
- Is the relevant evidence sufficient for a conviction?

5. Prepare your debate strategy using the *Debate Strategy Form* (Figure 1) provided by your instructor.

Figure 1 *Debate Strategy*

1	**Opening statement (2 minutes)**	Appoint one team member who will make a 2-minute opening statement that states your team's position and main supporting arguments.
2	**Main Arguments Supporting Team's Position (3 minutes)**	Each member of the team can present different arguments that support your team's position. Provide specific information and any data that support your statements. The more evidence you provide to support your statements, the stronger your argument. List the names of the team members, and write down the main idea of each member's argument. Record the main evidence or data used to support the argument.
3	**Prepare Questions for Opponents (Rebuttal Preparation, 2 minutes)**	Prior to the debate, prepare five to ten questions that you can ask each of your opponents. You need to anticipate what their main arguments are so that you will be ready with questions. These questions should be brief and to the point.
4	**Take Notes on Opponents' Presentation**	As your opponents present their case, take careful notes on each of their arguments. You will want to formulate rebuttals that disprove their points.
5	**Rebuttal (3 minutes)**	After you have presented your arguments, your opponents will have an opportunity to ask questions. A strong debater knows how to anticipate questions. Write down questions you expect from your opponents, and then prepare a response to them.
6	**Closing Statement (2 minutes)**	Select one team member to present your closing statement. In the closing statement, you should repeat your main idea and restate the main arguments used to support your idea.

6. Review the *Performance Evaluation Form* provided by your instructor (see Figure 2) to help you fine-tune your debate strategy and performance. This form will be used by your instructor and classmates to evaluate your debating skills. Note that your performance will be negatively affected by the following:

   - Personal attacks or insults directed toward members of an opposing team
   - Interruptions of an opponent's presentation
   - Talking and whispering during a presentation

7. Conduct the debate. The time allowed for each team's presentation is as follows:

Opening Statement	2 minutes
Arguments	3 minutes
Rebuttal Preparation	2 minutes
Rebuttal	3 minutes
Closing Statement	2 minutes

8. Use the *Performance Evaluation Form* to evaluate each of the debates. Circle the statement under the "points" column that best describes the debater's performance. Be sure to add positive comments and justify any low evaluation scores.

6. Before student teams develop their debate strategies, review the tips in the text on effective debating and what *not* to do while debating.

7. Each team prepares its CP-3 *Debate Strategy Form* before the debate. Students can also use the CP-3 *Performance Evaluation Form* to fine-tune their own debate strategy and performance.

8. Students use the second copy of the CP-3 *Performance Evaluation Form* to assess one other debate team. Make sure students know which debate team they are evaluating. Be sure students understand how to use the form. They should circle only one statement per row. The highest score a team can earn is 24 points. In the "Additional comments" section of the form, students explain any low evaluation scores.

Teaching Tip

You may wish to obtain and provide students with a copy of the article "Qualifying Value of Forensic Evidence" discussed in CP-3 TN *Qualifying Evidence* on the IRCD, Capstone 3.

Teaching Tip

Show students the *Frontline* episode entitled "The Real CSI" from April 17, 2012. You can find it at PBS online at http://www.pbs .org/wgbh/pages/frontline/real-csi

Figure 2 *Performance Evaluation Form.*

	1 Point	2 Points	3 Points	4 Points
1. Opening statement	Position not clearly stated. Failed to state arguments that would be used.	Stated arguments and positions, but provided irrelevant details with the statement.	Stated position and stated arguments to be presented.	Clearly stated the position and stated what arguments were to be presented.
2. Organization of materials	Not clear.	Somewhat clear.	Very clear and orderly.	Completely clear and logical.
3. Support of arguments or ideas	Few or no supporting statements and evidence.	Some supporting statements and examples of supporting evidence.	Many supporting statements and some examples of evidence.	Most relevant supporting statements and many examples of evidence.
4. Quality of rebuttal questions for the other team	No questions, indicating a lack of preparation.	Few questions for rebuttal that failed to counter arguments.	Several good questions for rebuttal prepared.	Many pertinent questions for the other team; clearly planned in advance.
5. Answers to opponents' rebuttal	No effective response.	Few effective responses.	Some effective responses.	Most effective rebuttal.
6. Style, enthusiasm, tone of voice, body movements	Unenthusiastic response by team members; voice demonstrated a lack of commitment to arguments.	Not all members demonstrated enthusiasm or good voice tone.	Demonstrated enthusiasm, good voice tone, and positive body language.	Very enthusiastic; sounded confident of information and committed to ideas.

Total points _____

Additional comments:

Going Further

Read one of the following articles. Report your findings to the class.

Gertner, Nancy. "National Academy of Sciences Report." *Criminal Justice*, Volume 27, Number 1, Spring 2012.

Hsu, Spencer. "Finding Forensic Errors by FBI Lab Unit Spanned Two Decades." *The Washington Post*, 30 Jul 2014.

http://www.nist.gov/forensics/osac/index.cfm (OSAC organization)

http://www.nap.edu/openbook.php?record_id=12589 (National Academy of Sciences Report 2009: "Strengthening Forensic Science in the United States: A Path Forward")

http://www.innocenceproject.org/docs/DNA_Exonerations_Forensic _Science.pdf ("Wrongful Convictions Involving Unvalidated or Improper Forensic Science That Were Later Overturned through DNA Testing." The Innocence Project)

PROJECT 4

Landmark Cases in Acceptance of Evidence

By the end of this project, you will be able to:

✔ Discuss landmark court cases involving acceptance of forensic evidence.

✔ Explain the significance of these cases on the status of evidence acceptability in the courts today.

INTRODUCTION

Testimony and evidence authenticated by experts have not always been accepted at trial. In this project, you will investigate landmark court cases revolving around the acceptance of testimony and evidence provided by experts.

MATERIALS

- CP-4 SH *Landmark Cases in Acceptance of Evidence Form*
- CP-4 SH *Technology and Evidence Analysis Form*

PROCEDURE

1. Your instructor will present the first court case, *Frye v. United States.* In the *Landmark Cases in Acceptance of Evidence Form* provided by your instructor, fill in the following information from your instructor's presentation:
   - Date
   - Case number
   - Case summary and decision
   - Impact on acceptance of evidence

Background

A hundred years ago, it was very difficult to convict a particular suspect for a specific crime. Courts had to rely on confessions or eyewitness testimony.

With technological advances in fingerprinting and DNA analysis, and the improvements made in microscopy and the development of new tools, it became easier to convict suspects. However, evidence obtained from new technology was not always accepted by the courts.

In this project, students investigate five landmark court cases that have extended the range of what is admissible as forensic evidence at trial.

Teaching Tip

Refer to the *Capstone Project 4 Instructor Notes* found on the IRCD, Capstone 4.

Procedures

1. Print, copy, and distribute the CP-4 *Landmark Cases in Acceptance of Evidence Form* found on the IRCD, Capstone 4.

CAPSTONE PROJECTS **631**

2. Students complete the information on each case in their CP-4 *Landmark Cases in Acceptance of Evidence Form.* To help students get started, you should discuss and model the first court case, *Frye v. United States.*

3. When you have completed your presentation of *Frye,* students should work in teams of two to research *one* of the other cases listed.

4. Have teams meet as directed in Procedure Steps 5 and 6 of the text so that each team eventually meets with a team researching each of the other cases. When they are done meeting, the teams should have completed their CP-4 *Landmark Cases in Acceptance of Evidence Form.*

5. In Procedure Step 7, go over the discussion questions with the class. Answers for these discussion questions are provided below.

   a. Frye *stated that all evidence must be generally accepted as reliable in the relevant scientific community.* Daubert *stated that the rigid requirement of* Frye *had been superseded by Rule 701 of the Federal Rules of Evidence. Judges could now determine at pretrial if evidence met* Daubert's *relevant factors. Judges became the gatekeepers; they could either allow or disallow the evidence at pretrial.*

   b. *The five* Daubert *factors:*

      i. *Whether the theory or testimony could be or has been tested.*

      ii. *Whether the theory or technique has been subjected to peer review and publication.*

      iii. *Is there a known or potential error rate?*

2. Working in teams of two, select one of the following court cases to research.

   • *Frye v. United States*
   • *Daubert v. Merrell Dow Pharmaceuticals*
   • *United States v. Starzecpyzel*
   • *Kumho Tire v. Carmichael*
   • *United States v. Prime*
   • *Maryland v. King*

3. Record the information you research on your selected case in the *Landmark Cases in Acceptance of Evidence Form.*

4. If other teams in your class are researching the same case, meet with them to compare your findings.

5. Meet with a team researching a case different from yours. For example, if you researched Case A, then meet with a team that researched Case B; if you researched Case C, then meet with a team that researched Case D. Share information about your case with the other team, and complete that section of your *Landmark Cases in Acceptance of Evidence Form.*

6. Continue the exchange of information with other teams, and record the information on your *Landmark Cases in Acceptance of Evidence Form.*

7. As a class, discuss the court cases and their effect on the acceptability of testimony and evidence provided by experts in the courts today. Some discussion questions:

   a. What is the main difference between the rulings of *Frye v. United States* and *Daubert v. Merrell Dow Pharmaceuticals*?

   b. After the ruling of *Daubert v. Merrell Dow Pharmaceuticals*, judges had to view the evidence at pretrial hearings to determine if the evidence could be admitted. List the five Daubert factors that judges need to consider in order to admit the evidence.

   c. If handwriting evidence was not yet considered to be scientific evidence at the time of *United States v. Starzecpyzel*, how was it admissible as reliable evidence?

   d. How did the ruling in *Kumho Tire v. Carmichael* affect how expert witness testimony would be accepted?

   e. In *United States v. Prime*, the Court viewed handwriting analysis testimony differently from how it was viewed in 1993. What are some of the reasons that the court now considered handwriting analysis as better able to meet the Daubert standard? What had changed?

   f. Explain the significance of Supreme Court Justice Scalia's claim that taking arrestee DNA was a violation of the Fourth Amendment.

   iv. *The existence and maintenance of standards controlling the techniques' operation.*

   v. *"General acceptance" can still have a bearing on the inquiry.*

   c. *In* United States v. Starzecpyzel, *handwriting evidence did not satisfy the* Daubert *standard but the case found handwriting analysis to be considered technical and admissible. The case did not meet the* Daubert *standard because handwriting*

   analysis had not been subjected as yet to rigorous testing, the error rate was not known, and published article reports differed from those in scientific journals.

   d. Kumho Tire v. Carmichael *expanded use of the* Daubert *standards to all types of expert witness testimony and not just scientific expert testimony.*

Further Study

1. Research the history of the acceptance of other types of evidence, such as
   a. DNA
   b. Dental impressions
   c. Blood-spatter analysis
   d. Glass analysis
   e. Hair and fiber analysis
   f. Fingerprint analysis
   g. Ballistics evidence
   h. Handwriting evidence
   i. Botanical evidence involving annual tree rings

2. Technology has improved evidence analysis and acceptance in courts. Evidence that was formerly considered class evidence can now be considered individual evidence because of advances in technology. Investigate the technological advances in evidence analysis for each of the following, and then complete the *Technology and Evidence Analysis Form* provided by your instructor.

   (1) Gas chromatography
   (2) High-performance liquid chromatography (HPLC)
   (3) Electron microscopy
   (4) Digital scanners in fingerprint analysis
   (5) Comparison microscopy
   (6) Spectophotometry
   (7) Polymerase chain reaction (PCR) amplification of DNA
   (8) X-ray applications
   (9) Computer software applications
   (10) Retinal scans
   (11) Short tandem repeat (STR) analysis
   (12) Thermal imaging
   (13) Computer software
   (14) Rapid DNA analysis
   (15) Magneto-optical sensor technology

e. *The Court believes that today there is more "general acceptance" of handwriting analysis based upon its use by Scotland Yard, the Secret Service, the FBI, and the CIA, and the Court upheld that handwriting analysis now met the Daubert standard for admissibility.*

f. *Fifteen universities now offer courses in forensics that include handwriting analysis.*

Teaching Tips

Confer with any teachers in your school who might be teaching law-related material for additional information.

Research the history of court acceptance for the following types of evidence: fingerprints, blood typing, tool marks, blood-spatter patterns, entomology, and DNA.

Further Research and Extensions

To complete the *Further Study* portion of the project, students investigate the technological advances in evidence analysis for each of the types of evidence listed. Print, copy, and distribute the CP-4 SH *Technology and Evidence Analysis Form* found on the IRCD, Capstone 4. They record their information on this form. You may want to suggest other types of evidence for students to research in addition to those listed in the text.

Background

For this project, you will need to record or arrange to stream an episode of a forensics-related TV show that students will view during a class period. Shows to consider include *CSI, Bones, Cold Case,* or *NCIS*.

As students view the episode, they will record all examples of contrived lab testing, poor procedures, incorrect weapons handling, improper assignment of jobs, etc., that they observe in the episode. They should look for examples that vary from real-life crime scenes and police activities they have studied in this course.

Teaching Tips

Refer to the *Capstone Project 5 Instructor Notes* found on the IRCD, Capstone 5. You can find a list of many common errors made in forensics television shows in that document.

Because of the graphic and violent nature of some forensics TV shows, you should check your school's policy on showing the episode to students and any requirements for obtaining permission from parents or guardians.

PROJECT 5

Analysis of a Forensic Science TV Show Episode

OBJECTIVES

By the end of this project, you will be able to:

✔ Identify contrived or misrepresented procedures or events portrayed in an episode of a forensic science television program.

✔ Document a correct method for the procedure or an improved representation of the event.

INTRODUCTION

Television provides us with many hours of forensic investigations. The writers for forensic science shows have searched high and low for ideas and unusual cases. Some of the techniques and forensic science concepts demonstrated in these shows have been contrived or misrepresented for the sake of entertainment and filling the allotted time slot. In this project, you will be charged with detecting and documenting how the TV portrayal of a crime-scene investigation varies from what happens in real life.

MATERIALS

- CP-5 SH *TV Episode Summary Form*
- CP-5 SH *Episode Evaluation Form*
- Computers with Internet access (optional)
- Reference materials, such as Katherine Ramsland's *Forensic Science of C.S.I., The C.S.I. Effect*, and *True Stories of C.S.I.* (optional)

PROCEDURE

1. Watch an episode of a forensic science TV show. Identify the episode by name, if possible, and the date it was first broadcast. Complete the *Episode Summary Form* provided by your instructor.

2. Use the *Episode Evaluation Form* provided by your instructor (shown in Figure 1) to list all examples of contrived lab testing, sloppy or improper procedures, incorrect evidence handling, erroneous division of labor, etc., that you observe as you watch the episode. You should look for procedures and activities that are not consistent with those you have learned in this text.

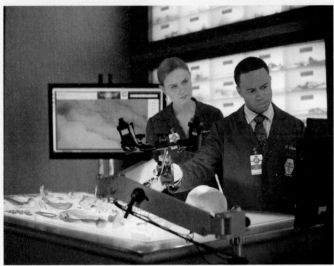

FOX Image Collection/Getty Images

3. After you have viewed the entire episode, form groups of three or four. Compare your list with those of other members of your team. Combine and consolidate your lists into one team list.

4. You may refer to your textbook, the Internet, or other reference materials to verify the correctness of your list.

5. Develop a summary of your list. This report can be in the format of a poster, PowerPoint presentation, blog, or talk show. The summary should discuss each inaccuracy your team identified and explain why you thought it was an inaccurate portrayal.

6. Present your team's summary to the class for evaluation.

Procedures

1. Print, copy, and distribute the following documents found on the IRCD, Capstone 5.
   - CP-5 *Episode Evaluation Form* (Figure 1)
   - CP-5 SH *TV Episode summary Form*

2. Working independently, students are to list on their CP-5 *Episode Evaluation Form* examples of procedures and activities that are not consistent with those they have learned in this text.

3. After students have viewed the entire episode, instruct them to form groups of three or four in which they compare and consolidate their individual lists. Allow some class time for reference checks (on computers, textbooks, etc.) of suspected contrivances. Students may find materials, such as Katherine Ramsland's *Forensic Science of C.S.I., The C.S.I. Effect,* and *True Stories of C.S.I.* very helpful. If computers or reference materials are unavailable in the classroom, assign as homework or refer students to the appropriate sections in the textbook.

4. During the next class period, have a representative from each group present the finalized list to the class for evaluation.

This same activity can be applied to popular books and magazine articles on forensics.

Teaching Tip

The CP-5 TV Episode Summary Form asks students to describe
- the crime
- the victims
- the suspects
- the securing of the crime scene
- any compromise of the evidence as a result of the processing.

Students also list examples of biological, trace, circumstantial, direct, and individual evidence.

Finally, they state and explain the most useful evidence in solving the crime.

7. If time permits, select one of the items on your team list and research advances in technology that have assisted in solving the crime.

Figure 1 *Episode Evaluation Form.*

Name of Program:			
Title of Episode:			
Date Aired:			
Time in minutes from start of episode that event occurred	**Event**	**Inconsistency with real procedure**	**How it actually is done**

DIFFERENTIATED LEARNING

Teaching Gifted Students

Have students demonstrate an improper technique, point out the error that occurred, and follow with a demonstration of the correct technique.

Forensic Dumpster Diving— What the Garbage Can Tell Us

OBJECTIVES

By the end of this project, you will be able to:

✔ Properly collect, document, and analyze evidence from garbage found at a crime scene.

✔ Analyze information derived from trash examination to describe the characteristics of a certain household, person, and/or a crime scene.

✔ Use your data to link a suspect to a crime scene.

INTRODUCTION

One of the richest sources of information about a person or household is the garbage. Items found in household garbage can help investigators of a crime scene create a profile of the inhabitant(s) as well as a timeline of events. It can help them identify the preferences and activities of suspects related to a crime.

MATERIALS: (per team of four students)

- CP-6 SH *Trash Recording Form*
- CP-6 SH *Household Profile Form*
- Bag of trash
- Gloves
- Hand lenses
- Forceps

CAPSTONE PROJECTS **637**

Background

This project will require one 40-minute class period for student teams to complete. It provides practice in examining and labeling trash "evidence." Described in the scenario.

Teaching Tip

Refer to the *Capstone Project 6 Instructor Notes* found on the IRCD, Capstone 6.

Teaching Tip

Before starting this activity, engage the class in a brainstorming activity about what might be learned from someone by analyzing his or her trash?

DIFFERENTIATED LEARNING

Teaching Gifted Students
Encourage motivated students to explore the legal issues behind examining someone's trash or recycling without their knowledge. Is it legal if the trash is on their property? At curbside on trash day? In a public trash can?

Safety Precautions

Make sure all students wear gloves when handling trash.

Procedures

1. You will need to provide student teams with a bag of trash. The bag should include items such as
   - Grocery and gas receipts
   - Cigarette butts
   - Fast food wrappers
   - Candy wrappers
   - Ketchup, mustard, and other condiment packages
   - Water bottles
   - Beverage cans
   - Envelopes from various sources (remove contents with names and use envelopes only)
   - Magazines (covers only)
   - Personal care products and medication bottles
   - Materials related to hobbies or work
   - Movie, sports, or concert tickets
   - Broken toys

   Check your own trash for ideas!

2. Print, copy, and distribute the following documents found on the IRCD, Capstone 6. Each team will need a copy of both documents for each scenario.
   - CP-6 SH *Trash Recording Form* (Figure 1)
   - CP-6 SH *Household Profile Form* (Figure 2)

- Glass container with lid
- Plastic bags
- Butcher paper or brown paper bag
- Paper towels
- Repackaging evidence containers
- Marking pens
- Pencils
- Evidence labels
- Digital camera
- Ruler
- Tape

SAFETY PRECAUTIONS

Wear gloves when handling trash.

Introduction

In this part of the project, you will develop profiles of members of a household through examination of their trash. All evidence should be photographed and properly bagged according to the rules of evidence collection discussed in Chapter 2.

PROCEDURE

1. Assign the roles of trash handler, recorder, examiner, and photographer to members of the team.
2. Open the bag of trash carefully and separate contents onto clean pieces of butcher paper or brown paper bags. Classify contents into categories, such as food, prints or impressions, written or typed material, hair, fibers, etc.
3. Separate any wet trash onto clean paper towels for drying and label toweling in pencil. Damp or wet items should be allowed to air dry and then bagged in a brown paper bag. (If DNA is to be later extracted, this may preserve it.) Liquid or semi-solid items can be sealed in plastic or glass containers. Dry items can be packaged in plastic bags.
4. Examine the trash and record your findings on the *Trash Recording Form* provided by your instructor (see Figure 1).

Figure 1 *Trash Recording Form.*

Case No.:				
Location:				
Date:				

Evidence Item No.	Description	Category	Name of Collector	Identifying Information

5. As a group, determine what trash should be photographed and labeled as evidence. Include a ruler in the photo to provide scale.
6. Decide which items are significant, or relevant, in developing a profile for household members.
7. Separately bag and correctly label all items that are considered evidence.
8. Complete the *Household Profile Form* provided by your instructor (see Figure 2 on the next page).

Further Study

1. Write a short story describing a crime that was solved, in part, with trash evidence.
2. Research the use of trash as evidence in court cases. Is trash evidence admissible in a trial in your state? Cite specific court rulings.

3. Make sure each team assigns the roles of trash handler, recorder, examiner, and photographer to members of the team. Explain that all significant evidence should be individually bagged and tagged as evidence. Students should separate any wet trash items to air dry on clean, separate paper toweling during examination. Damp or wet items should be bagged in brown paper bags. The recorder is responsible for entering information on the CP-6 SH *Trash Recording Form*. Once the team members have examined the trash and recorded their information, they should complete the CP-6 SH *Household Profile Form*.

Teaching Tip

The activity continues on the next page.

Be sure to remove the names, account numbers, etc., from your collection of garbage to protect personal identity.

Several weeks prior to this activity, start collecting items to be used from friends, family, etc. You should try to obtain trash from a variety of resources.

Review proper handling and evidence labeling from Chapter 2.

Figure 2 *Household Profile Form.*

Name of Occupant(s):		
Address:		
Name(s) of Evidence Collector(s):		
Date of Collection:		Time of Collection:

Category	Evidence
1. Number of household members	
2. Gender of each household member	
3. Age of each household member	
4. Relationship of household members	
5. Income level	
6. Owner of property	
7. Marital status	
8. Level of education	
9. Interests or hobbies	
10. Head of household (who pays the bills)	

Inferences: political persuasions, schools, organizations, favorite foods and/or beverages, frugal vs. wasteful, state of health, religious affiliations, favorite restaurant(s), supermarket(s), gas station(s), pharmacy, health club, and stores

Generalization	Evidence

Further Study

1. Students are asked to write a summary of the information that can be learned from a study of trash. Answers will vary, but most students should note that a good profile of household members can be obtained by studying trash.

2. Students are to research the use of trash as evidence in court cases and to find out if trash evidence is admissible in a trial in your state. This varies by state. If it is admissible in your state, make sure students cite specific court rulings.

PROJECT 7

Forensic Science Career Exploration

By the end of this project, you will be able to:

✔ Identify different types of careers in forensic science.

✔ Discuss the education requirements, job skills, job training, salary ranges, etc., of different careers in forensic science.

INTRODUCTION

In this project, you explore various career opportunities in forensic science. Research a career in forensic science and present your findings to the class.

MATERIALS

- Computer with Internet access (optional)
- CP-7 SH *Careers in Forensic Science Signup Form*
- CP-7 SH *Career Research Questions* list

PROCEDURE

1. In small groups, brainstorm careers related to forensic science and record your list. To help you get started, review the following list of career categories in forensic science.
   - Medicine and pathology
   - Physics and engineering
   - Chemistry and toxicology

Background

The goal of this project is to expose students to the many different occupations in the field of forensic science. When they have completed their research, student teams will prepare presentations on selected careers to share with the class.

Teaching Tip

Refer to the *Capstone Project 7 Instructor Notes* found on the IRCD, Capstone 7.

Procedures

1. Student groups will brainstorm a list of different types of careers. Allow groups sufficient time to develop a comprehensive list. Then, print, copy, and distribute the document CP-7 SH *Careers in Forensic Science Sign-up Form* on the IRCD, Capstone 7. Student groups should list careers in addition to those on the signup sheet in the space provided at the bottom of the form.

2. In Procedure Step 3 of this project, students compose a list of questions they will research to provide them with a better understanding of the forensic career. Make sure all students in each group contribute to the list of questions.

When student groups have completed their brainstorming, provide them with the CP-7 SH *Career Research Questions* list on the IRCD, Capstone 7. This list is intended to *supplement* the career questions each team generates on its own.

- Photographer or videographer
- Police science
- Psychiatry and behavioral science
- Document analysis and fraud
- Forensic specialties (e.g., forensic anthropology, blood-spatter, DNA, firearms)

Think about the characters from your favorite forensic TV programs, movies, or novels, and the jobs they hold. Recall articles you've read in magazines and newspapers about crime-scene investigations to help remind you of the many and diverse forensic careers.

Review the career profiles found at the end of each chapter. Refer to Figure 1 below, *Careers in Forensics*, for a list of the individuals and their careers along with their chapter and page references.

2. After brainstorming careers, refer to the *Careers in Forensic Science Signup Form* provided by your instructor. Compare your group's list with the careers listed in the table. If your team identified other forensic careers, add them to the bottom of the list on the form.

Figure 1 *Careers in Forensics.*

Career	Chapter	Page	Specialist Cited
Forensic Psychologist	1	12	Paul Ekman
Crime-Scene Investigator	2	35	Carl Williams
Chemical Researcher	3	63	William J. Walsh
Fiber Analyst	4	92	Irene Good
Forensic Palynologist	5	133	Dr. Lynne Milne
Art Conservator	6	171	Peter Paul Biro
DNA Expert	7	207	Kary Banks Mullis
Bloodstain Pattern Analyst	8	246	T. Paulette Sutton
Pharmacologist	9	296	Dr. Don Catlin
Document Examiner	10	330	Lloyd Cunningham
Forensic Entomologist	11	366	Dr. Neal Haskell
Forensic Pathologist	12	401	Dr. Michael Baden
Forensic Geologist	13	429	None cited
Forensic Anthropologist	14	463	Clyde Snow
Criminalist	15	497	David Green
Medical Examiner	16	532	Dr. Thomas Noguchi
Tool-Mark Expert	17	570	Dr. David P. Baldwin
Firearms Examiner	18	601	Gregory Klees

3. With your group, brainstorm questions you would like to research about a career in forensic science. Your research should include the following:

- Nature of the work
- Work environment
- Types of skills and knowledge needed to be successful
- Education and training requirements
- Salary and benefits
- Employment outlook
- Opportunities for advancement
- Benefits and drawbacks of working in this career
- Other skills and interests that would be useful in this career
- Other related jobs in this field

4. As directed by your instructor, each team selects a specific career from the *Careers in Forensic Science Signup Form.*

5. Use the list of questions your team developed in Step 3, along with the *Career Research Questions* provided by your instructor, to research the selected forensics career.

6. Plan how your team will research the information. Refer to the following Websites to aid in your research.

- **American Academy of Forensic Sciences:** *http://www.aafs.org*

  The American Academy of Forensic Sciences is a multidisciplinary professional organization that provides leadership to advance science and its application to the legal system. The objectives of the Academy are to promote education, foster research, improve practice, and encourage collaboration in the forensic sciences.

- **Crime-Scene Investigator Network:** *http://www.crime-scene-investigator .net* and *http://www.crime-scene-investigator.net/becomeone.html*

  These sites include guidelines, videos, articles, books, college training sites, job postings, and more regarding careers in forensics.

- **Salary Calculator:** *http://www.cbsalary.com/salary-calculator.aspx*

  You can research salary information on specific jobs in a selected career. After you enter information in the search box, you may see a page that advertises educational opportunities. Click the "No, thank you" link to exit the page and display the salary information page.

- **Bureau of Labor Statistics:** *http://www.bls.gov/OCO*

  The *Occupational Outlook Handbook* published by the Bureau of Labor Statistics provides information on hundreds of different jobs in the U.S. labor market. You can find information on education and training requirements, earnings, job prospects, what workers do, and working conditions.

3. Students should pair up with a classmate from their group to complete the rest of the project. For Step 4, student pairs select the career they would like to explore from the CP-7 SH *Careers in Forensic Science Sign-up Form*. Or, assign student pairs a career so that each team researches a different career. Since they will create a presentation on their selected career to share with the class, students will benefit more from this project if each team researches a different career.

4. Student teams use the questions they composed in Step 3 as well as the CP-7 SH *Career Research Questions* to investigate and gather information on their selected career. Be sure to specify exactly what you expect students to gather *at a minimum* in their research.

5. Each team will present its career research to the class. Discuss the different presentational formats suggested in Procedure Step 7. With mixed classes, it is important to offer alternative types of assessment opportunities. Encourage students to suggest a new format for their presentation. This not only stimulates creativity but also provides a more interesting set of presentations for the class to view.

In addition to the *Occupational Outlook Handbook*, the Bureau of Labor Statistics offers other sources of career information that you might find useful. The *Occupational Outlook Quarterly* is a career guidance magazine that includes articles about specific occupations and industries, types of training and education, and methods for exploring careers and finding jobs. This magazine also previews occupations that will be added to the next edition of the *Handbook*, summarizes current labor market research, and presents profiles of unusual careers.

The *Career Guide to Industries* provides career guidance information from an industry perspective. It describes employment opportunities and prospects in many industries, along with a description of the industry, key occupations in the industry, and training requirements for these occupations.

For the most detailed employment projections, visit the Employment Projections Website at *http://www.bls.gov/emp/*. This site includes data tables, searchable databases, and technical publications about the projections.

For comprehensive data on employment and earnings by occupation, visit the Occupational Employment Statistics (OES) Survey home page at *http://www.bls.gov/oes/*. The OES Survey provides earnings and employment data for more than 800 occupations and shows how earnings and employment vary by geographic area and industry. For comprehensive data on earnings, hours, and employment by industry, see the Current Employment Statistics (CES) Survey home page at *http://www.bls.gov/ces/*.

To find employment and earnings data related to demographic variables—such as age, sex, race, and educational attainment—visit the Current Population Survey home page at *http://www.bls.gov/cps/*.

- *Careers in Forensics* **End-of-Chapter Feature**

  As suggested, you might also review the profiles provided in the *Careers in Forensics* feature at the end of each chapter in this text. Refer to Figure 1 for a listing of the profiles.

- **Other Resources**

  In addition to the resources listed, you might consider conducting informational interviews with employers and those working in the field you are researching. Contact guidance and career counselors as well as post-secondary institutions that offer programs in the career you've selected. Professional societies, trade groups, and labor unions might also be helpful resources.

7. Each team presents its research to the class. Select one of the following formats for presenting your work (or use a different format with your instructor's approval):

- Slide show
- Video
- Animation
- Pamphlet
- Poster
- Role-playing (i.e., job interviewer and interviewee)
- Creative writing, such as a short story
- Blog

Be sure to correctly cite and list all references in a bibliography.

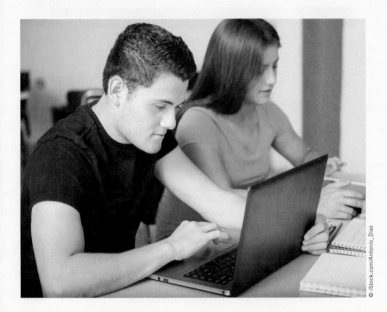

© iStock.com/Antonio_Diaz

Background

In this project, students work in teams to set up a mock crime scene. The number and size of teams will depend on the size of your class and the physical space in which students can work. Students should use the knowledge gained throughout this course to set up the crime scene, to secure and examine the crime scene, and to properly collect evidence.

PROJECT 8

Mock Crime-Scene Development and Processing

OBJECTIVES

By the end of this project, you will be able to:

✔ Create a mock crime scene for others to investigate.

✔ Work with a team to investigate a mock crime scene.

✔ Solve a crime using the evidence obtained from a mock crime scene.

INTRODUCTION

Solving a crime begins with the crime scene. You learned in Chapter 2 how a crime scene is photographed and processed, and how evidence is labeled, collected, and used to link a suspect to a crime. In this project, you will set up a mock crime scene. Your crime scene could be a model of an actual crime scene or you can create your own crime-scene scenario.

Keep the following in mind as you set up your crime scene:

1. Keep the crime scene simple.
2. Do not try to include too many different types of evidence.
3. Either create a scenario or model an actual case.
4. Set up your crime scene in an area that will not be disturbed for several days.

Teaching Tip
Refer to the *Capstone Project 8 Instructor Notes* found on the IRCD, Capstone 8.

You will also be a member of a team investigating a mock crime scene. Keep the following in mind as your team investigates the scene:

1. Follow the Seven Ss of crime-scene investigation discussed in Chapter 2.
2. Assign team members different roles, such as first responder, recorder, photographer, etc.
3. Photograph the crime scene, triangulate and document locations where evidence is found, and package and process all evidence properly while maintaining the proper chain of custody.

MATERIALS

Materials you need depend on the evidence at your crime scene. Evidence will vary according to the type of scenario you develop. Suggestions for evidence to include at your crime scene are in Figure 1 in the Procedure section.

- Evidence bags
- Compass
- Forceps
- Gloves
- Bunny suit (optional)
- Microscope
- Slides
- Rulers, meter sticks, measuring tape
- Sketch pads
- Black permanent labeling pen
- Pencils
- Graph paper
- Digital camera
- Crime-scene tape
- CP-8 SH Crime-Scene Investigator checklists
- CP-8 SH *Evidence Inventory Label*
- CP-8 SH *Evidence Marker*
- CP-8 SH *Site and Evidence Form*

Procedures

1. Print, copy, and distribute the following documents found on the IRCD, Capstone 8.
   - CP-8 SH *Site and Evidence Form*
   - CP-8 SH *Evidence Inventory Label*
   - CP-8 SH *Evidence Markers*
   - CP-8 SH *Evidence Collector*
   - CP-8 SH *First Responder*
   - CP-8 SH *Photographer*
   - CP-8 SH *Recorder*
   - CP-8 SH *Sketch Artist*

2. Students may develop a crime scene after completing an individual chapter using only the evidence discussed in that chapter. Or the crime scene can be developed using a variety of evidence types discussed in several chapters.

3. Student teams will need a space, such as a closet or unused corner of a room, that will not be disturbed by others for the duration of the scene development and processing. Note that, ideally, each team will have the opportunity to set up a mock crime scene *and* to investigate and process a mock crime scene.

4. Make sure the investigating teams assign different roles before they start processing the crime scene.

5. Encourage students to use the evidence they collected for the Personal Evidence Portfolio they assembled in Capstone Project 2.

PROCEDURE

Part 1: Setting Up the Crime Scene

Working in teams, follow these steps:

1. Choose an authentic crime scene to duplicate or create your own.

2. Select an area where your crime scene can be set up and left undisturbed for several days. This could be as small as a closet, but it must be large enough to accommodate four people who will be processing the crime scene. Measurements can be taken from nearby permanent objects (windows, doors, etc.) that can be used to triangulate the location of discovered evidence.

3. Determine how many types of evidence you will use. You may use evidence that you collected for the personal evidence portfolio you created in Capstone Project 2. Depending on the time available, you might include only one type of evidence or you can create a more involved crime scene with a variety of types of evidence. Forms of evidence that you may include in your crime scene are listed in Figure 1.

4. Place evidence in a location that is consistent with the crime. If referencing an actual crime scene, use photographs if available.

Figure 1 *Suggested Forms of Evidence*

Trace	DNA	Impressions	Blood	Forensic Entomology and Death	Weapons	Ballistics	Occupation-Related	Other
– Hair (human or animal)	– Hair	– Bite marks in sandwich or cheese	– Blood spatter	– Insect eggs, larva, or pupa	– Knife	– Cartridge casing	– Grease, oil (mechanic)	– Candy wrapper
– Fibers and/or textiles	– Blood	– Footprints	– Bloody bandage or shirt	– Evidence from livor mortis, rigor mortis, or algor mortis	– Screwdriver	– Bullet holes in wall or window	– Sugar, flour (baker)	– Cigarette wrapper
– Pollen	– Soda can or cigarette butt with saliva	– Tire impressions		– Reports from coroner, medical examiner, or toxicologist	– Hammer	– Gun	– Sawdust (carpenter)	– Button
– Dandruff		– Handprints			– Bloody rock	– Gunshot residue on surface	– Grass cuttings (landscaper)	– Ladder
– Makeup		– Fingerprints					– Manure (farmer)	– Flashlight
– Soil, mud, or sand		– Tool marks					– Beach sand (lifeguard)	– Open soda can
– Sawdust							– Uniform articles (firefighter, military, hospital personnel)	– Fast food wrapper
– Glass fragments								– Movie stub
								– Store receipts
								– Written notes

Part 2: Processing the Crime Scene

Working in teams, follow these steps:

1. Review the procedures in Chapter 2 for processing a crime scene.

2. Assign roles to members of the team processing the scene. These include first responder, recorder, photographer, artist, and evidence collector. You may have more than one evidence collector.

3. Make sure members of the team have copies of the appropriate checklists. For example, the member assigned to be first responder should have the *First Responder's Checklist*; the member assigned to be the photographer should have the *Photographer's Checklist*, etc. Your instructor will provide these checklists.

4. Sketch the crime scene. Include all objects (measured from two immovable landmarks; see Chapter 2); the position of the body, if there is one; and which side of the scene represents the direction north. Refer to page 25 for more information on sketching a crime scene.

Jochen Tack/Alamy

5. Follow the rules of evidence collection, documentation, and handling outlined in Chapter 2. Evidence should be properly labeled and the chain of custody maintained using the *Evidence Inventory Label* forms provided by your instructor.

6. The *Site and Evidence Form* should be completed as the scene is being processed. Information for the site should include:
   - Case number
   - Date
   - Time
   - Name of agency
   - Name of investigator
   - Location of scene
   - General description of the scene
   - Habitat assessment

7. For each item collected as evidence at the scene, complete the *Evidence Collection Form* provided by your instructor, listing:
   - Item number
   - Description
   - Distance and direction, including
     (a) Compass direction
     (b) Distance to Subdatum Point 1
     (c) Distance to Subdatum Point 2
   - Disposition of the evidence

8. Prioritize the analysis of evidence and determine who will receive and process the evidence.

9. Team members assigned to process evidence should document any lab results and analyses.

10. Collaborate with other team investigators and review the evidence. Try to recreate the crime based on the evidence.

11. Generate a final report that is consistent with the evidence. Include crime-scene photos, sketches, and any written reports or documents. All evidence should be available for examination in containers that are properly labeled and show a complete chain of custody. The final report can be written or in the form of a slide show.

Further Research and Extensions

Ask a crime-scene investigator to visit your classroom to describe actual crime scenes.

Invite a forensics conservation officer to describe working with wildlife and environmental crime issues.

DIFFERENTIATED LEARNING

Teaching Gifted Students
- Have students interview a local lawyer or judge about cases where evidence was not used because it was improperly handled or labeled, or the chain of custody was not maintained.
- Another activity for gifted students is to have them use a computer program to diagram a final version of their crime scene.

PROJECT 9

How to Read Calipers

Background

Reading calipers is a useful skill for many science classes and careers, but it is not necessarily intuitive. In Activity 17-2, Hammers and Hammer Impressions, students' caliper-reading skills are put to the test. Consider using this Capstone to prepare them for that activity or for extra practice after that activity.

Safety Precautions

There are no safety concerns with this activity.

Teaching Tip

You may also photograph various caliper readings and project the images, allowing students to practice reading measurements in that way.

OBJECTIVE

By the end of this project, you will be able to:

✔ Use calipers to obtain inside or outside measurement readings accurate to 0.1 mm.

INTRODUCTION

Taking measurements to the nearest 0.1 mm with the unaided eye is difficult. However, with the aid of calipers and a little practice, you'll be able to obtain measurements with an accuracy of 0.1 mm easily.

BACKGROUND

Calipers are designed so that either an inside measurement (such as a nasal opening) or an outside measurement (such as the length and width of a blood droplet) can be easily measured. Errors in measurement are made when you use the inside scale to measure an outside distance or vice versa. When reading calipers, using a hand lens helps. If you have a cell phone or computer tablet, taking a photo and enlarging it onscreen also helps.

MATERIALS: (per group of two students)

- CP-9 SH *How to Read Calipers*
- Calipers with a vernier scale accurate to 0.1 mm
- Hand lens or projecting device
- Computer tablet, cell phone, or digital camera (optional)

SAFETY

There are no safety concerns with this activity.

Procedures

1. Print, copy, and distribute CP-9 SH *How to Read Calipers*, found on the IRCD, Capstone 9. Answers to the SH activity are found on the CP-9 TN *How to Read Calipers* on the IRCD, Capstone 9.

2. Students should work in groups of two.

3. Point out the outside and inside scales of the calipers to students before they begin their group work. Encourage them to gently slide the jaw back and forth to feel how it works. Explain the difference between the scales (whole millimeters and tenths of millimeters).

Teaching Tip

Suggest that students with vision problems take a digital photo of the calipers with their phones or tablets and enlarge the images onscreen.

Teaching Tip

The inside scale might be used to measure the diameter of a pipe or the inside of a nasal cavity.

PROCEDURE

1. Refer to the calipers in Figure 1. Notice there is an *outside* scale located on the top of the calipers and an *inside* scale at the bottom of the calipers. (See the red arrows in Figure 1.) Be sure you read the correct scale, inside or outside, for whatever you are measuring. Slide the jaw back and forth to see how the scales move.

Figure 1 *Calipers.*

2. For the first example, you will make a measurement requiring the *outside* scale, as if you were measuring the diameter of a small bone. To determine the number of *whole millimeters*, locate the zero mark on the top scale (green arrow). The zero falls between 12 and 13 millimeters on the scale below it. Therefore, the measurement is a bit more than 12 mm.

3. In the next steps, you will learn how to read calipers to the nearest 0.1 mm. To determine the measurement to the nearest 0.1 mm using the outside scale, refer to the top scale in Figure 2. It is called a *vernier* scale. The units are between 0 and 1.0. Find a line on this top scale that is *aligned directly above a vertical line on the scale below it* (red arrows). The line you are looking for is at 0.3, which means 0.3 mm. By reading the calipers using the outside scale, you see a measurement of 12 mm + 0.3 mm = 12.3 mm.

Figure 2 *Vernier scale of calipers.*

4. To take a measurement such as the opening of the *inside* of a nasal cavity on a skull (Figure 3), read the calipers in a similar manner, except use the *inside* scale of the calipers.

Figure 3 *Model of human skull.*

© 2016 Cengage Learning®

(Project continued next page)

4. Have hand lenses and a camera (or smartphone or computer tablet with high-quality photographic capabilities) available for students who need help reading the calipers.

Teaching Tip

Project enlarged images of caliper readings.

- Distinguish between the inside and outside scales and when you might use each
- Once you determine which scale to read, have students determine the number of whole mm
- Show students on the projected image how to obtain the reading to the nearest 0.1 mm

Explore

Encourage students to measure the inside and outside diameters of objects around the classroom and compare their results with other students.

5. Refer to Figure 4 below.

   The inside and outside scales are indicated by the blue arrows.

Figure 4 *Vernier scale for inside measurement.*

6. To determine the number of whole millimeters in Figure 4, locate the zero mark on the bottom scale. (Refer to the green arrow.) This measurement is a bit more than 31 mm.

7. To determine the measurement to the nearest 0.1 mm, find a line on the bottom scale (from 0 to 1.0) that is in perfect alignment with a line above it. The line you are looking for is at 0.7, which means 0.7 mm (see red arrow). So the inside caliper reading is 31 mm + 0.7 mm = 31.7 mm.

8. Refer to the photos of the calipers in *CP-9 SH Reading Calipers*, which has been provided by your instructor. If needed, use a magnifying lens to help read the calipers. Another way to make a caliper reading easier to see is to take a digital photo and enlarge it onscreen. It will be much easier to see the alignment of the lines in the enlargement.

9. Determine the measurements of each of the caliper settings to the nearest 0.1 mm, and record the answer on *CP-9 SH*.

Further Research

Allow students to extend the activity, and other activities throughout the text, by using the calipers in the following ways:

• Measure a blood droplet and calculate the angle of impact. (Ch. 8 activities)
• Measure the diameter of a cartridge casing. (Ch. 18)
• Measure the height and spacing of capital letters in a writing sample. (Ch. 10)
• Measure the width of the dental impressions you made. (Ch. 16)

PROJECT 10

Gravesite Excavation

OBJECTIVES

By the end of this project, you will be able to:

✔ Apply information learned in previous chapters to locate a recent gravesite.

✔ Establish a crime-scene perimeter around the gravesite.

✔ Apply correct procedures for documenting and photographing the crime scene, collecting evidence from the crime scene, and storing the evidence.

✔ Using datum and subdatum points, establish and mark with stakes the collecting area around the gravesite.

✔ Gradually sift through the soil to locate, photograph, document, and package all evidence from the gravesite.

✔ Complete the *Site and Evidence Form* for the crime scene

✔ Create a profile of who was buried in that gravesite based on the biological and physical evidence found in the gravesite.

INTRODUCTION

Police received a telephone tip regarding the location of a missing person. The caller stated that the body was buried in large wooded area. How do the police know where to search for this recent gravesite in such a large location? What environmental and botanical clues can help to narrow the search area? Once the recent gravesite is located, how do they set up the collection site and how is the evidence recorded? Answers to these questions can be found in the sections listed below. Review the sections before starting this activity.

- Chapter 5, How Forensic Botany Is Used to Solve Cases
- Chapter 13, Finding Gravesites
- Chapter 2, Securing and Collecting Evidence

Background

Have students review the sections listed in the Introduction. Discuss how recent gravesites can be located using both botanical and physical clues. Review with students how to set up a collection site using both datum and subdatum points. Print, copy, and distribute the CP-10 SH shown in the Materials list from the the IRCD, Capstone 10.

Safety Precautions

It is important that evidence is handled and labeled properly to avoid any contamination. Safety guidelines for handling evidence should be followed for each type of evidence. Guidelines are discussed in Chapter 2.

Teaching Tip

Appoint one student as the site manager for each gravesite. This student assigns specific roles to other students and distributes the appropriate Crime-Scene Investigator checklists to each student.

Teaching Tip

Planted evidence could include items from the list below. Place the evidence 2–12 inches below the surface.

- Artificial bones or written description of the bones if bones are not available
- Hair (human or animal)
- (Artificial) blood or blood-soaked clothing
- Pollen
- Botanical evidence such as fruits, nuts, seeds, leaves, or roots
- Spent cartridges
- Fibers or clothing
- Insect evidence
- Buttons
- Shoes
- Jewelry
- Personal forms of ID found in wallets or pockets
- Trace evidence that could provide clues to one's occupation
- Sports equipment
- Toys
- Receipts or tickets showing dates
- Letters, wills, or other documents
- Evidence of restraints: handcuffs, adhesive tape across mouth, feet tied
- Evidence of injuries

Teaching Tip

Prepare reports that students may access after excavating their gravesite. Examples: autopsy, forensic entomology, DNA analysis, toxicology.

MATERIALS: (for each team of four students)

- CP-10 SH *Evidence Marker*
- CP-10 SH *Site and Evidence Form*
- CP-10 SH *Evidence Inv Label*
- CP-10 SH Crime-Scene Investigator checklists
- Trowels
- Old paintbrushes and old toothbrushes
- String
- Compass
- 4 stakes
- Hammer (to pound stakes into the ground)
- Crime-scene tape
- Tape measure
- Sifters
- Digital camera
- Identification (numbered) flags or evidence markers
- Evidence containers with evidence inventory labels
- Pencil
- Pails or coffee cans
- Boxes and brown paper bags (for evidence containers)
- Gloves and protective gear
- Metal detector (optional)

PROCEDURE

In this Capstone project, your team will search for a recent gravesite and excavate the gravesite applying proper forensic procedures. All crime-scene information and evidence should be photographed and documented using the *Site and Evidence Form*. You will apply information from your textbook to develop a profile of the person who is buried in the gravesite, based on the biological and physical evidence recovered from the gravesite.

Part A

Select a student to be the site manager. That person will limit the number of investigators working at the gravesite and he or she will secure the area. The site manager assigns the roles of photographer, recorder, evidence collector, and artist to those working the crime scene. (Refer to the individual checklists for the duties of each of those persons.)

1. The first decision to be made by the site manager is to determine the extent of the crime-scene (work) area. The actual gravesite should be near the center of the larger work area where investigators will process evidence. Twenty feet in all directions from the gravesite will provide a reasonable working area and crime-scene tape should be placed approximately at that distance.

2. The *Site and Evidence Form* provided by your instructor is completed by the recorder and evidence collectors as the crime scene is processed.

3. The photographer takes photos of the crime scene both close up and at a distance, facing north, south, east, and west. The recorder keeps a record of all photos that are taken by the photographer.

4. The crime-scene sketch artist prepares a rough sketch of the crime scene and marks the location of any evidence, indicating north and locations from the datum and subdatum sites.

5. The surface of the gravesite is documented and photographed to record its general appearance, type of vegetation, and any disturbances. The plants surrounding the gravesite are also documented and photographed.

6. Evidence collectors gather samples of the plant life (if any) that are present on the top of the gravesite as well as samples of the plants surrounding the collection area. The recorder keeps a record of all evidence in the *Site and Evidence Form*.

7. Mapping an outdoor crime scene is described in Chapter 2. The edge of the gravesite can often be determined by the color difference or soil contour where undisturbed soil meets a newly dug area. A square or rectangular staked perimeter should be established about a foot outside the edge of the disturbed soil in the undisturbed soil around the gravesite. The corners should be marked with reference to the directions northwest, southwest, northeast, and southeast. String should be secured around the stakes to outline the area. Distance measurements for evidence locations are the perpendicular distances from two adjacent sides of the collection site. For example, an object might be found 8 inches from the northeast string and 5 inches from the northwest string. Depth of the evidence should also be recorded in *Site and Evidence Form*. As the plant evidence is removed, examine the surface soil for the presence of any trace evidence. Soil samples should also be photographed, documented, and collected.

8. Remember that all evidence is first photographed in place in the gravesite and then photographed again after it has been removed from the site. Each form of evidence is separately collected, labeled, and properly packaged.

Procedures

1. Print, copy, and distribute the following documents found on the IRCD, Capstone 10:
   - CP-10 SH *Evidence Marker*
   - CP-10 SH *Evidence Inventory Label*
   - CP-10 SH *Site and Evidence Form*
   - CP-10 SH *Evidence Collector*
   - CP-10 *Artist*
   - CP-10 *First Responder*
   - CP-10 *Photographer*
   - CP-10 *Recorder*

2. Students should work in groups of four. The instructor establishes four dig sites with different forms of evidence to be investigated by the four student teams.

3. You may prefer to have the students work in teams of four to create four gravesites using different types of evidence. Student teams then excavate and analyze another group's gravesite and its planted evidence. Challenge the teams to properly excavate the gravesite and recover and properly document all evidence. Students should prepare a profile of the person found in the grave based on both biological and physical evidence.

This Capstone Activity is a way to integrate information from many different chapters. It requires students to apply knowledge of

- locating gravesites based on botanical and soil evidence
- mapping a collection site
- documenting, photographing, and storing different types of evidence
- creating a biological profile of a person based on evidence
- estimating PMI

9. Soil removal should progress slowly, layer by layer. Use trowels and brushes to expose the evidence. Do not use a shovel. Remove approximately 1 inch of soil from the entire gravesite area before digging deeper.

10. Carefully place the removed soil in buckets. Each bucket of soil needs to be sifted to recover smaller pieces of evidence such as teeth, small bones, jewelry, and spent cartridge casings. Each piece of evidence found should be photographed, documented, and stored properly.

11. Continue to remove soil and sift it. Dig to a depth of at least 12 inches.

Part B: Analysis of Evidence

1. Examine and analyze all forms of biological and physical evidence. Try to find evidence that would help determine the following:
   a. Person's identity: age, sex, height, health, physical condition, and ethnic background
   b. When the body was buried
   c. Whether the person was injured prior to burial
   d. Whether the body was restrained when buried
   e. Whether the body was moved from a different location and buried in its present location

2. List additional tests that should be performed on the evidence that would provide more information.

3. Based on the physical and biological evidence found during the grave excavation, each group prepares a presentation (of their choosing) to profile this person. Evidence from the grave excavation should substantiate any claims.

DIFFERENTIATED LEARNING

To raise the level of this activity, have students prepare written reports containing additional information regarding the identity of the person found in the gravesite. Each report should contain information that would be obtained by one of the following crime-scene investigators:

- Medical examiner
- Pathologist
- Serologist
- X-ray technician
- DNA analyst
- Forensic entomologist
- Forensic geologist

Students may use this information to develop a more accurate profile of the missing person.

A

abrasion mark a mark produced when pressure is applied as a surface slides across another surface

accumulated degree hours (ADH) the number of hours at an adjusted average temperature it takes for an insect species to develop to a given stage

addiction a physical process associated with drug use whereby a person craves a drug; failure to take the drug can result in withdrawal symptoms.

agglutination clumping of cells caused by an antigen–antibody response

algor mortis cooling of the body after death

allele an alternative form of a gene

amorphous without a defined shape or form; fibers composed of a loose arrangement of polymers that are soft, elastic, and absorbent (for example, cotton); applied to a solid, it refers to having atoms that are arranged randomly instead of in a distinctive pattern

analytical skills the ability to identify a concept or problem, to isolate its component parts, to organize information for decision making, to establish criteria for evaluation, and to draw appropriate conclusions

angiosperm a flowering plant that produces seeds within a fruit

angle of impact angle at which blood strikes a target surface relative to the horizontal plane of the target surface

antibodies proteins secreted by white blood cells that attach to specific antigens

antigen substance that provokes an immune response in the body

antigen–antibody response reaction in which antibodies attach to specific antigens; causes agglutination in cross blood-type transfusions

arch a fingerprint pattern in which the ridge pattern originates from one side of the print and continues to the other side

area of convergence two-dimensional view of the intersection of lines formed by drawing a line through the main axis of at least two drops of blood that indicates the general area of the source of the blood spatter

area of origin the location of the blood source viewed in three dimensions as determined by projecting angles of impact of individual bloodstains

assemblage group of plant species in an area dominated by one species that share the same habitat requirements

autolysis the breakdown of cells as they self-digest

autopsy medical examination to determine the cause of death

B

backscatter fragments of glass left on the side of an impact

ballistics the study of a projectile in flight; includes the launch and behavior of the projectile

biological profile estimation of the deceased's sex, age, stature, and ancestry, along with diseases and injuries, as derived from analysis of skeletal remains

breech the end of the barrel attached to the firing mechanism of a firearm; where the cartridge is loaded and unloaded

bullet the projectile that is fired when a firearm is discharged

bullet-resistant ("bulletproof") glass a laminated and tempered glass composed of two layers

C

caliber the inside diameter of a firearm barrel

cartridge a case that holds a bullet, primer powder, and gunpowder

cast-off pattern blood projected onto a surface as a result of being flung from an object in motion

cause of death the injury or condition responsible for a person's death (such as heart attack, kidney failure)

chain of custody the documented and unbroken transfer of evidence

chromosome nuclear cell structure that contains DNA in humans

circumstantial evidence (indirect evidence) evidence used to imply a fact but not support it directly

class evidence material that connects an individual or thing to a certain group (see *individual evidence*)

clay the finest soil particles that can absorb and hold water

Combined DNA Index System (CODIS) the FBI's computerized criminal DNA databases as well as the software used to run these databases; includes the National DNA Index System (NDIS)

comparison microscope a compound microscope that allows the side-by-side comparison of samples, such as hair or fibers

complete metamorphosis body development in four stages: egg, larva, pupa, and adult

concentric fracture circular pattern of cracks that forms around a point of impact

controlled substance a drug or other chemical compound whose manufacture, distribution, possession, and use are regulated by the legal system

Controlled Substances Act law that established penalties for possession, use, or distribution of illegal drugs and established five schedules for classifying drugs

core a center of a loop

coroner an elected official, either a layman or physician, who certifies deaths and can order additional investigations of suspicious deaths

cortex the region of a hair located outside the medulla that contains granules of pigment

counterfeiting typically, the forging of currency; also the forging of other government-issued documents (postage stamps, for example) and production of fake name-brand products for profit

crime-scene investigation a multidisciplinary approach in which scientific and legal professionals work together to solve a crime

crime-scene reconstruction a hypothesis of the sequence of events from before the crime was committed through its commission

crop a digestive organ used for storage of food

crystalline geometrically shaped; fibers composed of polymers packed side by side, which makes them stiff and strong (for example, flax)

currency a printed document issued by a bank, guaranteeing payment to the holder on demand

cuticle the tough outer covering of a hair that is composed of overlapping scales

cutting mark a mark produced along the edge of a surface as it is cut

D

datum point a permanent, fixed point of reference used in mapping a crime scene

decomposition the breakdown of once-living matter by living organisms

deductive reasoning deriving a conclusion from the facts using a series of logical steps

delta a triangular ridge pattern

density the ratio of the mass of an object to its volume, expressed by the equation $density = \dfrac{mass}{volume}$

dependency powerful craving for a drug; dependency, unlike addiction, does not result in physical withdrawal symptoms upon discontinuation of the drug

depressant a substance that decreases or inhibits the nervous system, reducing alertness

diaphysis the shaft of a bone

direct evidence evidence that (if authentic) supports an alleged fact of a case

direct transfer the passing of evidence, such as a fiber, from victim to suspect or vice versa

DNA fingerprint (profile) pattern of DNA fragments obtained by analyzing a person's unique sequences of noncoding DNA

document analysis the examination of questioned documents with known material using a variety of criteria, such as authenticity, alterations, erasures, and obliterations

document expert a person who scientifically analyzes handwritten, typewritten, photocopied, and computer-generated documents and their materials for authenticity

E

electrophoresis a method of separating molecules, such as DNA, according to size

entomology study of insects and related arthropods

epiphysis the unattached end of a bone that eventually becomes fused with the bone shaft

exemplar a standard document of known origin and authorship used in handwriting analysis for comparison to documents of unknown authorship (questioned documents)

exon portion of gene that is expressed

eyewitness a person who has seen someone or something related to a crime and can communicate his or her observations

F

fact a statement or information that can be verified

fiber the smallest indivisible unit of a textile; it must be at least 100 times longer than wide

fingerprint an impression left on any surface that consists of patterns made by the ridges on a finger

firearm a portable gun that uses a confined propellant to expel a projectile out of a barrel

first responder the first safety official to arrive at a crime scene

forensic relating to the application of scientific knowledge to legal questions

forensic anthropology the use of skeletal anatomy to identify remains for legal purposes

forensic botany the application of plant science to crime-scene analysis for use in the resolution of legal cases

forensic entomology application of entomology to civil and criminal legal cases

forensic palynology the use of pollen and spore evidence to help solve criminal cases

forgery the making, altering, or falsifying of personal documents or other objects with the intention of deception

fraudulence (fraud) deliberate deception practiced to secure unfair or illegal financial gain

G

gas chromatography a method of separating chemicals to establish their quantities

gene segment of DNA that codes for a trait

genome all the DNA found in human cells

geology the study of soil and rocks

glass a hard, transparent, amorphous, brittle solid made by heating a mixture of silica and other materials

groove (of a tire) a depression in the tread

growth plate (epiphyseal plate) area of cartilage between the shaft and cap of an immature bone responsible for the lengthening of bone

grub wormlike beetle larva

gunshot residue (GSR) soot and particles of unburned gunpowder deposited on a person who discharges a firearm; may also be found on close-range victims and adjacent surfaces

gymnosperm a plant with "naked" seeds that are not enclosed in a protective organ (fruit); most are evergreens

H

hair follicle the actively growing base of a hair that contains DNA and living cells

hair shaft part of the hair above the follicle; contains mitochondrial DNA

hallucinogen a drug that changes a person's perceptions and thinking during intoxication

humus material in the uppermost layer of soil made up of the decaying remains of plants and animals

I

IAFIS (Integrated Automated Fingerprint Identification System) FBI-developed national database of more than 76 million criminal fingerprints and criminal histories

illegal drug a drug that causes addiction, habituation, or a marked change in the consciousness, has limited or no medical use, and is listed in Schedule 1 of the U.S. Controlled Substances Act

indentation mark a mark or impression made by a tool pressed directly onto a softer surface

individual evidence a kind of evidence that identifies a particular person or thing

insect succession a predictable sequence of changing species that inhabit a decomposing body

instar each of the three different larval stages of flies in species that undergo complete metamorphosis

intron portion of a gene that is not expressed

J

joints locations where bones meet

K

karyotype picture of the paired homologous chromosomes and sex chromosomes in a cell

keratin a type of fibrous protein that makes up the majority of the cortex of a hair

L

laminated glass a double layer of glass held together by a middle layer of polyvinyl butyral (plastic); a type of safety glass used for windshields

lands and grooves the ridges (lands) and depressions (grooves) found on the inside of a firearm's barrel that are created when the firearm is manufactured

larva wormlike stage of insect development after egg

latent fingerprint a concealed fingerprint made visible through the use of powders or forensic techniques

latent impression impression requiring special techniques to be visible to the unaided eye

lead glass (crystal) glass containing lead oxide

livor mortis the pooling of the blood in tissues after death that results in a red skin color

logical reasoned from facts

loop a fingerprint pattern in which the ridge pattern flows inward and returns in the direction of the origin

M

maggot wormlike fly larva

manner of death one of five ways in which a person's death is classified (i.e., natural, accidental, suicidal, homicidal, or undetermined)

mechanism of death the specific physiological, physical, or chemical event that stops life

medical examiner a physician who performs autopsies, determines the cause and manner of death, and oversees death investigations

medulla the central core of a hair

melanin granules particles of pigment found in the cortex of a hair

mineral a naturally occurring, crystalline solid formed over time

mineral fiber a collection of mineral crystals formed into a recognizable pattern

minutiae the combination of details in the shapes and positions of ridges in fingerprints that makes each unique; also called ridge characteristics

mitochondrial DNA (mtDNA) genetic material in the mitochondria of the cytoplasm of a cell; only inherited from the mother

monomer small, repeating molecules that can link to form polymers

N

narcotic an addictive, sleep-inducing drug, often derived from opium, that acts as a central nervous system depressant and suppresses pain

natural fiber a fiber produced naturally and harvested from animal, plant, or mineral sources

normal line a line drawn perpendicular to the interface of the surfaces of two different media

nuclear DNA genetic material in the nucleus of a cell

O

observation what a person perceives using his or her senses

opinion personal belief founded on judgment rather than on direct experience or knowledge

ossification the process that replaces cartilage with bone by the deposition of minerals

osteoporosis loss of bone density that can result in an increased risk of fractures

oviposition depositing, or laying, of eggs

P

palynology the study of pollen and spores

paper bindle a folded paper used to hold trace evidence

passive drop blood drop created solely as a result of gravity

patent fingerprint a visible fingerprint that happens when fingers coated with blood, ink, or some other substance touch a surface and transfer their fingerprint to that surface

patent impression impression visible to the unaided eye

perception information received from the senses

pistil the female reproductive part of a flower where eggs are produced

pistol a handgun with a barrel and chamber that are connected

plastic fingerprint a three-dimensional fingerprint made in soft material such as clay, soap, or putty

plastic impression impression in soft material such as soil, snow, or congealing blood

poison a natural or manufactured substance that can cause severe illness or death if ingested, inhaled, or absorbed through the skin

pollen "fingerprint" (pollen profile) the number and type of pollen grains found in a geographic area at a particular time of year

pollen grain a reproductive structure that contains the male gametes of seed plants

pollination the transfer of pollen from the male part to the female part of a seed plant

polymer a substance composed of long chains of repeating molecules (monomers)

polymerase chain reaction (PCR) a method of amplifying (duplicating) minute amounts of DNA evidence for use in investigations

polymorphism region of repeating DNA within an intron that is highly variable from person to person

postmortem interval (PMI) time elapsed between a person's death and discovery of the body

primary crime scene the location where the crime took place

primer sequence of DNA added to trigger replication of a specific section of DNA

pupa a nonfeeding stage of development between larva and adult

putrefaction destruction of soft tissue by bacteria that results in the release of waste gases and fluids

Q

questioned document any signature, handwriting, typewriting, or other mark whose source or authenticity is in dispute or uncertain

R

radiating fracture pattern of cracks that move outward from a point of impact

refraction the change in the direction of light as it changes speed when moving from one substance into another

refractive index a measure of how light bends as it passes from one substance to another

restriction enzyme "molecular scissors"; a molecule that cuts a DNA molecule at a specific base sequence

restriction fragment DNA fragment that restriction enzymes create, as in preparation for gel electrophoresis

revolver a handgun with a revolving cylinder

rib (of a tire) an individual ridge of tread running around the circumference

ridge count the number of ridges between the center of a delta and the core of a loop

ridge pattern the recognizable pattern of the ridges found in the end pads of fingers that form lines on the surfaces of objects in a fingerprint. They fall into three categories: arches, loops, and whorls

rifle a long gun that has a barrel with spiral grooves and that is fired from shoulder level

rifling the spiral pattern of lands and grooves in the barrel of a firearm

rigor mortis the stiffening of the skeletal muscles after death

S

sand granules of fine rock particles

satellite smaller droplets of blood projected from larger drops of blood upon impact with a surface

secondary crime scene a location other than the primary crime scene, but that is related to the crime; where evidence is found

secondary transfer the transfer of evidence such as a fiber from a source (for example, a carpet) to a person (suspect), and then to another person (victim)

sediment soil that has settled after having been transported to a new location by water, wind, or glaciers

short tandem repeat (STR) sequence of repeating bases in noncoding regions of DNA that are used in DNA profiling

silicon dioxide (SiO$_2$) the chemical name for silica, the primary ingredient in glass

silt a type of soil whose particles are coarser than clay and finer than sand

skeletal trauma analysis the investigation of bones and the marks on them to uncover a potential cause of death

soil a mixture of minerals, water, gases, and the remains of dead organisms that covers Earth's surface

soil profile a cross section of horizontal layers, or horizons, in the soil that have distinct compositions and properties

sole the bottom of a piece of footwear

spine elongated blood streak radiating away from the center of a bloodstain

spiracles respiratory organs of insects that are used by researchers to identify a larval stage as first, second, or third instar

spore an asexual reproductive structure that can develop into an adult; found in certain protists (algae), plants, and fungi

stamen the male reproductive part of a flower consisting of the anther and filament where pollen is produced

stimulant a substance affecting the nervous system by increasing alertness, attention, and energy, as well as elevating blood pressure, heart rate, and respiration

swipe blood pattern resulting from a lateral transfer from a moving source onto another surface

synthetic fiber a fiber made from a manufactured substance such as plastic

T

tempered glass heat- or chemically treated safety glass

ten card a form used to record and preserve a person's fingerprints

textile a flexible, flat material made by interlacing yarns (or "threads")

tolerance a condition occurring with consistent use of one drug whereby a person needs more and more of the drug to produce the same effect

tool mark any impression, scratch, or abrasion made when contact occurs between a tool and another object

toxicity the degree to which a substance is poisonous or can cause illness

toxicology the study of drugs, poisons, toxins, and other substances that harm a person when used for medical, recreational, or criminal purposes

toxin a substance naturally produced by a living thing that can cause illness or death in humans

trace evidence small but measurable amounts of physical or biological material found at a crime scene

track width the distance from the center of the tread of a left tire to the center of the tread of the corresponding right tire

trajectory the flight path of a projectile

tread the part of a tire that meets the road; the pattern on the sole of footwear

triangulation a mathematical method of estimating positions of objects at a location such as a crime scene, given locations of stationary objects

turning diameter the diameter of the smallest circle that can be driven by a vehicle

W

warp a lengthwise yarn or thread in a weave

weathering formation of soil through the actions of wind and water on rock

weft a crosswise yarn or thread in a weave

wheelbase the distance from the center of the front wheel of a vehicle to the center of the rear wheel on the same side

whorl a fingerprint pattern that resembles a bull's-eye

wipe smeared blood pattern created when an object moves through blood that is not completely dried

Y

yarn (thread) fibers that have been spun together

Table of Sines

Degrees	Sine	Degrees	Sine	Degrees	Sine	Degrees	Sine
0	0.0000	27	0.4539	54	0.8090	81	0.9876
1	0.0174	28	0.4694	55	0.8191	82	0.9902
2	0.0348	29	0.4848	56	0.8290	83	0.9925
3	0.0523	30	0.5000	57	0.8386	84	0.9945
4	0.0697	31	0.5150	58	0.8480	85	0.9961
5	0.0871	32	0.5299	59	0.8571	86	0.9975
6	0.1045	33	0.5446	60	0.8660	87	0.9986
7	0.1218	34	0.5591	61	0.8746	88	0.9993
8	0.1391	35	0.5735	62	0.8829	89	0.9998
9	0.1564	36	0.5877	63	0.8910	90	1.0000
10	0.1736	37	0.6018	64	0.8987		
11	0.1908	38	0.6156	65	0.9063		
12	0.2079	39	0.6293	66	0.9135		
13	0.2249	40	0.6427	67	0.9205		
14	0.2419	41	0.6560	68	0.9271		
15	0.2588	42	0.6691	69	0.9335		
16	0.2756	43	0.6819	70	0.9396		
17	0.2923	44	0.6946	71	0.9455		
18	0.3090	45	0.7071	72	0.9510		
19	0.3255	46	0.7193	73	0.9563		
20	0.3420	47	0.7313	74	0.9612		
21	0.3583	48	0.7431	75	0.9659		
22	0.3746	49	0.7547	76	0.9702		
23	0.3907	50	0.7660	77	0.9743		
24	0.4067	51	0.7771	78	0.9781		
25	0.4226	52	0.7880	79	0.9816		
26	0.4383	53	0.7986	80	0.9848		

APPENDIX B

Table of Tangents

Degrees	Tangent
0	0.0000
1	0.0175
2	0.0349
3	0.0524
4	0.0699
5	0.0875
6	0.1051
7	0.1228
8	0.1405
9	0.1584
10	0.1763
11	0.1944
12	0.2125
13	0.2309
14	0.2493
15	0.2679
16	0.2867
17	0.3057
18	0.3249
19	0.3443
20	0.3639
21	0.3838
22	0.4040
23	0.4244
24	0.4452
25	0.4663
26	0.4877

Degrees	Tangent
27	0.5095
28	0.5317
29	0.5543
30	0.5773
31	0.6008
32	0.6248
33	0.6493
34	0.6744
35	0.7001
36	0.7265
37	0.7535
38	0.7812
39	0.8097
40	0.8390
41	0.8692
42	0.9003
43	0.9324
44	0.9656
45	1.0000
46	1.0354
47	1.0723
48	1.1106
49	1.1503
50	1.1919
51	1.2348
52	1.2799
53	1.3269

Degrees	Tangent
54	1.3762
55	1.4281
56	1.4825
57	1.5398
58	1.6003
59	1.6642
60	1.7320
61	1.8040
62	1.8807
63	1.9626
64	2.0503
65	2.1445
66	2.2460
67	2.3558
68	2.4750
69	2.6050
70	2.7474
71	2.9042
72	3.0776
73	3.2708
74	3.4874
75	3.7320
76	4.0107
77	4.3314
78	4.7046
79	5.1445
80	5.6712

Degrees	Tangent
81	6.3137
82	7.1153
83	8.1443
84	9.5143
85	11.4300
86	14.3006
87	19.0811
88	28.6362
89	57.2899

APPENDIX C

Celsius–Fahrenheit Conversion Table

°Celsius	°Fahrenheit	°Celsius	°Fahrenheit	°Celsius	°Fahrenheit	°Celsius	°Fahrenheit	°Celsius	°Fahrenheit
−40	−40	−10	14.0	20	68.0	50	122.0	80	176.0
−39	−38.2	−9	15.8	21	69.8	51	123.8	81	177.8
−38	−36.4	−8	17.6	22	71.6	52	125.6	82	179.6
−37	−34.6	−7	19.4	23	73.4	53	127.4	83	181.4
−36	−32.8	−6	21.2	24	75.2	54	129.2	84	183.2
−35	−31.0	−5	23.0	25	77.0	55	131.0	85	185.0
−34	−29.2	−4	24.8	26	78.8	56	132.8	86	186.8
−33	−27.4	−3	26.6	27	80.6	57	134.6	87	188.6
−32	−25.6	−2	28.4	28	82.4	58	136.4	88	190.4
−31	−23.8	−1	30.2	29	84.2	59	138.2	89	192.2
−30	−22.0	0	32.0	30	86.0	60	140.0	90	194.0
−29	−20.2	+1	33.8	31	87.8	61	141.8	91	195.8
−28	−18.4	2	35.6	32	89.6	62	143.6	92	197.6
−27	−16.6	3	37.4	33	91.4	63	145.4	93	199.4
−26	−14.8	4	39.2	34	93.2	64	147.2	94	201.2
−25	−13.0	5	41.0	35	95.0	65	149.0	95	203.0
−24	−11.2	6	42.8	36	96.8	66	150.8	96	204.8
−23	−9.4	7	44.6	37	98.6	67	152.6	97	206.6
−22	−7.6	8	46.4	38	100.4	68	154.4	98	208.4
−21	−5.8	9	48.2	39	102.2	69	156.2	99	210.2
−20	−4.0	10	50.0	40	104.0	70	158.0	100	212.0
−19	−2.2	11	51.8	41	105.8	71	159.8		
−18	−0.4	12	53.6	42	107.6	72	161.6		
−17	+1.4	13	55.4	43	109.4	73	163.4		
−16	3.2	14	57.2	44	111.2	74	165.2		
−15	5.0	15	59.0	45	113.0	75	167.0		
−14	6.8	16	60.8	46	114.8	76	168.8		
−13	8.6	17	62.6	47	116.6	77	170.6		
−12	10.4	18	64.4	48	118.4	78	172.4		
−11	12.2	19	66.2	49	120.2	79	174.2		

Formulas: $\quad T_c = \dfrac{5}{9}(T_f - 32) \qquad T_f = \dfrac{9}{5}T_c + 32$

In this index *f* represents entries that can be found in figures.

A

A antigens, 234
Abagnale, Frank W., 314, 322
abrasion marks, 561
accidental death, 388–389
accidental whorl, 163
accident reconstruction, 526–527
accumulated degree hours (ADH), 361
acrylic fibers, 86
acute poisoning, 287
Adams, Marshall, 158
additions, in forgery, 322
adhesion, in blood spatter, 238, 239
Advanced Fingerprint Identification Technology (AFIT), 161
African Burial Ground (National Monument), New York City, 460–461
age, estimating, 452–453, 452*f*
agglutination, 234, 236
air reconnaissance, 426
alcohol, 282, 284, 290, 292–293
alcohol, forensic toxicology and, 292–293
alcohol metabolism, 293
algae, 117–118
algor mortis, death and, 390–391
allele frequencies, STR analysis and, 200
alleles, 194, 198
American Academy of Forensic Sciences, 114, 601
American Anthropological Association, 457
American Board of Chemists, 497
American Board of Forensic Document Examiners (ABFDE), 316, 445
American Board of Forensic Entomology (ABFE), 366
American Board of Forensic Odontology (ABFO), 528
American carrion beetle, decomposition and, 359*f*
Ames Laboratory, 566, 570
ammunition, 590. *See also* ballistics; firearms
amorphous fibers, 83–84
amorphous atomic arrangement (glass), 484

amphetamines, 292
anabolic steroids, forensic toxicology and, 293
anaerobic environments, soil and, 425
anagen stage, of hair, 56
analytical skills, 9
analyzing evidence, 31–32
ancestry, determine from bones, 455–456
Anderson, Anna, 202
Anderson, Gail, 353
Andrews, Tommie Lee, 205
Andrews v. Florida, 203*f*
angiosperms, 124–125
angle, table of *sin(e),* 665
animal bones, 446
animal-dispersed pollen, 128
animal fibers, 82–83
animal hair, 57–58
animals, pollination and, 125–126
Ansell, Mary, 294
Anthony, Casey, 365
anthropology. *See* forensic anthropology
antibodies, 233
antigen-antibody response, blood and, 235–236
antigens, 234
Apps
  anthropology, 463
  counterfeit currency detector, 330
  crime-scene investigation, 35
  firearms & ballistics, 601
  SmartInsect, 366
  time of death, 401
  witnesses and, 12
arches (fingerprints), 162, 163*f*, 164*f*
area of convergence, 240*f*
area of origin, blood-spatter patterns, 241
arm hair, 55
arsenic poisoning, 62, 285, 288*f*
arson, staged crime scenes and, 32
arterial gush, blood-spatter patterns, 240*f*
arthritis, 447*f*
Art of the Steal, The (Abagnale), 314
asbestos fibers, 85, 87*f*
assemblages, 115
Association of Firearms and Tool Mark Examiners, 601
ATF (Federal Bureau of Alcohol, Tobacco, Firearms, and Explosives), 597, 601
Atlanta child murders, 34, 78

Australia, counterfeit currency in, 325
autolysis, death and, 390
automobiles, identifying via tires, 524–525
autopsy, 394–396
autosomes, 194
Avdonin, Alexander, 202

B

baby teeth, 453
Bach, Johann Sebastian, 444
Backhouse, Graham, 245
backscatter, glass, 491
bacterial spores, 127
Baldwin, David P., 570
ballistics
  activities, 604–617
  bullets, rifling and, 588, 591, 597
  caliber, of cartridge, 590–591*f*, 594
  cartridge, anatomy of, 589
  cartridges, different types of, 588*f*
  case studies, 598–600
  databases, 596–597
  defined, 586
  evidence from bullets/cartridges, 591–593
  evidence standards, 597
  gunshot residue, 592–593
  marks on spent cartridges, 592
  Minié ball, lead bullet, 586
  sequence of events in firing of bullet, 590*f*
  shells and, 587*f*
  trajectory, 594–596
  See also firearms
ballistics gel, 591
Balthazard, Victor, 53, 238
B antigens, 234
barbiturates, 292
barrel, of firearm, 591
basket weave pattern, 89*f*
Bass, Bill, 366
beard hairs, 55
Beasley, Randy, 158
Becke lines, 489
beer, 292–293
Beethoven Research Project, 63
beetles, decomposition and, 358–359
Belushi, John, 532
Bendale-Taylor, Colyn, 245
Benjamin N. Cardozo School of Law, 7, 192

mercury poisoning, 287, 288*f*
metabolites, 284
methamphetamines, 292
microcrystalling test, 286
microfibers, 86
microscopy, of hair, chemical testing for substances in, 58–60
Midwest Forensics Resource Center (MFRC), 570
Midwestern Association of Forensic Scientists, 601
Mildenhall, Dallas, 131
Milne, Lynne, forensic palynologist, 133
mineral fibers, 85
minerals, 419
Minié ball, lead bullet, 586
Minor League Baseball, 296
minutiae, fingerprint, 164, 165*f*
Mirabel, Natalie, 115
mitochondrial DNA (mtDNA), 52, 53, 193, 201, 203*f*
  analysis, Y STR and, 201
  hair and, 56, 60
Mohr, Karl Fredrich, 285
molecular biology, 113
monomers, 85
Monroe, Marilyn, 532
Monteith, Cory, 282, 291
Moore, Fred, 599
Mormon document fraud, 324
morphology, of blowflies, 356–357
mtDNA. *See* mitochondrial DNA
mug shots, 161
Muhammad, John, 600
Mullis, Kary Banks, 203*f*, 207
multispectral imaging, 425
Munoz, John, 158
murder, staged crime scenes and, 32
Murphy, Erin, 201
muscles, skeletons and, 448
mushrooms, 126–127
muzzle flash, 593
muzzle loaders, 586
myiasis, 353

N

NAA. *See* neutron activation analysis
Napoleon, hair analysis, 62
narcotics, 291, 292. *See also* drug(s)
nasal index, 456

nasion, 456
National Bureau of Justice, 289
National Combined DNA Index System. *See* CODIS
National Commission on Forensic Science, 203*f*
National Institute of Science and Technology Council Subcommittee on Forensic Science, 601
National Institute of Standards and Technology (NIST), 287, 567
National Institute on Drug Abuse, 289
National Integrated Ballistic Information Network (NIBIN), 595, 597
National Missing Person DNA Database (NMPDD), 203*f*
National Museum of Natural History, 353
Native American Graves Protection and Repatriation Act (NAGPRA), 457
natural death, 388–389
natural fibers, 82–85
Neufeld, Peter J., 192, 203*f*
neutron activation analysis (NAA), 50, 62
New York University School of Law, 201
New Zealand, forensic botany in, 114, 130
Nickell, Stella, 295
nickel oxide, 485
nicks, tool marks, 563
nitrogenous base, 193
Nobel Prize, 193, 207
Noguchi, Thomas (coroner), 532
noncoding DNA, 194
nonimaged records comparison, skeletal analysis and, 458
non-STR locus (AMEL), 197
normal line, refractive index and, 487
Norris, Charles, 285, 294
nuclear DNA, 52, 193. *See also* DNA
nucleotide, 193
Nursall, James, 158
Nutt, Susan, 495–496
Nyhuis, Bun Chee, 442, 458
Nyhuis, Richard, 442
nylon fibers, 86

O

oblique light, 322
observation(s)
  activities, 15–19
  case studies, 10–11
  death scene, entomology and, 362
  defining, 4–5
  direct evidence, 23
  documentation and, 7–8
  in forensics, 9
  by witnesses, 5–8
occipital protuberance, 449
Oetting, Lillian, 34
off-road tires, 523
offspring, genotypes in, 198*f*
olefins, synthetic fibers, 86
opiates, 291
opinion, 7
Orfila, Mathieu, 285
Organization of Scientific Area Committees (OSAC), 166, 287, 316, 424, 445, 570
ossification, 446
osteoarthritis, 447
osteoporosis, 447
Oswald, Lee Harvey, 599
"Otzi the Iceman," 131
outdoor crime scenes, mapping, 29–31
overdose, drug, 282
oviposition (egg laying), 360
ovoid bodies, 57
ovules, 124
Owsley, Douglas, 459–460

P

packaging evidence, 27–29
palynology, 113
paper bindle, 27
Paracelsus, 285
patent fingerprints, 164–165
patent impressions, 518
patent tire patterns, 523
pathology, as career, 401
Paul, Henri, 52
Payant, Donna, 530
Payne, Roger, 90
Peabody Museum, Harvard University, 92
Peacock, Linda, 529
pelvis, determining sex from, 451–452